The TTL Data Book

Volume 1

TEXAS INSTRUMENTS

IMPORTANT NOTICE

Texas Instruments (TI) reserves the right to make changes in the devices or the device specifications identified in this publication without notice. TI advises its customers to obtain the latest version of device specifications to verify, before placing orders, that the information being relied upon by the customer is current.

Ti warrants performance of its semiconductor products, including SNJ and SMJ devices, to current specifications in accordance with TI's standard warranty. Testing and other quality control techniques are utilized to the extent TI deems such testing necessary to support this warranty. Unless mandated by government requirements, specific testing of all parameters of each device is not necessarily performed.

In the absence of written agreement to the contrary, TI assumes no liability for TI applications assistance, customer's product design, or infringement of patents or copyrights of third parties by or arising from use of semiconductor devices described herein. Nor does TI warrant or represent that any license, either express or implied, is granted under any patent right, copyright, or other intellectual property right of TI covering or relating to any combination, machine, or process in which such semiconductor devices might be or are used.

Specifications contained in this data book supersede all data for these products published by TI in the US before January 1985.

ISBN 3-88078-078-1

INTRODUCTION

In this volume, Texas Instruments presents pertinent technical information on the industry's broadest families of TTL integrated circuits.

You'll find complete specifications on the following product types:

- Standard TTL circuits
  Series 54/74
- Schottky TTL circuits
  Schottky clamped[†] Series 54LS/74LS and 54S/74S

This edition is designed for ease of circuit selection with an alphanumerical index as well as a functional index to all bipolar digital device types available or under development showing the available technologies for each type (Standard TTL, Schottky and Advanced Schottky, Low-Power Schottky and Advanced Low-Power Schottky). Included in the general information section is an explanation of the function tables, parameter measurement information, and typical characteristics related to the TTL products listed in this volume.

Package dimensions given in the Mechanical Data section of this book are in metric measurement (and parenthetically in inches) to simplify board layout for designers involved in metric conversion and new designs.

This volume is one in a series of Digital Bipolar data books available from Texas Instruments. The complete series is listed below:

- The TTL Data Book, Volume 1
  Standard TTL, Schottky, Low-Power Schottky
- The TTL Data Book, Volume 2
  Advanced Low-Power Schottky, Advanced Schottky

Complete technical data for any TI semiconductor/component products are available from your nearest TI field sales office or local authorized TI distributor.

We sincerely hope you will find the new TTL Data Book, Volume 1, a meaningful addition to your technical library.

[†] Integrated Schottky Barrier diode clamped transistor is patented by Texas Instruments. U.S. Patent Number 3,463,975.

The TTL Data Book

General Information 1

Functional Index 2

TTL Devices 3

Mechanical Data 4

1

GENERAL INFORMATION

1

GENERAL INFORMATION

1

GENERAL INFORMATION

ALPHANUMERICAL INDEX

1

GENERAL INFORMATION

TEXAS INSTRUMENTS

INTRODUCTION

These symbols, terms, and definitions are in accordance with those currently agreed upon by the JEDEC Council of the Electronic Industries Association (EIA) for use in the USA and by the International Electrotechnical Commission (IEC) for international use.

PART I — OPERATING CONDITIONS AND CHARACTERISTICS (IN SEQUENCE BY LETTER SYMBOLS)

f_{max} **Maximum clock frequency**

The highest rate at which the clock input of a bistable circuit can be driven through its required sequence while maintaining stable transitions of logic level at the output with input conditions established that should cause changes of output logic level in accordance with the specification.

I_{CC} **Supply current**

The current into* the V_{CC} supply terminal of an integrated circuit.

I_{CCH} **Supply current, outputs high**

The current into* the V_{CC} supply terminal of an integrated circuit when all (or a specified number) of the outputs are at the high level.

I_{CCL} **Supply current, outputs low**

The current into* the V_{CC} supply terminal of an integrated circuit when all (or a specified number) of the outputs are at the low level.

I_{IH} **High-level input current**

The current into* an input when a high-level voltage is applied to that input.

I_{IL} **Low-level input current**

The current into* an input when a low-level voltage is applied to that input.

I_{OH} **High-level output current**

The current into* an output with input conditions applied that, according to the product specification, will establish a high level at the output.

I_{OL} **Low-level output current**

The current into* an output with input conditions applied that, according to the product specification, will establish a low level at the output.

I_{OS} **Short-circuit output current**

The current into* an output when that output is short-circuited to ground (or other specified potential) with input conditions applied to establish the output logic level farthest from ground potential (or other specified potential).

I_{OZH} **Off-state (high-impedance-state) output current (of a three-state output) with high-level voltage applied**

The current flowing into* an output having three-state capability with input conditions established that, according to the product specification, will establish the high-impedance state at the output and with a high-level voltage applied to the output.

NOTE: This parameter is measured with other input conditions established that would cause the output to be at a low level if it were enabled.

*Current out of a terminal is given as a negative value.

GENERAL INFORMATION   **1**

GLOSSARY
TTL SYMBOLS, TERMS, AND DEFINITIONS

I_{OZL} **Off-state (high-impedance-state) output current (of a three-state output) with low-level voltage applied**

The current flowing into* an output having three-state capability with input conditions established that, according to the product specification, will establish the high-impedance state at the output and with a low-level voltage applied to the output.

NOTE: This parameter is measured with other input conditions established that would cause the output to be at a high level if it were enabled.

V_{IH} **High-level input voltage**

An input voltage within the more positive (less negative) of the two ranges of values used to represent the binary variables.

NOTE: A minimum is specified that is the least-positive value of high-level input voltage for which operation of the logic element within specification limits is guaranteed.

V_{IK} **Input clamp voltage**

An input voltage in a region of relatively low differential resistance that serves to limit the input voltage swing.

V_{IL} **Low-level input voltage**

An input voltage level within the less positive (more negative) of the two ranges of values used to represent the binary variables.

NOTE: A maximum is specified that is the most-positive value of low-level input voltage for which operation of the logic element within specification limits is guaranteed.

V_{OH} **High-level output voltage**

The voltage at an output terminal with input conditions applied that, according to the product specification, will establish a high level at the output.

V_{OL} **Low-level output voltage**

The voltage at an output terminal with input conditions applied that, according to the product specification, will establish a low level at the output.

t_a **Access time**

The time interval between the application of a specific input pulse and the availability of valid signals at an output.

t_{dis} **Disable time (of a three-state output)**

The time interval between the specified reference points on the input and output voltage waveforms, with the three-state output changing from either of the defined active levels (high or low) to a high-impedance (off) state. (t_{dis} = t_{PHZ} or t_{PLZ}).

t_{en} **Enable time (of a three-state output)**

The time interval between the specified reference points on the input and output voltage waveforms, with the three-state output changing from a high-impedance (off) state to either of the defined active levels (high or low). (t_{en} = t_{PZH} or t_{PZL}).

*Current out of a terminal is given as a negative value.

TEXAS
INSTRUMENTS

t_h **Hold time**

The time interval during which a signal is retained at a specified input terminal after an active transition occurs at another specified input terminal.

NOTES: 1.   The hold time is the actual time interval between two signal events and is determined by the system in which the digital circuit operates. A minimum value is specified that is the shortest interval for which correct operation of the digital circuit is guaranteed.

         2.   The hold time may have a negative value in which case the minimum limit defines the longest interval (between the release of the signal and the active transition) for which correct operation of the digital circuit is guaranteed.

t_{pd} **Propagation delay time**

The time between the specified reference points on the input and output voltage waveforms with the output changing from one defined level (high or low) to the other defined level. ($t_{pd} = t_{PHL}$ or t_{PLH}).

t_{PHL} **Propagation delay time, high-to-low-level output**

The time between the specified reference points on the input and output voltage waveforms with the output changing from the defined high level to the defined low level.

t_{PHZ} **Disable time (of a three-state output) from high level**

The time interval between the specified reference points on the input and output voltage waveforms with the three-state output changing from the defined high level to a high-impedance (off) state.

t_{PLH} **Propagation delay time, low-to-high-level output**

The time between the specified reference points on the input and output voltage waveforms with the output changing from the defined low level to the defined high level.

t_{PLZ} **Disable time (of a three-state output) from low level**

The time interval between the specified reference points on the input and output voltage waveforms with the three-state output changing from the defined low level to a high-impedance (off) state.

t_{PZH} **Enable time (of a three-state output) to high level**

The time interval between the specified reference points on the input and output voltage waveforms with the three-state output changing from a high-impedance (off) state to the defined high level.

t_{PZL} **Enable time (of a three-state output) to low level**

The time interval between the specified reference points on the input and output voltage waveforms with the three-state output changing from a high-impedance (off) state to the defined low level.

t_{sr} **Sense recovery time**

The time interval needed to switch a memory from a write mode to a read mode and to obtain valid data signals at the output.

t_{su} **Setup time**

The time interval between the application of a signal at a specified input terminal and a subsequent active transition at another specified input terminal.

NOTES: 1.   The setup time is the actual time interval between two signal events and is determined by the system in which the digital circuit operates. A minimum value is specified that is the shortest interval for which correct operation of the digital circuit is guaranteed.

         2.   The setup time may have a negative value in which case the minimum limit defines the longest interval (between the active transition and the application of the other signal) for which correct operation of the digital circuit is guaranteed.

t_w **Pulse duration (width)**

The time interval between specified reference points on the leading and trailing edges of the pulse waveform.

GENERAL INFORMATION   **1**

GLOSSARY
TTL SYMBOLS, TERMS, AND DEFINITIONS

PART II — CLASSIFICATION OF CIRCUIT COMPLEXITY

Gate Equivalent Circuit

A basic unit-of-measure of relative digital-circuit complexity. The number of gate equivalent circuits is that number of individual logic gates that would have to be interconnected to perform the same function.

Large-Scale Integration, LSI

A concept whereby a complete major subsystem or system function is fabricated as a single microcircuit. In this context a major subsystem or system, whether digital or linear, is considered to be one that contains 100 or more equivalent gates or circuitry of similar complexity.

Medium-Scale Integration, MSI

A concept whereby a complete subsystem or system function is fabricated as a single microcircuit. The subsystem or system is smaller than for LSI, but whether digital or linear, is considered to be one that contains 12 or more equivalent gates or circuitry of similar complexity.

Small-Scale Integration, SSI

Integrated circuits of less complexity than medium-scale integration (MSI).

Very-Large-Scale Integration, VLSI

The description of any IC technology that is much more complex than large-scale integration (LSI), and involves a much higher equivalent gate count. At this time an exact definition including a minimum gate count has not been standardized by JEDEC or the IEEE.

The following symbols are used in function tables on TI data sheets:

H	=	high level (steady state)
L	=	low level (steady state)
↑	=	transition from low to high level
↓	=	transition from high to low level
→	=	value/level or resulting value/level is routed to indicated destination
⌒	=	value/level is re-entered
X	=	irrelevant (any input, including transitions)
Z	=	off (high-impedance) state of a 3-state-output
a . . h	=	the level of steady-state inputs at inputs A through H respectively
Q_0	=	level of Q before the indicated steady-state input conditions were established
$\overline{Q}_0$	=	complement of Q_0 or level of $\overline{Q}$ before the indicated steady-state input conditions were established
Q_n	=	level of Q before the most recent active transition indicated by ↓ or ↑
⎍	=	one high-level pulse
⎍	=	one low-level pulse
TOGGLE	=	each output changes to the complement of its previous level on each active transition indicated by ↓ or ↑.

If, in the input columns, a row contains only the symbols H, L, and/or X, this means the indicated output is valid whenever the input configuration is achieved and regardless of the sequence in which it is achieved. The output persists so long as the input configuration is maintained.

If, in the input columns, a row contains H, L, and/or X together with ↑ and/or ↓, this means the output is valid whenever the input configuration is achieved but the transition(s) must occur following the achievement of the steady-state levels. If the output is shown as a level (H, L, Q_0, or $\overline{Q}_0$), it persists so long as the steady-state input levels and the levels that terminate indicated transitions are maintained. Unless otherwise indicated, input transitions in the opposite direction to those shown have no effect at the output. (If the output is shown as a pulse, ⎍ or ⎍, the pulse follows the indicated input transition and persists for an interval dependent on the circuit.)

GENERAL INFORMATION

1

Among the most complex function tables in this book are those of the shift registers. These embody most of the symbols used in any of the function tables, plus more. Below is the function table of a 4-bit bidirectional universal shift register, e.g., type SN74194.

FUNCTION TABLE

	INPUTS									OUTPUTS			
CLEAR	MODE		CLOCK	SERIAL		PARALLEL				Q_A	Q_B	Q_C	Q_D
	S1	S0		LEFT	RIGHT	A	B	C	D				
L	X	X	X	X	X	X	X	X	X	L	L	L	L
H	X	X	L	X	X	X	X	X	X	Q_{A0}	Q_{B0}	Q_{C0}	Q_{D0}
H	H	H	↑	X	X	a	b	c	d	a	b	c	d
H	L	H	↑	X	H	X	X	X	X	H	Q_{An}	Q_{Bn}	Q_{Cn}
H	L	H	↑	X	L	X	X	X	X	L	Q_{An}	Q_{Bn}	Q_{Cn}
H	H	L	↑	H	X	X	X	X	X	Q_{Bn}	Q_{Cn}	Q_{Dn}	H
H	H	L	↑	L	X	X	X	X	X	Q_{Bn}	Q_{Cn}	Q_{Dn}	L
H	L	L	X	X	X	X	X	X	X	Q_{A0}	Q_{B0}	Q_{C0}	Q_{D0}

The first line of the table represents a synchronous clearing of the register and says that if clear is low, all four outputs will be reset low regardless of the other inputs. In the following lines, clear is inactive (high) and so has no effect.

The second line shows that so long as the clock input remains low (while clear is high), no other input has any effect and the outputs maintain the levels they assumed before the steady-state combination of clear high and clock low was established. Since on other lines of the table only the rising transition of the clock is shown to be active, the second line implicitly shows that no further change in the outputs will occur while the clock remains high or on the high-to-low transition of the clock.

The third line of the table represents synchronous parallel loading of the register and says that if S1 and S0 are both high then, without regard to the serial input, the data entered at A will be at output Q_A, data entered at B will be at Q_B, and so forth, following a low-to-high clock transition.

The fourth and fifth lines represent the loading of high- and low-level data, respectively, from the shift-right serial input and the shifting of previously entered data one bit; data previously at Q_A is now at Q_B, the previous levels of Q_B and Q_C are now at Q_C and Q_D respectively, and the data previously at Q_D is no longer in the register. This entry of serial data and shift takes place on the low-to-high transition of the clock when S1 is low and S0 is high and the levels at inputs A through D have no effect.

The sixth and seventh lines represent the loading of high- and low-level data, respectively, from the shift-left serial input and the shifting of previously entered data one bit; data previously at Q_B is now at Q_A, the previous levels of Q_C and Q_D are now at Q_B and Q_C, respectively, and the data previously at Q_A is no longer in the register. This entry of serial data and shift takes place on the low-to-high transition of the clock when S1 is high and S0 is low and the levels at inputs A through D have no effect.

The last line shows that as long as both mode inputs are low, no other input has any effect and, as in the second line, the outputs maintain the levels they assumed before the steady-state combination of clear high and both mode inputs low was established.

TEXAS
INSTRUMENTS

PARAMETER MEASUREMENT INFORMATION

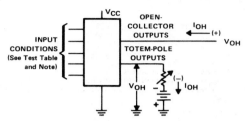

NOTE: For functions having three-state outputs, input conditions are maintained which will cause the outputs to be enabled (low-impedance).

TEST TABLE

FUNCTION	INPUT CONDITIONS
NAND	Input under test at V_{IL} max, all others at 4.5 V
AND	All inputs at V_{IH} min
NOR	All inputs at V_{IL} max
OR	Input under test at V_{IH} min, all others at GND
AND-OR INVERT	Inputs under test (a set including one input of each AND gate) at V_{IL} max, all others at 4.5 V
AND-OR	All inputs of AND gate under test at V_{IH} min, all others at GND

FIGURE 1. V_{IH}, V_{IL}, V_{OH}, I_{OH}

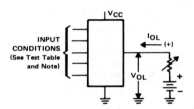

NOTE: For functions having three-state outputs, input conditions are maintained which will cause the outputs to be enabled (low-impedance).

TEST TABLE

FUNCTION	INPUT CONDITIONS
NAND	All inputs at V_{IH} min
AND	Input under test at V_{IL} max, all others at 4.5 V
NOR	Input under test at V_{IH} min, others at GND
OR	All inputs at V_{IL} max
AND-OR INVERT	All inputs of AND gate under test at V_{IH} min, all others at GND
AND-OR	Inputs under test (a set including one input of each AND gate) at V_{IH} min, all others at 4.5 V

FIGURE 2. V_{IH}, V_{IL}, V_{OL}

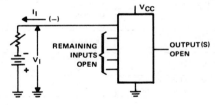

NOTE: Each input is tested separately.

FIGURE 3. V_I

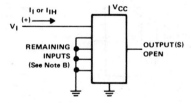

NOTES: A. Each input is tested separately.
B. When testing AND-OR-INVERT or AND-OR gates, each AND gate is tested separately with inputs of AND gates not under test open when testing I_I and grounded when testing I_{IH}.

FIGURE 4. I_I, I_{IH}

GENERAL INFORMATION

1

PARAMETER MEASUREMENT INFORMATION

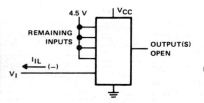

NOTES: A. Each input is tested separately.
B. When testing AND-OR-INVERT or AND-OR gates, each AND gate is tested separately with input of AND gates not under test open.

FIGURE 5. I_{IL}

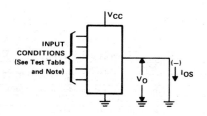

TEST TABLE

FUNCTION	INPUT CONDITIONS
NAND	All inputs at GND
AND	All inputs at 4.5 V
NOR	All inputs at GND
OR	All inputs at 4.5 V
AND-OR-INVERT	All inputs at GND
AND-OR	All inputs at 4.5 V

NOTE: For functions having three-state outputs, input conditions are maintained which will cause the outputs to be enabled (low-impedance).

FIGURE 6. I_{OS}, I_O

TEST TABLE

FUNCTION	INPUT CONDITIONS FOR I_{CCH}	INPUT CONDITIONS FOR I_{CCL}
NAND	All inputs at GND	All inputs at 4.5 V
AND	All inputs at 4.5 V	All inputs at GND
NOR	All inputs at GND	One input at 4.5 V, all others at GND
OR	One input at 4.5 V all others at GND	All inputs at GND
AND-OR-INVERT	All inputs at GND	All inputs of one AND gate at 4.5 V, all others at GND
AND-OR	All inputs of one AND gate at 4.5 V, all others at GND	All inputs at GND

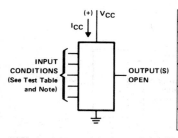

NOTE: I_{CC} is measured simultaneously for all functions in a package. The average-per-gate values are calculated from the appropriate one of the following equations.:

$$I_{CC}, I_{CCH}, \text{ or } I_{CCL} \text{ (average per gate or flip-flop)} = \frac{\text{total } I_{CC}, I_{CCH}, \text{ or } I_{CCL}}{\text{(number of gates or flip-flops in package)}}$$

$$I_{CC} \text{ (average per gate, 50\% duty cycle)} = \frac{I_{CCH} + I_{CCL}}{2 \text{ (number of gates in package)}}$$

FIGURE 7. I_{CC}

PARAMETER MEASUREMENT INFORMATION

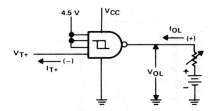

FIGURE 8. V_{T+}, I_{T+}, V_{OL}
(FOR NAND SCHMITT TRIGGERS)

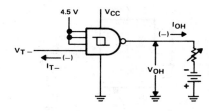

FIGURE 9. V_{T-}, I_{T-}, V_{OH}
(FOR NAND SCHMITT TRIGGERS)

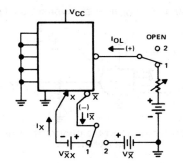

NOTES: A. Switches are in position 1 for SN54'/SN74', position
2 for SN54H'/SN74H'.

B. The $I_{\overline{X}}$ limit for SN54' and SN74' circuits may be
verified by an alternate equivalent procedure. The $V_{\overline{X}X}$
source is replaced by a resistor (see table below) in
parallel with a voltmeter between the X and $\overline{X}$ pins.
If the measured voltage, $V_{\overline{X}X}$, is less than 0.4, the
specified limit for $I_{\overline{X}}$ is met.

RESISTANCE VALUE TABLE

SN5423	114 Ω
SN5450, SN5453	138 Ω
SN7423	105 Ω
SN7450, SN7453	130 Ω

FIGURE 10. I_X **(FOR EXPANDABLE GATES)**

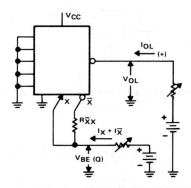

FIGURE 11. $V_{BE(Q)}$ **(FOR EXPANDABLE GATES)**

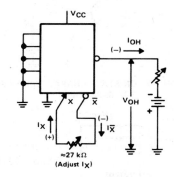

FIGURE 12. V_{OH} **(FOR EXPANDABLE GATES)**

1

GENERAL INFORMATION

TEXAS
INSTRUMENTS

1

PARAMETER MEASUREMENT INFORMATION

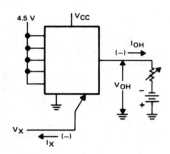

FIGURE 13. V_{OH} (FOR EXPANDABLE GATES)

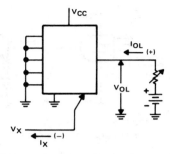

FIGURE 14. V_{OL} (FOR EXPANDABLE GATES)

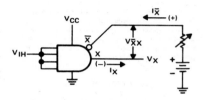

FIGURE 15. ON-STATE CHARACTERISTICS FOR EXPANDERS

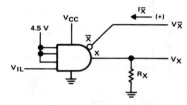

FIGURE 16. OFF-STATE CHARACTERISTICS FOR EXPANDERS

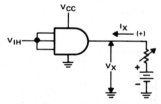

FIGURE 17. ON-STATE CHARACTERISTICS FOR EXPANDERS

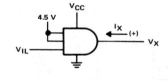

FIGURE 18. OFF-STATE CHARACTERISTICS FOR EXPANDERS

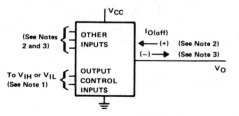

FIGURE 19. $I_{O(off)}$ (THREE-STATE OUTPUTS)

NOTES: 1. Input conditions are maintained which will ensure that the three-state output(s) is (are) disabled to the high-impedance state. See function table or logic for the particular device.
2. When testing for current into the output with a high-level output voltage, input conditions are applied that would cause the output to be low if it were enabled.
3. When testing for current out of the output with a low-level output voltage, input conditions are applied that would cause the output to be high if it were enabled.

TEXAS INSTRUMENTS

PARAMETER MEASUREMENT INFORMATION

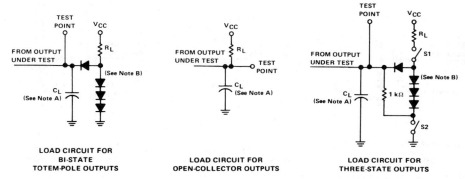

LOAD CIRCUIT FOR BI-STATE TOTEM-POLE OUTPUTS

LOAD CIRCUIT FOR OPEN-COLLECTOR OUTPUTS

LOAD CIRCUIT FOR THREE-STATE OUTPUTS

NOTES: A. C_L includes probe and jig capacitance.
         B. All diodes are 1N3064 or equivalent.

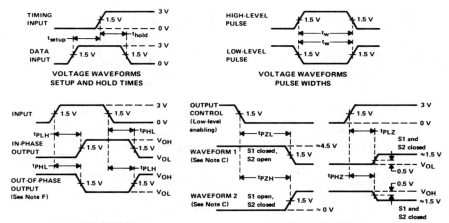

VOLTAGE WAVEFORMS
SETUP AND HOLD TIMES

VOLTAGE WAVEFORMS
PULSE WIDTHS

VOLTAGE WAVEFORMS
PROPAGATION DELAY TIMES

VOLTAGE WAVEFORMS
ENABLE AND DISABLE TIMES, THREE-STATE OUTPUTS

NOTES: C. Waveform 1 is for an output with internal conditions such that the output is low except when disabled by the output control.
         Waveform 2 is for an output with internal conditions such that the output is high except when disabled by the output control.
         D. In the examples above, the phase relationships between inputs and outputs have been chosen arbitrarily.
         E. All input pulses are supplied by generators having the following characteristics: PRR ≤ 1 MHz, Z_{out} ≈ 50 Ω and:
            For Series 54/74 and 54H/74H, t_r ≤ 7 ns, t_f ≤ 7 ns;
            For Specified[†] Series 54L/74L devices: t_r ≤ 10 ns, t_f ≤ 10 ns;
            For Series 54S/74S, t_r ≤ 2.5 ns, t_f ≤ 2.5 ns.
         F. When measuring propagation delay times of 3-state outputs, switches S1 and S2 are closed.
         G. The outputs are measured one at a time with one input transition per measurement.

[†]'L42, 'L43, 'L44, 'L46, 'L47, 'L75, 'L77, 'L96, 'L121, 'L122, 'L123, 'L153, 'L154, 'L157, 'L164

TEXAS INSTRUMENTS

GENERAL INFORMATION

1

PARAMETER MEASUREMENT INFORMATION

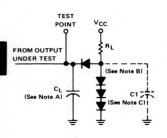

LOAD CIRCUIT FOR BI-STATE TOTEM-POLE OUTPUTS

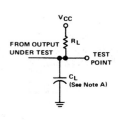

LOAD CIRCUIT FOR OPEN-COLLECTOR OUTPUTS

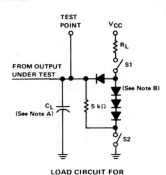

LOAD CIRCUIT FOR THREE-STATE OUTPUTS

NOTES: A. C_L includes probe and jig capacitance.
B. All diodes are 1N3064 or equivalent.
C. C1 (30 pF) is used for testing Series 54L devices only.

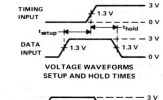

VOLTAGE WAVEFORMS SETUP AND HOLD TIMES

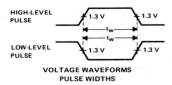

VOLTAGE WAVEFORMS PULSE WIDTHS

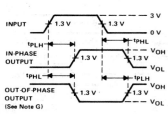

VOLTAGE WAVEFORMS PROPAGATION DELAY TIMES

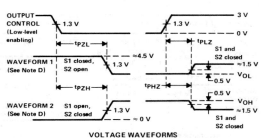

VOLTAGE WAVEFORMS ENABLE AND DISABLE TIMES, THREE-STATE OUTPUTS

NOTES: D. Waveform 1 is for an output with internal conditions such that the output is low except when disabled by the output control. Waveform 2 is for an output with internal conditions such that the output is high except when disabled by the output control.
E. In the examples above, the phase relationships between inputs and outputs have been chosen arbitrarily.
F. All input pulses are supplied by generators having the following characteristics: PRR ≤ 1 MHz, $Z_{out} \approx 50\ \Omega$ and:
For Series 54L/74L gates and inverters, $t_r = 60$ ns, $t_f = 60$ ns;
For Series 54L/74L flip-flops and MSI, $t_r \leq 25$ ns, $t_f \leq 25$ ns;
For Series 54LS/74LS, $t_r \leq 15$ ns, $t_f \leq 6$ ns.
G. When measuring propagation delay times of 3-state outputs, switches S1 and S2 are closed.
H. The outputs are measured one at a time with one input transition per measurement.

†'L42, 'L43, 'L44, 'L46, 'L47, 'L75, 'L77, 'L96, 'L121, 'L122, 'L123, 'L153, 'L154, 'L157, 'L164

TEXAS INSTRUMENTS

TYPICAL CHARACTERISTICS†

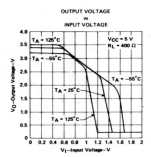

FIGURE A1

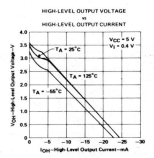

FIGURE A2

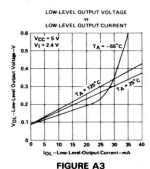

FIGURE A3

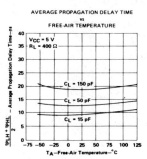

FIGURE A4

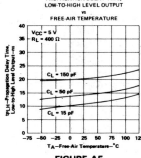

FIGURE A5

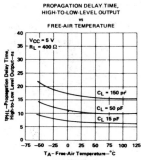

FIGURE A6

†Data for temperatures below 0°C and above 70°C are applicable for Series 54 circuits only.
Data as shown are applicable specifically for the NAND gates with totem-pole outputs.

1

GENERAL INFORMATION

TYPICAL CHARACTERISTICS†

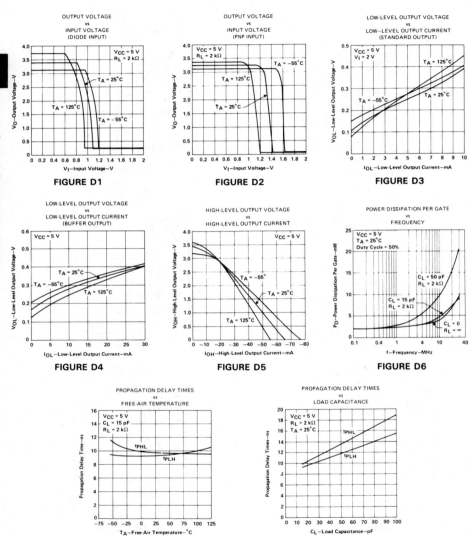

FIGURE D1

FIGURE D2

FIGURE D3

FIGURE D4

FIGURE D5

FIGURE D6

FIGURE D7

FIGURE D8

†Data for temperatures below 0°C and above 70°C are applicable for Series 54LS circuits only.

TEXAS
INSTRUMENTS

TYPICAL CHARACTERISTICS†

OUTPUT VOLTAGE
vs
INPUT VOLTAGE

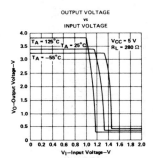

FIGURE E1

INPUT-CLAMPING-DIODE
FORWARD VOLTAGE
vs
FREE-AIR TEMPERATURE

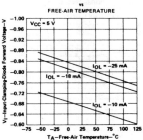

FIGURE E2

HIGH-LEVEL OUTPUT VOLTAGE
vs
HIGH-LEVEL OUTPUT CURRENT

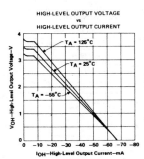

FIGURE E3

LOW-LEVEL OUTPUT VOLTAGE
vs
LOW-LEVEL OUTPUT CURRENT

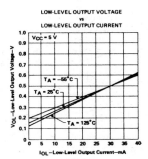

FIGURE E4

INPUT CURRENT
vs
INPUT VOLTAGE

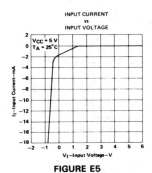

FIGURE E5

HIGH-LEVEL INPUT CURRENT
vs
FREE-AIR TEMPERATURE

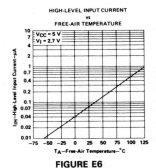

FIGURE E6

†Data for temperatures below 0 °C and above 70 °C are applicable for Series 54S circuits only.
Data as shown are applicable specifically for the NAND gates with totem-pole outputs.

GENERAL INFORMATION

1

TYPICAL CHARACTERISTICS[†]

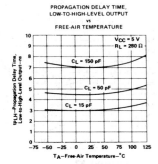

PROPAGATION DELAY TIME,
LOW-TO-HIGH-LEVEL OUTPUT
vs
FREE-AIR TEMPERATURE

FIGURE E7

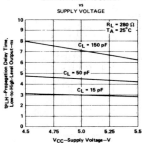

PROPAGATION DELAY TIME,
LOW-TO-HIGH-LEVEL OUTPUT
vs
SUPPLY VOLTAGE

FIGURE E8

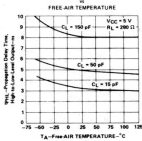

PROPAGATION DELAY TIME,
HIGH-TO-LOW-LEVEL OUTPUT
vs
FREE-AIR TEMPERATURE

FIGURE E9

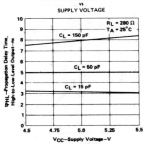

PROPAGATION DELAY TIME,
HIGH-TO-LOW-LEVEL OUTPUT
vs
SUPPLY VOLTAGE

FIGURE E10

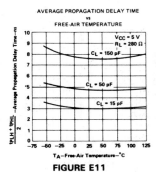

AVERAGE PROPAGATION DELAY TIME
vs
FREE-AIR TEMPERATURE

FIGURE E11

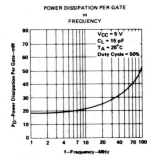

POWER DISSIPATION PER GATE
vs
FREQUENCY

FIGURE E12

[†]Data for temperatures below 0°C and above 70°C are applicable for Series 54S circuits only.
Data as shown are applicable specifically for the NAND gates with totem-pole outputs.

GENERAL INFORMATION

TYPICAL CHARACTERISTICS FOR FLIP-FLOPS†

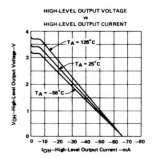

HIGH-LEVEL OUTPUT VOLTAGE
vs
HIGH-LEVEL OUTPUT CURRENT

FIGURE E13

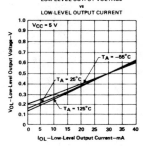

LOW-LEVEL OUTPUT VOLTAGE
vs
LOW-LEVEL OUTPUT CURRENT

FIGURE E14

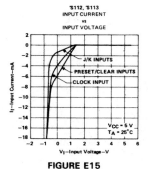

'S112, 'S113
INPUT CURRENT
vs
INPUT VOLTAGE

FIGURE E15

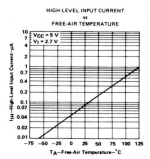

HIGH-LEVEL INPUT CURRENT
vs
FREE-AIR TEMPERATURE

FIGURE E16

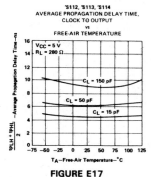

'S112, 'S113, 'S114
AVERAGE PROPAGATION DELAY TIME,
CLOCK TO OUTPUT
vs
FREE-AIR TEMPERATURE

FIGURE E17

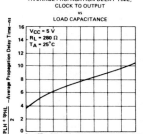

'S112, 'S113, 'S114
AVERAGE PROPAGATION DELAY TIME,
CLOCK TO OUTPUT
vs
LOAD CAPACITANCE

FIGURE E18

†Data for temperatures below 0 °C and above 70 °C are applicable for Series 54S circuits only.

General Information   **1**

Functional Index   **2**

TTL Devices   **3**

Mechanical Data   **4**

- All STD TTL, LS and Schottky Devices are included in TTL-Data Book Volume 1

- All ALS and AS Devices are included in TTL-Data Book Volume 2

- All PAL's® and Bipolar Memories are included in TTL-Data Book Volume 3

GATES AND INVERTERS

POSITIVE-NAND GATES AND INVERTERS

DESCRIPTION	TYPE	STD TTL	ALS	AS			LS	S
Hex 2-Input Gates	'804		●	B				
Hex Inverters	'04	●					●	●
	'04		A	●				
	'1004		●	●				
Quadruple 2-Input Gates	'00	●					●	●
	'00		A	●				
	'1000		A	●				
Triple 3-Input Gates	'10	●					●	●
	'10		A	●				
	'1010		A					
Dual 4-Input Gates	'20	●					●	●
	'20		A	●				
	'1020		A					
8-Input Gates	'30	●					●	●
	'30		A	●				
13-Input Gates	'133							●
			●					
Dual 2-Input Gates	'8003		●					

POSITIVE-NAND GATES AND INVERTERS WITH OPEN-COLLECTOR OUTPUTS

DESCRIPTION	TYPE	STD TTL	ALS	AS			LS	S
Hex Inverters	'05	●					●	●
	'1005		A					
	'1005		●					
Quadruple 2-Input Gates	'01	●					●	
	'01			●				
	'03	●					●	●
	'03		A					
	'1003		A					
Triple 3-Input Gates	'12	●					●	●
	'12		A					
Dual 4-Input Gates	'22	●					●	●
	'22			B				

POSITIVE-AND GATES WITH OPEN-COLLECTOR OUTPUTS

DESCRIPTION	TYPE	STD TTL	ALS	AS			LS	S
Quadruple 2-Input Gates	'09	●					●	●
	'09		●					
Triple 3-Input Gates	'15						●	●
	'15		● A					

POSITIVE-AND GATES

DESCRIPTION	TYPE	STD TTL	ALS	AS		LS	S
Hex 2-Input Gates	'808		●	B			
Quadruple 2-Input Gates	'08	●				●	●
	'08		●	●			
	'1008		A	●			
Triple 3-Input Gates	'11	●				●	●
	'11		A	●			
	'1011		A				
Dual 4-Input Gates	'21					●	
Triple 4-Input AND/NAND	'800			●			

POSITIVE-OR GATES

DESCRIPTION	TYPE	STD TTL	ALS	AS	LS	S
Hex 2-Input Gates	'832		●	B		
Quadruple 2-Input Gates	'32	●			●	●
	'32		●	●		
	'1032		A	●		
Triple 4-Input OR/NOR	'802			●		

POSITIVE-NOR GATES

DESCRIPTION	TYPE	STD TTL	ALS	AS		LS	S
Hex 2-Input Gates	'805		●	B			
Quadruple 2-Input Gates	'02	●				●	●
	'02		●	●			
	'1002		A				
Triple 3-Input Gates	'27	●				●	
	'27		●	●			
Dual 4-Input Gates with Strobe	'25	●					
Dual 5-Input Gates	'260						●

A Denotes "A" suffix version available in the technology indicated.
B Denotes "B" suffix version available in the technology indicated.

TEXAS
INSTRUMENTS

GATES AND INVERTERS

SCHMITT-TRIGGER POSITIVE-NAND GATES AND INVERTERS

DESCRIPTION	TYPE	TECHNOLOGY				
		STD TTL	ALS	AS	LS	S
Hex Inverters	'14	●			●	
	'19				●	
Octal Inverters	'619				●	
Dual 4-Input Positive-NAND	'13	●			●	
	'18				●	
Triple 4-Input Positive-NAND	'618				●	
Quadruple 2-Input Positive-NAND	'24				●	
	'132	●			●	●

DELAY ELEMENTS

DESCRIPTION	TYPE	TECHNOLOGY		
		ALS	AS	LS
Inverting and Noninverting Elements, 2-Input NAND Buffers	'31			●

FUNCTIONAL INDEX

2

GATES, EXPANDERS, BUFFERS, DRIVERS, AND TRANSCEIVERS

AND-OR-INVERT GATES

DESCRIPTION	TYPE	TECHNOLOGY					
		STD TTL	ALS	AS		LS	S
2-Wide 4-Input	'55					●	
4-Wide 4-2-3-2-Input	'64						●
4-Wide 2-2-3-2-Input	'54						
4-Wide 2-Input	'54	●					
4-Wide 2-3-3-2-Input	'54					●	
Dual 2-Wide 2-Input	'51	●				●	●

AND-OR-INVERT GATES WITH OPEN-COLLECTOR OUTPUTS

DESCRIPTION	TYPE	TECHNOLOGY			
		STD TTL	ALS	AS	S
4-Wide 4-2-3-2-Input	'65				●

EXPANDABLE GATES

DESCRIPTION	TYPE	TECHNOLOGY					
		STD TTL	ALS	AS			LS
Dual 4-Input Positive-NOR With Strobe	'23	●					
4-Wide AND-OR	'52						
4-Wide AND-OR-INVERT	'53	●					
2-Wide AND-OR-INVERT	'55						●
Dual 2-Wide AND-OR-INVERT	'50	●					

EXPANDERS

DESCRIPTION	TYPE	TECHNOLOGY		
		STD TTL	ALS	AS
Dual 4-Input	'60	●		
Triple 3-Input	'61			
3-2-2-3-Input AND-OR	'62			

BUFFER AND INTERFACE GATES WITH OPEN-COLLECTOR OUTPUTS

DESCRIPTION	TYPE	TECHNOLOGY				
		STD TTL	ALS	AS	LS	S
Hex	'07	●			●	
	'17	●				
	'35			●		
	'1035			●		
Hex Inverter	'06	●			●	
	'16	●				
	'1005			●		
Quad 2-Input Positive-NAND	'26	●			●	
	'38	●			●	●
			A, B			
	'39	●				
	'1003		A			
Quad 2-Input Positive-NOR	'33	●			●	
			A			

BUFFERS, DRIVERS, AND BUS TRANSCEIVERS WITH OPEN-COLLECTOR OUTPUTS

DESCRIPTION	TYPE	TECHNOLOGY				
		STD TTL	ALS	AS	LS	S
Noninverting Octal Buffers/Drivers	'743		●			
	'757		●	●		
	'760			●		
Inverting Octal Buffers/Drivers	'742		●			
	'756			●		
	'763		●	●		
Inverting and Noninverting Octal Buffers/Drivers	'762		●	●		
Noninverting Quad Transceivers	'759			●		
Inverting Quad Transceivers	'758			●		

2

FUNCTIONAL INDEX

A Denotes "A" suffix version available in the technology indicated.
B Denotes "B" suffix version available in the technology indicated.

GATES, EXPANDERS, BUFFERS, DRIVERS, AND TRANSCEIVERS

GATES, BUFFERS, DRIVERS, AND BUS TRANSCEIVERS WITH 3-STATE OUTPUTS

DESCRIPTION	TYPE	STD TTL	ALS	AS	LS	S
Noninverting Octal Buffers/Drivers	'241				•	•
			A	•		
	'244				•	•
			A	•		
	'465				•	
			A			
	'467				•	
			A			
	'541	•				
	'1241*	•				
	'1244*		A			
Inverting Octal Buffers/Drivers	'231		•	•		
	'240				•	•
			A	•		
	'466				•	
			A			
	'468				•	
			A			
	'540	•				
	'1240*	•				
Inverting and Noninverting Octal Buffers/Drivers	'230			•		
Octal Transceivers	'245				•	
			A	•		
	'1245		A			
Noninverting Hex Buffers/Drivers	'365	A			A	
			•			
	'367	A			A	
			•			
Inverting Hex Buffers/Drivers	'366	A			A	
			•			
	'368	A			A	
			•			
Quad Buffers/Drivers with Independent Output Controls	'125	•			A	
	'126	•			A	
	'426	•				
Noninverting Quad Transceivers	'243				•	
			A	•		
	'1243*		•			
Inverting Quad Transceivers	'242				•	
			A, B	•		
	'1242*		•			
Quad Transceivers with Storage	'226					•
12-Input NAND Gate	'134					•

50-OHM/75-OHM LINE DRIVERS

DESCRIPTION	TYPE	STD TTL	ALS	AS	S
Hex 2-Input Positive-NAND	'804		•	B	
Hex 2-Input Positive-NOR	'805		•	B	
Hex 2-Input Positive-AND	'808		•	B	
Hex 2-Input Positive-OR	'832		•	B	
Quad 2-Input Positive-NOR	'128	•			
Dual 4-Input Positive-NAND	'140				•

* Denotes very low power.
A Denotes "A" suffix version available in the technology indicated.
B Denotes "B" suffix version available in the technology indicated.

Texas Instruments

BUFFERS, DRIVERS, TRANSCEIVERS, AND CLOCK GENERATORS

BUFFERS, CLOCK/MEMORY DRIVERS

DESCRIPTION	TYPE	STD TTL	ALS	AS	LS	S
Hex 2-Input Positive-NAND	'804		●	B		
Hex 2-Input Positive-NOR	'805		●	B		
Hex 2-Input Positive-AND	'808		●	B		
Hex 2-Input Positive-OR	'832		●	B		
Hex Inverter	'1004		●	B		
Hex Buffer	'34		●	●		
	'1034		●	●		
Quad 2-Input Positive-NAND	'37	●			●	●
	'1000		A	●		
Quad 2-Input Positive-NOR	'28	●			●	
	'1002		A			
	'1036			●		
Quad 2-Input Positive-AND	'1008		A	●		
Quad 2-Input Positive-OR	1032		A	●		
Triple 3-Input Positive-NAND	'1010		A			
Triple 3-Input Positive-AND	'1011		A			
Triple 4-Input AND-NAND	'800			●		
Triple 4-Input OR-NOR	'802			●		
Dual 4-Input Positive-NAND	'40	●			●	●
	'1020		A			
Line Driver/Memory Driver with Series Damping Resistor	'436					●
Line Driver/Memory Driver	'437					●

OCTAL BUS TRANSCEIVERS/MOS DRIVERS

DESCRIPTION	TYPE	STD TTL	ALS	AS	LS	S
Inverting Outputs, 3-State	'2620			●		
	'2640			●		
True Outputs, 3-State	'2623			●		
	'2645			●		

DESCRIPTION		TYPE	STD TTL	ALS	AS	LS	S
Input Resistors	Inverting Outputs	'746	●				
	Noninverting Outputs	'747	●				
Output Resistors	Inverting Outputs	'2540	●				
	Noninverting Outputs	'2541	●				

BI-/TRI-DIRECTIONAL BUS TRANSCEIVERS AND DRIVERS

DESCRIPTION	TYPE OF OUTPUT	TYPE	ALS	AS	LS	S
Quad with Bit Direction	3-State	'446			●	
Controls	3-State	'449			●	
Quad Tridirection	OC	'440			●	
	OC	'441			●	
	3-State	'442			●	
	3-State	'443			●	
	3-State	'444			●	
4-Bit with Storage	3-State	'226				●

2

FUNCTIONAL INDEX

A Denotes "A" suffix version available in the technology indicated.
B Denotes "B" suffix version available in the technology indicated.

BUFFERS, DRIVERS, TRANSCEIVERS, AND CLOCK GENERATORS

OCTAL BI-/TRI-DIRECTIONAL BUS TRANSCEIVERS

DESCRIPTION	TYPE OF OUTPUT	TYPE	ALS	AS	LS
12 mA, 24 mA, 48 mA, 64 mA Sink, True Outputs	Low Power	3-State	'245	A	●	
						●
		OC	'621	A	●	
		3-State	'623	A	●	
						●
		OC, 3-State	'639	A	●	
						●
		3-State	'652	●	●	
						●
		OC, 3-State	'654	●		
	Very Low Power	OC	'1621	●		
		3-State	'1623	●		
		OC, 3-State	'1639	●		
12 mA, 24 mA, 48 mA, 64 mA Sink, Inverting Outputs	Low Power	3-State	'620	A	●	
						●
		OC	'622	A	●	
						●
		OC, 3-State	'638	A	●	
						●
		3-State	'651	●	●	
						●
		OC, 3-State	'653	●		
						●
	Very Low Power	3-State	'1620	●		
		OC	'1622	●		
		OC, 3-State	'1638	●		
12 mA, 24 mA, 48 mA, 64 mA Sink, True Outputs	Low Power	OC	'641	A	●	
						●
		3-State	'645	A	●	
						●
	Very Low Power	OC	'1641	●		
		3-State	'1645	A		
12 mA, 24 mA, 48 mA, 64 mA Sink, Inverting Outputs	Low Power	3-State	'640	A	●	
						●
		OC	'642	A	●	
						●
	Very Low Power	3-State	'1640	A		
		OC	'1642	●		
12 mA, 24 mA, 48 mA, 64 mA Sink, True and Inverting Outputs	Low Power	3-State	'643	A	●	
		OC	'644	A	●	
						●
	Very Low Power	3-State	'1643	●		
		OC	'1644	●		

OCTAL BI-/TRI-DIRECTIONAL BUS TRANSCEIVERS

DESCRIPTION	TYPE OF OUTPUT	TYPE	ALS	AS	LS
Registered with Multiplexed 12 mA, 24 mA, 48 mA, 64 mA True Outputs	3-State	'646	●	●	
						●
	OC	'647	●		
						●
Registered with Multiplexed 12 mA, 24 mA, 48 mA, 64 mA Inverting Outputs	3-State	'648	●	●	
						●
	OC	'649	●		
						●
Universal Transceiver Port Controllers	3-State	'877		●	
		'852		●	
		'856		●	

A Denotes "A" suffix version available in the technology indicated.

TEXAS
INSTRUMENTS

FLIP-FLOPS

DUAL AND SINGLE FLIP-FLOPS

DESCRIPTION	TYPE	TECHNOLOGY						
		STD TTL	ALS	AS			LS	S
Dual J-K Edge Triggered	'73	●						A
	'76							A
	'78							A
	'103							
	'106							
	'107	●						A
	'108							
	'109	●						A
			A	●				
	'112						A	●
			A	●				
	'113						A	●
			A	●				
	'114						A	●
			A	●				
Single J-K Edge Triggered	'70	●						
	'101							
	'102							
Dual Pulse Triggered	'73	●						
	'76	●						
	'78							
	'107	●						
Single Pulse Triggered	'71							
	'72	●						
	'104	●						
	'105	●						
Dual J-K with Data Lockout	'111	●						
Single J-K with Data Lockout	'110	●						
Dual D Type	'74	●					A	●
			A	●				

QUAD AND HEX FLIP-FLOPS

DESCRIPTION	NO. OF FFs	OUTPUTS	TYPE	TECHNOLOGY				
				STD TTL	ALS	AS	LS	S
D Type	6	Q	'174	●			●	●
			'378		●	●		
			'171				●	
	4	Q, Q̄	'175	●			●	●
			'379		●	●		
J-K	4	Q	'276	●				
			'376	●				

OCTAL, 9-BIT, AND 10-BIT D-TYPE FLIP-FLOPS

DESCRIPTION	NO. OF BITS	OUTPUTS	TYPE	TECHNOLOGY				
				STD TTL	ALS	AS	LS	S
True Data	Octal	3-State	'374		●	●		
			'574				●	●
True Data with Clear	Octal	2-State	'273	●			●	
		3-State	'575		●	●		
		3-State	'874		●	●		
		3-State	'878		●	●		
True with Enable	Octal	2-State	'377				●	
Inverting	Octal	3-State	'534		●	●		
		3-State	'564		●	●		
		3-State	'576		●	●		
Inverting with Clear	Octal	3-State	'577		●	●		
		3-State	'879		●	●		
Inverting with Preset	Octal	3-State	'876		●	●		
True	Octal	3-State	'825				●	
Inverting	Octal	3-State	'826				●	
True	9-Bit	3-State	'823				●	
Inverting	9-Bit	3-State	'824				●	
True	10-Bit	3-State	'821				●	
Inverting	10-Bit	3-State	'822				●	

2

FUNCTIONAL INDEX

A Denotes "A" suffix version available in the technology indicated.
B Denotes "B" suffix version available in the technology indicated.

TEXAS
INSTRUMENTS

LATCHES AND MULTIVIBRATORS

QUAD LATCHES

DESCRIPTION	OUTPUT	TYPE	STD TTL	ALS	AS	LS
Dual 2-Bit Transparent	2-State	'75	●			●
Dual 2-Bit Transparent	2-State	'77	●			●
Dual 2-Bit Transparent	2-State	'375				●
S-R	2-State	'279	●			A

RETRIGGERABLE MONOSTABLE MULTIVIBRATORS

DESCRIPTION	TYPE	STD TTL	ALS	AS	LS
Single	'122	●			●
Single	'130	●			
Single	'422				●
Dual	'123	●			●
Dual	'423				●

D-TYPE
OCTAL, 9-BIT, AND 10-BIT READ-BACK LATCHES

DESCRIPTION	NO. OF BITS	TYPE	STD TTL	ALS	AS	LS	S
Edge Triggered Inverting and Noninverting	Octal	'996		●			
Transparent True	Octal	'990		●			
Transparent True	9-Bit	'992		●			
Transparent True	10-Bit	'994		●			
Transparent Noninverting	Octal	'991		●			
Transparent Noninverting	9-Bit	'992		●			
Transparent Noninverting	10-Bit	'994		●			
Transparent with Clear True Outputs	Octal	'666		●			
Transparent with Clear Inverting Outputs	Octal	'667		●			

OCTAL, 9-BIT, AND 10-BIT LATCHES

DESCRIPTION	NO. OF BITS	OUTPUT	TYPE	STD TTL	ALS	AS	LS	S
Transparent	Octal	3-State	'268					●
Transparent	Octal	3-State	'373				●	●
Transparent	Octal	3-State	'573		●	●		
Dual 4-Bit Transparent	Octal	2-State	'116	●				
Dual 4-Bit Transparent	Octal	3-State	'873		●	●		
Inverting Transparent	Octal	3-State	'533		●	●		
Inverting Transparent	Octal	3-State	'563		●			
Inverting Transparent	Octal	3-State	'580		●	●		
Dual 4-Bit Inverting Transparent	Octal	3-State	'880		●	●		
2-Input Multiplexed	Octal	3-State	'604				●	
2-Input Multiplexed	Octal	3-State	'606				●	
2-Input Multiplexed	Octal	OC	'607				●	
Addressable	Octal	2-State	'259	●	●		●	
True	Octal	3-State	'845		●	●		
Inverting	Octal	3-State	'846		●	●		
True	9-Bit	3-State	'843		●	●		
Inverting	9-Bit	3-State	'844		●	●		
True	10-Bit	3-State	'841		●	●		
Inverting	10-Bit	3-State	'842		●	●		

MONOSTABLE MULTIVIBRATORS WITH SCHMITT-TRIGGER INPUTS

DESCRIPTION	TYPE	STD TTL	ALS	AS	LS	S
Single	'121	●				
Dual	'221	●			●	

TEXAS
INSTRUMENTS

REGISTERS

SHIFT REGISTERS

DESCRIPTION	NO. OF BITS	S-R	S-L	LOAD	HOLD	TYPE	STD TTL	ALS	AS	LS	S
Sign Protected			X	X	X	'322				A	
Parallel In, Parallel Out, Bidirectional	8	X	X	X	X	'198	•				
		X	X	X	X	'299				•	•
		X	X	X	X	'323		•	•	•	
	4	X	X	X	X	'194	•		•	A	•
Parallel In, Parallel Out, Registered Outputs	4	X	X	X	X	'671				•	
		X	X	X	X	'672				•	
Parallel In, Parallel Out	8	X		X	X	'199	•			•	
	5	X				'96	•			•	
	4	X	X			'95	A		•		B
		X	X			'99					
		X	X	X		'178	•				
		X	X			'195	•		•	A	•
		X	X			'295					B
		X	X			'395			•	A	
Serial In, Parallel Out	16	X		X	X	'673				•	
	8	X				'164	•		•	•	
Parallel In, Serial Out	16	X		X	X	'674				•	
	8	X		X	X	'165	•		•	A	
		X		X	X	'166	•		•	A	
Serial In, Serial Out	8	X				'91	A			•	
	4	X		X		'94	•				

SHIFT REGISTERS WITH LATCHES

DESCRIPTION	NO. OF BITS	OUTPUTS	TYPE	ALS	AS	LS
Parallel In, Parallel Out with Output Latches	4	3-State	'671			•
		3-State	'672			•
	16	2-State	'673			•
Serial In, Parallel Out with Output Latches	8	Buffered	'594			•
		3-State	'595			•
		OC	'596			•
		OC	'599			•
Parallel in, Serial Out with Input Latches	8	2-State	'597			•
Parallel I/O Ports with Input Latches, Multiplexed Serial Inputs	8	3-State	'598			•

SIGN-PROTECTED REGISTERS

DESCRIPTION	NO. OF BITS	S-R	S-L	LOAD	HOLD	TYPE	ALS	AS	LS
Sign Protected Register	8	X		X	X	'322			A

REGISTER FILES

DESCRIPTION	OUTPUT	TYPE	STD TTL	ALS	AS	LS
8 Words x 2 Bits	3-State	'172	•			
4 Words x 4 Bits	OC	'170	•			•
	3-State	'670				•
Dual 16 Words x 4 Bits	3-State	'870			•	
	3-State	'871			•	

OTHER REGISTERS

DESCRIPTION	TYPE	STD TTL	ALS	AS	LS	S
Quadruple Multiplexers with Storage	'98					
	'298	•			•	
	'398			•		
	'399					
8-Bit Universal Shift Registers	'299		•	•	•	•
Quadruple Bus Buffer Registers	'173	•			A	
Octal Storage Register	'396				•	

A Denotes "A" suffix version available in the technology indicated.
B Denotes "B" suffix version available in the technology indicated.

FUNCTIONAL INDEX 2

COUNTERS

SYNCHRONOUS COUNTERS — POSITIVE-EDGE TRIGGERED

DESCRIPTION	PARALLEL LOAD	TYPE	STD TTL	ALS	AS		LS	S
Decade	Sync	'160	•				A	
				B	•			
	Sync	'162	•				A	•
				B	•			
	Sync	'560	A					
	Sync	'668					•	
	Sync	'690					•	
Decade Up/Down	Sync	'168					B	
				B	•			
	Async	'190	•				•	
					•			
	Async	'192	•				•	
					•			
	Sync	'568	A					
	Sync	'696					•	
Decade Rate Multipler, $\frac{1}{N10}$	Async Set-to-9	'167	•					
4-Bit Binary	Sync	'161	•				A	
				B	•			
	Sync	'163	•				A	•
				B	•			
	Sync	'561	A					
	Sync	'669					•	
	Sync	'691					•	
	Sync	'693					•	
4-Bit Binary Up/Down	Sync	'169					B	•
				B	•			
	Async	'191	•				•	
					•			
	Async	'193	•				•	
					•			
	Sync	'569	A					
	Sync	'697					•	
	Sync	'699					•	
6-Bit Binary Rate Multipler, $\frac{1}{N2}$		'97	•					
8-Bit Up/Down	Async CLR	'867			•			
	Sync CLR	'869			•			

ASYNCHRONOUS COUNTERS (RIPPLE CLOCK) — NEGATIVE-EDGE TRIGGERED

DESCRIPTION	PARALLEL LOAD	TYPE	STD TTL	ALS	AS		LS	S
Decode	Set-to-9	'90	A				•	
		'68					•	
	Yes	'176	•				•	
	Yes	'196	•				•	•
	Set-to-9	'290	•				•	
4-Bit Binary	None	'93	A				•	
		'69					•	
	Yes	'177	•				•	
	Yes	'197	•				•	•
	None	'293	•				•	
Divide by 12	None	'92	A				•	
Dual Decode	None	'390	•				•	
	Set-to-9	'490					•	
Dual 4-Bit Binary	None	'393	•				•	

8-BIT BINARY COUNTERS WITH REGISTERS

DESCRIPTION	TYPE OF OUTPUT	TYPE	ALS	AS	LS
Parallel Register	3-State	'590			•
Outputs	OC	'591			•
Parallel Register Inputs	2-State	'592			•
Parallel I/O	3-State	'593			•

FREQUENCY DIVIDERS, RATE MULTIPLEXERS

DESCRIPTION	TYPE	STD TTL	ALS	AS	LS
50-to-1 Frequency Divider	'56				•
60-to-1 Frequency Divider	'57				•
60-Bit Binary Rate Multiplier	'97	•			
Decade Rate Multiplier	'167	•			

A Denotes "A" suffix version available in the technology indicated.
B Denotes "B" suffix version available in the technology indicated.

DECODERS, ENCODERS, DATA SELECTORS/MULTIPLEXERS AND SHIFTERS

DATA SELECTORS MULTIPLEXERS

DESCRIPTION	TYPE OF OUTPUT	TYPE	STD TTL	ALS	AS	LS	S
16-to-1	2-State	'150	●				
	3-State	'250			●		
	3-State	'850			●		
	3-State	'851			●		
Dual 8-to-1	3-State	'351	●				
8-to-1	2-State	'151	A			●	●
				●	●		
	2-State	'152	A			●	
	3-State	'251	●			●	●
				●	●		
	3-State	'354				●	
	2-State	'355				●	
	3-State	'356				●	
Dual 4-to-1	3-State	'153	●			●	●
				●	●		
	3-State	'253				●	●
				●	●		
	3-State	'352				●	
				●	●		
	3-State	'353				●	
				●	●		
Octal 2-to-1 with Storage	3-State	'604				●	
	OC	'605				●	
	3-State	'606				●	
	OC	'607				●	
Quad 2-to-1 with Storage	2-State	'98				●	
	2-State	'298	●			●	
					●		
	2-State	'399				●	
Quad 2-to-1	2-State	'157	●			●	●
				●	●		
	2-State	'158				●	●
				●	●		
	3-State	'257				B	●
				A	●		
	3-State	'258				B	●
				A	●		
6-to-1 Universal Multiplexer	3-State	'857		●	●		

DECODERS/DEMULTIPLEXERS

DESCRIPTION	TYPE OF OUTPUT	TYPE	STD TTL	ALS	AS	LS	S
4-to-16	3-State	'154	●				
	OC	'159	●				
4-to-10 BCD-to-Decimal	2-State	'42	A			●	
4-to-10 Excess-3-to-Decimal	2-State	'43	A				
4-to-10 Excess 3 Gray-to-Decimal	2-State	'44	A				
3-to-8 with Address Latches	2-State	'131		●	●		
		'137		●	●	●	
3-to-8	2-State	'138		●	●	●	●
	3-State	'538		●			
Dual 2-to-4	2-State	'139		●	●	A	●
	2-State	'155	●			A	
	OC	'156	●			●	
Dual 1-to-4 Decoders	3-State	'539		●		●	●

CODE CONVERTERS

DESCRIPTION	TYPE	STD TTL	S
BCD to Binary Converters	'484		A
Binary to BCD Converters	'485		A

PRIORITY ENCODERS/REGISTERS

DESCRIPTION	TYPE	STD TTL	ALS	AS	LS
Full BCD	'147	●			●
Cascadable Octal	'148	●			●
Cascadable Octal with 3-State Outputs	'348				●
4-Bit Cascadable with Registers	'278	●			

SHIFTERS

DESCRIPTION	OUTPUT	TYPE	STD TTL	ALS	AS	LS	S
4-Bit Shifter	3-State	'350					●
Parallel 16-Bit Multi Mode Barrel Shifter	3-State	'897			●		

A Denotes "A" suffix version available in the technology indicated.
B Denotes "B" suffix version available in the technology indicated.

FUNCTIONAL INDEX

2

Texas Instruments

DISPLAY DECODERS/DRIVERS, MEMORY/MICROPROCESSOR CONTROLLERS, AND VOLTAGE-CONTROLLED OSCILLATORS

OPEN-COLLECTOR DISPLAY DECODERS/DRIVERS

DESCRIPTION	OFF-STATE OUTPUT VOLTAGE	TYPE	TECHNOLOGY			
			STD TTL	ALS	AS	LS
BCD to Decimal	30 V	'45	●			
	15 V	'145	●			●
	7 V	'445				●
BCD-to-Seven-Segment	30 V	'46	A			
	15 V	'47	A			●
	5.5 V	'48	●			●
	5.5 V	'49	●			●
	30 V	'246	●			
	15 V	'247	●			●
	7 V	'447				●
	5.5 V	'248	●			●

OPEN COLLECTOR DISPLAY DECODERS/DRIVERS WITH COUNTERS/LATCH

DESCRIPTION	TYPE	TECHNOLOGY		
		STD TTL	ALS	AS
BCD Counter/4-Bit Latch/BCD-to-Decimal Decoder/Driver	'142	●		
BCD Counter/4-Bit Latch/BCD-to-Seven-Segment Decoder/Lad Driver	'143	●		

VOLTAGE-CONTROLLED OSCILLATORS

No. VCOs	COMP'L ZOUT	ENABLE	RANGE INPUT	Rext	fmax MHz	TYPE	TECHNOLOGY	
							LS	S
Single	Yes	Yes	Yes	No	20	'624	●	
Single	Yes	Yes	Yes	Yes	20	'628	●	
Dual	No	Yes	Yes	No	60	'124		●
Dual	Yes	Yes	No	No	20	'626	●	
Dual	No	No	No	No	20	'627	●	
Dual	No	Yes	Yes	No	20	'629	●	

MEMORY/MICROPROCESSOR CONTROLLERS

DESCRIPTION		TYPE	TECHNOLOGY			
			ALS	AS	LS	S
System Controllers, Universal or For 8881		'890	●			
Memory Refresh Controllers	Transparent, Burst Modes	4K, 16K	'600			A	
		64K	'601			A	
	Cycle Steal, Burst Modes	64K	'603			A	
Memory Mappers	3-State	'612			●	
	OC	'613			●	
Memory Mappers With Output Latches	3-State	'610			●	
	OC	'611			●	
Multi Mode Latches (8080A Applications)		'412				●

CLOCK GENERATOR CIRCUITS

DESCRIPTION	TYPE	TECHNOLOGY				
		STD TTL	ALS	AS	LS	S
Quadruple Complementary-Output Logic Elements	'265	●				
Dual Pulse Synchronizers/Drivers	'120	●				
Crystal Controlled Oscillators	'320				●	
	'321				●	
Digital Phase-Lock Loop	'297				●	
Programmable Frequency Dividers Digital Timers	'292				●	
	'294				●	
Triple 4-Input AND NAND Drivers	'800			●		
Triple 4-Input OR NOR Drivers	'802			●		
Dual VCO	'124					●

A Denotes "A" suffix version available in the technology indicated.

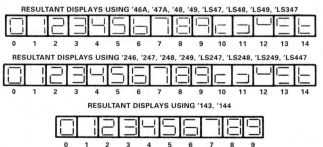

RESULTANT DISPLAYS USING '46A, '47A, '48, '49, 'LS47, 'LS48, 'LS49, 'LS347

0 1 2 3 4 5 6 7 8 9 10 11 12 13 14

RESULTANT DISPLAYS USING '246, '247, '248, '249, 'LS247, 'LS248, 'LS249, 'LS447

0 1 2 3 4 5 6 7 8 9 10 11 12 13 14

RESULTANT DISPLAYS USING '143, '144

0 1 2 3 4 5 6 7 8 9

TEXAS INSTRUMENTS

COMPARATORS AND ERROR DETECTION CIRCUITS

4-BIT COMPARATORS

DESCRIPTION					TYPE	TECHNOLOGY				
P=Q	P>Q	P<Q	OUTPUT	OUTPUT ENABLE		STD TTL	ALS	AS	LS	S
Yes	Yes	No	2-State	No	'85	●			●	●

8-BIT COMPARATORS

DESCRIPTION								TYPE	TECHNOLOGY		
INPUTS	P=Q	P̄=Q̄	P>Q	P<Q	OUTPUT	OUTPUT ENABLE			ALS	AS	LS
20 kΩ Pull Up	Yes	No	No	No	OC	Yes	'518	●		
	No	Yes	No	No	2-State	Yes	'520	●		
	No	Yes	No	No	OC	Yes	'522	●		
	Yes	No	Yes	No	2-State	No	'682			●
	Yes	No	Yes	No	OC	No	'683			●
Standard	Yes	No	No	No	OC	Yes	'519	●		
	No	Yes	No	No	2-State	Yes	'521	●		
	Yes	No	Yes	No	2-State	No	'684			●
	Yes	No	Yes	No	OC	No	'685			●
	Yes	No	Yes	No	2-State	Yes	'686			●
	Yes	No	Yes	No	OC	Yes	'687			●
	No	Yes	No	Yes	2-State	Yes	'688	●		●
	No	Yes	No	No	OC	Yes	'689	●		●
Latched P	No	No	Yes	Yes	2-State	Yes	'885		●	
Latched P and Q	Yes	No	Yes	Yes	Latched	Yes	'866		●	

ADDRESS COMPARATORS

DESCRIPTION	OUTPUT ENABLE	LATCHED OUTPUT	TYPE	TECHNOLOGY	
				ALS	AS
16-Bit to 4-Bit	Yes		'677	●	
		Yes	'678	●	
12-Bit to 4-Bit	Yes		'679	●	
		Yes	'680	●	

PARITY GENERATORS/CHECKERS, ERROR DETECTION AND CORRECTION CIRCUITS

DESCRIPTION		NO. OF BITS	TYPE	TECHNOLOGY				
				STD TTL	ALS	AS	LS	S
Odd Even Parity Generators Checkers		8	'180	●				
		9	'280				●	●
		9	'286			●		
Parallel Error Detection Correction Circuits	3-State	8	'636				●	
	OC	8	'637				●	
	3-State	16	'616		●	●		
	OC	16	'617		●			
	3-State	16	'630				●	
	OC	16	'631				●	
	3-State	32	'632		A			
	OC	32	'633		●			
	3-State	32	'634		●			
	OC	32	'635		●			

FUSE-PROGRAMMABLE COMPARATORS

DESCRIPTION	TYPE	TECHNOLOGY			
		STD TTL	ALS	AS	LS	S
16-Bit Identity Comparator	'526		●		
12-Bit Identity Comparator	'528		●		
8-Bit Identity Comparator and 4-Bit Comparator	'527		●		

2

TEXAS
INSTRUMENTS

ARITHMETIC CIRCUITS AND PROCESSOR ELEMENTS

PARALLEL BINARY ADDERS

DESCRIPTION	TYPE	STD TTL	ALS	AS		LS	S
1-Bit Gated	'80	●					
4-Bit	'83	A				A	
	'283	●				●	●
Dual 1-Bit Carry Save	'183					●	

ACCUMULATORS, ARITHMETIC LOGIC UNITS, LOOK-AHEAD CARRY GENERATORS

DESCRIPTION		TYPE	STD TTL	ALS	AS	LS	S
4-Bit parallel Binary Accumulators		'281					●
		'681			●		
4-Bit Arithmetic Logic Units/ Function Generators		'181				●	●
		'381			A		
					A		
		'881			A		●
4-Bit Arithmetic Logic Unit with Ripple Carry		'382				●	
Look-Ahead Carry Generators	16 Bit	'182			●		●
		'282			●		
	32 Bit	'882			●		
Quad Serial Adder/Subtractor		'385				●	
8-Bit Slice Elements		'888			●		

MULTIPLIERS

DESCRIPTION	TYPE	STD TTL	ALS	AS	LS	S
2-Bit-by-4-Bit Parallel Binary Multipliers	'261				●	
4-Bit-by-4-Bit Parallel Binary Multipliers	'285	●				
25-MHz 6-Bit Binary Rate Multipliers	'97	●				
25-MHz Decade Rate Multipliers	'167	●				
8-Bit x 1-Bit 2's Complement Multipliers	'384				●	
16-Bit Multimode Multiplier	'1616		●			

OTHER ARITHMETIC OPERATORS

DESCRIPTION	TYPE	STD TTL	ALS	AS		LS	S
Quad 2-Input Exclusive-OR Gates with Totem-Pole Outputs	'86	●				A	●
	'386		●			A	
Quad 2-Input Exclusive-OR Gates with Open-Collector Outputs	'136	●					●
			●				
Quad 2-Input Exclusive-NOR Gates	'256					●	
	'810		●	●			
Quad 2-Input Exclusive-NOR Gates with Open-Collector Outputs	'811		●	●			
Quad Exclusive OR/NOR Gates	'135						●
4-Bit True/Complement, Element	'87						

BIPOLAR BIT/SLICE PROCESSOR ELEMENTS

DESCRIPTION	CASCADABLE TO N-BITS	TYPE	ALS	AS	LS	S
8-Bit Slice	Yes	'888		●		

A Denotes "A" suffix version available in the technology indicated.

MEMORIES

USER-PROGRAMMABLE READ-ONLY MEMORIES (PROM's)
STANDARD PROM's

DESCRIPTION	TYPE	ORGANIZATION	TYPE OUTPUT	S
16K-Bit Arrays	TBP28S166	2048W x 8B	3-State	●
	TBP38S165	2048W x 8B	3-State	●
	TBP38S166	2048W x 8B	3-State	●
	TBP38SA165	2048W x 8B	OC	●
	TBP38SA166	2048W x 8B	OC	●
	TBP34S162	4096W x 4B	3-State	●
	TBP34SA162	4096W x 4B	OC	●
8K-Bit Arrays	TBP24S81	2048W x 4B	3-State	●
	TBP24SA81	2048W x 4B	OC	●
	TBP28S85A	1024W x 8B	3-State	●
	TBP28S86A	1024W x 8B	3-State	●
	TBP28SA86A	1024W x 8B	OC	●
	TBP38S85	1024W x 8B	3-State	●
	TBP38S86	1024W x 8B	3-State	●
	TBP38SA85	1024W x 8B	OC	●
	TBP38SA86	1024W x 8B	OC	●
4K-Bit Arrays	TBP24S41	1024W x 4B	3-State	●
	TBP24SA41	1024W x 4B	OC	●
	TBP28S42	512W x 8B	3-State	●
	TBP28SA42	512W x 8B	OC	●
	TBP28S46	512W x 8B	3-State	●
	TBP28SA46	512W x 8B	OC	●
2K-Bit Arrays	TBP38S22	256W x 8B	3-State	●
	TBP38SA22	256W x 8B	OC	●
1K-Bit Arrays	TBP24S10	256W x 4B	3-State	●
	TBP24SA10	256W x 4B	OC	●
	TBP34S10	256W x 4B	3-State	●
	TBP34SA10	256W x 4B	OC	●
256-Bit Arrays	TBP18S030	32W x 8B	3-State	●
	TBP18SA030	32W x 8B	OC	●
	TBP38S030	32W x 8B	3-State	●
	TBP38SA030	32W x 8B	OC	●

LOW-POWER PROM's

DESCRIPTION	TYPE	ORGANIZATION	TYPE OUTPUT	S
16K-Bit Arrays	TBP28L166	2048W x 8B	3-State	●
	TBP38L165	2048W x 8B	3-State	●
	TBP28L166	2048W x 8B	3-State	●
	TBP34L162	4096W x 4B	3-State	●
8K-Bit Arrays	TBP28L85A	1024W x 8B	3-State	●
	TBP28L86A	1024W x 8B	3-State	●
	TBP38L85	1024W x 8B	3-State	●
	TBP38L86	1024W x 8B	3-State	●
4K-Bit Arrays	TBP28L42	512W x 8B	3-State	●
	TBP28L46	512W x 8B	3-State	●
2K-Bit Arrays	TBP28L22	256W x 8B	3-State	●
	TBP28LA22	256W x 8B	OC	●
	TBP38L22	256W x 8B	3-State	●
1K-Bit Arrays	TBP34L10	256W x 4B	3-State	●
256-Bit Arrays	TBP38L030	32W x 8B	3-State	●

A Denotes "A" suffix version available in the technology indicated.
B Denotes "B" suffix version available in the technology indicated.

REGISTERED PROM's

DESCRIPTION	TYPE	ORGANIZATION	TYPE OUTPUT	S
16K Bit Arrays	TBP34R162	4096W x 4B	3-State	●
	TBP34SR165	4096W x 4B	3-State	●

RANDOM-ACCESS READ-WRITE MEMORIES (RAM's)

DESCRIPTION	ORGANI-ZATION	TYPE OF OUTPUT	TYPE	STD TTL	ALS	AS	LS	S
256-Bit Arrays	256 x 1	3-State	'201					●
		OC	'301					●
64-Bit-Arrays	16 x 4	OC	'89	●				
		3-State	'189				A	B
		3-State	'219			A		
		OC	'289				A	B
		OC	'319			A		
16-Bit Multiple-Port Register File	8 x 2	3-State	'172	●				
16-Bit Register File	4 x 4	OC	'170	●			●	
		3-State	'670	●			●	
Dual 64-Bit Register Files	16 x 4	3-State	'870			●		
			'871			●		

FIRST-IN FIRST-OUT MEMORIES (FIFO's)

DESCRIPTION	TYPE OF OUTPUT	TYPE	ALS	AS	LS	LS
16 Words x 5 Bits	3-State	'225				●
64 Words x 5 Bits	3-State	'233	●			
64 Words x 4 Bits	3-State	'232	●			

2

FUNCTIONAL INDEX

FUNCTIONAL INDEX

PROGRAMMABLE LOGIC ARRAYS

PROGRAMMABLE LOGIC ARRAYS

DESCRIPTION	INPUTS	NO.	OUTPUTS TYPE	TYPE NO.	ALS	NO. OF PINS
Impact PAL® Circuits	16	8	Active-Low	PAL16L8-15	●	20
		4		PAL16R4-15	●	
		6	Registered	PAL16R6-15	●	
		8		PAL16R8-15	●	
Half-Power Impact Circuits	16	8	Active-Low	PAL16L8-25	●	20
		4		PAL16R4-25	●	
		6	Registered	PAL16R6-25	●	
		8		PAL16R8-25	●	
High-Perfomance PAL® Circuits	16	8	Active-Low	PAL16L8A	●	20
		4		PAL16R4A	●	
		6	Registered	PAL16R6A	●	
		8		PAL16R8A	●	
Half-Power PAL® Circuits	16	8	Active-Low	PAL16L8A-2	●	20
		4		PAL16R4A-2	●	
		6	Registered	PAL16R6A-2	●	
		8		PAL16R8A-2	●	
High-Performance PAL® Circuits	20	8	Active-Low	PAL20L8A	●	24
		4		PAL20R4A	●	
		6	Registered	PAL20R6A	●	
		8		PAL20R8A	●	
Half-Power PAL® Circuits	20	8	Active-Low	PAL20L8A-2	●	24
		4		PAL20R4A-2	●	
		6	Registered	PAL20R6A-2	●	
		8		PAL20R8A-2	●	
Exclusive-OR PAL® Circuits	20	10	Active-Low	PAL20L10-20	●	24
		4		PAL20X4-20	●	
		8	Registered	PAL20X8-20	●	
		10		PAL20X10-20	●	
Exclusive-OR PAL® Circuits	20	8	Active-Low	PALR19L8-35	●	24
		4		PAL20X4-35	●	
		8	Registered	PAL20X8-35	●	
		10		PAL20X10-35	●	
Registered-Input PAL® Circuits	19	8	Active-Low	PAL19L8-25	●	24
		4		PALR19R4-25	●	
		6	Registered	PALR19R6-25	●	
		8		PALR19R8-25	●	
Registered-Input PAL® Circuits	19	8	Active-Low	PALR19L8-40	●	24
		4		PALR19R4-40	●	
		6	Registered	PALR19R6-40	●	
		8		PALR19R8-40	●	
Latched-Input PAL® Circuits	19	8	Active-Low	PALT19L8-25	●	24
		4		PALT19R4-25	●	
		6	Registered	PALT19R6-25	●	
		8		PALT19R8-25	●	
Latched-Input PAL® Circuits	19	8	Active-Low	PALT19L8-40	●	24
		4		PALT19R4-40	●	
		6	Registered	PALT19R6-40	●	
		8		PALT19R8-40	●	
Field-Programmable 14 x 32 x 6 Logic Arrays	14	6	3-State	FPLA839	●	24
			OC	FPLA840	●	

® PAL is a Registered Trademark of Monolithic Memories Incorporated.

TEXAS
INSTRUMENTS

General Information | 1

Functional Index | 2

TTL Devices | 3

Mechanical Data | 4

3

TTL DEVICES

- Package Options Include Both Plastic and Ceramic Chip Carriers in Addition to Plastic and Ceramic DIPs
- Dependable Texas Instruments Quality and Reliability

description

These devices contain four independent 2-input NAND gates.

The SN5400, and SN54LS00, and SN54S00 are characterized for operation over the full military temperature range of −55°C to 125°C. The SN7400, SN74LS00, and SN74S00 are characterized for operation from 0°C to 70°C.

FUNCTION TABLE (each gate)

INPUTS		OUTPUT
A	B	Y
H	H	L
L	X	H
X	L	H

logic diagram (each gate)

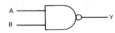

positive logic

$$Y = \overline{A \cdot B} \ \text{ or } \ Y = \overline{A} + \overline{B}$$

SN5400 . . . J PACKAGE
SN54LS00, SN54S00 . . . J OR W PACKAGE
SN7400 . . . J OR N PACKAGE
SN74LS00, SN74S00 . . . D, J OR N PACKAGE
(TOP VIEW)

SN5400 . . . W PACKAGE
(TOP VIEW)

SN54LS00, SN54S00 . . . FK PACKAGE
SN74LS00, SN74S00
(TOP VIEW)

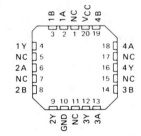

NC - No internal connection

3

TTL DEVICES

TEXAS
INSTRUMENTS

3-3

schematics (each gate)

'00

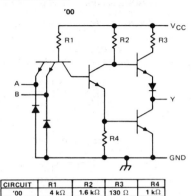

CIRCUIT	R1	R2	R3	R4
'00	4 kΩ	1.6 kΩ	130 Ω	1 kΩ

'LS00

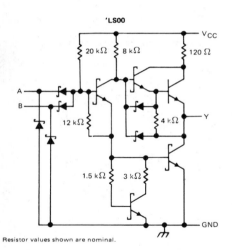

'S00

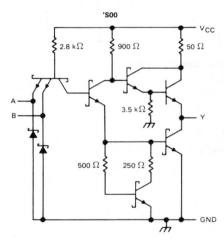

Resistor values shown are nominal.

absolute maximum ratings over operating free-air temperature range (unless otherwise noted)

Supply voltage, V_{CC} (see Note 1) '00, 'LS00, 'S00 . . . . 7 V

Input voltage: '00, 'S00 . . . . 5.5 V

'LS00 . . . . 7 V

Operating free-air temperature range: SN54' . . . . −55°C to 125°C

SN74' . . . . 0°C to 70°C

Storage temperature range . . . . −65°C to 150°C

NOTE 1: Voltage values are with respect to network ground terminal.

TEXAS
INSTRUMENTS

recommended operating conditions

		SN5400			SN7400			UNIT
		MIN	NOM	MAX	MIN	NOM	MAX	
V_{CC}	Supply voltage	4.5	5	5.5	4.75	5	5.25	V
V_{IH}	High-level input voltage	2			2			V
V_{IL}	Low-level input voltage			0.8			0.8	V
I_{OH}	High-level output current			−0.4			−0.4	mA
I_{OL}	Low-level output current			16			16	mA
T_A	Operating free-air temperature	−55		125	0		70	°C

electrical characteristics over recommended operating free-air temperature range (unless otherwise noted)

PARAMETER	TEST CONDITIONS †			SN5400			SN7400			UNIT
				MIN	TYP‡	MAX	MIN	TYP‡	MAX	
V_{IK}	V_{CC} = MIN,	I_I = −12 mA				−1.5			−1.5	V
V_{OH}	V_{CC} = MIN,	V_{IL} = 0.8 V,	I_{OH} = −0.4 mA	2.4	3.4		2.4	3.4		V
V_{OL}	V_{CC} = MIN,	V_{IH} = 2 V,	I_{OL} = 16 mA		0.2	0.4		0.2	0.4	V
I_I	V_{CC} = MAX,	V_I = 5.5 V				1			1	mA
I_{IH}	V_{CC} = MAX,	V_I = 2.4 V				40			40	µA
I_{IL}	V_{CC} = MAX,	V_I = 0.4 V				−1.6			−1.6	mA
I_{OS}§	V_{CC} = MAX			−20		−55	−18		−55	mA
I_{CCH}	V_{CC} = MAX,	V_I = 0 V			4	8		4	8	mA
I_{CCL}	V_{CC} = MAX,	V_I = 4.5 V			12	22		12	22	mA

† For conditions shown as MIN or MAX, use the appropriate value specified under recommended operating conditions.
‡ All typical values are at V_{CC} = 5 V, T_A = 25°C.
§ Not more than one output should be shorted at a time.

switching characteristics, V_{CC} = 5 V, T_A = 25°C (see note 2)

PARAMETER	FROM (INPUT)	TO (OUTPUT)	TEST CONDITIONS		MIN	TYP	MAX	UNIT
t_{PLH}	A or B	Y	R_L = 400 Ω,	C_L = 15 pF		11	22	ns
t_{PHL}						7	15	ns

NOTE 2: See General Information Section for load circuits and voltage waveforms.

3

TTL DEVICES

TEXAS
INSTRUMENTS

recommended operating conditions

		SN54LS00			SN74LS00			UNIT
		MIN	NOM	MAX	MIN	NOM	MAX	
V_{CC}	Supply voltage	4.5	5	5.5	4.75	5	5.25	V
V_{IH}	High-level input voltage	2			2			V
V_{IL}	Low-level input voltage			0.7			0.8	V
I_{OH}	High-level output current			-0.4			-0.4	mA
I_{OL}	Low-level output current			4			8	mA
T_A	Operating free-air temperature	-55		125	0		70	°C

electrical characteristics over recommended operating free-air temperature range (unless otherwise noted)

PARAMETER	TEST CONDITIONS †		SN54LS00			SN74LS00			UNIT
			MIN	TYP‡	MAX	MIN	TYP‡	MAX	
V_{IK}	V_{CC} = MIN,	$I_I = -18$ mA			-1.5			-1.5	V
V_{OH}	V_{CC} = MIN,	V_{IL} = MAX, $I_{OH} = -0.4$ mA	2.5	3.4		2.7	3.4		V
V_{OL}	V_{CC} = MIN,	V_{IH} = 2 V, I_{OL} = 4 mA		0.25	0.4		0.25	0.4	V
	V_{CC} = MIN,	V_{IH} = 2 V, I_{OL} = 8 mA					0.35	0.5	
I_I	V_{CC} = MAX,	V_I = 7 V			0.1			0.1	mA
I_{IH}	V_{CC} = MAX,	V_I = 2.7 V			20			20	µA
I_{IL}	V_{CC} = MAX,	V_I = 0.4 V			-0.4			-0.4	mA
I_{OS} §	V_{CC} = MAX		-20		-100	-20		-100	mA
I_{CCH}	V_{CC} = MAX,	V_I = 0 V		0.8	1.6		0.8	1.6	mA
I_{CCL}	V_{CC} = MAX,	V_I = 4.5 V		2.4	4.4		2.4	4.4	mA

† For conditions shown as MIN or MAX, use the appropriate value specified under recommended operating conditions.
‡ All typical values are at V_{CC} = 5 V, T_A = 25°C
§ Not more than one output should be shorted at a time, and the duration of the short-circuit should not exceed one second.

switching characteristics, V_{CC} = 5 V, T_A = 25°C (see note 2)

PARAMETER	FROM (INPUT)	TO (OUTPUT)	TEST CONDITIONS		MIN	TYP	MAX	UNIT
t_{PLH}	A or B	Y	R_L = 2 kΩ,	C_L = 15 pF		9	15	ns
t_{PHL}						10	15	ns

NOTE 2: See General Information Section for load circuits and voltage waveforms.

3

TTL DEVICES

TEXAS
INSTRUMENTS

recommended operating conditions

		SN54S00			SN74S00			UNIT
		MIN	NOM	MAX	MIN	NOM	MAX	
V_{CC}	Supply voltage	4.5	5	5.5	4.75	5	5.25	V
V_{IH}	High-level input voltage	2			2			V
V_{IL}	Low-level input voltage			0.8			0.8	V
I_{OH}	High-level output current			-1			-1	mA
I_{OL}	Low-level output current			20			20	mA
T_A	Operating free-air temperature	-55		125	0		70	$^\circ$C

electrical characteristics over recommended operating free-air temperature range (unless otherwise noted)

PARAMETER	TEST CONDITIONS †			SN54S00			SN74S00			UNIT
				MIN	TYP‡	MAX	MIN	TYP‡	MAX	
V_{IK}	V_{CC} = MIN,	$I_I = -18$ mA				-1.2			-1.2	V
V_{OH}	V_{CC} = MIN,	$V_{IL} = 0.8$ V,	$I_{OH} = -1$ mA	2.5	3.4		2.7	3.4		V
V_{OL}	V_{CC} = MIN,	$V_{IH} = 2$ V,	$I_{OL} = 20$ mA			0.5			0.5	V
I_I	V_{CC} = MAX,	$V_I = 5.5$ V				1			1	mA
I_{IH}	V_{CC} = MAX,	$V_I = 2.7$ V				50			50	μA
I_{IL}	V_{CC} = MAX,	$V_I = 0.5$ V				-2			-2	mA
I_{OS}§	V_{CC} = MAX			-40		-100	-40		-100	mA
I_{CCH}	V_{CC} = MAX,	$V_I = 0$ V			10	16		10	16	mA
I_{CCL}	V_{CC} = MAX,	$V_I = 4.5$ V			20	36		20	36	mA

† For conditions shown as MIN or MAX, use the appropriate value specified under recommended operating conditions.
‡ All typical values are at V_{CC} = 5 V, T_A = 25°C.
§ Not more than one output should be shorted at a time, and the duration of the short-circuit should not exceed one second.

switching characteristics, V_{CC} = 5 V, T_A = 25°C (see note 2)

PARAMETER	FROM (INPUT)	TO (OUTPUT)	TEST CONDITIONS		MIN	TYP	MAX	UNIT
t_{PLH}	A or B	Y	$R_L = 280\ \Omega$,	$C_L = 15$ pF		3	4.5	ns
t_{PHL}						3	5	ns
t_{PLH}			$R_L = 280\ \Omega$,	$C_L = 50$ pF			4.5	ns
t_{PHL}							5	ns

NOTE 2: See General Information Section for load circuits and voltage waveforms.

3

TTL DEVICES

TEXAS
INSTRUMENTS

- Package Options Include both Plastic and Ceramic Chip Carriers in Addition to Plastic and Ceramic DIPS

- Dependable Texas Instruments Quality and Reliability

description

These devices contain four independent 2-input-NAND gates. The open-collector outputs require pull-up resistors to perform correctly. They may be connected to other open-collector outputs to implement active-low wired-OR or active-high wired-AND functions. Open-collector devices are often used to generate higher V_{OH} levels.

The SN5401, and SN54LS01 are characterized for operation over the full military temperature ranges of −55°C to 125°C. The SN7401, and SN74S01 are characterized for operation from 0°C to 70°C.

FUNCTION TABLE (each gate)

INPUTS		OUTPUT
A	B	Y
H	H	L
L	X	H
X	L	H

logic diagram (each gate)

positive logic

$$Y = \overline{A \cdot B} \quad \text{or} \quad Y = \overline{A} + \overline{B}$$

SN5401 . . . J PACKAGE
SN54LS01 . . . J OR W PACKAGE
SN7401 . . . J OR N PACKAGE
SN74LS01 . . . D, J OR N PACKAGE
(TOP VIEW)

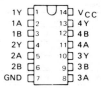

SN5401 . . . W PACKAGE
(TOP VIEW)

SN54LS01 . . . FK PACKAGE
SN74LS01
(TOP VIEW)

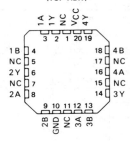

NC   No internal connection

3

TTL DEVICES

schematics (each gate)

'01

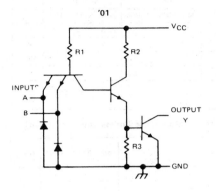

'LS01

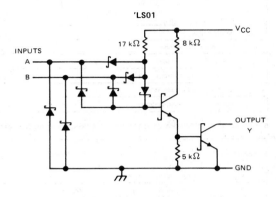

CIRCUITS	R1	R2	R3
'01	4 kΩ	1.6 kΩ	1 kΩ

Resistor values shown are nominal.

absolute maximum ratings over operating free-air temperature range(unless otherwise noted)

Supply voltage, V_{CC} (see Note 1): '01, 'H01, 'LS01 . . . . 7 V
Input voltage: '01 . . . . 5.5 V
            'LS01 . . . . 7 V
Off-state output voltage . . . . 7 V
Operating free-air temperature range: SN54' . . . . −55°C to 125°C
                                  SN74' . . . . 0°C to 70°C
Storage temperature range . . . . −65°C to 150°C

NOTE 1: Voltage values are with respect to network ground terminal.

3

TTL DEVICES

TEXAS
INSTRUMENTS

recommended operating conditions

		SN5401			SN7401			UNIT
		MIN	NOM	MAX	MIN	NOM	MAX	
V_{CC}	Supply voltage	4.5	5	5.5	4.75	5	5.25	V
V_{IH}	High-level input voltage	2			2			V
V_{IL}	Low-level input voltage			0.8			0.8	V
V_{OH}	High-level output voltage			5.5			5.5	V
I_{OL}	Low-level output current			16			16	mA
T_A	Operating free-air temperature	−55		125	0		70	°C

electrical characteristics over recommended operating free-air temperature range (unless otherwise noted)

PARAMETER	TEST CONDITIONS†			MIN	TYP‡	MAX	UNIT
V_{IK}	V_{CC} = MIN,	$I_I = -12$ mA				−1.5	V
I_{OH}	V_{CC} = MIN,	V_{IL} = 0.8 V,	V_{OH} = 5.5 V			0.25	mA
V_{OL}	V_{CC} = MIN,	V_{IH} = 2 V,	I_{OL} = 16 mA		0.2	0.4	V
I_I	V_{CC} = MAX,	V_I = 5.5 V				1	mA
I_{IH}	V_{CC} = MAX,	V_I = 2.4 V				40	µA
I_{IL}	V_{CC} = MAX,	V_I = 0.4 V				−1.6	mA
I_{CCH}	V_{CC} = MAX,	V_I = 0 V			4	8	mA
I_{CCL}	V_{CC} = MAX,	V_I = 4.5 V			12	22	mA

† For conditions shown as MIN or MAX, use the appropriate value specified under recommended operating conditions.
‡ All typical values are at V_{CC} = 5 V, T_A = 25°C.

switching characteristics, V_{CC} = 5 V, T_A = 25°C (see note 2)

PARAMETER	FROM (INPUT)	TO (OUTPUT)	TEST CONDITIONS		MIN	TYP	MAX	UNIT
t_{PLH}	A or B	Y	R_L = 4 kΩ,	C_L = 15 pF		35	55	ns
t_{PHL}			R_L = 400 Ω,	C_L = 15 pF		8	15	ns

NOTE 2: See General Information Section for load circuits and voltage waveforms.

TEXAS
INSTRUMENTS

recommended operating conditions

		SN54LS01			SN74LS01			UNIT
		MIN	NOM	MAX	MIN	NOM	MAX	
V_{CC}	Supply voltage	4.5	5	5.5	4.75	5	5.25	V
V_{IH}	High-level input voltage	2			2			V
V_{IL}	Low-level input voltage			0.7			0.8	V
V_{OH}	High-level output voltage			5.5			5.5	V
I_{OL}	Low-level output current			4			8	mA
T_A	Operating free-air temperature	-55		125	0		70	$^\circ$C

electrical characteristics over recommended operating free-air temperature range (unless otherwise noted)

PARAMETER	TEST CONDITIONS†			SN54LS01			SN74LS01			UNIT
				MIN	TYP‡	MAX	MIN	TYP‡	MAX	
V_{IK}	V_{CC} = MIN,	I_I = $-$18 mA				-1.5			-1.5	V
I_{OH}	V_{CC} = MIN,	V_{IL} = MAX,	V_{OH} = 5.5 V			0.1			0.1	mA
V_{OL}	V_{CC} = MIN,	V_{IH} = 2 V,	I_{OL} = 4 mA		0.25	0.4		0.25	0.4	V
	V_{CC} = MIN,	V_{IH} = 2 V,	I_{OL} = 8 mA					0.35	0.5	
I_I	V_{CC} = MAX,	V_I = 7 V				0.1			0.1	mA
I_{IH}	V_{CC} = MAX,	V_I = 2.7 V				20			20	μA
I_{IL}	V_{CC} = MAX,	V_I = 0.4 V				-0.4			-0.4	mA
I_{CCH}	V_{CC} = MAX,	V_I = 0 V			0.8	1.6		0.8	1.6	mA
I_{CCL}	V_{CC} = MAX,	V_I = 4.5 V			2.4	4.4		2.4	4.4	mA

† For conditions shown as MIN or MAX, use the appropriate value specified under recommended operating conditions.
‡ All typical values are at V_{CC} = 5 V, T_A = 25°C.

switching characteristics, V_{CC} = 5 V, T_A = 25°C (see note 2)

PARAMETER	FROM (INPUT)	TO (OUTPUT)	TEST CONDITIONS		MIN	TYP	MAX	UNIT
t_{PLH}	A or B	Y	R_L = 2 kΩ,	C_L = 15 pF		17	32	ns
t_{PHL}						15	28	ns

NOTE 2: See General Information Section for load circuits and voltage waveforms.

3

TTL DEVICES

TEXAS
INSTRUMENTS

- Package Options Include Both Plastic and Ceramic Chip Carriers in Addition to Plastic and Ceramic DIPs

- Dependable Texas Instruments Quality and Reliability

description

These devices contain four independent 2-input-NOR gates.

The SN5402, SN54LS02 and SN54S02 are characterized for operation over the full military temperature range of −55°C to 125°C. The SN7402, SN74LS02 and SN74S02 are characterized for operation from 0°C to 70°C.

FUNCTION TABLE (each gate)

INPUTS		OUTPUT
A	B	Y
H	X	L
X	H	L
L	L	H

logic diagram (each gate)

positive logic

$$Y = \overline{A} \cdot \overline{B} \text{ or } Y = \overline{A + B}$$

SN5402 . . . J PACKAGE
SN54LS02, SN54S02 . . . J OR W PACKAGE
SN7402 . . . J OR N PACKAGE
SN74LS02, SN74S02 . . . D, J OR N PACKAGE
(TOP VIEW)

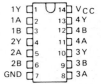

SN5402 . . . W PACKAGE
(TOP VIEW)

SN54LS02, SN54S02 . . . FK PACKAGE
SN74LS02, SN74S02
(TOP VIEW)

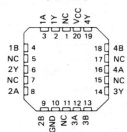

NC - No internal connection

TEXAS
INSTRUMENTS

3

TTL DEVICES

schematics (each gate)

'02

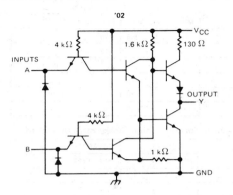

'LS02

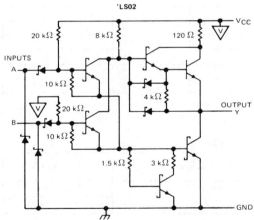

'S02

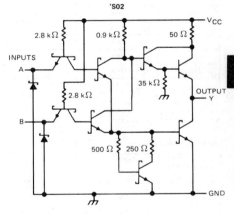

Resistor values shown are nominal.

absolute maximum ratings over operating free-air temperature range (unless otherwise noted)

Supply voltage, V_{CC} (see Note 1): '02, 'LS02, 'S02 .... 7 V

Input voltage: '02, 'S02 .... 5.5 V
             'LS02 .... 7 V
Off-state output voltage... 7 V
Operating free-air temperature range: SN54' .... -55°C to 125°C
                                SN74' .... 0°C to 70°C
Storage temperature range .... -65°C to 150°C

NOTE 1: Voltage values are with respect to network ground terminal.

TEXAS
INSTRUMENTS

3-13

recommended operating conditions

		SN5402 MIN	SN5402 NOM	SN5402 MAX	SN7402 MIN	SN7402 NOM	SN7402 MAX	UNIT
V_{CC}	Supply voltage	4.5	5	5.5	4.75	5	5.25	V
V_{IH}	High-level input voltage	2			2			V
V_{IL}	Low-level input voltage			0.8			0.8	V
I_{OH}	High-level output current			− 0.4			− 0.4	mA
I_{OL}	Low-level output current			16			16	mA
T_A	Operating free-air temperature	− 55		125	0		70	°C

electrical characteristics over recommended operating free-air temperature range (unless otherwise noted)

PARAMETER	TEST CONDITIONS†		SN5402 MIN	SN5402 TYP‡	SN5402 MAX	SN7402 MIN	SN7402 TYP‡	SN7402 MAX	UNIT
V_{IK}	V_{CC} = MIN,	I_I = − 12 mA			− 1.5			− 1.5	V
V_{OH}	V_{CC} = MIN,	V_{IL} = 0.8 V, I_{OH} = − 0.4 mA	2.4	3.4		2.4	3.4		V
V_{OL}	V_{CC} = MIN,	V_{IH} = 2 V, I_{OL} = 16 mA		0.2	0.4		0.2	0.4	V
I_I	V_{CC} = MAX,	V_I = 5.5 V			1			1	mA
I_{IH}	V_{CC} = MAX,	V_I = 2.4 V			40			40	µA
I_{IL}	V_{CC} = MAX,	V_I = 0.4 V			− 1.6			− 1.6	mA
I_{OS}§	V_{CC} = MAX		− 20		− 55	− 18		− 55	mA
I_{CCH}	V_{CC} = MAX,	V_I = 0 V		8	16		8	16	mA
I_{CCL}	V_{CC} = MAX,	See Note 2		14	27		14	27	mA

† For conditions shown as MIN or MAX, use the appropriate value specified under recommended operating conditions.
‡ All typical values are at V_{CC} = 5 V, T_A = 25°C.
§ Not more than one output should be shorted at a time.
NOTE 2: One input at 4.5 V, all others at GND.

switching characteristics, V_{CC} = 5 V, T_A = 25°C (see note 3)

PARAMETER	FROM (INPUT)	TO (OUTPUT)	TEST CONDITIONS		MIN	TYP	MAX	UNIT
t_{PLH}	A or B	Y	R_L = 400 Ω,	C_L = 15 pF		12	22	ns
t_{PHL}						8	15	ns

NOTE 3: See General Information Section for load circuits and voltage waveforms.

3

TTL DEVICES

recommended operating conditions

		SN54LS02			SN74LS02			UNIT
		MIN	NOM	MAX	MIN	NOM	MAX	
V_{CC}	Supply voltage	4.5	5	5.5	4.75	5	5.25	V
V_{IH}	High-level input voltage	2			2			V
V_{IL}	Low-level input voltage			0.7			0.8	V
I_{OH}	High-level output current			-0.4			-0.4	mA
I_{OL}	Low-level output current			4			8	mA
T_A	Operating free-air temperature	-55		125	0		70	°C

electrical characteristics over recommended operating free-air temperature range (unless otherwise noted)

PARAMETER	TEST CONDITIONS †			SN54LS02			SN74LS02			UNIT
				MIN	TYP‡	MAX	MIN	TYP‡	MAX	
V_{IK}	V_{CC} = MIN,	I_I = -18 mA				-1.5			-1.5	V
V_{OH}	V_{CC} = MIN,	V_{IL} = MAX,	I_{OH} = -0.4 mA	2.5	3.4		2.7	3.4		V
V_{OL}	V_{CC} = MIN,	V_{IH} = 2 V,	I_{OL} = 4 mA		0.25	0.4		0.25	0.4	V
	V_{CC} = MIN,	V_{IH} = 2 V,	I_{OL} = 8 mA					0.35	0.5	
I_I	V_{CC} = MAX,	V_I = 7 V				0.1			0.1	mA
I_{IH}	V_{CC} = MAX,	V_I = 2.7 V				20			20	μA
I_{IL}	V_{CC} = MAX,	V_I = 0.4 V				-0.4			-0.4	mA
I_{OS} §	V_{CC} = MAX			-20		-100	-20		-100	mA
I_{CCH}	V_{CC} = MAX,	V_I = 0 V			1.6	3.2		1.6	3.2	mA
I_{CCL}	V_{CC} = MAX,	See Note 2			2.8	5.4		2.8	5.4	mA

† For conditions shown as MIN or MAX, use the appropriate value specified under recommended operating conditions.
‡ All typical values are at V_{CC} = 5 V, T_A = 25°C
§ Not more than one output should be shorted at a time, and the duration of the short-circuit should not exceed one second.
NOTE 2: One input at 4.5 V, all others at GND.

switching characteristics, V_{CC} = 5 V, T_A = 25°C (see note 3)

PARAMETER	FROM (INPUT)	TO (OUTPUT)	TEST CONDITIONS		MIN	TYP	MAX	UNIT
t_{PLH}	A or B	Y	R_L = 2 kΩ,	C_L = 15 pF		10	15	ns
t_{PHL}						10	15	ns

NOTE 3: See General Information Section for load circuits and voltage waveforms.

TEXAS INSTRUMENTS

3

TTL DEVICES

recommended operating conditions

		SN54S02			SN74S02			UNIT
		MIN	NOM	MAX	MIN	NOM	MAX	
V_{CC}	Supply voltage	4.5	5	5.5	4.75	5	5.25	V
V_{IH}	High-level input voltage	2			2			V
V_{IL}	Low-level input voltage			0.8			0.8	V
I_{OH}	High-level output current			−1			−1	mA
I_{OL}	Low-level output current			20			20	mA
T_A	Operating free-air temperature	−55		125	0		70	°C

electrical characteristics over recommended operating free-air temperature range (unless otherwise noted)

PARAMETER	TEST CONDITIONS †			SN54S02			SN74S02			UNIT
				MIN	TYP‡	MAX	MIN	TYP‡	MAX	
V_{IK}	V_{CC} = MIN,	I_I = −18 mA				−1.2			−1.2	V
V_{OH}	V_{CC} = MIN,	V_{IL} = 0.8 V,	I_{OH} = −1 mA	2.5	3.4		2.7	3.4		V
V_{OL}	V_{CC} = MIN,	V_{IH} = 2 V,	I_{OL} = 20 mA			0.5			0.5	V
I_I	V_{CC} = MAX,	V_I = 5.5 V				1			1	mA
I_{IH}	V_{CC} = MAX,	V_I = 2.7 V				50			50	µA
I_{IL}	V_{CC} = MAX,	V_I = 0.5 V				−2			−2	mA
I_{OS} §	V_{CC} = MAX			−40		−100	−40		−100	mA
I_{CCH}	V_{CC} = MAX,	V_I = 0 V			17	29		17	29	mA
I_{CCL}	V_{CC} = MAX,	See Note 2			26	45		26	45	mA

† For conditions shown as MIN or MAX, use the appropriate value specified under recommended operating conditions.
‡ All typical values are at V_{CC} = 5 V, T_A = 25°C.
§ Not more than one output should be shorted at a time, and the duration of the short-circuit should not exceed one second.
NOTE 2: One input at 4.5 V, all others at GND.

switching characteristics, V_{CC} = 5 V, T_A = 25°C (see note 3)

PARAMETER	FROM (INPUT)	TO (OUTPUT)	TEST CONDITIONS		MIN	TYP	MAX	UNIT
t_{PLH}	A or B	Y	R_L = 280 Ω,	C_L = 15 pF		3.5	5.5	ns
t_{PHL}						3.5	5.5	ns
t_{PLH}			R_L = 280 Ω,	C_L = 50 pF		5		ns
t_{PHL}						5		ns

NOTE 3: See General Information Section for load circuits and voltage waveforms.

- **Package Options Include Both Plastic and Ceramic Chip Carriers in Addition to Plastic and Ceramic DIPs**

- **Dependable Texas Instruments Quality and Reliability**

description

These devices contain four independent 2-input NAND gates. The open-collector outputs require pull-up resistors to perform correctly. They may be connected to other open-collector outputs to implement active-low wired-OR or active-high wired-AND functions. Open-collector devices are often used to generate higher V_{OH} levels.

The SN5403, SN54LS03 and SN54S03 are characterized for operation over the full military temperature range of $-55°C$ to $125°C$. The SN7403, SN74LS03 and SN74S03 are characterized for operation from 0°C to 70°C.

SN5403 ... J PACKAGE
SN54LS03, SN54S03 ... J OR W PACKAGE
SN7403 ... J OR N PACKAGE
SN74LS03, SN74S03 ... D, J OR N PACKAGE
(TOP VIEW)

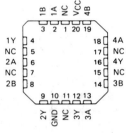

SN54LS03, SN54S03 ... FK PACKAGE
SN74LS03, SN74S03
(TOP VIEW)

NC - No internal connection

FUNCTION TABLE (each gate)

INPUTS		OUTPUT
A	B	Y
H	H	L
L	X	H
X	L	H

logic diagram (each gate)

positive logic

$$Y = \overline{A \cdot B} \text{ or } Y = \overline{A} + \overline{B}$$

TEXAS INSTRUMENTS

TTL DEVICES

3

TYPES SN5403, SN54LS03, SN54S03
SN7403, SN74LS03, SN74S03
QUADRUPLE 2-INPUT POSITIVE-NAND GATES WITH OPEN-COLLECTOR OUTPUTS

schematics (each gate)

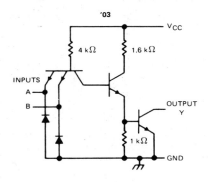

'03

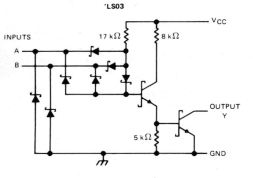

'LS03

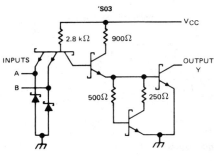

'S03

Resistor values shown are nominal.

absolute maximum ratings over operating free-air temperature range (unless otherwise noted)

Supply voltage, V_{CC} (see Note 1): '03, 'LS03, 'S03 . . . . 7 V

Input voltage: '03, 'S03 . . . . 5,5 V

'LS03 . . . . 7 V

Off-state output voltage: 'LS03, 'S03 . . . . 7 V

Operating free-air temperature range: SN54' . . . . -55°C to 125°C

SN74' . . . . 0°C to 70°C

Storage temperature range . . . . -65°C to 150°C

NOTE 1: Voltage values are with respect to network ground terminal.

3-18

TEXAS
INSTRUMENTS

recommended operating conditions

		SN5403			SN7403			UNIT
		MIN	NOM	MAX	MIN	NOM	MAX	
V_{CC}	Supply voltage	4.5	5	5.5	4.75	5	5.25	V
V_{IH}	High-level input voltage	2			2			V
V_{IL}	Low-level input voltage			0.8			0.8	V
V_{OH}	High-level output voltage			5.5			5.5	V
I_{OL}	Low-level output current			16			16	mA
T_A	Operating free-air temperature	−55		125	0		70	°C

electrical characteristics over recommended operating free-air temperature range (unless otherwise noted)

PARAMETER	TEST CONDITIONS†			MIN	TYP‡	MAX	UNIT
V_{IK}	V_{CC} = MIN,	I_I = −12 mA				−1.5	V
I_{OH}	V_{CC} = MIN,	V_{IL} = 0.8 V,	V_{OH} = 5.5 V			0.25	mA
V_{OL}	V_{CC} = MIN,	V_{IH} = 2 V,	I_{OL} = 16 mA		0.2	0.4	V
I_I	V_{CC} = MAX,	V_I = 5.5 V				1	mA
I_{IH}	V_{CC} = MAX,	V_I = 2.4 V				40	µA
I_{IL}	V_{CC} = MAX,	V_I = 0.4 V				−1.6	mA
I_{CCH}	V_{CC} = MAX,	V_I = 0 V			4	8	mA
I_{CCL}	V_{CC} = MAX,	V_I = 4.5 V			12	22	mA

† For conditions shown as MIN or MAX, use the appropriate value specified under recommended operating conditions.
‡ All typical values are at V_{CC} = 5 V, T_A = 25°C.

switching characteristics, V_{CC} = 5 V, T_A = 25°C (see note 2)

PARAMETER	FROM (INPUT)	TO (OUTPUT)	TEST CONDITIONS		MIN	TYP	MAX	UNIT
t_{PLH}	A or B	Y	R_L = 4 kΩ,	C_L = 15 pF		35	45	ns
t_{PHL}			R_L = 400 Ω,	C_L = 15 pF		8	15	ns

NOTE 2: See General Information Section for load circuits and voltage waveforms.

3.

TTL DEVICES

TEXAS
INSTRUMENTS

recommended operating conditions

		SN54LS03			SN74LS03			UNIT
		MIN	NOM	MAX	MIN	NOM	MAX	
V_{CC}	Supply voltage	4.5	5	5.5	4.75	5	5.25	V
V_{IH}	High-level input voltage	2			2			V
V_{IL}	Low-level input voltage			0.7			0.8	V
V_{OH}	High-level output voltage			5.5			5.5	V
I_{OL}	Low-level output current			4			8	mA
T_A	Operating free-air temperature	−55		125	0		70	°C

electrical characteristics over recommended operating free-air temperature range (unless otherwise noted)

PARAMETER	TEST CONDITIONS†	SN54LS03			SN74LS03			UNIT
		MIN	TYP‡	MAX	MIN	TYP‡	MAX	
V_{IK}	V_{CC} = MIN, I_I = −18 mA			−1.5			−1.5	V
I_{OH}	V_{CC} = MIN, V_{IL} = MAX, V_{OH} = 5.5 V			0.1			0.1	mA
V_{OL}	V_{CC} = MIN, V_{IH} = 2 V, I_{OL} = 4 mA		0.25	0.4		0.25	0.4	V
	V_{CC} = MIN, V_{IH} = 2 V, I_{OL} = 8 mA					0.35	0.5	
I_I	V_{CC} = MAX, V_I = 7 V			0.1			0.1	mA
I_{IH}	V_{CC} = MAX, V_I = 2.7 V			20			20	μA
I_{IL}	V_{CC} = MAX, V_I = 0.4 V			−0.4			−0.4	mA
I_{CCH}	V_{CC} = MAX, V_I = 0 V		0.8	1.6		0.8	1.6	mA
I_{CCL}	V_{CC} = MAX, V_I = 4.5 V		2.4	4.4		2.4	4.4	mA

† For conditions shown as MIN or MAX, use the appropriate value specified under recommended operating conditions.
‡ All typical values are at V_{CC} = 5 V, T_A = 25°C.

switching characteristics, V_{CC} = 5 V, T_A = 25°C (see note 2)

PARAMETER	FROM (INPUT)	TO (OUTPUT)	TEST CONDITIONS		MIN	TYP	MAX	UNIT
t_{PLH}	A or B	Y	R_L = 2 kΩ,	C_L = 15 pF		17	32	ns
t_{PHL}						15	28	ns

NOTE 2: See General Information Section for load circuits and voltage waveforms.

TEXAS
INSTRUMENTS

recommended operating conditions

		SN54S03			SN74S03			UNIT
		MIN	NOM	MAX	MIN	NOM	MAX	
V_{CC}	Supply voltage	4.5	5	5.5	4.75	5	5.25	V
V_{IH}	High-level input voltage	2			2			V
V_{IL}	Low-level input voltage			0.8			0.8	V
V_{OH}	High-level output voltage			5.5			5.5	V
I_{OL}	Low-level output current			20			20	mA
T_A	Operating free-air temperature	−55		125	0		70	°C

electrical characteristics over recommended operating free-air temperature range (unless otherwise noted)

PARAMETER	TEST CONDITIONS†			MIN	TYP‡	MAX	UNIT
V_{IK}	V_{CC} = MIN,	I_I = −18 mA				−1.2	V
I_{OH}	V_{CC} = MIN,	V_{IL} = 0.8 V,	V_{OH} = 5.5 V			0.25	mA
V_{OL}	V_{CC} = MIN,	V_{IH} = 2 V,	I_{OL} = 20 mA			0.5	V
I_I	V_{CC} = MAX,	V_I = 5.5 V				1	mA
I_{IH}	V_{CC} = MAX,	V_I = 2.7 V				50	μA
I_{IL}	V_{CC} = MAX,	V_I = 0.5 V				−2	mA
I_{CCH}	V_{CC} = MAX,	V_I = 0 V			6	13.2	mA
I_{CCL}	V_{CC} = MAX,	V_I = 4.5 V			20	36	mA

† For conditions shown as MIN or MAX, use the appropriate value specified under recommended operating conditions.
‡ All typical values are at V_{CC} = 5 V, T_A = 25°C.

switching characteristics, V_{CC} = 5 V, T_A = 25°C (see note 2)

PARAMETER	FROM (INPUT)	TO (OUTPUT)	TEST CONDITIONS		MIN	TYP	MAX	UNIT
t_{PLH}	A or B	Y	R_L = 280 Ω,	C_L = 15 pF	2	5	7.5	ns
t_{PHL}					2	4.5	7	ns
t_{PLH}			R_L = 280 Ω,	C_L = 50 pF			7.5	ns
t_{PHL}							7	ns

NOTE 2: See General Information Section for load circuits and voltage waveforms.

TEXAS INSTRUMENTS

3

TTL DEVICES

- Package Options Include Both Plastic and Ceramic Chip Carriers in Addition to Plastic and Ceramic DIPs
- Dependable Texas Instruments Quality and Reliability

description

These devices contain six independent inverters.

The SN5404, SN54LS04 and SN54S04 are characterized for operation over the full military temperature range of −55°C to 125°C. The SN7404, SN74LS04 and SN74S04 are characterized for operation from 0°C to 70°C.

FUNCTION TABLE (each inverter)

INPUTS A	OUTPUT Y
H	L
L	H

logic diagram (each inverter)

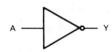

A ——▷○—— Y

positive logic

$$Y = \overline{A}$$

SN5404 ... J PACKAGE
SN54LS04, SN54S04 ... J OR PACKAGE
SN7404 ... J OR N PACKAGE
SN74LS04, SN74S04 ... D, J OR N PACKAGE
(TOP VIEW)

```
        ┌──┬─┐
  1A ─┤1   14├─ VCC
  1Y ─┤2   13├─ 6A
  2A ─┤3   12├─ 6Y
  2Y ─┤4   11├─ 5A
  3A ─┤5   10├─ 5Y
  3Y ─┤6    9├─ 4A
 GND ─┤7    8├─ 4Y
        └────┘
```

SN5404 ... W PACKAGE
(TOP VIEW)

```
        ┌──┬─┐
  1A ─┤1   14├─ 1Y
  2Y ─┤2   13├─ 6A
  2A ─┤3   12├─ 6Y
 VCC ─┤4   11├─ GND
  3A ─┤5   10├─ 5Y
  3Y ─┤6    9├─ 5A
  4A ─┤7    8├─ 4Y
        └────┘
```

SN54LS04, SN54S04 ... FK PACKAGE
SN74LS04, SN74S04
(TOP VIEW)

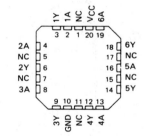

NC - No internal connection

TEXAS
INSTRUMENTS

3

TTL DEVICES

TYPES SN5404, SN54LS04, SN54S04
SN7404, SN74LS04, SN74S04
HEX INVERTERS

schematics (each gate)

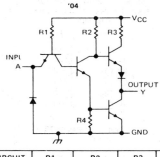

CIRCUIT	R1	R2	R3	R4
'04	4 kΩ	1.6 kΩ	130 Ω	1 kΩ

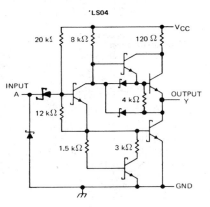

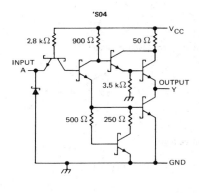

Resistor values shown are nominal.

absolute maximum ratings over operating free-air temperature range (unless otherwise noted)

Supply voltage, V_{CC} (see Note 1): '04, 'LS04, 'S04 . . . . 7 V

Input voltage: '04, 'S04 . . . . 5.5 V

'LS04 . . . . 7 V

Operating free-air temperature range: SN54' . . . . −55°C to 125°C

SN74' . . . . 0°C to 70°C

Storage temperature range . . . . −65°C to 150°C

NOTE 1: Voltage values are with respect to network ground terminal.

TEXAS
INSTRUMENTS

recommended operating conditions

		SN5404			SN7404			UNIT
		MIN	NOM	MAX	MIN	NOM	MAX	
V_{CC}	Supply voltage	4.5	5	5.5	4.75	5	5.25	V
V_{IH}	High-level input voltage	2			2			V
V_{IL}	Low-level input voltage			0.8			0.8	V
I_{OH}	High-level output current			− 0.4			− 0.4	mA
I_{OL}	Low-level output current			16			16	mA
T_A	Operating free-air temperature	− 55		125	0		70	°C

electrical characteristics over recommended operating free-air temperature range (unless otherwise noted)

PARAMETER	TEST CONDITIONS†	SN5404			SN7404			UNIT
		MIN	TYP‡	MAX	MIN	TYP‡	MAX	
V_{IK}	V_{CC} = MIN, I_I = − 12 mA			− 1.5			− 1.5	V
V_{OH}	V_{CC} = MIN, V_{IL} = 0.8 V, I_{OH} = − 0.4 mA	2.4	3.4		2.4	3.4		V
V_{OL}	V_{CC} = MIN, V_{IH} = 2 V, I_{OL} = 16 mA		0.2	0.4		0.2	0.4	V
I_I	V_{CC} = MAX, V_I = 5.5 V			1			1	mA
I_{IH}	V_{CC} = MAX, V_I = 2.4 V			40			40	μA
I_{IL}	V_{CC} = MAX, V_I = 0.4 V			− 1.6			− 1.6	mA
I_{OS} §	V_{CC} = MAX	− 20		− 55	− 18		− 55	mA
I_{CCH}	V_{CC} = MAX, V_I = 0 V		6	12		6	12	mA
I_{CCL}	V_{CC} = MAX, V_I = 4.5 V		18	33		18	33	mA

† For conditions shown as MIN or MAX, use the appropriate value specified under recommended operating conditions.
‡ All typical values are at V_{CC} = 5 V, T_A = 25°C.
§ Not more than one output should be shorted at a time.

switching characteristics, V_{CC} = 5 V, T_A = 25°C (see note 2)

PARAMETER	FROM (INPUT)	TO (OUTPUT)	TEST CONDITIONS		MIN	TYP	MAX	UNIT
t_{PLH}	A	Y	R_L = 400 Ω,	C_L = 15 pF		12	22	ns
t_{PHL}						8	15	ns

NOTE 2: See General Information Section for load circuits and voltage waveforms.

3

TTL DEVICES

TEXAS
INSTRUMENTS

recommended operating conditions

		SN54LS04			SN74LS04			UNIT
		MIN	NOM	MAX	MIN	NOM	MAX	
V_{CC}	Supply voltage	4.5	5	5.5	4.75	5	5.25	V
V_{IH}	High-level input voltage	2			2			V
V_{IL}	Low-level input voltage			0.7			0.8	V
I_{OH}	High-level output current			−0.4			−0.4	mA
I_{OL}	Low-level output current			4			8	mA
T_A	Operating free-air temperature	−55		125	0		70	°C

electrical characteristics over recommended operating free-air temperature range (unless otherwise noted)

PARAMETER	TEST CONDITIONS †			SN54LS04			SN74LS04			UNIT
				MIN	TYP ‡	MAX	MIN	TYP ‡	MAX	
V_{IK}	V_{CC} = MIN,	I_I = −18 mA				−1.5			−1.5	V
V_{OH}	V_{CC} = MIN,	V_{IL} = MAX,	I_{OH} = −0.4 mA	2.5	3.4		2.7	3.4		V
V_{OL}	V_{CC} = MIN,	V_{IH} = 2 V,	I_{OL} = 4 mA		0.25	0.4			0.4	V
	V_{CC} = MIN,	V_{IH} = 2 V,	I_{OL} = 8 mA					0.25	0.5	
I_I	V_{CC} = MAX,	V_I = 7 V				0.1			0.1	mA
I_{IH}	V_{CC} = MAX,	V_I = 2.7 V				20			20	μA
I_{IL}	V_{CC} = MAX,	V_I = 0.4 V				−0.4			−0.4	mA
I_{OS} §	V_{CC} = MAX			−20		−100	−20		−100	mA
I_{CCH}	V_{CC} = MAX,	V_I = 0 V			1.2	2.4		1.2	2.4	mA
I_{CCL}	V_{CC} = MAX,	V_I = 4.5 V			3.6	6.6		3.6	6.6	mA

† For conditions shown as MIN or MAX, use the appropriate value specified under recommended operating conditions.
‡ All typical values are at V_{CC} = 5 V, T_A = 25°C.
§ Not more than one output should be shorted at a time, and the duration of the short-circuit should not exceed one second.

switching characteristics, V_{CC} = 5 V, T_A = 25°C (see note 2)

PARAMETER	FROM (INPUT)	TO (OUTPUT)	TEST CONDITIONS		MIN	TYP	MAX	UNIT
t_{PLH}	A	Y	R_L = 2 kΩ,	C_L = 15 pF		9	15	ns
t_{PHL}						10	15	ns

NOTE 2: See General Information Section for load circuits and voltage waveforms.

TEXAS INSTRUMENTS

3

TTL DEVICES

recommended operating conditions

		SN54S04			SN74S04			UNIT
		MIN	NOM	MAX	MIN	NOM	MAX	
V_{CC}	Supply voltage	4.5	5	5.5	4.75	5	5.25	V
V_{IH}	High-level input voltage	2			2			V
V_{IL}	Low-level input voltage			0.8			0.8	V
I_{OH}	High-level output current			−1			−1	mA
I_{OL}	Low-level output current			20			20	mA
T_A	Operating free-air temperature	−55		125	0		70	°C

electrical characteristics over recommended operating free-air temperature range (unless otherwise noted)

PARAMETER	TEST CONDITIONS †	SN54S04			SN74S04			UNIT
		MIN	TYP ‡	MAX	MIN	TYP ‡	MAX	
V_{IK}	V_{CC} = MIN, $\quad I_I = -18$ mA			−1.2			−1.2	V
V_{OH}	V_{CC} = MIN, $\quad V_{IL} = 0.8$ V, $\quad I_{OH} = -1$ mA	2.5	3.4		2.7	3.4		V
V_{OL}	V_{CC} = MIN, $\quad V_{IH} = 2$ V, $\quad I_{OL} = 20$ mA			0.5			0.5	V
I_I	V_{CC} = MAX, $\quad V_I = 5.5$ V			1			1	mA
I_{IH}	V_{CC} = MAX, $\quad V_I = 2.7$ V			50			50	µA
I_{IL}	V_{CC} = MAX, $\quad V_I = 0.5$ V			−2			−2	mA
I_{OS} §	V_{CC} = MAX	−40		−100	−40		−100	mA
I_{CCH}	V_{CC} = MAX, $\quad V_I = 0$ V		15	24		15	24	mA
I_{CCL}	V_{CC} = MAX, $\quad V_I = 4.5$ V		30	54		30	54	mA

† For conditions shown as MIN or MAX, use the appropriate value specified under recommended operating conditions.
‡ All typical values are at V_{CC} = 5 V, T_A = 25°C.
§ Not more than one output should be shorted at a time, and the duration of the short-circuit should not exceed one second.

switching characteristics, V_{CC} = 5 V, T_A = 25°C (see note 2)

PARAMETER	FROM (INPUT)	TO (OUTPUT)	TEST CONDITIONS	MIN	TYP	MAX	UNIT
t_{PLH}	A	Y	$R_L = 280\ \Omega$, $\quad C_L = 15$ pF		3	4.5	ns
t_{PHL}					3	5	ns
t_{PLH}			$R_L = 280\ \Omega$, $\quad C_L = 50$ pF		4.5		ns
t_{PHL}					5		ns

NOTE 2: See General Information Section for load circuits and voltage waveforms.

3

TTL DEVICES

- Package Options Include Both Plastic and Ceramic Chip Carriers in Addition to Plastic and Ceramic DIPs

- Dependable Texas Instruments Quality and Reliability

description

These devices contain six independent inverters. The open-collector outputs require pull-up resistors to perform correctly. They may be connected to other open-collector outputs to implement active-low wired-OR or active-high wired-AND functions. Open collector devices are often used to generate high V_{OH} levels.

The SN5405, SN54LS05 and SN54S05 are characterized for operation over the full military temperature range of $-55°C$ to $125°C$. The SN7405, SN74LS05 and SN74S05 are characterized for operation from 0°C to 70°C.

FUNCTION TABLE (each inverter)

INPUT	OUTPUT
A	Y
H	L
L	H

logic diagram (each inverter)

positive logic

$$Y = \overline{A}$$

SN5405 . . . J PACKAGE
SN54LS05, SN54S05 . . . J OR W PACKAGE
SN7405 . . . J OR N PACKAGE
SN74LS05, SN74S05 . . . D, J OR N PACKAGE
(TOP VIEW)

SN5405 . . . W PACKAGE
(TOP VIEW)

SN54LS05, SN54S05 . . . FK PACKAGE
SN74LS05, SN74S05
(TOP VIEW)

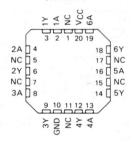

NC - No internal connection

PRODUCTION DATA
This document contains information current as of publication date. Products conform to specifications per the terms of Texas Instruments standard warranty. Production processing does not necessarily include testing of all parameters.

schematics (each inverter)

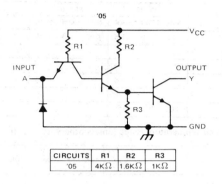

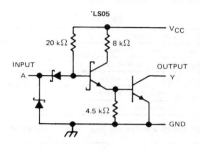

CIRCUITS	R1	R2	R3
'05	4KΩ	1.6KΩ	1KΩ

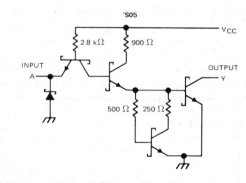

Resistor values are nominal.

absolute maximum ratings over operating free-air temperature range (unless otherwise noted)

Supply voltage, V_{CC} (see Note 1): '05, 'LS05, 'S05 . . . . 7 V

Input voltage: '05, 'S05 . . . . 5.5 V

      'LS05 . . . . 7 V

Off-state output voltage . . . . 7 V

Operating free-air temperature range: SN54' . . . . −55°C to 125°C

                SN74' . . . . 0°C to 70°C

Storage temperature range . . . . −65°C to 150°C

NOTE 1: Voltage values are with respect to network ground terminal.

3

TTL DEVICES

recommended operating conditions

		SN5405			SN7405			UNIT
		MIN	NOM	MAX	MIN	NOM	MAX	
V_{CC}	Supply voltage	4.5	5	5.5	4.75	5	5.25	V
V_{IH}	High-level input voltage	2			2			V
V_{IL}	Low-level input voltage			0.8			0.8	V
V_{OH}	High-level output voltage			5.5			5.5	V
I_{OL}	Low-level output current			16			16	mA
T_A	Operating free-air temperature	-55		125	0		70	°C

electrical characteristics over recommended operating free-air temperature range (unless otherwise noted)

PARAMETER	TEST CONDITIONS†			MIN	TYP‡	MAX	UNIT
V_{IK}	V_{CC} = MIN,	I_I = -12 mA				-1.5	V
I_{OH}	V_{CC} = MIN,	V_{IL} = 0.8 V,	V_{OH} = 5.5 V			0.25	mA
V_{OL}	V_{CC} = MIN,	V_{IH} = 2 V,	I_{OL} = 16 mA		0.2	0.4	V
I_I	V_{CC} = MAX,	V_I = 5.5 V				1	mA
I_{IH}	V_{CC} = MAX,	V_I = 2.4 V				40	μA
I_{IL}	V_{CC} = MAX,	V_I = 0.4 V				-1.6	mA
I_{CCH}	V_{CC} = MAX,	V_I = 0 V			6	12	mA
I_{CCL}	V_{CC} = MAX,	V_I = 4.5 V			18	33	mA

† For conditions shown as MIN or MAX, use the appropriate value specified under recommended operating conditions.
‡ All typical values are at V_{CC} = 5 V, T_A = 25°C.

switching characteristics, V_{CC} = 5 V, T_A = 25°C (see note 2)

PARAMETER	FROM (INPUT)	TO (OUTPUT)	TEST CONDITIONS		MIN	TYP	MAX	UNIT
t_{PLH}	A	Y	R_L = 4 kΩ,	C_L = 15 pF		40	55	ns
t_{PHL}			R_L = 400 Ω,	C_L = 15 pF		8	15	ns

NOTE 2: See General Information Section for load circuits and voltage waveforms.

TEXAS
INSTRUMENTS

3

TTL DEVICES

recommended operating conditions

		SN54LS05			SN74LS05			UNIT
		MIN	NOM	MAX	MIN	NOM	MAX	
V_{CC}	Supply voltage	4.5	5	5.5	4.75	5	5.25	V
V_{IH}	High-level input voltage	2			2			V
V_{IL}	Low-level input voltage			0.7			0.8	V
V_{OH}	High-level output voltage			5.5			5.5	V
I_{OL}	Low-level output current			4			8	mA
T_A	Operating free-air temperature	−55		125	0		70	°C

electrical characteristics over recommended operating free-air temperature range (unless otherwise noted)

PARAMETER	TEST CONDITIONS†			SN54LS05			SN74LS05			UNIT
				MIN	TYP‡	MAX	MIN	TYP‡	MAX	
V_{IK}	V_{CC} = MIN,	I_I = −18 mA				−1.5			−1.5	V
I_{OH}	V_{CC} = MIN,	V_{IL} = MAX,	V_{OH} = 5.5 V			0.1			0.1	mA
V_{OL}	V_{CC} = MIN,	V_{IH} = 2 V,	I_{OL} = 4 mA	0.25	0.4		0.25	0.4		V
	V_{CC} = MIN,	V_{IH} = 2 V,	I_{OL} = 8 mA					0.35	0.5	
I_I	V_{CC} = MAX,	V_I = 7 V				0.1			0.1	mA
I_{IH}	V_{CC} = MAX,	V_I = 2.7 V				20			20	µA
I_{IL}	V_{CC} = MAX,	V_I = 0.4 V				−0.4			−0.4	mA
I_{CCH}	V_{CC} = MAX,	V_I = 0 V			1.2	2.4		1.2	2.4	mA
I_{CCL}	V_{CC} = MAX,	V_I = 4.5 V			3.6	6.6		3.6	6.6	mA

† For conditions shown as MIN or MAX, use the appropriate value specified under recommended operating conditions.
‡ All typical values are at V_{CC} = 5 V, T_A = 25°C.

switching characteristics, V_{CC} = 5 V, T_A = 25°C (see note 2)

PARAMETER	FROM (INPUT)	TO (OUTPUT)	TEST CONDITIONS		MIN	TYP	MAX	UNIT
t_{PLH}	A	Y	R_L = 2 kΩ,	C_L = 15 pF		17	32	ns
t_{PHL}						15	28	ns

NOTE 2: See General Information Section for load circuits and voltage waveforms.

TTL DEVICES 3

TEXAS INSTRUMENTS

recommended operating conditions

		SN54S05			SN74S05			UNIT
		MIN	NOM	MAX	MIN	NOM	MAX	
V_{CC}	Supply voltage	4.5	5	5.5	4.75	5	5.25	V
V_{IH}	High-level input voltage	2			2			V
V_{IL}	Low-level input voltage			0.8			0.8	V
V_{OH}	High-level output voltage			5.5			5.5	V
I_{OL}	Low-level output current			20			20	mA
T_A	Operating free-air temperature	−55		125	0		70	°C

electrical characteristics over recommended operating free-air temperature range (unless otherwise noted)

PARAMETER	TEST CONDITIONS †			SN54S05			SN74S05			UNIT
			MIN	TYP‡	MAX	MIN	TYP‡	MAX		
V_{IK}	V_{CC} = MIN,	I_I = −18 mA				−1.2			−1.2	V
I_{OH}	V_{CC} = MIN,	V_{IL} = 0.8 V, V_{OH} = 5.5 V				0.25			0.25	mA
V_{OL}	V_{CC} = MIN,	V_{IH} = 2 V, I_{OL} = 20 mA				0.5			0.5	V
I_I	V_{CC} = MAX,	V_I = 5.5 V				1			1	mA
I_{IH}	V_{CC} = MAX,	V_I = 2.7 V				50			50	µA
I_{IL}	V_{CC} = MAX,	V_I = 0.5 V				−2			−2	mA
I_{CCH}	V_{CC} = MAX,	V_I = 0 V		9		19.8	9		19.8	mA
I_{CCL}	V_{CC} = MAX,	V_I = 4.5 V		30		54	30		54	mA

† For conditions shown as MIN or MAX, use the appropriate value specified under recommended operating conditions.
‡ All typical values are at V_{CC} = 5 V, T_A = 25°C.

switching characteristics, V_{CC} = 5 V, T_A = 25°C (see note 2)

PARAMETER	FROM (INPUT)	TO (OUTPUT)	TEST CONDITIONS		MIN	TYP	MAX	UNIT
t_{PLH}			R_L = 280 Ω,	C_L = 15 pF	2	5	7.5	ns
t_{PHL}	A	Y			2	4.5	7	ns
t_{PLH}			R_L = 280 Ω,	C_L = 50 pF			7.5	ns
t_{PHL}							7	ns

NOTE 2: See General Information Section for load circuits and voltage waveforms.

TEXAS
INSTRUMENTS

ADVANCE (SN74LS06)
INFORMATION

- Converts TTL Voltage Levels to MOS Levels
- High Sink-Current Capability
- Input Clamping Diodes Simplify System Design
- Open-Collector Driver for Indicator Lamps and Relays
- Inputs Fully Compatible with Most TTL Circuits

SN5406, SN5416 ... J OR W PACKAGE
SN7406, SN7416 ... J OR N PACKAGE
SN74LS06 ... N PACKAGE
(TOP VIEW)

1A	1	14	V_CC
1Y	2	13	6A
2A	3	12	6Y
2Y	4	11	5A
3A	5	10	5Y
3Y	6	9	4A
GND	7	8	4Y

description

These monolithic TTL hex inverter buffers/drivers feature high-voltage open-collector outputs for interfacing with high-level circuits (such as MOS), or for driving high-current loads (such as lamps or relays), and are also characterized for use as inverter buffers for driving TTL inputs. The SN5406, SN7406, and SN74LS06 have minimum breakdown voltages of 30 volts and the SN5416 and SN7416 have minimum breakdown voltages of 15 volts. The maximum sink current is 30 milliamperes for the SN5406 and SN5416, and 40 milliamperes for the SN7406, SN7416 and SN74LS06.

logic diagram

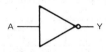

positive logic

$$Y = \overline{A}$$

schematic

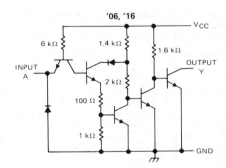

'06, '16

Resistor values shown are nominal
not for SN74LS06

3

TTL DEVICES

TEXAS INSTRUMENTS

absolute maximum ratings over operating free-air temerature range (unless otherwise noted)

Supply voltage, V_{CC} (see Note 1) .... 7 V
Input voltage (see Note 1) .... 7 V
Output voltage (see Note 1 and 2): SN5406, SN7406 Circuits .... 30 V
SN5416, SN7416 Circuits .... 15 V
Operating free-air temperature range: SN5406, SN5416 Circuits .... −55°C to 125°C
SN7406, SN7416 Circuits .... 0°C to 70°C
Storage temperature range .... −65°C to 150°C

NOTES: 1. Voltage values are with respect to network ground terminal.
2. This is the maximum voltage which should be applied to any output when it is in the off state.

recommended operating conditions

			SN5406 SN5416			SN7406 SN7416			UNIT
			MIN	NOM	MAX	MIN	NOM	MAX	
V_{CC}	Supply voltage		4.5	5	5.5	4.75	5	5.25	V
V_{IH}	High-level input voltage		2			2			V
V_{IL}	Low-level input voltage				0.8			0.8	V
V_{OH}	High-level output voltage	'06			30			30	V
		'16			15			15	
I_{OL}	Low-level output current				30			40	mA
T_A	Operating free-air temperature		−55		125	0		70	°C

electrical characteristics over recommended operating free-air temperature range (unless otherwise noted)

PARAMETER	TEST CONDITIONS[†]			SN5406 SN5416			SN7406 SN7416			UNIT
				MIN	TYP[*]	MAX	MIN	TYP[*]	MAX	
V_{IK}	V_{CC} = MIN,	I_I = −12 mA				−1.5			−1.5	V
I_{OH}	V_{CC} = MIN,	V_{IL} = 0.8 V,	V_{OH} = §			0.25			0.25	mA
V_{OL}	V_{CC} = MIN,	V_{IH} = 2 V	I_{OL} = 16 mA			0.4			0.4	V
			I_{OL} = £			0.7			0.7	
I_I	V_{CC} = MAX,	V_I = 5.5 V				1			1	mA
I_{IH}	V_{CC} = MAX,	V_{IH} = 2.4 V				40			40	μA
I_{IL}	V_{CC} = MAX,	V_{IL} = 0.4 V				−1.6			−1.6	mA
I_{CCH}	V_{CC} = MAX				30	48		30	48	mA
I_{CCL}	V_{CC} = MAX				32	51		32	51	mA

† For conditions shown as MIN or MAX, use the appropriate value specified under recommended operating conditions.
* All typical values are at V_{CC} = 5 V, T_A = 25°C.
§ V_{OH} = 30 V for '06 and 15 V for '16.
£ I_{OL} = 30 mA for SN54' and 40 mA for SN74'.

SN5406, SN7406, SN5416, SN7416 switching characteristics, V_{CC} = 5 V, T_A = 25°C (see note 3)

PARAMETER	FROM (INPUT)	TO (OUTPUT)	TEST CONDITIONS		MIN	TYP	MAX	UNIT
t_{PLH}	A	Y	R_L = 110 Ω	C_L = 15 pF		10	15	ns
t_{PHL}						15	23	ns

NOTE 3: See General Information Section for load circuits and voltage waveforms.

PRODUCTION DATA
This document contains information current as of
publication date. Products conform to specifications per the terms of Texas Instruments standard
warranty. Production processing does not necessarily include testing of all parameters.

TEXAS
INSTRUMENTS

absolute maximum ratings over operating free-air temperature range (unless otherwise noted)

Supply voltage, V_{CC} (see Note 1) . . . . 7 V
Input voltage (see Note 1) . . . . 7 V
Output voltage (see Note 1 and 2): SN74LS06 . . . . 30 V
Operating free-air temperature range: SN74LS06 . . . . 0° to 70°C
Storage temperature range . . . . −65°C to 150°C

NOTES: 1. Voltage values are with respect to network ground terminal.
2. This is the maximum voltage which should be applied to any output when it is in the off state.

recommended operating conditions

		SN74LS06			UNIT
		MIN	NOM	MAX	
V_{CC}	Supply voltage	4.75	5	5.25	V
V_{IH}	High-level input voltage	2			V
V_{IL}	Low-level input voltage			0.8	V
V_{OH}	High-level output voltage			30	V
I_{OL}	Low-level output current			40	mA
T_A	Operating free-air temperature	0		70	°C

electrical characteristics over recommended operating free-air temperature range (unless otherwise noted)

PARAMETER	TEST CONDITIONS*		SN74LS06			UNIT
			MIN	TYP*†	MAX	
V_{IK}	V_{CC} = MIN,	I_I = −12 mA			−1.5	V
I_{OH}	V_{CC} = MIN,	V_{IL} = 0.8 V			0.25	mA
V_{OL}	V_{CC} = MIN, V_{IH} = 2 V	I_{OL} = 16 mA			0.4	V
		I_{OL} = 40 mA			0.7	
I_I	V_{CC} = MAX,	V_I = 5,5 V			0.1	mA
I_{IH}	V_{CC} = MAX,	V_{IH} = 2.4 V			30	μA
I_{IL}	V_{CC} = MAX,	V_{IL} = 0.4 V			−0.2	mA
I_{CCH}	V_{CC} = MAX			9	18	mA
I_{CCL}	V_{CC} = MAX			35	60	mA

† For conditions shown as MIN or MAX, use the appropriate value specified under recommended operating conditions.
* All typical values are at V_{CC} = 5 V, T_A = 25°C.

SN74LS06 switching characteristics, V_{CC} = 5 V, T_A = 25°C (see note 3)

PARAMETER	FROM (INPUT)	TO (OUTPUT)	TEST CONDITIONS		MIN	TYP	MAX	UNIT
t_{PLH}	A	Y	R_L = 110 Ω	C_L = 15 pF		7	15	ns
t_{PHL}						10	20	ns

NOTE 3: See General Information Section for load circuits and voltage waveforms.

TEXAS
INSTRUMENTS

3

TTL DEVICES

ADVANCE (SN74LS07)
INFORMATION

- Converts TTL Voltage Levels to MOS Levels
- High Sink-Current Capability
- Input Clamping Diodes Simplify System Design
- Open-Collector Driver for Indicator Lamps and Relays
- Inputs Fully Compatible with Most TTL Circuits

SN5407, SN5417 ... J OR W PACKAGE
SN7407, SN7417 ... J OR N PACKAGE
(TOP VIEW)

```
        ___ ___
1A  [ 1  U  14 ] Vcc
1Y  [ 2     13 ] 6A
2A  [ 3     12 ] 6Y
2Y  [ 4     11 ] 5A
3A  [ 5     10 ] 5Y
3Y  [ 6      9 ] 4A
GND [ 7      8 ] 4Y
```

description

These monolithic TTL hex buffers/drivers feature high-voltage open-collector outputs for interfacing with high-level circuits (such as MOS), or for driving high-current loads (such as lamps or relays, and are also characterized for use as buffers for driving TTL inputs. The SN5407, SN7407, and SN74LS07 have minimum breakdown voltages of 30 volts and the SN5417 and SN7417 have minimum breakdown voltages of 15 volts. The maximum sink current is 30 milliamperes for the SN5407 and SN5417, and 40 milliamperes for the SN7407, SN7417, and SN74LS07.

These circuits are completely compatible with most TTL families. Inputs are diode-clamped to minimize transmission-line effects witch simplifies design. Typical power dissipation is 145 milliwatts and average propagation delay time is 14 nanoseconds. The SN5407 and SN5417 are characterized for operation over the full military temperature range of $-55°$C to $125°$C; the SN7404, SN7417, and SN74LS07 are characterized for operation from $0°$C to $70°$C.

logic diagram (each gate)

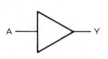

positive logic (each gate)

$$Y = A$$

schematic

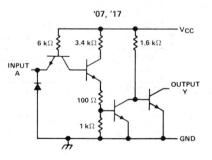

Resistor values shown are nominal
not for SN74LS07

TEXAS
INSTRUMENTS

3

TTL DEVICES

TYPES SN5407, SN5417, SN7407, SN7417
HEX BUFFERS/DRIVERS WITH
OPEN-COLLECTOR HIGH VOLTAGE OUTPUTS

absolute maximum ratings over operating free-air temerature range (unless otherwise noted)

Supply voltage, V_{CC} (see Note 1) .... 7 V
Input voltage (see Note 1) .... 5.5 V
Output voltage (see Note 1 and 2): SN5407, SN7407 Circuits .... 30 V
SN5417, SN7417 Circuits .... 15 V
Operating free-air temperature range: SN5407, SN5417 Circuits .... −55°C to 125°C
SN7407, SN7417 Circuits .... 0°C to 70°C
Storage temperature range .... −65°C to 150°C

NOTES: 1. Voltage values are with respect to network ground terminal.
2. This is the maximum voltage which should be applied to any output when it is in the off state.

recommended operating conditions

			SN5407 SN5417			SN7407 SN7417			UNIT
			MIN	NOM	MAX	MIN	NOM	MAX	
V_{CC}	Supply voltage		4.5	5	5.5	4.75	5	5.25	V
V_{IH}	High-level input voltage		2			2			V
V_{IL}	Low-level input voltage				0.8			0.8	V
V_{OH}	High-level output voltage	'0.7			30			30	V
		'17			15			15	
I_{OL}	Low-level output current				30			40	mA
T_A	Operating free-air temperature		−55		125	0		70	°C

electrical characteristics over recommended operating free-air temperature range (unless otherwise noted)

PARAMETER	TEST CONDITIONS[†]			SN5407 SN5417			SN7407 SN7417			UNIT
				MIN	TYP[*]	MAX	MIN	TYP[*]	MAX	
V_{IK}	V_{CC} = MIN,	I_I = −12 mA				−1.5			−1.5	V
I_{OH}	V_{CC} = MIN,	V_{IL} = 0.8 V,	V_{OH} = §			0.25			0.25	mA
V_{OL}	V_{CC} = MIN,	V_{IH} = 2 V	I_{OL} = 16 mA			0.4			0.4	V
			I_{OL} = £			0.7			0.7	
I_I	V_{CC} = MAX,	V_I = 5.5 V				1			1	mA
I_{IH}	V_{CC} = MAX,	V_{IH} = 2.4 V				40			40	μA
I_{IL}	V_{CC} = MAX,	V_{IL} = 0.4 V				−1.6			−1.6	mA
I_{CCH}	V_{CC} = MAX				29	41		29	41	mA
I_{CCL}	V_{CC} = MAX				21	30		21	30	mA

[†] For conditions shown as MIN or MAX, use the appropriate value specified under recommended operating conditions.
[*] All typical values are at V_{CC} = 5 V, T_A = 25°C.
§ V_{OH} = 30 V for '06 and 15 V for '17.
£ I_{OL} = 30 mA for SN54' and 40 mA for SN74'.

SN5407, SN7407, SN5417, SN7417 switching characteristics, V_{CC} = 5 V, T_A = 25°C (see note 3)

PARAMETER	FROM (INPUT)	TO (OUTPUT)	TEST CONDITIONS		MIN	TYP	MAX	UNIT
t_{PLH}	A	Y	R_L = 110 Ω	C_L = 15 pF		6	10	ns
t_{PHL}						20	30	ns

NOTE 3: See General Information Section for load circuits and voltage waveforms.

TEXAS
INSTRUMENTS

3 TTL DEVICES

absolute maximum ratings over operating free-air temperature range (unless otherwise noted)

Supply voltage, V_{CC} (see Note 1) .... 7 V
Input voltage (see Note 1) .... 7 V
Output voltage (see Note 1 and 2): SN74LS07 .... 30 V
Operating free-air temperature range: SN74LS07 .... 0° to 70°C
Storage temperature range .... −65°C to 150°C

NOTES: 1. Voltage values are with respect to network ground terminal.
2. This is the maximum voltage which should be applied to any output when it is in the off state.

recommended operating conditions

				SN74LS07		UNIT
			MIN	NOM	MAX	
V_{CC}	Supply voltage		4.75	5	5.25	V
V_{IH}	High-level input voltage		2			V
V_{IL}	Low-level input voltage				0.8	V
V_{OH}	High-level output voltage	'07			30	V
I_{OL}	Low-level output current				40	mA
T_A	Operating free-air temperature		0		70	°C

electrical characteristics over recommended operating free-air temperature range (unless otherwise noted)

PARAMETER	TEST CONDITIONS[†]			SN74LS07			UNIT
				MIN	TYP[*]	MAX	
V_{IK}	V_{CC} = MIN,	I_I = −12 mA				−1.5	V
I_{OH}	V_{CC} = MIN,	V_{IH} = 2 V,	V_{OH} = §			0.25	mA
V_{OL}	V_{CC} = MIN,	V_{IL} = 0.8 V	I_{OL} = 16 mA			0.4	V
			I_{OL} = £			0.7	
I_I	V_{CC} = MAX,	V_I = 5,5 V				0.1	mA
I_{IH}	V_{CC} = MAX,	V_{IH} = 2.4 V				30	μA
I_{IL}	V_{CC} = MAX,	V_{IL} = 0.4 V				−0.2	mA
I_{CCH}	V_{CC} = MAX				7	14	mA
I_{CCL}	V_{CC} = MAX				25	45	mA

† For conditions shown as MIN or MAX, use the appropriate value specified under recommended operating conditions.
* All typical values are at V_{CC} = 5 V, T_A = 25°C.
§ V_{OH} = 30 V for '07 and 15 V for '17.
£ I_{OL} = 30 mA for SN54' and 40 mA for SN74'.

SN74LS07 switching characteristics, V_{CC} = 5 V, T_A = 25°C (see note 3)

PARAMETER	FROM (INPUT)	TO (OUTPUT)	TEST CONDITIONS		MIN	TYP	MAX	UNIT
t_{PLH}	A	Y	R_L = 110 Ω	C_L = 15 pF		6	10	ns
t_{PHL}						18	30	ns

NOTE 3: See General Information Section for load circuits and voltage waveforms.

3

TTL DEVICES

TEXAS
INSTRUMENTS

- **Package Options Include Both Plastic and Ceramic Chip Carriers in Addition to Plastic and Ceramic DIPs**

- **Dependable Texas Instruments Quality and Reliability**

description

These devices contain four independent 2-input AND gates.

The SN5408, SN54LS08, and SN54S08 are characterized for operation over the full military temperature range of −55°C to 125°C. The SN7408, SN74LS08 and SN74S08 are characterized for operation from 0°C to 70°C.

SN5408, SN54LS08, SN54S08 . . . J OR W PACKAGE
SN7408 . . . J OR N PACKAGE
SN74LS08, SN74S08 . . . D, J OR N PACKAGE
(TOP VIEW)

1A	1	14	V_{CC}
1B	2	13	4B
1Y	3	12	4A
2A	4	11	4Y
2B	5	10	3B
2Y	6	9	3A
GND	7	8	3Y

SN54LS08, SN54S08 . . . FK PACKAGE
SN74LS08, SN74S08
(TOP VIEW)

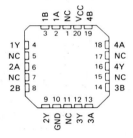

NC - No internal connection

FUNCTION TABLE (each gate)

INPUTS		OUTPUT
A	B	Y
H	H	H
L	X	L
X	L	L

logic diagram (each gate)

positive logic

$$Y = A \cdot B \text{ or } Y = \overline{\overline{A} + \overline{B}}$$

TTL DEVICES

3

schematics (each gate)

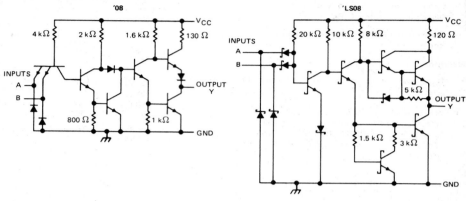

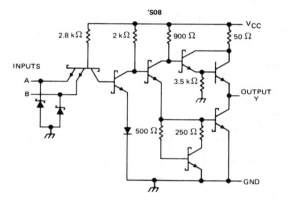

Resistor values are nominal.

absolute maximum ratings over operating free-air temperature range (unless otherwise noted)

Supply voltage, V_{CC} (see Note 1) .... 7 V
Input voltage: '08, 'S08 .... 5.5 V
              'LS08 .... 7 V
Operating free-air temperature range: SN54' .... -55°C to 125°C
                                 SN74' .... 0°C to 70°C
Storage temperature range .... -65°C to 150°C

NOTE 1: Voltage values are with respect to network ground terminal.

TEXAS
INSTRUMENTS

recommended operating conditions

		SN5408			SN7408			UNIT
		MIN	NOM	MAX	MIN	NOM	MAX	
V_{CC}	Supply voltage	4.5	5	5.5	4.75	5	5.25	V
V_{IH}	High-level input voltage	2			2			V
V_{IL}	Low-level input voltage			0.8			0.8	V
I_{OH}	High-level output current			− 0.8			− 0.8	mA
I_{OL}	Low-level output current			16			16	mA
T_A	Operating free-air temperature	− 55		125	0		70	°C

electrical characteristics over recommended operating free-air temperature range (unless otherwise noted)

PARAMETER	TEST CONDITIONS†			SN5408			SN7408			UNIT
				MIN	TYP‡	MAX	MIN	TYP‡	MAX	
V_{IK}	V_{CC} = MIN,	I_I = − 12 mA				− 1.5			− 1.5	V
V_{OH}	V_{CC} = MIN,	V_{IH} = 2 V,	I_{OH} = − 0.8 mA	2.4	3.4		2.4	3.4		V
V_{OL}	V_{CC} = MIN,	V_{IL} = 0.8 V,	I_{OL} = 16 mA		0.2	0.4		0.2	0.4	V
I_I	V_{CC} = MAX,	V_I = 5.5 V				1			1	mA
I_{IH}	V_{CC} = MAX,	V_I = 2.4 V				40			40	µA
I_{IL}	V_{CC} = MAX,	V_I = 0.4 V				− 1.6			− 1.6	mA
I_{OS}§	V_{CC} = MAX			− 20		− 55	− 18		− 55	mA
I_{CCH}	V_{CC} = MAX,	V_I = 4.5 V			11	21		11	21	mA
I_{CCL}	V_{CC} = MAX,	V_I = 0 V			20	33		20	33	mA

† For conditions shown as MIN or MAX, use the appropriate value specified under recommended operating conditions.
‡ All typical values are at V_{CC} = 5 V, T_A = 25°C.
§ Not more than one output should be shorted at a time.

switching characteristics, V_{CC} = 5 V, T_A = 25°C (see note 2)

PARAMETER	FROM (INPUT)	TO (OUTPUT)	TEST CONDITIONS		MIN	TYP	MAX	UNIT
t_{PLH}	A or B	Y	R_L = 400 Ω,	C_L = 15 pF		17.5	27	ns
t_{PHL}						12	19	ns

NOTE 2: See General Information Section for load circuits and voltage waveforms.

3

TTL DEVICES

TEXAS
INSTRUMENTS

recommended operating conditions

		SN54LS08			SN74LS08			UNIT
		MIN	NOM	MAX	MIN	NOM	MAX	
V_{CC}	Supply voltage	4.5	5	5.5	4.75	5	5.25	V
V_{IH}	High-level input voltage	2			2			V
V_{IL}	Low-level input voltage			0.7			0.8	V
I_{OH}	High-level output current			−0.4			−0.4	mA
I_{OL}	Low-level output current			4			8	mA
T_A	Operating free-air temperature	−55		125	0		70	°C

electrical characteristics over recommended operating free-air temperature range (unless otherwise noted)

PARAMETER	TEST CONDITIONS †		SN54LS08			SN74LS08			UNIT
			MIN	TYP‡	MAX	MIN	TYP‡	MAX	
V_{IK}	V_{CC} = MIN,	I_I = −18 mA			−1.5			−1.5	V
V_{OH}	V_{CC} = MIN,	V_{IH} = 2 V, I_{OH} = −0.4 mA	2.5	3.4		2.7	3.4		V
V_{OL}	V_{CC} = MIN,	V_{IL} = MAX, I_{OL} = 4 mA		0.25	0.4		0.25	0.4	V
	V_{CC} = MIN,	V_{IL} = MAX, I_{OL} = 8 mA					0.35	0.5	
I_I	V_{CC} = MAX,	V_I = 7 V			0.1			0.1	mA
I_{IH}	V_{CC} = MAX,	V_I = 2.7 V			20			20	µA
I_{IL}	V_{CC} = MAX,	V_I = 0.4 V			−0.4			−0.4	mA
I_{OS}§	V_{CC} = MAX		−20		−100	−20		−100	mA
I_{CCH}	V_{CC} = MAX,	V_I = 4.5 V		2.4	4.8		2.4	4.8	mA
I_{CCL}	V_{CC} = MAX,	V_I = 0 V		4.4	8.8		4.4	8.8	mA

† For conditions shown as MIN or MAX, use the appropriate value specified under recommended operating conditions.
‡ All typical values are at V_{CC} = 5 V, T_A = 25°C
§ Not more than one output should be shorted at a time, and the duration of the short-circuit should not exceed one second.

switching characteristics, V_{CC} = 5 V, T_A = 25°C (see note 2)

PARAMETER	FROM (INPUT)	TO (OUTPUT)	TEST CONDITIONS	MIN	TYP	MAX	UNIT
t_{PLH}	A or B	Y	R_L = 2 kΩ, C_L = 15 pF		8	15	ns
t_{PHL}					10	20	ns

NOTE 2: See General Information Section for load circuits and voltage waveforms.

TEXAS
INSTRUMENTS

3

TTL DEVICES

recommended operating conditions

		SN54S08			SN74S08			UNIT
		MIN	NOM	MAX	MIN	NOM	MAX	
V_{CC}	Supply voltage	4.5	5	5.5	4.75	5	5.25	V
V_{IH}	High-level input voltage	2			2			V
V_{IL}	Low-level input voltage			0.8			0.8	V
I_{OH}	High-level output current			-1			-1	mA
I_{OL}	Low-level output current			20			20	mA
T_A	Operating free-air temperature	-55		125	0		70	$^{\circ}C$

electrical characteristics over recommended operating free-air temperature range (unless otherwise noted)

PARAMETER	TEST CONDITIONS †			SN54S08			SN74S08			UNIT
				MIN	TYP‡	MAX	MIN	TYP‡	MAX	
V_{IK}	V_{CC} = MIN,	$I_I = -18$ mA				-1.2			-1.2	V
V_{OH}	V_{CC} = MIN,	$V_{IH} = 2$ V,	$I_{OH} = -1$ mA	2.5	3.4		2.7	3.4		V
V_{OL}	V_{CC} = MIN,	$V_{IL} = 0.8$ V	$I_{OL} = 20$ mA			0.5			0.5	V
I_I	V_{CC} = MAX,	$V_I = 5.5$ V				1			1	mA
I_{IH}	V_{CC} = MAX,	$V_I = 2.7$ V				50			50	μA
I_{IL}	V_{CC} = MAX,	$V_I = 0.5$ V				-2			-2	mA
I_{OS} §	V_{CC} = MAX			-40		-100	-40		-100	mA
I_{CCH}	V_{CC} = MAX,	$V_I = 4.5$ V			18	32		18	32	mA
I_{CCL}	V_{CC} = MAX,	$V_I = 0$ V			32	57		32	57	mA

† For conditions shown as MIN or MAX, use the appropriate value specified under recommended operating conditions.
‡ All typical values are at V_{CC} = 5 V, T_A = 25°C.
§ Not more than one output should be shorted at a time, and the duration of the short-circuit should not exceed one second.

switching characteristics, V_{CC} = 5 V, T_A = 25°C (see note 2)

PARAMETER	FROM (INPUT)	TO (OUTPUT)	TEST CONDITIONS		MIN	TYP	MAX	UNIT
t_{PLH}			$R_L = 280$ Ω,	$C_L = 15$ pF		4.5	7	ns
t_{PHL}	A or B	Y				5	7.5	ns
t_{PLH}			$R_L = 280$ Ω,	$C_L = 50$ pF		6		ns
t_{PHL}						7.5		ns

NOTE 2: See General Information Section for load circuits and voltage waveforms.

3

TTL DEVICES

TEXAS
INSTRUMENTS

- **Package Options Include Both Plastic and Ceramic Chip Carriers in Addition to Plastic and Ceramic DIPs**

- **Dependable Texas Instruments Quality and Reliability**

description

These devices contain four independent 2-input AND gates. The open-collector outputs require pull-up resistors to perform correctly. They may be connected to other open-collector outputs to implement active-low wired-OR or active-high wired-AND functions. Open-collector devices are often used to generate higher V_{OH} levels.

The SN5409, SN54LS09, and SN54S09 are characterized for operation over the full military temperature range of $-55\,°C$ to $125\,°C$. The SN7409, SN74LS09 and SN74S09 are characterized for operation from $0\,°C$ to $70\,°C$.

SN5409, SN54LS09, SN54S09 . . . J OR W PACKAGE
SN7409 . . . J OR N PACKAGE
SN74LS09, SN74S09 . . . D, J OR N PACKAGE
(TOP VIEW)

SN54LS09, SN54S09 . . . FK PACKAGE
SN74LS09, SN74S09
(TOP VIEW)

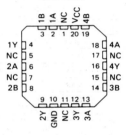

NC - No internal connection

FUNCTION TABLE (each gate)

INPUTS		OUTPUT
A	B	Y
H	H	H
L	X	L
X	L	L

logic diagram (each gate)

positive logic

$$Y = A \cdot B \text{ or } Y = \overline{\overline{A} + \overline{B}}$$

TEXAS
INSTRUMENTS

3

TTL DEVICES

3

TTL DEVICES

schematics (each gate)

'09

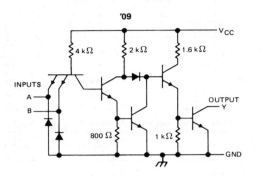

'LS09

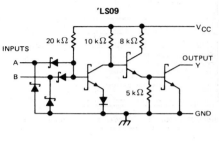

'S09

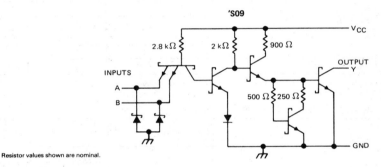

Resistor values shown are nominal.

absolute maximum ratings over operating free-air temperature range (unless otherwise noted)

Supply voltage, V_{CC} (see Note 1) . . . . 7 V
Input voltage: '09, 'S09 . . . . 5.5 V
    'LS09 . . . . 7 V
Off-state output voltage . . . . 7 V
Operating free-air temperature range: SN54' . . . . -55°C to 125°C
    SN74' . . . . 0°C to 70°C
Storage temperature range . . . . -65°C to 150°C

NOTE 1: Voltage values are with respect to network ground terminal.

recommended operating conditions

		SN5409			SN7409			UNIT
		MIN	NOM	MAX	MIN	NOM	MAX	
V_{CC}	Supply voltage	4.5	5	5.5	4.75	5	5.25	V
V_{IH}	High-level input voltage	2			2			V
V_{IL}	Low-level input voltage			0.8			0.8	V
V_{OH}	High-level output voltage			5.5			5.5	V
I_{OL}	Low-level output current			16			16	mA
T_A	Operating free-air temperature	-55		125	0		70	°C

electrical characteristics over recommended operating free-air temperature range (unless otherwise noted)

PARAMETER	TEST CONDITIONS†		MIN	TYP‡	MAX	UNIT
V_{IK}	V_{CC} = MIN,	I_I = -12 mA			-1.5	V
I_{OH}	V_{CC} = MIN,	V_{IH} = 2 V, V_{OH} = 5.5 V			0.25	mA
V_{OL}	V_{CC} = MIN,	V_{IL} = 0.8 V I_{OL} = 16 mA		0.2	0.4	V
I_I	V_{CC} = MAX,	V_I = 5.5 V			1	mA
I_{IH}	V_{CC} = MAX,	V_I = 2.4 V			40	µA
I_{IL}	V_{CC} = MAX,	V_I = 0.4 V			-1.6	mA
I_{CCH}	V_{CC} = MAX,	V_I = 4.5 V		11	21	mA
I_{CCL}	V_{CC} = MAX,	V_I = 0 V		20	33	mA

† For conditions shown as MIN or MAX, use the appropriate value specified under recommended operating conditions.
‡ All typical values are at V_{CC} = 5 V, T_A = 25°C.

switching characteristics, V_{CC} = 5 V, T_A = 25°C (see note 2)

PARAMETER	FROM (INPUT)	TO (OUTPUT)	TEST CONDITIONS		MIN	TYP	MAX	UNIT
t_{PLH}	A or B	Y	R_L = 400 Ω,	C_L = 15 pF		21	32	ns
t_{PHL}						16	24	ns

NOTE 2: See General Information Section for load circuits and voltage waveforms.

TEXAS
INSTRUMENTS

QUADRUPLE 2-INPUT POSITIVE-AND GATES WITH OPEN-COLLECTOR OUTPUTS

recommended operating conditions

		SN54LS09			SN74LS09			UNIT
		MIN	NOM	MAX	MIN	NOM	MAX	
V_{CC}	Supply voltage	4.5	5	5.5	4.75	5	5.25	V
V_{IH}	High-level input voltage	2			2			V
V_{IL}	Low-level input voltage			0.7			0.8	V
V_{OH}	High-level output voltage			5.5			5.5	V
I_{OL}	Low-level output current			4			8	mA
T_A	Operating free-air temperature	−55		125	0		70	°C

electrical characteristics over recommended operating free-air temperature range (unless otherwise noted)

PARAMETER	TEST CONDITIONS†	SN54LS09			SN74LS09			UNIT
		MIN	TYP‡	MAX	MIN	TYP‡	MAX	
V_{IK}	V_{CC} = MIN, I_I = −18 mA			−1.5			−1.5	V
I_{OH}	V_{CC} = MIN, V_{IH} = 2 V, V_{OH} = 5.5 V			0.1			0.1	mA
V_{OL}	V_{CC} = MIN, V_{IL} = MAX, I_{OL} = 4 mA		0.25	0.4		0.25	0.4	V
	V_{CC} = MIN, V_{IL} = MAX, I_{OL} = 8 mA					0.35	0.5	
I_I	V_{CC} = MAX, V_I = 7 V			0.1			0.1	mA
I_{IH}	V_{CC} = MAX, V_I = 2.7 V			20			20	µA
I_{IL}	V_{CC} = MAX, V_I = 0.4 V			−0.4			−0.4	mA
I_{CCH}	V_{CC} = MAX, V_I = 4.5 V		2.4	4.8		2.4	4.8	mA
I_{CCL}	V_{CC} = MAX, V_I = 0 V		4.4	8.8		4.4	8.8	mA

† For conditions shown as MIN or MAX, use the appropriate value specified under recommended operating conditions.
‡ All typical values are at V_{CC} = 5 V, T_A = 25°C.

switching characteristics, V_{CC} = 5 V, T_A = 25°C (see note 2)

PARAMETER	FROM (INPUT)	TO (OUTPUT)	TEST CONDITIONS	MIN	TYP	MAX	UNIT
t_{PLH}	A or B	Y	R_L = 2 kΩ, C_L = 15 pF		20	35	ns
t_{PHL}					17	35	ns

NOTE 2: See General Information Section for load circuits and voltage waveforms.

TEXAS INSTRUMENTS

recommended operating conditions

		SN54S09			SN74S09			UNIT
		MIN	NOM	MAX	MIN	NOM	MAX	
V_{CC}	Supply voltage	4.5	5	5.5	4.75	5	5.25	V
V_{IH}	High-level input voltage	2			2			V
V_{IL}	Low-level input voltage			0.8			0.8	V
V_{OH}	High-level output voltage			5.5			5.5	V
I_{OL}	Low-level output current			20			20	mA
T_A	Operating free-air temperature	−55		125	0		70	°C

electrical characteristics over recommended operating free-air temperature range (unless otherwise noted)

PARAMETER	TEST CONDITIONS†		MIN	TYP‡	MAX	UNIT
V_{IK}	V_{CC} = MIN,	I_I = −18 mA			−1.2	V
I_{OH}	V_{CC} = MIN,	V_{IH} = 2 V, V_{OH} = 5.5 V			0.25	mA
V_{OL}	V_{CC} = MIN,	V_{IL} = 0.8 V, I_{OL} = 20 mA			0.5	V
I_I	V_{CC} = MAX,	V_I = 5.5 V			1	mA
I_{IH}	V_{CC} = MAX,	V_I = 2.7 V			50	μA
I_{IL}	V_{CC} = MAX,	V_I = 0.5 V			−2	mA
I_{CCH}	V_{CC} = MAX,	V_I = 4.5 V		18	32	mA
I_{CCL}	V_{CC} = MAX,	V_I = 0 V		32	57	mA

† For conditions shown as MIN or MAX, use the appropriate value specified under recommended operating conditions.
‡ All typical values are at V_{CC} = 5 V, T_A = 25°C.

switching characteristics, V_{CC} = 5 V, T_A = 25°C (see note 2)

PARAMETER	FROM (INPUT)	TO (OUTPUT)	TEST CONDITIONS		MIN	TYP	MAX	UNIT
t_{PLH}	A or B	Y	R_L = 280 Ω,	C_L = 15 pF		6.5	10	ns
t_{PHL}						6.5	10	ns
t_{PLH}			R_L = 280 Ω,	C_L = 50 pF		9		ns
t_{PHL}						9		ns

NOTE 2: See General Information Section for load circuits and voltage waveforms.

- **Package Options Include Both Plastic and Ceramic Chip Carriers in Addition to Plastic and Ceramic DIPs**

- **Dependable Texas Instruments Quality and Reliability**

description

These devices contain three independent 3-input NAND gates.

The SN5410, SN54LS10 and SN54S10 are characterized for operation over the full military temperature range of −55°C to 125°C. The SN7410, SN74LS10 and SN74S10 are characterized for operation from 0°C to 70°C.

FUNCTION TABLE (each gate)

INPUTS			OUTPUT
A	B	C	Y
H	H	H	L
L	X	X	H
X	L	X	H
X	X	L	H

logic diagram (each gate)

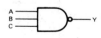

positive logic

$$Y = \overline{A \cdot B \cdot C} \text{ or } Y = \overline{A} + \overline{B} + \overline{C}$$

SN5410 . . . J PACKAGE
SN54LS10, SN54S10 . . . J OR W PACKAGE
SN7410 . . . J OR N PACKAGE
SN74LS10, SN74S10 . . . D, J OR N PACKAGE

(TOP VIEW)

1A	1	14	V_CC
1B	2	13	1C
2A	3	12	1Y
2B	4	11	3C
2C	5	10	3B
2Y	6	9	3A
GND	7	8	3Y

SN5410 . . . W PACKAGE

(TOP VIEW)

1A	1	14	1C
1B	2	13	3Y
1Y	3	12	3C
V_CC	4	11	GND
2Y	5	10	3B
2A	6	9	3A
2B	7	8	2C

SN54LS10, SN54S10 . . . FK PACKAGE
SN74LS10, SN74S10

(TOP VIEW)

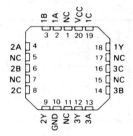

NC - No internal connection

TEXAS
INSTRUMENTS

3-51

TTL DEVICES

3

schematics (each gate)

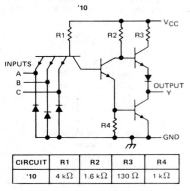

'10

CIRCUIT	R1	R2	R3	R4
'10	4 kΩ	1.6 kΩ	130 Ω	1 kΩ

Input clamp diodes not on SN54L10 circuit.

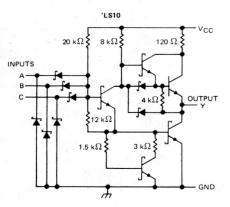

'LS10

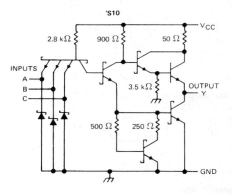

'S10

Resistor values shown are nominal.

absolute maximum ratings over operating free-air temperature range (unless otherwise noted)

Supply voltage, V_{CC} (see Note 1): '10, 'LS10, 'S10 . . . . 7 V

Input voltage: '10, 'S10 . . . . 5.5 V

'LS10 . . . . 7 V

Operating free-air temperature range: SN54' . . . . −55°C to 125°C

SN74' . . . . 0°C to 70°C

Storage temperature range . . . . −65°C to 150°C

NOTE 1: Voltage values are with respect to network ground terminal.

TEXAS
INSTRUMENTS

recommended operating conditions

		SN5410			SN7410			UNIT
		MIN	NOM	MAX	MIN	NOM	MAX	
V_{CC}	Supply voltage	4.5	5	5.5	4.75	5	5.25	V
V_{IH}	High-level input voltage	2			2			V
V_{IL}	Low-level input voltage			0.8			0.8	V
I_{OH}	High-level output current			−0.4			−0.4	mA
I_{OL}	Low-level output current			16			16	mA
T_A	Operating free-air temperature	−55		125	0		70	°C

electrical characteristics over recommended operating free-air temperature range (unless otherwise noted)

PARAMETER	TEST CONDITIONS†			SN5410			SN7410			UNIT
			MIN	TYP‡	MAX	MIN	TYP‡	MAX		
V_{IK}	V_{CC} = MIN,	$I_I = -12$ mA			−1.5			−1.5		V
V_{OH}	V_{CC} = MIN,	V_{IL} = 0.8 V, $I_{OH} = -0.4$ mA	2.4	3.4		2.4	3.4			V
V_{OL}	V_{CC} = MIN,	V_{IH} = 2 V, I_{OL} = 16 mA		0.2	0.4		0.2	0.4		V
I_I	V_{CC} = MAX,	V_I = 5.5 V			1			1		mA
I_{IH}	V_{CC} = MAX,	V_I = 2.4 V			40			40		µA
I_{IL}	V_{CC} = MAX,	V_I = 0.4 V			−1.6			−1.6		mA
I_{OS}§	V_{CC} = MAX		−20		−55	−18		−55		mA
I_{CCH}	V_{CC} = MAX,	V_I = 0 V		3	6		3	6		mA
I_{CCL}	V_{CC} = MAX,	V_I = 4.5 V		9	16.5		9	16.5		mA

† For conditions shown as MIN or MAX, use the appropriate value specified under recommended operating conditions.
‡ All typical values are at V_{CC} = 5 V, T_A = 25°C.
§ Not more than one output should be shorted at a time.

switching characteristics, V_{CC} = 5 V, T_A = 25°C (see note 2)

PARAMETER	FROM (INPUT)	TO (OUTPUT)	TEST CONDITIONS		MIN	TYP	MAX	UNIT
t_{PLH}	A, B or C	Y	R_L = 400 Ω,	C_L = 15 pF		11	22	ns
t_{PHL}						7	15	ns

NOTE 2: See General Information Section for load circuits and voltage waveforms.

3

TTL DEVICES

TEXAS INSTRUMENTS

recommended operating conditions

		SN54LS10 MIN	NOM	MAX	SN74LS10 MIN	NOM	MAX	UNIT
V_{CC}	Supply voltage	4.5	5	5.5	4.75	5	5.25	V
V_{IH}	High-level input voltage	2			2			V
V_{IL}	Low-level input voltage			0.7			0.8	V
I_{OH}	High-level output current			− 0.4			− 0.4	mA
I_{OL}	Low-level output current			4			8	mA
T_A	Operating free-air temperature	− 55		125	0		70	°C

electrical characteristics over recommended operating free-air temperature range (unless otherwise noted)

PARAMETER	TEST CONDITIONS †			SN54LS10 MIN	TYP‡	MAX	SN74LS10 MIN	TYP‡	MAX	UNIT
V_{IK}	V_{CC} = MIN,	I_I = − 18 mA				− 1.5			− 1.5	V
V_{OH}	V_{CC} = MIN,	V_{IL} = MAX,	I_{OH} = − 0.4 mA	2.5	3.4		2.7	3.4		V
V_{OL}	V_{CC} = MIN,	V_{IH} = 2 V,	I_{OL} = 4 mA		0.25	0.4			0.4	V
	V_{CC} = MIN,	V_{IH} = 2 V,	I_{OL} = 8 mA					0.25	0.5	
I_I	V_{CC} = MAX,	V_I = 7 V				0.1			0.1	mA
I_{IH}	V_{CC} = MAX,	V_I = 2.7 V				20			20	µA
I_{IL}	V_{CC} = MAX,	V_I = 0.4 V				− 0.4			− 0.4	mA
I_{OS} §	V_{CC} = MAX			− 20		− 100	− 20		− 100	mA
I_{CCH}	V_{CC} = MAX,	V_I = 0 V			0.6	1.2		0.6	1.2	mA
I_{CCL}	V_{CC} = MAX,	V_I = 4.5 V			1.8	3.3		1.8	3.3	mA

† For conditions shown as MIN or MAX, use the appropriate value specified under recommended operating conditions.
‡ All typical values are at V_{CC} = 5 V, T_A = 25°C.
§ Not more than one output should be shorted at a time, and the duration of the short-circuit should not exceed one second.

switching characteristics, V_{CC} = 5 V, T_A = 25°C (see note 2)

PARAMETER	FROM (INPUT)	TO (OUTPUT)	TEST CONDITIONS		MIN	TYP	MAX	UNIT
t_{PLH}	A, B or C	Y	R_L = 2 kΩ,	C_L = 15 pF		9	15	ns
t_{PHL}						10	15	ns

NOTE 2: See General Information Section for load circuits and voltage waveforms.

TEXAS
INSTRUMENTS

3
TTL DEVICES

recommended operating conditions

		SN54S10			SN74S10			UNIT
		MIN	NOM	MAX	MIN	NOM	MAX	
V_{CC}	Supply voltage	4.5	5	5.5	4.75	5	5.25	V
V_{IH}	High-level input voltage	2			2			V
V_{IL}	Low-level input voltage			0.8			0.8	V
I_{OH}	High-level output current			−1			−1	mA
I_{OL}	Low-level output current			20			20	mA
T_A	Operating free-air temperature	−55		125	0		70	°C

electrical characteristics over recommended operating free-air temperature range (unless otherwise noted)

PARAMETER	TEST CONDITIONS †		SN54S10			SN74S10			UNIT
			MIN	TYP‡	MAX	MIN	TYP‡	MAX	
V_{IK}	V_{CC} = MIN,	I_I = −18 mA			−1.2			−1.2	V
V_{OH}	V_{CC} = MIN,	V_{IL} = 0.8 V, I_{OH} = −1 mA	2.5	3.4		2.7	3.4		V
V_{OL}	V_{CC} = MIN,	V_{IH} = 2 V, I_{OL} = 20 mA			0.5			0.5	V
I_I	V_{CC} = MAX,	V_I = 5.5 V			1			1	mA
I_{IH}	V_{CC} = MAX,	V_I = 2.7 V			50			50	µA
I_{IL}	V_{CC} = MAX,	V_I = 0.5 V			−2			−2	mA
I_{OS} §	V_{CC} = MAX		−40		−100	−40		−100	mA
I_{CCH}	V_{CC} = MAX,	V_I = 0 V		7.5	12		7.5	12	mA
I_{CCL}	V_{CC} = MAX,	V_I = 4.5 V		15	27		15	27	mA

† For conditions shown as MIN or MAX, use the appropriate value specified under recommended operating conditions.
‡ All typical values are at V_{CC} = 5 V, T_A = 25°C.
§ Not more than one output should be shorted at a time, and the duration of the short-circuit should not exceed one second.

switching characteristics, V_{CC} = 5 V, T_A = 25°C (see note 2)

PARAMETER	FROM (INPUT)	TO (OUTPUT)	TEST CONDITIONS		MIN	TYP	MAX	UNIT
t_{PLH}			R_L = 280 Ω,	C_L = 15 pF		3	4.5	ns
t_{PHL}	A, B or C	Y				3	5	ns
t_{PLH}			R_L = 280 Ω,	C_L = 50 pF			4.5	ns
t_{PHL}							5	ns

NOTE 2: See General Information Section for load circuits and voltage waveforms.

3

TTL DEVICES

TEXAS
INSTRUMENTS

- Package Options Include Both Plastic and Ceramic Chip Carriers in Addition to Plastic and Ceramic DIPs

- Dependable Texas Instruments Quality and Reliability

description

These devices contain three independent 3-input AND gates.

The SN54LS11 and SN54S11 are characterized for operation over the full military temperature range of −55°C to 125°C. The SN74LS11, and SN74S11 are characterized for operation from 0°C to 70°C.

FUNCTION TABLE (each gate)

INPUTS			OUTPUT
A	B	C	Y
H	H	H	H
L	X	X	L
X	L	X	L
X	X	L	L

logic diagram (each gate)

positive logic

$$Y = A \cdot B \cdot C \text{ or } Y = \overline{\overline{A} + \overline{B} + \overline{C}}$$

SN54LS11, SN54S11 . . . J OR W PACKAGE
SN74LS11, SN74S11 . . . D, J OR N PACKAGE
(TOP VIEW)

SN54LS11, SN54S11 . . . FK PACKAGE
SN74LS11, SN74S11
(TOP VIEW)

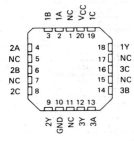

NC - No internal connection

3

TTL DEVICES

schematics (each gate)

'LS11

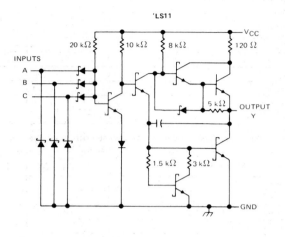

'S11

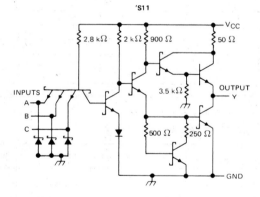

Resistor values shown are nominal.

absolute maximum ratings over operating free-air temperature range (unless otherwise noted)

Supply voltage, V_{CC} (see Note 1) . . . . 7 V

Input voltage: 'S11 . . . . 5.5 V

'LS11 . . . . 7 V

Operating free-air temperature: SN54' . . . . −55°C to 125°C

SN74' . . . . 0°C to 70°C

Storage temperature range . . . . −65°C to 150°C

NOTE 1: Voltage values are with respect to network ground terminal.

TEXAS
INSTRUMENTS

3

TTL DEVICES

recommended operating conditions

PARAMETER		SN54LS11			SN74LS11			UNIT
		MIN	NOM	MAX	MIN	NOM	MAX	
V_{CC}	Supply voltage	4.5	5	5.5	4.75	5	5.25	V
V_{IH}	High-level input voltage	2			2			V
V_{IL}	Low-level input voltage			0.7			0.8	V
I_{OH}	High-level output current			− 0.4			− 0.4	mA
I_{OL}	Low-level output current			4			8	mA
T_A	Operating free-air temperature	− 55		125	0		70	$^\circ$C

electrical characteristics over recommended operating free-air temperature range (unless otherwise noted)

PARAMETER	TEST CONDITIONS †			SN54LS11			SN74LS11			UNIT
				MIN	TYP‡	MAX	MIN	TYP‡	MAX	
V_{IK}	V_{CC} = MIN,	I_I = − 18 mA				− 1.5			− 1.5	V
V_{OH}	V_{CC} = MIN,	V_{IH} = 2 V,	I_{OH} = − 0.4 mA	2.5	3.4		2.7	3.4		V
V_{OL}	V_{CC} = MIN,	V_{IL} = MAX,	I_{OL} = 4 mA		0.25	0.4		0.25	0.4	V
	V_{CC} = MIN,	V_{IL} = MAX,	I_{OL} = 8 mA					0.35	0.5	
I_I	V_{CC} = MAX,	V_I = 7 V				0.1			0.1	mA
I_{IH}	V_{CC} = MAX,	V_I = 2.7 V				20			20	μA
I_{IL}	V_{CC} = MAX,	V_I = 0.4 V				− 0.4			− 0.4	mA
I_{OS} §	V_{CC} = MAX			− 20		− 100	− 20		− 100	mA
I_{CCH}	V_{CC} = MAX,	V_I = 4.5 V			1.8	3.6		1.8	3.6	mA
I_{CCL}	V_{CC} = MAX,	V_I = 0 V			3.3	6.6		3.3	6.6	mA

† For conditions shown as MIN or MAX, use the appropriate value specified under recommended operating conditions.
‡ All typical values are at V_{CC} = 5 V, T_A = 25°C.
§ Not more than one output should be shorted at a time, and the duration of the short-circuit should not exceed one second.

switching characteristics, V_{CC} = 5 V, T_A = 25°C (see note 2)

PARAMETER	FROM (INPUT)	TO (OUTPUT)	TEST CONDITIONS		MIN	TYP	MAX	UNIT
t_{PLH}	A, B or C	Y	R_L = 2 kΩ,	C_L = 15 pF		8	15	ns
t_{PHL}						10	20	ns

NOTE 2: See General Information Section for load circuits and voltage waveforms.

TEXAS
INSTRUMENTS

3

TTL DEVICES

recommended operating conditions

		SN54S11			SN74S11			UNIT
		MIN	NOM	MAX	MIN	NOM	MAX	
V_{CC}	Supply voltage	4.5	5	5.5	4.75	5	5.25	V
V_{IH}	High-level input voltage	2			2			V
V_{IL}	Low-level input voltage			0.8			0.8	V
I_{OH}	High-level output current			−1			−1	mA
I_{OL}	Low-level output current			20			20	mA
T_A	Operating free-air temperature	−55		125	0		70	°C

electrical characteristics over recommended operating free-air temperature range (unless otherwise noted)

PARAMETER	TEST CONDITIONS †		SN54S11			SN74S11			UNIT
			MIN	TYP ‡	MAX	MIN	TYP ‡	MAX	
V_{IK}	V_{CC} = MIN,	I_I = −18 mA			−1.2			−1.2	V
V_{OH}	V_{CC} = MIN,	V_{IH} = 2 V, I_{OH} = −1 mA	2.5	3.4		2.7	3.4		V
V_{OL}	V_{CC} = MIN,	V_{IL} = 0.8 V, I_{OL} = 20 mA			0.5			0.5	V
I_I	V_{CC} = MAX,	V_I = 5.5 V			1			1	mA
I_{IH}	V_{CC} = MAX,	V_I = 2.7 V			50			50	μA
I_{IL}	V_{CC} = MAX,	V_I = 0.5 V			−2			−2	mA
I_{OS} §	V_{CC} = MAX		−40		−100	−40		−100	mA
I_{CCH}	V_{CC} = MAX,	V_I = 4.5 V		13.5	24		13.5	24	mA
I_{CCL}	V_{CC} = MAX,	V_I = 0 V		24	42		24	42	mA

† For conditions shown as MIN or MAX, use the appropriate value specified under recommended operating conditions.
‡ All typical values are at V_{CC} = 5 V, T_A = 25°C.
§ Not more than one output should be shorted at a time, and the duration of the short-circuit should not exceed one second.

switching characteristics, V_{CC} = 5 V, T_A = 25°C (see note 2)

PARAMETER	FROM (INPUT)	TO (OUTPUT)	TEST CONDITIONS		MIN	TYP	MAX	UNIT
t_{PLH}			R_L = 280 Ω,	C_L = 15 pF		4.5	7	ns
t_{PHL}	A, B or C	Y				5	7.5	ns
t_{PLH}			R_L = 280 Ω,	C_L = 50 pF		6		ns
t_{PHL}						7.5		ns

NOTE 2: See General Information Section for load circuits and voltage waveforms.

3

TTL DEVICES

- **Package Options Include Both Plastic and Ceramic Chip Carriers in Addition to Plastic and Ceramic DIPs**

- **Dependable Texas Instruments Quality and Reliability**

description

These devices contain three independent 3-input NAND gates with open-collector outputs. The open-collector outputs require pull-up resistors to perform correctly. They may be connected to other open-collector outputs to implement active-low wired-OR or active-high wired-AND functions. Open-collector devices are often used to generate higher V_{OH} levels.

The SN5412 and SN54LS12 are characterized for operation over the full military range of $-55\,°C$ to $125\,°C$. The SN7412 and SN74LS12 are characterized for operation from $0\,°C$ to $70\,°C$.

SN5412, SN54LS12 . . . J OR W PACKAGE
SN7412 . . . J OR N PACKAGE
SN74LS12 . . . D, J OR N PACKAGE
(TOP VIEW)

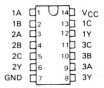

SN54LS12 . . . FK PACKAGE
SN74LS12
(TOP VIEW)

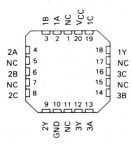

NC - No internal connection

FUNCTION TABLE (each gate)

INPUTS			OUTPUT
A	B	C	Y
H	H	H	L
L	X	X	H
X	L	X	H
X	X	L	H

logic diagram (each gate)

positive logic

$$Y = \overline{A \cdot B \cdot C} \quad \text{or} \quad Y = \overline{A} + \overline{B} + \overline{C}$$

TEXAS INSTRUMENTS

schematics (each gate)

'12

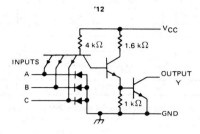

Resistor values shown are nominal.

'LS12

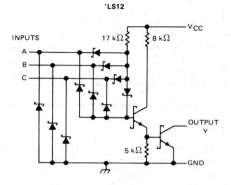

absolute maximum ratings over operating free-air temperature range (unless otherwise noted)

Supply voltage, V_{CC} (see Note 1) .... 7 V
Input voltage: '12 .... 5.5 V
           'LS12 .... 7 V
Off-state output voltage .... 7 V
Operating free-air temperature: SN54' .... -55°C to 125°C
                  SN74' .... 0°C to 70°C
Storage temperature range .... -65°C to 150°C

NOTE 1: Voltage values are with respect to network ground terminal.

3

TTL DEVICES

recommended operating conditions

		SN5412			SN7412			UNIT
		MIN	NOM	MAX	MIN	NOM	MAX	
V_{CC}	Supply voltage	4.5	5	5.5	4.75	5	5.25	V
V_{IH}	High-level input voltage	2			2			V
V_{IL}	Low-level input voltage			0.8			0.8	V
V_{OH}	High-level output voltage			5.5			5.5	V
I_{OL}	Low-level output current			16			16	mA
T_A	Operating free-air temperature	−55		125	0		70	°C

electrical characteristics over recommended operating free-air temperature range (unless otherwise noted)

PARAMETER	TEST CONDITIONS†			MIN	TYP‡	MAX	UNIT
V_{IK}	V_{CC} = MIN,	I_I = −12 mA				−1.5	V
I_{OH}	V_{CC} = MIN,	V_{IL} = 0.8 V,	V_{OH} = 5.5 V			0.25	mA
V_{OL}	V_{CC} = MIN,	V_{IH} = 2 V,	I_{OL} = 16 mA		0.2	0.4	V
I_I	V_{CC} = MAX,	V_I = 5.5 V				1	mA
I_{IH}	V_{CC} = MAX,	V_I = 2.4 V				40	μA
I_{IL}	V_{CC} = MAX,	V_I = 0.4 V				−1.6	mA
I_{CCH}	V_{CC} = MAX,	V_I = 0 V			3	6	mA
I_{CCL}	V_{CC} = MAX,	V_I = 4.5 V			9	16.5	mA

† For conditions shown as MIN or MAX, use the appropriate value specified under recommended operating conditions.
‡ All typical values are at V_{CC} = 5 V, T_A = 25°C.

switching characteristics, V_{CC} = 5 V, T_A = 25°C (see note 2)

PARAMETER	FROM (INPUT)	TO (OUTPUT)	TEST CONDITIONS		MIN	TYP	MAX	UNIT
t_{PLH}	A, B or C	Y	R_L = 4 kΩ,	C_L = 15 pF		35	45	ns
t_{PHL}			R_L = 400 Ω,	C_L = 15 pF		8	15	ns

NOTE 2: See General Information Section for load circuits and voltage waveforms.

Texas
INSTRUMENTS

recommended operating conditions

		SN54LS12			SN74LS12			UNIT
		MIN	NOM	MAX	MIN	NOM	MAX	
V_{CC}	Supply voltage	4.5	5	5.5	4.75	5	5.25	V
V_{IH}	High-level input voltage	2			2			V
V_{IL}	Low-level input voltage			0.7			0.8	V
V_{OH}	High-level output voltage			5.5			5.5	V
I_{OL}	Low-level output current			4			8	mA
T_A	Operating free-air temperature	−55		125	0		70	°C

electrical characteristics over recommended operating free-air temperature range (unless otherwise noted)

PARAMETER	TEST CONDITIONS†			SN54LS12			SN74LS12			UNIT
				MIN	TYP‡	MAX	MIN	TYP‡	MAX	
V_{IK}	V_{CC} = MIN,	I_I = −18 mA				−1.5			−1.5	V
I_{OH}	V_{CC} = MIN,	V_{IL} = MAX,	V_{OH} = 5.5 V			0.1			0.1	mA
V_{OL}	V_{CC} = MIN,	V_{IH} = 2 V,	I_{OL} = 4 mA	0.25	0.4		0.25	0.4		V
	V_{CC} = MIN,	V_{IH} = 2 V,	I_{OL} = 8 mA				0.35	0.5		
I_I	V_{CC} = MAX,	V_I = 7 V				0.1			0.1	mA
I_{IH}	V_{CC} = MAX,	V_I = 2.7 V				20			20	μA
I_{IL}	V_{CC} = MAX,	V_I = 0.4 V				−0.4			−0.4	mA
I_{CCH}	V_{CC} = MAX,	V_I = 0 V		0.7	1.4		0.7	1.4		mA
I_{CCL}	V_{CC} = MAX,	V_I = 4.5 V		1.8	3.3		1.8	3.3		mA

† For conditions shown as MIN or MAX, use the appropriate value specified under recommended operating conditions.
‡ All typical values are at V_{CC} = 5 V, T_A = 25°C.

switching characteristics, V_{CC} = 5 V, T_A = 25°C (see note 2)

PARAMETER	FROM (INPUT)	TO (OUTPUT)	TEST CONDITIONS		MIN	TYP	MAX	UNIT
t_{PLH}	A, B or C	Y	R_L = 2 kΩ,	C_L = 15 pF		17	32	ns
t_{PHL}						15	28	ns

NOTE 2: See General Information Section for load circuits and voltage waveforms.

TEXAS
INSTRUMENTS

- **Operation from Very Slow Edges**
- **Improved Line-Receiving Characteristics**
- **High Noise Immunity**

description

Each circuit functions as a 4-input NAND gate, but because of the Schmitt action, it has different input threshold levels for positive (V_{T+}) and for negative going (V_{T-}) signals.

These circuits are temperature-compensated and can be triggered from the slowest of input ramps and still give clean, jitter-free output signals.

The SN5413 and SN54LS13 are characterized for operation over the full military temperature range of $-55°C$ to $125°C$. The SN7413 and SN74LS13 are characterized for operation from $0°C$ to $70°C$.

logic diagram

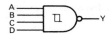

positive logic

$$Y = \overline{ABCD}$$

SN5413, SN54LS13 . . . J OR W PACKAGE
SN7413 . . . J OR N PACKAGE
SN74LS13 . . . D, J OR N PACKAGE
(TOP VIEW)

SN54LS13 . . . FK PACKAGE
SN74LS13
(TOP VIEW)

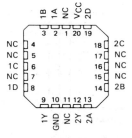

NC – No internal connection

TTL DEVICES

3

TEXAS
INSTRUMENTS

schematics

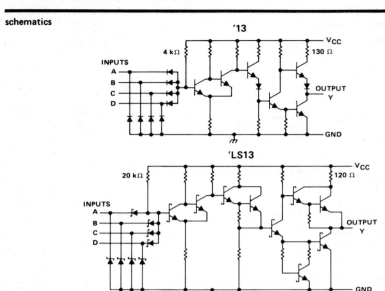

Resistor values are nominal.

absolute maximum ratings over operating free-air temperature range (unless otherwise noted)

Supply voltage, V_{CC} (see Note 1) .... 7 V

Input voltage: '13 .... 5.5 V

'LS13 .... 7 V

Operating free-air temperature: SN54' .... -55°C to 125°C

SN74' .... 0°C to 70°C

Storage temperature range .... -65°C to 150°C

NOTE 1: Voltage values are with respect to network ground terminal.

TEXAS
INSTRUMENTS

recommended operating conditions

		SN5413			SN7413			UNIT
		MIN	NOM	MAX	MIN	NOM	MAX	
V_{CC}	Supply voltage	4.5	5	5.5	4.75	5	5.25	V
I_{OH}	High-level output current			−0.8			−0.8	mA
I_{OL}	Low-level output current			16			16	mA
T_A	Operating free-air temperature	−55		125	0		70	°C

electrical characteristics over recommended operating free-air temperature range (unless otherwise noted)

PARAMETER	TEST CONDITIONS[†]			MIN	TYP[‡]	MAX	UNIT
V_{T+}	$V_{CC} = 5\ V$			1.5	1.7	2	V
V_{T-}	$V_{CC} = 5\ V$			0.6	0.9	1.1	V
Hysteresis $(V_{T+} - V_{T-})$	$V_{CC} = 5\ V$			0.4	0.8		V
V_{IK}	$V_{CC} = MIN,$	$I_I = -12\ mA$				−1.5	V
V_{OH}	$V_{CC} = MIN,$	$V_I = 0.6\ V,$	$I_{OH} = -0.8\ mA$	2.4	3.4		V
V_{OL}	$V_{CC} = MIN,$	$V_I = 2\ V,$	$I_{OL} = 16\ mA$		0.2	0.4	V
I_{T+}	$V_{CC} = 5\ V,$	$V_I = V_{T+}$			−0.65		mA
I_{T-}	$V_{CC} = 5\ V,$	$V_I = V_{T-}$			−0.85		mA
I_I	$V_{CC} = MAX,$	$V_I = 5.5\ V$				1	mA
I_{IH}	$V_{CC} = MAX,$	$V_{IH} = 2.4\ V$				40	µA
I_{IL}	$V_{CC} = MAX,$	$V_{IL} = 0.4\ V$			−1	−1.6	mA
I_{OS} [§]	$V_{CC} = MAX,$			−18		−55	mA
I_{CCH}	$V_{CC} = MAX$				14	23	mA
I_{CCL}	$V_{CC} = MAX$				20	32	mA

[†] For conditions shown as MIN or MAX, use the appropriate value specified under recommended operating conditions.
[‡] All typical values are at $V_{CC} = 5\ V$, $T_A = 25°C$.
[§] Not more than one output should be shorted at a time.

switching characteristics, $V_{CC} = 5\ V$, $T_A = 25°C$

PARAMETER	FROM (INPUT)	TO (OUTPUT)	TEST CONDITIONS		MIN	TYP	MAX	UNIT
t_{PLH}	Any	Y	$R_L = 400\ \Omega,$	$C_L = 15\ pF$		18	27	ns
t_{PHL}						15	22	ns

3

TTL DEVICES

TEXAS
INSTRUMENTS

recommended operating conditions

		SN54LS13			SN74LS13			UNIT
		MIN	NOM	MAX	MIN	NOM	MAX	
V_{CC}	Supply voltage	4.5	5	5.5	4.75	5	5.25	V
I_{OH}	High-level output current			−0.4			−0.4	mA
I_{OL}	Low-level output current			4			8	mA
T_A	Operating free-air temperature	−55		125	0		70	°C

electrical characteristics over recommended operating free-air temperature range (unless otherwise noted)

PARAMETER	TEST CONDITIONS[†]		SN54LS13			SN74LS13			UNIT
			MIN	TYP[‡]	MAX	MIN	TYP[‡]	MAX	
V_{T+}	$V_{CC} = 5$ V		1.4	1.6	1.9	1.4	1.6	1.9	V
V_{T-}	$V_{CC} = 5$ V		0.5	0.8	1	0.5	0.8	1	V
Hysteresis $(V_{T+} - V_{T-})$	$V_{CC} = 5$ V		0.4	0.8		0.4	0.8		V
V_{IK}	$V_{CC} = $ MIN, $\quad I_I = -18$ mA				−1.5			−1.5	V
V_{OH}	$V_{CC} = $ MIN, $\quad V_I = 0.5$ V, $\quad I_{OH} = -0.4$ mA		2.5	3.4		2.7	3.4		V
V_{OL}	$V_{CC} = $ MIN, $\quad V_I = 1.9$ V	$I_{OL} = 4$ mA		0.25	0.4		0.25	0.4	V
		$I_{OL} = 8$ mA					0.35	0.5	
I_{T+}	$V_{CC} = 5$ V, $\quad V_I = V_{T+}$			−0.14			−0.14		mA
I_{T-}	$V_{CC} = 5$ V, $\quad V_I = V_{T-}$			−0.18			−0.18		mA
I_I	$V_{CC} = $ MAX, $\quad V_I = 7$ V				0.1			0.1	mA
I_{IH}	$V_{CC} = $ MAX, $\quad V_{IH} = 2.7$ V				20			20	μA
I_{IL}	$V_{CC} = $ MAX, $\quad V_{IL} = 0.4$ V				−0.4			−0.4	mA
I_{OS} [§]	$V_{CC} = $ MAX		−20		−100	−20		−100	mA
I_{CCH}	$V_{CC} = $ MAX			2.9	6		2.9	6	mA
I_{CCL}	$V_{CC} = $ MAX			4.1	7		4.1	7	mA

† For conditions shown as MIN or MAX, use the appropriate value specified under recommended operating conditions.
‡ All typical values are at $V_{CC} = 5$ V, $T_A = 25$°C.
§ Not more than one output should be shorted at a time, and duration of the short-circuit should not exceed one second.

switching characteristics, $V_{CC} = 5$ V, $T_A = 25$°C

PARAMETER	FROM (INPUT)	TO (OUTPUT)	TEST CONDITIONS		MIN	TYP	MAX	UNIT
t_{PLH}	Any	Y	$R_L = 2$ kΩ,	$C_L = 15$ pF		15	22	ns
t_{PHL}						18	27	ns

TEXAS INSTRUMENTS

PARAMETER MEASUREMENT INFORMATION

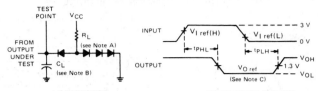

LOAD CIRCUIT

VOLTAGE WAVEFORMS

NOTES: A. All diodes are 1N3064 or equivalent.
B. C_L includes probe and jig capacitance.
C. Generator characteristics and reference voltages are:

	Generator Characteristics				Reference Voltages		
	Z_{out}	PRR	t_r	t_f	$V_{I\ ref(H)}$	$V_{I\ ref(L)}$	$V_{O\ ref}$
SN54'/SN74'	50 Ω	1 MHz	10 ns	10 ns	1.7 V	0.9 V	1.5 V
SN54LS'/SN74LS'	50 Ω	1 MHz	15 ns	6 ns	1.6 V	0.8 V	1.3 V

TYPICAL CHARACTERISTICS OF '13 CIRCUITS

POSITIVE-GOING THRESHOLD VOLTAGE
vs
FREE-AIR TEMPERATURE

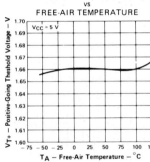

FIGURE 1

NEGATIVE-GOING THRESHOLD VOLTAGE
vs
FREE-AIR TEMPERATURE

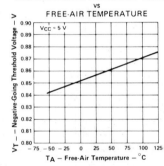

FIGURE 2

HYSTERESIS
vs
FREE-AIR TEMPERATURE

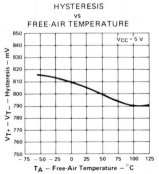

FIGURE 3

Data for temperatures below 0°C and 70°C and supply voltages below 4.75 V and above 5.25 V are applicable for SN5413 only.

3

TTL DEVICES

TYPICAL CHARACTERISTICS OF '13 CIRCUITS

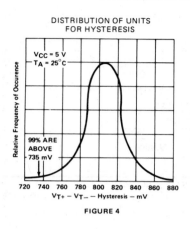

DISTRIBUTION OF UNITS
FOR HYSTERESIS

FIGURE 4

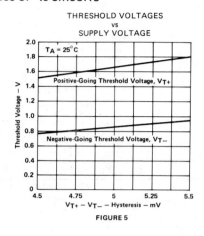

THRESHOLD VOLTAGES
vs
SUPPLY VOLTAGE

FIGURE 5

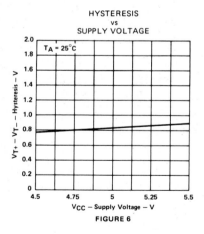

HYSTERESIS
vs
SUPPLY VOLTAGE

FIGURE 6

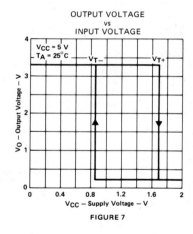

OUTPUT VOLTAGE
vs
INPUT VOLTAGE

FIGURE 7

Data for temperatures below 0°C and 70°C and supply voltages below 4.75 V and above 5.25 V are applicable for SN5413 only.

TEXAS
INSTRUMENTS

TYPICAL CHARACTERISTICS OF 'LS13 CIRCUITS

POSITIVE-GOING THRESHOLD VOLTAGE
vs
FREE-AIR TEMPERATURE

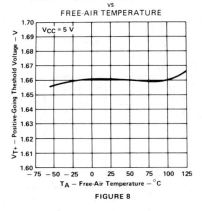

FIGURE 8

NEGATIVE-GOING THRESHOLD VOLTAGE
vs
FREE-AIR TEMPERATURE

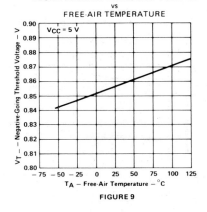

FIGURE 9

HYSTERESIS
vs
FREE-AIR TEMPERATURE

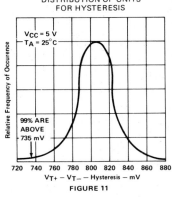

FIGURE 10

DISTRIBUTION OF UNITS
FOR HYSTERESIS

FIGURE 11

Data for temperatures below 0°C and above 70°C and supply voltages below 4.75 V and above 5.25 V are applicable for SN54LS13 only.

3

TTL DEVICES

TYPICAL CHARACTERISTICS OF 'LS13 CIRCUITS

THRESHOLD VOLTAGES AND HYSTERESIS
vs
SUPPLY VOLTAGE

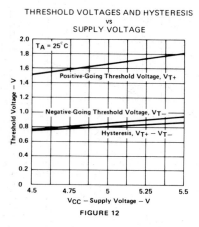

FIGURE 12

OUTPUT VOLTAGE
vs
INPUT VOLTAGE

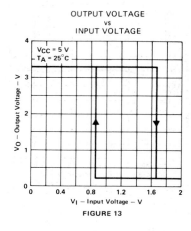

FIGURE 13

Data for temperatures below 0°C and above 70°C and supply voltages below 4.75 V and above 5.25 V are applicable for SN54LS13 only.

TEXAS
INSTRUMENTS

TYPICAL APPLICATION DATA

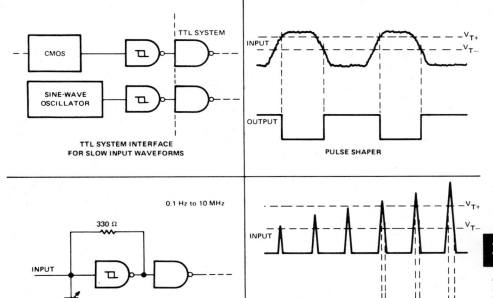

TTL SYSTEM INTERFACE
FOR SLOW INPUT WAVEFORMS

PULSE SHAPER

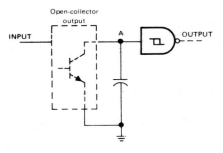

MULTIVIBRATOR

THRESHOLD DETECTOR

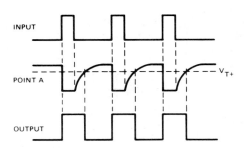

PULSE STRETCHER

3

TTL DEVICES

3

- **Operation from Very Slow Edges**
- **Improved Line-Receiving Characteristics**
- **High Noise Immunity**

description

Each circuit functions as an inverter, but because of the Schmitt action, it has different input threshold levels for positive (V_{T+}) and for negative going (V_{T-}) signals.

These circuits are temperature-compensated and can be triggered from the slowest of input ramps and still give clean, jitter-free output signals.

The SN5414 and SN54LS14 are characterized for operation over the full military temperature range of $-55°C$ to $125°C$. The SN7414 and the SN74LS14 are characterized for operation from $0°C$ to $70°C$.

logic diagram

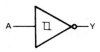

positive logic

$$Y = \overline{A}$$

SN5414, SN54LS14 ... J OR W PACKAGE
SN7414 ... J OR N PACKAGE
SN74LS14 ... D, J OR N PACKAGE
(TOP VIEW)

1A	1	14	V_{CC}
1Y	2	13	6A
2A	3	12	6Y
2Y	4	11	5A
3A	5	10	5Y
3Y	6	9	4A
GND	7	8	4Y

SN54LS14 ... FK PACKAGE
SN74LS14
(TOP VIEW)

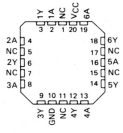

NC – No internal connection

TEXAS
INSTRUMENTS

3

TTL DEVICES

TYPES SN5414, SN54LS14, SN7414, SN74LS14
HEX SCHMITT-TRIGGER INVERTERS

schematics

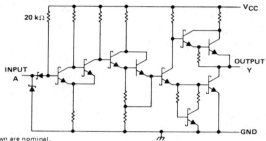

Resistor values shown are nominal.

absolute maximum ratings over operating free-air temperature range (unless otherwise noted)

Supply voltage, V_{CC} (see Note 1) .... 7 V

Input voltage: '14 .... 5.5 V

'LS14 .... 7 V

Operating free-air temperature: SN54' .... -55°C to 125°C

SN74' .... 0°C to 70°C

Storage temperature range .... -65°C to 150°C

NOTE 1: Voltage values are with respect to network ground terminal.

3

TTL DEVICES

recommended operating conditions

		SN5414			SN7414			UNIT
		MIN	NOM	MAX	MIN	NOM	MAX	
V_{CC}	Supply voltage	4.5	5	5.5	4.75	5	5.25	V
I_{OH}	High-level output current			-0.8			-0.8	mA
I_{OL}	Low-level output current			16			16	mA
T_A	Operating free-air temperature	-55		125	0		70	$^\circ$C

electrical characteristics over recommended operating free-air temperature range (unless otherwise noted)

PARAMETER	TEST CONDITIONS†			MIN	TYP‡	MAX	UNIT
V_{T+}	$V_{CC} = 5$ V			1.5	1.7	2	V
V_{T-}	$V_{CC} = 5$ V			0.6	0.9	1.1	V
Hysteresis $(V_{T+} - V_{T-})$	$V_{CC} = 5$ V			0.4	C.8		V
V_{IK}	$V_{CC} = $ MIN,	$I_I = -12$ mA				-1.5	V
V_{OH}	$V_{CC} = $ MIN,	$V_I = 0.6$ V,	$I_{OH} = -0.8$ mA	2.4	3.4		V
V_{OL}	$V_{CC} = $ MIN,	$V_I = 2$ V,	$I_{OL} = 16$ mA		0.2	0.4	V
I_{T+}	$V_{CC} = 5$ V,	$V_I = V_{T+}$			-0.43		mA
I_{T-}	$V_{CC} = 5$ V,	$V_I = V_{T-}$			-0.56		mA
I_I	$V_{CC} = $ MAX,	$V_I = 5.5$ V				1	mA
I_{IH}	$V_{CC} = $ MAX,	$V_{IH} = 2.4$ V				40	μA
I_{IL}	$V_{CC} = $ MAX,	$V_{IL} = 0.4$ V			-0.8	-1.2	mA
I_{OS}§	$V_{CC} = $ MAX			-18		-55	mA
I_{CCH}	$V_{CC} = $ MAX				22	36	mA
I_{CCL}	$V_{CC} = $ MAX				39	60	mA

† For conditions shown as MIN or MAX, use the appropriate value specified under recommended operating conditions.
‡ All typical values are at $V_{CC} = 5$ V, $T_A = 25^\circ$C.
§ Not more than one output should be shorted at a time.

switching characteristics, $V_{CC} = 5$ V, $T_A = 25^\circ$C

PARAMETER	FROM (INPUT)	TO (OUTPUT)	TEST CONDITIONS		MIN	TYP	MAX	UNIT
t_{PLH}	A	Y	$R_L = 400$ Ω,	$C_L = 15$ pF		15	22	ns
t_{PHL}						15	22	ns

3

TTL DEVICES

recommended operating conditions

		SN54LS14 MIN	NOM	MAX	SN74LS14 MIN	NOM	MAX	UNIT
V_{CC}	Supply voltage	4.5	5	5.5	4.75	5	5.25	V
I_{OH}	High-level output current			− 0.4			− 0.4	mA
I_{OL}	Low-level output current			4			8	mA
T_A	Operating free-air temperature	− 55		125	0		70	°C

electrical characteristics over recommended operating free-air temperature range (unless otherwise noted)

PARAMETER	TEST CONDITIONS[†]		SN54LS14 MIN	TYP[‡]	MAX	SN74LS14 MIN	TYP[‡]	MAX	UNIT
V_{T+}	V_{CC} = 5 V		1.4	1.6	1.9	1.4	1.6	1.9	V
V_{T-}	V_{CC} = 5 V		0.5	0.8	1	0.5	0.8	1	V
Hysteresis $(V_{T+} - V_{T-})$	V_{CC} = 5 V		0.4	0.8		0.4	0.8		V
V_{IK}	V_{CC} = MIN, I_I = − 18 mA				− 1.5			− 1.5	V
V_{OH}	V_{CC} = MIN, V_I = 0.5 V, I_{OH} = − 0.4 mA		2.5	3.4		2.7	3.4		V
V_{OL}	V_{CC} = MIN, V_I = 1.9 V	I_{OL} = 4 mA		0.25	0.4		0.25	0.4	V
		I_{OL} = 8 mA					0.35	0.5	
I_{T+}	V_{CC} = 5 V, V_I = V_{T+}			− 0.14			− 0.14		mA
I_{T-}	V_{CC} = 5 V, V_I = V_{T-}			− 0.18			− 0.18		mA
I_I	V_{CC} = MAX, V_I = 7 V				0.1			0.1	mA
I_{IH}	V_{CC} = MAX, V_{IH} = 2.7 V				20			20	µA
I_{IL}	V_{CC} = MAX, V_{IL} = 0.4 V				− 0.4			− 0.4	mA
I_{OS} [§]	V_{CC} = MAX		− 20		− 100	− 20		− 100	mA
I_{CCH}	V_{CC} = MAX			8.6	16		8.6	16	mA
I_{CCL}	V_{CC} = MAX			12	21		12	21	mA

[†] For conditions shown as MIN or MAX, use the appropriate value specified under recommended operating conditions.
[‡] All typical values are at V_{CC} = 5 V, T_A = 25°C.
[§] Not more than one output should be shorted at a time, and duration of the short-circuit should not exceed one second.

switching characteristics, V_{CC} = 5 V, T_A = 25°C

PARAMETER	FROM (INPUT)	TO (OUTPUT)	TEST CONDITIONS		MIN	TYP	MAX	UNIT
t_{PLH}	A	Y	R_L = 2 kΩ,	C_L = 15 pF		15	22	ns
t_{PHL}						15	22	ns

TEXAS
INSTRUMENTS

TYPES SN5414, SN54LS14, SN7414, SN74LS14
HEX SCHMITT-TRIGGER INVERTERS

PARAMETER MEASUREMENT INFORMATION

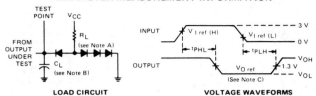

LOAD CIRCUIT   VOLTAGE WAVEFORMS

NOTES: A. All diodes are 1N3064 or equivalent.
B. C_L includes probe and jig capacitance.
C. Generator characteristics and reference voltage are:

	Generator Characteristics				Reference Voltages		
	Z_{out}	PRR	t_r	t_f	$V_{I\,ref(H)}$	$V_{I\,ref(L)}$	$V_{O\,ref}$
SN54'/SN74'	50 Ω	1 MHz	10 ns	10 ns	1.7 V	0.9 V	1.5 V
SN54LS'/SN74LS'	50 Ω	1 MHz	15 ns	6 ns	1.6 V	0.8 V	1.3 V

TYPICAL CHARACTERISTICS OF '14 CIRCUITS

POSITIVE-GOING THRESHOLD VOLTAGE
vs
FREE-AIR TEMPERATURE

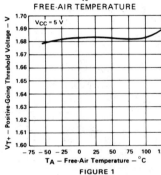

FIGURE 1

NEGATIVE-GOING THRESHOLD VOLTAGE
vs
FREE-AIR TEMPERATURE

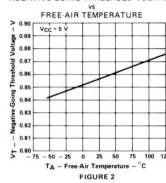

FIGURE 2

HYSTERESIS
vs
FREE-AIR TEMPERATURE

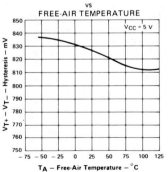

FIGURE 3

Data for temperatures below 0°C and 70°C and supply voltages below 4.75V and above 5.25 V are applicable for SN5414 only.

3 TTL DEVICES

3

TTL DEVICES

TYPICAL CHARACTERISTICS OF '14 CIRCUITS

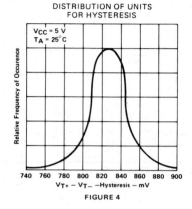

DISTRIBUTION OF UNITS
FOR HYSTERESIS

FIGURE 4

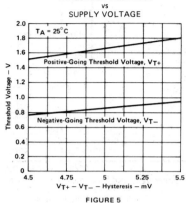

THRESHOLD VOLTAGES
vs
SUPPLY VOLTAGE

FIGURE 5

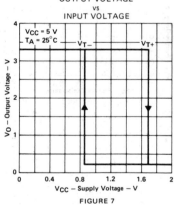

HYSTERESIS
vs
SUPPLY VOLTAGE

FIGURE 6

OUTPUT VOLTAGE
vs
INPUT VOLTAGE

FIGURE 7

Data for temperatures below $0°C$ and $70°C$ and supply voltages below 4.75 V and above 5.25 V are applicable for SN5414 only.

TEXAS
INSTRUMENTS

TYPICAL CHARACTERISTICS OF 'LS14 CIRCUITS

POSITIVE-GOING THRESHOLD VOLTAGE
vs
FREE-AIR TEMPERATURE

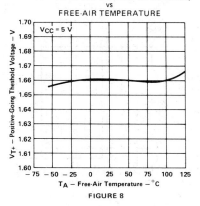

FIGURE 8

NEGATIVE-GOING THRESHOLD VOLTAGE
vs
FREE-AIR TEMPERATURE

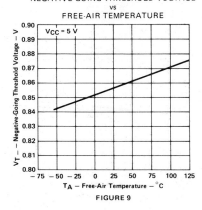

FIGURE 9

HYSTERESIS
vs
FREE-AIR TEMPERATURE

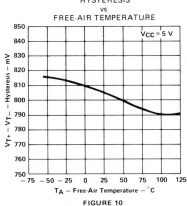

FIGURE 10

DISTRIBUTION OF UNITS
FOR HYSTERESIS

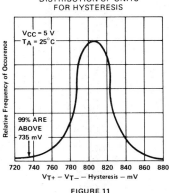

FIGURE 11

Data for temperatures below 0°C and above 70°C and supply voltages below 4.75 V and above 5.25 V are applicable for SN54LS14 only.

3

TTL DEVICES

TYPES SN54LS14, SN74LS14
HEX SCHMITT-TRIGGER INVERTERS

TYPICAL CHARACTERISTICS OF 'LS14 CIRCUITS

THRESHOLD VOLTAGES AND HYSTERESIS
vs
SUPPLY VOLTAGE

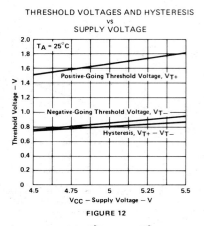

FIGURE 12

OUTPUT VOLTAGE
vs
INPUT VOLTAGE

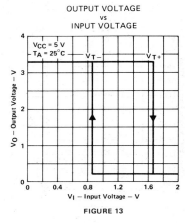

FIGURE 13

Data for temperatures below 0°C and above 70°C and supply voltages below 4.75 V and above 5.25 V are applicable for SN54LS14 only.

TEXAS INSTRUMENTS

TYPICAL APPLICATION DATA

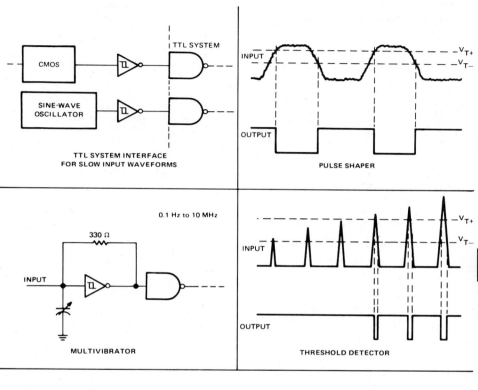

TTL SYSTEM INTERFACE
FOR SLOW INPUT WAVEFORMS

PULSE SHAPER

0.1 Hz to 10 MHz

330 Ω

INPUT

MULTIVIBRATOR

THRESHOLD DETECTOR

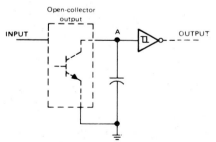

Open-collector
output

INPUT

A

OUTPUT

PULSE STRETCHER

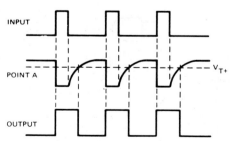

INPUT

POINT A

OUTPUT

3

TTL DEVICES

- **Package Options Include Both Plastic and Ceramic Chip Carriers in Addition to Plastic and Ceramic DIPs**

- **Dependable Texas Instruments Quality and Reliability**

description

These devices contain three independent 3-input AND gates with open-collector outputs. The open-collector outputs require pull-up resistors to perform correctly. They may be connected to other open-collector outputs to implement active-low wired-OR or active-high wired-AND functions. Open-collector devices are often used to generate high V_{OH} levels.

The SN54LS15 and SN54S15 are characterized for operation over the full military temperature range of −55°C to 125°C. The SN74LS15, and SN74S15 are characterized for operation from 0°C to 70°C.

SN54LS15, SN54S15 . . . J OR W PACKAGE

SN74LS15, SN74S15 . . . D, J OR N PACKAGE

(TOP VIEW)

1A [1	14] V_{CC}
1B [2	13] 1C
2A [3	12] 1Y
2B [4	11] 3C
2C [5	10] 3B
2Y [6	9] 3A
GND [7	8] 3Y

SN54LS15, SN54S15 . . . FK PACKAGE
SN74LS15, SN74S15

(TOP VIEW)

2A [4   18] 1Y
NC [5   17] NC
2B [6   16] 3C
NC [7   15] NC
2C [8   14] 3B

NC - No internal connection

FUNCTION TABLE (each gate)

INPUTS			OUTPUT
A	B	C	Y
H	H	H	H
L	X	X	L
X	L	X	L
X	X	L	L

logic diagram (each gate)

positive logic

$$Y = A \cdot B \cdot C \text{ or } Y = \overline{\overline{A} + \overline{B} + \overline{C}}$$

TEXAS
INSTRUMENTS

schematics (each gate)

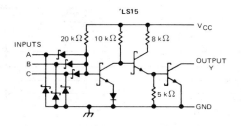

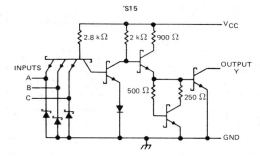

Resistor values shown are nominal.

absolute maximum ratings over operating free-air temperature range (unless otherwise noted)

Supply voltage, V_{CC} (see Note 1): .... 7 V

Input voltage: 'S15 .... 5.5 V

              'LS15 .... 7 V

Operating free-air temperature range: SN54' .... -55°C to 125°C

                              SN74' .... 0°C to 70°C

Storage temperature range .... -65°C to 150°C

NOTE 1: Voltage values are with respect to network ground terminal.

recommended operating conditions

		SN54LS15			SN74LS15			UNIT
		MIN	NOM	MAX	MIN	NOM	MAX	
V_{CC}	Supply voltage	4.5	5	5.5	4.75	5	5.25	V
V_{IH}	High-level input voltage	2			2			V
V_{IL}	Low-level input voltage			0.7			0.8	V
V_{OH}	High-level output voltage			5.5			5.5	V
I_{OL}	Low-level output current			4			8	mA
T_A	Operating free-air temperature	−55		125	0		70	°C

electrical characteristics over recommended operating free-air temperature range (unless otherwise noted)

PARAMETER	TEST CONDITIONS†		SN54LS15			SN74LS15			UNIT
			MIN	TYP‡	MAX	MIN	TYP‡	MAX	
V_{IK}	V_{CC} = MIN,	I_I = −18 mA			−1.5			−1.5	V
I_{OH}	V_{CC} = MIN, V_{IH} = 2 V,	V_{OH} = 5.5 V			0.1			0.1	mA
V_{OL}	V_{CC} = MIN, V_{IH} = 2 V,	I_{OL} = 4 mA	0.25	0.4		0.25	0.4		V
	V_{CC} = MIN, V_{IH} = 2 V,	I_{OL} = 8 mA				0.35	0.5		
I_I	V_{CC} = MAX,	V_I = 7 V			0.1			0.1	mA
I_{IH}	V_{CC} = MAX,	V_I = 2.7 V			20			20	µA
I_{IL}	V_{CC} = MAX,	V_I = 0.4 V			−0.4			−0.4	mA
I_{CCH}	V_{CC} = MAX,	V_I = 4.5 V		1.8	3.6		1.8	3.6	mA
I_{CCL}	V_{CC} = MAX,	V_I = 0 V		3.3	6.6		3.3	6.6	mA

† For conditions shown as MIN or MAX, use the appropriate value specified under recommended operating conditions.
‡ All typical values are at V_{CC} = 5 V, T_A = 25°C.

switching characteristics, V_{CC} = 5 V, T_A = 25°C (see note 2)

PARAMETER	FROM (INPUT)	TO (OUTPUT)	TEST CONDITIONS		MIN	TYP	MAX	UNIT
t_{PLH}	A, B, or C	Y	R_L = 2 kΩ,	C_L = 15 pF		20	35	ns
t_{PHL}						17	35	ns

NOTE 2: See General Information Section for load circuits and voltage waveforms.

3

TTL DEVICES

TEXAS
INSTRUMENTS

TRIPLE 3-INPUT POSITIVE-AND GATES WITH OPEN-COLLECTOR OUTPUTS

recommended operating conditions

		SN54S15			SN74S15			UNIT
		MIN	NOM	MAX	MIN	NOM	MAX	
V_{CC}	Supply voltage	4.5	5	5.5	4.75	5	5.25	V
V_{IH}	High-level input voltage	2			2			V
V_{IL}	Low-level input voltage			0.8			0.8	V
V_{OH}	High-level output voltage			5.5			5.5	V
I_{OL}	Low-level output current			20			20	mA
T_A	Operating free-air temperature	-55		125	0		70	°C

electrical characteristics over recommended operating free-air temperature range (unless otherwise noted)

PARAMETER	TEST CONDITIONS†			MIN	TYP‡	MAX	UNIT
V_{IK}	V_{CC} = MIN,	$I_I = -12$ mA				-1.2	V
I_{OH}	V_{CC} = MIN,	V_{IH} = 2 V,	V_{OH} = 5.5 V			0.25	mA
V_{OL}	V_{CC} = MIN,	V_{IH} = 2 V,	I_{OL} = 16 mA			0.5	V
I_I	V_{CC} = MAX,	V_I = 5.5 V				1	mA
I_{IH}	V_{CC} = MAX,	V_I = 2.7 V				50	µA
I_{IL}	V_{CC} = MAX,	V_I = 0.5 V				-2	mA
I_{CCH}	V_{CC} = MAX,	V_I = 4.5 V			10.5	19.5	mA
I_{CCL}	V_{CC} = MAX,	V_I = 0 V			24	42	mA

† For conditions shown as MIN or MAX, use the appropriate value specified under recommended operating conditions.
‡ All typical values are at V_{CC} = 5 V, T_A = 25°C.

switching characteristics, V_{CC} = 5 V, T_A = 25°C (see note 2)

PARAMETER	FROM (INPUT)	TO (OUTPUT)	TEST CONDITIONS		MIN	TYP	MAX	UNIT
t_{PLH}	A, B, or C	Y	R_L = 280 Ω,	C_L = 15 pF		5.5	8.5	ns
t_{PHL}						6	9	ns
t_{PLH}			R_L = 280 Ω,	C_L = 50 pF		8.5		ns
t_{PHL}						8		ns

NOTE 2: See General Information Section for load circuits and voltage waveforms.

3

TTL DEVICES

TEXAS
INSTRUMENTS

3

TTL DEVICES

- Functionally and Mechanically Identical To 'LS13, 'LS14, and 'LS132, Respectively
- Improved Line-Receiving Characteristics
- P-N-P Inputs Reduce System Loading
- Excellent Noise Immunity With Typical Hysteresis of 0.7 V

SN74LS18A ... D, J OR N PACKAGE
(TOP VIEW)

```
      ___  ___
1A  [ 1  U  14 ] VCC
1B  [ 2     13 ] 2D
NC  [ 3     12 ] 2C
1C  [ 4     11 ] NC
1D  [ 5     10 ] 2B
1Y  [ 6      9 ] 2A
GND [ 7      8 ] 2Y
```

description

Each circuit functions as a NAND gate or inverter, but because of the Schmitt action, it has different input threshold levels for positive (V_{T+}) and for negative going (V_{T-}) signals. The hysteresis or backlash, which is the difference between the two threshold levels ($V_{T+} - V_{T-}$), is typically 900 millivolts.

These circuits are temperature-compensated and can be triggered from the slowest of input ramps and still give clean, jitter-free output signals.

logic diagram (each gate or inverter)

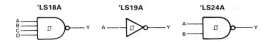

'LS18A   'LS19A   'LS24A

SN74LS19A ... D, J OR N PACKAGE
(TOP VIEW)

```
      ___  ___
1A  [ 1  U  14 ] VCC
1Y  [ 2     13 ] 6A
2A  [ 3     12 ] 6Y
2Y  [ 4     11 ] 5A
3A  [ 5     10 ] 5Y
3Y  [ 6      9 ] 4A
GND [ 7      8 ] 4Y
```

SN74LS24A ... D, J OR N PACKAGE
(TOP VIEW)

```
      ___  ___
1A  [ 1  U  14 ] VCC
1B  [ 2     13 ] 4B
1Y  [ 3     12 ] 4A
2A  [ 4     11 ] 4Y
2B  [ 5     10 ] 3B
2Y  [ 6      9 ] 3A
GND [ 7      8 ] 3Y
```

3

TTL DEVICES

TEXAS
INSTRUMENTS

3-89

schematic (each gate)

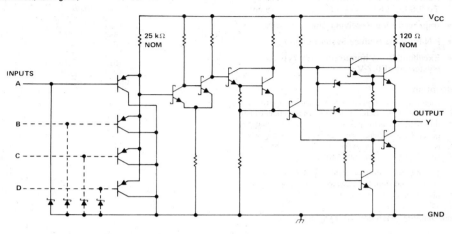

absolute maximum ratings over operating free-air temperature range (unless otherwise noted)

Supply voltage, V_{CC} (see Note 1) . . . . 7 V
Input voltage . . . . 7 V
Operating free-air temperature range: SN74LS' . . . . 0°C to 70°C
Storage temperature range . . . . −65°C to 150°C

recommended operating conditions

	SN74LS'			UNIT
	MIN	NOM	MAX	
Supply voltage, V_{CC}	4.75	5	5.25	V
High-level output current, I_{OH}			−400	µA
Low-level output current, I_{OL}			8	mA
Operating free-air temperature, T_A	0		70	°C

TEXAS
INSTRUMENTS

electrical characteristics over recommended operating free-air temperature range (unless otherwise noted)

PARAMETER	TEST CONDITIONS[†]			SN74LS' MIN	SN74LS' TYP[‡]	SN74LS' MAX	UNIT
V_{T+}	$V_{CC} = 5 V$			1.65	1.9	2.15	V
V_{T-}	$V_{CC} = 5 V$			0.75	1.0	1.25	V
Hysteresis $(V_{T+} - V_{T-})$	$V_{CC} = 5 V$			0.4	0.9		V
V_{IK}	$V_{CC} = MIN,$	$I_I = -18 mA$				-1.5	V
V_{OH}	$V_{CC} = MIN,$	$V_I = V_{T-}min$	$I_{OH} = -0.4 mA$	2.7	3.4		V
V_{OL}	$V_{CC} = MIN,$	$V_I = V_{T+}max$	$I_{OL} = 4 mA$		0.25	0.4	V
			$I_{OL} = 8 mA$		0.35	0.5	
I_{T+}	$V_{CC} = 5 V,$	$V_I = V_{T+}$			-2	-20	µA
I_{T-}	$V_{CC} = 5 V,$	$V_I = V_{T-}$			-5	-30	µA
I_I	$V_{CC} = MAX,$	$V_I = 7 V$				0.1	mA
I_{IH}	$V_{CC} = MAX,$	$V_I = 2.7 V$				20	µA
I_{IL}	$V_{CC} = MAX,$	$V_I = 0.4 V$				-50	µA
I_{OS}[§]	$V_{CC} = MAX,$	$V_I = V_O = 0 V$		-20		-100	mA
I_{CCH}	$V_{CC} = MAX,$	$V_I = 0 V$	'LS18A		3.3	6	mA
			'LS19A		9.9	18	
			'LS24A		6.6	12	
I_{CCL}	$V_{CC} = MAX,$	$V_I = 4.5 V$	'LS18A		5.7	10	mA
			'LS19A		17	30	
			'LS24A		11	20	

[†]For conditions shown as MIN or MAX, use the appropriate value specified under recommended operating conditions.
[‡]All typical values are at $V_{CC} = 5 V$, $T_A = 25°C$.
[§]Not more than one output should be shorted at a time, and the duration of the short-circuit should not exceed one second.

switching characteristics, $V_{CC} = 5 V$, $T_A = 25°C$, see figure 1

PARAMETER	FROM (INPUT)	TO (OUTPUT)	TEST CONDITIONS	'LS18A MIN	'LS18A TYP	'LS18A MAX	'LS19A MIN	'LS19A TYP	'LS19A MAX	'LS24A MIN	'LS24A TYP	'LS24A MAX	UNIT
t_{PLH}	Any	Y	$R_L = 2 kΩ,$ $C_L = 15 pF$		13	20		13	20		13	20	ns
t_{PHL}	Any	Y			37	55		18	30		25	40	ns

t_{PLH} – Propagation delay time, low-to-high-level output
t_{PHL} – Propagation delay time, high-to-low-level output

3

TTL DEVICES

TEXAS
INSTRUMENTS

TYPES SN74LS18A, SN74LS19A, SN74LS24A
SCHMITT-TRIGGER POSITIVE-NAND GATES
AND INVERTERS WITH TOTEM-POLE OUTPUTS

PARAMETER MEASUREMENT INFORMATION

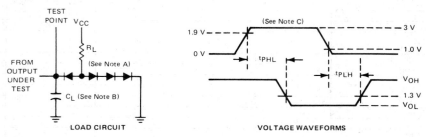

LOAD CIRCUIT

VOLTAGE WAVEFORMS

NOTES: A. All diodes are IN3064 or equivalent.
B. C_L includes probe and circuit capacitance.
C. The generator characteristics are; P_{RR} = IMHz, t_r = 15 ns,
t_p = 6 ns, Z_{out} = 50 Ω.

FIGURE 1

TEXAS
INSTRUMENTS

- Package Options Include Both Plastic and Ceramic Chip Carriers in Addition to Plastic and Ceramic DIPs

- Dependable Texas Instruments Quality and Reliability

description

These devices contain two independent 4-input NAND gates.

The SN5420, SN54LS20 and SN54S20 are characterized for operation over the full military temperature range of −55°C to 125°C. The SN7420, SN74LS20 and SN74S20 are characterized for operation from 0°C to 70°C.

FUNCTION TABLE (each gate)

INPUTS				OUTPUT
A	B	C	D	Y
H	H	H	H	L
L	X	X	X	H
X	L	X	X	H
X	X	L	X	H
X	X	X	L	H

logic diagram (each gate)

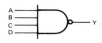

positive logic

$$Y = \overline{A \cdot B \cdot C \cdot D} \text{ or } Y = \overline{A} + \overline{B} + \overline{C} + \overline{D}$$

SN5420 . . . J PACKAGE
SN54LS20, SN54S20 . . . J OR W PACKAGE
SN7420 . . . J OR N PACKAGE
SN74LS20, SN74S20 . . . D, J OR N PACKAGE
(TOP VIEW)

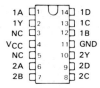

SN5420 . . . W PACKAGE
(TOP VIEW)

1A	1	14	1D
1Y	2	13	1C
NC	3	12	1B
VCC	4	11	GND
NC	5	10	2Y
2A	6	9	2D
2B	7	8	2C

SN54LS20, SN54S20 . . . FK PACKAGE
SN74LS20, SN74S20
(TOP VIEW)

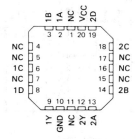

NC - No internal connection

TTL DEVICES

3

TEXAS
INSTRUMENTS

TYPES SN5420, SN54LS20, SN54S20
SN7420, SN74LS20, SN74S20
DUAL 4-INPUT POSITIVE-NAND GATES

schematics (each gate)

'20

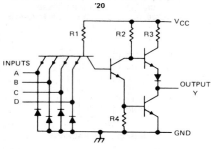

CIRCUIT	R1	R2	R3	R4
'20	4 kΩ	1.6 kΩ	130 Ω	1 kΩ

'LS20

'S20

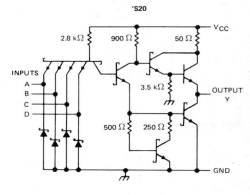

Resistor values shown are nominal.

absolute maximum ratings over operating free-air temperature range (unless otherwise noted)

Supply voltage, V_{CC} (see Note 1): '20, 'LS20, 'S20 .... 7 V

Input voltage: '20, 'S20 .... 5.5 V

             'LS20 .... 7 V

Operating free-air temperature: SN54' .... -55°C to 125°C

                        SN74' .... 0°C to 70°C

Storage temperature range .... -65°C to 150°C

NOTE 1: Voltage values are with respect to network ground terminal.

TEXAS
INSTRUMENTS

recommended operating conditions

		SN5420			SN7420			UNIT
		MIN	NOM	MAX	MIN	NOM	MAX	
V_{CC}	Supply voltage	4.5	5	5.5	4.75	5	5.25	V
V_{IH}	High-level input voltage	2			2			V
V_{IL}	Low-level input voltage			0.8			0.8	V
I_{OH}	High-level output current			−0.4			−0.4	mA
I_{OL}	Low-level output current			16			16	mA
T_A	Operating free-air temperature	−55		125	0		70	°C

electrical characteristics over recommended operating free-air temperature range (unless otherwise noted)

PARAMETER	TEST CONDITIONS†			SN5420			SN7420			UNIT
			MIN	TYP‡	MAX	MIN	TYP‡	MAX		
V_{IK}	V_{CC} = MIN,	I_I = −12 mA			−1.5			−1.5		V
V_{OH}	V_{CC} = MIN,	V_{IL} = 0.8 V, I_{OH} = −0.4 mA	2.4	3.4		2.4	3.4			V
V_{OL}	V_{CC} = MIN,	V_{IH} = 2 V, I_{OL} = 16 mA		0.2	0.4		0.2	0.4		V
I_I	V_{CC} = MAX,	V_I = 5.5 V			1			1		mA
I_{IH}	V_{CC} = MAX,	V_I = 2.4 V			40			40		µA
I_{IL}	V_{CC} = MAX,	V_I = 0.4 V			−1.6			−1.6		mA
I_{OS}§	V_{CC} = MAX		−20		−55	−18		−55		mA
I_{CCH}	V_{CC} = MAX,	V_I = 0 V		2	4		2	4		mA
I_{CCL}	V_{CC} = MAX,	V_I = 4.5 V		6	11		6	11		mA

† For conditions shown as MIN or MAX, use the appropriate value specified under recommended operating conditions.
‡ All typical values are at V_{CC} = 5 V, T_A = 25°C.
§ Not more than one output should be shorted at a time.

switching characteristics, V_{CC} = 5 V, T_A = 25°C (see note 2)

PARAMETER	FROM (INPUT)	TO (OUTPUT)	TEST CONDITIONS		MIN	TYP	MAX	UNIT
t_{PLH}	Any	Y	R_L = 400 Ω,	C_L = 15 pF		12	22	ns
t_{PHL}						8	15	ns

NOTE 2: See General Information Section for load circuits and voltage waveforms.

3

TTL DEVICES

TEXAS
INSTRUMENTS

recommended operating conditions

		SN54LS20			SN74LS20			UNIT
		MIN	NOM	MAX	MIN	NOM	MAX	
V_{CC}	Supply voltage	4.5	5	5.5	4.75	5	5.25	V
V_{IH}	High-level input voltage	2			2			V
V_{IL}	Low-level input voltage			0.7			0.8	V
I_{OH}	High-level output current			-0.4			-0.4	mA
I_{OL}	Low-level output current			4			8	mA
T_A	Operating free-air temperature	-55		125	0		70	°C

electrical characteristics over recommended operating free-air temperature range (unless otherwise noted)

PARAMETER	TEST CONDITIONS †			SN54LS20			SN74LS20			UNIT
				MIN	TYP‡	MAX	MIN	TYP‡	MAX	
V_{IK}	V_{CC} = MIN,	$I_I = -18$ mA				-1.5			-1.5	V
V_{OH}	V_{CC} = MIN,	V_{IL} = MAX,	$I_{OH} = -0.4$ mA	2.5	3.4		2.7	3.4		V
V_{OL}	V_{CC} = MIN,	V_{IH} = 2 V,	I_{OL} = 4 mA		0.25	0.4			0.4	V
	V_{CC} = MIN,	V_{IH} = 2 V,	I_{OL} = 8 mA					0.25	0.5	
I_I	V_{CC} = MAX,	V_I = 7 V				0.1			0.1	mA
I_{IH}	V_{CC} = MAX,	V_I = 2.7 V				20			20	µA
I_{IL}	V_{CC} = MAX,	V_I = 0.4 V				-0.4			-0.4	mA
I_{OS} §	V_{CC} = MAX			-20		-100	-20		-100	mA
I_{CCH}	V_{CC} = MAX,	V_I = 0 V			0.4	0.8		0.4	0.8	mA
I_{CCL}	V_{CC} = MAX,	V_I = 4.5 V			1.2	2.2		1.2	2.2	mA

† For conditions shown as MIN or MAX, use the appropriate value specified under recommended operating conditions.
‡ All typical values are at V_{CC} = 5 V, T_A = 25°C.
§ Not more than one output should be shorted at a time, and the duration of the short-circuit should not exceed one second.

switching characteristics, V_{CC} = 5 V, T_A = 25°C (see note 2)

PARAMETER	FROM (INPUT)	TO (OUTPUT)	TEST CONDITIONS		MIN	TYP	MAX	UNIT
t_{PLH}	Any	Y	R_L = 2 kΩ,	C_L = 15 pF		9	15	ns
t_{PHL}						10	15	ns

NOTE 2: See General Information Section for load circuits and voltage waveforms.

TEXAS
INSTRUMENTS

3
TTL DEVICES

recommended operating conditions

		SN54S20			SN74S20			UNIT
		MIN	NOM	MAX	MIN	NOM	MAX	
V_{CC}	Supply voltage	4.5	5	5.5	4.75	5	5.25	V
V_{IH}	High-level input voltage	2			2			V
V_{IL}	Low-level input voltage			0.8			0.8	V
I_{OH}	High-level output current			−1			−1	mA
I_{OL}	Low-level output current			20			20	mA
T_A	Operating free-air temperature	−55		125	0		70	°C

electrical characteristics over recommended operating free-air temperature range (unless otherwise noted)

PARAMETER	TEST CONDITIONS †			SN54S20			SN74S20			UNIT
				MIN	TYP‡	MAX	MIN	TYP‡	MAX	
V_{IK}	V_{CC} = MIN,	I_I = −18 mA				−1.2			−1.2	V
V_{OH}	V_{CC} = MIN,	V_{IL} = 0.8 V,	I_{OH} = −1 mA	2.5	3.4		2.7	3.4		V
V_{OL}	V_{CC} = MIN,	V_{IH} = 2 V,	I_{OL} = 20 mA			0.5			0.5	V
I_I	V_{CC} = MAX,	V_I = 5.5 V				1			1	mA
I_{IH}	V_{CC} = MAX,	V_I = 2.7 V				50			50	μA
I_{IL}	V_{CC} = MAX,	V_I = 0.5 V				−2			−2	mA
I_{OS} §	V_{CC} = MAX			−40		−100	−40		−100	mA
I_{CCH}	V_{CC} = MAX,	V_I = 0 V			5	8		5	8	mA
I_{CCL}	V_{CC} = MAX,	V_I = 4.5 V			10	18		10	18	mA

† For conditions shown as MIN or MAX, use the appropriate value specified under recommended operating conditions.
‡ All typical values are at V_{CC} = 5 V, T_A = 25°C.
§ Not more than one output should be shorted at a time, and the duration of the short-circuit should not exceed one second.

switching characteristics, V_{CC} = 5 V, T_A = 25°C (see note 2)

PARAMETER	FROM (INPUT)	TO (OUTPUT)	TEST CONDITIONS		MIN	TYP	MAX	UNIT
t_{PLH}	A, B, C or D	Y	R_L = 280 Ω,	C_L = 15 pF		3	4.5	ns
t_{PHL}						3	5	ns
t_{PLH}			R_L = 280 Ω,	C_L = 50 pF			4.5	ns
t_{PHL}							5	ns

NOTE 2: See General Information Section for load circuits and voltage waveforms.

TTL DEVICES

3

TEXAS
INSTRUMENTS

- Package Options Include Both Plastic and Ceramic Chip Carriers in Addition to Plastic and Ceramic DIPs

- Dependable Texas Instruments Quality and Reliability

description

These devices contain two independent 4-input AND gates.

The SN54LS21 is characterized for operation over the full military temperature range of −55°C to 125°C. The SN74LS21 is characterized for operation from 0°C to 70°C.

FUNCTION TABLE (each gate)

INPUTS				OUTPUT
A	B	C	D	Y
H	H	H	H	H
L	X	X	X	L
X	L	X	X	L
X	X	L	X	L
X	X	X	L	L

SN54LS21 . . . J OR W PACKAGE
SN74LS21 . . . D, J OR N PACKAGE
(TOP VIEW)

1A	1	14 VCC
1B	2	13 2D
NC	3	12 2C
1C	4	11 NC
1D	5	10 2B
1Y	6	9 2A
GND	7	8 2Y

SN54LS21 . . . FK PACKAGE
SN74LS21
(TOP VIEW)

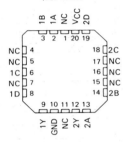

NC - No internal connection

logic diagram (each gate)

positive logic

$$Y = A \cdot B \cdot C \cdot D \ \text{or} \ Y = \overline{\overline{A} + \overline{B} + \overline{C} + \overline{D}}$$

TEXAS
INSTRUMENTS

schematics (each gate)

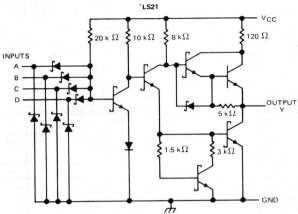

Resistor values shown are nominal.

absolute maximum ratings over operating free-air temperature range (unless otherwise noted)

Supply voltage, V_{CC} (see Note 1) .... 7 V
Input voltage: 'LS21 .... 7 V
Operating temperature range: SN54' .... -55°C to 125°C
SN74' .... 0°C to 70°C
Storage temperature range .... -65°C to 150°C

NOTE 1: Voltage values are with respect to network ground terminal.

3

TTL DEVICES

recommended operating conditions

		SN54LS21			SN74LS21			UNIT
		MIN	NOM	MAX	MIN	NOM	MAX	
V_{CC}	Supply voltage	4.5	5	5.5	4.75	5	5.25	V
V_{IH}	High-level input voltage	2			2			V
V_{IL}	Low-level input voltage			0.7			0.8	V
I_{OH}	High-level output current			− 0.4			− 0.4	mA
I_{OL}	Low-level output current			4			8	mA
T_A	Operating free-air temperature	− 55		125	0		70	°C

electrical characteristics over recommended operating free-air temperature range (unless otherwise noted)

PARAMETER	TEST CONDITIONS †		SN54LS21			SN74LS21			UNIT
			MIN	TYP‡	MAX	MIN	TYP‡	MAX	
V_{IK}	V_{CC} = MIN,	I_I = − 18 mA			− 1.5			− 1.5	V
V_{OH}	V_{CC} = MIN,	V_{IH} = 2 V, $\quad I_{OH}$ = − 0.4 mA	2.5	3.4		2.7	3.4		V
V_{OL}	V_{CC} = MIN,	V_{IL} = MAX, $\quad I_{OL}$ = 4 mA		0.25	0.4		0.25	0.4	V
	V_{CC} = MIN,	V_{IL} = MAX, $\quad I_{OL}$ = 8 mA					0.35	0.5	
I_I	V_{CC} = MAX,	V_I = 7 V			0.1			0.1	mA
I_{IH}	V_{CC} = MAX,	V_I = 2.7 V			20			20	µA
I_{IL}	V_{CC} = MAX,	V_I = 0.4 V			− 0.4			− 0.4	mA
I_{OS} §	V_{CC} = MAX		− 20		− 100	− 20		− 100	mA
I_{CCH}	V_{CC} = MAX,	V_I = 4.5 V		1.2	2.4		1.2	2.4	mA
I_{CCL}	V_{CC} = MAX,	V_I = 0 V		2.2	4.4		2.2	4.4	mA

† For conditions shown as MIN or MAX, use the appropriate value specified under recommended operating conditions.
‡ All typical values are at V_{CC} = 5 V, T_A = 25°C.
§ Not more than one output should be shorted at a time, and the duration of the short-circuit should not exceed one second.

switching characteristics, V_{CC} = 5 V, T_A = 25°C (see note 2)

PARAMETER	FROM (INPUT)	TO (OUTPUT)	TEST CONDITIONS		MIN	TYP	MAX	UNIT
t_{PLH}	Any	Y	R_L = 2 kΩ,	C_L = 15 pF		8	15	ns
t_{PHL}						10	20	ns

NOTE 2: See General Information Section for load circuits and voltage waveforms.

3

TTL DEVICES

- **Package Options Include Both Plastic and Ceramic Chip Carriers in Addition to Plastic and Ceramic DIPs**

- **Dependable Texas Instruments Quality and Reliability**

description

These devices contain two independent 4-input NAND gates. The open-collector outputs require pull-up resistors to perform correctly. They may be connected to other open-collector outputs to implement active-low wired-OR or active-high wired-AND functions. Open-collector devices are often used to generate higher V_{OH} levels.

The SN5422, SN54LS22 and SN54S22 are characterized for operation over the full military temperature range of −55°C to 125°C. The SN7422, SN74LS22 and SN74S22 are characterized for operation from 0°C to 70°C.

SN5422, SN54LS22, SN54S22 . . . J OR W PACKAGE

SN7422 . . . J OR N PACKAGE

SN74LS22, SN74S22 . . . D, J OR N PACKAGE

(TOP VIEW)

1A	1	14 V_{CC}
1B	2	13 2D
NC	3	12 2C
1C	4	11 NC
1D	5	10 2B
1Y	6	9 2A
GND	7	8 2Y

SN54LS22, SN54S22 . . . FK PACKAGE
SN74LS22, SN74S22

(TOP VIEW)

NC — No international connection

FUNCTION TABLE (each gate)

INPUTS				OUTPUT
A	B	C	D	Y
H	H	H	H	L
L	X	X	X	H
X	L	X	X	H
X	X	L	X	H
X	X	X	L	H

logic diagram (each gate)

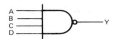

A
B
C
D
—Y

positive logic

$$Y = \overline{A \cdot B \cdot C \cdot D} \text{ or } Y = \overline{A} + \overline{B} + \overline{C} + \overline{D}$$

3

TTL DEVICES

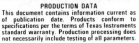

TEXAS
INSTRUMENTS

schematics (each gate)

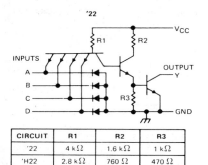

'22

CIRCUIT	R1	R2	R3
'22	4 kΩ	1.6 kΩ	1 kΩ
'H22	2.8 kΩ	760 Ω	470 Ω

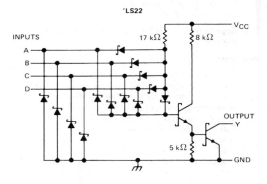

'LS22

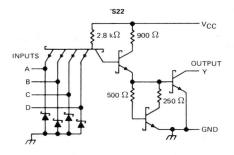

'S22

Resistor values shown are nominal.

absolute maximum ratings over operating free-air temperature range (unless otherwise noted)

Supply voltage, V_{CC} (see Note 1) . . . . 7 V

Input voltage: '22, 'S22 . . . . 5.5 V

              'LS22 . . . . 7 V

Operating free-air temperature: SN54' . . . . −55°C to 125°C

                                 SN74' . . . . 0°C to 70°C

Storage temperature range . . . . −65°C to 150°C

NOTE 1: Voltage values are with respect to network ground terminal.

TEXAS
INSTRUMENTS

3

TTL DEVICES

recommended operating conditions

		SN5422			SN7422			UNIT
		MIN	NOM	MAX	MIN	NOM	MAX	
V_{CC}	Supply voltage	4.5	5	5.5	4.75	5	5.25	V
V_{IH}	High-level input voltage	2			2			V
V_{IL}	Low-level input voltage			0.8			0.8	V
V_{OH}	High-level output voltage			5.5			5.5	V
I_{OL}	Low-level output current			16			16	mA
T_A	Operating free-air temperature	−55		125	0		70	°C

electrical characteristics over recommended operating free-air temperature range (unless otherwise noted)

PARAMETER	TEST CONDITIONS†			MIN	TYP‡	MAX	UNIT
V_{IK}	V_{CC} = MIN,	I_I = −12 mA				−1.5	V
I_{OH}	V_{CC} = MIN,	V_{IL} = 0.8 V,	V_{OH} = 5.5 V			0.25	mA
V_{OL}	V_{CC} = MIN,	V_{IH} = 2 V,	I_{OL} = 16 mA		0.2	0.4	V
I_I	V_{CC} = MAX,	V_I = 5.5 V				1	mA
I_{IH}	V_{CC} = MAX,	V_I = 2.4 V				40	µA
I_{IL}	V_{CC} = MAX,	V_I = 0.4 V				−1.6	mA
I_{CCH}	V_{CC} = MAX,	V_I = 0 V			2	4	mA
I_{CCL}	V_{CC} = MAX,	V_I = 4.5 V			6	11	mA

† For conditions shown as MIN or MAX, use the appropriate value specified under recommended operating conditions.
‡ All typical values are at V_{CC} = 5 V, T_A = 25°C.

switching characteristics, V_{CC} = 5 V, T_A = 25°C (see note 2)

PARAMETER	FROM (INPUT)	TO (OUTPUT)	TEST CONDITIONS		MIN	TYP	MAX	UNIT
t_{PLH}	Any	Y	R_L = 4 kΩ,	C_L = 15 pF		35	45	ns
t_{PHL}			R_L = 400 Ω,	C_L = 15 pF		8	15	ns

NOTE 2: See General Information Section for load circuits and voltage waveforms.

3

TTL DEVICES

TEXAS INSTRUMENTS

recommended operating conditions

		SN54LS22 MIN	NOM	MAX	SN74LS22 MIN	NOM	MAX	UNIT
V_{CC}	Supply voltage	4.5	5	5.5	4.75	5	5.25	V
V_{IH}	High-level input voltage	2			2			V
V_{IL}	Low-level input voltage			0.7			0.8	V
V_{OH}	High-level output voltage			5.5			5.5	V
I_{OL}	Low-level output current			4			8	mA
T_A	Operating free-air temperature	−55		125	0		70	°C

electrical characteristics over recommended operating free-air temperature range (unless otherwise noted)

PARAMETER	TEST CONDITIONS†	SN54LS22 MIN	TYP‡	MAX	SN74LS22 MIN	TYP‡	MAX	UNIT
V_{IK}	V_{CC} = MIN, I_I = −18 mA			−1.5			−1.5	V
I_{OH}	V_{CC} = MIN, V_{IL} = MAX, V_{OH} = 5.5 V			0.1			0.1	mA
V_{OL}	V_{CC} = MIN, V_{IH} = 2 V, I_{OL} = 4 mA		0.25	0.4		0.25	0.4	V
	V_{CC} = MIN, V_{IH} = 2 V, I_{OL} = 8 mA					0.35	0.5	
I_I	V_{CC} = MAX, V_I = 7 V			0.1			0.1	mA
I_{IH}	V_{CC} = MAX, V_I = 2.7 V			20			20	μA
I_{IL}	V_{CC} = MAX, V_I = 0.4 V			−0.4			−0.4	mA
I_{CCH}	V_{CC} = MAX, V_I = 0 V		0.4	0.8		0.4	0.8	mA
I_{CCL}	V_{CC} = MAX, V_I = 4.5 V		1.2	2.2		1.2	2.2	mA

† For conditions shown as MIN or MAX, use the appropriate value specified under recommended operating conditions.
‡ All typical values are at V_{CC} = 5 V, T_A = 25°C.

switching characteristics, V_{CC} = 5 V, T_A = 25°C (see note 2)

PARAMETER	FROM (INPUT)	TO (OUTPUT)	TEST CONDITIONS	MIN	TYP	MAX	UNIT
t_{PLH}	Any	Y	R_L = 2 kΩ, C_L = 15 pF		17	32	ns
t_{PHL}					15	28	ns

NOTE 2: See General Information Section for load circuits and voltage waveforms.

TEXAS INSTRUMENTS

recommended operating conditions

		SN54S22			SN74S22			UNIT
		MIN	NOM	MAX	MIN	NOM	MAX	
V_{CC}	Supply voltage	4.5	5	5.5	4.75	5	5.25	V
V_{IH}	High-level input voltage	2			2			V
V_{IL}	Low-level input voltage			0.8			0.8	V
V_{OH}	High-level output voltage			5.5			5.5	V
I_{OL}	Low-level output current			20			20	mA
T_A	Operating free-air temperature	−55		125	0		70	°C

electrical characteristics over recommended operating free-air temperature range (unless otherwise noted)

PARAMETER	TEST CONDITIONS†			MIN	TYP‡	MAX	UNIT
V_{IK}	V_{CC} = MIN,	I_I = −18 mA				−1.2	V
I_{OH}	V_{CC} = MIN,	V_{IL} = 0.8 V,	V_{OH} = 5.5 V			0.25	mA
V_{OL}	V_{CC} = MIN,	V_{IH} = 2 V,	I_{OL} = 20 mA			0.5	V
I_I	V_{CC} = MAX,	V_I = 5.5 V				1	mA
I_{IH}	V_{CC} = MAX,	V_I = 2.7 V				50	μA
I_{IL}	V_{CC} = MAX,	V_I = 0.5 V				−2	mA
I_{CCH}	V_{CC} = MAX,	V_I = 0 V			3	6.6	mA
I_{CCL}	V_{CC} = MAX,	V_I = 4.5 V			10	18	mA

† For conditions shown as MIN or MAX, use the appropriate value specified under recommended operating conditions.
‡ All typical values are at V_{CC} = 5 V, T_A = 25°C.

switching characteristics, V_{CC} = 5 V, T_A = 25°C (see note 2)

PARAMETER	FROM (INPUT)	TO (OUTPUT)	TEST CONDITIONS		MIN	TYP	MAX	UNIT
t_{PLH}			R_L = 280 Ω,	C_L = 15 pF	2	5	7.5	ns
t_{PHL}	Any	Y			2	4.5	7	ns
t_{PLH}			R_L = 280 Ω,	C_L = 50 pF		7.5		ns
t_{PHL}						7		ns

NOTE 2: See General Information Section for load circuits and voltage waveforms.

3

TTL DEVICES

TEXAS
INSTRUMENTS

3

TTL DEVICES

- **Package Options Include Plastic and Ceramic DIPs**
- **Dependable Texas Instruments Quality and Reliability**

description

These devices contain dual 4-input positive NOR gates with strobe. The SN5423 and SN7423 are expandable, and perform the Boolean functions:

$$1Y \quad \overline{1G(1A \cdot 1B \cdot 1C \cdot 1D) \cdot X} \text{ and}$$
$$2Y \quad \overline{2G(2A \cdot 2B \cdot 2C \cdot 2D)}$$

with X output of SN5460/SN7460. The SN5425 and SN7425 perform the Boolean function:

$$Y \quad \overline{G(A \cdot B \cdot C \cdot D)}$$

The SN5423 and the SN5425 are characterized for operation over the full military temperature range of 55 C to 125 C. The SN7423 and the SN7425 are characterized for operation from 0 C to 70 C.

schematic (each gate)

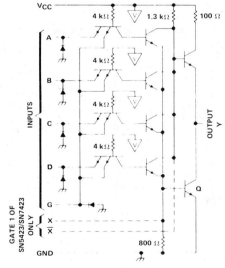

Notes: A. Component values shown are nominal.
         B. Both expander inputs are used simultaneously for expanding.
         C. If expander is not used leave X and X open.
         D. A total of four expander gates can be connected to
             the expander inputs.

         ▽   V_CC bus

SN5423 . . . J OR W PACKAGE
SN7423 . . . J OR N PACKAGE
(TOP VIEW)

```
        1X [ 1    16 ] VCC
        1A [ 2    15 ] 1X
        1B [ 3    14 ] 2D
        1G [ 4    13 ] 2C
        1C [ 5    12 ] 2G
        1D [ 6    11 ] 2B
        1Y [ 7    10 ] 2A
       GND [ 8     9 ] 2Y
```

SN5425 . . . J OR W PACKAGE
SN7425 . . . J OR N PACKAGE
(TOP VIEW)

```
        1A [ 1    14 ] VCC
        1B [ 2    13 ] 2D
        1G [ 3    12 ] 2C
        1C [ 4    11 ] 2G
        1D [ 5    10 ] 2B
        1Y [ 6     9 ] 2A
       GND [ 7     8 ] 2Y
```

logic diagram

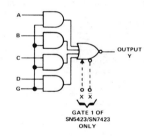

GATE 1 OF
SN5423/SN7423
ONLY

TRUTH TABLE

INPUTS					OUTPUT
A	B	C	D	G	Y
H	X	X	X	H	L
X	H	X	X	H	L
X	X	H	X	H	L
X	X	X	H	H	L
L	L	L	L	X	H
X	X	X	X	L	H

Expander inputs are open.
H high level, L low level, X irrelevant

3

TTL DEVICES

TYPES SN5423, SN5425, SN7423, SN7425
DUAL 4-INPUT NOR GATES WITH STROBE

absolute maximum ratings over operating free-air temperature range (unless otherwise noted)

Supply voltage V_{CC} (see Note 1) . . . . 7 V

Input voltage (see Note 1) . . . . 5.5 V

Interemitter voltage (see Note 2) . . . . 5.5 V

Operating free-air temperature range: SN5423, SN5425 Circuits . . . . -55°C to 125°C

SN7423, SN7425 Circuits . . . . 0°C to 70°C

Storage temperature range . . . . -65°C to 150°C

NOTES: 1. Voltage values, except interemitter voltage, are with respect to network ground terminal.
2. This is the voltage between two emitters of a multiple-emitter transistor.

recommended operating conditions

			'23, '25 MIN	'23, '25 NOM	'23, '25 MAX	UNIT
V_{CC}	Supply voltage	54 Family	4.5	5	5.5	V
		74 Family	4.75	5	5.25	
V_{IH}	High-level input voltage		2			V
V_{IL}	Low-level input voltage				0.8	V
I_{OH}	High-level output current				-0.8	mA
I_{OL}	Low-level output current	54 Family			16	mA
		74 Family			16	
T_A	Operating free-air temperature range	54 Family	-55		125	$^{\circ}$C
		74 Family	0		70	

The '23 is designed for use with up to four '60 expanders.

electrical characteristics over recommended operating free-air temperature range (unless otherwise noted)

PARAMETER		TEST CONDITIONS[†]			MIN	TYP[‡]	MAX	UNIT
V_I		V_{CC} = MIN,	$I_I = -12$ mA				-1.5	V
V_{OH}		V_{CC} = MIN,	V_{IL} = 0.8 V,	$I_{OH} = -0.8$ mA	2.4	3.4		V
V_{OL}		V_{CC} = MIN,	V_{IH} = 2 V,	I_{OL} = 16 mA		0.2	0.4	V
I_I		V_{CC} = MAX,	V_I = 5.5 V				1	mA
I_{IH}	data inputs	V_{CC} = MAX,	V_I = 2.4 V				40	μA
	strobe inputs						160	
I_{IL}	data inputs	V_{CC} = MAX,	V_I = 0.4 V				-1.6	mA
	strobe inputs						-6.4	
I_{OS}[§]		V_{CC} = MAX		54 Family	-20		-55	mA
				74 Family	-18		-55	
I_{CCH}		V_{CC} = MAX,	All inputs at 0 V			8	16	mA
I_{CCL}		V_{CC} = MAX,	All inputs at 5 V			10	19	mA

[†] For conditions shown as MIN or MAX, use the appropriate value specified under recommended operating conditions for the applicable device type. Expander inputs X and $\overline{X}$ are open.
[‡] All typical values are at V_{CC} = 5 V, T_A = 25°C.
[§] Not more than one output should be shorted at a time.

TEXAS INSTRUMENTS

electrical characteristics (SN5423 circuits) using expander inputs, V_{CC} = 4.5 V, T_A = −55°C

	PARAMETER	TEST CONDITIONS			MIN	TYP†	MAX	UNIT
$I_{\overline{X}}$	Expander current	$V_{X\overline{X}}$ = 0.4 V,	I_{OL} = 16 mA				−3.5	mA
$V_{BE(Q)}$	Base-Emitter voltage of output transistor (Q)	I_{OL} = 16 mA,	$I_X + I_{\overline{X}}$ = 0.41 mA,	$R_{X\overline{X}}$ = 0			1.1	V
V_{OH}	High-level output voltage	I_{OH} = −0.4 mA,	I_X = 0.15 mA,	$I_{\overline{X}}$ = −0.15 mA	2.4	3.4		V
V_{OL}	Low-level output voltage	I_{OL} = 16 mA,	$I_X + I_{\overline{X}}$ = 0.3 mA,	$R_{X\overline{X}}$ = 114 Ω		0.2	0.4	V

electrical characteristics (SN7423 circuits) using expander inputs, V_{CC} = 4.75 V, T_A = 0°C

	PARAMETER	TEST CONDITIONS			MIN	TYP†	MAX	UNIT
$I_{\overline{X}}$	Expander current	$V_{X\overline{X}}$ = 0.4 V,	I_{OL} = 16 mA.				−3.8	mA
$V_{BE(Q)}$	Base-Emitter voltage of output transistor (Q)	I_{OL} = 16 mA,	$I_X + I_{\overline{X}}$ = 0.62 mA,	$R_{X\overline{X}}$ = 0			1	V
V_{OH}	High-level output voltage	I_{OH} = −0.4 mA,	I_X = 0.27 mA,	$I_{\overline{X}}$ = −0.27 mA	2.4	3.4		V
V_{OL}	Low-level output voltage	I_{OL} = 16 mA,	$I_X + I_{\overline{X}}$ = 0.43 mA,	$R_{X\overline{X}}$ = 130 Ω		0.2	0.4	V

† All typical values are at V_{CC} = 5 V, T_A = 25°C.

switching characteristics, V_{CC} = 5 V, T_A = 25°C, N = 10, (see note 3)

PARAMETER	TEST CONDITIONS		MIN	TYP	MAX	UNIT
t_{PLH}	R_L = 400 Ω,	C_L = 15 pF		13	22	ns
t_{PHL}	R_L = 400 Ω,	C_L = 15 pF		8	15	ns

NOTE 3: Switching characteristics of the SN5423 and SN7424 are tested with the expander pins open.

3

TTL DEVICES

- **For Driving Low-Threshold-Voltage MOS Inputs**

description

These 2-input open-collector NAND gates feature high-output voltage ratings for interfacing with low-threshold-voltage MOS logic circuits or other 12-volt systems. Although the output is rated to withstand 15 volts, the V_{CC} terminal is connected to the standard 5-volt source.

The SN5426 and SN54LS26 are characterized for operation over the full military temperature range of $-55\,°C$ to $125\,°C$. The SN7426 and SN74LS26 are characterized for operation from $0\,°C$ to $70\,°C$.

logic diagram (each gate)

SN5426 . . . J PACKAGE
SN54LS26 . . . J OR W PACKAGE
SN7426 . . . J OR N PACKAGE
SN74LS26 . . . D, J OR N PACKAGE
(TOP VIEW)

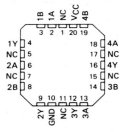

SN54LS26 . . . FK PACKAGE
SN74LS26
(TOP VIEW)

NC - No internal connection

positive logic

$$Y = \overline{AB}$$

TEXAS
INSTRUMENTS

3
TTL DEVICES

schematics

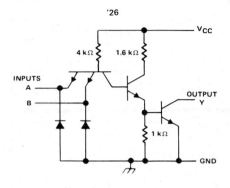

'26

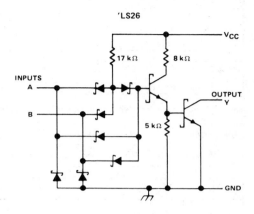

'LS26

Resistor values shown are nominal.

absolute maximum ratings over operating free-air temperature range (unless otherwise noted)

Supply voltage, V_{CC} (see Note 1) .... 7 V
Input voltage: '26 .... 5.5 V
              'LS26 .... 7 V
Operating free-air temperature: SN54' .... $-55°C$ to $125°C$
                  SN74' .... $0°C$ to $70°C$
Storage temperature range .... $-65°C$ to $150°C$

NOTE 1: Voltage values are with respect to network ground terminal.

3

TTL DEVICES

recommended operating conditions

		SN5426			SN7426			UNIT
		MIN	NOM	MAX	MIN	NOM	MAX	
V_{CC}	Supply voltage	4.5	5	5.5	4.75	5	5.25	V
V_{IH}	High-level input voltage	2			2			V
V_{IL}	Low-level input voltage			0.8			0.8	V
V_{OH}	High-level output voltage			15			15	V
I_{OL}	Low-level output current			16			16	mA
T_A	Operating free-air temperature	−55		125	0		70	°C

electrical characteristics over recommended operating free-air temperature range (unless otherwise noted)

PARAMETER	TEST CONDITIONS[†]			SN5426			SN7426			UNIT
				MIN	TYP[‡]	MAX	MIN	TYP[‡]	MAX	
V_{IK}	V_{CC} = MIN,	I_I = −12 mA				−1.5			−1.5	V
I_{OH}	V_{CC} = MIN,	V_{IL} = 0.8 V,	V_{OH} = 12 V			50			50	μA
	V_{CC} = MIN,	V_{IL} = 0.8 V,	V_{OH} = 15 V			1			1	mA
V_{OL}	V_{CC} = MIN,	V_{IH} = 2 V,	I_{OL} = 16 mA			0.4			0.4	V
I_I	V_{CC} = MAX,	V_I = 5.5 V				1			1	mA
I_{IH}	V_{CC} = MAX,	V_{IH} = 2.4 V				40			40	μA
I_{IL}	V_{CC} = MAX,	V_{IL} = 0.4 V				−1.6			−1.6	mA
I_{CCH}	V_{CC} = MAX,	V_I = 0 V			4	8		4	8	mA
I_{CCL}	V_{CC} = MAX,	V_I = 4.5 V			12	22		12	22	mA

[†] For conditions shown as MIN or MAX, use the appropriate value specified under recommended operating conditions.
[‡] All typical values are at V_{CC} = 5 V, T_A = 25°C.

switching characteristics, V_{CC} = 5 V, T_A = 25°C (see note 2)

PARAMETER	FROM (INPUT)	TO (OUTPUT)	TEST CONDITIONS		MIN	TYP	MAX	UNIT
t_{PLH}	A or B	Y	R_L = 1 kΩ,	C_L = 15 pF		16	24	ns
t_{PHL}						11	17	ns

NOTE 2: See General Information Section for load circuits and voltage waveforms.

3

TTL DEVICES

TEXAS
INSTRUMENTS

recommended operating conditions

		SN54LS26			SN74LS26			UNIT
		MIN	NOM	MAX	MIN	NOM	MAX	
V_{CC}	Supply voltage	4.5	5	5.5	4.75	5	5.25	V
V_{IH}	High-level input voltage	2			2			V
V_{IL}	Low-level input voltage			0.7			0.8	V
V_{OH}	High-level output voltage			15			15	V
I_{OL}	Low-level output current			4			8	mA
T_A	Operating free-air temperature	-55		125	0		70	$^\circ$C

electrical characteristics over recommended operating free-air temperature range (unless otherwise noted)

PARAMETER	TEST CONDITIONS[†]			SN54LS26			SN74LS26			UNIT
				MIN	TYP[‡]	MAX	MIN	TYP[‡]	MAX	
V_{IK}	$V_{CC} = $ MIN,	$I_I = -18$ mA				-1.5			-1.5	V
I_{OH}	$V_{CC} = $ MIN,	$V_{IL} = $ MAX,	$V_{OH} = 12$ V			50			50	μA
	$V_{CC} = $ MIN,	$V_{IL} = $ MAX,	$V_{OH} = 15$ V			1			1	mA
V_{OL}	$V_{CC} = $ MIN,	$V_{IH} = 2$ V,	$I_{OL} = 4$ mA	0.25	0.4		0.25	0.4		V
	$V_{CC} = $ MIN,	$V_{IH} = 2$ V,	$I_{OL} = 8$ mA				0.35	0.5		
I_I	$V_{CC} = $ MAX,	$V_I = 7$ V				0.1			0.1	mA
I_{IH}	$V_{CC} = $ MAX,	$V_{IH} = 2.7$ V				20			20	μA
I_{IL}	$V_{CC} = $ MAX,	$V_{IL} = 0.4$ V				-0.4			-0.4	mA
I_{CCH}	$V_{CC} = $ MAX,	$V_I = 0$ V		0.8	1.6		0.8	1.6		mA
I_{CCL}	$V_{CC} = $ MAX,	$V_I = 4.5$ V		2.4	4.4		2.4	4.4		

[†] For conditions shown as MIN or MAX, use the appropriate value specified under recommended operating conditions.
[‡] All typical values are at $V_{CC} = 5$ V, $T_A = 25^\circ$C.

switching characteristics, $V_{CC} = 5$ V, $T_A = 25^\circ$C (see note 2)

PARAMETER	FROM (INPUT)	TO (OUTPUT)	TEST CONDITIONS	MIN	TYP	MAX	UNIT
t_{PLH}	A or B	Y	$R_L = 2$ kΩ, $C_L = 15$ pF		17	32	ns
t_{PHL}					15	28	ns

NOTE 2: See General Information Section for load circuits and voltage waveforms.

3

TTL DEVICES

- **Package Options Include Both Plastic and Ceramic Chip Carriers in Addition to Plastic and Ceramic DIPs**

- **Dependable Texas Instruments Quality and Reliability**

description

These devices contain three independent 3-input NOR gates.

The SN5427 and SN54LS27 are characterized for operation over the full military temperature range of −55 °C to 125 °C. The SN7427 and SN74LS27 are characterized for operation from 0 °C to 70 °C.

FUNCTION TABLE (each gate)

INPUTS			OUTPUT
A	B	C	Y
H	X	X	L
X	H	X	L
X	X	H	L
L	L	L	H

SN5427, SN54LS27 . . . J OR W PACKAGE
SN7427 . . . J OR N PACKAGE
SN74LS27 . . . D, J OR N PACKAGE
(TOP VIEW)

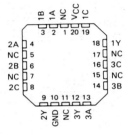

```
1A  [1   U  14]  VCC
1B  [2      13]  1C
2A  [3      12]  1Y
2B  [4      11]  3C
2C  [5      10]  3B
2Y  [6       9]  3A
GND [7       8]  3Y
```

SN54LS27 . . . FK PACKAGE
SN74LS27
(TOP VIEW)

```
        1B 1A NC VCC 1C
         3  2  1 20 19
2A [4              18] 1Y
NC [5              17] NC
2B [6              16] 3C
NC [7              15] NC
2C [8              14] 3B
         9 10 11 12 13
        2Y GND NC 3Y 3A
```

NC - No internal connection

logic diagram (each gate)

positive logic

$$Y = \overline{A + B + C} \text{ or } Y = \overline{A} \cdot \overline{B} \cdot \overline{C}$$

TEXAS
INSTRUMENTS

3

TTL DEVICES

schematics (each gate)

'27

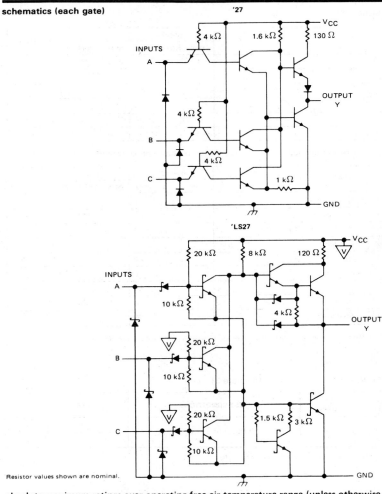

'LS27

Resistor values shown are nominal.

absolute maximum ratings over operating free-air temperature range (unless otherwise noted)

Supply voltage, V_{CC} (see Note 1) . . . . 7 V
Input voltage: '27 . . . . 5.5 V
               'LS27 . . . . 7 V
Operating free-air temperature: SN54' . . . . -55°C to 125°C
                           SN74' . . . . 0°C to 70°C
Storage temperature range . . . . -65°C to 150°C

NOTE 1: Voltage values are with respect to network ground terminal.

TEXAS INSTRUMENTS

3-115

TTL DEVICES

3

recommended operating conditions

		SN5427 MIN	SN5427 NOM	SN5427 MAX	SN7427 MIN	SN7427 NOM	SN7427 MAX	UNIT
V_{CC}	Supply voltage	4.5	5	5.5	4.75	5	5.25	V
V_{IH}	High-level input voltage	2			2			V
V_{IL}	Low-level input voltage			0.8			0.8	V
I_{OH}	High-level output current			−0.8			−0.8	mA
I_{OL}	Low-level output current			16			16	mA
T_A	Operating free-air temperature	−55		125	0		70	°C

electrical characteristics over recommended operating free-air temperature range (unless otherwise noted)

PARAMETER	TEST CONDITIONS †	SN5427 MIN	SN5427 TYP ‡	SN5427 MAX	SN7427 MIN	SN7427 TYP ‡	SN7427 MAX	UNIT
V_{IK}	V_{CC} = MIN, I_I = −12 mA			−1.5			−1.5	V
V_{OH}	V_{CC} = MIN, V_{IL} = 0.8 V, I_{OH} = −0.8 mA	2.4	3.4		2.4	3.4		V
V_{OL}	V_{CC} = MIN, V_{IH} = 2 V, I_{OL} = 16 mA		0.2	0.4		0.2	0.4	V
I_I	V_{CC} = MAX, V_I = 5.5 V			1			1	mA
I_{IH}	V_{CC} = MAX, V_I = 2.4 V			40			40	µA
I_{IL}	V_{CC} = MAX, V_I = 0.4 V			−1.6			−1.6	mA
I_{OS} §	V_{CC} = MAX	−20		−55	−18		−55	mA
I_{CCH}	V_{CC} = MAX, V_I = 0 V		10	16		10	16	mA
I_{CCL}	V_{CC} = MAX, See Note 2		16	26		16	26	mA

† For conditions shown as MIN or MAX, use the appropriate value specified under recommended operating conditions.
‡ All typical values are at V_{CC} = 5 V, T_A = 25°C.
§ Not more than one output should be shorted at a time.
NOTE 2: One input at 4.5 V, all others at GND.

switching characteristics, V_{CC} = 5 V, T_A = 25°C (see note 3)

PARAMETER	FROM (INPUT)	TO (OUTPUT)	TEST CONDITIONS	MIN	TYP	MAX	UNIT
t_{PLH}	A, B or C	Y	R_L = 400 Ω, C_L = 15 pF		10	15	ns
t_{PHL}					7	11	ns

NOTE 3: See General Information Section for load circuits and voltage waveforms.

TEXAS
INSTRUMENTS

3

TTL DEVICES

recommended operating conditions

		SN54LS27			SN74LS27			UNIT
		MIN	NOM	MAX	MIN	NOM	MAX	
V_{CC}	Supply voltage	4.5	5	5.5	4.75	5	5.25	V
V_{IH}	High-level input voltage	2			2			V
V_{IL}	Low-level input voltage			0.7			0.8	V
I_{OH}	High-level output current			-0.4			-0.4	mA
I_{OL}	Low-level output current			4			8	mA
T_A	Operating free-air temperature	-55		125	0		70	$^\circ$C

electrical characteristics over recommended operating free-air temperature range (unless otherwise noted)

PARAMETER	TEST CONDITIONS †			SN54LS27			SN74LS27			UNIT
				MIN	TYP‡	MAX	MIN	TYP‡	MAX	
V_{IK}	$V_{CC} = $ MIN,	$I_I = -18$ mA				-1.5			-1.5	V
V_{OH}	$V_{CC} = $ MIN,	$V_{IL} = $ MAX,	$I_{OH} = -0.4$ mA	2.5	3.4		2.7	3.4		V
V_{OL}	$V_{CC} = $ MIN,	$V_{IH} = 2$ V,	$I_{OL} = 4$ mA		0.25	0.4		0.25	0.4	V
	$V_{CC} = $ MIN,	$V_{IH} = 2$ V,	$I_{OL} = 8$ mA					0.35	0.5	
I_I	$V_{CC} = $ MAX,	$V_I = 7$ V				0.1			0.1	mA
I_{IH}	$V_{CC} = $ MAX,	$V_I = 2.7$ V				20			20	μA
I_{IL}	$V_{CC} = $ MAX,	$V_I = 0.4$ V				-0.4			-0.4	mA
I_{OS} §	$V_{CC} = $ MAX			-20		-100	-20		-100	mA
I_{CCH}	$V_{CC} = $ MAX,	$V_I = 0$ V			2	4		2	4	mA
I_{CCL}	$V_{CC} = $ MAX,	See Note 2			3.4	6.8		3.4	6.8	mA

† For conditions shown as MIN or MAX, use the appropriate value specified under recommended operating conditions.
‡ All typical values are at $V_{CC} = 5$ V, $T_A = 25^\circ$C.
§ Not more than one output should be shorted at a time, and the duration of the short-circuit should not exceed one second.
NOTE 2: One input at 4.5 V, all others at GND.

switching characteristics, $V_{CC} = 5$ V, $T_A = 25^\circ$C (see note 3)

PARAMETER	FROM (INPUT)	TO (OUTPUT)	TEST CONDITIONS		MIN	TYP	MAX	UNIT
t_{PLH}	A, B or C	Y	$R_L = 2$ kΩ,	$C_L = 15$ pF		10	15	ns
t_{PHL}						10	15	ns

NOTE 3: See General Information Section for load circuits and voltage waveforms.

3

TTL DEVICES

TEXAS
INSTRUMENTS

- **Package Options Include Both Plastic and Ceramic Chip Carriers in Addition to Plastic and Ceramic DIPs**

- **Dependable Texas Instruments Quality and Reliability**

description

These devices contain four independent 2-input NOR buffer gates.

The SN5428, and SN54LS28 are characterized for operation over the full military temperature range of −55°C to 125°C. The SN7428, and SN74LS28 are characterized for operation from 0°C to 70°C.

SN5428, SN54LS28 . . . J OR W PACKAGE
SN7428 . . . J OR N PACKAGE
SN74LS28 . . . D, J OR N PACKAGE
(TOP VIEW)

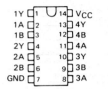

SN54LS28 . . . FK PACKAGE
SN74LS28
(TOP VIEW)

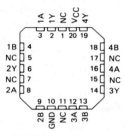

NC - No internal connection

FUNCTION TABLE (each gate)

INPUTS		OUTPUT
A	B	Y
H	X	L
X	H	L
L	L	H

logic diagram (each gate)

positive logic

$$Y = \overline{A + B} \text{ or } Y = \overline{A} \cdot \overline{B}$$

3

TTL DEVICES

TEXAS
INSTRUMENTS

schematics (each gate)

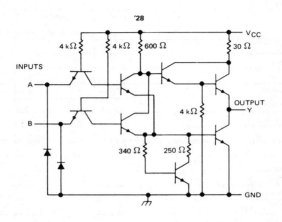

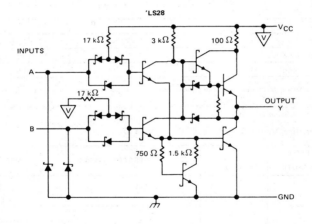

Resistor values shown are nominal.

absolute maximum ratings over operating free-air temperature range (unless otherwise noted)

Supply voltage, V_{CC} (see Note 1)	7 V
Input voltage: '28	5.5 V
'LS28	7 V
Operating free-air temperature: SN54'	-55°C to 125°C
SN74'	0°C to 70°C
Storage temperature range	-65°C to 150°C

NOTE 1: Voltage values are with respect to network ground terminal.

recommended operating conditions

		SN5428			SN7428			UNIT
		MIN	NOM	MAX	MIN	NOM	MAX	
V_{CC}	Supply voltage	4.5	5	5.5	4.75	5	5.25	V
V_{IH}	High-level input voltage	2			2			V
V_{IL}	Low-level input voltage			0.8			0.8	V
I_{OH}	High-level output current			−2.4			−2.4	mA
I_{OL}	Low-level output current			48			48	mA
T_A	Operating free-air temperature	−55		125	0		70	°C

electrical characteristics over recommended operating free-air temperature range (unless otherwise noted)

PARAMETER	TEST CONDITIONS †			MIN	TYP‡	MAX	UNIT
V_{IK}	V_{CC} = MIN,	I_I = −12mA				−1.5	V
V_{OH}	V_{CC} = MIN,	V_{IL} = 0.8 V,	I_{OH} = −2.4 mA	2.4	3.4		V
V_{OL}	V_{CC} = MIN,	V_{IH} = 2 V,	I_{OL} = 48 mA		0.2	0.4	V
I_I	V_{CC} = MAX,	V_I = 5.5 V				1	mA
I_{IH}	V_{CC} = MAX,	V_I = 2.4 V				40	μA
I_{IL}	V_{CC} = MAX,	V_I = 0.4 V				−1.6	mA
I_{OS}§	V_{CC} = MAX			−70		−180	mA
I_{CCH}	V_{CC} = MAX,	V_I = 0 V			12	21	mA
I_{CCL}	V_{CC} = MAX,	See Note 2			33	57	mA

† For conditions shown as MIN or MAX, use the appropriate value specified under recommended operating conditions.
‡ All typical values are at V_{CC} = 5 V, T_A = 25°C.
§ Not more than one output should be shorted at a time and the duration of the short circuit should not exceed one second.
NOTE 2: One input at 4.5 V, all others at GND.

switching characteristics, V_{CC} = 5 V, T_A = 25°C (see note 3)

PARAMETER	FROM (INPUT)	TO (OUTPUT)	TEST CONDITIONS		MIN	TYP	MAX	UNIT
t_{PLH}	A or B	Y	R_L = 133 Ω,	C_L = 50 pF		6	9	ns
t_{PHL}						8	12	ns
t_{PLH}			R_L = 133 Ω,	C_L = 150 pF		10	15	ns
t_{PHL}						12	18	ns

NOTE 3: See General Information Section for load circuits and voltage waveforms.

Texas
INSTRUMENTS

recommended operating conditions

		SN54LS28			SN74LS28			UNIT
		MIN	NOM	MAX	MIN	NOM	MAX	
V_{CC}	Supply voltage	4.5	5	5.5	4.75	5	5.25	V
V_{IH}	High-level input voltage	2			2			V
V_{IL}	Low-level input voltage			0.7			0.8	V
I_{OH}	High-level output current			-1.2			-1.2	mA
I_{OL}	Low-level output current			12			24	mA
T_A	Operating free-air temperature	-55		125	0		70	$^{\circ}C$

electrical characteristics over recommended operating free-air temperature range (unless otherwise noted)

PARAMETER	TEST CONDITIONS †			SN54LS28			SN74LS28			UNIT
				MIN	TYP‡	MAX	MIN	TYP‡	MAX	
V_{IK}	V_{CC} = MIN,	$I_I = -18$ mA				-1.5			-1.5	V
V_{OH}	V_{CC} = MIN,	V_{IL} = MAX,	$I_{OH} = -1.2$ mA	2.5	3.4		2.7	3.4		V
V_{OL}	V_{CC} = MIN,	V_{IH} = 2 V,	I_{OL} = 12 mA		0.25	0.4		0.24	0.4	V
	V_{CC} = MIN,	V_{IH} = 2 V,	I_{OL} = 24 mA					0.35	0.5	
I_I	V_{CC} = MAX,	V_I = 7 V				0.1			0.1	mA
I_{IH}	V_{CC} = MAX,	V_I = 2.7 V				20			20	μA
I_{IL}	V_{CC} = MAX,	V_I = 0.4 V				-0.4			-0.4	mA
I_{OS} §	V_{CC} = MAX			-30		-130	-30		-130	mA
I_{CCH}	V_{CC} = MAX,	V_I = 0 V			1.8	3.6		1.8	3.6	mA
I_{CCL}	V_{CC} = MAX,	See Note 2			6.9	13.8		6.9	13.8	mA

† For conditions shown as MIN or MAX, use the appropriate value specified under recommended operating conditions.
‡ All typical values are at V_{CC} = 5 V, T_A = 25°C.
§ Not more than one output should be shorted at a time and the duration of the short circuit should not exceed one second.
NOTE 2: One input at 4.5 V, all others at GND.

switching characteristics, V_{CC} = 5 V, T_A = 25°C (see note 3)

PARAMETER	FROM (INPUT)	TO (OUTPUT)	TEST CONDITIONS		MIN	TYP	MAX	UNIT
t_{PLH}	A or B	Y	R_L = 667 Ω,	C_L = 45 pF		12	24	ns
t_{PHL}						12	24	ns

NOTE 3: See General Information Section for load circuits and voltage waveforms.

3

TTL DEVICES

3

TTL DEVICES

- **Package Options Include Both Plastic and Ceramic Chip Carriers in Addition to Plastic and Ceramic DIPs**

- **Dependable Texas Instruments Quality and Reliability**

description

These devices contain a single 8-input NAND gate.

The SN5430, SN54LS30, and SN54S30 are characterized for operation over the full military temperature range of −55°C to 125°C. The SN7430, SN74LS30, and SN74S30 are characterized for operation from 0°C to 70°C.

FUNCTION TABLE

INPUTS A THRU H	OUTPUT Y
All inputs H	L
One or more inputs L	H

logic diagram

positive logic

$$Y = \overline{A \cdot B \cdot C \cdot D \cdot E \cdot F \cdot G \cdot H} \quad \text{or}$$
$$Y = \overline{A} + \overline{B} + \overline{C} + \overline{D} + \overline{E} + \overline{F} + \overline{G} + \overline{H}$$

SN5430 . . . J PACKAGE
SN54LS30, SN54S30 . . . J OR W PACKAGE
SN7430 . . . J OR N PACKAGE
SN74LS30, SN74S30 . . . D, J OR N PACKAGE
(TOP VIEW)

```
       A [ 1  U  14 ] VCC
       B [ 2     13 ] NC
       C [ 3     12 ] H
       D [ 4     11 ] G
       E [ 5     10 ] NC
       F [ 6      9 ] NC
     GND [ 7      8 ] Y
```

SN5430 . . . W PACKAGE
(TOP VIEW)

```
      NC [ 1  U  14 ] NC
       A [ 2     13 ] NC
       B [ 3     12 ] Y
     VCC [ 4     11 ] GND
       C [ 5     10 ] H
       D [ 6      9 ] G
       E [ 7      8 ] F
```

SN54LS30, SN54S30 . . . FK PACKAGE
SN74LS30, SN74S30
(TOP VIEW)

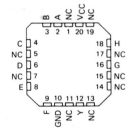

NC - No internal connection

PRODUCTION DATA
This document contains information current as of publication date. Products conform to specifications per the terms of Texas Instruments standard warranty. Production processing does not necessarily include testing of all parameters.

TEXAS
INSTRUMENTS

schematics (each gate)

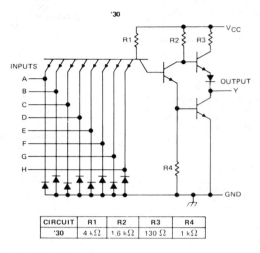

CIRCUIT	R1	R2	R3	R4
'30	4 kΩ	1.6 kΩ	130 Ω	1 kΩ

Input clamp diodes not on SN54L30 circuit.

TEXAS
INSTRUMENTS

schematics (each gate)

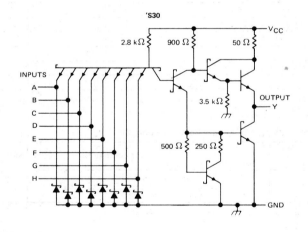

Resistor values shown are nominal.

absolute maximum ratings over operating free-air temperature range (unless otherwise noted)

Supply voltage, V_{CC} (see Note 1): '30, 'LS30, 'S30 . . . . 7 V

Input voltage: '30, 'S30 . . . . 5.5 V

'LS30 . . . . 7 V

Operating free-air temperature: SN54' . . . . −55°C to 125°C

SN74' . . . . 0°C to 70°C

Storage temperature range . . . . −65°C to 150°C

NOTE 1: Voltage values are with respect to network ground terminal.

TEXAS INSTRUMENTS

recommended operating conditions

		SN5430			SN7430			UNIT
		MIN	NOM	MAX	MIN	NOM	MAX	
V_{CC}	Supply voltage	4.5	5	5.5	4.75	5	5.25	V
V_{IH}	High-level input voltage	2			2			V
V_{IL}	Low-level input voltage			0.8			0.8	V
I_{OH}	High-level output current			−0.4			−0.4	mA
I_{OL}	Low-level output current			16			16	mA
T_A	Operating free-air temperature	−55		125	0		70	°C

electrical characteristics over recommended operating free-air temperature range (unless otherwise noted)

PARAMETER	TEST CONDITIONS†	SN5430			SN7430			UNIT
		MIN	TYP‡	MAX	MIN	TYP‡	MAX	
V_{IK}	V_{CC} = MIN, I_I = −12 mA			−1.5			−1.5	V
V_{OH}	V_{CC} = MIN, V_{IL} = 0.8 V, I_{OH} = −0.4 mA	2.4	3.4		2.4	3.4		V
V_{OL}	V_{CC} = MIN, V_{IH} = 2 V, I_{OL} = 16 mA		0.2	0.4		0.2	0.4	V
I_I	V_{CC} = MAX, V_I = 5.5 V			1			1	mA
I_{IH}	V_{CC} = MAX, V_I = 2.4 V			40			40	µA
I_{IL}	V_{CC} = MAX, V_I = 0.4 V			−1.6			−1.6	mA
I_{OS}§	V_{CC} = MAX	−20		−55	−18		−55	mA
I_{CCH}	V_{CC} = MAX, V_I = 0 V		1	2		1	2	mA
I_{CCL}	V_{CC} = MAX, V_I = 4.5 V		3	6		3	6	mA

† For conditions shown as MIN or MAX, use the appropriate value specified under recommended operating conditions.
‡ All typical values are at V_{CC} = 5 V, T_A = 25°C.
§ Not more than one output should be shorted at a time.

switching characteristics, V_{CC} = 5 V, T_A = 25°C (see note 2)

PARAMETER	FROM (INPUT)	TO (OUTPUT)	TEST CONDITIONS	MIN	TYP	MAX	UNIT
t_{PLH}	Any	Y	R_L = 400 Ω, C_L = 15 pF		13	22	ns
t_{PHL}					8	15	ns

NOTE 2: See General Information Section for load circuits and voltage waveforms.

Texas
INSTRUMENTS

recommended operating conditions

		SN54LS30			SN74LS30			UNIT
		MIN	NOM	MAX	MIN	NOM	MAX	
V_{CC}	Supply voltage	4.5	5	5.5	4.75	5	5.25	V
V_{IH}	High-level input voltage	2			2			V
V_{IL}	Low-level input voltage			0.7			0.8	V
I_{OH}	High-level output current			−0.4			−0.4	mA
I_{OL}	Low-level output current			4			8	mA
T_A	Operating free-air temperature	−55		125	0		70	°C

electrical characteristics over recommended operating free-air temperature range (unless otherwise noted)

PARAMETER	TEST CONDITIONS †		SN54LS30			SN74LS30			UNIT
		MIN	TYP‡	MAX	MIN	TYP‡	MAX	
V_{IK}	V_{CC} = MIN,	I_I = −18 mA			−1.5			−1.5	V
V_{OH}	V_{CC} = MIN,	V_{IL} = MAX, I_{OH} = −0.4 mA	2.5	3.4		2.7	3.4		V
V_{OL}	V_{CC} = MIN,	V_{IH} = 2 V, I_{OL} = 4 mA		0.25	0.4			0.4	V
	V_{CC} = MIN,	V_{IH} = 2 V, I_{OL} = 8 mA					0.25	0.5	
I_I	V_{CC} = MAX,	V_I = 7 V			0.1			0.1	mA
I_{IH}	V_{CC} = MAX,	V_I = 2.7 V			20			20	μA
I_{IL}	V_{CC} = MAX,	V_I = 0.4 V			−0.4			−0.4	mA
I_{OS}§	V_{CC} = MAX		−20		−100	−20		−100	mA
I_{CCH}	V_{CC} = MAX,	V_I = 0 V		0.35	0.5		0.35	0.5	mA
I_{CCL}	V_{CC} = MAX,	V_I = 4.5 V		0.6	1.1		0.6	1.1	mA

† For conditions shown as MIN or MAX, use the appropriate value specified under recommended operating conditions.
‡ All typical values are at V_{CC} = 5 V, T_A = 25°C
§ Not more than one output should be shorted at a time, and the duration of the short-circuit should not exceed one second.

switching characteristics, V_{CC} = 5 V, T_A = 25°C (see note 2)

PARAMETER	FROM (INPUT)	TO (OUTPUT)	TEST CONDITIONS	MIN	TYP	MAX	UNIT
t_{PLH}	Any	Y	R_L = 2 kΩ, C_L = 15 pF		8	15	ns
t_{PHL}					13	20	ns

NOTE 2: See General Information Section for load circuits and voltage waveforms.

3

TTL DEVICES

TEXAS
INSTRUMENTS

recommended operating conditions

		SN54S30			SN74S30			UNIT
		MIN	NOM	MAX	MIN	NOM	MAX	
V_{CC}	Supply voltage	4.5	5	5.5	4.75	5	5.25	V
V_{IH}	High-level input voltage	2			2			V
V_{IL}	Low-level input voltage			0.8			0.8	V
I_{OH}	High-level output current			-1			-1	mA
I_{OL}	Low-level output current			20			20	mA
T_A	Operating free-air temperature	-55		125	0		70	°C

electrical characteristics over recommended operating free-air temperature range (unless otherwise noted)

PARAMETER	TEST CONDITIONS †		SN54S30			SN74S30			UNIT
			MIN	TYP‡	MAX	MIN	TYP‡	MAX	
V_{IK}	V_{CC} = MIN,	$I_I = -18$ mA			-1.2			-1.2	V
V_{OH}	V_{CC} = MIN,	V_{IL} = 0.8 V, $I_{OH} = -1$ mA	2.5	3.4		2.7	3.4		V
V_{OL}	V_{CC} = MIN,	V_{IH} = 2 V, I_{OL} = 20 mA			0.5			0.5	V
I_I	V_{CC} = MAX,	V_I = 5.5 V			1			1	mA
I_{IH}	V_{CC} = MAX,	V_I = 2.7 V			50			50	μA
I_{IL}	V_{CC} = MAX,	V_I = 0.5 V			-2			-2	mA
I_{OS} §	V_{CC} = MAX		-40		-100	-40		-100	mA
I_{CCH}	V_{CC} = MAX,	V_I = 0 V		3	5		3	5	mA
I_{CCL}	V_{CC} = MAX,	V_I = 4.5 V		5.5	10		5.5	10	mA

† For conditions shown as MIN or MAX, use the appropriate value specified under recommended operating conditions.
‡ All typical values are at V_{CC} = 5 V, T_A = 25°C.
§ Not more than one output should be shorted at a time, and the duration of the short-circuit should not exceed one second.

switching characteristics, V_{CC} = 5 V, T_A = 25°C (see note 2)

PARAMETER	FROM (INPUT)	TO (OUTPUT)	TEST CONDITIONS		MIN	TYP	MAX	UNIT
t_{PLH}	Any	Y	R_L = 280 Ω,	C_L = 15 pF		4	6	ns
t_{PHL}						4.5	7	ns
t_{PLH}			R_L = 280 Ω,	C_L = 50 pF		5.5		ns
t_{PHL}						6.5		ns

NOTE 2: See General Information Section for load circuits and voltage waveforms.

TEXAS
INSTRUMENTS

REVISED DECEMBER 1983

- **Delay Elements for Generating Delay Lines**
- **Inverting and Non-inverting Elements**
- **Buffer NAND Elements Rated at I_{OL} of 12/24 mA**
- **PNP Inputs Reduce Fan-In ($I_{IL} = -0.2$ mA MAX)**
- **Worst Case MIN/MAX Delays Guaranteed Across Temperature and V_{CC} Ranges**

description

These 'LS31 delay elements are intended to provide well-defined delays across both temperature and V_{CC} ranges. Used in cascade, a limitless range of delay gating is possible.

All inputs are PNP with I_{IL} MAX of -0.2 mA. Gates 1, 2, 5, and 6 have standard Low-Power Schottky output sink current capability of 4 and 8 mA I_{OL}. Buffers 3 and 4 are rated at 12 and 24 mA.

The SN54LS31 is characterized for operation over the full military temperature range of $-55\,°C$ to $125\,°C$. The SN74LS31 is characterized for operation from $0\,°C$ to $70\,°C$.

SN54LS31 . . . J OR W PACKAGE
SN74LS31 . . . D, J OR N PACKAGE
(TOP VIEW)

SN54LS31 . . . FK PACKAGE
SN74LS31
(TOP VIEW)

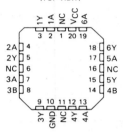

NC - No internal connection

logic symbol†

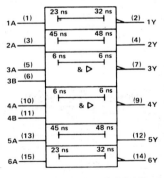

†Pin numbers shown on logic notation are for D, J and N packages only.

TTL DEVICES

3

TEXAS
INSTRUMENTS

Delay Element	Logic	Typical Delays			Rated I_{OL}
		t_{PLH}	t_{PHL}	AVG.	
Gates 1 and 6	Inverting	32 ns	23 ns	27.5 ns	4 and 8 mA
Gates 2 and 5	Non-Inverting	45 ns	48 ns	46.5 ns	4 and 8 mA
Buffers 3 and 4	2-Input NAND	6 ns	6 ns	6 ns	12 and 24 mA

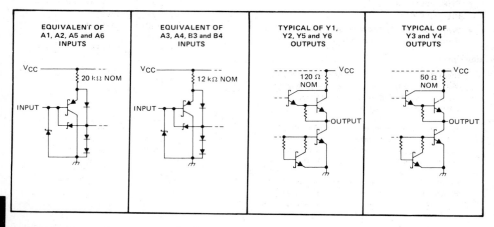

| | EQUIVALENT OF A1, A2, A5 and A6 INPUTS | EQUIVALENT OF A3, A4, B3 and B4 INPUTS | TYPICAL OF Y1, Y2, Y5 and Y6 OUTPUTS | TYPICAL OF Y3 and Y4 OUTPUTS |

absolute maximum ratings over operating free air temperature range (unless otherwise noted)

Supply voltage, V_{CC} (See Note 1) . . . . 7 V

Input voltage, V_I: All inputs . . . . 7 V

Operating free-air temperature range: SN54LS31 . . . . −55°C to 125°C

SN74LS31 . . . . 0°C to 70°C

Storage temperature range . . . . −65°C to 150°C

NOTE 1: Voltage values are with respect to network ground terminal.

recommended operating conditions

			SN54LS31			SN74LS31			UNIT
			MIN	NOM	MAX	MIN	NOM	MAX	
V_{CC}	Supply voltage		4.5	5	55	4.75	5	5.25	V
V_{IH}	High-level input voltage		2			2			V
V_{IL}	Low-level input voltage				0.7			0.8	V
I_{OH}	High-level output current	Y3, Y4 outputs			−1.2			−1.2	mA
		All other outpus			−0.4			−0.4	
I_{OL}	Low-level output current	Y3, Y4 outputs			12			24	mA
		All other outputs			4			8	
T_A	Operating free-air temperature		−55		125	0		70	°C

TEXAS
INSTRUMENTS

electrical characteristics over recommended operating free-air temperature range (unless otherwise noted)

PARAMETER		TEST CONDITIONS[†]			SN54LS31 MIN	TYP[‡]	MAX	SN74LS31 MIN	TYP[‡]	MAX	UNIT
V_{IK}		V_{CC} = MIN, I_I = $-$18 mA					-1.5			-1.5	V
V_{OH}		V_{CC} = MIN, V_{IH} = 2 V, V_{IL} = MAX	Y3, Y4	I_{OH} = $-$1.2 mA	2.4	3.1		2.4	3.1		V
			Others	I_{OH} = $-$0.4 mA	2.5	3.1		2.7	3.1		
V_{OL}		V_{CC} = MIN, V_{IH} = 2 V, V_{IL} = MAX	Y3, Y4	I_{OL} = 12 mA		0.25	0.4		0.25	0.4	V
				I_{OL} = 24 mA					0.35	0.5	
			Others	I_{OL} = 4 mA		0.25	0.4		0.25	0.4	
				I_{OL} = 8 mA					0.35	0.5	
I_I		V_{CC} = MAX, V_I = 7 V					0.1			0.1	mA
I_{IH}		V_{CC} = MAX, V_I = 2.7 V					20			20	µA
I_{IL}		V_{CC} = MAX, V_I = 0.4 V					-0.2			-0.2	mA
I_{OS}[§]		V_{CC} = MAX, A3, A4, B3, B4 = 0 V	Y3, Y4		-30		-130	-30		-130	mA
		V_{CC} = MAX, A1, A6 = 0 V, A2, A5 = 4.5 V	Y1, Y2, Y5, Y6		-20		-100	-20		-100	
I_{CC}	I_{CCH}	V_{CC} = MAX, A2, A5 = 4.5 V, all other inputs 0 V				2.3	4		2.3	4	mA
	I_{CCL}	V_{CC} = MAX, A2, A5 = 0 V, all other inputs 4.5 V				13	20		13	20	

† For conditions shown as MIN or MAX, use the appropriate value specified under recommended operating conditions.
‡ All typical values are at V_{CC} = 5 V, T_A = 25°C.
§ Not more than one output should be shorted at a time and the duration of the short-circuit should not exceed one second.

switching characteristics, (see note 2)

PARAMETER	FROM (INPUT)	TO (OUTPUT)	SN54LS31 MIN	TYP	MAX	SN74LS31 MIN	TYP	MAX	UNIT
t_{PLH}	A1, A6	Y1, Y6	15		70	22		65	ns
t_{PHL}			9		50	13		45	ns
t_{PLH}	A2, A5	Y2, Y5	22		90	31		80	ns
t_{PHL}			20		105	30		95	ns
t_{PLH}	A3, B3, A4, Y4	Y3, Y4	2		20	2		15	ns
t_{PHL}			2		20	2		15	ns

NOTE 2: V_{CC} = MIN to MAX
R_L = 667 Ω, C_L = 45 pF for Y3 and Y4.
R_L = 2 kΩ, C_L = 15 pF for Y1, Y2, Y5 and Y6.
T_A = MIN to MAX
See General Information Section for load circuits and voltage waveforms.

3

TTL DEVICES

TEXAS
INSTRUMENTS

- **Package Options Include Both Plastic and Ceramic Chip Carriers in Addition to Plastic and Ceramic DIPs**

- **Dependable Texas Instruments Quality and Reliability**

description

These devices contain four independent 2-input OR gates.

The SN5432, SN54LS32 and SN54S32 are characterized for operation over the full military range of −55 °C to 125 °C. The SN7432, SN74LS32 and SN74S32 are characterized for operation from 0 °C to 70 °C.

FUNCTION TABLE (each gate)

INPUTS		OUTPUT
A	**B**	**Y**
H	X	H
X	H	H
L	L	L

logic diagram (each gate)

positive logic

$$Y = A + B \quad \text{or} \quad Y = \overline{\overline{A} \cdot \overline{B}}$$

SN5432, SN54LS32, SN54S32 . . . J OR W PACKAGE
SN7432 . . . J OR N PACKAGE
SN74LS32, SN74S32 . . . D, J or N PACKAGE
(TOP VIEW)

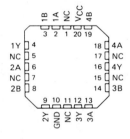

SN54LS32, SN54S32 . . . FK PACKAGE
SN74LS32, SN74S32
(TOP VIEW)

NC - No internal connection

3

TTL DEVICES

TEXAS INSTRUMENTS

schematics (each gate)

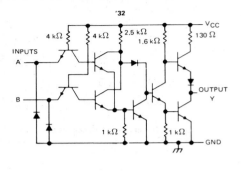

'32

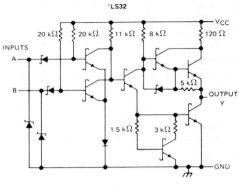

'LS32

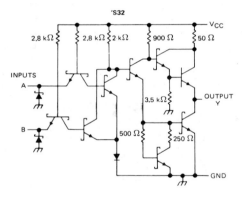

'S32

Resistor values shown are nominal.

absolute maximum ratings over operating free-air temperature range (unless otherwise noted)

Supply voltage, V_{CC} (see Note 1)	7 V
Input voltage: '32, 'S32	5.5 V
'LS32	7 V
Operating free-air temperature: SN54'	-55°C to 125°C
SN74'	0°C to 70°C
Storage temperature range	-65°C to 150°C

NOTE 1: Voltage values are with respect to network ground terminal.

TEXAS
INSTRUMENTS

recommended operating conditions

		SN5432			SN7432			UNIT
		MIN	NOM	MAX	MIN	NOM	MAX	
V_{CC}	Supply voltage	4.5	5	5.5	4.75	5	5.25	V
V_{IH}	High-level input voltage	2			2			V
V_{IL}	Low-level input voltage			0.8			0.8	V
I_{OH}	High-level output current			−0.8			−0.8	mA
I_{OL}	Low-level output current			16			16	mA
T_A	Operating free-air temperature	−55		125	0		70	°C

electrical characteristics over recommended operating free-air temperature range (unless otherwise noted)

PARAMETER	TEST CONDITIONS†			SN5432			SN7432			UNIT
				MIN	TYP‡	MAX	MIN	TYP‡	MAX	
V_{IK}	V_{CC} = MIN,	I_I = −12 mA				−1.5			−1.5	V
V_{OH}	V_{CC} = MIN,	V_{IH} = 2 V,	I_{OH} = −0.8 mA	2.4	3.4		2.4	3.4		V
V_{OL}	V_{CC} = MIN,	V_{IL} = 0.8 V,	I_{OL} = 16 mA		0.2	0.4		0.2	0.4	V
I_I	V_{CC} = MAX,	V_I = 5.5 V				1			1	mA
I_{IH}	V_{CC} = MAX,	V_I = 2.4 V				40			40	µA
I_{IL}	V_{CC} = MAX,	V_I = 0.4 V				−1.6			−1.6	mA
I_{OS}§	V_{CC} = MAX			−20		−55	−18		−55	mA
I_{CCH}	V_{CC} = MAX,	See Note 2			15	22		15	22	mA
I_{CCL}	V_{CC} = MAX,	V_I = 0 V			23	38		23	38	mA

† For conditions shown as MIN or MAX, use the appropriate value specified under recommended operating conditions.
‡ All typical values are at V_{CC} = 5 V, T_A = 25°C.
§ Not more than one output should be shorted at a time.
NOTE 2: One input at 4.5 V, all others at GND.

switching characteristics, V_{CC} = 5 V, T_A = 25°C (see note 3)

PARAMETER	FROM (INPUT)	TO (OUTPUT)	TEST CONDITIONS		MIN	TYP	MAX	UNIT
t_{PLH}	A or B	Y	R_L = 400 Ω,	C_L = 15 pF		10	15	ns
t_{PHL}						14	22	ns

NOTE 3: See General Information Section for load circuits and voltage waveforms.

3

TTL DEVICES

TYPES SN54LS32, SN74LS32
QUADRUPLE 2-INPUT POSITIVE-OR GATES

recommended operating conditions

		SN54LS32			SN74LS32			UNIT
		MIN	NOM	MAX	MIN	NOM	MAX	
V_{CC}	Supply voltage	4.5	5	5.5	4.75	5	5.25	V
V_{IH}	Hgh-level input voltage	2			2			V
V_{IL}	Low-level input voltage			0.7			0.8	V
I_{OH}	High-level output current			-0.4			-0.4	mA
I_{OL}	Low-level output current			4			8	mA
T_A	Opertating free-air temperature	-55		125	0		70	°C

electrical characteristics over recommended operating free-air temperature range (unless otherwise noted)

PARAMETER	TEST CONDITIONS †			SN54LS32			SN74LS32			UNIT
				MIN	TYP‡	MAX	MIN	TYP‡	MAX	
V_{IK}	$V_{CC} = $ MIN,	$I_I = -18$ mA				-1.5			-1.5	V
V_{OH}	$V_{CC} = $ MIN,	$V_{IH} = 2$ V,	$I_{OH} = -0.4$ mA	2.5	3.4		2.7	3.4		V
V_{OL}	$V_{CC} = $ MIN,	$V_{IL} = $ MAX,	$I_{OL} = 4$ mA		0.25	0.4		0.25	0.4	V
	$V_{CC} = $ MIN,	$V_{IL} = $ MAX,	$I_{OL} = 8$ mA					0.35	0.5	
I_I	$V_{CC} = $ MAX,	$V_I = 7$ V				0.1			0.1	mA
I_{IH}	$V_{CC} = $ MAX,	$V_I = 2.7$ V				20			20	µA
I_{IL}	$V_{CC} = $ MAX,	$V_I = 0.4$ V				-0.4			-0.4	mA
$I_{OS}§$	$V_{CC} = $ MAX			-20		-100	-20		-100	mA
I_{CCH}	$V_{CC} = $ MAX,	See Note 2			3.1	6.2		3.1	6.2	mA
I_{CCL}	$V_{CC} = $ MAX,	$V_I = 0$ V			4.9	9.8		4.9	9.8	mA

† For conditions shown as MIN or MAX, use the appropriate value specified under recommended operating conditions.
‡ All typical values are at $V_{CC} = 5$ V, $T_A = 25°$C.
§ Not more than one output should be shorted at a time and the duration of the short-circuit should not exceed one second.
NOTE 2: One input at 4.5 V, all others at GND.

switching characteristics, $V_{CC} = 5$ V, $T_A = 25°$C (see note 3)

PARAMETER	FROM (INPUT)	TO (OUTPUT)	TEST CONDITIONS		MIN	TYP	MAX	UNIT
t_{PLH}	A or B	Y	$R_L = 2$ kΩ,	$C_L = 15$ pF		14	22	ns
t_{PHL}						14	22	ns

NOTE 3: See General Information Section for load circuits and voltage waveforms.

3

TTL DEVICES

Texas
Instruments

recommended operating conditions

		SN54S32 MIN	NOM	MAX	SN74S32 MIN	NOM	MAX	UNIT
V_{CC}	Supply voltage	4.5	5	5.5	4.75	5	5.25	V
V_{IH}	High-level input voltage	2			2			V
V_{IL}	Low-level input voltage			0.8			0.8	V
I_{OH}	High-level output current			−1			−1	mA
I_{OL}	Low-level output current			20			20	mA
T_A	Operating free-air temperature	−55		125	0		70	°C

electrical characteristics over recommended operating free-air temperature range (unless otherwise noted)

PARAMETER	TEST CONDITIONS †	SN54S32 MIN	TYP‡	MAX	SN74S32 MIN	TYP‡	MAX	UNIT
V_{IK}	V_{CC} = MIN, I_I = −18 mA			−1.2			−1.2	V
V_{OH}	V_{CC} = MIN, V_{IH} = 2 V, I_{OH} = −1 mA	2.5	3.4		2.7	3.4		V
V_{OL}	V_{CC} = MIN, V_{IL} = 0.8 V, I_{OL} = 20 mA			0.5			0.5	V
I_I	V_{CC} = MAX, V_I = 5.5 V			1			1	mA
I_{IH}	V_{CC} = MAX, V_I = 2.7 V			50			50	µA
I_{IL}	V_{CC} = MAX, V_I = 0.5 V			−2			−2	mA
I_{OS} §	V_{CC} = MAX	−40		−100	−40		−100	mA
I_{CCH}	V_{CC} = MAX, See Note 2		18	32		18	32	mA
I_{CCL}	V_{CC} = MAX, V_I = 0 V		38	68		38	68	mA

† For conditions shown as MIN or MAX, use the appropriate value specified under recommended operating conditions.
‡ All typical values are at V_{CC} = 5 V, T_A = 25°C.
§ Not more than one output should be shorted at a time and the duration of the short-circuit should not exceed one second.
NOTE 2: One input at 4.5 V, all others at GND.

switching characteristics, V_{CC} = 5 V, T_A = 25°C (see note 3)

PARAMETER	FROM (INPUT)	TO (OUTPUT)	TEST CONDITIONS	MIN	TYP	MAX	UNIT
t_{PLH}	A or B	Y	R_L = 280 Ω, C_L = 15 pF		4	7	ns
t_{PHL}	A or B	Y	R_L = 280 Ω, C_L = 15 pF		4	7	ns
t_{PLH}	A or B	Y	R_L = 280 Ω, C_L = 50 pF		5		ns
t_{PHL}	A or B	Y	R_L = 280 Ω, C_L = 50 pF		5		ns

NOTE 3: See General Information Section for load circuits and voltage waveforms.

3

TTL DEVICES

- **Package Options Include Both Plastic and Ceramic Chip Carriers in Addition to Plastic and Ceramic DIPs**

- **Dependable Texas Instruments Quality and Reliability**

description

These devices contain four independent 2-input NOR buffer gates with open-collector outputs. Open-collector outputs require resistive pull-up to perform logically but can deliver higher V_{OH} levels and are commonly used in wired-AND applications.

The SN5433, and SN54LS33 are characterized for operation over the full military temperature range of −55°C to 125°C. The SN7433, and SN74LS33 are characterized for operation from 0°C to 70°C.

FUNCTION TABLE (each gate)

INPUTS		OUTPUT
A	**B**	**Y**
H	X	L
X	H	L
L	L	H

logic diagram (each gate)

positive logic

$$Y = \overline{A + B} \quad \text{or} \quad Y = \overline{A} \cdot \overline{B}$$

SN5433, SN54LS33 . . . J OR W PACKAGE
SN7433 . . . J OR N PACKAGE
SN74LS33 . . . D, J OR N PACKAGE
(TOP VIEW)

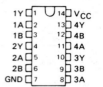

SN54LS33 . . . FK PACKAGE
SN74LS33
(TOP VIEW)

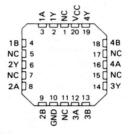

NC - No internal connection

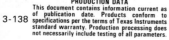

3

TTL DEVICES

schematics (each gate)

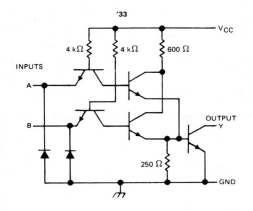

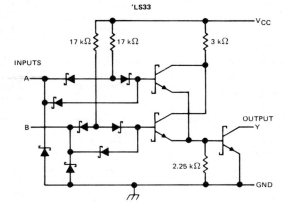

Resistor values shown are nominal.

absolute maximum ratings over operating free-air temperature range (unless otherwise noted)

Supply voltage, V_{CC} (see Note 1) .... 7 V
Input voltage: '33 .... 5.5 V
              'LS33 .... 7 V
Off-state output voltage .... 7 V
Operating free-air temperature: SN54' .... -55°C to 125°C
                     SN74' .... 0°C to 70°C
Storage temperature range .... -65°C to 150°C

NOTE 1: Voltage values are with respect to network ground terminal.

TEXAS
INSTRUMENTS

3-139

3

TTL DEVICES

recommended operating conditions

		SN5433			SN7433			UNIT
		MIN	NOM	MAX	MIN	NOM	MAX	
V_{CC}	Supply voltage	4.5	5	5.5	4.75	5	5.25	V
V_{IH}	High-level input voltage	2			2			V
V_{IL}	Low-level input voltage			0.8			0.8	V
V_{OH}	High-level output voltage			5.5			5.5	V
I_{OL}	Low-level output current			48			48	mA
T_A	Operating free-air temperature	-55		125	0		70	°C

electrical characteristics over recommended operating free-air temperature range (unless otherwise noted)

PARAMETER	TEST CONDITIONS †		SN5433			SN7433			UNIT
			MIN	TYP‡	MAX	MIN	TYP‡	MAX	
V_{IK}	V_{CC} = MIN,	$I_I = -12$ mA			-1.5			-1.5	V
I_{OH}	V_{CC} = MIN,	V_{IH} = 2 V, V_{OH} = 5.5 V			0.25			0.25	mA
V_{OL}	V_{CC} = MIN,	V_{IL} = 0.8 V, I_{OL} = 48 mA			0.4			0.4	V
I_I	V_{CC} = MAX,	V_I = 5.5 V			1			1	mA
I_{IH}	V_{CC} = MAX,	V_I = 2.4 V			40			40	μA
I_{IL}	V_{CC} = MAX,	V_I = 0.4 V			-1.6			-1.6	mA
I_{CCH}	V_{CC} = MAX,	V_I = 0V		12	21		12	21	mA
I_{CCL}	V_{CC} = MAX,	See Note 2		33	57		33	57	mA

† For conditions shown as MIN or MAX, use the appropriate value specified under recommended operating conditions.
‡ All typical values are at V_{CC} = 5 V, T_A = 25°C.
NOTE 2: One input at 4.5 V, all others at GND.

switching characteristics, V_{CC} = 5 V, T_A = 25°C (see note 3)

PARAMETER	FROM (INPUT)	TO (OUTPUT)	TEST CONDITIONS		MIN	TYP	MAX	UNIT
t_{PLH}	A or B	Y	R_L = 133 Ω,	C_L = 50 pF		10	15	ns
t_{PHL}						12	18	ns
t_{PLH}			R_L = 133 Ω,	C_L = 150 pF		15	22	ns
t_{PHL}						16	24	ns

NOTE 3: See General Information Section for load circuits and voltage waveforms.

TEXAS
INSTRUMENTS

3

TTL DEVICES

recommended operating conditions

		SN54LS33			SN74LS33			UNIT
		MIN	NOM	MAX	MIN	NOM	MAX	
V_{CC}	Supply voltage	4.5	5	5.5	4.75	5	5.25	V
V_{IH}	High-level input voltage	2			2			V
V_{IL}	Low-level input voltage			0.7			0.8	V
V_{OH}	High-level output voltage			5.5			5.5	V
I_{OL}	Low-level output current			12			24	mA
T_A	Operating free-air temperature	−55		125	0		70	°C

electrical characteristics over recommended operating free-air temperature range (unless otherwise noted)

PARAMETER	TEST CONDITIONS†			SN54LS33			SN74LS33			UNIT
			MIN	TYP‡	MAX	MIN	TYP‡	MAX		
V_{IK}	V_{CC} = MIN,	I_I = −18 mA			−1.5			−1.5		V
I_{OH}	V_{CC} = MIN,	V_{IH} = 2 V, V_{OH} = 5.5 V			0.25			0.25		mA
V_{OL}	V_{CC} = MIN,	V_{IL} = MAX, I_{OL} = 12 mA		0.25	0.4		0.25	0.4		V
	V_{CC} = MIN,	V_{IL} = MAX, I_{OL} = 24 mA					0.35	0.5		
I_I	V_{CC} = MAX,	V_I = 7 V			0.1			0.1		mA
I_{IH}	V_{CC} = MAX,	V_I = 2.7 V			20			20		µA
I_{IL}	V_{CC} = MAX,	V_I = 0.4 V			−0.4			−0.4		mA
I_{CCH}	V_{CC} = MAX,	V_I = 0 V		1.8	3.6		1.8	3.6		mA
I_{CCL}	V_{CC} = MAX,	See Note 2		6.9	13.8		6.9	13.8		mA

†For conditions shown as MIN or MAX, use the appropriate value specified under recommended operating conditions.
‡All typical values are at V_{CC} = 5 V, T_A = 25°C.
NOTE 2: One input at 4.5 V, all others at GND.

switching characteristics, V_{CC} = 5 V, T_A = 25°C (see note 3)

PARAMETER	FROM (INPUT)	TO (OUTPUT)	TEST CONDITIONS		MIN	TYP	MAX	UNIT
t_{PLH}	A or B	Y	R_L = 667 Ω,	C_L = 45 pF		20	32	ns
t_{PHL}						18	28	ns

NOTE 3: See General Information Section for load circuits and voltage waveforms.

3

TTL DEVICES

- **Package Options Include Both Plastic and Ceramic Chip Carriers in Addition to Plastic and Ceramic DIPs**

- **Dependable Texas Instruments Quality and Reliability**

description

These devices contain four independent 2-input NAND buffer gates.

The SN5437, SN54LS37 and SN54S37 are characterized for operation over the full military range of $-55\,°C$ to $125\,°C$. The SN7437, SN74LS37 and SN74S37 are characterized for operation from $0\,°C$ to $70\,°C$.

SN5437, SN54LS37, SN54S37 . . . J OR W PACKAGE
SN7437 . . . J OR N PACKAGE
SN74LS37, SN74S37 . . . D, J OR N PACKAGE

(TOP VIEW)

1A 1	14 V_{CC}
1B 2	13 4B
1Y 3	12 4A
2A 4	11 4Y
2B 5	10 3B
2Y 6	9 3A
GND 7	8 3Y

FUNCTION TABLE (each gate)

INPUTS		OUTPUT
A	B	Y
H	H	L
L	X	H
X	L	H

SN54LS37, SN54S37 . . . FK PACKAGE
SN74LS37, SN74S37

(TOP VIEW)

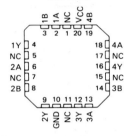

NC - No internal connection

logic diagram (each gate)

positive logic

$$Y = \overline{A \cdot B} \ \text{or} \ Y = \overline{A} + \overline{B}$$

3

TTL DEVICES

TEXAS
INSTRUMENTS

schematics (each gate)

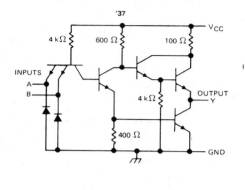

'37

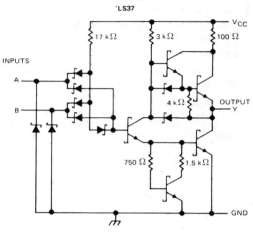

'LS37

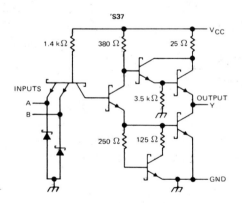

'S37

Resistor values shown are nominal.

absolute maximum ratings over operating free-air temperature range (unless otherwise noted)

Supply voltage, V_{CC} (see Note 1) . . . . 7 V
Input voltage: '37, 'S37 . . . . 5.5 V
'LS37 . . . . 7 V
Operating free-air temperature: SN54' . . . . $-55°$C to $125°$C
SN74' . . . . $0°$C to $70°$C
Storage temperature range . . . . $-65°$C to $150°$C

NOTE 1: Voltage values are with respect to network ground terminal.

TEXAS
INSTRUMENTS

3

TTL DEVICES

recommended operating conditions

		SN5437			SN7437			UNIT
		MIN	NOM	MAX	MIN	NOM	MAX	
V_{CC}	Supply voltage	4.5	5	5.5	4.75	5	5.25	V
V_{IH}	High-level input voltage	2			2			V
V_{IL}	Low-level input voltage			0.8			0.8	V
I_{OH}	High-level output current			-1.2			-1.2	mA
I_{OL}	Low-level output current			48			48	mA
T_A	Operating free-air temperature	-55		125	0		70	$^\circ$C

electrical characteristics over recommended operating free-air temperature range (unless otherwise noted)

PARAMETER	TEST CONDITIONS †			SN5437			SN7437			UNIT
			MIN	TYP‡	MAX	MIN	TYP‡	MAX		
V_{IK}	V_{CC} = MIN,	I_I = -12 mA			-1.5			-1.5		V
V_{OH}	V_{CC} = MIN,	V_{IL} = 0.8 V, I_{OH} = -1.2 mA	2.4	3.3		2.4	3.3			V
V_{OL}	V_{CC} = MIN,	V_{IH} = 2 V, I_{OL} = 48 mA		0.2	0.4		0.2	0.4		V
I_I	V_{CC} = MAX,	V_I = 5.5 V			1			1		mA
I_{IH}	V_{CC} = MAX,	V_I = 2.4 V			40			40		μA
I_{IL}	V_{CC} = MAX,	V_I = 0.4 V			-1.6			-1.6		mA
I_{OS} §	V_{CC} = MAX		-20		-70	-18		-70		mA
I_{CCH}	V_{CC} = MAX,	V_I = 0 V		9	15.5		9	15.5		mA
I_{CCL}	V_{CC} = MAX,	V_I = 4.5 V		34	54		34	54		mA

† For conditions shown as MIN or MAX, use the appropriate value specified under recommended operating conditions.
‡ All typical values are at V_{CC} = 5 V, T_A = 25°C.
§ Not more than one output should be shorted at a time, and the duration of the short circuit should not exceed one second.

switching characteristics, V_{CC} = 5 V, T_A = 25°C (see note 2)

PARAMETER	FROM (INPUT)	TO (OUTPUT)	TEST CONDITIONS	MIN	TYP	MAX	UNIT
t_{PLH}	A or B	Y	R_L = 133 Ω, C_L = 45 pF		13	22	ns
t_{PHL}					8	15	ns

NOTE 2: See General Information Section for load circuits and voltage waveforms.

3

TTL DEVICES

recommended operating conditions

		SN54LS37			SN74LS37			UNIT
		MIN	NOM	MAX	MIN	NOM	MAX	
V_{CC}	Supply voltage	4.5	5	5.5	4.75	5	5.25	V
V_{IH}	High-level input voltage	2			2			V
V_{IL}	Low-level input voltage			0.7			0.8	V
I_{OH}	High-level output current			-1.2			-1.2	mA
I_{OL}	Low-level output current			12			24	mA
T_A	Operating free-air temperature	-55		125	0		70	$^{\circ}C$

electrical characteristics over recommended operating free-air temperature range (unless otherwise noted)

PARAMETER	TEST CONDITIONS†			SN54LS37			SN74LS37			UNIT
				MIN	TYP‡	MAX	MIN	TYP‡	MAX	
V_{IK}	V_{CC} = MIN,	I_I = -18 mA				-1.5			-1.5	V
V_{OH}	V_{CC} = MIN,	V_{IL} = MAX,	I_{OH} = -1.2 mA	2.5	3.4		2.7	3.4		V
V_{OL}	V_{CC} = MIN,	V_{IH} = 2 V,	I_{OL} = 12 mA		0.25	0.4		0.25	0.4	V
	V_{CC} = MIN,	V_{IH} = 2 V,	I_{OL} = 24 mA					0.35	0.5	
I_I	V_{CC} = MAX,	V_I = 7 V				0.1			0.1	mA
I_{IH}	V_{CC} = MAX,	V_I = 2.7 V				20			20	μA
I_{IL}	V_{CC} = MAX,	V_I = 0.4 V				-0.4			-0.4	mA
I_{OS}§	V_{CC} = MAX			-30		-130	-30		-130	mA
I_{CCH}	V_{CC} = MAX,	V_I = 0 V			0.9	2		0.9	2	mA
I_{CCL}	V_{CC} = MAX,	V_I = 4.5 V			6	12		6	12	mA

† For conditions shown as MIN or MAX, use the appropriate value specified under recommended operating conditions.
‡ All typical values are at V_{CC} = 5 V, T_A = 25°C.
§ Not more than one output should be shorted at a time, and the duration of the short-circuit should not exceed one second.

switching characteristics, V_{CC} = 5 V, T_A = 25°C (see note 2)

PARAMETER	FROM (INPUT)	TO (OUTPUT)	TEST CONDITIONS		MIN	TYP	MAX	UNIT
t_{PLH}	A or B	Y	R_L = 667 Ω,	C_L = 45 pF		12	24	ns
t_{PHL}						12	24	ns

NOTE 2: See General Information Section for load circuits and voltage waveforms.

3

TTL DEVICES

recommended operating conditions

		SN54S37			SN74S37			UNIT
		MIN	NOM	MAX	MIN	NOM	MAX	
V_{CC}	Supply voltage	4.5	5	5.5	4.75	5	5.25	V
V_{IH}	High-level input voltage	2			2			V
V_{IL}	Low-level input voltage			0.8			0.8	V
I_{OH}	High-level output current			-3			-3	mA
I_{OL}	Low-level output current			60			60	mA
T_A	Operating free-air temperature	-55		125	0		70	°C

electrical characteristics over recommended operating free-air temperature range (unless otherwise noted)

PARAMETER	TEST CONDITIONS †			SN54S37			SN74S37			UNIT
				MIN	TYP‡	MAX	MIN	TYP‡	MAX	
V_{IK}	V_{CC} = MIN,	$I_I = -18$ mA				-1.2			-1.2	V
V_{OH}	V_{CC} = MIN,	V_{IL} = 0.8 V,	$I_{OH} = -3$ mA	2.5	3.4		2.7	3.4		V
V_{OL}	V_{CC} = MIN,	V_{IH} = 2 V,	I_{OL} = 60 mA			0.5			0.5	V
I_I	V_{CC} = MAX,	V_I = 5.5 V				1			1	mA
I_{IH}	V_{CC} = MAX,	V_I = 2.7 V				0.1			0.1	mA
I_{IL}	V_{CC} = MAX,	V_I = 0.5 V				-4			-4	mA
I_{OS} §	V_{CC} = MAX			-50		-225	-50		-225	mA
I_{CCH}	V_{CC} = MAX,	V_I = 0 V			20	36		20	36	mA
I_{CCL}	V_{CC} = MAX,	V_I = 4.5			46	80		46	80	mA

† For conditions shown as MIN or MAX, use the appropriate value specified under recommended operating conditions.
‡ All typical values are at V_{CC} = 5 V, T_A = 25°C.
§ Not more than one output should be shorted at a time, and the duration of the short circuit should not exceed 100 milliseconds.

switching characteristics, V_{CC} = 5 V, T_A = 25°C (see note 2)

PARAMETER	FROM (INPUT)	TO (OUTPUT)	TEST CONDITIONS		MIN	TYP	MAX	UNIT
t_{PLH}	A or B	Y	$R_L = 93\ \Omega$,	C_L = 50 pF		4	6.5	ns
t_{PHL}						4	6.5	ns
t_{PLH}			$R_L = 93\ \Omega$,	C_L = 150 pF		6		ns
t_{PHL}						6		ns

NOTE 2: See General Information Section for load circuits and voltage waveforms.

3

TTL DEVICES

TEXAS
INSTRUMENTS

- **Package Options Include Both Plastic and Ceramic Chip Carriers in Addition to Plastic and Ceramic DIPs**

- **Dependable Texas Instruments Quality and Reliability**

description

These devices contain four independent 2-input NAND buffer gates with open-collector outputs. The open-collector outputs require pull-up resistors to perform correctly. They may be connected to other open-collector outputs to implement active-low wired-OR or active-high wired-AND functions. Open-collector devices are often used to generate high V_{OH} levels.

The SN5438, SN54LS38, and SN54S38 are characterized for operation over the full military temperature range of $-55°C$ to $125°C$. The SN7438, SN74LS38, and SN74S38 are characterized for operation from $0°C$ to $70°C$.

SN5438, SN54LS38, SN54S38 . . . J OR W PACKAGE
SN7438 . . . J OR N PACKAGE
SN74LS38, SN74S38 . . . D, J OR N PACKAGE
(TOP VIEW)

SN54LS38, SN54S38 . . . FK PACKAGE
SN74LS38, SN74S38
(TOP VIEW)

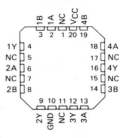

NC - No internal connection

FUNCTION TABLE (each gate)

INPUTS		OUTPUT
A	**B**	**Y**
H	H	L
L	X	H
X	L	H

logic diagram (each gate)

positive logic

$$Y = \overline{A \cdot B} \text{ or } Y = \overline{A} + \overline{B}$$

3

TTL DEVICES

TEXAS INSTRUMENTS

schematics (each gate)

'38

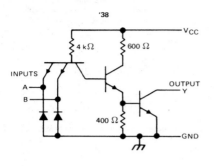

'LS38

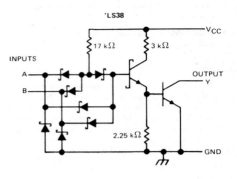

'S38

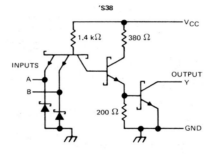

Resistor values shown are nominal.

absolute maximum ratings over operating free-air temperature (unless otherwise noted)

Supply voltage, V_{CC} (see Note 1) . . . . 7 V
Input voltage: '38 . . . . 5.5 V
             LS38 . . . . 7 V
Off-state output voltage . . . . 7 V
Operating free-air temperature range: SN54' . . . . $-55°C$ to $125°C$
                             SN74' . . . . $0°C$ to $70°C$
Storage temperature range . . . . $-65°C$ to $150°C$

NOTE 1: Voltage values are with respect to network ground terminal.

TEXAS
INSTRUMENTS

QUADRUPLE 2-INPUT POSITIVE-NAND BUFFERS WITH OPEN-COLLECTOR OUTPUTS

recommended operating conditions

		SN5438 MIN	SN5438 NOM	SN5438 MAX	SN7438 MIN	SN7438 NOM	SN7438 MAX	UNIT
V_{CC}	Supply voltage	4.5	5	5.5	4.75	5	5.25	V
V_{IH}	High-level input voltage	2			2			V
V_{IL}	Low-level input voltage			0.8			0.8	V
V_{OH}	High-level output voltage			5.5			5.5	V
I_{OL}	Low-level output current			48			48	mA
T_A	Operating free-air temperature	-55		125	0		70	°C

electrical characteristics over recommended operating free-air temperature range (unless otherwise noted)

PARAMETER	TEST CONDITIONS†			MIN	TYP‡	MAX	UNIT
V_{IK}	V_{CC} = MIN,	$I_I = -12$ mA				-1.5	V
I_{OH}	V_{CC} = MIN,	V_{IL} = 0.8 V,	V_{OH} = 5.5 V			0.25	mA
V_{OL}	V_{CC} = MIN,	V_{IH} = 2 V,	I_{OL} = 16 mA			0.4	V
I_I	V_{CC} = MAX,	V_I = 5.5 V				1	mA
I_{IH}	V_{CC} = MAX,	V_I = 2.4 V				40	μA
I_{IL}	V_{CC} = MAX,	V_I = 0.4 V				-1.6	mA
I_{CCH}	V_{CC} = MAX,	V_I = 0 V			5	8.5	mA
I_{CCL}	V_{CC} = MAX,	V_I = 4.5 V			34	54	mA

† For conditions shown as MIN or MAX, use the appropriate value specified under recommended operating conditions.
‡ All typical values are at V_{CC} = 5 V, T_A = 25°C.

switching characteristics, V_{CC} = 5 V, T_A = 25°C (see note 2)

PARAMETER	FROM (INPUT)	TO (OUTPUT)	TEST CONDITIONS		MIN	TYP	MAX	UNIT
t_{PLH}	A or B	Y	R_L = 133 Ω,	C_L = 45 pF		14	22	ns
t_{PHL}						11	18	ns

NOTE 2: See General Information Section for load circuits and voltage waveforms.

3

TTL DEVICES

TEXAS
INSTRUMENTS

recommended operating conditions

		SN54LS38			SN74LS38			UNIT
		MIN	NOM	MAX	MIN	NOM	MAX	
V_{CC}	Supply voltage	4.5	5	5.5	4.75	5	5.25	V
V_{IH}	High-level input voltage	2			2			V
V_{IL}	Low-level input voltage			0.7			0.8	V
V_{OH}	High-level output voltage			5.5			5.5	V
I_{OL}	Low-level output current			12			24	mA
T_A	Operating free-air temperature	−55		125	0		70	°C

electrical characteristics over recommended operating free-air temperature range (unless otherwise noted)

PARAMETER	TEST CONDITIONS†			SN54LS38			SN74LS38			UNIT
				MIN	TYP‡	MAX	MIN	TYP‡	MAX	
V_{IK}	V_{CC} = MIN,	I_I = −18 mA				−1.5			−1.5	V
I_{OH}	V_{CC} = MIN,	V_{IL} = MAX,	V_{OH} = 5.5 V			0.25			0.25	mA
V_{OL}	V_{CC} = MIN,	V_{IH} = 2 V,	I_{OL} = 12 mA	0.25	0.4		0.25	0.4		V
	V_{CC} = MIN,	V_{IH} = 2 V,	I_{OL} = 24 mA				0.35	0.5		
I_I	V_{CC} = MAX,	V_I = 7 V				0.1			0.1	mA
I_{IH}	V_{CC} = MAX,	V_I = 2.7 V				20			20	μA
I_{IL}	V_{CC} = MAX,	V_I = 0.4 V				−0.4			−0.4	mA
I_{CCH}	V_{CC} = MAX,	V_I = 0 V		0.9	2		0.9	2		mA
I_{CCL}	V_{CC} = MAX,	V_I = 4.5 V		6	12		6	12		mA

† For conditons shown as MIN or MAX, use the appropriate value specified under recommended operating conditions.
‡ All typical values are at V_{CC} = 5 V, T_A = 25°C.

switching characteristics, V_{CC} = 5 V, T_A = 25°C (see note 2)

PARAMETER	FROM (INPUT)	TO (OUTPUT)	TEST CONDITIONS		MIN	TYP	MAX	UNIT
t_{PLH}	A or B	Y	R_L = 667 Ω,	C_L = 45 pF		20	32	ns
t_{PHL}						18	28	ns

NOTE 2: See General Information Section for load circuits and voltage waveforms.

TEXAS
INSTRUMENTS

3

TTL DEVICES

recommended operating conditions

		SN54S38 MIN	SN54S38 NOM	SN54S38 MAX	SN74S38 MIN	SN74S38 NOM	SN74S38 MAX	UNIT
V_{CC}	Supply voltage	4.5	5	5.5	4.75	5	5.25	V
V_{IH}	High-level input voltage	2			2			V
V_{IL}	Low-level input voltage			0.8			0.8	V
V_{OH}	High-level output voltage			5.5			5.5	V
I_{OL}	Low-level output current			60			60	mA
T_A	Operating free-air temperature	−55		125	0		70	°C

electrical characteristics over recommended operating free-air temperature range (unless otherwise noted)

PARAMETER	TEST CONDITIONS †			MIN	TYP‡	MAX	UNIT
V_{IK}	V_{CC} = MIN,	I_I = −18 mA				−1.2	V
I_{OH}	V_{CC} = MIN,	V_{IL} = 0.8 V,	V_{OH} = 5.5 V			0.25	mA
V_{OL}	V_{CC} = MIN,	V_{IH} = 2 V,	I_{OL} = 60 mA			0.5	V
I_I	V_{CC} = MAX,	V_I = 5.5 V				1	mA
I_{IH}	V_{CC} = MAX,	V_I = 2.7 V				0.1	mA
I_{IL}	V_{CC} = MAX,	V_I = 0.5 V				−4	mA
I_{CCH}	V_{CC} = MAX,	V_I = 0 V			20	36	mA
I_{CCL}	V_{CC} = MAX,	V_I = 4.5 V			46	80	mA

† For conditions shown as MIN or MAX, use the appropriate value specified under recommended operating conditions.
‡ All typical values are at V_{CC} = 5 V, T_A = 25°C.

switching characteristics, V_{CC} = 5 V, T_A = 25°C (see note 2)

PARAMETER	FROM (INPUT)	TO (OUTPUT)	TEST CONDITIONS		MIN	TYP	MAX	UNIT
t_{PLH}	A or B	Y	R_L = 93 Ω,	C_L = 50 pF		6.5	10	ns
t_{PHL}						6.5	10	ns
t_{PLH}			R_L = 93 Ω,	C_L = 150 pF		9		ns
t_{PHL}						8.5		ns

NOTE 2: See General Information Section for load circuits and voltage waveforms.

3

TTL DEVICES

- **Current Sinking Capability up to 80 mA**
- **Guaranteed Fan-Out of 30 Series 54/74 Loads**
- **Dependable Texas Instruments Quality and Reliability**

description

These devices contain four independent 2-input NAND buffers. The open-collector outputs require pull-up resistors to perform correctly. They may be connected to other open-collector outputs to implement active-low wired-OR or active-high wired-AND functions. Open-collector devices are often used to generate higher V_{OH} levels.

The SN5439 is characterized for operation over the full military temperature range of $-55°C$ to $125°C$. The SN7439 is characterized for operation from $0°C$ to $70°C$.

SN5439 . . . J PACKAGE
SN7439 . . . J OR N PACKAGE
(TOP VIEW)

```
        ___  ___
1Y  [ 1      14 ]  VCC
1A  [ 2      13 ]  4Y
1B  [ 3      12 ]  4B
2Y  [ 4      11 ]  4A
2A  [ 5      10 ]  3Y
2B  [ 6       9 ]  3B
GND [ 7       8 ]  3A
```

positive logic

$$Y = \overline{A \cdot B} \text{ or } Y = \overline{A} + \overline{B}$$

schematics (each gate)

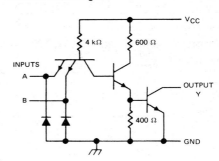

FUNCTION TABLE (each gate)

INPUTS		OUTPUT
A	**B**	**Y**
H	H	L
L	X	H
X	L	H

logic symbol †

```
1A ─(2)─┐ & ▷      ◇ ┌─(1)── 1Y
1B ─(3)─┘
2A ─(5)─┐         ┌─(4)── 2Y
2B ─(6)─┘
3A ─(8)─┐         ┌─(10)─ 3Y
3B ─(9)─┘
4A ─(11)┐         ┌─(13)─ 4Y
4B ─(12)┘
```

Pin numbers shown on logic notation are for J or N packages.

TEXAS INSTRUMENTS

3
TTL DEVICES

absolute maximum ratings over operating free-air temperature range (unless otherwise noted)

Supply voltage, V_{CC} (see Note 1) 7V
Input voltage 7V
Off-state output voltage 7V
Operating free-air temperature range: SN5439 . . . . −55°C to 125°C
                                        SN7439 . . . . 0°C to 70°C
Storage temperature range . . . . −65°C to 150°C

NOTE 1: Voltage values are with respect to network ground terminal.

recommended operating conditions

		SN5439			SN7439			UNIT
		MIN	NOM	MAX	MIN	NOM	MAX	
V_{CC}	Supply voltage	4.5	5	5.5	4.5	5	5.5	V
V_{IH}	High-level input voltage	2			2			V
V_{IL}	Low-level input voltage			0.8			0.8	V
V_{OH}	High-level output voltage			5.5			5.5	V
I_{OL}	Low-level output voltage			60			60	mA
							80†	
T_A	Operating free-air temperature	−55		125	0		70	°C

† The extended limit applies only if V_{CC} is maintained between 4.75 and 5.25 V.

electrical characteristics over recommended operating free-air temperature range (unless otherwise noted)

PARAMETER	TEST CONDITIONS†		SN5439			SN7439			UNIT
			MIN	TYP	MAX	MIN	TYP	MAX	
V_{IK}	$V_{CC} = MIN,$	$I_I = -12$ mA			−1.5			−1.5	V
I_{OH}	$V_{CC} = MIN,$	$V_{OH} = 5.5$ V			−0.25			−0.25	mA
V_{OL}	$V_{CC} = MIN,$	$I_{OL} = 48$ mA			0.4			0.4	V
	$V_{CC} = MIN,$	$I_{OL} = 60$ mA			0.5			0.5	
	$V_{CC} = 4.75$ V,	$I_{OL} = 80$ mA						0.6	
I_I	$V_{CC} = MAX,$	$V_I = 5.5$ V			1			1	mA
I_{IH}	$V_{CC} = MAX,$	$V_I = 2.4$ V			40			40	µA
I_{IL}	$V_{CC} = MAX,$	$V_I = 0.4$ V			−1.6			−1.6	mA
I_{CCH}	$V_{CC} = MAX,$	$V_I = 0V$			54			54	mA

† For conditions shown as MIN or MAX, use the appropriate value specified under recommended operating conditions.

switching characteristics, V_{CC} = 5 V, T_A = 25°C (see note 2)

PARAMETER	FROM (INPUT)	TO (OUTPUT)	TEST CONDITIONS		SN5439		SN7439		UNIT
					MIN	MAX	MIN	MAX	
t_{PLH}	A or B	Y	$R_L = 133\,\Omega,$	$C_L = 45$ pF		22		22	ns
t_{PHL}						18		18	

NOTE 2: See General Information Section for load circuits and voltage waveforms.

TEXAS
INSTRUMENTS

TTL DEVICES

3

- Package Options Include Both Plastic and Ceramic Chip Carriers in Addition to Plastic and Ceramic DIPs

- Dependable Texas Instruments Quality and Reliability

description

These devices contain two independent 4-input NAND buffer gates.

The SN5440, SN54LS40, and SN54S40 are characterized for operation over the full military temperature range of −55°C to 125°C. The SN7440, SN74LS40 and SN74S40 are characterized for operation from 0°C to 70°C.

FUNCTION TABLE (each gate)

INPUTS				OUTPUT
A	B	C	D	Y
H	H	H	H	L
L	X	X	X	H
X	L	X	X	H
X	X	L	X	H
X	X	X	L	H

logic diagram (each gate)

positive logic

$$Y = \overline{A \cdot B \cdot C \cdot D} \text{ or } Y = \overline{A} + \overline{B} + \overline{C} + \overline{D}$$

SN5440 . . . J PACKAGE
SN54LS40, SN54S40 . . . J OR W PACKAGE
SN7440 . . . J OR N PACKAGE
SN74LS40, SN74S40 . . . D, J OR N PACKAGE
(TOP VIEW)

1A	1	14	V_CC
1B	2	13	2D
NC	3	12	2C
1C	4	11	NC
1D	5	10	2B
1Y	6	9	2A
GND	7	8	2Y

SN5440 . . . W PACKAGE
(TOP VIEW)

1A	1	14	1D
1Y	2	13	1C
NC	3	12	1B
V_CC	4	11	GND
NC	5	10	2Y
2A	6	9	2D
2B	7	8	2C

SN54LS40, SN54S40 . . . FK PACKAGE
SN74LS40, SN74S40
(TOP VIEW)

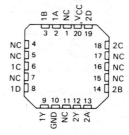

NC - No internal connection

PRODUCTION DATA
This document contains information current as of publication date. Products conform to specifications per the terms of Texas Instruments standard warranty. Production processing does not necessarily include testing of all parameters.

TEXAS INSTRUMENTS

schematics (each gate)

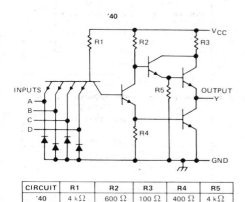

'40

CIRCUIT	R1	R2	R3	R4	R5
'40	4 kΩ	600 Ω	100 Ω	400 Ω	4 kΩ

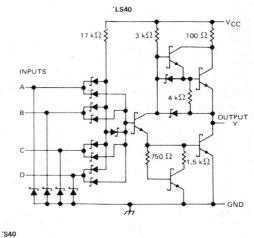

'LS40

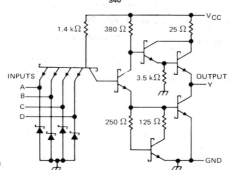

'S40

Resistor values shown are nominal.

absolute maximum ratings over operating free-air temperature range (unless otherwise noted)

Supply voltage, V_CC (see Note 1) .... 7 V

Input voltage: '40, 'S40 .... 5.5 V

            'LS40 .... 7 V

Operating free-air temperature: SN54' .... −55°C to 125°C

                    SN74' .... 0°C to 70°C

Storage temperature range .... −65°C to 150°C

NOTE 1: Voltage values are with respect to network ground terminal.

TTL DEVICES

3

TYPES SN5440, SN7440
DUAL 4-INPUT POSITIVE-NAND BUFFERS

recommended operating conditions

		SN5440			SN7440			UNIT
		MIN	NOM	MAX	MIN	NOM	MAX	
V_{CC}	Supply voltage	4.5	5	5.5	4.75	5	5.25	V
V_{IH}	High-level input voltage	2			2			V
V_{IL}	Low-level input voltage			0.8			0.8	V
I_{OH}	High-level output current			−1.2			−1.2	mA
I_{OL}	Low-level output current			48			48	mA
T_A	Operating free-air temperature	−55		125	0		70	°C

electrical characteristics over recommended operating free-air temperature range (unless otherwise noted)

PARAMETER	TEST CONDITIONS †			SN5440			SN7440			UNIT
			MIN	TYP‡	MAX	MIN	TYP‡	MAX		
V_{IK}	V_{CC} = MIN,	I_I = −12 mA			−1.5			−1.5		V
V_{OH}	V_{CC} = MIN,	V_{IL} = 0.8 V,	I_{OH} = −1.2 mA	2.4	3.3		2.4	3.3		V
V_{OL}	V_{CC} = MIN,	V_{IH} = 2 V,	I_{OL} = 48 mA		0.2	0.4		0.2	0.4	V
I_I	V_{CC} = MAX,	V_I = 5.5 V			1			1		mA
I_{IH}	V_{CC} = MAX,	V_I = 2.4 V			40			40		µA
I_{IL}	V_{CC} = MAX,	V_I = 0.4 V			−1.6			−1.6		mA
I_{OS}§	V_{CC} = MAX		−20		−70	−18		−70		mA
I_{CCH}	V_{CC} = MAX,	V_I = 0 V		4	8		4	8		mA
I_{CCL}	V_{CC} = MAX,	V_I = 4.5 V		17	27		17	27		mA

† For conditions shown as MIN or MAX, use the appropriate value specified under recommended operating conditions.
‡ All typical values are at V_{CC} = 5 V, T_A = 25°C.
§ Not more than one output should be shorted at a time, and the duration of the short circuit should not exceed 100 milliseconds.

switching characteristics, V_{CC} = 5 V, T_A = 25°C (see note 2)

PARAMETER	FROM (INPUT)	TO (OUTPUT)	TEST CONDITIONS		MIN	TYP	MAX	UNIT
t_{PLH}	Any	Y	R_L = 133 Ω,	C_L = 15 pF		13	22	ns
t_{PHL}						8	15	ns

NOTE 2: See General Information Section for load circuits and voltage waveforms.

Texas
Instruments

recommended operating conditions

		SN54LS40 MIN	NOM	MAX	SN74LS40 MIN	NOM	MAX	UNIT
V_{CC}	Supply voltage	4.5	5	5.5	4.75	5	5.25	V
V_{IH}	High-level input voltage	2			2			V
V_{IL}	Low-level input voltage			0.7			08	V
I_{OH}	High-level output current			−1.2			−1.2	mA
I_{OL}	Low-level output current			12			24	mA
T_A	Operating free-air temperature	−55		125	0		70	°C

electrical characteristics over recommended operating free-air temperature range (unless otherwise noted)

PARAMETER	TEST CONDITIONS†		SN54LS40 MIN	TYP‡	MAX	SN74LS40 MIN	TYP‡	MAX	UNIT
V_{IK}	V_{CC} = MIN,	I_I = −18 mA			−1.5			−1.5	V
V_{OH}	V_{CC} = MIN,	V_{IL} = MAX, I_{OH} = −1.2 mA	2.5	3.4		2.7	3.4		V
V_{OL}	V_{CC} = MIN,	V_{IH} = 2 V, I_{OL} = 12 mA		0.25	0.4		0.25	0.4	V
	V_{CC} = MIN,	V_{IH} = 2 V, I_{OL} = 24 mA					0.35	0.5	
I_I	V_{CC} = MAX,	V_I = 7 V			0.1			0.1	mA
I_{IH}	V_{CC} = MAX,	V_I = 2.7 V			20			20	µA
I_{IL}	V_{CC} = MAX,	V_I = 0.4 V			−0.4			−0.4	mA
I_{OS}§	V_{CC} = MAX		−30		−130	−30		−130	mA
I_{CCH}	V_{CC} = MAX,	V_I = 0 V		0.45	1		0.45	1	mA
I_{CCL}	V_{CC} = MAX,	V_I = 4.5 V		3	6		3	6	mA

† For conditions shown as MIN or MAX, use the appropriate value specified under recommended operating conditions.
‡ All typical values are at V_{CC} = 5 V, T_A = 25°C.
§ Not more than one output should be shorted at a time, and the duration of the short circuit should not exceed one second.

switching characteristics, V_{CC} = 5 V, T_A = 25°C (see note 2)

PARAMETER	FROM (INPUT)	TO (OUTPUT)	TEST CONDITIONS	MIN	TYP	MAX	UNIT
t_{PLH}	Any	Y	R_L = 667 Ω, C_L = 45 pF		12	24	ns
t_{PHL}					12	24	ns

NOTE 2: See General Information Section for load circuits and voltage waveforms.

3

TTL DEVICES

recommended operating conditions

		SN54S40			SN74S40			UNIT
		MIN	NOM	MAX	MIN	NOM	MAX	
V_{CC}	Supply voltage	4.5	5	5.5	4.75	5	5.25	V
V_{IH}	High-level input voltage	2			2			V
V_{IL}	Low-level input voltage			0.8			0.8	V
I_{OH}	High-level output current			−3			−3	mA
I_{OL}	Low-level output current			60			60	mA
T_A	Operating free-air temperature	−55		125	0		70	°C

electrical characteristics over recommended operating free-air temperature range (unless otherwise noted)

PARAMETER	TEST CONDITIONS †		SN54S40			SN74S40			UNIT
			MIN	TYP‡	MAX	MIN	TYP‡	MAX	
V_{IK}	V_{CC} = MIN,	I_I = −18 mA			−1.2			−1.2	V
V_{OH}	V_{CC} = MIN,	V_{IL} = 0.8 V, I_{OH} = −3 mA	2.5	3.4		2.7	3.4		V
V_{OL}	V_{CC} = MIN,	V_{IH} = 2 V, I_{OL} = 60 mA			0.5			0.5	V
I_I	V_{CC} = MAX,	V_I = 5.5 V			1			1	mA
I_{IH}	V_{CC} = MAX,	V_I = 2.7 V			0.1			0.1	mA
I_{IL}	V_{CC} = MAX,	V_I = 0.5 V			−4			−4	mA
I_{OS}§	V_{CC} = MAX		−50		−225	−50		−225	mA
I_{CCH}	V_{CC} = MAX,	V_I = 0 V		10	18		10	18	mA
I_{CCL}	V_{CC} = MAX,	V_I = 4.5 V		25	44		25	44	mA

† For conditions shown as MIN or MAX, use the appropriate value specified under recommended operating conditions.
‡ All typical values are at V_{CC} = 5 V, T_A = 25°C.
§ Not more than one output should be shorted at a time, and the duration of the short-circuit should not exceed 100 milliseconds.

switching characteristics, V_{CC} = 5 V, T_A = 25°C (see note 2)

PARAMETER	FROM (INPUT)	TO (OUTPUT)	TEST CONDITIONS		MIN	TYP	MAX	UNIT
t_{PLH}	Any	Y	R_L = 93 Ω,	C_L = 50 pF		4	6.5	ns
t_{PHL}						4	6.5	ns
t_{PLH}			R_L = 93 Ω,	C_L = 150 pF		6		ns
t_{PHL}						6		ns

NOTE 2: See General Information Section for load circuits and voltage waveforms.

3

TTL DEVICES

TEXAS
INSTRUMENTS

'42A, 'LS42 . . . BCD-TO-DECIMAL
EXCESS-3-TO-DECIMAL
GRAY-TO-DECIMAL

- **All Outputs Are High for Invalid Input Conditions**

- **Also for Application as**
  4-Line-to-16-Line Decoders
  3-Line-to-8-Line Decoders

- **Diode-Clamped Inputs**

TYPES	TYPICAL POWER DISSIPATION	TYPICAL PROPAGATION DELAYS
'42A	140 mW	17 ns
'LS42	35 mW	17 ns

SN5442A, SN54LS42 . . . . . . J OR W PACKAGE
SN7442A . . . J OR N PACKAGE
SN74LS42 . . . D, J OR N PACKAGE
(TOP VIEW)

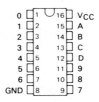

0	1	16	V_CC
1	2	15	A
2	3	14	B
3	4	13	C
4	5	12	D
5	6	11	9
6	7	10	8
GND	8	9	7

SN54LS42 . . . FK PACKAGE
SN74LS42
(TOP VIEW)

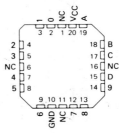

NC - No internal connection

description

These monolithic decimal decoders consist of eight inverters and ten four-input NAND gates. The inverters are connected in pairs to make BCD input data available for decoding by the NAND gates. Full decoding of valid input logic ensures that all outputs remain off for all invalid input conditions.

The '42A, and 'LS42 BCD-to-decimal decoders feature inputs and outputs that are compatible for use with most TTL and other saturated low-level logic circuits. DC noise margins are typically one volt.

Series 54, and 54LS circuits are characterized for operation over the full military temperature range of −55°C to 125°C; Series 74, and 74LS circuits are characterized for operation from 0°C to 70°C.

3

TTL DEVICES

TEXAS INSTRUMENTS

logic diagrams

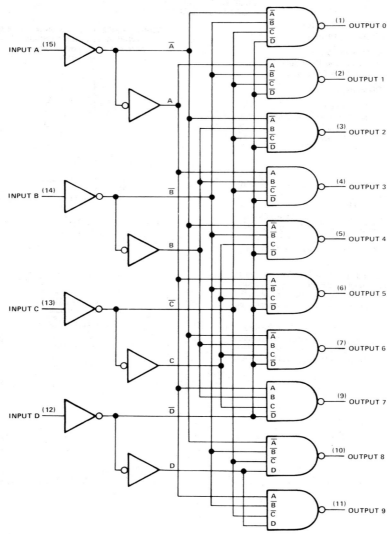

Pin numbers shown on logic notation are for D, J or N packages.

schematics of inputs and outputs

'42A

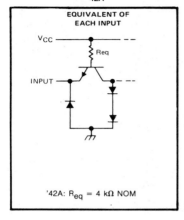

'LS42

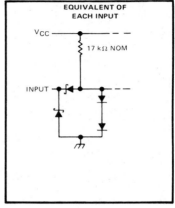

'42A

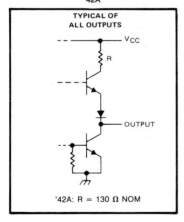

'LS42

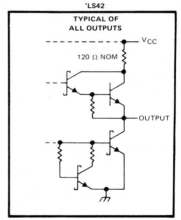

TTL DEVICES

3

TEXAS
INSTRUMENTS

FUNCTION TABLE

NO.	'42A, 'LS42 BCD INPUT				ALL TYPES DECIMAL OUTPUT									
	D	C	B	A	0	1	2	3	4	5	6	7	8	9
0	L	L	L	L	L	H	H	H	H	H	H	H	H	H
1	L	L	L	H	H	L	H	H	H	H	H	H	H	H
2	L	L	H	L	H	H	L	H	H	H	H	H	H	H
3	L	L	H	H	H	H	H	L	H	H	H	H	H	H
4	L	H	L	L	H	H	H	H	L	H	H	H	H	H
5	L	H	L	H	H	H	H	H	H	L	H	H	H	H
6	L	H	H	L	H	H	H	H	H	H	L	H	H	H
7	L	H	H	H	H	H	H	H	H	H	H	L	H	H
8	H	L	L	L	H	H	H	H	H	H	H	H	L	H
9	H	L	L	H	H	H	H	H	H	H	H	H	H	L
INVALID	H	L	H	L	H	H	H	H	H	H	H	H	H	H
INVALID	H	L	H	H	H	H	H	H	H	H	H	H	H	H
INVALID	H	H	L	L	H	H	H	H	H	H	H	H	H	H
INVALID	H	H	L	H	H	H	H	H	H	H	H	H	H	H
INVALID	H	H	H	L	H	H	H	H	H	H	H	H	H	H
INVALID	H	H	H	H	H	H	H	H	H	H	H	H	H	H

H = high level, L = low level

absolute maximum ratings over operating free-air temperature range (unless otherwise noted)

Supply voltage, V_{CC} (see Note 1) . . . . 7 V
Input voltage: '42A . . . . 5.5 V
              'LS42 . . . . 7 V
Operating free-air temperature: SN54' . . . . −55°C to 125°C
                        SN74' . . . . 0°C to 70°C
Storage temperature range . . . . −65°C to 150°C

NOTE 1: Voltage values are with respect to network ground terminal.

TEXAS
INSTRUMENTS

recommended operating conditions

	SN5442A MIN	SN5442A NOM	SN5442A MAX	SN7442A MIN	SN7442A NOM	SN7442A MAX	UNIT
Supply voltage, V_{CC}	4.5	5	5.5	4.75	5	5.25	V
High-level output current, I_{OH}			-800			-800	µA
Low-level output current, I_{OL}			16			16	mA
Operating free-air temperature, T_A	-55		125	0		70	°C

electrical characteristics over recommended operating free-air temperature range (unless otherwise noted)

PARAMETER		TEST CONDITIONS†	SN5442A MIN	SN5442A TYP‡	SN5442A MAX	SN7442A MIN	SN7442A TYP‡	SN7442A MAX	UNIT
V_{IH}	High-level input voltage		2			2			V
V_{IL}	Low-level input voltage				0.8			0.8	V
V_{IK}	Input clamp voltage	V_{CC} = MIN, I_I = -12 mA			1.5			-1.5	V
V_{OH}	High-level output voltage	V_{CC} = MIN, V_{IH} = 2 V, V_{IL} = 0.8 V, I_{OH} = -800 µA	2.4	3.4		2.4	3.4		V
V_{OL}	Low-level output voltage	V_{CC} = MIN, V_{IH} = 2 V, V_{IL} = 0.8 V, I_{OL} = 16 mA		0.2	0.4		0.2	0.4	V
I_I	Input current at maximum input voltage	V_{CC} = MAX, V_I = 5.5 V			1			1	mA
I_{IH}	High-level input current	V_{CC} = MAX, V_I = 2.4 V			40			40	µA
I_{IL}	Low-level input current	V_{CC} = MAX, V_I = 0.4 V			-1.6			-1.6	mA
I_{OS}	Short-circuit output current §	V_{CC} = MAX	-20		-55	-18		-55	mA
I_{CC}	Supply current	V_{CC} = MAX, See Note 2		28	41		28	56	mA

†For conditions shown as MIN or MAX, use the appropriate values specified under recommended operating conditions.
‡All typical values are at V_{CC} = 5 V, T_A = 25°C.
§Not more than one output should be shorted at a time.
NOTE 2: I_{CC} is measured with all outputs open and all inputs grounded.

switching characteristics, V_{CC} = 5 V, T_A = 25°C

PARAMETER		TEST CONDITIONS	MIN	TYP	MAX	UNIT
t_{PHL}	Propagation delay time, high-to-low-level output from A, B, C, or D through 2 levels of logic			14	25	ns
t_{PHL}	Propagation delay time, high-to-low-level output from A, B, C, or D through 3 levels of logic	C_L = 15 pF, R_L = 400 Ω, See Note 3		17	30	ns
t_{PLH}	Propagation delay time, low-to-high-level output from A, B, C, and D through 2 levels of logic			10	25	ns
t_{PLH}	Propagation delay time, low-to-high-level output from A, B, C, and D through 3 levels of logic			17	30	ns

NOTE 3: See General Information Section for load circuits and voltage waveforms.

TTL DEVICES

3

TEXAS
INSTRUMENTS

recommended operating conditions

	SN54LS42 MIN	SN54LS42 NOM	SN54LS42 MAX	SN74LS42 MIN	SN74LS42 NOM	SN74LS42 MAX	UNIT
Supply voltage, V_{CC}	4.5	5	5.5	4.75	5	5.25	V
High-level output current, I_{OH}			−400			−400	μA
Low-level output current, I_{OL}			4			8	mA
Operating free-air temperature, T_A	−55		125	0		70	°C

electrical characteristics over recommended operating free-air temperature range (unless otherwise noted)

PARAMETER		TEST CONDITIONS[†]		SN54LS42 MIN	SN54LS42 TYP[‡]	SN54LS42 MAX	SN74LS42 MIN	SN74LS42 TYP[‡]	SN74LS42 MAX	UNIT
V_{IH}	High-level input voltage			2			2			V
V_{IL}	Low-level input voltage					0.7			0.8	V
V_{IK}	Input clamp voltage	V_{CC} = MIN, I_I = −18 mA				−1.5			−1.5	V
V_{OH}	High-level output voltage	V_{CC} = MIN, V_{IH} = 2 V, V_{IL} = V_{IL} max, I_{OH} = −400 μA		2.5	3.5		2.7	3.5		V
V_{OL}	Low-level output voltage	V_{CC} = MIN, V_{IH} = 2 V, V_{IL} = V_{IL} max	I_{OL} = 4 mA		0.25	0.4		0.25	0.4	V
			I_{OL} = 8 mA					0.35	0.5	
I_I	Input current at maximum input voltage	V_{CC} = MAX, V_I = 7 V				0.1			0.1	mA
I_{IH}	High-level input current	V_{CC} = MAX, V_I = 2.7 V				20			20	μA
I_{IL}	Low-level input current	V_{CC} = MAX, V_I = 0.4 V				−0.4			−0.4	mA
I_{OS}	Short-circuit output current[§]	V_{CC} = MAX		−20		−100	−20		−100	mA
I_{CC}	Supply current	V_{CC} = MAX, See Note 2			7	13		7	13	mA

[†] For conditions shown as MIN or MAX, use the appropriate value specified under recommended operating conditions.
[‡] All typical values are at V_{CC} = 5 V, T_A = 25°C.
[§] Not more than one output should be shorted at a time, and duration of the short-circuit should not exceed one second.
NOTE 2. I_{CC} is measured with all outputs open and inputs grounded.

switching characteristics, V_{CC} = 5 V, T_A = 25°C

PARAMETER		TEST CONDITIONS	MIN	TYP	MAX	UNIT
t_{PHL}	Propagation delay time, high-to-low-level output from A, B, C, or D through 2 levels of logic			15	25	ns
t_{PHL}	Propagation delay time, high-to-low-level output from A, B, C, or D through 3 levels of logic	C_L = 15 pF, R_L = 2 kΩ, See Note 3		20	30	ns
t_{PLH}	Propagation delay time, low-to-high-level output from A, B, C, and D through 2 levels of logic			15	25	ns
t_{PLH}	Propagation delay time, low-to-high-level output from A, B, C, and D through 3 levels of logic			20	30	ns

Note 3: See General Information Section for load circuits and voltage waveforms.

TEXAS
INSTRUMENTS

FOR USE AS LAMP, RELAY, OR MOS DRIVERS

featuring

- **Full Decoding of Input Logic**
- **80-mA Sink-Current Capability**
- **All Outputs Are Off for Invalid BCD Input Conditions**

logic

FUNCTION TABLE

NO.	INPUTS				OUTPUTS									
	D	C	B	A	0	1	2	3	4	5	6	7	8	9
0	L	L	L	L	L	H	H	H	H	H	H	H	H	H
1	L	L	L	H	H	L	H	H	H	H	H	H	H	H
2	L	L	H	L	H	H	L	H	H	H	H	H	H	H
3	L	L	H	H	H	H	H	L	H	H	H	H	H	H
4	L	H	L	L	H	H	H	H	L	H	H	H	H	H
5	L	H	L	H	H	H	H	H	H	L	H	H	H	H
6	L	H	H	L	H	H	H	H	H	H	L	H	H	H
7	L	H	H	H	H	H	H	H	H	H	H	L	H	H
8	H	L	L	L	H	H	H	H	H	H	H	H	L	H
9	H	L	L	H	H	H	H	H	H	H	H	H	H	L
INVALID	H	L	H	L	H	H	H	H	H	H	H	H	H	H
	H	L	H	H	H	H	H	H	H	H	H	H	H	H
	H	H	L	L	H	H	H	H	H	H	H	H	H	H
	H	H	L	H	H	H	H	H	H	H	H	H	H	H
	H	H	H	L	H	H	H	H	H	H	H	H	H	H
	H	H	H	H	H	H	H	H	H	H	H	H	H	H

H = high level (off), L = low level (on)

description

These monolithic BCD-to-decimal decoders/drivers consist of eight inverters and ten four-input NAND gates. The inverters are connected in pairs to make BCD input data available for decoding by the NAND gates. Full decoding of valid BCD input logic ensures that all outputs remain off for all invalid binary input conditions. These decoders feature TTL inputs and high-performance, n-p-n output transistors designed for use as indicator/relay drivers or as open-collector logic-circuit drivers. Each of the high-breakdown output transistors (30 volts) will sink up to 80 milliamperes of current. Each input is one normalized Series 54/74 load. Inputs and outputs are entirely compatible for use with TTL logic circuits, and the outputs are compatible for interfacing with most MOS integrated circuits. Power dissipation is typically 215 milliwatts.

PRODUCTION DATA
This document contains information current as of publication date. Products conform to specifications per the terms of Texas Instruments standard warranty. Production processing does not necessarily include testing of all parameters.

SN5445 . . . J OR W PACKAGE
SN7445 . . . J OR N PACKAGE
(TOP VIEW)

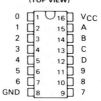

```
0  [1   16]  VCC
1  [2   15]  A
2  [3   14]  B
3  [4   13]  C
4  [5   12]  D
5  [6   11]  9
6  [7   10]  8
GND [8   9]  7
```

logic diagram

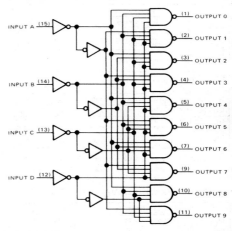

INPUT A (15)
INPUT B (14)
INPUT C (13)
INPUT D (12)

(1) OUTPUT 0
(2) OUTPUT 1
(3) OUTPUT 2
(4) OUTPUT 3
(5) OUTPUT 4
(6) OUTPUT 5
(7) OUTPUT 6
(9) OUTPUT 7
(10) OUTPUT 8
(11) OUTPUT 9

logic symbol

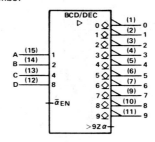

Pin numbers shown in logic notation are for J or N packages.

TTL DEVICES

3

TEXAS INSTRUMENTS

3-167

absolute maximum ratings over operating free-air temperature range (unless otherwise noted)

Supply voltage, V_{CC} (see Note 1)	7 V
Input voltage	5.5 V
Maximum current into any output (off-state)	1 mA
Operating free-air temperature range: SN5445 Circuits	-55°C to 125°C
SN7445 Circuits	0°C to 70°C
Storage temperature range	-65°C to 150°C

NOTE 1: Voltage values are with respect to network ground terminal.

recommended operating conditions

	SN5445			SN7445			UNIT
	MIN	NOM	MAX	MIN	NOM	MAX	
Supply voltage, V_{CC}	4.5	5	5.5	4.75	5	5.25	V
Off-state output voltage			30			30	V
Operating free-air temperature, T_A	-55		125	0		70	°C

electrical characteristics over recommended operating free-air temperature range (unless otherwise noted)

	PARAMETER	TEST CONDITIONS[†]		MIN	TYP[‡]	MAX	UNIT
V_{IH}	High-level input voltage			2			V
V_{IL}	Low-level input voltage					0.8	V
V_{IK}	Input clamp voltage	V_{CC} = MIN, I_I = -12 mA				-1.5	V
$V_{O(on)}$	On-state output voltage	V_{CC} = MIN, V_{IH} = 2 V,	$I_{O(on)}$ = 80 mA		0.5	0.9	V
		V_{IL} = 0.8 V	$I_{O(on)}$ = 20 mA			0.4	
$I_{O(off)}$	Off-state output current	V_{CC} = MIN, V_{IH} = 2 V, V_{IL} = 0.8 V, $V_{O(off)}$ = 30 V				250	μA
I_I	Input current at maximum input voltage	V_{CC} = MAX, V_I = 5.5 V				1	mA
I_{IH}	High-level input current	V_{CC} = MAX, V_I = 2.4 V				40	μA
I_{IL}	Low-level input current	V_{CC} = MAX, V_I = 0.4 V				-1.6	mA
I_{CC}	Supply current	V_{CC} = MAX, See Note 2	SN5445		43	62	mA
			SN7445		43	70	

[†]For conditions shown as MIN or MAX, use the appropriate value specified under recommended operating conditions for the applicable type.
[‡]All typical values are at V_{CC} = 5 V, T_A = 25°C.
NOTE 2: I_{CC} is measured with all inputs grounded and outputs open.

switching characteristics, V_{CC} = 5 V, T_A = 25°C

	PARAMETER	TEST CONDITIONS	MIN	TYP	MAX	UNIT
t_{PLH}	Propagation delay time, low-to-high-level output	C_L = 15 pF, R_L = 100 Ω, See Note 3			50	ns
t_{PHL}	Propagation delay time, high-to-low-level output				50	ns

NOTE 3: See General Information Section for load circuits and voltage waveforms.

schematics of inputs and outputs

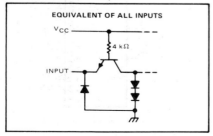

EQUIVALENT OF ALL INPUTS

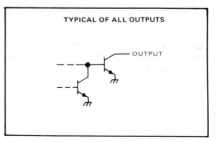

TYPICAL OF ALL OUTPUTS

TEXAS
INSTRUMENTS

'46A, '47A, 'LS47 feature	'48, 'LS48 feature	'49, 'LS49 feature
• **Open-Collector Outputs Drive Indicators Directly**	• **Internal Pull-Ups Eliminate Need for External Resistors**	• **Open-Collector Outputs**
• **Lamp-Test Provision**	• **Lamp-Test Provision**	• **Blanking Input**
• **Leading/Trailing Zero Suppression**	• **Leading/Trailing Zero Suppression**	

SN5446A, SN5447A, SN54LS47, SN5448,
SN54LS48 . . . J OR W PACKAGE
SN7446A, SN7447A,
SN7448 . . . J OR N PACKAGE
SN74LS47, SN74LS48 . . . D, J OR N PACKAGE
(TOP VIEW)

SN54LS47, SN54LS48 . . . FK PACKAGE
SN74LS47, SN74LS48
(TOP VIEW)

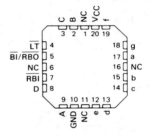

SN5449 . . . W PACKAGE
SN54LS49 . . . J OR W PACKAGE
SN74LS49 . . . D, J OR N PACKAGE
(TOP VIEW)

SN54LS49 . . . FK PACKAGE
SN74LS49
(TOP VIEW)

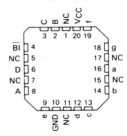

NC — No internal connection

TTL DEVICES

3

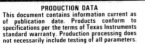

TEXAS
INSTRUMENTS

TYPES SN5446A, '47A, '48, '49, SN54LS47, 'LS48, 'LS49, SN7446A, '47A, '48, SN74LS47, 'LS48, 'LS49
BCD-TO-SEVEN-SEGMENT DECODERS/DRIVERS

- All Circuit Types Feature Lamp Intensity Modulation Capability

| TYPE | DRIVER OUTPUTS | | | | TYPICAL | PACKAGES |
	ACTIVE LEVEL	OUTPUT CONFIGURATION	SINK CURRENT	MAX VOLTAGE	POWER DISSIPATION	
SN5446A	low	open-collector	40 mA	30 V	320 mW	J, W
SN5447A	low	open-collector	40 mA	15 V	320 mW	J, W
SN5448	high	2-kΩ pull-up	6.4 mA	5.5 V	265 mW	J, W
SN5449	high	open-collector	10 mA	5.5 V	165 mW	W
SN54LS47	low	open-collector	12 mA	15 V	35 mW	J, W
SN54LS48	high	2-kΩ pull-up	2 mA	5.5 V	125 mW	J, W
SN54LS49	high	open-collector	4 mA	5.5 V	40 mW	J, W
SN7446A	low	open-collector	40 mA	30 V	320 mW	J, N
SN7447A	low	open-collector	40 mA	15 V	320 mW	J, N
SN7448	high	2-kΩ pull-up	6.4 mA	5.5 V	265 mW	J, N
SN74LS47	low	open-collector	24 mA	15 V	35 mW	J, N
SN74LS48	high	2-kΩ pull-up	6 mA	5.5 V	125 mW	J, N
SN74LS49	high	open-collector	8 mA	5.5 V	40 mW	J, N

logic symbols

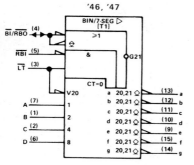

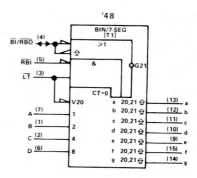

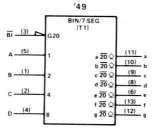

Pin numbers shown on logic notation are for D, J or N packages.

TEXAS
INSTRUMENTS

description

The '46A, '47A, and 'LS47 feature active-low outputs designed for driving common-anode VLEDs or incandescent indicators directly, and the '48, '49, 'LS48, 'LS49 feature active-high outputs for driving lamp buffers or common-cathode VLEDs. All of the circuits except '49 and 'LS49 have full ripple-blanking input/output controls and a lamp test input. The '49 and 'LS49 circuits incorporate a direct blanking input. Segment identification and resultant displays are shown below. Display patterns for BCD input counts above 9 are unique symbols to authenticate input conditions.

The '46A, '47A, '48, 'LS47, and 'LS48 circuits incorporate automatic leading and/or trailing-edge zero-blanking control ($\overline{RBI}$ and $\overline{RBO}$). Lamp test ($\overline{LT}$) of these types may be performed at any time when the $\overline{BI}/\overline{RBO}$ node is at a high level. All types (including the '49 and 'LS49) contain an overriding blanking input ($\overline{BI}$) which can be used to control the lamp intensity by pulsing or to inhibit the outputs. Inputs and outputs are entirely compatible for use with TTL logic outputs.

The SN54246/SN74246 through '249 and the SN54LS247/SN74LS247 through 'LS249 compose the 6 and the 9 with tails and have been designed to offer the designer a choice between two indicator fonts. The SN54249/SN74249 and SN54LS249/SN74LS249 are 16-pin versions of the 14-pin SN5449 and 'LS49. Included in the '249 circuit and 'LS249 circuits are the full functional capability for lamp test and ripple blanking, which is not available in the '49 or 'LS49 circuit.

SEGMENT IDENTIFICATION

NUMERICAL DESIGNATIONS AND RESULTANT DISPLAYS

'46A, '47A, 'LS47 FUNCTION TABLE

DECIMAL OR FUNCTION	INPUTS						$\overline{BI}/\overline{RBO}$†	OUTPUTS							NOTE
	$\overline{LT}$	$\overline{RBI}$	D	C	B	A		a	b	c	d	e	f	g	
0	H	H	L	L	L	L	H	ON	ON	ON	ON	ON	ON	OFF	
1	H	X	L	L	L	H	H	OFF	ON	ON	OFF	OFF	OFF	OFF	
2	H	X	L	L	H	L	H	ON	ON	OFF	ON	ON	OFF	ON	
3	H	X	L	L	H	H	H	ON	ON	ON	ON	OFF	OFF	ON	
4	H	X	L	H	L	L	H	OFF	ON	ON	OFF	OFF	ON	ON	
5	H	X	L	H	L	H	H	ON	OFF	ON	ON	OFF	ON	ON	
6	H	X	L	H	H	L	H	OFF	OFF	ON	ON	ON	ON	ON	
7	H	X	L	H	H	H	H	ON	ON	ON	OFF	OFF	OFF	OFF	1
8	H	X	H	L	L	L	H	ON	ON	ON	ON	ON	ON	ON	
9	H	X	H	L	L	H	H	ON	ON	ON	OFF	OFF	ON	ON	
10	H	X	H	L	H	L	H	OFF	OFF	OFF	ON	ON	OFF	ON	
11	H	X	H	L	H	H	H	OFF	OFF	ON	ON	OFF	OFF	ON	
12	H	X	H	H	L	L	H	OFF	ON	OFF	OFF	OFF	ON	ON	
13	H	X	H	H	L	H	H	ON	OFF	OFF	ON	OFF	ON	ON	
14	H	X	H	H	H	L	H	OFF	OFF	OFF	ON	ON	ON	ON	
15	H	X	H	H	H	H	H	OFF	OFF	OFF	OFF	OFF	OFF	OFF	
BI	X	X	X	X	X	X	L	OFF	OFF	OFF	OFF	OFF	OFF	OFF	2
RBI	H	L	L	L	L	L	L	OFF	OFF	OFF	OFF	OFF	OFF	OFF	3
LT	L	X	X	X	X	X	H	ON	ON	ON	ON	ON	ON	ON	4

H = high level, L = low level, X = irrelevant

NOTES: 1. The blanking input ($\overline{BI}$) must be open or held at a high logic level when output functions 0 through 15 are desired. The ripple blanking input ($\overline{RBI}$) must be open or high if blanking of a decimal zero is not desired.

2. When a low logic level is applied directly to the blanking input ($\overline{BI}$), all segment outputs are off regardless of the level of any other input.

3. When ripple blanking input ($\overline{RBI}$) and inputs A, B, C, and D are at a low level with the lamp test input high, all segment outputs go off and the ripple blanking output ($\overline{RBO}$) goes to a low level (response condition).

4. When the blanking input/ripple blanking output ($\overline{BI}/\overline{RBO}$) is open or held high and a low is applied to the lamp test input, all segment outputs are on.

† $\overline{BI}/\overline{RBO}$ is wire-AND logic serving as blanking input ($\overline{BI}$) and/or ripple blanking output ($\overline{RBO}$).

TTL DEVICES **3**

TEXAS INSTRUMENTS

TYPES SN5446A, '47A, '48, '49, SN54LS47, 'LS48, 'LS49, SN7446A, '47A, '48, SN74LS47, 'LS48, 'LS49 BCD-TO-SEVEN-SEGMENT DECODERS/DRIVERS

'48, 'LS48 FUNCTION TABLE

DECIMAL OR FUNCTION	INPUTS						BI/RBO†	OUTPUTS							NOTE
	LT	RBI	D	C	B	A		a	b	c	d	e	f	g	
0	H	H	L	L	L	L	H	H	H	H	H	H	H	L	
1	H	X	L	L	L	H	H	L	H	H	L	L	L	L	
2	H	X	L	L	H	L	H	H	H	L	H	H	L	H	
3	H	X	L	L	H	H	H	H	H	H	H	L	L	H	
4	H	X	L	H	L	L	H	L	H	H	L	L	H	H	
5	H	X	L	H	L	H	H	H	L	H	H	L	H	H	
6	H	X	L	H	H	L	H	L	L	H	H	H	H	H	
7	H	X	L	H	H	H	H	H	H	H	L	L	L	L	
8	H	X	H	L	L	L	H	H	H	H	H	H	H	H	1
9	H	X	H	L	L	H	H	H	H	H	H	L	H	H	
10	H	X	H	L	H	L	H	L	L	L	H	H	L	H	
11	H	X	H	L	H	H	H	L	L	H	H	L	L	H	
12	H	X	H	H	L	L	H	L	H	L	L	L	H	H	
13	H	X	H	H	L	H	H	H	L	L	H	L	H	H	
14	H	X	H	H	H	L	H	L	L	L	H	H	H	H	
15	H	X	H	H	H	H	H	L	L	L	L	L	L	L	
BI	X	X	X	X	X	X	L	L	L	L	L	L	L	L	2
RBI	H	L	L	L	L	L	L	L	L	L	L	L	L	L	3
LT	L	X	X	X	X	X	H	H	H	H	H	H	H	H	4

H = high level, L = low level, X = irrelevant

NOTES: 1. The blanking input (BI) must be open or held at a high logic level when output functions 0 through 15 are desired. The ripple-blanking input (RBI) must be open or high, if blanking of a decimal zero is not desired.

2. When a low logic level is applied directly to the blanking input (BI), all segment outputs are low regardless of the level of any other input.

3. When ripple-blanking input (RBI) and inputs A, B, C, and D are at a low level with the lamp-test input high, all segment outputs go low and the ripple-blanking output (RBO) goes to a low level (response condition).

4. When the blanking input/ripple-blanking output (BI/RBO) is open or held high and a low is applied to the lamp-test input, all segment outputs are high.

† BI/RBO is wire-AND logic serving as blanking input (BI) and/or ripple blanking output (RBO).

'49, 'LS49 FUNCTION TABLE

DECIMAL OR FUNCTION	INPUTS					OUTPUTS							NOTE
	D	C	B	A	BI	a	b	c	d	e	f	g	
0	L	L	L	L	H	H	H	H	H	H	H	L	
1	L	L	L	H	H	L	H	H	L	L	L	L	
2	L	L	H	L	H	H	H	L	H	H	L	H	
3	L	L	H	H	H	H	H	H	H	L	L	H	
4	L	H	L	L	H	L	H	H	L	L	H	H	
5	L	H	L	H	H	H	L	H	H	L	H	H	
6	L	H	H	L	H	L	L	H	H	H	H	H	
7	L	H	H	H	H	H	H	H	L	L	L	L	
8	H	L	L	L	H	H	H	H	H	H	H	H	1
9	H	L	L	H	H	H	H	H	H	L	H	H	
10	H	L	H	L	H	L	L	L	H	H	L	H	
11	H	L	H	H	H	L	L	H	H	L	L	H	
12	H	H	L	L	H	L	H	L	L	L	H	H	
13	H	H	L	H	H	H	L	L	H	L	H	H	
14	H	H	H	L	H	L	L	L	H	H	H	H	
15	H	H	H	H	H	L	L	L	L	L	L	L	
BI	X	X	X	X	L	L	L	L	L	L	L	L	2

H = high level, L = low level, X = irrelevant

NOTES: 1. The blanking input (BI) must be open or held at a high logic level when output functions 0 through 15 are desired.

2. When a low logic level is applied directly to the blanking input (BI), all segment outputs are low regardless of the level of any other input.

TEXAS
INSTRUMENTS

logic diagrams

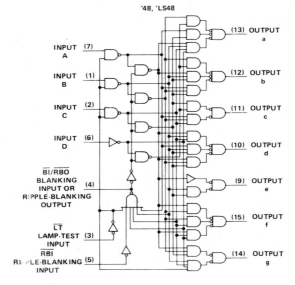

Pin numbers shown on logic notation are for D, J or N packages.

3

TTL DEVICES

logic diagrams (continued)

'49, 'LS49

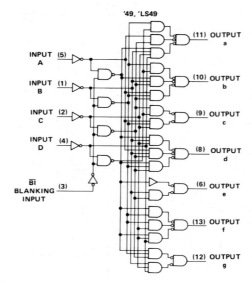

Pin numbers shown on logic notation are for D, J or N packages.

TEXAS
INSTRUMENTS

schematics of inputs and outputs

'46A, '47A, '48, '49

EQUIVALENT OF EACH INPUT EXCEPT $\overline{BI}/\overline{RBO}$

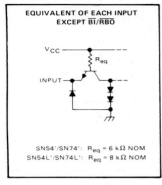

SN54'/SN74': R_{eq} = 6 kΩ NOM
SN54L'/SN74L': R_{eq} = 8 kΩ NOM

'46A, '47A, '48

EQUIVALENT OF $\overline{BI}/\overline{RBO}$

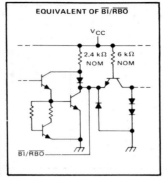

'46A, '47A

TYPICAL OF OUTPUTS
a THRU g

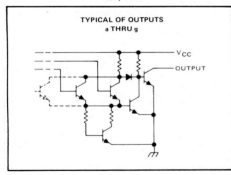

'48

TYPICAL OF OUTPUTS
a THRU g

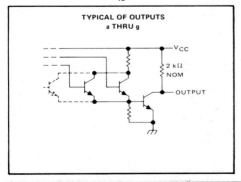

'49

TYPICAL OF ALL OUTPUTS

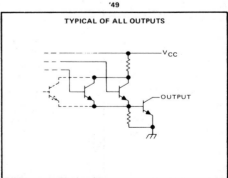

3

TTL DEVICES

TYPES SN54LS47, 'LS48, 'LS49, SN74LS47, 'LS48, 'LS49
BCD-TO-SEVEN-SEGMENT DECODERS/DRIVERS

schematics of inputs and outputs

'LS47, 'LS48, 'LS49

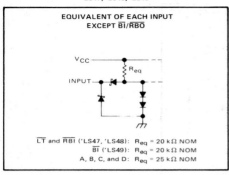

EQUIVALENT OF EACH INPUT
EXCEPT $\overline{BI}/\overline{RBO}$

$\overline{LT}$ and $\overline{RBI}$ ('LS47, 'LS48): R_{eq} = 20 kΩ NOM
$\overline{BI}$ ('LS49): R_{eq} = 20 kΩ NOM
A, B, C, and D: R_{eq} = 25 kΩ NOM

'LS47, 'LS48, 'LS49

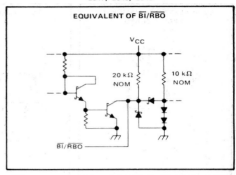

EQUIVALENT OF $\overline{BI}/\overline{RBO}$

'LS47

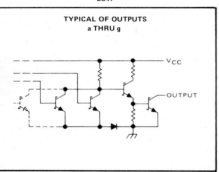

TYPICAL OF OUTPUTS
a THRU g

'LS48

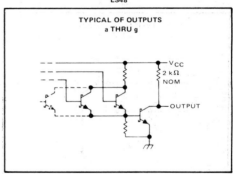

TYPICAL OF OUTPUTS
a THRU g

'LS49

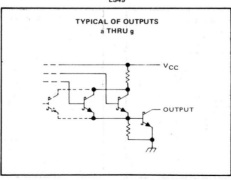

TYPICAL OF OUTPUTS
a THRU g

3

TTL DEVICES

TEXAS
INSTRUMENTS

absolute maximum ratings over operating free-air temperature range (unless otherwise noted)

Supply voltage, V_{CC} (see Note 1)	7 V
Input voltage	5.5 V
Current forced into any output in the off state	1 mA
Operating free-air temperature range: SN5446A, SN5447A	$-55°C$ to $125°C$
SN7446A, SN7447A	$0°C$ to $70°C$
Storage temperature range	$-65°C$ to $150°C$

NOTE 1: Voltage values are with respect to network ground terminal.

recommended operating conditions

		SN5446A			SN5447A			SN7446A			SN7447A			UNIT
		MIN	NOM	MAX	MIN	NOM	MAX	MIN	NOM	MAX	MIN	NOM	MAX	
Supply voltage, V_{CC}		4.5	5	5.5	4.5	5	5.5	4.75	5	5.25	4.75	5	5.25	V
Off-state output voltage, $V_{O(off)}$	a thru g			30			15			30			15	V
On-state output current, $I_{O(on)}$	a thru g			40			40			40			40	mA
High-level output current, I_{OH}	$\overline{BI}/\overline{RBO}$			−200			−200			−200			−200	μA
Low-level output current, I_{OL}	$\overline{BI}/\overline{RBO}$			8			8			8			8	mA
Operating free-air temperature, T_A		−55		125	−55		125	0		70	0		70	°C

electrical characteristics over recommended operating free-air temperature range (unless otherwise noted)

	PARAMETER		TEST CONDITIONS[†]		MIN	TYP[‡]	MAX	UNIT
V_{IH}	High-level input voltage				2			V
V_{IL}	Low-level input voltage						0.8	V
V_{IK}	Input clamp voltage		V_{CC} = MIN, I_I = −12 mA				−1.5	V
V_{OH}	High-level output voltage	$\overline{BI}/\overline{RBO}$	V_{CC} = MIN, V_{IH} = 2 V, V_{IL} = 0.8 V, I_{OH} = −200 μA		2.4	3.7		V
V_{OL}	Low-level output voltage	$\overline{BI}/\overline{RBO}$	V_{CC} = MIN, V_{IH} = 2 V, V_{IL} = 0.8 V, I_{OL} = 8 mA			0.27	0.4	V
$I_{O(off)}$	Off-state output current	a thru g	V_{CC} = MAX, V_{IH} = 2 V, V_{IL} = 0.8 V, $V_{O(off)}$ = MAX				250	μA
$V_{O(on)}$	On-state output voltage	a thru g	V_{CC} = MIN, V_{IH} = 2 V, V_{IL} = 0.8 V, $I_{O(on)}$ = 40 mA			0.3	0.4	V
I_I	Input current at maximum input voltage	Any input except $\overline{BI}/\overline{RBO}$	V_{CC} = MAX, V_I = 5.5 V				1	mA
I_{IH}	High-level input current	Any input except $\overline{BI}/\overline{RBO}$	V_{CC} = MAX, V_I = 2.4 V				40	μA
I_{IL}	Low-level input current	Any input except $\overline{BI}/\overline{RBO}$	V_{CC} = MAX, V_I = 0.4 V				−1.6	mA
		$\overline{BI}/\overline{RBO}$					−4	
I_{OS}	Short-circuit output current	$\overline{BI}/\overline{RBO}$	V_{CC} = MAX				−4	mA
I_{CC}	Supply current		V_{CC} = MAX, See Note 2	SN54′		64	85	mA
				SN74′		64	103	

[†]For conditions shown as MIN or MAX, use the appropriate value specified under recommended operating conditions.
[‡]All typical values are at V_{CC} = 5 V, T_A = 25°C.
NOTE 2: I_{CC} is measured with all outputs open and all inputs at 4.5 V.

switching characteristics, V_{CC} = 5 V, T_A = 25°C

	PARAMETER	TEST CONDITIONS	MIN	TYP	MAX	UNIT
t_{off}	Turn-off time from A input				100	ns
t_{on}	Turn-on time from A input	C_L = 15 pF, R_L = 120 Ω, See Note 3			100	
t_{off}	Turn-off time from $\overline{RBI}$ input				100	ns
t_{on}	Turn-on time from $\overline{RBI}$ input				100	

NOTE 3: See General Information Section for load circuits and voltage waveforms. t_{off} corresponds to t_{PLH} and t_{on} corresponds to t_{PHL}.

TEXAS
INSTRUMENTS

3-177

3

TTL DEVICES

absolute maximum ratings over operating free-air temperature range (unless otherwise noted)

Supply voltage, V_{CC} (see Note 1) . . . . 7 V
Input voltage . . . . 7 V
Peak output current ($t_w \leqslant$ 1 ms, duty cycle $\leqslant$ 10%) . . . . 200 mA
Current forced into any output in the off state . . . . 1 mA
Operating free-air temperature range: SN54LS47 . . . . $-55°C$ to $125°C$
            SN74LS47 . . . . $0°C$ to $70°C$
Storage temperature range . . . . $-65°C$ to $150°C$

NOTE 1: Voltage values are with respect to network ground terminal.

recommended operating conditions

		SN54LS47			SN74LS47			UNIT
		MIN	NOM	MAX	MIN	NOM	MAX	
Supply voltage, V_{CC}		4.5	5	5.5	4.75	5	5.25	V
Off-state output voltage, $V_{O(off)}$	a thru g			15			15	V
On-state output current, $I_{O(on)}$	a thru g			12			24	mA
High-level output current, I_{OH}	$\overline{BI}/\overline{RBO}$			-50			-50	μA
Low-level output current, I_{OL}	$\overline{BI}/\overline{RBO}$			1.6			3.2	mA
Operating free-air temperature, T_A		-55		125	0		70	$°C$

electrical characteristics over recommended operating free-air temperature range (unless otherwise noted)

PARAMETER		TEST CONDITIONS[†]		SN54LS47			SN74LS47			UNIT
				MIN	TYP[‡]	MAX	MIN	TYP[‡]	MAX	
V_{IH}	High-level input voltage			2			2			V
V_{IL}	Low-level input voltage					0.7			0.8	V
V_{IK}	Input clamp voltage	V_{CC} = MIN,	$I_I = -18$ mA			-1.5			-1.5	V
V_{OH}	High-level output voltage	$\overline{BI}/\overline{RBO}$	V_{CC} = MIN, V_{IH} = 2 V, $V_{IL} = V_{IL}$ max, $I_{OH} = -50$ μA	2.4	4.2		2.4	4.2		V
V_{OL}	Low-level output voltage	$\overline{BI}/\overline{RBO}$	V_{CC} = MIN, V_{IH} = 2 V, $V_{IL} = V_{IL}$ max	I_{OL} = 1.6 mA	0.25	0.4		0.25	0.4	V
				I_{OL} = 3.2 mA				0.35	0.5	
$I_{O(off)}$	Off-state output current	a thru g	V_{CC} = MAX, V_{IH} = 2 V, $V_{IL} = V_{IL}$ max, $V_{O(off)}$ = 15 V			250			250	μA
$V_{O(on)}$	On-state output voltage	a thru g	V_{CC} = MIN, V_{IH} = 2 V, $V_{IL} = V_{IL}$ max	$I_{O(on)}$ = 12 mA	0.25	0.4		0.25	0.4	V
				$I_{O(on)}$ = 24 mA				0.35	0.5	
I_I	Input current at maximum input voltage		V_{CC} = MAX, V_I = 7 V			0.1			0.1	mA
I_{IH}	High-level input current		V_{CC} = MAX, V_I = 2.7 V			20			20	μA
I_{IL}	Low-level input current	Any input except $\overline{BI}/\overline{RBO}$	V_{CC} = MAX, V_I = 0.4 V			-0.4			-0.4	mA
		$\overline{BI}/\overline{RBO}$				-1.2			-1.2	
I_{OS}	Short-circuit output current	$\overline{BI}/\overline{RBO}$	V_{CC} = MAX	-0.3		-2	-0.3		-2	mA
I_{CC}	Supply current		V_{CC} = MAX, See Note 2		7	13		7	13	mA

[†]For conditions shown as MIN or MAX, use the appropriate value specified under recommended operating conditions.
[‡] All typical values are at V_{CC} = 5 V, $T_A = 25°C$.
NOTE 2: I_{CC} is measured with all outputs open and all inputs at 4.5 V.

switching characteristics, V_{CC} = 5 V, $T_A = 25°C$

PARAMETER		TEST CONDITIONS	MIN	TYP	MAX	UNIT
t_{off}	Turn-off time from A input				100	ns
t_{on}	Turn-on time from A input	C_L = 15 pF, R_L = 665 Ω, See Note 3			100	
t_{off}	Turn-off time from $\overline{RBI}$ input				100	ns
t_{on}	Turn-on time from $\overline{RBI}$ input				100	

NOTE 3: See General Information Section for load circuits and voltage waveforms.

TEXAS
INSTRUMENTS

absolute maximum ratings over operating free-air temperature range (unless otherwise noted)

Supply voltage, V_{CC} (see Note 1) . . . . 7 V
Input voltage . . . . 5.5 V
Operating free-air temperature range: SN5448 . . . . -55°C to 125°C
  SN7448 . . . . 0°C to 70°C
Storage temperature range . . . . -65°C to 150°C

NOTE 1: Voltage values are with respect to network ground terminal.

recommended operating conditions

		SN5448			SN7448			UNIT
		MIN	NOM	MAX	MIN	NOM	MAX	
Supply voltage, V_{CC}		4.5	5	5.5	4.75	5	5.25	V
High-level output current, I_{OH}	a thru g			−400			−400	μA
	$\overline{BI}/\overline{RBO}$			−200			−200	
Low-level output current, I_{OL}	a thru g			6.4			6.4	mA
	$\overline{BI}/\overline{RBO}$			8			8	
Operating free-air temperature, T_A		−55		125	0		70	°C

electrical characteristics over recommended operating free-air temperature range (unless otherwise noted)

PARAMETER			TEST CONDITIONS†		MIN	TYP‡	MAX	UNIT
V_{IH}	High-level input voltage				2			V
V_{IL}	Low-level input voltage						0.8	V
V_{IK}	Input clamp voltage		V_{CC} = MIN, I_I = −12 mA				−1.5	V
V_{OH}	High-level output voltage	a thru g	V_{CC} = MIN, V_{IH} = 2 V,		2.4	4.2		V
		$\overline{BI}/\overline{RBO}$	V_{IL} = 0.8 V, I_{OH} = MAX		2.4	3.7		
I_O	Output current	a thru g	V_{CC} = MIN, V_O = 0.85 V, Input conditions as for V_{OH}		−1.3	−2		mA
V_{OL}	Low-level output voltage		V_{CC} = MIN, V_{IH} = 2 V, V_{IL} = 0.8 V, I_{OL} = MAX			0.27	0.4	V
I_I	Input current at maximum input voltage	Any input except $\overline{BI}/\overline{RBO}$	V_{CC} = MAX, V_I = 5.5 V				1	mA
I_{IH}	High-level input current	Any input except $\overline{BI}/\overline{RBO}$	V_{CC} = MAX, V_I = 2.4 V				40	μA
I_{IL}	Low-level input current	Any input except $\overline{BI}/\overline{RBO}$	V_{CC} = MAX, V_I = 0.4 V				−1.6	mA
		$\overline{BI}/\overline{RBO}$					−4	
I_{OS}	Short-circuit output current	$\overline{BI}/\overline{RBO}$	V_{CC} = MAX				−4	mA
I_{CC}	Supply current		V_{CC} = MAX, See Note 2	SN5448		53	76	mA
				SN7448		53	90	

†For conditions shown as MIN or MAX, use the appropriate value specified under recommended operating conditions.
‡All typical values are at V_{CC} = 5 V, T_A = 25°C.
NOTE 2: I_{CC} is measured with all outputs open and all inputs at 4.5 V.

switching characteristics, V_{CC} = 5 V, T_A = 25°C

PARAMETER		TEST CONDITIONS	MIN	TYP	MAX	UNIT
t_{PHL}	Propagation delay time, high-to-low-level output from A input	C_L = 15 pF, R_L = 1 kΩ, See Note 3			100	ns
t_{PLH}	Propagation delay time, low-to-high-level output from A input				100	
t_{PHL}	Propagation delay time, high-to-low-level output from $\overline{RBI}$ input				100	ns
t_{PLH}	Propagation delay time, low-to-high-level output from $\overline{RBI}$ input				100	

NOTE 3: See General Information Section for load circuits and voltage waveforms.

3

TTL DEVICES

TEXAS
INSTRUMENTS

TYPES SN54LS48, SN74LS48
BCD-TO-SEVEN-SEGMENT DECODERS/DRIVERS

absolute maximum ratings over operating free-air temperature range (unless otherwise noted)

Supply voltage, V_{CC} (see Note 1) . . . . 7 V
Input voltage . . . . 7 V
Operating free-air temperature range: SN54LS48 . . . . $-55°C$ to $125°C$
                                SN74LS48 . . . . $0°C$ to $70°C$
Storage temperature range . . . . $-65°C$ to $150°C$

NOTE 1: Voltage values are with respect to network ground terminal.

recommended operating conditions

			SN54LS48			SN74LS48			UNIT
			MIN	NOM	MAX	MIN	NOM	MAX	
Supply voltage, V_{CC}			4.5	5	5.5	4.75	5	5.25	V
High-level output current, I_{OH}	a thru g				-100			-100	μA
	$\overline{BI}/\overline{RBO}$				-50			-50	
Low-level output current, I_{OL}	a thru g				2			6	mA
	$\overline{BI}/\overline{RBO}$				1.6			3.2	
Operating free-air temperature, T_A			-55		125	0		70	°C

electrical characteristics over recommended operating free-air temperature range (unless otherwise noted)

	PARAMETER	TEST CONDITIONS[†]			SN54LS48			SN74LS48			UNIT
					MIN	TYP[‡]	MAX	MIN	TYP[‡]	MAX	
V_{IH}	High-level input voltage				2			2			V
V_{IL}	Low-level input voltage						0.7			0.8	V
V_{IK}	Input clamp voltage	V_{CC} = MIN,	$I_I = -18$ mA				-1.5			-1.5	V
V_{OH}	High-level output voltage	a thru g and $\overline{BI}/\overline{RBO}$	V_{CC} = MIN, V_{IH} = 2 V, $V_{IL} = V_{IL}$ max, I_{OH} = MAX		2.4	4.2		2.4	4.2		V
I_O	Output current	a thru g	V_{CC} = MIN, V_O = 0.85 V, Input conditions as for V_{OH}		-1.3	-2		-1.3	-2		mA
V_{OL}	Low-level output voltage	a thru g	V_{CC} = MIN, V_{IH} = 2 V, $V_{IL} = V_{IL}$ max	I_{OL} = 2 mA		0.25	0.4		0.25	0.4	V
				I_{OL} = 6 mA					0.35	0.5	
		$\overline{BI}/\overline{RBO}$	V_{CC} = MIN, V_{IH} = 2 V, $V_{IL} = V_{IL}$ max	I_{OL} = 1.6 mA		0.25	0.4		0.25	0.4	V
				I_{OL} = 3.2 mA					0.35	0.5	
I_I	Input current at maximum input voltage	Any input except $\overline{BI}/\overline{BRO}$	V_{CC} = MAX, V_I = 7 V				0.1			0.1	mA
I_{IH}	High-level input current	Any input except $\overline{BI}/\overline{RBO}$	V_{CC} = MAX, V_I = 2.7 V				20			20	μA
I_{IL}	Low-level input current	Any input except $\overline{BI}/\overline{RBO}$	V_{CC} = MAX, V_I = 0.4 V				-0.4			-0.4	mA
		$\overline{BI}/\overline{RBO}$					-1.2			-1.2	
I_{OS}	Short-circuit output current	$\overline{BI}/\overline{RBO}$	V_{CC} = MAX		-0.3		-2	-0.3		-2	mA
I_{CC}	Supply current		V_{CC} = MAX, See Note 2			25	38		25	38	mA

[†]For conditions shown as MIN or MAX, use the appropriate value specified under recommended operating conditions.
[‡]All typical values are at V_{CC} = 5 V, T_A 25°C.
NOTE 2: I_{CC} is measured with all outputs open and all inputs at 4.5 V.

switching characteristics, V_{CC} = 5 V, T_A = 25°C

	PARAMETER	TEST CONDITIONS	MIN	TYP	MAX	UNIT
t_{PHL}	Propagation delay time, high-to-low-level output from A input	C_L = 15 pF, R_L = 4 kΩ, See Note 3			100	ns
t_{PLH}	Propagation delay time, low-to-high-level output from A input				100	
t_{PHL}	Propagation delay time, high-to-low-level output from $\overline{RBI}$ input	C_L = 15 pF, R_L = 6 kΩ, See Note 3			100	ns
t_{PLH}	Propagation delay time, low-to-high-level output from $\overline{RBI}$ input				100	

NOTE 3: See General Information Section for load circuits and voltage waveforms.

TEXAS INSTRUMENTS

absolute maximum ratings over operating free-air temperature range (unless otherwise noted)

Supply voltage, V_{CC} (see Note 1) . . . . 7 V
Input voltage . . . . 5.5 V
Current forced into any output in the off state . . . . 1 mA
Operating free-air temperature range . . . . −55°C to 125°C
Storage temperature range . . . . −65°C to 150°C

NOTE 1: Voltage values are with respect to network ground terminal.

recommended operating conditions

	SN5449			UNIT
	MIN	NOM	MAX	
Supply voltage, V_{CC}	4.5	5	5.5	V
High-level output voltage, V_{OH}			5.5	V
Low-level output current, I_{OL}			10	mA
Operating free-air temperature, T_A	−55		125	°C

electrical characteristics over recommended operating free-air temperature range (unless otherwise noted)

	PARAMETER	TEST CONDITIONS†	SN5449			UNIT
			MIN	TYP‡	MAX	
V_{IH}	High-level input voltage		2			V
V_{IL}	Low-level input voltage				0.6	V
V_{IK}	Input clamp voltage	V_{CC} = MIN, I_I = −10 mA			−1.5	V
I_{OH}	High-level output current	V_{CC} = MIN, V_{IH} = 2 V, V_{IL} = 0.8 V, V_{OH} = 5.5 V			250	μA
V_{OL}	Low-level output voltage	V_{CC} = MIN, V_{IH} = 2 V, V_{IL} = 0.8 V, I_{OL} = 10 mA		0.27	0.4	V
I_I	Input current at maximum input voltage	V_{CC} = MAX, V_I = 5.5 V			1	mA
I_{IH}	High-level input current	V_{CC} = MAX, V_I = 2.4 V			40	μA
I_{IL}	Low-level input current	V_{CC} = MAX, V_I = 0.4 V			−1.6	mA
I_{CC}	Supply current	V_{CC} = MAX, See Note 2		33	47	mA

†For conditions shown as MIN or MAX, use the appropriate value specified under recommended operating conditions.
‡All typical values are at V_{CC} = 5 V, T_A = 25°C.
NOTE 2: I_{CC} is measured with all outputs open and all inputs at 4.5 V.

switching characteristics, V_{CC} = 5 V, T_A = 25°C

	PARAMETER	TEST CONDITIONS	MIN	TYP	MAX	UNIT
t_{PHL}	Propagation delay time, high-to-low-level output from A input				100	ns
t_{PLH}	Propagation delay time, low-to-high-level output from A input	C_L = 15 pF, R_L = 667 Ω, See Note 3			100	
t_{PHL}	Propagation delay time, high-to-low-level output from $\overline{RBI}$ input				100	ns
t_{PLH}	Propagation delay time, low-to-high-level output from $\overline{RBI}$ input				100	

NOTE 3: See General Information Section for load circuits and voltage waveforms.

TEXAS
INSTRUMENTS

3

TTL DEVICES

absolute maximum ratings over operating free-air temperature range (unless otherwise noted)

Supply voltage, V_{CC} (see Note 1)	7 V
Input voltage	7 V
Current forced into any output in the off state	1 mA
Operating free-air temperature range: SN54LS49	-55°C to 125°C
SN74LS49	0°C to 70°C
Storage temperature range	-65°C to 150°C

NOTE 1: Voltage values are with respect to network ground terminal.

recommended operating conditions

	SN54LS49			SN74LS49			UNIT
	MIN	NOM	MAX	MIN	NOM	MAX	
Supply voltage, V_{CC}	4.5	5	5.5	4.75	5	5.25	V
High-level output voltage, V_{OH}			5.5			5.5	V
Low-level output current, I_{OL}			4			8	mA
Operating free-air temperature, T_A	-55		125	0		70	$^\circ$C

electrical characteristics over recommended operating free-air temperature range (unless otherwise noted)

PARAMETER		TEST CONDITIONS[†]		SN54LS49			SN74LS49			UNIT
				MIN	TYP[‡]	MAX	MIN	TYP[‡]	MAX	
V_{IH}	High-level input voltage			2			2			V
V_{IL}	Low-level input voltage					0.7			0.8	V
V_{IK}	Input clamp voltage	V_{CC} = MIN,	$I_I = -18$ mA			-1.5			-1.5	V
I_{OH}	High-level output current	V_{CC} = MIN, V_{IH} = 2 V, $V_{IL} = V_{IL}$ max, V_{OH} = 5.5 V				250			250	μA
V_{OL}	Low-level output voltage	V_{CC} = MIN, V_{IH} = 2 V, $V_{IL} = V_{IL}$ max	I_{OL} = 4 mA	0.25		0.4	0.25		0.4	V
			I_{OL} = 8 mA				0.35		0.5	
I_I	Input current at maximum input voltage	V_{CC} = MAX,	V_I = 7 V			0.1			0.1	mA
I_{IH}	High-level input current	V_{CC} = MAX,	V_I = 2.7 V			20			20	μA
I_{IL}	Low-level input current	V_{CC} = MAX,	V_I = 0.4 V			-0.4			-0.4	mA
I_{CC}	Supply current	V_{CC} = MAX,	See Note 2	8		15	8		15	mA

[†]For conditions shown as MIN or MAX, use the appropriate value specified under recommended operating conditions.
[‡]All typical values are at V_{CC} = 5 V, $T_A = 25^\circ$C.
NOTE 2: I_{CC} is measured with all outputs open and all inputs at 4.5 V.

switching characteristics, V_{CC} = 5 V, $T_A = 25^\circ$C

PARAMETER		TEST CONDITIONS	MIN	TYP	MAX	UNIT
t_{PHL}	Propagation delay time, high-to-low-level output from A input	C_L = 15 pF, R_L = 2 kΩ, See Note 3			100	ns
t_{PLH}	Propagation delay time, low-to-high-level output from A input				100	
t_{PHL}	Propagation delay time, high-to-low-level output from $\overline{RBI}$ input	C_L = 15 pF, R_L = 6 kΩ, See Note 3			100	ns
t_{PLH}	Propagation delay time, low-to-high-level output from $\overline{RBI}$ input				100	

NOTE 3: See General Information Section for load circuits and voltage waveforms.

TEXAS
INSTRUMENTS

- Package Options Include Plastic and Ceramic DIPs

- Dependable Texas Instruments Quality and Reliability

SN5450 . . . J PACKAGE
SN7450 . . . J OR N PACKAGE
(TOP VIEW)

1A	1	14	V_{CC}
2A	2	13	1B
2B	3	12	$1\overline{X}$
2C	4	11	1X
2D	5	10	1D
2Y	6	9	1C
GND	7	8	1Y

description

These devices contain two independent 2-wide 2-input AND-OR-INVERT gates with one gate expandable. They perform the Boolean function $Y = \overline{AB + CD + X}$ with X = output of SN5460/SN7460 for the SN5450/SN7450.

The SN5450 is characterized for operation over the full military temperature range of −55°C to 125°C. The SN7450 is characterized for operation from 0°C to 70°C.

SN5450 . . . W PACKAGE
(TOP VIEW)

$1\overline{X}$	1	14	1D
$1\overline{X}$	2	13	1C
1A	3	12	1Y
V_{CC}	4	11	GND
1B	5	10	2Y
2A	6	9	2D
2B	7	8	2C

logic diagram

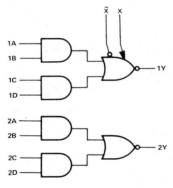

3

TTL DEVICES

TEXAS
INSTRUMENTS

3-183

schematic

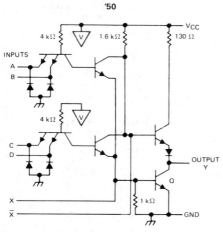

'50

Resistor values shown are nominal.
If expander is not used, leave X and $\overline{X}$ open.

absolute maximum ratings over operating free-air temperature range (unless otherwise noted)

Supply voltage, V_{CC} (see Note 1)	7 V
Input voltage	5.5 V
Operating free-air temperature range: SN54'	$-55°C$ to $125°C$
SN74'	$0°C$ to $70°C$
Storage temperature range	$-65°C$ to $150°C$

NOTE 1: Voltage values are with respect to network ground terminal.

TEXAS
INSTRUMENTS

3

TTL DEVICES

recommended operating conditions

		SN5450			SN7450			UNIT
		MIN	NOM	MAX	MIN	NOM	MAX	
V_{CC}	Supply voltage	4.5	5	5.5	4.75	5	5.25	V
V_{IH}	High-level input voltage	2			2			V
V_{IL}	Low-level input voltage			0.8			0.8	V
I_{OH}	High-level output current			-0.4			-0.4	mA
I_{OL}	Low-level output current			16			16	mA
T_A	Operating free-air temperature	-55		125	0		70	°C

electrical characteristics over recommended operating free-air temperature range (unless otherwise noted)

PARAMETER	TEST CONDITIONS†			SN5450			SN7450			UNIT
				MIN	TYP‡	MAX	MIN	TYP‡	MAX	
V_{IK}	V_{CC} = MIN,	$I_I = -12$ mA				-1.5			-1.5	V
V_{OH}	V_{CC} = MIN,	V_{IL} = 0.8 V,	$I_{OH} = -0.4$ mA	2.4	3.4		2.4	3.4		V
V_{OL}	V_{CC} = MIN,	V_{IH} = 2 V,	I_{OL} = 16 mA		0.2	0.4		0.2	0.4	V
I_I	V_{CC} = MAX,	V_I = 5.5 V				1			1	mA
I_{IH}	V_{CC} = MAX,	V_{IH} = 2.4 V				40			40	µA
I_{IL}	V_{CC} = MAX,	V_{IL} = 0.4 V				-1.6			-1.6	mA
I_{OS}§	V_{CC} = MAX			-20		-55	-18		-55	mA
I_{CCH}	V_{CC} = MAX,	V_I = 0 V			4	8		4	8	mA
I_{CCL}	V_{CC} = MAX,	See Note 2			7.4	14		7.4	14	mA
$I_{\overline{X}}$▲	$V_{\overline{X}X}$ = 0.4 V,	I_{OL} = 16 mA				-2.9			-3.1	mA
$V_{BE(Q)}$▲	$I_X + I_{\overline{X}}$ = 0.41 mA,	$R_{\overline{X}X}$ = 0,	I_{OL} = 16 mA		1.1					V
	$I_X + I_{\overline{X}}$ = 0.62 mA,	$R_{\overline{X}X}$ = 0,	I_{OL} = 16 mA					1		V
V_{OH}▲	I_X = 0.15 mA,	$I_{\overline{X}} = -0.15$ mA,	$I_{OH} = -0.4$ mA	2.4	3.4					V
	I_X = 0.27 mA,	$I_{\overline{X}} = -0.27$ mA,	$I_{OH} = -0.4$ mA				2.4	3.4		V
V_{OL}▲	$I_X + I_{\overline{X}}$ = 0.3 mA,	$R_{\overline{X}X}$ = 138 Ω,	I_{OL} = 16 mA		0.2	0.4				V
	$I_X + I_{\overline{X}}$ = 0.43 mA,	$R_{\overline{X}X}$ = 130 Ω,	I_{OL} = 16 mA					0.2	0.4	V

† For conditions shown as MIN or MAX, use the appropriate value specified under recommended operating conditions.
‡ All typical values are at V_{CC} = 5 V, $T_A = 25°$C.
§ Not more than one output should be shorted at a time.
▲ Using expander inputs, V_{CC} = MIN, T_A = MIN, except typical values.
NOTE 2: All inputs of one AND gate at 4.5 V, all others at GND.

switching characteristics, V_{CC} = 5 V, T_A = 25°C (see note 3)

PARAMETER	FROM (INPUT)	TO (OUTPUT)	TEST CONDITIONS		MIN	TYP	MAX	UNIT
t_{PLH}	Any	Y	R_L = 400 Ω,	C_L = 15 pF		13	22	ns
t_{PHL}			Expander pins open			8	15	ns

NOTE 3: See General Information Section for load circuits and voltage waveforms.

TTL DEVICES

3

Texas Instruments

3

TTL DEVICES

- Package Options Include Both Plastic and Ceramic Chip Carriers in Addition to Plastic and Ceramic DIPs

- Dependable Texas Instruments Quality and Reliability

description

The '51, and 'S51 contain two independent 2-wide 2-input AND-OR-INVERT gates. They perform the Boolean function $Y = \overline{AB + CD}$.

The 'LS51 contains one 2-wide 3-input and one 2-wide 2-input AND-OR-INVERT gates. They perform the Boolean functions $1Y = \overline{(1A \cdot 1B \cdot 1C) + (1D \cdot 1E \cdot 1F)}$ and $2Y = \overline{(2A \cdot 2B) + (2C \cdot 2D)}$.

The SN5451, SN54LS51 and SN54S51 are characterized for operation over the full military temperature range of −55°C to 125°C. The SN7451, SN74LS51 and SN74S51 are characterized for operation from 0°C to 70°C.

logic diagrams

'51, 'S51

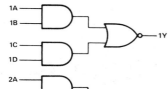

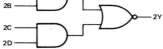

'L51, 'LS51

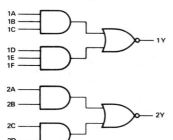

SN5451 ... J PACKAGE
SN54LS51 ... J OR W PACKAGE
SN7451 ... J OR N PACKAGE
SN74S51 ... D, J OR N PACKAGE
(TOP VIEW)

```
1A  [ 1    14 ]  VCC
2A  [ 2    13 ]  1B
2B  [ 3    12 ]  NU
2C  [ 4    11 ]  NU
2D  [ 5    10 ]  1D
2Y  [ 6     9 ]  1C
GND [ 7     8 ]  1Y
```

SN5451 ... W PACKAGE
(TOP VIEW)

```
NU  [ 1    14 ]  1D
NU  [ 2    13 ]  1C
1A  [ 3    12 ]  1Y
VCC [ 4    11 ]  GND
1B  [ 5    10 ]  2Y
2A  [ 6     9 ]  2D
2B  [ 7     8 ]  2C
```

SN54LS51 ... J OR W PACKAGE
SN74LS51 ... D, J OR N PACKAGE
(TOP VIEW)

```
1A  [ 1    14 ]  VCC
2A  [ 2    13 ]  1C
2B  [ 3    12 ]  1B
2C  [ 4    11 ]  1F
2D  [ 5    10 ]  1E
2Y  [ 6     9 ]  1D
GND [ 7     8 ]  1Y
```

NC- No internal connection
NU - Make no external connection

3

TTL DEVICES

TEXAS
INSTRUMENTS

TYPES SN5451, SN7451
AND-OR-INVERT GATES

SN54S51 . . . FK PACKAGE
SN74S51
(TOP VIEW)

```
          2A  1A  NC  VCC 1B
           3   2   1   20  19
    2B  4                      18  NU
    NC  5                      17  NC
    2C  6                      16  NU
    NC  7                      15  NC
    2D  8                      14  1D
           9  10  11  12  13
          2Y  GND NC  1Y  1C
```

SN54LS51 . . . FK PACKAGE
SN74LS51
(TOP VIEW)

```
          2A  1A  NC  VCC 1C
           3   2   1   20  19
    2B  4                      18  1B
    NC  5                      17  NC
    2C  6                      16  1F
    NC  7                      15  NC
    2D  8                      14  1E
           9  10  11  12  13
          2Y  GND NC  1Y  1D
```

NC - No internal connection
NU - Make no external connection

schematics

'51

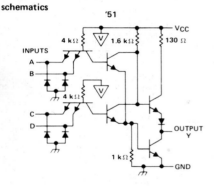

**TEXAS
INSTRUMENTS**

schematics

'LS51

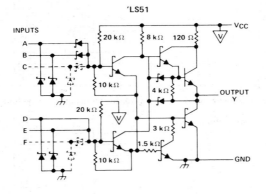

'S51

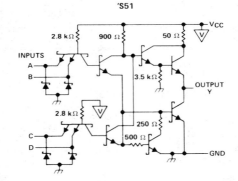

absolute maximum ratings over operating free-air temperature range (unless otherwise noted)

Supply voltage, V_{CC} (see Note 1): '51, 'LS51, 'S51 .... 7 V

Input voltage: '51, 'S51 .... 5.5 V

'LS51 .... 7 V

Operating free-air temperature range: SN54' .... -55°C to 125°C

SN74' .... 0°C to 70°C

Storage temperature range .... -65°C to 150°C

NOTE 1: Voltage values are with respect to network ground terminal.

TTL DEVICES

3

recommended operating conditions

		SN5451 MIN	SN5451 NOM	SN5451 MAX	SN7451 MIN	SN7451 NOM	SN7451 MAX	UNIT
V_{CC}	Supply voltage	4.5	5	5.5	4.75	5	5.25	V
V_{IH}	High-level input voltage	2			2			V
V_{IL}	Low-level input voltage			0.8			0.8	V
I_{OH}	High-level output current			−0.4			−0.4	mA
I_{OL}	Low-level output current			16			16	mA
T_A	Operating free-air temperature	−55		125	0		70	°C

electrical characteristics over recommended operating free-air temperature range (unless otherwise noted)

PARAMETER	TEST CONDITIONS †	SN5451 MIN	SN5451 TYP‡	SN5451 MAX	SN7451 MIN	SN7451 TYP‡	SN7451 MAX	UNIT
V_{IK}	V_{CC} = MIN, I_I = −12 mA			−1.5			−1.5	V
V_{OH}	V_{CC} = MIN, V_{IL} = 0.8 V, I_{OH} = −0.4 mA	2.4	3.4		2.4	3.4		V
V_{OL}	V_{CC} = MIN, V_{IH} = 2 V, I_{OL} = 16 mA		0.2	0.4		0.2	0.4	V
I_I	V_{CC} = MAX, V_I = 5.5 V			1			1	mA
I_{IH}	V_{CC} = MAX, V_I = 2.4 V			40			40	µA
I_{IL}	V_{CC} = MAX, V_I = 0.4 V			−1.6			−1.6	mA
I_{OS} §	V_{CC} = MAX	−20		−55	−18		−55	mA
I_{CCH}	V_{CC} = MAX, V_I = 0 V		4	8		4	8	mA
I_{CCL}	V_{CC} = MAX, See Note 2		7.4	14		7.4	14	mA

† For conditions shown as MIN or MAX, use the appropriate value specified under recommended operating conditions.
‡ All typical values are at V_{CC} = 5 V, T_A = 25°C.
§ Not more than one output should be shorted at a time.
NOTE 2: All inputs of one AND gate at 4.5 V, all others at GND.

switching characteristics, V_{CC} = 5 V, T_A = 25°C (see note 3)

PARAMETER	FROM (INPUT)	TO (OUTPUT)	TEST CONDITIONS	MIN	TYP	MAX	UNIT
t_{PLH}	Any	Y	R_L = 400 Ω, C_L = 15 pF		13	22	ns
t_{PHL}					8	15	

NOTE 3: See General Information Section for load circuits and voltage waveforms.

TEXAS
INSTRUMENTS

recommended operating conditions

		SN54LS51			SN74LS51			UNIT
		MIN	NOM	MAX	MIN	NOM	MAX	
V_{CC}	Supply voltage	4.5	5	5.5	4.75	5	5.25	V
V_{IH}	High-level input voltage	2			2			V
V_{IL}	Low-level input voltage			0.7			0.8	V
I_{OH}	High-level output current			−0.4			−0.4	mA
I_{OL}	Low-level output current			4			8	mA
T_A	Operating free-air temperature	−55		125	0		70	°C

electrical characteristics over recommended operating free-air temperature range (unless otherwise noted)

PARAMETER	TEST CONDITIONS †	SN54LS51			SN74LS51			UNIT
		MIN	TYP‡	MAX	MIN	TYP‡	MAX	
V_{IK}	V_{CC} = MIN, I_I = −18 mA			−1.5			−1.5	V
V_{OH}	V_{CC} = MIN, V_{IL} = MAX, I_{OH} = −0.4 mA	2.5	3.4		2.7	3.4		V
V_{OL}	V_{CC} = MIN, V_{IH} = 2 V, I_{OL} = 4 mA		0.25	0.4		0.25	0.4	V
	V_{CC} = MIN, V_{IH} = 2 V, I_{OL} = 8 mA					0.35	0.5	
I_I	V_{CC} = MAX, V_I = 7 V			0.1			0.1	mA
I_{IH}	V_{CC} = MAX, V_I = 2.7 V			20			20	µA
I_{IL}	V_{CC} = MAX, V_I = 0.4 V			−0.4			−0.4	mA
I_{OS}§	V_{CC} = MAX	−20		−100	−20		−100	mA
I_{CCH}	V_{CC} = MAX, V_I = 0 V		0.8	1.6		0.8	1.6	mA
I_{CCL}	V_{CC} = MAX, See Note 2		1.4	2.8		1.4	2.8	mA

† For conditions shown as MIN or MAX, use the appropriate value specified under recommended operating conditions.
‡ All typical values are at V_{CC} = 5 V, T_A = 25°C.
§ Not more than one output should be shorted at a time, and the duration of the short-circuit should not exceed one second.
NOTE 2: All inputs of one AND gate at 4.5 V, all others at GND.

switching characteristics, V_{CC} = 5 V, T_A = 25°C (see note 3)

PARAMETER	FROM (INPUT)	TO (OUTPUT)	TEST CONDITIONS	MIN	TYP	MAX	UNIT
t_{PLH}	Any	Y	R_L = 2 kΩ, C_L = 15 pF		12	20	ns
t_{PHL}					12.5	20	ns

NOTE 3: See General Information Section for load circuits and voltage waveforms.

3

TTL DEVICES

TEXAS INSTRUMENTS

TYPES SN54S51, SN74S51
AND-OR-INVERT GATES

recommended operating conditions

		SN54S51			SN74S51			UNIT
		MIN	NOM	MAX	MIN	NOM	MAX	
V_{CC}	Supply voltage	4.5	5	5.5	4.75	5	5.25	V
V_{IH}	High-level input voltage	2			2			V
V_{IL}	Low-level input voltage			0.8			0.8	V
I_{OH}	High-level output current			−1			−1	mA
I_{OL}	Low-level output current			20			20	mA
T_A	Operating free-air temperature	−55		125	0		70	°C

electrical characteristics over recommended operating free-air temperature range (unless otherwise noted)

PARAMETER	TEST CONDITIONS †			SN54S51			SN74S51			UNIT
				MIN	TYP ‡	MAX	MIN	TYP ‡	MAX	
V_{IK}	V_{CC} = MIN,	I_I = −18 mA				−1.2			−1.2	V
V_{OH}	V_{CC} = MIN,	V_{IL} = 0.8 V,	I_{OH} = −1 mA	2.5	3.4		2.7	3.4		V
V_{OL}	V_{CC} = MIN,	V_{IH} = 2 V,	I_{OL} = 20 mA			0.5			0.5	V
I_I	V_{CC} = MAX,	V_I = 5.5 V				1			1	mA
I_{IH}	V_{CC} = MAX,	V_I = 2.7 V				50			50	μA
I_{IL}	V_{CC} = MAX,	V_I = 0.5 V				−2			−2	mA
I_{OS} §	V_{CC} = MAX			−40		−100	−40		−100	mA
I_{CCH}	V_{CC} = MAX,	V_I = 0 V			8.2	17.8		8.2	17.8	mA
I_{CCL}	V_{CC} = MAX,	See Note 2			13.6	22		13.6	22	mA

† For conditions shown as MIN or MAX, use the appropriate value specified under recommended operating conditions.
‡ All typical values are at V_{CC} = 5 V, T_A = 25°C.
§ Not more than one output should be shorted at a time, and the duration of the short-circuit should not exceed one second.
NOTE 2: All inputs of one AND gate at 4.5 V, all others at GND.

switching characteristics, V_{CC} = 5 V, T_A = 25°C (see note 3)

PARAMETER	FROM (INPUT)	TO (OUTPUT)	TEST CONDITIONS		MIN	TYP	MAX	UNIT
t_{PLH}			R_L = 280 Ω,	C_L = 15 pF		3.5	5.5	ns
t_{PHL}						3.5	5.5	ns
t_{PLH}	Any	Y	R_L = 280 Ω,	C_L = 50 pF		5		ns
t_{PHL}							5.5	ns

NOTE 3: See General Information Section for load circuits and voltage waveforms.

3

TTL DEVICES

TEXAS
INSTRUMENTS

- **Package Options Include Plastic and Ceramic DIPs**

- **Dependable Texas Instruments Quality and Reliability**

description

These devices contain expandable 4-wide AND-OR-INVERT gates. The '53 perform the Boolean function $Y = \overline{AB + CD + EF + GH + X}$ = output of SN5460/SN7460.

The SN5453 is characterized for operation over the full military temperature range of −55°C to 125°C. The SN7453 is characterized for operation from 0°C to 70°C.

SN5453 . . . J PACKAGE
SN7453 . . . J OR N PACKAGE
(TOP VIEW)

A	1	14	V_{CC}
C	2	13	B
D	3	12	$\overline{X}$
E	4	11	X
F	5	10	H
NC	6	9	G
GND	7	8	Y

SN5453 . . . W PACKAGE
(TOP VIEW)

X	1	14	H
$\overline{X}$	2	13	G
A	3	12	Y
V_{CC}	4	11	GND
B	5	10	NC
C	6	9	F
D	7	8	E

logic diagram

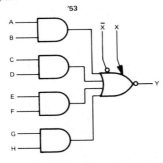

'53

TEXAS
INSTRUMENTS

3

TTL DEVICES

TYPES SN5453, SN7453
EXPANDABLE 4-WIDE AND-OR-INVERT GATES

schematic

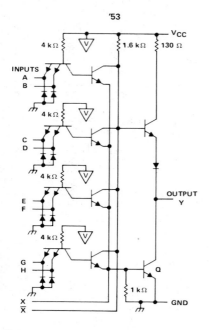

Resistor values shown are nominal.
If expander is not used, leave X and X̄ open.

absolute maximum ratings over operating free-air temperature range (unless otherwise noted)

Supply voltage, V_{CC} (see Note 1) .... 7 V

Input voltage .... 5.5 V

Operating free-air temperature range: SN54′ .... −55°C to 125°C

SN74′ .... 0°C to 70°C

Storage temperature range .... −65°C to 150°C

NOTE 1: Voltage values are with respect to network ground terminal.

recommended operating conditions

		SN5453			SN7453			UNIT
		MIN	NOM	MAX	MIN	NOM	MAX	
V_{CC}	Supply voltage	4.5	5	5.5	4.75	5	5.25	V
V_{IH}	High-level input voltage	2			2			V
V_{IL}	Low-level input voltage			0.8			0.8	V
I_{OH}	High-level output current			−0.4			−0.4	mA
I_{OL}	Low-level output current			16			16	mA
T_A	Operating free-air temperature	−55		125	0		70	°C

electrical characteristics over recommended operating free-air temperature range (unless otherwise noted)

PARAMETER	TEST CONDITIONS[†]			SN5453			SN7453			UNIT
				MIN	TYP[‡]	MAX	MIN	TYP[‡]	MAX	
V_{IK}	$V_{CC} = $ MIN,	$I_I = -12$ mA				−1.5			−1.5	V
V_{OH}	$V_{CC} = $ MIN,	$V_{IL} = 0.8$ V,	$I_{OH} = -0.4$ mA	2.4	3.4		2.4	3.4		V
V_{OL}	$V_{CC} = $ MIN,	$V_{IH} = 2$ V,	$I_{OL} = 16$ mA		0.2	0.4		0.2	0.4	V
I_I	$V_{CC} = $ MAX,	$V_I = 5.5$ V				1			1	mA
I_{IH}	$V_{CC} = $ MAX,	$V_{IH} = 2.4$ V				40			40	μA
I_{IL}	$V_{CC} = $ MAX,	$V_{IL} = 0.4$ V				−1.6			−1.6	mA
I_{OS}§	$V_{CC} = $ MAX			−20		−55	−18		−55	mA
I_{CCH}	$V_{CC} = $ MAX,	$V_I = 0$ V			4	8		4	8	mA
I_{CCL}	$V_{CC} = $ MAX,	See Note 2			5.1	9.5		5.1	9.5	mA
$I_{\overline{X}}$▲	$V_{\overline{X}X} = 0.4$ V,	$I_{OL} = 16$ mA				−2.9			−3.1	mA
$V_{BE(Q)}$▲	$I_X + I_{\overline{X}} = 0.41$ mA	$R_{\overline{X}X} = 0$,	$I_{OL} = 16$ mA		1.1					V
	$I_X + I_{\overline{X}} = 0.62$ mA,	$R_{\overline{X}X} = 0$,	$I_{OL} = 16$ mA					1		
V_{OH}▲	$I_X = 0.15$ mA,	$I_{\overline{X}} = -0.15$ mA,	$I_{OH} = -0.4$ mA	2.4	3.4					V
	$I_X = 0.27$ mA,	$I_{\overline{X}} = -0.27$ mA,	$I_{OH} = -0.4$ mA				2.4	3.4		
V_{OL}▲	$I_X + I_{\overline{X}} = 0.3$ mA,	$R_{\overline{X}X} = 138$ Ω,	$I_{OL} = 16$ mA		0.2	0.4				V
	$I_X + I_{\overline{X}} = 0.43$ mA,	$R_{\overline{X}X} = 130$ Ω,	$I_{OL} = 16$ mA					0.2	0.4	

† For conditions shown as MIN or MAX, use the appropriate value specified under recommended operating conditions.
‡ All typical values are at $V_{CC} = 5$ V, $T_A = 25°$C,
§Not more than one output should be shorted at a time.
▲Using expander inputs, $V_{CC} = $ MIN, $T_A = $ MIN, except typical values
NOTE 2: All inputs of one AND gate at 4.5 V, all others at GND.

switching characteristics, $V_{CC} = 5$ V, $T_A = 25°$C (see note 3)

PARAMETER	FROM (INPUT)	TO (OUTPUT)	TEST CONDITIONS	MIN	TYP	MAX	UNIT
t_{PLH}	Any	Y	$R_L = 400$ Ω, $\quad C_L = 15$ pF ¶		13	22	ns
t_{PHL}					8	15	ns

¶ Expander pins open.
NOTE 3: See General Information Section for load circuits and voltage waveforms.

TEXAS
INSTRUMENTS

3

TTL DEVICES

- **Package Options Include Both Plastic and Ceramic Chip Carriers in Addition to Plastic and Ceramic DIPs**

- **Dependable Texas Instruments Quality and Reliability**

description

These devices contain 4-wide AND-OR-INVERT gates. They perform the following Boolean functions:

'54 $Y = \overline{AB + CD + EF + GH}$

LS54 $Y = \overline{AB + CDE + FGH + IJ}$

The SN5454 and the SN54LS54 are characterized for operation over the full military temperature range of −55°C to 125°C. The SN7454 and the SN74LS54 are characterized for operation from 0°C to 70°C.

SN5454 . . . J PACKAGE
SN7454 . . . J OR N PACKAGE

(TOP VIEW)

A	1	14	V_CC
C	2	13	B
D	3	12	NU
E	4	11	NU
F	5	10	H
NC	6	9	G
GND	7	8	Y

SN5454 . . . W PACKAGE

(TOP VIEW)

NU	1	14	H
NU	2	13	G
A	3	12	Y
V_CC	4	11	GND
B	5	10	NC
C	6	9	F
D	7	8	E

logic diagrams

'54

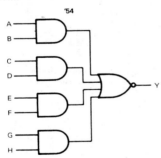

Y

TTL DEVICES

3

TEXAS INSTRUMENTS

logic diagrams (continued)

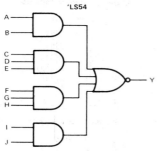

'LS54

schematics

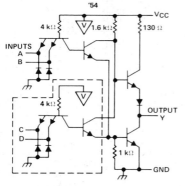

'54

Resistor values shown are nominal.
The portion of the circuits within the dashed lines is repeated for each additional AND section.

SN54LS54 . . . J OR W PACKAGE
SN74LS54 . . . D, J OR N PACKAGE
(TOP VIEW)

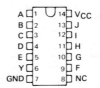

SN54LS54 . . . FK PACKAGE
SN74LS54
(TOP VIEW)

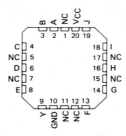

NC - No internal connection
NU - Make no external connection

TEXAS
INSTRUMENTS

schematics (continued)

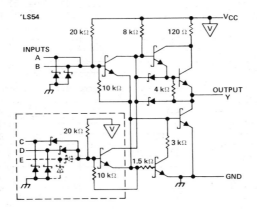

Resistor values shown are nominal.
In 'LS54 circuits, 3-input gate represented by additonal dashed line.
The portion of the circuits within the dashed lines is repeated for each additional AND section.

absolute maximum ratings over operating free-air temperature range (unless otherwise noted)

Supply voltage, V_{CC} (see Note 1): '54, 'LS54 .... 7 V
Input voltage: '54 .... 5.5 V
          'LS54 .... 7 V
Operating free-air temperature range: SN54' .... $-55°C$ to $125°C$
                       SN74' .... $0°C$ to $70°C$
Storage temperature range .... $-65°C$ to $150°C$

NOTE 1: Voltage values are with respect to network ground terminal.

3

TTL DEVICES

recommended operating conditions

		SN5454			SN7454			UNIT
		MIN	NOM	MAX	MIN	NOM	MAX	
V_{CC}	Supply voltage	4.5	5	5.5	4.75	5	5.25	V
V_{IH}	High-level input voltage	2			2			V
V_{IL}	Low-level input voltage			0.8			0.8	V
I_{OH}	High-level output current			−0.4			−0.4	mA
I_{OL}	Low-level output current			16			16	mA
T_A	Operating free-air temperature	−55		125	0		70	°C

electrical characterics over recommended operating free-air temperature range (unless otherwise noted)

PARAMETER	TEST CONDITIONS[†]			SN5454			SN7454			UNIT
				MIN	TYP[‡]	MAX	MIN	TYP[‡]	MAX	
V_{IK}	V_{CC} = MIN,	I_I = −12 mA				−1.5			−1.5	V
V_{OH}	V_{CC} = MIN,	V_{IL} = 0.8 V,	I_{OH} = −0.4 mA	2.4	3.4		2.4	3.4		V
V_{OL}	V_{CC} = MIN,	V_{IH} = 2 V,	I_{OL} = 16 mA		0.2	0.4		0.2	0.4	V
I_I	V_{CC} = MAX,	V_I = 5.5 V				1			1	mA
I_{IH}	V_{CC} = MAX,	V_I = 2.4 V				40			40	µA
I_{IL}	V_{CC} = MAX,	V_I = 0.4 V				−1.6			−1.6	mA
I_{OS}§	V_{CC} = MAX			−20		−55	−18		−55	mA
I_{CCH}	V_{CC} = MAX,	V_I = 0 V			4	8		4	8	mA
I_{CCL}	V_{CC} = MAX,	See Note 2			5.1	9.5		5.1	9.5	mA

† For conditions shown as MIN or MAX, use the appropriate value specified under recommended operating conditions.
‡ All typical values are at V_{CC} = 5 V, T_A = 25°C.
§ Not more than one output should be shorted at a time.
NOTE 2: All inputs of one AND gate at 4.5 V, all others at GND.

switching characteristics, V_{CC} = 5 V, T_A = 25°C (see note 3)

PARAMETER	FROM (INPUT)	TO (OUTPUT)	TEST CONDITIONS		MIN	TYP	MAX	UNIT
t_{PLH}	Any	Y	R_L = 400 Ω,	C_L = 15 pF		13	22	ns
t_{PHL}						8	15	ns

NOTE 3: See General Information Section for load circuits and voltage waveforms.

TEXAS
INSTRUMENTS

recommended operating conditions

		SN54LS54			SN74LS54			UNIT
		MIN	NOM	MAX	MIN	NOM	MAX	
V_{CC}	Supply voltage	4.5	5	5.5	4.75	5	5.25	V
V_{IH}	High-level input voltage	2			2			V
V_{IL}	Low-level input voltage			0.7			0.8	V
I_{OH}	High-level output current			-0.4			-0.4	mA
I_{OL}	Low-level output current			4			8	mA
T_A	Operating free-air temperature	-55		125	0		70	$^\circ$C

electrical characteristics over recommended operating free-air temperature range (unless otherwise noted)

PARAMETER	TEST CONDITIONS[†]			SN54LS54			SN74LS54			UNIT
				MIN	TYP[‡]	MAX	MIN	TYP[‡]	MAX	
V_{IK}	V_{CC} = MIN,	$I_I = -18$ mA				-1.5			-1.5	V
V_{OH}	V_{CC} = MIN,	V_{IL} = MAX,	$I_{OH} = -0.4$ mA	2.5	3.4		2.7	3.4		V
V_{OL}	V_{CC} = MIN,	V_{IH} = 2 V,	I_{OL} = 4 mA		0.25	0.4		0.25	0.4	V
	V_{CC} = MIN,	V_{IH} = 2 V,	I_{OL} = 8 mA					0.35	0.5	
I_I	V_{CC} = MAX,	V_I = 7 V				0.1			0.1	mA
I_{IH}	V_{CC} = MAX,	V_I = 2.7 V				20			20	μA
I_{IL}	V_{CC} = MAX,	V_I = 0.4 V				-0.4			-0.4	mA
I_{OS}§	V_{CC} = MAX			-20		-100	-20		-100	mA
I_{CCH}	V_{CC} = MAX,	V_I = 0 V			0.8	1.6		0.8	1.6	mA
I_{CCL}	V_{CC} = MAX,	See Note 2			1	2		1	2	mA

[†] For conditions shown as MIN or MAX, use the appropriate value specified under recommended operating conditions.
[‡] All typical values are at V_{CC} = 5 V, T_A = 25°C.
§Not more than one output should be shorted at a time, and the duration of the short-circuit should not exceed one second.
NOTE 2: All inputs of one AND gate at 4.5 V, all others at GND.

switching characteristics, V_{CC} = 5 V, T_A = 25°C (see note 3)

PARAMETER	FROM (INPUT)	TO (OUTPUT)	TEST CONDITIONS		MIN	TYP	MAX	UNIT
t_{PLH}	Any	Y	$R_L = 2$ kΩ,	C_L = 15 pF		12	20	ns
t_{PHL}						12.5	20	ns

NOTE 3: See General Information Section for load circuits and voltage waveforms.

- **Package Options Include Both Plastic and Ceramic Chip Carriers in Addition to Plastic and Ceramic DIPs**

- **Dependable Texas Instruments Quality and Reliability**

description

These devices contain 2-wide 4-input AND-OR-INVERT gates. 'LS55 perform the Boolean function Y = ABCD + EFGH.

The SN54LS55 is characterized for operation over the full military temperature range of −55°C to 125°C. The SN74LS55 is characterized for operation from 0°C to 70°C.

logic diagram

'L55, 'LS55

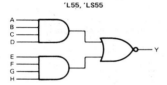

SN54LS55 . . . J OR W PACKAGE
SN74LS55 . . . D, J OR N PACKAGE
(TOP VIEW)

SN54LS55 . . . FK PACKAGE
SN74LS55
(TOP VIEW)

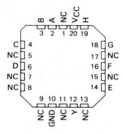

NC - No internal connection

3

TTL DEVICES

schematic

'LS55

Resistor values shown are nominal.

absolute maximum ratings over operating free-air temperature range (unless otherwise noted)

Supply voltage, V_{CC} (see Note 1)... 7 V
Input voltage: 'H55, 'L55 .... 5.5 V
             'LS55 .... 7 V
Operating free-air temperature range: SN54', ... $-55°C$ to $125°C$
                              SN74' .... $0°C$ to $70°C$
Storage temperature range .... $-65°C$ to $150°C$

NOTE 1: Voltage values are with respect to network ground terminal.

3

TTL DEVICES

TEXAS
INSTRUMENTS

recommended operating conditions

		SN54LS55			SN74LS55			UNIT
		MIN	NOM	MAX	MIN	NOM	MAX	
V_{CC}	Supply voltage	4.5	5	5.5	4.75	5	5.25	V
V_{IH}	High-level input voltage	2			2			V
V_{IL}	Low-level input voltage			0.7			0.8	V
I_{OH}	High-level output current			− 0.4			− 0.4	mA
I_{OL}	Low-level output current			4			8	mA
T_A	Operating free-air temperature	− 55		125	0		70	°C

electrical characteristics over recommended operating free-air temperature range (unless otherwise noted)

PARAMETER	TEST CONDITIONS[†]			SN54LS55			SN74LS55			UNIT
				MIN	TYP‡	MAX	MIN	TYP‡	MAX	
V_{IK}	V_{CC} = MIN,	I_I = − 18 mA				− 1.5			− 1.5	V
V_{OH}	V_{CC} = MIN,	V_{IL} = MAX,	I_{OH} = − 0.4 mA	2.5	3.4		2.7	3.4		V
V_{OL}	V_{CC} = MIN,	V_{IH} = 2 V,	I_{OL} = 4 mA		0.25	0.4		0.25	0.4	V
	V_{CC} = MIN,	V_{IH} = 2 V,	I_{OL} = 8 mA					0.35	0.5	
I_I	V_{CC} = MAX,	V_I = 7 V				0.1			0.1	mA
I_{IH}	V_{CC} = MAX,	V_I = 2.7 V				20			20	µA
I_{IL}	V_{CC} = MAX,	V_I = 0.4 V				− 0.4			− 0.4	mA
I_{OS}§	V_{CC} = MAX			− 20		− 100	− 20		− 100	mA
I_{CCH}	V_{CC} = MAX,	V_I = 0 V			0.4	0.8		0.4	0.8	mA
I_{CCL}	V_{CC} = MAX,	See Note 2			0.7	1.3		0.7	1.3	mA

† For conditions shown as MIN or MAX, use the appropriate value specified under recommended operating conditions.
‡ All typical values are at V_{CC} = 5 V, T_A = 25°C.
§ Not more than one output should be shorted at a time, and the duration of the short-circuit should not exceed one second.
NOTE 2: All outputs of one AND gate at 4.5 V, all others at GND.

switching characteristics, V_{CC} = 5 V, T_A = 25°C (see note 3)

PARAMETER	FROM (INPUT)	TO (OUTPUT)	TEST CONDITIONS		MIN	TYP	MAX	UNIT
t_{PLH}	Any	Y	R_L = 2 kΩ,	C_L = 15 pF		12	20	ns
t_{PHL}						12.5	20	ns

NOTE 3: See General Information Section for load circuits and voltage waveforms.

3

TTL DEVICES

REVISED DECEMBER 1983

- **'LS56 Performs 50 to 1 Frequency Division (5 to 1, 5 to 1, and 10 to 1)**

- **'LS57 Performs 60 to 1 Frequency Division (6 to 1, 5 to 1, and 10 to 1)**

- **Available in P or JG package (two P or JG Packages Fit in a Single 16-pin Socket)**

- **Maximum Clock Frequency 25 MHz Typical**

SN54LS56, SN54LS57 . . . JG PACKAGE
SN74LS56, SN74LS57 . . . JG OR P PACKAGE

(TOP VIEW)

```
CLKB [ 1    8 ] Q_C
V_CC [ 2    7 ] Q_B
 Q_A [ 3    6 ] CLR
 GND [ 4    5 ] CLKA
```

FOR CHIP CARRIER INFORMATION, CONTACT THE FACTORY.

description

These frequency dividers are particularly useful in generating one second or one hour timing pulses from 50 Hz (European standard frequency) or 60 Hz (United States standard frequency). 50 to 1 frequency division is accomplished in the 'LS56 by connecting output Q_A to input CLKB. 60 to 1 frequency division in the 'LS57 is accomplished in the same way. More universal capabilities are evidenced by the 25 MHz typical f_{max} and the almost limitless frequency division possibilities when used in cascade. Two 'LS56 packages may be interconnected to give frequency division of 2500 to 1, 625 to 1, 100 to 1, etc. Two 'LS57 packages can be connected to generate frequency divisions of 3600 to 1, 1800 to 1, 900 to 1 etc.

The 'LS56 and 'LS57 frequency dividers consist of three separate counters, A, B, and C on a single monolithic substrate. The A counter divides by 5 to 1 in the 'LS56 and by 6 to 1 in the 'LS57. The B counter divides by 5 to 1 in both devices and is internally tied to the C counter which divides by 2 to 1. The resulting C counter output is 10 to 1. Both the 'LS56 and 'LS57 feature a clear pin which is common to all three counters, A, B, and C. When the clear pin is low, the counters are enabled. When the clear is high, the counters are disabled and their outputs are set to a low-level.

All three counters, A, B, and C trigger on the high-to-low transition of the clock input. All output waveforms are symmetrical except for the 5 to 1 outputs (A and B of the 'LS56 and B of the 'LS57). See the output waveform drawings below.

input and output waveforms

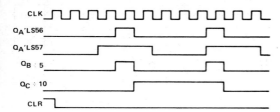

logic diagram

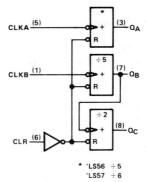

```
* 'LS56  ÷5
  'LS57  ÷6
```

PRODUCTION DATA
This document contains information current as of publication date. Products conform to these specifications per the terms of Texas Instruments standard warranty. Production processing does not necessarily include testing of all parameters.

TEXAS
INSTRUMENTS

schematics of inputs and outputs

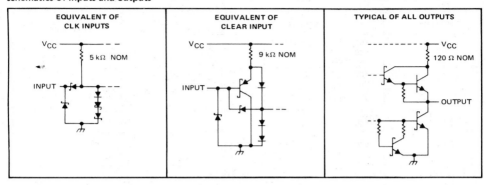

| EQUIVALENT OF CLK INPUTS | EQUIVALENT OF CLEAR INPUT | TYPICAL OF ALL OUTPUTS |

absolute maximum ratings over operating free-air temperature range (unless otherwise noted)

Supply voltage, V_{CC} (see Note 1) . . . . 7 V

Input voltage: CLR . . . . 7 V

CLKA, CLKB . . . . 5.5 V

Operating free-air temperature range: SN54LS′ . . . . −55°C to 125°C

SN74LS′ . . . . −0°C to 70°C

Storage temperature range . . . . −65°C to 150°C

NOTE 1: Voltage values are with respect to network ground terminal.

recommended operating conditions

		SN54LS′			SN74LS′			UNIT
		MIN	NOM	MAX	MIN	NOM	MAX	
V_{CC}	Supply voltage	4.5	5	5.5	4.75	5	5.25	V
V_{IH}	High-level input voltage	2			2			V
V_{IL}	Low-level input voltage			0.7			0.8	V
I_{OH}	High-level output current			−1			−1	mA
I_{OL}	Low-level output current			8			16	mA
f_{clock}	Clock frequency	0		15	0		15	MHz
t_r, t_f	Rise and fall time of clock			50			50	ns
t_w	Pulse width of clock or clear	30			30			ns
t_{su}	Clear inactive state set-up time	25			25			ns
T_A	Operating free-air temperature	−55		125	0		70	°C

3

TTL DEVICES

TEXAS INSTRUMENTS

electrical characteristics over recommended operating free-air temperature range (unless otherwise noted)

PARAMETER		TEST CONDITIONS†			SN54LS' MIN	TYP‡	MAX	SN74LS' MIN	TYP‡	MAX	UNIT
V_{IK}		V_{CC} = MIN,	I_I = -18 mA				-1.5			-1.5	V
V_{OH}		V_{CC} = MIN, V_{IH} = 2 V, V_{IL} = MAX	I_{OH} = -1 mA		2.5	3.4		2.7	3.4		V
V_{OL}		V_{CC} = MIN, V_{IH} = 2 V, V_{IL} = MAX	I_{OL} = 8 mA			0.25	0.4		0.25	0.4	V
			I_{OL} = 16 mA						0.35	0.5	
I_I	CLKA, CLKB	V_{CC} = MAX	V_I = 5.5 V				0.2			0.2	mA
	CLR		V_I = 7 V				0.1			0.1	
I_{IH}	CLKA, CLKB	V_{CC} = MAX, V_I = 2.7 V					80			80	µA
	CLR						20			20	
I_{IL}	CLKA, CLKB	V_{CC} = MAX, CLR = 0 V,	V_I = 0.4 V				-3.2			-3.2	mA
	CLR						-0.2			-0.2	
I_{OS}§		V_{CC} = MAX, CLR = 0 V,	V_O = 0 V		-20		-100	-20		-100	mA
I_{CC}		V_{CC} = MAX, See Note 2				17	30		17	30	mA

† For conditions shown as MIN or MAX, use the appropriate value specified under recommended operating conditions.
‡ All typical values are at V_{CC} = 5 V, T_A = 25°C.
§ Not more than one output should be shorted at a time and the duration of the short-circuit should not exceed one second.
NOTE 2: I_{CC} is measured by applying 4.5 V to the CLR pin with all other inputs grounded and the outputs open.

switching characteristics, V_{CC} = 5 V, T_A = 25°C (see note 3)

PARAMETER	FROM (INPUT)	TO (OUTPUT)	TEST CONDITIONS	'LS56 MIN	TYP	MAX	'LS57 MIN	TYP	MAX	UNIT
f_{max}	CLKA	Q_A		15	25		15	25		MHz
f_{max}	CLKB	Q_B, Q_C		15	25		15	25		MHz
t_{PLH}	CLKB	Q_B			8	15		8	15	ns
t_{PHL}					14	25		14	25	ns
t_{PLH}*	CLKB	Q_C	R_L = 1 kΩ, C_L = 30 pF		18	30		18	30	ns
t_{PHL}*					24	35		24	35	ns
t_{PLH}	CLKA	Q_A			12	20		14	25	ns
t_{PHL}					14	25		18	30	ns
t_{PHL}	CLR	Q_A			17	30		17	30	ns
t_{PHL}	CLR	Q_B			17	30		17	30	ns
t_{PHL}	CLR	Q_C			17	30		17	30	ns

* Times measured from CLKB to output Q_C are taken with output Q_B unloaded.
NOTE 3: See General Information Section for load circuits and voltage waveforms.

TEXAS
INSTRUMENTS

- **Package Options Include Both Plastic and Ceramic Chip Carriers in Addition to Plastic and Ceramic DIPs**

- **Dependable Texas Instruments Quality and Reliability**

description

These devices contain 4-2-3-2 input AND-OR-INVERT gates. They perform the Boolean function $Y = \overline{ABCD + EF + GHI + JK}$. The 'S64 has totem-pole outputs and the 'S65 has open-collector outputs.

The SN54S64 and the SN54S65 are characterized for operation over the full military temperature range of −55 °C to 125 °C. The SN74S64 and the SN74S65 are characterized for operation from 0 °C to 70 °C.

logic diagram (each device)

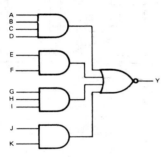

SN54S64, SN54S65 . . . J OR W PACKAGE
SN74S64, SN74S65 . . . D, J OR N PACKAGE
(TOP VIEW)

SN54S64, SN54S65 . . . FK PACKAGE
SN74S64, SN74S65
(TOP VIEW)

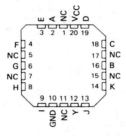

NC - No internal connection

TEXAS
INSTRUMENTS

3

TTL DEVICES

schematics (each gate)

'S64

'S65

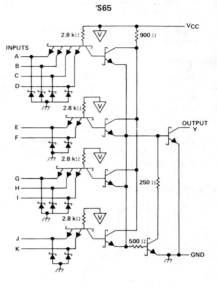

Resistor values shown are nominal and in ohms.

absolute maximum ratings over operating free-air temperature range (unless otherwise noted)

Supply voltage, V_{CC} (see Note 1)	7 V
Input voltage	5.5 V
Off-state output voltage, 'S65	7 V
Operating free-air temperature range: SN54'	−55°C to 125°C
SN74'	0°C to 70°C
Storage temperature range	−65°C to 150°C

NOTE 1: Voltage values are with respect to network ground terminal.

TEXAS
INSTRUMENTS

recommended operating conditions

		SN54S64			SN74S64			UNIT
		MIN	NOM	MAX	MIN	NOM	MAX	
V_{CC}	Supply voltage	4.5	5	5.5	4.75	5	5.25	V
V_{IH}	High-level input voltage	2			2			V
V_{IL}	Low-level input voltage			0.8			0.8	V
I_{OH}	High-level output current			−1			−1	mA
I_{OL}	Low-level output current			20			20	mA
T_A	Operating free-air temperature	−55		125	0		70	°C

electrical characteristics over recommended operating free-air temperature range (unless otherwise noted)

PARAMETER	TEST CONDITIONS †			SN54S64			SN74S64			UNIT
				MIN	TYP‡	MAX	MIN	TYP‡	MAX	
V_{IK}	V_{CC} = MIN,	I_I = −18 mA				−1.2			−1.2	V
V_{OH}	V_{CC} = MIN,	V_{IL} = 0.8 V,	I_{OH} = −1 mA	2.5	3.4		2.7	3.4		V
V_{OL}	V_{CC} = MIN,	V_{IH} = 2 V,	I_{OL} = 20 mA			0.5			0.5	V
I_I	V_{CC} = MAX,	V_I = 5.5 V				1			1	mA
I_{IH}	V_{CC} = MAX,	V_I = 2.7 V				50			50	µA
I_{IL}	V_{CC} = MAX,	V_I = 0.5 V				−2			−2	mA
I_{OS}§	V_{CC} = MAX			−40		−100	−40		−100	mA
I_{CCH}	V_{CC} = MAX,	V_I = 0 V			7	12.5		7	12.5	mA
I_{CCL}	V_{CC} = MAX,	V_I = 4.5 V			8.5	16		8.5	16	mA

† For conditions shown as MIN or MAX, use the appropriate value specified under recommended operating conditions.
‡ All typical values are at V_{CC} = 5 V, T_A = 25°C.
§ Not more than one output should be shorted at a time, and the duration of the short-circuit should not exceed one second.

switching characteristics, V_{CC} = 5 V, T_A = 25°C (see note 2)

PARAMETER	FROM (INPUT)	TO (OUTPUT)	TEST CONDITIONS		MIN	TYP	MAX	UNIT
t_{PLH}	Any	Y	R_L = 280 Ω,	C_L = 15 pF		3.5	5.5	ns
t_{PHL}						3.5	5.5	ns
t_{PLH}			R_L = 280 Ω,	C_L = 50 pF		5		ns
t_{PHL}						5.5		ns

NOTE 2: See General Information Section for load circuits and voltage waveforms.

TYPES SN54S65, SN74S65
4-2-3-2 INPUT AND-OR-INVERT GATES

recommended operating conditions

		SN54S65			SN74S65			UNIT
		MIN	NOM	MAX	MIN	NOM	MAX	
V_{CC}	Supply voltage	4.5	5	5.5	4.75	5	5.25	V
V_{IH}	High-level input voltage	2			2			V
V_{IL}	Low-level input voltage			0.8			0.8	V
V_{OH}	High-level output voltage			5.5			5.5	V
I_{OL}	Low-level output current			20			20	mA
T_A	Operating free-air temperature	−55		125	0		70	°C

electrical characteristics over operating free-air temperature range (unless otherwise noted)

PARAMETER	TEST CONDITIONS †		MIN	TYP‡	MAX	UNIT
V_{IK}	V_{CC} = MIN,	$I_I = -18$ mA			−1.2	V
I_{OH}	V_{CC} = MIN,	V_{IL} = 0.8 V, V_{OH} = 5.5 V			0.25	mA
V_{OL}	V_{CC} = MIN,	V_{IH} = 2 V, I_{OL} = 20 mA			0.5	V
I_I	V_{CC} = MAX,	V_I = 5.5 V			1	mA
I_{IH}	V_{CC} = MAX,	V_I = 2.7 V			50	µA
I_{IL}	V_{CC} = MAX,	V_I = 0.5 V			−2	mA
I_{CCH}	V_{CC} = MAX,	V_I = 0 V		6	11	mA
I_{CCL}	V_{CC} = MAX,	V_I = 4.5 V		8.5	16	mA

† For conditions shown as MIN or MAX, use the appropriate value specified under recommended operating conditions.
‡ All typical values are at V_{CC} = 5 V, T_A = 25°C.

switching characteristics, V_{CC} = 5 V, T_A = 25°C (see note 2)

PARAMETER	FROM (INPUT)	TO (OUTPUT)	TEST CONDITIONS		MIN	TYP	MAX	UNIT
t_{PLH}	Any	Y	R_L = 280 Ω,	C_L = 15 pF	2	5	7.5	ns
t_{PHL}					2	5.5	8.5	ns
t_{PLH}			R_L = 280 Ω,	C_L = 50 pF		8		ns
t_{PHL}						6.5		ns

NOTE 2: See General Information Section for load circuits and voltage waveforms.

3

TTL DEVICES

TEXAS
INSTRUMENTS

- Heavy Duty Outputs I_{OL} Rated at 8mA/16 mA
- Counter One of Either 'LS68 or 'LS69 Has Individual Clicks for the A Flip-Flop
- Direct Clear for Each 4-Bit Counter
- Guaranteed Maximum Count Frequency is 50 MHz for 'LS69 and 40 MHz for 'LS68

description

Each of the 'LS68 and 'LS69 circuits contain two four-bit counters. The 'LS68 is a dual decade counter, while the 'LS69 is a dual binary counter. Counter number one of both the 'LS68 and 'LS69 has two clock pins. Clock 1 is for the A flip-flop, while clock 2 is for the B, C, D flip-flops. Counter one of the 'LS68 can perform bi-quinary counting. All $1Q_A$ outputs are rated with sufficient I_{OL} to drive clock 2 while maintaining a full fan-out.

All clocks trigger on the high-to-low transition of the clock pulse. All counters have direct overriding clear pins which, when low, reset Q_A, Q_B, Q_C, and Q_D low regardless of the state of the clock.

The SN54LS68 and SN54LS69 circuits are characterized for operation over the full military temperature range of $-55\,°C$ to $125\,°C$. The SN74LS68 and SN74LS69 circuits are characterized for operation from $0\,°C$ to $70\,°C$

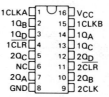

SN54LS68, SN54LS69 . . . J PACKAGE
SN74LS68, SN74LS69 . . . D, J OR N PACKAGE
(TOP VIEW)

1CLKA	1	16	V_{CC}
$1Q_B$	2	15	1CLKB
$1Q_D$	3	14	$1Q_A$
1CLR	4	13	$1Q_C$
$2Q_C$	5	12	$2Q_D$
NC	6	11	2CLR
$2Q_A$	7	10	$2Q_B$
GND	8	9	2CLK

SN54LS68, SN54LS69 . . . FK PACKAGE
SN74LS68, SN74LS69
(TOP VIEW)

Pins (top): $1Q_B$, 1CLKA, NC, V_{CC}, 1CLKB — 3 2 1 20 19

$1Q_D$	4	18	$1Q_A$
1CLR	5	17	$1Q_C$
NC	6	16	NC
$2Q_C$	7	15	$2Q_D$
NC	8	14	2CLR

Pins (bottom): 9 10 11 12 13 — $2Q_A$, GND, NC, 2CLK, $2Q_B$

NC – No internal connection

3

TTL DEVICES

TEXAS
INSTRUMENTS

TYPES SN54LS68, SN54LS69, SN74LS68, SN74LS69
DUAL 4-BIT DECADE OR BINARY COUNTERS

count sequence tables

'LS68 DECADE COUNTER
BCD COUNT SEQUENCE
(See Note 1)
Applies to Counters 1 & 2

COUNT	OUTPUT			
	Q_D	Q_C	Q_B	Q_A
0	L	L	L	L
1	L	L	L	H
2	L	L	H	L
3	L	L	H	H
4	L	H	L	L
5	L	H	L	H
6	L	H	H	L
7	L	H	H	H
8	H	L	L	L
9	H	L	L	H

'LS68 DECADE COUNTER
BI-QUINARY SEQUENCE
(See Note 2)
Applies to Counter 1 only

COUNT	OUTPUT			
	Q_A	Q_D	Q_C	Q_B
0	L	L	L	L
1	L	L	L	H
2	L	L	H	L
3	L	L	H	H
4	L	H	L	L
5	H	L	L	L
6	H	L	L	H
7	H	L	H	L
8	H	L	H	H
9	H	H	L	L

'LS69 BINARY COUNTER
BCD COUNT SEQUENCE
(See Note 3)
Applies to Counters 1 & 2

COUNT	OUTPUT			
	Q_D	Q_C	Q_B	Q_A
0	L	L	L	L
1	L	L	L	H
2	L	L	H	L
3	L	L	H	H
4	L	H	L	L
5	L	H	L	H
6	L	H	H	L
7	L	H	H	H
8	H	L	L	L
9	H	L	L	H
10	H	L	H	L
11	H	L	H	H
12	H	H	L	L
13	H	H	L	H
14	H	H	H	L
15	H	H	H	H

NOTES: 1. Output $1Q_A$ is connected to 1CLK2 for BCD count.
2. Output $1Q_A$ is connected to 1CLK1 for bi-quinary count.
3. Output $1Q_A$ is connected to 1CLK2 for binary count.

schematics of inputs and outputs

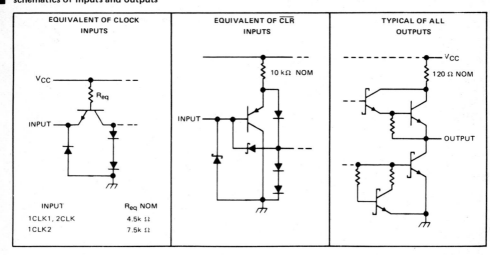

EQUIVALENT OF CLOCK INPUTS		EQUIVALENT OF $\overline{CLR}$ INPUTS	TYPICAL OF ALL OUTPUTS

INPUT	R_{eq} NOM
1CLK1, 2CLK	4.5k Ω
1CLK2	7.5k Ω

TEXAS
INSTRUMENTS

logic diagrams

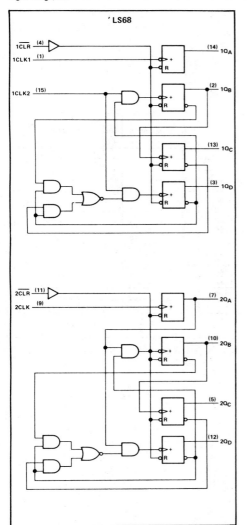

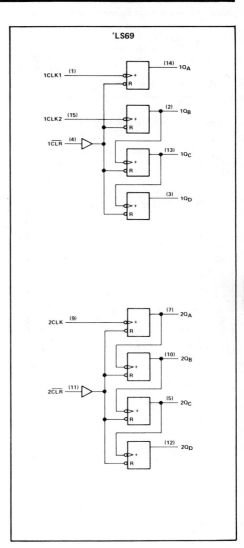

Pin numbers shown on logic notation are for D, J or N packages.

3

TTL DEVICES

absolute maximum ratings over operating free-air temperature range (unless otherwise noted)

Supply voltage, V_{CC} (see Note 4) . . . . 7 V
Input voltage: Clear inputs . . . . 7 V
             Clock inputs . . . . 5.5 V
Operating free-air temperature range: SN54LS' . . . . $-55°C$ to $125°C$
                                  SN74LS' . . . . $0°C$ to $70°C$
Storage temperature range . . . . $-65°C$ to $150°C$

NOTE 4: Voltage values are with respect to network ground terminal.

recommended operating conditions

				SN54LS'			SN74LS'			UNIT
				MIN	NOM	MAX	MIN	NOM	MAX	
V_{CC}	Supply voltage			4.5	5	5.5	4.75	5	5.25	V
V_{IH}	High-level input voltage			2			2			V
V_{IL}	Low-level input voltage					0.7			0.8	V
I_{OH}	High-level output current					-1			-1	mA
I_{OL}	Low-level output current					8			16	mA
f_{max}	Clock frequency	1CLK1		0		50	0		50	MHz
		1CLK2	'LS68	0		20	0		20	
			'LS69	0		25	0		25	
		2CLK	'LS68	0		40	0		40	
			'LS69	0		50	0		50	
t_w	Pulse width	1CLK1		10			10			ns
		1CLK2	'LS68	25			25			
			'LS69	20			20			
		2CLK	'LS68	13			13			
			'LS69	10			10			
		CLEAR		15			15			
t_{su}	Clear inactive-state set-up time			25			25			ns
T_A	Operating free-air temperature			-55		125	0		70	$°C$

3

TTL DEVICES

electrical characteristics over recommended operating free-air temperature range (unless otherwise noted)

PARAMETER		TEST CONDITIONS†			SN54LS'			SN74LS'			UNIT
					MIN	TYP‡	MAX	MIN	TYP‡	MAX	
V_{IK}		V_{CC} = MIN,	I_I = −18 mA				−1.5			−1.5	V
V_{OH}		V_{CC} = MIN, V_{IH} = 2 V, V_{IL} = MAX		I_{OH} = −1 mA	2.5	3.4		2.7	3.4		V
V_{OL}		V_{CC} = MIN, V_{IH} = 2 V, V_{IL} = MAX		I_{OL} = 8 mA		0.25	0.4		0.25	0.4	V
				I_{OL} = 16 mA					0.35	0.5	
I_I	CLK	V_{CC} = MAX,	V_I = 5.5 V				0.1			0.1	mA
	$\overline{CLR}$	V_{CC} = MAX,	V_I = 7 V				0.1			0.1	
I_{IH}	CLK	V_{CC} = MAX,	V_I = 2.7 V				40			40	µA
	$\overline{CLR}$						20			20	
I_{IL}	1CLK1, 2CLK	V_{CC} = MAX,	V_I = 0.4 V				−2			−2	mA
	1CLK2						−1.2			−1.2	
	$\overline{CLR}$						−0.2			−0.2	
I_{OS}§		V_{CC} = MAX,	V_O = 0 V		−20		−100	−20		−100	mA
I_{CC}		V_{CC} = MAX,	see Note 5			36	54		36	54	mA

† For conditions shown as MIN or MAX, use the appropriate value specified under recommended operating conditions.
‡ All typical values are at V_{CC} = 5 V, T_A = 25°C.
§ Not more than one output should be shorted at a time, and duration of the short-circuit should not exceed one second.
NOTE 5: I_{CC} is measured with all inputs grounded and all outputs open.

switching characteristics, V_{CC} = 5 V, T_A = 25°C (see note 6)

PARAMETER	FROM (INPUT)	TO (OUTPUT)	TEST CONDITIONS	'LS68			'LS69			UNIT
				MIN	TYP	MAX	MIN	TYP	MAX	
f_{max}	1CLK1	$1Q_A$		50	70		50	70		MHz
f_{max}		$1Q_B, 1Q_C, 1Q_D$		20	30		25	35		MHz
f_{max}		$2Q_A, 2Q_B, 2Q_C, 2Q_D$		40	60		50	70		MHz
t_{PLH}	1CLK1	$1Q_A$			7	11		7	11	ns
t_{PHL}					14	21		14	21	
t_{PLH}		$1Q_B$			8	12		7	11	
t_{PHL}					12	18		14	21	
t_{PLH}	1CLK2	$1Q_C$			15	23		16	24	ns
t_{PHL}			R_L = 1 kΩ, C_L = 30 pF		21	32		21	32	
t_{PLH}		$1Q_D$			8	12		25	38	
t_{PHL}					13	20		30	45	
t_{PLH}		$2Q_A$			7	11		7	11	
t_{PHL}					14	21		14	21	
t_{PLH}		$2Q_B$			16	24		14	21	
t_{PHL}	2CLK				19	29		19	29	ns
t_{PLH}		$2Q_C$			23	35		23	35	
t_{PHL}					27	40		27	40	
t_{PLH}		$2Q_D$			16	24		32	48	
t_{PHL}					19	29		36	54	
t_{PHL}	Any $\overline{CLR}$	Any Q			20	30		20	30	ns

NOTE 6: See General Information Section for load circuits and voltage waveforms.

3

TTL DEVICES

TTL DEVICES

- **Package Options Include Plastic and Ceramic DIPs**
- **Dependable Texas Instruments Quality and Reliability**

description

These monolithic, edge-triggered J-K flip-flops feature gated inputs, direct clear and preset inputs, and complementary Q and $\overline{Q}$ outputs. Input information is transferred to the outputs on the positive edge of the clock pulse.

Direct-coupled clock triggering occurs at a specific voltage level of the clock pulse, and after the clock input threshold voltage has been passed, the gated inputs are locked out.

These flip-flops are ideally suited for medium-to-high-speed applications and can result in a significant saving in system power dissipation and package count where input gating is required.

The SN5470 is characterized for operation over the full military temperature range of $-55°C$ to $125°C$. The SN7470 is characterized for operation from $0°C$ to $70°C$.

SN5470 . . . J PACKAGE
SN7470 . . . J OR N PACKAGE
(TOP VIEW)

NC	1	14 V_{CC}
$\overline{CLR}$	2	13 $\overline{PRE}$
J1	3	12 CLK
J2	4	11 K2
$\overline{J}$	5	10 K1
$\overline{Q}$	6	9 $\overline{K}$
GND	7	8 Q

SN5470 . . . W PACKAGE
(TOP VIEW)

K1	1	14 K2
CLK	2	13 $\overline{K}$
$\overline{PRE}$	3	12 Q
V_{CC}	4	11 GND
$\overline{CLR}$	5	10 $\overline{Q}$
NC	6	9 $\overline{J}$
J1	7	8 J2

NC - No internal connection

logic symbol

Pin numbers shown are for J and N packages only.

positive logic

$$J = J1 \cdot J2 \cdot \overline{J}$$
$$K = K1 \cdot K2 \cdot \overline{K}$$

FUNCTION TABLE

INPUTS					OUTPUTS	
PRE	CLR	CLK	J	K	Q	$\overline{Q}$
L	H	L	X	X	H	L
H	L	L	X	X	L	H
L	L	X	X	X	L†	L†
H	H	↑	L	L	Q_0	Q_0
H	H	↑	H	L	H	L
H	H	↑	L	H	L	H
H	H	↑	H	H	TOGGLE	
H	H	L	X	X	Q_0	Q_0

If inputs J and K are not used, they must be grounded. Preset or clear function can occur only when the clock input is low.
†This configuration is nonstable; that is, it will not persist when preset and clear inputs return to their inactive (high) level.

TEXAS INSTRUMENTS

3
TTL DEVICES

logic diagram

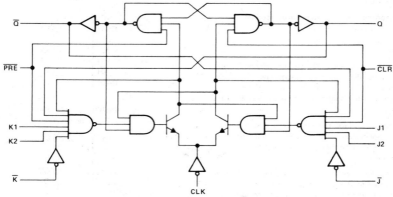

'70-GATED J-K WITH CLEAR AND PRESET

schematics of input and outputs

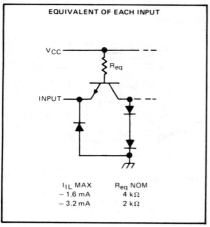

EQUIVALENT OF EACH INPUT

I_{IL} MAX	R_{eq} NOM
−1.6 mA	4 kΩ
−3.2 mA	2 kΩ

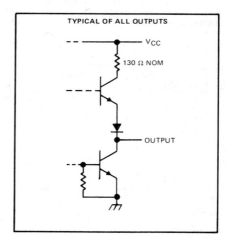

TYPICAL OF ALL OUTPUTS

130 Ω NOM

**TEXAS
INSTRUMENTS**

absolute maximum ratings over operating free-air temperature range (unless otherwise noted)

Supply voltage, V_{CC} (see Note 1) . . . . .7 V

Input voltage . . . . 5.5 V

Operating free-air temperature: SN5470 . . . . -55°C to 125°C

SN7470 . . . . 0°C to 70°C

Storage temperature range . . . . -65°C to 150°C

NOTE 1: All voltage values are with respect to network ground terminal.

recommended operating conditions

			SN5470			SN7470			UNIT
			MIN	NOM	MAX	MIN	NOM	MAX	
V_{CC}	Supply voltage		4.5	5	5.5	4.75	5	5.25	V
V_{IH}	High-level input voltage		2			2			V
V_{IL}	Low-level input voltage				0.8			0.8	V
I_{OH}	High-level output current				-0.4			-0.4	mA
I_{OL}	Low-level output current				16			16	mA
t_w	Pulse duration	CLK high	20			20			ns
		CLK low	30			30			
		$\overline{PRE}$ or $\overline{CLR}$ low	25			25			
t_{su}	Setup time before CLK ↑		20			20			ns
t_h	Hold time-Data after CLK↑		5			5			ns
T_A	Operating free-air temperature		-55		125	0		70	$^{\circ}$C

↑↓ The arrow indicates the edge of the clock pulse used for reference: ↑ for the rising edge, ↓ for the falling edge.

electrical characteristics over recommended operating free-air temperature range (unless otherwise noted)

PARAMETER		TEST CONDITIONS†	SN5470			SN7470			UNIT
			MIN	TYP‡	MAX	MIN	TYP‡	MAX	
V_{IK}		V_{CC} = MIN, I_I = -12 mA			-1.5			-1.5	V
V_{OH}		V_{CC} = MIN, V_{IH} = 2 V, V_{IL} = 0.8 V, I_{OH} = -0.4 mA	2.4	3.4		2.4	3.4		V
V_{OL}		V_{CC} = MIN, V_{IH} = 2 V, V_{IL} = 0.8 V, I_{OL} = 16 mA		0.2	0.4		0.2	0.4	V
I_I		V_{CC} = MAX, V_I = 5.5 V			1			1	mA
I_{IH}	$\overline{PRE}$ or $\overline{CLR}$	V_{CC} = MAX, V_I = 2.4 V			80			80	μA
	All other				40			40	
I_{IL}	$\overline{PRE}$ or $\overline{CLR}$★	V_{CC} = MAX, V_I = 0.4 V			-3.2			-3.2	mA
	All other				-1.6			-1.6	
I_{OS}§		V_{CC} = MAX	-20		-57	-18		-57	mA
I_{CC}		V_{CC} = MAX, See Note 2		13	26		13	26	mA

† For conditions shown as MIN or MAX, use the appropriate value specified under recommended operating conditions.

‡ All typical values are at V_{CC} = 5 V, T_A = 25°C.

§ Not more than one output should be shorted at a time.

★ Clear is tested with preset high and preset is tested with clear high.

NOTE 2: With all outputs open, I_{CC} is measured with the Q and $\overline{Q}$ outputs high in turn. At the time of measurement, the clock input is at 4.5 V.

3

TTL DEVICES

TEXAS
INSTRUMENTS

switching characteristics, V_{CC} = 5 V, T_A = 25°C (see note 3)

PARAMETER¶	FROM (INPUT)	TO (OUTPUT)	TEST CONDITIONS	MIN	TYP	MAX	UNIT
f_{max}				20	35		MHz
t_{PLH}	$\overline{PRE}$ or $\overline{CLR}$	Q or $\overline{Q}$				50	ns
t_{PHL}			R_L = 400 Ω, $\quad$ C_L = 15 pF			50	ns
t_{PLH}	CLK	Q or $\overline{Q}$			27	50	ns
t_{PHL}					18	50	ns

¶ f_{max} maximum clock frequency; t_{PLH} = propagation delay time, low-to-high level output;
t_{PHL} propagation delay time, high-to-low level output.
NOTE 3: See General Information Section for load circuits and voltage waveforms.

TEXAS
INSTRUMENTS

- **Package Options Include Plastic and Ceramic DIPs**
- **Dependable Texas Instruments Quality and Reliability**

description

These J-K flip-flops are based on the master-slave principle and each has AND gate inputs for entry into the master section which are controlled by the clock pulse. The clock pulse also regulates the state of the coupling transistors which connect the master and slave sections. The sequence of operation is as follows:

1. Isolate slave from master
2. Enter information from AND gate inputs to master
3. Disable AND gate inputs
4. Transfer information from master to slave

Logical state of J and K inputs must not be allowed to change when the clock pulse is in a high state.

The SN5472 is characterized for operation over the full military temperature range of −55°C to 125°C. The SN7472 is characterized for operation from 0°C to 70°C.

SN5472 . . . J PACKAGE
SN7472 . . . J OR N PACKAGE
(TOP VIEW)

NC	1	14	V_CC
CLR	2	13	PRE
J1	3	12	CLK
J2	4	11	K3
J3	5	10	K2
Q	6	9	K1
GND	7	8	Q

SN5472 . . . W PACKAGE
(TOP VIEW)

K1	1	14	K3
CLK	2	13	K2
PRE	3	12	Q
V_CC	4	11	GND
CLR	5	10	Q
NC	6	9	J3
J1	7	8	J2

NC - No internal connection

logic symbol

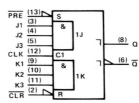

PRE (13)	S
J1 (3)	&
J2 (4)	1J
J3 (5)	
CLK (12)	C1
K1 (9)	&
K2 (10)	1K
K3 (11)	
CLR (2)	R

(8) Q
(6) Q̄

Pin numbers shown are for J and N packages.

positive logic

$$J = J1 \cdot J2 \cdot J3$$
$$K = K1 \cdot K2 \cdot K3$$

FUNCTION TABLE

INPUTS					OUTPUTS	
PRE	CLR	CLK	J	K	Q	Q̄
L	H	X	X	X	H	L
H	L	X	X	X	L	H
L	L	X	X	X	H†	H†
H	H	⊓	L	L	Q_0	$\overline{Q}_0$
H	H	⊓	H	L	H	L
H	H	⊓	L	H	L	H
H	H	⊓	H	H	TOGGLE	

† This configuration is nonstable; that is, it will not persist when either preset or clear returns to its inactive (high) level.

TEXAS INSTRUMENTS

3

TTL DEVICES

logic diagram
'72

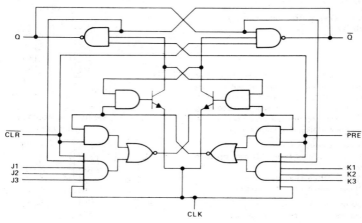

TEXAS
INSTRUMENTS

schematics of inputs and outputs

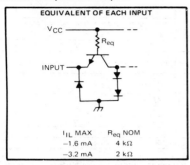

'72

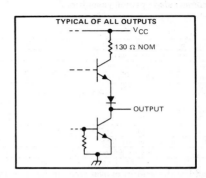

absolute maximum ratings over operating free-air temperature range (unless otherwise noted)

Supply voltage, V_{CC} (see Note 1) .... 7 V

Input voltage .... 5.5 V

Operating free-air temperature: SN54′ .... $-55°C$ to $125°C$

SN74′ .... $0°C$ to $70°C$

Storage temperature range .... $-65°C$ to $150°C$

NOTE 1: Voltage values are with respect to network ground terminal.

TTL DEVICES

3

recommended operating conditions

			SN5472			SN7472			UNIT
			MIN	NOM	MAX	MIN	NOM	MAX	
V_{CC}	Supply voltage		4.5	5	5.5	4.75	5	5.25	V
V_{IH}	High-level input voltage		2			2			V
V_{IL}	Low-level input voltage				0.8			0.8	V
I_{OH}	High-level output current				−0.4			−0.4	mA
I_{OL}	Low-level output current				16			16	mA
t_w	Pulse duration	CLK high	20			20			ns
		CLK low	47			47			
		PRE or CLR	25			25			
t_{su}	Input setup time before CLK ↑		0			0			ns
t_h	Input hold time-data after CLK ↓		0			0			ns
T_A	Operating free-air temperature		−55		125	0		70	°C

electrical characteristics over recommended operating free-air temperature range (unless otherwise noted)

PARAMETER		TEST CONDITIONS †	SN5472			SN7472			UNIT
			MIN	TYP‡	MAX	MIN	TYP‡	MAX	
V_{IK}		V_{CC} = MIN, I_I = −12 mA			−1.5			−1.5	V
V_{OH}		V_{CC} = MIN, V_{IH} = 2 V, V_{IL} = 0.8 V, I_{OH} = −0.4 mA	2.4	3.4		2.4	3.4		V
V_{OL}		V_{CC} = MIN, V_{IH} = 2 V, V_{IL} = 0.8 V, I_{OL} = 16 mA		0.2	0.4		0.2	0.4	V
I_I		V_{CC} = MAX, V_I = 5.5 V			1			1	mA
I_{IH}	J or K	V_{CC} = MAX, V_I = 2.4 V			40			40	µA
	All other				80			80	
I_{IL}	J or K	V_{CC} = MAX, V_I = 0.4 V			−1.6			−1.6	mA
	All other				−3.2			−3.2	
I_{OS} §		V_{CC} = MAX	−20		−57	−18		−57	mA
I_{CC}		V_{CC} = MAX, See Note 2		10	20		10	20	mA

† For conditions shown as MIN or MAX, use the appropriate value specified under recommended operating conditions.
‡ All typical values are at V_{CC} = 5 V, T_A = 25°C.
§ Not more than one output should be shorted at a time.
NOTE 2: With all outputs open, I_{CC} is measured with the Q and $\overline{Q}$ outputs high in turn. At the time of measurement, the clock input is grounded.

switching characteristics, V_{CC} = 5 V, T_A = 25°C (see note 3)

PARAMETER	FROM (INPUT)	TO (OUTPUT)	TEST CONDITIONS	MIN	TYP	MAX	UNIT
f_{max}				15	20		MHz
t_{PLH}	PRE or CLR	Q or $\overline{Q}$	R_L = 400 Ω, C_L = 15 pF		16	25	ns
t_{PHL}					25	40	ns
t_{PLH}	CLK	Q or $\overline{Q}$			16	25	ns
t_{PHL}					25	40	ns

NOTE 3: See General Information Section for load circuits and voltage waveforms.

TEXAS
INSTRUMENTS

- **Package Options Include Plastic and Ceramic DIPs**

- **Dependable Texas Instruments Quality and Reliability**

description

The '73, contain two independent J-K flip-flops with individual J-K, clock, and direct clear inputs. The '73 are positive pulsetriggered flip-flops. J-K input is loaded into the master while the clock is high and transferred to the slave on the high-to-low transition. For these devices the J and K inputs must be stable while the clock is high.

The 'LS73A contain two independent negative-edge-triggered flip-flops. The J and K inputs must be stable one setup time prior to the high-to-low clock transition for predictable operation. When the clear is low, it overrides the clock and data inputs forcing the Q output low and the $\overline{Q}$ output high.

The SN5473 and the SN54LS73A are characterized for operation over the full military temperature range of −55°C to 125°C. The SN7473 and the SN74LS73A are characterized for operation from 0°C to 70°C.

SN5473, SN54LS73A . . . J OR W PACKAGE
SN7473 . . . J OR N PACKAGE
SN74LS73A . . . D, J OR N PACKAGE

(TOP VIEW)

```
         ┌──┬──┐
 1CLK  [1 ∪  14] 1J
 1CLR  [2    13] 1Q
   1K  [3    12] 1Q̄
  Vcc  [4    11] GND
 2CLK  [5    10] 2K
 2CLR  [6     9] 2Q
   2J  [7     8] 2Q̄
         └─────┘
```

'73
FUNCTION TABLE

INPUTS				OUTPUTS	
$\overline{\text{CLR}}$	CLK	J	K	Q	$\overline{Q}$
L	X	X	X	L	H
H	$\sqcap\sqcup$	L	L	Q_0	$\overline{Q}_0$
H	$\sqcap\sqcup$	H	L	H	L
H	$\sqcap\sqcup$	L	H	L	H
H	$\sqcap\sqcup$	H	H	TOGGLE	

'LS73A
FUNCTION TABLE

INPUTS				OUTPUTS	
$\overline{\text{CLR}}$	CLK	J	K	Q	$\overline{Q}$
L	X	X	X	L	H
H	↓	L	L	Q_0	$\overline{Q}_0$
H	↓	H	L	H	L
H	↓	L	H	L	H
H	↓	H	H	TOGGLE	
H	H	X	X	Q_0	Q_0

FOR CHIP CARRIER INFORMATION,
CONTACT THE FACTORY

3

TTL DEVICES

TEXAS
INSTRUMENTS

TYPES SN5473, SN54LS73A
SN7473, SN74LS73A
DUAL J-K FLIP-FLOPS WITH CLEAR

logic symbols

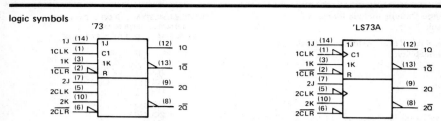

Pin numbers shown on logic notation are for D, J or N packages.

schematics of inputs and outputs

'73

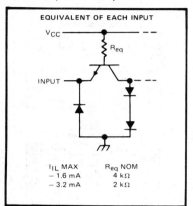

I_{IL} MAX	R_{eq} NOM
− 1.6 mA	4 kΩ
− 3.2 mA	2 kΩ

TYPICAL OF ALL OUTPUTS

130 Ω NOM

OUTPUT

TEXAS
INSTRUMENTS

3

TTL DEVICES

schematics of inputs and outputs (continued)

'LS73A

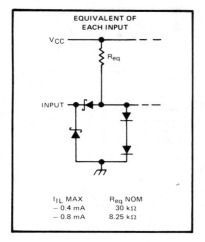

EQUIVALENT OF
EACH INPUT

I_{IL} MAX	R_{eq} NOM
− 0.4 mA	30 kΩ
− 0.8 mA	8.25 kΩ

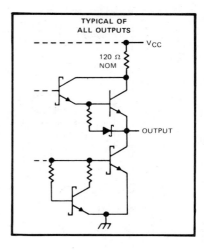

TYPICAL OF
ALL OUTPUTS

3

TTL DEVICES

logic diagrams

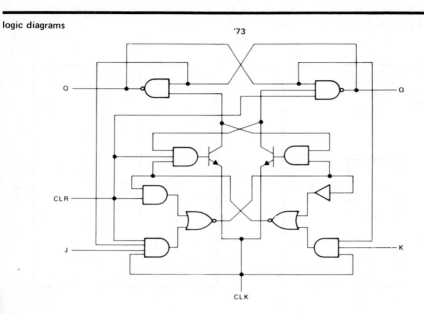

logic diagrams (continued)

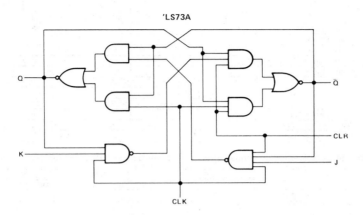

'LS73A

absolute maximum ratings over operating free-air temperature range (unless otherwise noted)

Supply voltage, V_{CC} (see Note 1) . . . . 7 V
Input voltage: '73 . . . . 5.5 V
            'LS73A . . . . 7 V
Operating free-air temperature range: SN54' . . . . $-55^{\circ}C$ to $125^{\circ}C$
                         SN74' . . . . $0^{\circ}C$ to $70^{\circ}C$
Storage temperature range . . . . $-65^{\circ}C$ to $150^{\circ}C$

NOTE 1: Voltage values are with respect to network ground terminal.

3

TTL DEVICES

recommended operating conditions

		SN5473			SN7473			UNIT
		MIN	NOM	MAX	MIN	NOM	MAX	
V_{CC}	Supply voltage	4.5	5	5 5	4.75	5	5.25	V
V_{IH}	High-level input voltage	2			2			V
V_{IL}	Low-level input voltage			0.8			0.8	V
I_{OH}	High-level output current			−0.4			−0.4	mA
I_{OL}	Low-level output current			16			16	mA
t_w	Pulse duration CLK high	20			20			ns
	CLK low	47			47			
	$\overline{CLR}$ low	25			25			
t_{su}	Input setup time before CLK↑	0			0			ns
t_h	Input hold time data after CLK↓	0			0			ns
T_A	Operating free-air temperature	−55		125	0		70	°C

electrical characteristics over recommended operating free-air temperature range (unless otherwise noted)

PARAMETER		TEST CONDITIONS†			SN5473			SN7473			UNIT
					MIN	TYP‡	MAX	MIN	TYP‡	MAX	
V_{IK}		V_{CC} = MIN,	I_I = −12 mA				−1.5			−1.5	V
V_{OH}		V_{CC} = MIN,	V_{IH} = 2 V,	V_{IL} = 0.8 V,	2.4	3.4		2.4	3.4		V
		I_{OH} = −0.4 mA									
V_{OL}		V_{CC} = MIN,	V_{IH} = 2 V,	V_{IL} = 0.8 V,		0.2	0.4		0.2	0.4	V
		I_{OL} = 16 mA									
I_I		V_{CC} = MAX,	V_I = 5.5 V				1			1	mA
I_{IH}	J or K	V_{CC} = MAX,	V_I = 2.4 V				40			40	μA
	$\overline{CLR}$ or CLK						80			80	
I_{IL}	J or K	V_{CC} = MAX,	V_I = 0.4 V				−1.6			−1.6	mA
	$\overline{CLR}$						−3.2			−3.2	
	CLK						−3.2			−3.2	
I_{OS}§		V_{CC} = MAX			−20		−57	−18		−57	mA
I_{CC}		V_{CC} = MAX,	See Note 2			10	20		10	20	mA

† For conditions shown as MIN or MAX, use the appropriate value specified under recommended operating conditions.
‡ All typical values are at V_{CC} = 5 V, T_A = 25°C.
§ Not more than one output should be shorted at a time.
NOTE 2: With all outputs open, I_{CC} is measured with the Q and Q̄ outputs high in turn.
At the time of measurement, the clock input is grounded.

switching characteristics, V_{CC} = 5 V, T_A = 25°C (see note 3)

PARAMETER¶	FROM (INPUT)	TO (OUTPUT)	TEST CONDITIONS		MIN	TYP	MAX	UNIT
f_{max}					15	20		MHz
t_{PLH}	$\overline{CLR}$	$\overline{Q}$	R_L = 400 Ω,	C_L = 15 pF		16	25	ns
t_{PHL}		Q				25	40	ns
t_{PLH}	CLK	Q or $\overline{Q}$				16	25	ns
t_{PHL}						25	40	ns

¶ f_{max} maximum clock frequency; t_{PLH} propagation delay time, low-to-high-level output; t_{PHL} propagation delay time, high-to-low-level output.
NOTE 3: See General Information Section for load circuits and voltage waveforms.

TEXAS
INSTRUMENTS

3

TTL DEVICES

recommended operating conditions

			SN54LS73A			SN74LS73A			UNIT
			MIN	NOM	MAX	MIN	NOM	MAX	
V_{CC}	Supply voltage		4.5	5	5.5	4.75	5	5.25	V
V_{IH}	High-level input voltage		2			2			V
V_{IL}	Low-level input voltage				0.7			0.8	V
I_{OH}	High-level output current				− 0.4			− 0.4	mA
I_{OL}	Low-level output current				4			8	mA
f_{clock}	Clock frequency		0		30	0		30	MHz
t_w	Pulse duration	CLK high	20			20			ns
		$\overline{CLR}$ low	25			20			
t_{su}	Set up time-before CLK↓	data high or low	20			20			ns
		$\overline{CLR}$ inactive	20			20			
t_h	Hold time-data after CLK↓		0			0			ns
T_A	Operating free-air temperature		− 55		125	0		70	°C

electrical characteristics over recommended operating free-air temperature range (unless otherwise noted)

PARAMETER		TEST CONDITIONS†	SN54LS73A			SN74LS73A			UNIT
			MIN	TYP‡	MAX	MIN	TYP‡	MAX	
V_{IK}		$V_{CC} = $ MIN, $I_I = -18$ mA			− 1.5			− 1.5	V
V_{OH}		$V_{CC} = $ MIN, $V_{IH} = 2$ V, $V_{IL} = $ MAX, $I_{OH} = -0.4$ mA	2.5	3.4		2.7	3.4		V
V_{OL}		$V_{CC} = $ MIN, $V_{IL} = $ MAX, $V_{IH} = 2$ V, $I_{OL} = 4$ mA		0.25	0.4		0.25	0.4	V
		$V_{CC} = $ MIN, $V_{IL} = $ MAX, $V_{IH} = 2$ V, $I_{OL} = 8$ mA					0.35	0.5	
I_I	J or K	$V_{CC} = $ MAX, $V_I = 7$ V			0.1			0.1	mA
	$\overline{CLR}$				0.3			0.3	
	CLK				0.4			0.4	
I_{IH}	J or K	$V_{CC} = $ MAX, $V_I = 2.7$ V			20			20	μA
	$\overline{CLR}$				60			60	
	CLK				80			80	
I_{IL}	J or K	$V_{CC} = $ MAX, $V_I = 0.4$ V			− 0.4			− 0.4	mA
	$\overline{CLR}$ or CLK				− 0.8			− 0.8	
I_{OS}§		$V_{CC} = $ MAX, See Note 4	− 20		− 100	− 20		− 100	mA
I_{CC}		$V_{CC} = $ MAX, See Note 2		4	6		4	6	mA

† For conditions shown as MIN or MAX, use the appropriate value specified under recommended operating conditions.
‡ All typical values are at $V_{CC} = 5$ V, $T_A = 25°$C.
§ Not more than one output should be shorted at a time, and the duration of the short circuit should not exceed one second.
NOTE 2: With all outputs open, I_{CC} is measured with the Q and $\overline{Q}$ outputs high in turn. At the time of measurement, the clock input is grounded.
NOTE 4: For certain devices where state commutation can be caused by shorting an output to ground, an equivalent test may be performed with $V_O = 2.25$ V and 2.125 V for the 54 family and the 74 family, respectively, with the minimum and maximum limits reduced to one half of their stated values.

switching characteristics, $V_{CC} = 5$ V, $T_A = 25°$C (see note 3)

PARAMETER	FROM (INPUT)	TO (OUTPUT)	TEST CONDITIONS		MIN	TYP	MAX	UNIT
f_{max}			$R_L = 2$ kΩ,	$C_L = 15$ pF	30	45		MHz
t_{PLH}	$\overline{CLR}$ or CLK	Q or $\overline{Q}$				15	20	ns
t_{PHL}						15	20	ns

NOTE 3: See General Information Section for load circuits and voltage waveforms.

TEXAS
INSTRUMENTS

3

TTL DEVICES

TYPES SN5474, SN54LS74A, SN54S74
SN7474, SN74LS74A, SN74S74
DUAL D-TYPE POSITIVE-EDGE-TRIGGERED FLIP-FLOPS WITH PRESET AND CLEAR

REVISED DECEMBER 1983

- **Package Options Include Both Plastic and Ceramic Chip Carriers in Addition to Plastic and Ceramic DIPs**

- **Dependable Texas Instruments Quality and Reliability**

description

These devices contain two independent D-type positive-edge-triggered flip-flops. A low level at the preset or clear inputs sets or resets the outputs regardless of the levels of the other inputs. When preset and clear are inactive (high), data at the D input meeting the setup time requirements are transferred to the outputs on the positive-going edge of the clock pulse. Clock triggering occurs at a voltage level and is not directly related to the rise time of the clock pulse. Following the hold time interval, data at the D input may be changed without affecting the levels at the outputs.

The SN54' family is characterized for operation over the full military temperature range of $-55\,°C$ to $125\,°C$. The SN74' family is characterized for operation from $0\,°C$ to $70\,°C$.

SN5474 . . . J PACKAGE
SN54LS74A, SN54S74 . . . J OR W PACKAGE
SN7474 . . . J OR N PACKAGE
SN74LS74A, SN74S74 . . . D, J OR N PACKAGE
(TOP VIEW)

1CLR [1	14] VCC
1D [2	13] 2CLR
1CLK [3	12] 2D
1PRE [4	11] 2CLK
1Q [5	10] 2PRE
1Q̄ [6	9] 2Q
GND [7	8] 2Q̄

SN5474 . . . W PACKAGE
(TOP VIEW)

1CLK [1	14] 1PRE
1D [2	13] 1Q
1CLR [3	12] 1Q̄
VCC [4	11] GND
2CLR [5	10] 2Q̄
2D [6	9] 2Q
2CLK [7	8] 2PRE

SN54LS74A, SN54S74 . . . FK PACKAGE
SN74LS74A, SN74S74
(TOP VIEW)

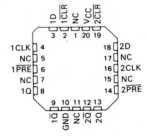

NC - No internal connection

FUNCTION TABLE

INPUTS				OUTPUTS	
PRE	CLR	CLK	D	Q	Q̄
L	H	X	X	H	L
H	L	X	X	L	H
L	L	X	X	H†	H†
H	H	↑	H	H	L
H	H	↑	L	L	H
H	H	L	X	Q₀	Q̄₀

† The output levels in this configuration are not guaranteed to meet the minimum levels in V_{OH} if the lows at preset and clear are near V_{IL} maximum. Furthermore, this configuration is nonstable; that is, it will not persist when either preset or clear returns to its inactive (high) level.

logic symbol

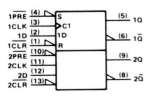

Pin numbers shown on logic notation are for D, J or N packages.

logic diagram

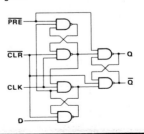

TEXAS INSTRUMENTS

3 TTL DEVICES

schematics of inputs and outputs

'74

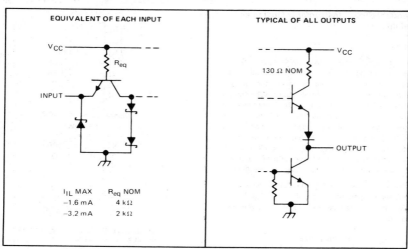

EQUIVALENT OF EACH INPUT	TYPICAL OF ALL OUTPUTS

I_{IL} MAX R_{eq} NOM

I_{IL} MAX	R_{eq} NOM
−1.6 mA	4 kΩ
−3.2 mA	2 kΩ

3

TTL DEVICES

TEXAS
INSTRUMENTS

schematics of inputs and outputs (continued)

'S74

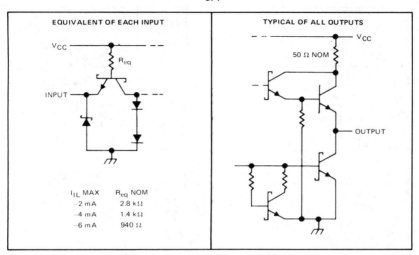

EQUIVALENT OF EACH INPUT	TYPICAL OF ALL OUTPUTS

I_{IL} MAX	R_{eq} NOM
−2 mA	2.8 kΩ
−4 mA	1.4 kΩ
−6 mA	940 Ω

schematic

'LS74A

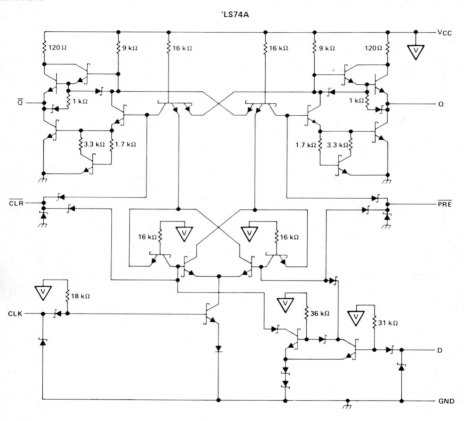

absolute maximum ratings over operating free-air temperature range (unless otherwise noted)

Supply voltage, V_{CC} (see Note 1) . . . . 7 V
Input voltage: '74, 'S74 . . . . 5.5 V
          'LS74A . . . . 7 V
Operating free-air temperature range: SN54' . . . . $-55°C$ to $125°C$
                                   SN74' . . . . $0°C$ to $70°C$
Storage temperature range . . . . $-65°C$ to $150°C$

NOTE 1: Voltage values are with respect to network ground terminal.

recommended operating conditions

			SN5474			SN7474			UNIT
			MIN	NOM	MAX	MIN	NOM	MAX	
V_{CC}	Supply voltage		4.5	5	5.5	4.75	5	5.25	V
V_{IH}	High-level input voltage		2			2			V
V_{IL}	Low-level input voltage				0.8			0.8	V
I_{OH}	High-level output current				−0.4			−0.4	mA
I_{OL}	Low-level output current				16			16	mA
t_w	Pulse duration	CLK high	30			30			ns
		CLK low	37			37			
		$\overline{PRE}$ or $\overline{CLR}$ low	30			30			
t_{su}	Input setup time before CLK ↑		20			20			ns
t_h	Input hold time-data after CLK ↑		5			5			ns
T_A	Operating free-air temperature		−55		125	0		70	°C

electrical characteristics over recommended operating free-air temperature range (unless otherwise noted)

PARAMETER		TEST CONDITIONS†		SN5474			SN7474			UNIT
				MIN	TYP‡	MAX	MIN	TYP‡	MAX	
V_{IK}		V_{CC} = MIN,	I_I = −12 mA			−1.5			−1.5	V
V_{OH}		V_{CC} = MIN, V_{IH} = 2 V, V_{IL} = 0.8 V, I_{OH} = −0.4 mA		2.4	3.4		2.4	3.4		V
V_{OL}		V_{CC} = MIN, V_{IH} = 2 V, V_{IL} = 0.8 V, I_{OL} = 16 mA			0.2	0.4		0.2	0.4	V
I_I		V_{CC} = MAX,	V_I = 5.5 V			1			1	mA
I_{IH}	D					40			40	mA
	$\overline{CLR}$	V_{CC} = MAX,	V_I = 2.4 V			120			120	
	All Other					80			80	
I_{IL}	D					−1.6			−1.6	mA
	$\overline{PRE}$★	V_{CC} = MAX,	V_I = 0.4 V			−1.6			−1.6	
	$\overline{CLR}$★					−3.2			−3.2	
	CLK					−3.2			−3.2	
I_{OS}§		V_{CC} = MAX		−20		−57	−18		−57	mA
I_{CC} Supply Current (average per Flip-Flop)		V_{CC} = MAX,	See Note 2		8.5	15		8.5	15	mA

† For conditions shown as MIN or MAX, use the appropriate value specified under recommended operating conditions.
‡ All typical values are at V_{CC} = 5 V, T_A = 25°C.
★ Clear is tested with preset high and preset is tested with clear high.
§ Not more than one output should be shorted at a time.
NOTE 2: With all outputs open, I_{CC} is measured with the Q and $\overline{Q}$ outputs high in turn. At the time of measurement, the clock input is grounded.

switching charateristics, V_{CC} = 5 V, T_A = 25°C (see note 3)

PARAMETER	FROM (INPUT)	TO (OUTPUT)	TEST CONDITIONS		MIN	TYP	MAX	UNIT
f_{max}					15	25		MHz
t_{PLH}	$\overline{PRE}$ or $\overline{CLR}$	Q or $\overline{Q}$	R_L = 400 Ω,	C_L = 15 pF			25	ns
t_{PHL}							40	ns
t_{PLH}	CLK	Q or $\overline{Q}$				14	25	ns
t_{PHL}						20	40	ns

NOTE 3: See General Information Section for load circuits and voltage waveforms.

3

TTL DEVICES

recommended operating conditions

			SN54LS74A			SN74LS74A			UNIT
			MIN	NOM	MAX	MIN	NOM	MAX	
V_{CC}	Supply voltage		4.5	5	5.5	4.75	5	5.25	V
V_{IH}	High-level input voltage		2			2			V
V_{IL}	Low-level input voltage				0.7			0.8	V
I_{OH}	High-level output current				-0.4			-0.4	mA
I_{OL}	Low-level output current				4			8	mA
f_{clock}	Clock frequency		0		25	0		25	MHz
t_w	Pulse duration	CLK high	25			25			ns
		$\overline{PRE}$ or $\overline{CLR}$ low	25			25			
t_{su}	Setup time-before CLK ↑	High-level data	20			20			ns
		Low-level data	20			20			
t_h	Hold time-data after CLK ↑		5			5			ns
T_A	Operating free-air temperature		-55		125	0		70	°C

electrical characteristics over recommended operating free-air temperature range (unless otherwise noted)

PARAMETER		TEST CONDITIONS†			SN54LS74A			SN74LS74A			UNIT
					MIN	TYP‡	MAX	MIN	TYP‡	MAX	
V_{IK}		V_{CC} = MIN,	$I_I = -18$ mA				-1.5			-1.5	V
V_{OH}		V_{CC} = MIN, $I_{OH} = -0.4$ mA	V_{IH} = 2 V,	V_{IL} = MAX,	2.5	3.4		2.7	3.4		V
V_{OL}		V_{CC} = MIN, I_{OL} = 4 mA	V_{IL} = MAX,	V_{IH} = 2 V,		0.25	0.4		0.25	0.4	V
		V_{CC} = MIN, I_{OL} = 8 mA	V_{IL} = MAX,	V_{IH} = 2 V,					0.35	0.5	
I_I	D or CLK	V_{CC} = MAX,	V_I = 7 V				0.1			0.1	mA
	$\overline{CLR}$ or $\overline{PRE}$						0.2			0.2	
I_{IH}	D or CLK	V_{CC} = MAX,	V_I = 2.7 V				20			20	µA
	$\overline{CLR}$ or $\overline{PRE}$						40			40	
I_{IL}	D or CLK	V_{CC} = MAX,	V_I = 0.4 V				-0.4			-0.4	mA
	$\overline{CLR}$ or $\overline{PRE}$						-0.8			-0.8	
I_{OS}§		V_{CC} = MAX,	See Note 4		-20		-100	-20		-100	mA
I_{CC}		V_{CC} = MAX,	See Note 2			4	8		4	8	mA

† For conditions shown as MIN or MAX, use the appropriate value specified under recommended operating conditions.
‡ All typical values are at V_{CC} = 5 V, T_A = 25°C.
§ Not more than one output should be shorted at a time, and the duration of the short circuit should not exceed one second.
NOTE 2: With all outputs open, I_{CC} is measured with the Q and $\overline{Q}$ outputs high in turn. At the time of measurement, the clock input is grounded.
NOTE 4: For certain devices where state commutation can be caused by shorting an output to ground, an equivalent test may be performed with V_O = 2.25 V and 2.125 V for the 54 family and the 74 family, respectively, with the minimum and maximum limits reduced to one half of their stated values.

switching characteristics, V_{CC} = 5 V, T_A = 25°C (see note 3)

PARAMETER	FROM (INPUT)	TO (OUTPUT)	TEST CONDITIONS		MIN	TYP	MAX	UNIT
f_{max}			R_L = 2 kΩ,	C_L = 15 pF	25	33		MHz
t_{PLH}	$\overline{CLR}$, $\overline{PRE}$ or CLK	Q or $\overline{Q}$				13	25	ns
t_{PHL}						25	40	ns

NOTE 3: See General Information Section for load circuits and voltage waveforms.

TEXAS
INSTRUMENTS

recommended operating conditions

			SN54S74			SN74S74			UNIT
			MIN	NOM	MAX	MIN	NOM	MAX	
V_{CC}	Supply voltage		4.5	5	5.5	4.75	5	5.25	V
V_{IH}	High-level input voltage		2			2			V
V_{IL}	Low-level input voltage				0.8			0.8	V
I_{OH}	High-level output current				−1			−1	mA
I_{OL}	Low-level output current				20			20	mA
t_w	Pulse duration	CLK high	6			6			ns
		CLK low	7.3			7.3			
		$\overline{CLR}$ or $\overline{PRE}$ low	7			7			
t_{su}	Setup time, before CLK ↑	High-level data	3			3			ns
		Low-level data	3			3			
t_h	Input hold time - data after CLK ↑		2			2			ns
T_A	Operating free-air temperature		−55		125	0		70	°C

electrical characteristics over recommended operating free-air temperature range (unless otherwise noted)

PARAMETER		TEST CONDITIONS†		SN54S74			SN74S74			UNIT
				MIN	TYP‡	MAX	MIN	TYP‡	MAX	
V_{IK}		V_{CC} = MIN,	I_I = −18 mA,			−1.2			−1.2	V
V_{OH}		V_{CC} = MIN,	V_{IH} = 2 V, V_{IL} = 0.8 V,	2.5	3.4		2.7	3.4		V
		I_{OH} = −1 mA								
V_{OL}		V_{CC} = MIN,	V_{IH} = 2 V, V_{IL} = 0.8 V,			0.5			0.5	V
		I_{OL} = 20 mA								
I_I		V_{CC} = MAX,	V_I = 5.5 V			1			1	mA
I_{IH}	D	V_{CC} = MAX,	V_I = 2.7 V			50			50	mA
	$\overline{CLR}$					150			150	
	$\overline{PRE}$ or CLK					100			100	
I_{IL}	D	V_{CC} = MAX,	V_I = 0.5 V			−2			−2	mA
	$\overline{CLR}$★					−6			−6	
	$\overline{PRE}$★					−4			−4	
	CLK					−4			−4	
I_{OS}§		V_{CC} = MAX		−40		−100	−40		−100	mA
I_{CC} Supply Current (average per Flip-Flop)		V_{CC} = MAX,	See Note 2		15	25		15	25	mA

† For conditions shown as MIN or MAX, use the appropriate value specified under recommended operating conditions.
‡ All typical values are at V_{CC} = 5 V, T_A = 25°C.
§ Not more than one output should be shorted at a time, and the duration of the short circuit should not exceed one second.
★ Clear is tested with preset high and preset is tested with clear high.
NOTE 2: All outputs open, I_{CC} is measured with the Q and $\overline{Q}$ outputs high in turn. At the time of measurement, the clock input is grounded.

switching characteristics, V_{CC} = 5 V, T_A = 25°C (see note 3)

PARAMETER	FROM (INPUT)	TO (OUTPUT)	TEST CONDITIONS		MIN	TYP	MAX	UNIT
f_{max}					75	110		MHz
t_{PLH}	$\overline{PRE}$ or $\overline{CLR}$	Q or $\overline{Q}$				4	6	ns
t_{PHL}	$\overline{PRE}$ or $\overline{CLR}$ (CLK high)	$\overline{Q}$ or Q	R_L = 280 Ω, C_L = 15 pF			9	13.5	ns
	$\overline{PRE}$ or $\overline{CLR}$ (CLK low)					5	8	
t_{PLH}	CLK	Q or $\overline{Q}$				6	9	ns
t_{PHL}						6	9	ns

NOTE 3: See General Information Section for load circuits and voltage waveforms.

3

TTL DEVICES

logic

FUNCTION TABLE
(each latch)

INPUTS		OUTPUTS	
D	C	Q	$\overline{Q}$
L	H	L	H
H	H	H	L
X	L	Q_0	$\overline{Q_0}$

H = high level, L = low level, X = irrelevant

Q_0 = the level of Q before the high-to-low transition of G

SN5475, SN54LS75 . . . J OR W PACKAGE
SN7475 . . . J OR N PACKAGE
SN74LS75 . . . D, J OR N PACKAGE

(TOP VIEW)

```
        ___  ___
1Q  [ 1  U  16 ] 1Q
1D  [ 2     15 ] 2Q
2D  [ 3     14 ] 2Q
3C, 4C [ 4  13 ] 1C, 2C
VCC [ 5     12 ] GND
3D  [ 6     11 ] 3Q
4D  [ 7     10 ] 3Q
4Q  [ 8      9 ] 4Q
```

SN5477, SN54LS77 . . . W PACKAGE

(TOP VIEW)

```
         ___  ___
1D  [ 1   U  14 ] 1Q
2D  [ 2      13 ] 2Q
3C, 4C [ 3  12 ] 1C, 2C
VCC [ 4      11 ] GND
3D  [ 5      10 ] NC
4D  [ 6       9 ] 3Q
NC  [ 7       8 ] 4Q
```

NC - No internal connection

**FOR CHIP CARRIER INFORMATION,
CONTACT THE FACTORY**

description

These latches are ideally suited for use as temporary storage for binary information between processing units and input/output or indicator units. Information present at a data (D) input is transferred to the Q output when the enable (C) is high and the Q output will follow the data input as long as the enable remains high. When the enable goes low, the information (that was present at the data input at the time the transition occurred) is retained at the Q output until the enable is permitted to go high.

The '75, and 'LS75 feature complementary Q and $\overline{Q}$ outputs from a 4-bit latch, and are available in various 16-pin packages. For higher component density applications, the '77, and 'LS77 4-bit latches are available in 14-pin flat packages.

These circuits are completely compatible with all popular TTL families. All inputs are diode-clamped to minimize transmission-line effects and simplify system design. Series 54, and 54LS devices are characterized for operation over the fully military temperature range of −55°C to 125°C; Series 74, and 74LS devices are characterized for operation from 0°C to 70°C.

absolute maximum ratings over operating free-air temperature range (unless otherwise noted)

Supply voltage, V_{CC} (see Note 1) . . . . 7 V
Input voltage: '75, '77 . . . . 5.5 V
              'LS75, 'LS77 . . . . 7 V
Interemitter voltage (see Note 2) . . . . 5.5 V
Operating free-air temperature range: SN54' . . . . −55°C to 125°C
                                   SN74' . . . . 0°C to 70°C
Storage temperature range . . . . −65°C to 150°C

NOTES: 1. Voltage values are with respect to network ground terminal.
       2. This is the voltage between two emitters of a multiple-emitter input transistor and is not applicable to the 'LS75 and 'LS77.

3
TTL DEVICES

TEXAS
INSTRUMENTS

logic diagrams (each latch)

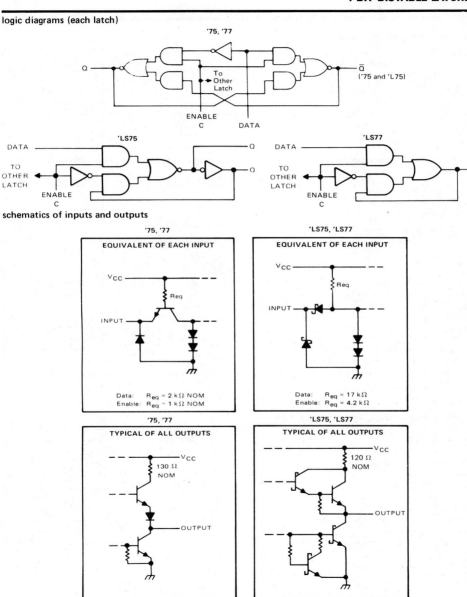

schematics of inputs and outputs

recommended operating conditions

	SN5475, SN5477			SN7475			UNIT
	MIN	NOM	MAX	MIN	NOM	MAX	
Supply voltage, V_{CC}	4.5	5	5.5	4.75	5	5.25	V
High-level output current, I_{OH}			−400			−400	μA
Low-level output current, I_{OL}			16			16	mA
Width of enabling pulse, t_w	20			20			ns
Setup time, t_{su}	20			20			ns
Hold time, t_h	5			5			ns
Operating free-air temperature, T_A	−55		125	0		70	°C

electrical characteristics over recommended operating free-air temperature range (unless otherwise noted)

PARAMETER		TEST CONDITIONS[†]		MIN	TYP[‡]	MAX	UNIT
V_{IH} High-level input voltage				2			V
V_{IL} Low-level input voltage						0.8	V
V_{IK} Input clamp voltage		V_{CC} = MIN,	I_I = −12 mA			−1.5	V
V_{OH} High-level output voltage		V_{CC} = MIN, V_{IL} = 0.8 V,	V_{IH} = 2 V, I_{OH} = −400 μA	2.4	3.4		V
V_{OL} Low-level output voltage		V_{CC} = MIN, V_{IL} = 0.8 V,	V_{IH} = 2 V, I_{OL} = 16 mA		0.2	0.4	V
I_I Input current at maximum input voltage		V_{CC} = MAX,	V_I = 5.5 V			1	mA
I_{IH} High-level input current	D input	V_{CC} = MAX,	V_I = 2.4 V			80	μA
	C input					160	
I_{IL} Low-level input current	D input	V_{CC} = MAX,	V_I = 0.4 V			−3.2	mA
	C input					−6.4	
I_{OS} Short-circuit output current[§]		V_{CC} = MAX	SN54′	−20		−57	mA
			SN74′	−18		−57	
I_{CC} Supply current		V_{CC} = MAX, See Note 3	SN54′		32	46	mA
			SN74′		32	53	

[†]For conditions shown as MIN or MAX, use the appropriate value specified under recommended operating conditions.
[‡]All typical values are at V_{CC} = 5 V, T_A = 25°C.
[§]Not more than one output should be shorted at a time.
NOTE 3: I_{CC} is tested with all inputs grounded and all outputs open.

switching characteristics, V_{CC} = 5 V, T_A = 25°C

PARAMETER	FROM (INPUT)	TO (OUTPUT)	TEST CONDITIONS	MIN	TYP	MAX	UNIT
t_{PLH}	D	Q			16	30	ns
t_{PHL}					14	25	
t_{PLH}[◀]	D	$\bar{Q}$	C_L = 15 pF, R_L = 400 Ω, See Figure 1		24	40	ns
t_{PHL}[◀]					7	15	
t_{PLH}	C	Q			16	30	ns
t_{PHL}					7	15	
t_{PLH}[◀]	C	$\bar{Q}$			16	30	ns
t_{PHL}[◀]					7	15	

t_{PLH} propagation delay time, low-to-high-level output
t_{PHL} propagation delay time, high-to-low-level output
[◀] These parameters are not applicable for the SN5477.

TEXAS
INSTRUMENTS

recommended operating conditions

		SN54LS75 SN54LS77			SN74LS75			UNIT
		MIN	NOM	MAX	MIN	NOM	MAX	
Supply voltage, V_{CC}		4.5	5	5.5	4.75	5	5.25	V
High-level output current, I_{OH}				−400			−400	μA
Low-level output current, I_{OL}				4			8	mA
Width of enabling pulse, t_w		20			20			ns
Setup time, t_{su}		20			20			ns
Hold time, t_h		5			5			ns
Operating free-air temperature, T_A		−55		125	0		70	°C

electrical characteristics over recommended operating free-air temperature range (unless otherwise noted)

PARAMETER		TEST CONDITIONS[†]		SN54LS75 SN54LS77			SN74LS75			UNIT
				MIN	TYP[‡]	MAX	MIN	TYP[‡]	MAX	
V_{IH}	High-level input voltage			2			2			V
V_{IL}	Low-level input voltage					0.7			0.8	V
V_{IK}	Input clamp voltage	V_{CC} = MIN,	I_I = −18 mA			−1.5			−1.5	V
V_{OH}	High-level output voltage	V_{CC} = MIN, V_{IH} = 2 V, V_{IL} = V_{IL} max, I_{OH} = −400 μA		2.5	3.5		2.7	3.5		V
V_{OL}	Low-level output voltage	V_{CC} = MIN, V_{IH} = 2 V, V_{IL} = V_{IL} max	I_{OL} = 4 mA	0.25		0.4	0.25		0.4	V
			I_{OL} = 8 mA				0.35		0.5	
I_I	Input current at maximum input voltage	V_{CC} = MAX, V_I = 7 V	D input			0.1			0.1	mA
			C input			0.4			0.4	
I_{IH}	High-level input current	V_{CC} = MAX, V_I = 2.7 V	D input			20			20	μA
			C input			80			80	
I_{IL}	Low-level input current	V_{CC} = MAX, V_I = 0.4 V	D input			−0.4			−0.4	mA
			C input			−1.6			−1.6	
I_{OS}	Short-circuit output current[§]	V_{CC} = MAX		−20		−100	−20		−100	mA
I_{CC}	Supply current	V_{CC} = MAX, See Note 2	'LS75		6.3	12		6.3	12	mA
			'LS77		6.9	13				

[†] For conditions shown as MIN or MAX, use the appropriate value specified under recommended operating conditions.
[‡] All typical values are at V_{CC} = 5 V, T_A = 25 C.
[§] Not more than one output should be shorted at a time, and duration of the short-circuit should not exceed one second
NOTE 2: I_{CC} is tested with all inputs grounded and all outputs open.

switching characteristics, V_{CC} = 5 V, T_A = 25° C

PARAMETER[◆]	FROM (INPUT)	TO (OUTPUT)	TEST CONDITIONS	'LS75			'LS77			UNIT
				MIN	TYP	MAX	MIN	TYP	MAX	
t_{PLH}	D	Q			15	27		11	19	ns
t_{PHL}					9	17		9	17	
t_{PLH}	D	$\overline{Q}$			12	20				ns
t_{PHL}			C_L = 15 pF, R_L = 2 kΩ, See Figure 1		7	15				
t_{PLH}	C	Q			15	27		10	18	ns
t_{PHL}					14	25		10	18	
t_{PLH}	C	$\overline{Q}$			16	30				ns
t_{PHL}					7	15				

[◆] t_{PLH} = propagation delay time, low-to-high-level output
t_{PLH} = propagation delay time, high-to-low-level output

3

TTL DEVICES

TEXAS
INSTRUMENTS

TYPES SN5475, SN5477, SN54LS75, SN54LS77, SN7475, SN74LS75
4-BIT BISTABLE LATCHES

PARAMETER MEASUREMENT INFORMATION

switching characteristics [†]

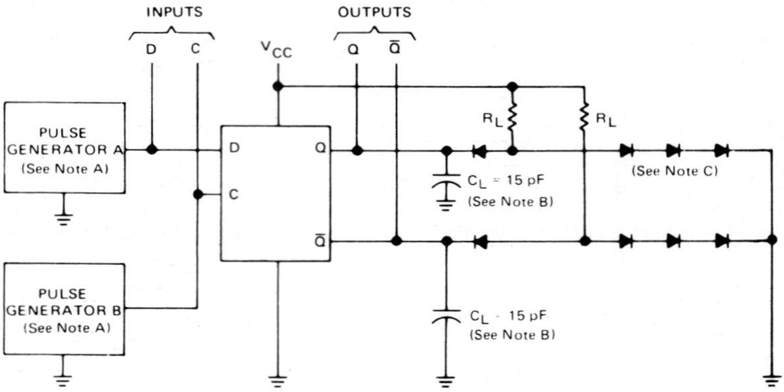

TEST CIRCUIT

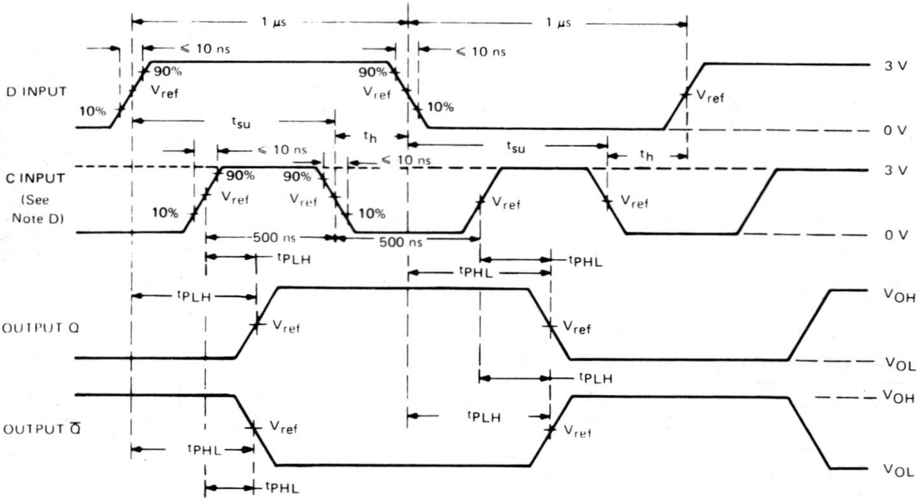

VOLTAGE WAVEFORMS

[†] Complementary Q outputs are on the '75, and 'LS75 only.

NOTES: A. The pulse generators have the following characteristics: $Z_{out} \approx 50\ \Omega$; for pulse generator A, PRR ≤ 500 kHz; for pulse generator B, PRR ≤ 1 MHz. Positions of D and C input pulses are varied with respect to each other to verify setup times.
B. C_L includes probe and jig capacitance.
C. All diodes are 1N3064 or equivalent.
D. When measuring propagation delay times from the D input, the corresponding C input must be held high.
E. For '75 and '77, V_{ref} = 1.5 V; for 'LS75 and 'LS77, V_{ref} = 1.3 V.

FIGURE 1

TEXAS INSTRUMENTS

- **Package Options Include Plastic and Ceramic DIPs**

- **Dependable Texas Instruments Quality and Reliability**

SN5476, SN54LS76A . . . J OR W PACKAGE
SN7476 . . . J OR N PACKAGE
SN74LS76A . . . D, J OR N PACKAGE
(TOP VIEW)

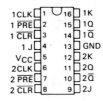

1CLK	1	16	1K
1 $\overline{PRE}$	2	15	1Q
1 $\overline{CLR}$	3	14	1$\overline{Q}$
1 J	4	13	GND
V$_{CC}$	5	12	2K
2CLK	6	11	2Q
2 $\overline{PRE}$	7	10	2$\overline{Q}$
2 $\overline{CLR}$	8	9	2J

description

The '76 contain two independent J-K flip-flops with individual J-K, clock, preset, and clear inputs. The '76 are positive-edge-triggered flip-flops. J-K input is loaded into the master while the clock is high and transferred to the slave on the high-to-low transition. For these devices the J and K inputs must be stable while the clock is high.

The 'LS76A contain two independent negative-edge-triggered flip-flops. The J and K inputs must be stable one setup time prior to the high-to-low clock transition for predictable operation. The preset and clear are asynchronous active low inputs. When low they override the clock and data inputs forcing the outputs to the steady state levels as shown in the function table.

The SN5476, and the SN54LS76A are characterized for operation over the full military temperature range of −55°C to 125°C. The SN7476 and the SN74LS76A are characterized for operation from 0°C to 70°C.

'76
FUNCTION TABLE

INPUTS					OUTPUTS	
$\overline{PRE}$	$\overline{CLR}$	CLK	J	K	Q	$\overline{Q}$
L	H	X	X	X	H	L
H	L	X	X	X	L	H
L	L	X	X	X	H[†]	H[†]
H	H	⊓	L	L	Q$_0$	$\overline{Q}_0$
H	H	⊓	H	L	H	L
H	H	⊓	L	H	L	H
H	H	⊓	H	H	TOGGLE	

'LS76A
FUNCTION TABLE

INPUTS					OUTPUTS	
$\overline{PRE}$	$\overline{CLR}$	CLK	J	K	Q	$\overline{Q}$
L	H	X	X	X	H	L
H	L	X	X	X	L	H
L	L	X	X	X	H[†]	H[†]
H	H	↓	L	L	Q$_0$	$\overline{Q}_0$
H	H	↓	H	L	H	L
H	H	↓	L	H	L	H
H	H	↓	H	H	TOGGLE	
H	H	H	X	X	Q$_0$	$\overline{Q}_0$

† This configuration is nonstable; that is, it will not persist when either preset or clear returns to its inactive (high) level.

FOR CHIP CARRIER INFORMATION,
CONTACT THE FACTORY

TEXAS INSTRUMENTS

TTL DEVICES 3

logic diagrams

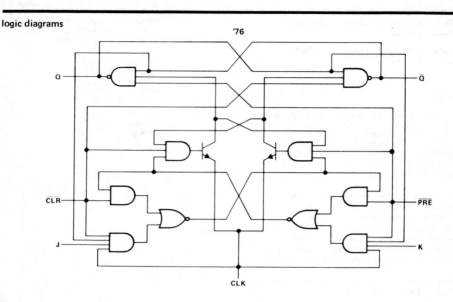

3

TTL DEVICES

logic diagrams (continued)

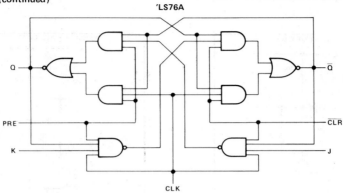

'LS76A

logic symbols

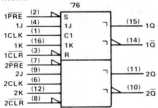

'76

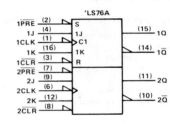

'LS76A

Pin numbers shown on logic notation are for D, J or N packages.

schematics of inputs and outputs

'76

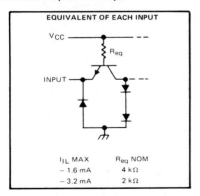

EQUIVALENT OF EACH INPUT

I_{IL} MAX	R_{eq} NOM
− 1.6 mA	4 kΩ
− 3.2 mA	2 kΩ

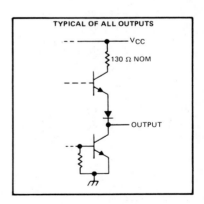

TYPICAL OF ALL OUTPUTS

130 Ω NOM

TTL DEVICES

3

schematics of inputs and outputs (continued)

'LS76A

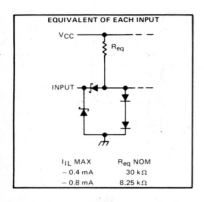

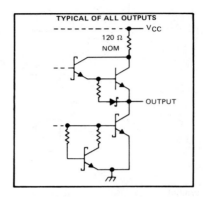

I_{IL} MAX	R_{eq} NOM
− 0.4 mA	30 kΩ
− 0.8 mA	8.25 kΩ

absolute maximum ratings over operating free-air temperature range (unless otherwise noted)

Supply voltage, V_{CC} (see Note 1) . . . . 7 V
Input voltage: '76 . . . . 5.5 V
　　　　　　'LS76A . . . . 7 V
Operating free-air temperature range: SN54' . . . . − 55°C to 125°C
　　　　　　　　　　　　　　　　SN74' . . . . 0°C to 70°C
Storage temperature range . . . . − 65°C to 150°C
NOTE 1: Voltage values are with respect to network ground terminal.

TEXAS
INSTRUMENTS

3

TTL DEVICES

recommended operating conditions

			SN5476			SN7476			UNIT
			MIN	NOM	MAX	MIN	NOM	MAX	
V_{CC}	Supply voltage		4.5	5	5.5	4.75	5	5.25	V
V_{IH}	High-level input voltage		2			2			V
V_{IL}	Low-level input voltage				0.8			0.8	V
I_{OH}	High-level output current				−0.4			−0.4	mA
I_{OL}	Low-level output current				16			16	mA
t_W	Pulse duration	CLK high	20			20			ns
		CLK low	47			47			
		$\overline{PRE}$ or $\overline{CLR}$ low	25			25			
t_{su}	Input setup time before CLK ↑		0			0			ns
t_h	Input hold time-data after CLK ↓		0			0			ns
T_A	Operating free-air temperature		−55		125	0		70	°C

electrical characteristics over recommended operating free-air temperature range (unless otherwise noted)

PARAMETER		TEST CONDITIONS†		SN5476			SN7476			UNIT
				MIN	TYP	MAX	MIN	TYP	MAX	
V_{IK}		V_{CC} = MIN,	I_I = −12 mA			−1.5			−1.5	V
V_{OH}		V_{CC} = MIN, V_{IH} = 2 V, V_{IL} = 0.8 V, I_{OH} = −0.4 mA		2.4	3.4		2.4	3.4		V
V_{OL}		V_{CC} = MIN, V_{IH} = 2 V, V_{IL} = 0.8 V, I_{OL} = 16 mA			0.2	0.4		0.2	0.4	V
I_I		V_{CC} = MAX,	V_I = 5.5 V			1			1	mA
I_{IH}	J or K	V_{CC} = MAX,	V_I = 2.4 V			40			40	μA
	All other					80			80	
I_{IL}	J or K	V_{CC} = MAX,	V_I = 0.4 V			−1.6			−1.6	mA
	All other★					−3.2			−3.2	
I_{OS}§		V_{CC} = MAX		−20		−57	−18		−57	mA
I_{CC} Supply Current (average per Flip-Flop)		V_{CC} = MAX,	See Note 2		10	20		10	20	mA

† For conditions shown as MIN or MAX, use the appropriate value specified under recommended operating conditions.
‡ All typical values are at V_{CC} = 5 V, T_A = 25°C.
§ Not more than one output should be shorted at a time.
★ Clear is tested with preset high and preset is tested with clear high.
NOTE 2: With all outputs open, I_{CC} is measured with the Q and $\overline{Q}$ outputs high in turn. At the time of measurement, the clock input is grounded.

switching characteristics, V_{CC} = 5 V, T_A = 25°C (see note 3)

PARAMETER	FROM (INPUT)	TO (OUTPUT)	TEST CONDITIONS		MIN	TYP	MAX	UNIT
f_{max}			R_L = 400 Ω,	C_L = 15 pF	15	20		MHz
t_{PLH}	$\overline{PRE}$ or $\overline{CLR}$	Q or $\overline{Q}$				16	25	ns
t_{PHL}						25	40	ns
t_{PLH}	CLK	Q or $\overline{Q}$				16	25	ns
t_{PHL}						25	40	ns

NOTE 3: See General Information Section for load circuits and voltage waveforms.

TEXAS
INSTRUMENTS

recommended operating conditions

			SN54LS76A			SN74LS76A			UNIT
			MIN	NOM	MAX	MIN	NOM	MAX	
V_{CC}	Supply voltage		4.5	5	5.5	4.75	5	5.75	V
V_{IH}	High-level input voltage		2			2			V
V_{IL}	Low-level input voltage				0.7			0.8	V
I_{OH}	High-level output current				−0.4			−0.4	mA
I_{OL}	Low-level output current				4			8	mA
f_{clock}	Clock frequency		0		30	0		30	MHz
t_w	Pulse duration	CLK high	20			20			ns
		PRE or CLR low	25			25			
t_{su}	Setup time before CLK↓	data high or low	20			20			ns
		CLR inactive	20			20			
		PRE inactive	25			25			
t_h	Hold time-data after CLK↓		0			0			ns
T_A	Operating free-air temperature		−55		125	0		70	°C

electrical characteristics over recommended operating free-air temperature range (unless otherwise noted)

PARAMETER		TEST CONDITIONS[†]			SN54LS76A			SN74LS76A			UNIT
					MIN	TYP[‡]	MAX	MIN	TYP[‡]	MAX	
V_{IK}		V_{CC} = MIN,	I_I = −18 mA				−1.5			−1.5	V
V_{OH}		V_{CC} = MIN,	V_{IH} = 2 V,	V_{IL} = MAX,	2.5	3.4		2.7	3.4		V
		I_{OH} = −0.4 mA									
V_{OL}		V_{CC} = MIN,	V_{IL} = MAX,	V_{IH} = 2 V,		0.25	0.4		0.25	0.4	V
		I_{OL} = 4 mA									
		V_{CC} = MIN,	V_{IL} = MAX,	V_{IH} = 2 V,					0.35	0.5	
		I_{OL} = 8 mA									
I_I	J or K	V_{CC} = MAX,	V_I = 7 V				0.1			0.1	mA
	CLR or PRE						0.3			0.3	
	CLK						0.4			0.4	
I_{IH}	J or K	V_{CC} = MAX,	V_I = 2.7 V				20			20	μA
	CLR or PRE						60			60	
	CLK						80			80	
I_{IL}	J or K	V_{CC} = MAX,	V_I = 0.4 V				−0.4			−0.4	mA
	All other						−0.8			−0.8	
I_{OS}[§]		V_{CC} = MAX,	See Note 4		−20		−100	−20		−100	mA
I_{CC}		V_{CC} = MAX,	See Note 2			4	6		4	6	mA

† For conditions shown as MIN or MAX, use the appropriate value specified under recommended operating conditions.
‡ All typical values are at V_{CC} = 5 V, T_A = 25°C.
§ Not more than one output should be shorted at a time, and the duration of the short circuit should not exceed one second.
NOTE 2: With all outputs open, I_{CC} is measured with the Q and Q̄ outputs high in turn. At the time of measurement, the clock input is grounded.
NOTE 4: For certain devices where state commutation can be caused by shorting an output to ground, an equivalent test may be performed with V_O = 2.25 V and 2.125 V for the 54 family and the 74 family, respectively, with the minimum and maximum limits reduced to one half of their stated values.

switching characteristics, V_{CC} = 5 V, T_A = 25°C (see note 3)

PARAMETER	FROM (INPUT)	TO (OUTPUT)	TEST CONDITIONS		MIN	TYP	MAX	UNIT
f_{max}			R_L = 2 kΩ,	C_L = 15 pF	30	45		MHz
t_{PLH}	PRE, CLR or CLK	Q or Q̄				15	20	ns
t_{PHL}						15	20	ns

NOTE 3: See General Information Section for load circuits and voltage waveforms.

TEXAS
INSTRUMENTS

- **Package Options Include Plastic and Ceramic DIPs**

- **Dependable Texas Instruments Quality and Reliability**

description

The 'LS78A contain two negative-edge-triggered flip-flops with individual J-K, preset inputs, and common clock and common clear inputs. The logic levels at the J and K inputs may be allowed to change while the clock pulse is high and the flip-flop will perform according to the function table as long as minimum setup and hold times are observed. The preset and clear are asynchronous active low inputs. When low they override the clock and data inputs forcing the outputs to the steady state levels as shown in the function table.

The SN54LS78A is characterized for operation over the full military temperature range of −55°C to 125°C. The SN74LS78A is characterized for operation from 0°C to 70°C.

**FOR CHIP CARRIER INFORMATION,
CONTACT THE FACTORY**

SN54LS78A . . . J OR W PACKAGE
SN74LS78A . . . D, J OR N PACKAGE
(TOP VIEW)

CLK	1	14 1K
1 $\overline{PRE}$	2	13 1Q
1J	3	12 1$\overline{Q}$
V$_{CC}$	4	11 GND
$\overline{CLR}$	5	10 2J
2 $\overline{PRE}$	6	9 2$\overline{Q}$
2K	7	8 2Q

'LS78A

INPUTS					OUTPUTS	
$\overline{PRE}$	$\overline{CLR}$	CLK	J	K	Q	$\overline{Q}$
L	H	X	X	X	H	L
H	L	X	X	X	L	H
L	L	X	X	X	H†	H†
H	H	↓	L	L	Q_0	$\overline{Q}_0$
H	H	↓	H	L	H	L
H	H	↓	L	H	L	H
H	H	↓	H	H	TOGGLE	
H	H	H	X	X	Q_0	$\overline{Q}_0$

† This configuration is nonstable; that is, it will not persist when preset and clear inputs return to their inactive (high) level.

TTL DEVICES

3

logic diagram

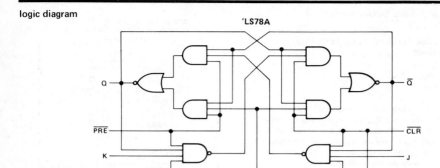

'LS78A

logic symbol

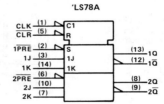

'LS78A

Pin numbers shown on logic notation are for D, J or N packages.

3

TTL DEVICES

schematics of inputs and outputs

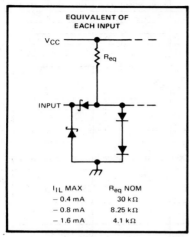

'LS78A

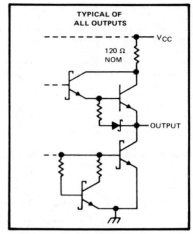

I_{IL} MAX	R_{eq} NOM
− 0.4 mA	30 kΩ
− 0.8 mA	8.25 kΩ
− 1.6 mA	4.1 kΩ

absolute maximum ratings over operating free-air temperature range (unless otherwise noted)

Supply voltage, V_{CC} (see Note 1) . . . . 7 V

Input voltage: 'LS78A . . . . 7 V

Operating free-air temperature range: SN54'. . . . . − 55˚C to 125˚C

SN74'. . . . . 0˚C to 70˚C

Storage temperature range . . . . − 65˚C to 150˚C

NOTE 1: Voltage values are with respect to network ground terminal.

TTL DEVICES

3

recommended operating conditions

		SN54LS78A			SN74LS78A			UNIT
		MIN	NOM	MAX	MIN	NOM	MAX	
V_{CC}	Supply voltage	4.5	5	5.5	4.75	5	5.75	V
V_{IH}	High-level input voltage	2			2			V
V_{IL}	Low-level input voltage			0.7			0.8	V
I_{OH}	High-level output current			− 0.4			− 0.4	mA
I_{OL}	Low-level output current			4			8	mA
f_{clock}	Clock frequency	0		30	0		30	MHz
t_w	Pulse duration — CLK high	20			20			ns
	Pulse duration — $\overline{PRE}$ or $\overline{CLR}$ low	25			25			
t_{su}	Setup time before CLK ↓ — data high or low	20			20			ns
	Setup time before CLK ↓ — $\overline{PRE}$ or $\overline{CLR}$ inactive	20			20			
t_h	Hold time-data after CLK ↓	0			0			ns
T_A	Operating free-air temperature	− 55		125	0		70	°C

electrical characteristics over recommended operating free-air temperature range (unless otherwise noted)

PARAMETER		TEST CONDITIONS†			SN54LS78A			SN74LS78A			UNIT
					MIN	TYP‡	MAX	MIN	TYP‡	MAX	
V_{IK}		V_{CC} = MIN,	I_I = − 18 mA				− 1.5			− 1.5	V
V_{OH}		V_{CC} = MIN, I_{OH} = − 0.4 mA	V_{IH} = 2 V,	V_{IL} = 0.7 V,	2.5	3.4					V
		V_{CC} = MIN, I_{OH} = − 0.4 mA	V_{IH} = 2 V,	V_{IL} = 0.8 V,				2.7	3.4		
V_{OL}		V_{CC} = MIN, I_{OL} = 4 mA	V_{IL} = MAX,	V_{IH} = 2 V,		0.25	0.4		0.25	0.4	V
		V_{CC} = MIN, I_{OL} = 8 mA	V_{IL} = MAX,	V_{IH} = 2 V,					0.35	0.5	
I_I	J or K	V_{CC} = MAX,	V_I = 7 V				0.1			0.1	mA
	$\overline{CLR}$						0.6			0.6	
	$\overline{PRE}$						0.3			0.3	
	CLK						0.8			0.8	
I_{IH}	J or K	V_{CC} = MAX,	V_I = 2.7 V				20			20	μA
	$\overline{CLR}$						120			120	
	$\overline{PRE}$						60			60	
	CLK						160			160	
I_{IL}	J or K	V_{CC} = MAX,	V_I = 0.4 V				− 0.4			− 0.4	mA
	$\overline{CLR}$						− 1.6			− 1.6	
	$\overline{PRE}$						− 0.8			− 0.8	
	CLK						− 1.6			− 1.6	
I_{OS} §		V_{CC} = MAX,	See Note 4		− 20		− 100	− 20		− 100	mA
I_{CC}		V_{CC} = MAX,	See Note 2			4	6		4	6	mA

† For conditions shown as MIN or MAX, use the appropriate value specified under recommended operating conditions.
‡ All typical values are at V_{CC} = 5 V, T_A = 25°C.
§ Not more than one output should be shorted at a time, and the duration of the short circuit should not exceed one second.
NOTE 2: With all outputs open, I_{CC} is measured with the Q and $\overline{Q}$ outputs high in turn. At the time of measurement, the clock input is grounded.
NOTE 4: For certain devices where state commutation can be caused by shorting an output to ground, an equivalent test may be performed with V_O = 2.25 V and 2.125 V for the 54 family and the 74 family, respectively, with the minimum and maximum limits reduced to one half of their stated values.

TEXAS
INSTRUMENTS

3 TTL DEVICES

switching characteristics, V_{CC} = 5 V, T_A = 25°C (see note 3)

PARAMETER	FROM (INPUT)	TO (OUTPUT)	TEST CONDITIONS	MIN	TYP	MAX	UNIT
f_{max}			R_L = 2 kΩ, C_L = 15 pF	30	45		MHz
t_{PLH}	$\overline{PRE}$, $\overline{CLR}$ or CLK	Q or $\overline{Q}$			15	20	ns
t_{PHL}					15	20	ns

NOTE 3: See General Information Section for load circuits and voltage waveforms.

TTL DEVICES

3

- Full-Carry Look-Ahead across the Four Bits
- Systems Achieve Partial Look-Ahead Performance with the Economy of Ripple Carry
- SN54283/SN74283 and SN54LS283/SN74LS283 Are Recommended For New Designs as They Feature Supply Voltage and Ground on Corner Pins to Simplify Board Layout

TYPE	TYPICAL ADD TIMES		TYPICAL POWER DISSIPATION PER 4-BIT ADDER
	TWO 8-BIT WORDS	TWO 16-BIT WORDS	
'83A	23 ns	43 ns	310 mW
'LS83A	25 ns	45 ns	95 mW

SN5483A, SN54LS83A ... J OR W PACKAGE
SN7483A ... J OR N PACKAGE
SN74LS83A ... D, J OR N PACKAGE
(TOP VIEW)

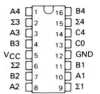

A4	1	16	B4
Σ3	2	15	Σ4
A3	3	14	C4
B3	4	13	C0
VCC	5	12	GND
Σ2	6	11	B1
B2	7	10	A1
A2	8	9	Σ1

SN54LS83A ... FK PACKAGE
SN74LS83A
(TOP VIEW)

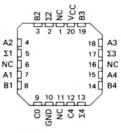

NC - No internal connection

description

These improved full adders perform the addition of two 4-bit binary numbers. The sum (Σ) outputs are provided for each bit and the resultant carry (C4) is obtained from the fourth bit. These adders feature full internal look ahead across all four bits generating the carry term in ten nanoseconds typically. This provides the system designer with partial look-ahead performance at the economy and reduced package count of a ripple-carry implementation.

The adder logic, including the carry, is implemented in its true form meaning that the end-around carry can be accomplished without the need for logic or level inversion.

Designed for medium-speed applications, the circuits utilize transistor-transistor logic that is compatible with most other TTL families and other saturated low-level logic families.

Series 54 and 54LS circuits are characterized for operation over the full military temperature range of −55°C to 125°C, and Series 74 and 74LS circuits are characterized for operation from 0°C to 70°C.

FUNCTION TABLE

INPUT				OUTPUT					
				WHEN C0 = L			WHEN C0 = H		
						WHEN C2 = L			WHEN C2 = H
A1	B1	A2	B2	Σ1	Σ2	C2	Σ1	Σ2	C2
A2	B3	A4	B4	Σ3	Σ4	C4	Σ3	Σ4	C4
L	L	L	L	L	L	L	L	L	L
H	L	L	L	H	L	L	L	H	L
L	H	L	L	H	L	L	L	H	L
H	H	L	L	L	H	L	H	L	L
L	L	H	L	L	H	L	H	L	L
H	L	H	L	H	H	L	L	L	H
L	H	H	L	H	H	L	L	L	H
H	H	H	L	L	L	H	H	L	L
L	L	L	H	L	L	H	H	L	L
H	L	L	H	H	H	L	L	L	H
L	H	L	H	H	H	L	L	L	H
H	H	L	H	L	L	H	H	L	H
L	L	H	H	L	L	H	H	L	H
H	L	H	H	H	L	H	L	H	H
L	H	H	H	H	L	H	L	H	H
H	H	H	H	L	H	H	H	H	H

H = high level, L = low level

NOTE: Input conditions at A1, B1, A2, B2, and C0 are used to determine outputs Σ1 and Σ2 and the value of the internal carry C2. The values at C2, A3, B3, A4, and B4 are then used to determine outputs Σ3, Σ4, and C4.

3

TTL DEVICES

TEXAS
INSTRUMENTS

TYPES SN5483A, SN54LS83A, SN7483A, SN74LS83A
4-BIT BINARY FULL ADDERS WITH FAST CARRY

schematics of inputs and outputs

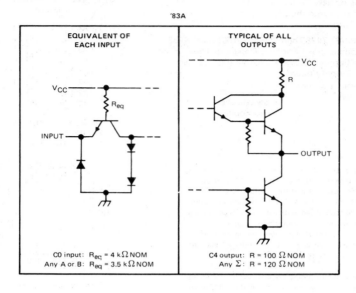

'83A

EQUIVALENT OF EACH INPUT

TYPICAL OF ALL OUTPUTS

C0 input: R_{eq} = 4 kΩ NOM
Any A or B: R_{eq} = 3.5 kΩ NOM

C4 output: R = 100 Ω NOM
Any Σ: R = 120 Ω NOM

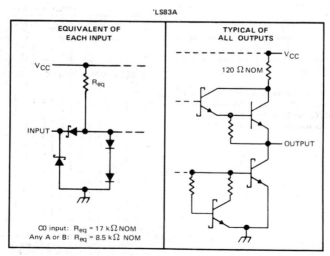

'LS83A

EQUIVALENT OF EACH INPUT

TYPICAL OF ALL OUTPUTS

120 Ω NOM

C0 input: R_{eq} = 17 kΩ NOM
Any A or B: R_{eq} = 8.5 kΩ NOM

TEXAS
INSTRUMENTS

3

TTL DEVICES

logic diagram

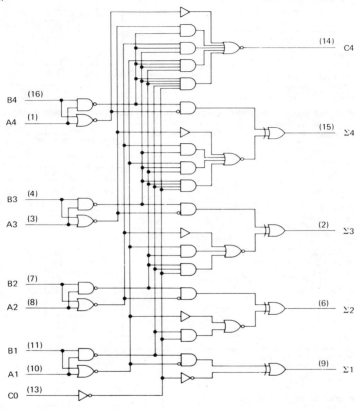

Pin numbers shown on logic notation are for D, J or N packages.

absolute maximum ratings over operating free-air temperature range (unless otherwise noted)

Supply voltage, V_{CC} (see Note 1) . . . . 7 V
Input voltage: '83A . . . . 5.5 V
             'LS83A . . . . 7 V
Interemitter voltage (see Note 2) . . . . 5.5 V
Operating free-air temperature range: SN5483A, SN54LS83A . . . . −55°C to 125°C
                              SN7483A, SN74LS83A . . . . 0°C to 70°C
Storage temperature range . . . . 65°C to 150°C

NOTES: 1. Voltage values, except interemitter voltage, are with respect to network ground terminal.
2. This is the voltage between two emitters of a multiple emitter transistor. This rating applies for the '83A only between the following pairs: A1 and B1, A2 and B2, A3 and B3, A4 and B4.

TTL DEVICES

3

recommended operating conditions

		SN5483A MIN	SN5483A NOM	SN5483A MAX	SN7483A MIN	SN7483A NOM	SN7483A MAX	UNIT
Supply Voltage, V_{CC}		4.5	5	5.5	4.75	5	5.25	V
High-level output current, I_{OH}	Any output except C4			-800			800	μA
	Output C4			400			400	
Low-level output current, I_{OL}	Any output except C4			16			16	mA
	Output C4			8			8	
Operating free-air temperature, T_A		-55		125	0		70	C

electrical characteristics over recommended operating free-air temperature range (unless otherwise noted)

PARAMETER		TEST CONDITIONS[†]	SN5483A MIN	SN5483A TYP[‡]	SN5483A MAX	SN7483A MIN	SN7483A TYP[‡]	SN7483A MAX	UNIT
V_{IH}	High-level input voltage		2			2			V
V_{IL}	Low-level input voltage				0.8			0.8	V
V_{IK}	Input clamp voltage	V_{CC} = MIN, I_I = -12 mA			-1.5			-1.5	V
V_{OH}	High-level output voltage	V_{CC} = MIN, V_{IH} = 2 V, V_{IL} = 0.8 V, I_{OH} = MAX	2.4	3.4		2.4	3.4		V
V_{OL}	Low-level output voltage	V_{CC} = MIN, V_{IH} = 2 V, V_{IL} = 0.8 V, I_{OL} = MAX		0.2	0.4		0.2	0.4	V
I_I	Input current at maximum input voltage	V_{CC} = MAX, V_I = 5.5 V			1			1	mA
I_{IH}	High-level input current	V_{CC} = MAX, V_I = 2.4 V			40			40	μA
I_{IL}	Low-level input current	V_{CC} = MAX, V_I = 0.4 V			-1.6			-1.6	mA
I_{OS}	Short-circuit output current[§] Any output except C4	V_{CC} = MAX	-20		-55	-18		-55	mA
	Output C4		-20		-70	-18		-70	
I_{CC}	Supply current	V_{CC} = MAX, Outputs open — All B low, other inputs at 4.5 V		56			56		mA
		All inputs at 4.5 V		66	99		66	110	

† For conditions shown as MIN or MAX, use the appropriate value specified under recommended operating conditions.
‡ All typical values are at V_{CC} = 5 V, T_A = 25°C.
§ Only one output should be shorted at a time.

switching characteristics, V_{CC} = 5 V, T_A = 25°C

PARAMETER[¶]	FROM (INPUT)	TO (OUTPUT)	TEST CONDITIONS	MIN	TYP	MAX	UNIT
t_{PLH}	C0	Any Σ	C_L = 15 pF, R_L = 400 Ω, See Note 3		14	21	ns
t_{PHL}					12	21	
t_{PLH}	A_i or B_i	Σ_i			16	24	ns
t_{PHL}					16	24	
t_{PLH}	C0	C4	C_L = 15 pF, R_L = 780 Ω, See Note 3		9	14	ns
t_{PHL}					11	16	
t_{PLH}	A_i or B_i	C4			9	14	ns
t_{PHL}					11	16	

¶ t_{PLH} Propagation delay time, low to high level output
t_{PHL} Propagation delay time, high to low level output
NOTE 3: See General Information Section for load circuits and voltage waveforms.

TEXAS
INSTRUMENTS

recommended operating conditions

		SN54LS83A			SN74LS83A			UNIT
		MIN	NOM	MAX	MIN	NOM	MAX	
Supply voltage, V_{CC}		4.5	5	5.5	4.75	5	5.25	V
High-level output current, I_{OH}				−400			−400	μA
Low-level output current, I_{OL}				4			8	mA
Operating free-air temperature, T_A		−55		125	0		70	C

electrical characteristics over recommended operating free-air temperature range (unless otherwise noted)

PARAMETER			TEST CONDITIONS[†]		SN54LS83A			SN74LS83A			UNIT
					MIN	TYP[‡]	MAX	MIN	TYP[‡]	MAX	
V_{IH}	High-level input voltage				2			2			V
V_{IL}	Low-level input voltage						0.7			0.8	V
V_{IK}	Input clamp voltage		V_{CC} = MIN, I_I = −18 mA				−1.5			−1.5	V
V_{OH}	High-level output voltage		V_{CC} = MIN, V_{IH} = 2 V, V_{IL} = V_{IL} max, I_{OH} = −400 μA		2.5	3.4		2.7	3.4		V
V_{OL}	Low-level output voltage		V_{CC} = MIN, V_{IH} = 2 V, V_{IL} = V_{IL} max	I_{OL} = 4 mA		0.25	0.4		0.25	0.4	V
				I_{OL} = 8 mA					0.35	0.5	
I_I	Input current at maximum input voltage	Any A or B	V_{CC} = MAX, V_I = 7 V				0.2			0.2	mA
		C0					0.1			0.1	
I_{IH}	High-level input current	Any A or B	V_{CC} = MAX, V_I = 2.7 V				40			40	μA
		C0					20			20	
I_{IL}	Low-level input current	Any A or B	V_{CC} = MAX, V_I = 0.4 V				−0.8			−0.8	mA
		C0					−0.4			−0.4	
I_{OS}	Short-circuit output current [§]		V_{CC} = MAX		−20		−100	−20		−100	mA
I_{CC}	Supply current		V_{CC} = MAX, Outputs open	All inputs grounded		22	39		22	39	mA
				All B low, other inputs at 4.5 V		19	34		19	34	
				All inputs at 4.5 V		19	34		19	34	

[†] For conditions shown as MIN or MAX, use the appropriate value specified under recommended operating conditions.
[‡] All typical values are at V_{CC} = 5 V, T_A = 25°C.
[§] Only one output should be shorted at a time, and duration of the short-circuit should not exceed one second.

switching characteristics, V_{CC} = 5 V, T_A = 25°C

PARAMETER[¶]	FROM (INPUT)	TO (OUTPUT)	TEST CONDITIONS	MIN	TYP	MAX	UNIT
t_{PLH}	C0	Any Σ			16	24	ns
t_{PHL}					15	24	
t_{PLH}	A_i or B_i	Σ_i	C_L = 15 pF, R_L = 2 kΩ, See Note 4		15	24	ns
t_{PHL}					15	24	
t_{PLH}	C0	C4			11	17	ns
t_{PHL}					15	22	
t_{PLH}	A_i or B_i	C4			11	17	ns
t_{PHL}					12	17	

[¶] t_{PLH} Propagation delay time, low to high level output
t_{PHL} Propagation delay time, high to low level output
Note 4: See General Information Section for load circuits and voltage waveforms.

3

TTL DEVICES

TYPE	TYPICAL POWER DISSIPATION	TYPICAL DELAY (4-BIT WORDS)
'85	275 mW	23 ns
'LS85	52 mW	24 ns
'S85	365 mW	11 ns

description

These four-bit magnitude comparators perform comparison of straight binary and straight BCD (8-4-2-1) codes. Three fully decoded decisions about two 4-bit words (A, B) are made and are externally available at three outputs. These devices are fully expandable to any number of bits without external gates. Words of greater length may be compared by connecting comparators in cascade. The A > B, A < B, and A = B outputs of a stage handling less-significant bits are connected to the corresponding A > B, A < B, and A = B inputs of the next stage handling more-significant bits. The stage handling the least-significant bits must have a high-level voltage applied to the A = B input. The cascading paths of the '85, 'LS85, and 'S85 are implemented with only a two-gate-level delay to reduce overall comparison times for long words. An alternate method of cascading which further reduces the comparison time is shown in the typical application data.

SN5485, SN54LS85, SN54S85 . . . J OR W PACKAGE
SN7485 . . . J OR N PACKAGE
SN74LS85, SN74S85 . . . D, J OR N PACKAGE
(TOP VIEW)

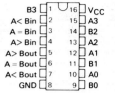

```
        B3  [ 1   U  16 ]  VCC
    A< Bin  [ 2      15 ]  A3
    A = Bin [ 3      14 ]  B2
    A> Bin  [ 4      13 ]  A2
   A> Bout  [ 5      12 ]  A1
   A = Bout [ 6      11 ]  B1
   A< Bout  [ 7      10 ]  A0
       GND  [ 8       9 ]  B0
```

SN54LS85, SN54S85 . . . FK PACKAGE
SN74LS85, SN74S85
(TOP VIEW)

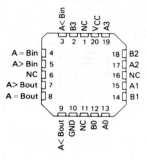

```
             A< Bin  B3  NC  VCC  A3
                3    2   1   20   19
   A = Bin [ 4                    18 ] B2
   A> Bin  [ 5                    17 ] A2
      NC   [ 6                    16 ] NC
  A> Bout  [ 7                    15 ] A1
  A = Bout [ 8                    14 ] B1
                9   10  11  12  13
             A< Bout  GND  NC  B0  A0
```

NC - No internal connection

FUNCTION TABLES

COMPARING INPUTS				CASCADING INPUTS			OUTPUTS		
A3, B3	A2, B2	A1, B1	A0, B0	A > B	A < B	A = B	A > B	A < B	A = B
A3 > B3	X	X	X	X	X	X	H	L	L
A3 < B3	X	X	X	X	X	X	L	H	L
A3 = B3	A2 > B2	X	X	X	X	X	H	L	L
A3 = B3	A2 < B2	X	X	X	X	X	L	H	L
A3 = B3	A2 = B2	A1 > B1	X	X	X	X	H	L	L
A3 = B3	A2 = B2	A1 < B1	X	X	X	X	L	H	L
A3 = B3	A2 = B2	A1 = B1	A0 > B0	X	X	X	H	L	L
A3 = B3	A2 = B2	A1 = B1	A0 < B0	X	X	X	L	H	L
A3 = B3	A2 = B2	A1 = B1	A0 = B0	H	L	L	H	L	L
A3 = B3	A2 = B2	A1 = B1	A0 = B0	L	H	L	L	H	L
A3 = B3	A2 = B2	A1 = B1	A0 = B0	L	L	H	L	L	H

'85, 'LS85, 'S85

A3 = B3	A2 = B2	A1 = B1	A0 = B0	X	X	H	L	L	H
A3 = B3	A2 = B2	A1 = B1	A0 = B0	H	H	L	L	L	L
A3 = B3	A2 = B2	A1 = B1	A0 = B0	L	L	L	H	H	L

TEXAS
INSTRUMENTS

3

TTL DEVICES

logic diagram

'85, 'LS85, 'S85

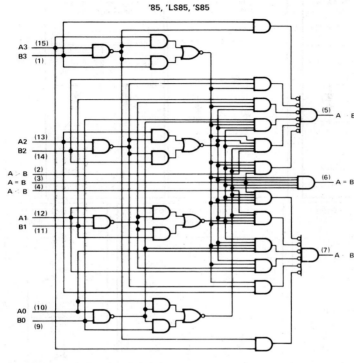

Pin numbers shown on logic notation are for D, J or N packages.

schematics of inputs and outputs

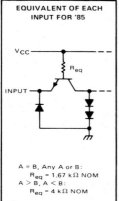

EQUIVALENT OF EACH
INPUT FOR '85

V_{CC}

R_{eq}

INPUT

A = B, Any A or B:
$R_{eq} = 1.67\ k\Omega$ NOM
A > B, A < B:
$R_{eq} = 4\ k\Omega$ NOM

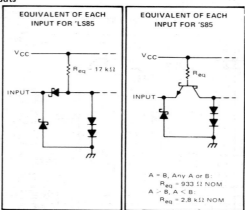

EQUIVALENT OF EACH
INPUT FOR 'LS85

V_{CC}

$R_{eq} \sim 17\ k\Omega$

INPUT

EQUIVALENT OF EACH
INPUT FOR 'S85

V_{CC}

R_{eq}

INPUT

A = B, Any A or B:
$R_{eq} = 933\ \Omega$ NOM
A > B, A < B:
$R_{eq} = 2.8\ k\Omega$ NOM

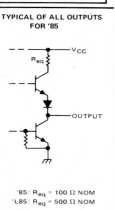

TYPICAL OF ALL OUTPUTS
FOR '85

V_{CC}

R_{eq}

OUTPUT

'85: $R_{eq} = 100\ \Omega$ NOM
'L85: $R_{eq} = 500\ \Omega$ NOM

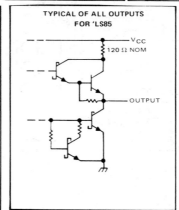

TYPICAL OF ALL OUTPUTS
FOR 'LS85

V_{CC}
120 Ω NOM

OUTPUT

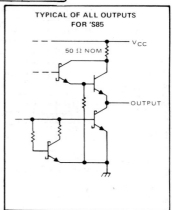

TYPICAL OF ALL OUTPUTS
FOR 'S85

V_{CC}

50 Ω NOM

OUTPUT

absolute maximum ratings over operating free-air temperature range (unless otherwise noted)

	SN54' SN54S'		SN54LS'	SN74' SN74S'	SN74LS	UNIT
Supply voltage, V_{CC} (see Note 1)	7		7	7	7	V
Input voltage	5.5		7	5.5	7	V
Interemitter voltage (see Note 2)	5.5			5.5		V
Operating free-air temperature range	−55 to 125			−0 to 70		°C
Storage temperature range	−65 to 150			−65 to 150		°C

NOTES: 1. Voltage values, except interemitter voltage, are with respect to network ground terminal.

2. This is the voltage between two emitters of a multiple-emitter input transistor. This rating applies to each A input in conjunction with its respective B input of the '85 and 'S85.

TEXAS
INSTRUMENTS

recommended operating conditions

	SN5485 MIN	SN5485 NOM	SN5485 MAX	SN7485 MIN	SN7485 NOM	SN7485 MAX	UNIT
Supply voltage, V_{CC}	4.5	5	5.5	4.75	5	5.25	V
High-level output current, I_{OH}			−400			−400	μA
Low-level output current, I_{OL}			16			16	mA
Operating free-air temperature, T_A	−55		125	0		70	°C

electrical characteristics over recommended operating free-air temperature range (unless otherwise noted)

	PARAMETER		TEST CONDITIONS†			MIN	TYP‡	MAX	UNIT
V_{IH}	High-level input voltage					2			V
V_{IL}	Low-level input voltage							0.8	V
V_{IK}	Input clamp voltage		V_{CC} = MIN,		I_I = −12 mA			−1.5	V
V_{OH}	High-level output voltage		V_{CC} = MIN, V_{IL} = 0.8 V,	V_{IH} = 2 V, I_{OH} = −400 μA		2.4	3.4		V
V_{OL}	Low-level output voltage		V_{CC} = MIN, V_{IL} = 0.8 V,	V_{IH} = 2 V, I_{OL} = 16 mA			0.2	0.4	V
I_I	Input current at maximum input voltage		V_{CC} = MAX,	V_I = 5.5 V				1	mA
I_{IH}	High-level input current	A < B, A > B inputs	V_{CC} = MAX,	V_I = 2.4 V				40	μA
		all other inputs						120	
I_{IL}	Low-level input current	A < B, A > B inputs	V_{CC} = MAX,	V_I = 0.4 V				−1.6	mA
		all other inputs						−4.8	
I_{OS}	Short-circuit output current§		V_{CC} = MAX, V_O = 0		SN5485	−20		−55	mA
					SN7485	−18		−55	
I_{CC}	Supply current		V_{CC} = MAX, See Note 4				55	88	mA

†For conditions shown as MIN or MAX, use the appropriate value specified under recommended operating conditions.
‡All typical values are at V_{CC} = 5 V, T_A = 25°C.
§Not more than one output should be shorted at a time.
NOTE 4: I_{CC} is measured with outputs open, A = B grounded, and all other inputs at 4.5 V.

switching characteristics, V_{CC} = 5 V, T_A = 25°C

PARAMETER¶	FROM INPUT	TO OUTPUT	NUMBER OF GATE LEVELS	TEST CONDITIONS	MIN	TYP	MAX	UNIT
t_{PLH}	Any A or B data input	A < B, A > B	1			7		ns
			2			12		
			3			17	26	
		A = B	4			23	35	
t_{PHL}	Any A or B data input	A < B, A > B	1			11		ns
			2	C_L = 15 pF,		15		
			3	R_L = 400 Ω,		20	30	
		A = B	4	See Note 5		20	30	
t_{PLH}	A < B or A = B	A > B	1			7	11	ns
t_{PHL}	A < B or A = B	A > B	1			11	17	ns
t_{PLH}	A = B	A = B	2			13	20	ns
t_{PHL}	A = B	A = B	2			11	17	ns
t_{PLH}	A > B or A = B	A < B	1			7	11	ns
t_{PHL}	A > B or A = B	A < B	1			11	17	ns

¶t_{PLH} ≡ propagation delay time, low-to-high-level output
t_{PHL} ≡ propagation delay time, high-to-low-level output.
NOTE 5: See General Information Section for load circuits and voltage waveforms.

TEXAS
INSTRUMENTS

TTL DEVICES

3

recommended operating conditions

	SN54LS85			SN74LS85			UNIT
	MIN	NOM	MAX	MIN	NOM	MAX	
Supply voltage, V_{CC}	4.5	5	5.5	4.75	5	5.25	V
High-level output current, I_{OH}			-400			-400	μA
Low-level output current, I_{OL}			4			8	mA
Operating free-air temperature, T_A	-55		125	0		70	°C

electrical characteristics over recommended operating free-air temperature range (unless otherwise noted)

PARAMETER			TEST CONDITIONS[†]		SN54LS85			SN74LS85			UNIT
					MIN	TYP[‡]	MAX	MIN	TYP[‡]	MAX	
V_{IH}	High-level input voltage				2			2			V
V_{IL}	Low-level input voltage						0.7			0.7	V
V_{IK}	Input clamp voltage		$V_{CC} = $ MIN,	$I_I = -18$ mA			-1.5			-1.5	V
V_{OH}	High-level output voltage		$V_{CC} = $ MIN, $V_{IL} = V_{IL}$ max,	$V_{IH} = 2$ V, $I_{OH} = -400 \mu$A	2.5	3.4		2.7	3.4		V
V_{OL}	Low-level output voltage		$V_{CC} = $ MIN, $V_{IH} = 2$ V,	$I_{OL} = 4$ mA		0.25	0.4		0.25	0.4	V
			$V_{IL} = V_{IL}$ max	$I_{OL} = 8$ mA					0.35	0.5	
I_I	Input current at maximum input voltage	$A < B, A > B$ inputs	$V_{CC} = $ MAX,	$V_I = 7$ V			0.1			0.1	mA
		all other inputs					0.3			0.3	
I_{IH}	High-level input current	$A < B, A > B$ inputs	$V_{CC} = $ MAX,	$V_I = 2.7$ V			20			20	μA
		all other inputs					60			60	
I_{IL}	Low-level input current	$A < B, A > B$ inputs	$V_{CC} = $ MAX,	$V_I = 0.4$ V			-0.4			-0.4	mA
		all other inputs					-1.2			-1.2	
I_{OS}	Short-circuit output current [§]		$V_{CC} = $ MAX		-20		-100	-20		-100	mA
I_{CC}	Supply current		$V_{CC} = $ MAX,	See Note 4		10.4	20		10.4	20	mA

[†] For conditions shown as MIN or MAX, use the appropriate value specified under recommended operating conditions.
[‡] All typical values are at $V_{CC} = 5$ V, $T_A = 25$°C.
[§] Not more than one output should be shorted at a time, and duration of the short-circuit should not exceed one second.
NOTE 4: I_{CC} is measured with outputs open, $A = B$ grounded, and all other inputs at 4.5 V.

switching characteristics, $V_{CC} = 5$ V, $T_A = 25$°C

PARAMETER[¶]	FROM INPUT	TO OUTPUT	NUMBER OF GATE LEVELS	TEST CONDITIONS	MIN	TYP	MAX	UNIT
t_{PLH}	Any A or B data input	$A < B, A > B$	1			14		ns
			2			19		
			3			24	36	
		$A = B$	4			27	45	
t_{PHL}	Any A or B data input	$A < B, A > B$	1	$C_L = 15$ pF, $R_L = 2$ kΩ, See Note 5		11		ns
			2			15		
			3			20	30	
		$A = B$	4			23	45	
t_{PLH}	$A < B$ or $A = B$	$A > B$	1			14	22	ns
t_{PHL}	$A < B$ or $A = B$	$A > B$	1			11	17	ns
t_{PLH}	$A = B$	$A = B$	2			13	20	ns
t_{PHL}	$A = B$	$A = B$	2			13	26	ns
t_{PLH}	$A > B$ or $A = B$	$A < B$	1			14	22	ns
t_{PHL}	$A > B$ or $A = B$	$A < B$	1			11	17	ns

[¶] t_{PLH} = propagation delay time, low-to-high-level output
t_{PHL} = propagation delay time, high-to-low-level output
NOTE 5: See General Information Section for load circuits and voltage waveforms.

TEXAS
INSTRUMENTS

recommended operating conditions

	SN54S85			SN74S85			UNIT
	MIN	NOM	MAX	MIN	NOM	MAX	
Supply voltage, V_{CC}	4.5	5	5.5	4.75	5	5.25	V
High-level output current, I_{OH}			−1			−1	mA
Low-level output current, I_{OL}			20			20	mA
Operating free-air temperature, T_A	−55		125	0		70	C

electrical characteristics over recommended operating free-air temperature range (unless otherwise noted)

PARAMETER		TEST CONDITIONS[†]		MIN	TYP[‡]	MAX	UNIT
V_{IH}	High-level input voltage			2			V
V_{IL}	Low-level input voltage					0.8	V
V_{IK}	Input clamp voltage	V_{CC} = MIN, I_I = −18 mA				−1.2	V
V_{OH}	High-level output voltage	V_{CC} = MIN, V_{IH} = 2 V,	SN54S85	2.5	3.4		V
		V_{IL} = 0.8 V, I_{OH} = −1 mA	SN74S85	2.7	3.4		
V_{OL}	Low-level output voltage	V_{CC} = MIN, V_{IH} = 2 V, V_{IL} = 0.8 V, I_{OL} = 20 mA				0.5	V
I_I	Input current at maximum input voltage	V_{CC} = MAX, V_I = 5.5 V				1	mA
I_{IH}	High-level input current	A < B, A > B inputs	V_{CC} = MAX, V_I = 2.7 V			50	μA
		all other inputs				150	
I_{IL}	Low-level input current	A < B, A > B inputs	V_{CC} = MAX, V_I = 0.5 V			−2	mA
		all other inputs				−6	
I_{OS}	Short-circuit output current[§]	V_{CC} = MAX		−40		−100	mA
I_{CC}	Supply current	V_{CC} = MAX, See Note 4			73	115	mA
		V_{CC} = MAX, T_A = 125 C, See Note 4	SN54S85W			110	

[†]For conditions shown as MIN or MAX, use the appropriate value specified under recommended operating conditions.
[‡]All typical values are at V_{CC} = 5 V, T_A = 25 C.
[§]Not more than one output should be shorted at a time, and duration of the short-circuit should not exceed one second.
NOTE 4: I_{CC} is measured with outputs open, A = B grounded, and all other inputs at 4.5 V.

switching characteristics, V_{CC} = 5 V, T_A = 25°C

PARAMETER[¶]	FROM INPUT	TO OUTPUT	NUMBER OF GATE LEVELS	TEST CONDITIONS	MIN	TYP	MAX	UNIT
t_{PLH}	Any A or B data input	A < B, A > B	1			5		ns
			2			7.5		
			3			10.5	16	
		A = B	4			12	18	
t_{PHL}	Any A or B data input	A < B, A > B	1			5.5		ns
			2	C_L = 15 pF,		7		
			3	R_L = 280 Ω,		11	16.5	
		A = B	4	See Note 5		11	16.5	
t_{PLH}	A < B or A = B	A > B	1			5	7.5	ns
t_{PHL}	A < B or A = B	A > B	1			5.5	8.5	ns
t_{PLH}	A = B	A = B	2			7	10.5	ns
t_{PHL}	A = B	A = B	2			5	7.5	ns
t_{PLH}	A > B or A = B	A < B	1			5	7.5	ns
t_{PHL}	A > B or A = B	A < B	1			5.5	8.5	ns

[¶]t_{PLH} propagation delay time, low-to-high-level output
t_{PHL} propagation delay time, high-to-low-level output
NOTE 5: See General Information Section for load circuits and voltage waveforms.

TEXAS
INSTRUMENTS

3

TTL DEVICES

TYPICAL APPLICATION DATA

COMPARISON OF TWO N-BIT WORDS

This application demonstrates how these magnitude comparators can be cascaded to compare longer words. The example illustrated shows the comparison of two 24-bit words; however, the design is expandable to n-bits. As an example, one comparator can be used with five of the 24-bit comparators illustrated to expand the word length to 120-bits. Typical comparison times for various word lengths using the '85, 'LS85, or 'S85 are:

WORD LENGTH	NUMBER OF PKGS	'85	'LS85	'S85
1-4 bits	1	23 ns	24 ns	11 ns
5-24 bits	2-6	46 ns	48 ns	22 ns
25-120 bits	8-31	69 ns	72 ns	33 ns

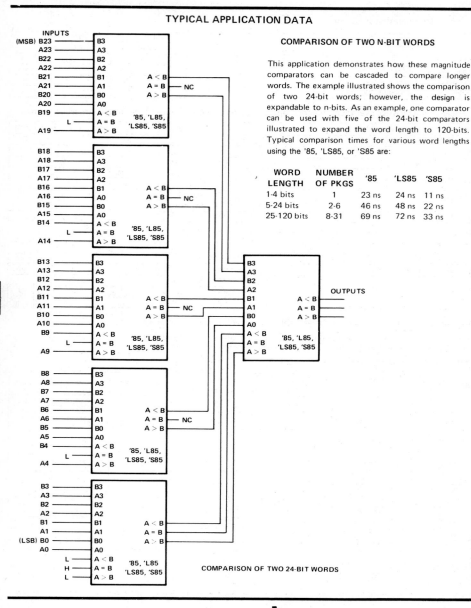

COMPARISON OF TWO 24-BIT WORDS

TEXAS
INSTRUMENTS

schematics of inputs and outputs

'86

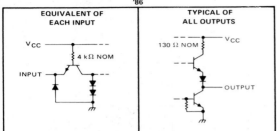

EQUIVALENT OF EACH INPUT	TYPICAL OF ALL OUTPUTS

V_CC — 4 kΩ NOM — INPUT

130 Ω NOM — V_CC — OUTPUT

'LS86A

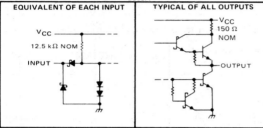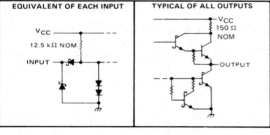

EQUIVALENT OF EACH INPUT	TYPICAL OF ALL OUTPUTS

V_CC — 12.5 kΩ NOM — INPUT

V_CC — 150 Ω NOM — OUTPUT

'S86

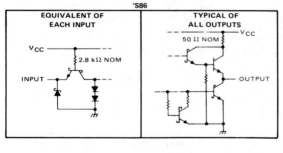

EQUIVALENT OF EACH INPUT	TYPICAL OF ALL OUTPUTS

V_CC — 2.8 kΩ NOM — INPUT

V_CC — 50 Ω NOM — OUTPUT

SN5486, SN54LS86A, SN54S86 . . . J OR W PACKAGE
SN7486 . . . J OR N PACKAGE
SN74LS86A, SN74S86 . . . D, J OR N PACKAGE

(TOP VIEW)

1A	1		14	V_CC
1B	2		13	4B
1Y	3		12	4A
2A	4		11	4Y
2B	5		10	3B
2Y	6		9	3A
GND	7		8	3Y

SN54LS86A, SN54S86 . . . FK PACKAGE
SN74LS86A, SN74S86

(TOP VIEW)

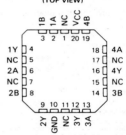

1B 1A NC V_CC 4B
3 2 1 20 19

1Y	4	18	4A
NC	5	17	NC
2A	6	16	4Y
NC	7	15	NC
2B	8	14	3B

9 10 11 12 13
2Y GND NC 3Y 3A

NC - No internal connection

FUNCTION TABLES

INPUTS		OUTPUT
A	B	Y
L	L	L
L	H	H
H	L	H
H	H	L

H = high level, L = low level

TYPE	TYPICAL AVERAGE PROPAGATION DELAY TIME	TYPICAL TOTAL POWER DISSIPATION
'86	14 ns	150 mW
'LS86A	10 ns	30.5 mW
'S86	7 ns	250 mW

3

TTL DEVICES

TEXAS INSTRUMENTS

absolute maximum ratings over operating free-air temperature range (unless otherwise noted)

Supply voltage, V_{CC} (see Note 1)	. . . .	7 V
Input voltage	. . . .	5.5 V
Operating free-air temperature range: SN5486	. . . .	-55°C to 125°C
SN7486	. . . .	0°C to 70°C
Storage temperature range	. . . .	-65°C to 150°C

NOTE 1: Voltage values are with respect to network ground terminal.

recommended operating conditions

	SN5486			SN7486			UNIT
	MIN	NOM	MAX	MIN	NOM	MAX	
Supply voltage, V_{CC}	4.5	5	5.5	4.75	5	5.25	V
High-level output current, I_{OH}			-800			-800	μA
Low-level output current, I_{OL}			16			16	mA
Operating free-air temperature, T_A	-55		125	0		70	$^\circ$C

electrical characteristics over recommended operating free-air temperature range (unless otherwise noted)

PARAMETER		TEST CONDITIONS[†]	SN5486			SN7486			UNIT
			MIN	TYP[‡]	MAX	MIN	TYP[‡]	MAX	
V_{IH}	High-level input voltage		2			2			V
V_{IL}	Low-level input voltage				0.8			0.8	V
V_{IK}	Input clamp voltage	V_{CC} = MIN, I_I = -8 mA			-1.5			-1.5	V
V_{OH}	High-level output voltage	V_{CC} = MIN, V_{IH} = 2 V, V_{IL} = 0.8 V, I_{OH} = $-800\,\mu$A	2.4	3.4		2.4	3.4		V
V_{OL}	Low-level output voltage	V_{CC} = MIN, V_{IH} = 2 V V_{IL} = 0.8 V, I_{OL} = 16 mA		0.2	0.4		0.2	0.4	V
I_I	Input current at maximum input voltage	V_{CC} = MAX, V_I = 5.5 V			1			1	mA
I_{IH}	High-level input current	V_{CC} = MAX, V_I = 2.4 V			40			40	μA
I_{IL}	Low-level input current	V_{CC} = MAX, V_I = 0.4 V			-1.6			-1.6	mA
I_{OS}	Short-circuit output current[§]	V_{CC} = MAX	-20		-55	-18		-55	mA
I_{CC}	Supply current	V_{CC} = MAX, See Note 2		30	43		30	50	mA

[†] For conditions shown as MIN or MAX, use the appropriate value specified under recommended operating conditions for the applicable type.
[‡] All typical values are at V_{CC} = 5 V, T_A = 25°C.
[§] Not more than one output should be shorted at a time.
NOTE 2: I_{CC} is measured with the inputs grounded and the outputs open.

switching characteristics, V_{CC} = 5 V, T_A = 25°C

PARAMETER[¶]	FROM (INPUT)	TEST CONDITIONS		MIN	TYP	MAX	UNIT
t_{PLH}	A or B	Other input low	C_L = 15 pF, R_L = 400 Ω, See Note 3		15	23	ns
t_{PHL}					11	17	
t_{PLH}	A or B	Other input high			18	30	ns
t_{PHL}					13	22	

[¶] t_{PLH} propagation delay time, low-to-high-level output
t_{PHL} propagation delay time, high-to-low-level output
NOTE 3: See General Information Section for load circuits and voltage waveforms.

TEXAS
INSTRUMENTS

absolute maximum ratings over operating free-air temperature range (unless otherwise noted)

Supply voltage, V_{CC} (see Note 1) . . . . 7 V
Input voltage . . . . 7 V
Operating free-air temperature range: SN54LS86A . . . . $-55°C$ to $125°C$
SN74LS86A . . . . $0°C$ to $70°C$
Storage temperature range . . . . $-65°C$ to $150°C$

NOTE 1: Voltage values are with respect to network ground terminal.

recommended operating conditions

	SN54LS86A			SN74LS86A			UNIT
	MIN	NOM	MAX	MIN	NOM	MAX	
Supply voltage, V_{CC}	4.5	5	5.5	4.75	5	5.25	V
High-level output current, I_{OH}			-400			-400	μA
Low-level output current, I_{OL}			4			8	mA
Operating free-air temperature, T_A	-55		125	0		70	°C

electrical characteristics over recommended operating free-air temperature range (unless otherwise noted)

PARAMETER		TEST CONDITIONS†		SN54LS86A			SN74LS86A			UNIT
				MIN	TYP‡	MAX	MIN	TYP‡	MAX	
V_{IH}	High-level input voltage			2			2			V
V_{IL}	Low-level input voltage					0.7			0.8	V
V_{IK}	Input clamp voltage	V_{CC} = MIN,	$I_I = -18$ mA			-1.5			-1.5	V
V_{OH}	High-level output voltage	V_{CC} = MIN, $V_{IL} = V_{IL}$ max,	$V_{IH} = 2$ V, $I_{OH} = -400 \mu A$	2.5	3.4		2.7	3.4		V
V_{OL}	Low-level output voltage	V_{CC} = MIN, $V_{IH} = 2$ V,	$I_{OL} = 4$ mA		0.25	0.4		0.25	0.4	V
		$V_{IL} = V_{IL}$ max	$I_{OL} = 8$ mA					0.35	0.5	
I_I	Input current at maximum input voltage	V_{CC} = MAX,	$V_I = 7$ V			0.2			0.2	mA
I_{IH}	High-level input current	V_{CC} = MAX,	$V_I = 2.7$ V			40			40	μA
I_{IL}	Low-level input current	V_{CC} = MAX,	$V_I = 0.4$ V			-0.8			-0.8	mA
I_{OS}	Short-circuit output current§	V_{CC} = MAX		-20		-100	-20		-100	mA
I_{CC}	Supply current	V_{CC} = MAX,	See Note 2		6.1	10		6.1	10	mA

†For conditions shown as MIN or MAX, use the appropriate value specified under recommended operating conditions for the applicable type.
‡All typical values are at V_{CC} = 5 V, $T_A = 25°C$.
§Not more than one output should be shorted at a time.
NOTE 2: I_{CC} is measured with the inputs grounded and the outputs open.

switching characteristics, V_{CC} = 5 V, $T_A = 25°C$

PARAMETER¶	FROM (INPUT)	TEST CONDITIONS		MIN	TYP	MAX	UNIT
t_{PLH}	A or B	Other input low	$C_L = 15$ pF, $R_L = 2$ kΩ, See Note 3		12	23	ns
t_{PHL}					10	17	
t_{PLH}	A or B	Other input high			20	30	ns
t_{PHL}					13	22	

¶t_{PLH} = propagation delay time, low-to-high-level output
t_{PHL} = propagation delay time, high-to-low-level output
NOTE 3: See General Information Section for load circuits and voltage waveforms.

3

TTL DEVICES

TYPES SN54S86, SN74S86
QUADRUPLE 2-INPUT EXCLUSIVE-OR GATES

absolute maximum ratings over operating free-air temperature range (unless otherwise noted)

Supply voltage, V_{CC} (see Note 1) . . . . 7 V

Input voltage . . . . 5.5 V

Operating free-air temperature range: SN54S86 . . . . $-55°C$ to $125°C$

SN74S86 . . . . $0°C$ to $70°C$

Storage temperature range . . . . $-65°C$ to $150°C$

NOTE 1: Voltage values are with respect to network ground terminal.

recommended operating conditions

	SN54S86			SN74S86			UNIT
	MIN	NOM	MAX	MIN	NOM	MAX	
Supply voltage, V_{CC}	4.5	5	5.5	4.75	5	5.25	V
High-level output current, I_{OH}			-1			-1	mA
Low-level output current, I_{OL}			20			20	mA
Operating free-air temperature, T_A	-55		125	0		70	°C

electrical characteristics over recommended operating free-air temperature range (unless otherwise noted)

PARAMETER		TEST CONDITIONS[†]	SN54S86			SN74S86			UNIT
			MIN	TYP[‡]	MAX	MIN	TYP[‡]	MAX	
V_{IH}	High-level input voltage		2			2			V
V_{IL}	Low-level input voltage				0.8			0.8	V
V_{IK}	Input clamp voltage	$V_{CC} = MIN$, $I_I = -18$ mA			-1.2			-1.2	V
V_{OH}	High-level output voltage	$V_{CC} = MIN$, $V_{IH} = 2$ V, $V_{IL} = 0.8$ V, $I_{OH} = -1$ mA	2.5	3.4		2.7	3.4		V
V_{OL}	Low-level output voltage	$V_{CC} = MIN$, $V_{IH} = 2$ V $V_{IL} = 0.8$ V, $I_{OL} = 20$ mA			0.5			0.5	V
I_I	Input current at maximum input voltage	$V_{CC} = MAX$, $V_I = 5.5$ V			1			1	mA
I_{IH}	High-level input current	$V_{CC} = MAX$, $V_I = 2.7$ V			50			50	μA
I_{IL}	Low-level input current	$V_{CC} = MAX$, $V_I = 0.5$ V			-2			-2	mA
I_{OS}	Short-circuit output current[§]	$V_{CC} = MAX$	-40		-100	-40		-100	mA
I_{CC}	Supply current	$V_{CC} = MAX$, See Note 2		50	75		50	75	mA

[†]For conditions shown as MIN or MAX, use the appropriate value specified under recommended operating conditions for the applicable type.

[‡]All typical values are at $V_{CC} = 5$ V, $T_A = 25°C$.

[§]Not more than one output should be shorted at a time, and duration of the short-circuit should not exceed one second.

NOTE 2: I_{CC} is measured with the inputs grounded and the outputs open.

switching characteristics, $V_{CC} = 5$ V, $T_A = 25°C$

PARAMETER[¶]	FROM (INPUT)	TEST CONDITIONS		MIN	TYP	MAX	UNIT
t_{PLH}	A or B	Other input low	$C_L = 15$ pF, $R_L = 280 \Omega$, See Note 3		7	10.5	ns
t_{PHL}					6.5	10	
t_{PLH}	A or B	Other input high			7	10.5	ns
t_{PHL}					6.5	10	

[¶]t_{PLH} propagation delay time, low-to-high-level output

t_{PHL} propagation delay time, high-to-low-level output

NOTE 3: See General Information Section for load circuits and voltage waveforms.

TEXAS
INSTRUMENTS

3

TTL DEVICES

MARCH 1974 – REVISED DECEMBER 1983

'90A, 'LS90 . . . DECADE COUNTERS

'92A, 'LS92 . . . DIVIDE-BY-TWELVE COUNTERS

'93A, 'LS93 . . . 4-BIT BINARY COUNTERS

TYPES	TYPICAL POWER DISSIPATION
'90A	145 mW
'LS90	45 mW
'92A, '93A	130 mW
'LS92, 'LS93	45 mW

description

Each of these monolithic counters contains four master-slave flip-flops and additional gating to provide a divide-by-two counter and a three-stage binary counter for which the count cycle length is divide-by-five for the '90A, and 'LS90, divide-by-six for the '92A and 'LS92, and divide-by-eight for the '93A, and 'LS93.

All of these counters have a gated zero reset and the '90A, and 'LS90 also have gated set-to-nine inputs for use in BCD nine's complement applications.

To use their maximum count length (decade, divide-by-twelve, or four-bit binary) of these counters, the CKB input is connected to the Q_A output. The input count pulses are applied to CKA input and the outputs are as described in the appropriate function table. A symmetrical divide-by-ten count can be obtained from the '90A, or 'LS90 counters by connecting the Q_D output to the CKA input and applying the input count to the CKB input which gives a divide-by-ten square wave at output Q_A.

SN5490A, SN54LS90 . . . J OR W PACKAGE
SN7490A . . . J OR N PACKAGE
SN74LS90 . . . D, J OR N PACKAGE
(TOP VIEW)

```
        ┌──┬──┐
 CKB  [1│  U  │14] CKA
R0(1) [2│     │13] NC
R0(2) [3│     │12] Q_A
 NC   [4│     │11] Q_D
 Vcc  [5│     │10] GND
R9(1) [6│     │9 ] Q_B
R9(2) [7│     │8 ] Q_C
        └─────┘
```

SN5492A, SN54LS92 . . . J OR W PACKAGE
SN7492A . . . J OR N PACKAGE
SN74LS92 . . . D, J OR N PACKAGE
(TOP VIEW)

```
        ┌──┬──┐
 CKB  [1│  U  │14] CKA
 NC   [2│     │13] NC
 NC   [3│     │12] Q_A
 NC   [4│     │11] Q_B
 Vcc  [5│     │10] GND
R0(1) [6│     │9 ] Q_C
R0(2) [7│     │8 ] Q_D
        └─────┘
```

SN5493A, SN54LS93 . . . J OR W PACKAGE
SN7493A . . . J OR N PACKAGE
SN74LS93 . . . D, J OR N PACKAGE
(TOP VIEW)

```
        ┌──┬──┐
 CKB  [1│  U  │14] CKA
R0(1) [2│     │13] NC
R0(2) [3│     │12] Q_A
 NC   [4│     │11] Q_D
 Vcc  [5│     │10] GND
 NC   [6│     │9 ] Q_B
 NC   [7│     │8 ] Q_C
        └─────┘
```

For new chip carrier design, use 'LS290, 'LS292, and 'LS293.

3

TTL DEVICES

TEXAS INSTRUMENTS

TYPES SN5490A, '92A, '93A, SN54LS90, 'LS92, 'LS93, SN7490A, '92A, '93A SN74LS90, 'LS92, 'LS93
DECADE, DIVIDE-BY-TWELVE, AND BINARY COUNTERS

'90A, 'LS90
BCD COUNT SEQUENCE
(See Note A)

COUNT	OUTPUT			
	Q_D	Q_C	Q_B	Q_A
0	L	L	L	L
1	L	L	L	H
2	L	L	H	L
3	L	L	H	H
4	L	H	L	L
5	L	H	L	H
6	L	H	H	L
7	L	H	H	H
8	H	L	L	L
9	H	L	L	H

'90A, 'LS90
BI-QUINARY (5-2)
(See Note B)

COUNT	OUTPUT			
	Q_A	Q_D	Q_C	Q_B
0	L	L	L	L
1	L	L	L	H
2	L	L	H	L
3	L	L	H	H
4	L	H	L	L
5	H	L	L	L
6	H	L	L	H
7	H	L	H	L
8	H	L	H	H
9	H	H	L	L

'92A, 'LS92
COUNT SEQUENCE
(See Note C)

COUNT	OUTPUT			
	Q_D	Q_C	Q_B	Q_A
0	L	L	L	L
1	L	L	L	H
2	L	L	H	L
3	L	L	H	H
4	L	H	L	L
5	L	H	L	H
6	H	L	L	L
7	H	L	L	H
8	H	L	H	L
9	H	L	H	H
10	H	H	L	L
11	H	H	L	H

'90A, 'LS90
RESET/COUNT FUNCTION TABLE

RESET INPUTS				OUTPUT			
$R_{0(1)}$	$R_{0(2)}$	$R_{9(1)}$	$R_{9(2)}$	Q_D	Q_C	Q_B	Q_A
H	H	L	X	L	L	L	L
H	H	X	L	L	L	L	L
X	X	H	H	H	L	L	H
X	L	X	L	COUNT			
L	X	L	X	COUNT			
L	X	X	L	COUNT			
X	L	L	X	COUNT			

'92A, 'LS92, '93A, 'LS93
RESET/COUNT FUNCTION TABLE

RESET INPUTS		OUTPUT			
$R_{0(1)}$	$R_{0(2)}$	Q_D	Q_C	Q_B	Q_A
H	H	L	L	L	L
L	X	COUNT			
X	L	COUNT			

'93A, 'LS93
COUNT SEQUENCE
(See Note C)

COUNT	OUTPUT			
	Q_D	Q_C	Q_B	Q_A
0	L	L	L	L
1	L	L	L	H
2	L	L	H	L
3	L	L	H	H
4	L	H	L	L
5	L	H	L	H
6	L	H	H	L
7	L	H	H	H
8	H	L	L	L
9	H	L	L	H
10	H	L	H	L
11	H	L	H	H
12	H	H	L	L
13	H	H	L	H
14	H	H	H	L
15	H	H	H	H

NOTES: A. Output Q_A is connected to input CKB for BCD count.
B. Output Q_D is connected to input CKA for bi-quinary count.
C. Output Q_A is connected to input CKB.
D. H = high level, L = low level, X = irrelevant

TEXAS
INSTRUMENTS

logic diagrams

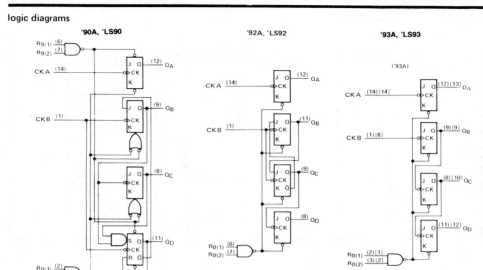

The J and K inputs shown without connection are for reference only and are functionally at a high level.

schematics of inputs and outputs

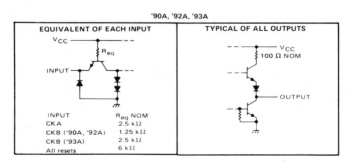

schematics of inputs and outputs (continued)

'LS90, 'LS92, 'LS93

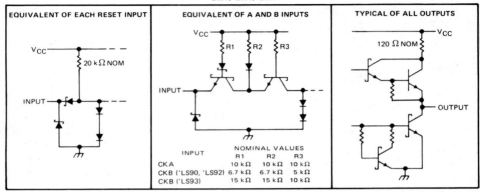

INPUT	NOMINAL VALUES		
	R1	R2	R3
CK A	10 kΩ	10 kΩ	10 kΩ
CKB ('LS90, 'LS92)	6.7 kΩ	6.7 kΩ	5 kΩ
CKB ('LS93)	15 kΩ	15 kΩ	10 kΩ

TEXAS
INSTRUMENTS

3

TTL DEVICES

absolute maximum ratings over operating free-air temperature range (unless otherwise noted)

Supply voltage, V_{CC} (see Note 1)	7 V
Input voltage	5.5 V
Interemitter voltage (see Note 2)	5.5 V
Operating free-air temperature range: SN5490A, SN5492A, SN5493A	-55°C to 125°C
SN7490A, SN7492A, SN7493A	0°C to 70°C
Storage temperature range	-65°C to 150°C

NOTES: 1. Voltage values, except interemitter voltage, are with respect to network ground terminal.
2. This is the voltage between two emitters of a multiple emitter transistor. For these circuits, this rating applies between the two R_0 inputs, and for the '90A circuit, it also applies between the two R_9 inputs.

recommended operating conditions

		SN5490A, SN5492A SN5493A			SN7490A, SN7492A SN7493A			UNIT
		MIN	NOM	MAX	MIN	NOM	MAX	
Supply voltage, V_{CC}		4.5	5	5.5	4.75	5	5.25	V
High-level output current, I_{OH}				−800			−800	μA
Low-level output current, I_{OL}				16			16	mA
Count frequency, f_{count} (see Figure 1)	A input	0		32	0		32	MHz
	B input	0		16	0		16	
Pulse width, t_w	A input	15			15			ns
	B input	30			30			
	Reset inputs	15			15			
Reset inactive-state setup time, t_{su}		25			25			ns
Operating free-air temperature, T_A		−55		125	0		70	°C

electrical characteristics over recommended operating free-air temperature range (unless otherwise noted)

PARAMETER [‡]		TEST CONDITIONS[†]	'90A			'92A			'93A			UNIT
			MIN	TYP[‡]	MAX	MIN	TYP[‡]	MAX	MIN	TYP[‡]	MAX	
V_{IH}	High-level input voltage		2			2			2			V
V_{IL}	Low-level input voltage				0.8			0.8			0.8	V
V_{IK}	Input clamp voltage	V_{CC} = MIN, I_I = −12 mA			−1.5			−1.5			−1.5	V
V_{OH}	High-level output voltage	V_{CC} = MIN, V_{IH} = 2 V, V_{IL} = 0.8 V, I_{OH} = −800 μA	2.4	3.4		2.4	3.4		2.4	3.4		V
V_{OL}	Low-level output voltage	V_{CC} = MIN, V_{IH} = 2 V, V_{IL} = 0.8 V, I_{OL} = 16 mA [◆]		0.2	0.4		0.2	0.4		0.2	0.4	V
I_I	Input current at maximum input voltage	V_{CC} = MAX, V_I = 5.5 V			1			1			1	mA
I_{IH}	High-level input current — Any reset	V_{CC} = MAX, V_I = 2.4 V			40			40			40	μA
	CKA				80			80			80	
	CKB				120			120			80	
I_{IL}	Low-level input current — Any reset	V_{CC} = MAX, V_I = 0.4 V			−1.6			−1.6			−1.6	mA
	CKA				−3.2			−3.2			−3.2	
	CKB				−4.8			−4.8			−3.2	
I_{OS}	Short-circuit output current [§] — SN54'	V_{CC} = MAX	−20		−57	−20		−57	−20		−57	mA
	SN74'		−18		−57	−18		−57	−18		−57	
I_{CC}	Supply current	V_{CC} = MAX, See Note 3		29	42		26	39		26	39	mA

[†]For conditions shown as MIN or MAX, use the appropriate value specified under recommended operating conditions.
[‡]All typical values are at V_{CC} = 5 V, T_A = 25°C.
[§]Not more than one output should be shorted at a time.
[◆] Q_A outputs are tested at I_{OL} = 16 mA plus the limit value for I_{IL} for the CKB input. This permits driving the CKB input while maintaining full fan out capability.
NOTE 3: I_{CC} is measured with all outputs open, both R_0 inputs grounded following momentary connection to 4.5 V, and all other inputs grounded.

TEXAS
INSTRUMENTS

3

TTL DEVICES

switching characteristics, V_{CC} = 5 V, T_A = 25°C

PARAMETER[^t]	FROM (INPUT)	TO (OUTPUT)	TEST CONDITIONS	'90A			'92A			'93A			UNIT
				MIN	TYP	MAX	MIN	TYP	MAX	MIN	TYP	MAX	
f_{max}	CKA	Q_A		32	42		32	42		32	42		MHz
	CKB	Q_B		16			16			16			
t_{PLH}	CKA	Q_A			10	16		10	16		10	16	ns
t_{PHL}					12	18		12	18		12	18	
t_{PLH}	CKA	Q_D			32	48		32	48		46	70	ns
t_{PHL}					34	50		34	50		46	70	
t_{PLH}	CKB	Q_B	C_L = 15 pF,		10	16		10	16		10	16	ns
t_{PHL}			R_L = 400 Ω,		14	21		14	21		14	21	
t_{PLH}	CKB	Q_C	See Figure 1		21	32		10	16		21	32	ns
t_{PHL}					23	35		14	21		23	35	
t_{PLH}	CKB	Q_D			21	32		21	32		34	51	ns
t_{PHL}					23	35		23	35		34	51	
t_{PHL}	Set-to-0	Any			26	40		26	40		26	40	ns
t_{PLH}	Set-to-9	Q_A, Q_D			20	30							ns
t_{PHL}		Q_B, Q_C			26	40							

[^t]:
f_{max} maximum count frequency
t_{PLH} propagation delay time, low to high level output
t_{PHL} propagation delay time, high to low level output

Texas
Instruments

absolute maximum ratings over operating free-air temperature range (unless otherwise noted)

Supply voltage, V_{CC} (see Note 1) . . . . 7 V
Input voltage: R inputs . . . . 7 V
            A and B inputs . . . . 5.5 V
Operating free-air temperature range: SN54LS' Circuits . . . . $-55°C$ to $125°C$
                          SN74LS' Circuits . . . . $0°C$ to $70°C$
Storage temperature range . . . . $-65°C$ to $150°C$

NOTE 1: Voltage values are with respect to network ground terminal.

recommended operating conditions

		SN54LS90 SN54LS92 SN54LS93			SN74LS90 SN74LS92 SN74LS93			UNIT
		MIN	NOM	MAX	MIN	NOM	MAX	
Supply voltage, V_{CC}		4.5	5	5.5	4.75	5	5.25	V
High-level output current, I_{OH}				-400			-400	μA
Low-level output current, I_{OL}				4			8	mA
Count frequency, f_{count} (see Figure 1)	A input	0		32	0		32	MHz
	B input	0		16	0		16	
Pulse width, t_w	A input	15			15			ns
	B input	30			30			
	Reset inputs	30			30			
Reset inactive-state setup time, t_{su}		25			25			ns
Operating free-air temperature, T_A		-55		125	0		70	°C

electrical characteristics over recommended operating free-air temperature range (unless otherwise noted)

PARAMETER		TEST CONDITIONS†		SN54LS90 SN54LS92			SN74LS90 SN74LS92			UNIT
				MIN	TYP‡	MAX	MIN	TYP‡	MAX	
V_{IH}	High-level input voltage			2			2			V
V_{IL}	Low-level input voltage					0.7			0.8	V
V_{IK}	Input clamp voltage	V_{CC} = MIN,	$I_I = -18$ mA			-1.5			-1.5	V
V_{OH}	High-level output voltage	V_{CC} = MIN, V_{IH} = 2 V, $V_{IL} = V_{IL}$max., $I_{OH} = -400\ \mu$A		2.5	3.4		2.7	3.4		V
V_{OL}	Low-level output voltage	V_{CC} = MIN, V_{IH} = 2 V, $V_{IL} = V_{IL}$ max.,	I_{OL} = 4 mA¶		0.25	0.4		0.25	0.4	V
			I_{OL} = 8 mA¶					0.35	0.5	
I_I	Input current at maximum input voltage	Any reset	V_{CC} = MAX, V_I = 7 V			0.1			0.1	mA
		CKA	V_{CC} = MAX, V_I = 5.5 V			0.2			0.2	
		CKB				0.4			0.4	
I_{IH}	High-level input current	Any reset	V_{CC} = MAX, V_I = 2.7 V			20			20	μA
		CKA				40			40	
		CKB				80			80	
I_{IL}	Low-level input current	Any reset	V_{CC} = MAX, V_I = 0.4 V			-0.4			-0.4	mA
		CKA				-2.4			-2.4	
		CKB				-3.2			-3.2	
I_{OS}	Short-circuit output current§	V_{CC} = MAX		-20		-100	-20		-100	mA
I_{CC}	Supply current	V_{CC} = MAX, See Note 3	'LS90		9	15		9	15	mA
			'LS92		9	15		9	15	

†For conditions shown as MIN or MAX, use the appropriate value specified under recommended operating conditions.

‡All typical values are at V_{CC} = 5 V, T_A = 25°C.

§Not more than one output should be shorted at a time, and duration of the short-circuit should not exceed one second.

¶Q_A outputs are tested at specified I_{OL} plus the limit value of I_{IL} for the CKB input. This permits driving the CKB input while maintaining full fan-out capability.

NOTE 3: I_{CC} is measured with all outputs open, both R_0 inputs grounded following momentary connection to 4.5 V, and all other inputs grounded.

TEXAS
INSTRUMENTS

electrical characteristics over recommended operating free-air temperature range (unless otherwise noted)

PARAMETER		TEST CONDITIONS[†]		SN54LS93 MIN	TYP[‡]	MAX	SN74LS93 MIN	TYP[‡]	MAX	UNIT
V_{IH}	High-level input voltage			2			2			V
V_{IL}	Low-level input voltage					0.7			0.8	V
V_{IK}	Input clamp voltage	V_{CC} = MIN, I_I = −18 mA				−1.5			−1.5	V
V_{OH}	High-level output voltage	V_{CC} = MIN, V_{IH} = 2 V, V_{IL} = V_{IL} max, I_{OH} = −400 μA		2.5	3.4		2.7	3.4		V
V_{OL}	Low-level output voltage	V_{CC} = MIN, V_{IH} = 2 V, V_{IL} = V_{IL} max	I_{OL} = 4 mA[¶]		0.25	0.4		0.25	0.4	V
			I_{OL} = 8 mA[¶]					0.35	0.5	
I_I	Input current at maximum input voltage	Any reset: V_{CC} = MAX, V_I = 7 V				0.1			0.1	mA
		CKA or CKB: V_{CC} = MAX, V_I = 5.5 V				0.2			0.2	
I_{IH}	High-level input current	Any reset: V_{CC} = MAX, V_I = 2.7 V				20			20	μA
		CKA or CKB				40			80	
I_{IL}	Low-level input current	Any reset: V_{CC} = MAX, V_I = 0.4 V				−0.4			−0.4	mA
		CKA				−2.4			−2.4	
		CKB				−1.6			−1.6	
I_{OS}	Short-circuit output current[§]	V_{CC} = MAX		−20		−100	−20		−100	mA
I_{CC}	Supply current	V_{CC} = MAX, See Note 3			9	15		9	15	mA

[†] For conditions shown as MIN or MAX, use the appropriate value specified under recommended operating conditions.
[‡] All typical values are at V_{CC} = 5 V, T_A = 25°C.
[§] Not more than one output should be shorted at a time, and duration of the short-circuit should not exceed one second.
[¶] Q_A outputs are tested at specified I_{OL} plus the limit value for I_{IL} for the CKB input. This permits driving the CKB input while maintaining full fan-out capability.
NOTE 3: I_{CC} is measured with all outputs open, both R_0 inputs grounded following momentary connection to 4.5 V, and all other inputs grounded.

switching characteristics, V_{CC} = 5 V, T_A = 25°C

PARAMETER[¶]	FROM (INPUT)	TO (OUTPUT)	TEST CONDITIONS	'LS90 MIN	TYP	MAX	'LS92 MIN	TYP	MAX	'LS93 MIN	TYP	MAX	UNIT
f_{max}	CKA	Q_A		32	42		32	42		32	42		MHz
	CKB	Q_B		16			16			16			
t_{PLH}	CKA	Q_A			10	16		10	16		10	16	ns
t_{PHL}					12	18		12	18		12	18	
t_{PLH}	CKA	Q_D			32	48		32	48		46	70	ns
t_{PHL}					34	50		34	50		46	70	
t_{PLH}	CKB	Q_B	C_L = 15 pF, R_L = 2 kΩ, See Figure 1		10	16		10	16		10	16	ns
t_{PHL}					14	21		14	21		14	21	
t_{PLH}	CKB	Q_C			21	32		10	16		21	32	ns
t_{PHL}					23	35		14	21		23	35	
t_{PLH}	CKB	Q_D			21	32		21	32		34	51	ns
t_{PHL}					23	35		23	35		34	51	
t_{PHL}	Set to 0	Any			26	40		26	40		26	40	ns
t_{PLH}	Set to 9	Q_A, Q_D			20	30								ns
t_{PHL}		Q_B, Q_C			26	40								

[¶] f_{max} — maximum count frequency
t_{PLH} — propagation delay time, low to high level output
t_{PHL} — propagation delay time, high to low level output

TEXAS INSTRUMENTS

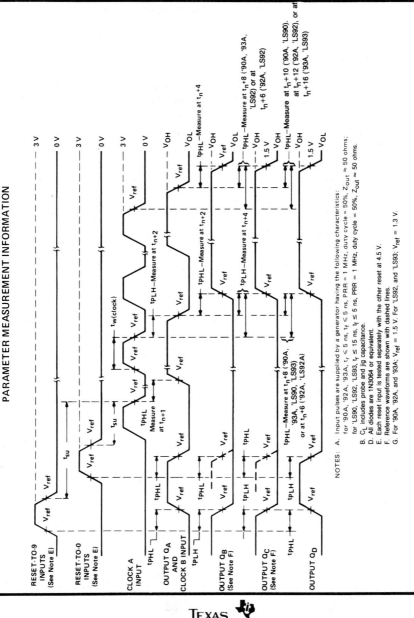

PARAMETER MEASUREMENT INFORMATION

NOTES: A. Input pulses are supplied by a generator having the following characteristics:
for '90A, '92A, '93A, $t_r \leqslant 5$ ns, $t_f \leqslant 5$ ns, PRR = 1 MHz, duty cycle = 50%, $Z_{out} \approx 50$ ohms;
for 'LS90, 'LS92, 'LS93, $t_r \leqslant 15$ ns, $t_f \leqslant 5$ ns, PRR = 1 MHz, duty cycle = 50%, $Z_{out} \approx 50$ ohms.
B. C_L includes probe and jig capacitance.
D. All diodes are 1N3064 or equivalent.
E. Each reset input is tested separately with the other reset at 4.5 V.
F. Reference waveforms are shown with dashed lines.
G. For '90A, '92A, and '93A; V_{ref} = 1.5 V. For 'LS92, and 'LS93; V_{ref} = 1.3 V.

FIGURE 1A

TTL DEVICES

3

TEXAS
INSTRUMENTS

TYPES SN5490A, SN5492A, SN5493A, SN54LS90, SN54LS92, SN54LS93, SN7490A, SN7492A, SN7493A, SN74LS90, SN74LS92, SN74LS93 DECADE, DIVIDE-BY-TWELVE, AND BINARY COUNTERS

PARAMETER MEASUREMENT INFORMATION

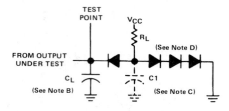

LOAD CIRCUIT

NOTES: A. Input pulses are supplied by a generator having the following characteristics:
for '90A, '92A, '93A, $t_r \leq 5$ ns, $t_f \leq 5$ ns, PRR = 1 MHz, duty cycle = 50%, $Z_{out} \approx 50$ ohms;
for 'LS90, 'LS92, 'LS93, $t_r \leq 15$ ns, $t_f \leq 5$ ns, PRR = 1 MHz, duty cycle = 50%, $Z_{out} \approx 50$ ohms.
B. C_L includes probe and jig capacitance.
D. All diodes are 1N3064 or equivalent.
E. Each reset input is tested separately with the other reset at 4.5 V.
F. Reference waveforms are shown with dashed lines.
G. For '90A, '92A, and '93A; $V_{ref} = 1.5$ V. For 'LS90, 'LS92, and 'LS93; $V_{ref} = 1.3$ V.

FIGURE 1B

TEXAS
INSTRUMENTS

- **For applications in:**
  Digital Computer Systems
  Data-Handling Systems
  Control Systems

TYPE	TYPICAL MAXIMUM CLOCK FREQUENCY	TYPICAL POWER DISSIPATION
'LS91	18 MHz	60 mW

SN54LS91 ... J PACKAGE
SN74LS91 ... D, J OR N PACKAGE
(TOP VIEW)

```
        ┌──┬─┐
  NC [1 │  U │14] Q̄H
  NC [2 │    │13] QH
  NC [3 │    │12] A
  NC [4 │    │11] B
 VCC [5 │    │10] GND
  NC [6 │    │ 9] CLK
  NC [7 │    │ 8] NC
        └────┘
```

SN54LS91 ... W PACKAGE
(TOP VIEW)

```
        ┌──┬─┐
  NC [1 │  U │14] Q̄H
  NC [2 │    │13] QH
  NC [3 │    │12] B
 VCC [4 │    │11] GND
  NC [5 │    │10] A
  NC [6 │    │ 9] CLK
  NC [7 │    │ 8] NC
        └────┘
```

NC - No internal connection

description

These monolithic serial-in, serial-out, 8-bit shift registers utilize transistor-transistor logic (TTL) circuits and are composed of eight R-S master-slave flip-flops, input gating, and a clock driver. Single-rail data and input control are gated through inputs A and B and an internal inverter to form the complementary inputs to the first bit of the shift register. Drive for the internal common clock line is provided by an inverting clock driver. This clock pulse inverter/driver causes these circuits to shift information one bit on the positive edge of an input clock pulse.

schematics of inputs and outputs

'LS91

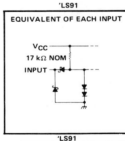

EQUIVALENT OF EACH INPUT

VCC
17 kΩ NOM
INPUT

'LS91

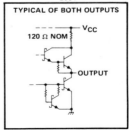

TYPICAL OF BOTH OUTPUTS

VCC
120 Ω NOM
OUTPUT

FUNCTION TABLE

INPUTS AT t_n		OUTPUTS AT t_{n+8}	
A	B	Q_H	$\bar{Q}_H$
H	H	H	L
L	X	L	H
X	L	L	H

t_n = Reference bit time, clock low

t_{n+8} = Bit time after 8 low-to-high clock transitions.

3

TTL DEVICES

TEXAS INSTRUMENTS

logic diagram

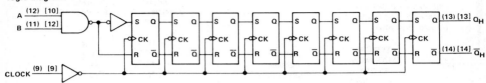

Pin numbers shown in ( ) are for the D, J or N packages and pin numbers shown in | | are for the W package.

TEXAS
INSTRUMENTS

absolute maximum ratings over operating free-air temperature range (unless otherwise noted)

Supply voltage, V_{CC} (see Note 1) . . . . 7 V
Input voltage . . . . 7 V
Operating free-air temperature range: SN54LS91 . . . . −55°C to 125°C
　　　　　　　　　　　　　　　　　　　 SN74LS91 . . . . 0°C to 70°C
Storage temperature range . . . . −65°C to 150°C

NOTES: 1. Voltage values are with respect to network ground terminal.

recommended operating conditions

	SN54LS91			SN74LS91			UNIT
	MIN	NOM	MAX	MIN	NOM	MAX	
Supply voltage, V_{CC}	4.5	5	5.5	4.75	5	5.25	V
High-level output current, I_{OH}			−400			−400	μA
Low-level output current, I_{OL}			4			8	mA
Width of clock input pulse, t_w	25			25			ns
Setup time, t_{su} (see Figure 1)	25			25			ns
Hold time, t_h (see Figure 1)	0			0			ns
Operating free-air temperature, T_A	−55		125	0		70	C

electrical characteristics over recommended operating free-air temperature range (unless otherwise noted)

PARAMETER	TEST CONDITIONS[†]		SN54LS91			SN74LS91			UNIT
			MIN	TYP[‡]	MAX	MIN	TYP[‡]	MAX	
V_{IH}　High-level input voltage			2			2			V
V_{IL}　Low-level input voltage					0.7			0.8	V
V_{IK}　Input clamp voltage	V_{CC} = MIN,	I_I = −18 mA			−1.5			−1.5	V
V_{OH}　High-level output voltage	V_{CC} = MIN, 　V_{IH} = 2 V, V_{IL} = V_{IL} max, I_{OH} = −400 μA		2.5	3.5		2.7	3.5		V
V_{OL}　Low-level output voltage	V_{CC} = MIN, 　V_{IH} = 2 V, V_{IL} = V_{IL} max	I_{OL} = 4 mA		0.25	0.4		0.25	0.4	V
		I_{OL} = 8 mA					0.35	0.5	
I_I　Input current at maximum input voltage	V_{CC} = MAX,	V_I = 7 V			0.1			0.1	mA
I_{IH}　High-level input current	V_{CC} = MAX,	V_I = 2.7 V			20			20	μA
I_{IL}　Low-level input current	V_{CC} = MAX,	V_I = 0.4 V			−0.4			−0.4	mA
I_{OS}　Short-circuit output current[§]	V_{CC} = MAX		−20		−100	−20		−100	mA
I_{CC}　Supply current	V_{CC} = MAX,	See Note 3		12	20		12	20	mA

[†]For conditions shown as MIN or MAX, use the appropriate value specified under recommended operating conditions.
[‡]All typical values are at V_{CC}　5 V, T_A　25 C.
[§]Not more than one output should be shorted at a time, and duration of the short-circuit should not exceed one second.
NOTE 3: I_{CC} is measured after the eighth clock pulse with the output open and A and B inputs grounded.

switching characteristics, V_{CC} = 5 V, T_A = 25°C

PARAMETER	TEST CONDITIONS	MIN	TYP	MAX	UNIT
f_{max}　Maximum clock frequency	C_L = 15 pF,	10	18		MHz
t_{PLH}　Propagation delay time, low-to-high-level output	R_L = 2 kΩ,		24	40	ns
t_{PHL}　Propagation delay time, high-to-low-level output	See Figure 1		27	40	ns

3

TTL DEVICES

TEXAS
INSTRUMENTS

PARAMETER MEASUREMENT INFORMATION

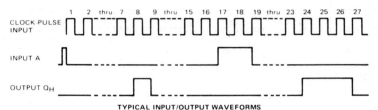

TEST CIRCUIT

TYPICAL INPUT/OUTPUT WAVEFORMS

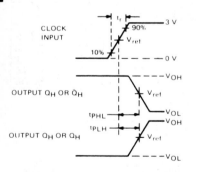

PROPAGATION DELAY TIMES VOLTAGE WAVEFORMS

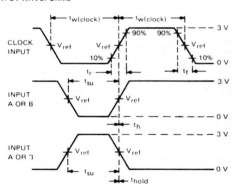

SWITCHING TIMES VOLTAGE WAVEFORMS

NOTES: A. The generator has the following characteristics: $t_{w(clock)} = 500$ ns, PRR ≤ 1 MHz, $Z_{out} \approx 50\ \Omega$. For SN54LS91, $t_r = 15$ ns, and $t_f = 6$ ns.
   B. C_L includes probe and jig capacitance.
   C. All diodes are 1N3064 or equivalent.
   D. $C_1 = 30$ pF and is used for SN54L91 only.
   E. For SN54LS91/SN74LS91, $V_{ref} = 1.3$ V.

FIGURE 1—SWITCHING TIMES

TEXAS
INSTRUMENTS

3

TTL DEVICES

TYPE	TYPICAL MAXIMUM CLOCK FREQUENCY	TYPICAL POWER DISSIPATION
'95A	36 MHz	195 mW
'LS95B	36 MHz	65 mW

description

These 4-bit registers feature parallel and serial inputs, parallel outputs, mode control, and two clock inputs. The registers have three modes of operation:

Parallel (broadside) load
Shift right (the direction Q_A toward Q_D)
Shift left (the direction Q_D toward Q_A)

Parallel loading is accomplished by applying the four bits of data and taking the mode control input high. The data is loaded into the associated flip-flops and appears at the outputs after the high-to-low transition of the clock-2 input. During loading, the entry of serial data is inhibited.

Shift right is accomplished on the high-to-low transition of clock 1 when the mode control is low; shift left is accomplished on the high-to-low transition of clock 2 when the mode control is high by connecting the output of each flip-flop to the parallel input of the previous flip-flop (Q_D to input C, etc.) and serial data is entered at input D. The clock input may be applied commonly to clock 1 and clock 2 if both modes can be clocked from the same source. Changes at the mode control input should normally be made while both clock inputs are low; however, conditions described in the last three lines of the function table will also ensure that register contents are protected.

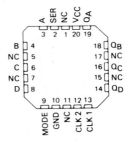

SN5495A, SN54LS95B . . . J OR W PACKAGE
SN7495A . . . J OR N PACKAGE
SN74LS95B . . . D, J OR N PACKAGE
(TOP VIEW)

SN54LS95B . . . FK PACKAGE
SN74LS95B
(TOP VIEW)

NC - No internal connection

FUNCTION TABLE

INPUTS								OUTPUTS			
MODE	CLOCKS		SERIAL	PARALLEL				Q_A	Q_B	Q_C	Q_D
CONTROL	2 (L)	1 (R)		A	B	C	D				
H	H	X	X	X	X	X	X	Q_{A0}	Q_{B0}	Q_{C0}	Q_{D0}
H	↓	X	X	a	b	c	d	a	b	c	d
H	↓	X	X	Q_B†	Q_C†	Q_D†	d	Q_{Bn}	Q_{Cn}	Q_{Dn}	d
L	L	H	X	X	X	X	X	Q_{A0}	Q_{B0}	Q_{C0}	Q_{D0}
L	X	↓	H	X	X	X	X	H	Q_{An}	Q_{Bn}	Q_{Cn}
L	X	↓	L	X	X	X	X	L	Q_{An}	Q_{Bn}	Q_{Cn}
↑	L	L	X	X	X	X	X	Q_{A0}	Q_{B0}	Q_{C0}	Q_{D0}
↓	L	L	X	X	X	X	X	Q_{A0}	Q_{B0}	Q_{C0}	Q_{D0}
↓	L	H	X	X	X	X	X	Q_{A0}	Q_{B0}	Q_{C0}	Q_{D0}
↑	H	L	X	X	X	X	X	Q_{A0}	Q_{B0}	Q_{C0}	Q_{D0}
↑	H	H	X	X	X	X	X	Q_{A0}	Q_{B0}	Q_{C0}	Q_{D0}

†Shifting left requires external connection of Q_B to A, Q_C to B, and Q_D to C. Serial data is entered at input D.
H = high level (steady state), L = low level (steady state), X = irrelevant (any input, including transitions)
↓ = transition from high to low level, ↑ = transition from low to high level
a, b, c, d = the level of steady-state input at inputs A, B, C, or D, respectively.
Q_{A0}, Q_{B0}, Q_{C0}, Q_{D0} = the level of Q_A, Q_B, Q_C, or Q_D, respectively, before the indicated steady state input conditions were established.
Q_{An}, Q_{Bn}, Q_{Cn}, Q_{Dn} = the level of Q_A, Q_B, Q_C, or Q_D, respectively, before the most-recent ↓ transition of the clock.

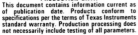

TEXAS
INSTRUMENTS

3

TTL DEVICES

TYPES SN5495A, SN54LS95B, SN7495A, SN74LS95B
4-BIT PARALLEL-ACCESS SHIFT REGISTERS

logic diagrams

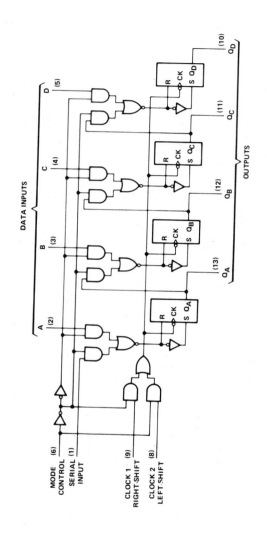

schematics of inputs and outputs

'95A

EQUIVALENT OF EACH INPUT

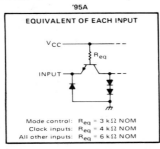

Mode control: R_{eq} = 3 kΩ NOM
Clock inputs: R_{eq} = 4 kΩ NOM
All other inputs: R_{eq} = 6 kΩ NOM

'95A

TYPICAL OF ALL OUTPUTS

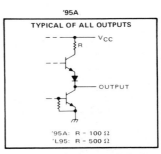

'95A: R = 100 Ω
'L95: R = 500 Ω

'LS95B

**EQUIVALENT OF CLOCK
AND MODE CONTROL INPUTS**

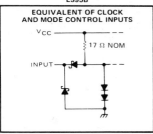

'LS95B

**EQUIVALENT OF DATA
AND SERIAL INPUTS**

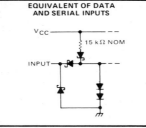

'LS95B

TYPICAL OF ALL OUTPUTS

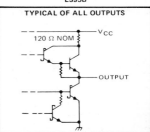

absolute maximum ratings over operating free-air temperature range (unless otherwise noted)

	SN54'		SN54LS'	SN74'	SN74LS'	UNIT
Supply voltage, V_{CC} (see Note 1)	7		7	7	7	V
Input voltage	5.5		7	5.5	7	V
Interemitter voltage (see Note 2)	5.5			5.5		V
Operating free-air temperature range	− 55 to 125			0 to 70		°C
Storage temperature range	− 65 to 150			− 65 to 150		°C

NOTES: 1. Voltage values, except interemitter voltage, are with respect to network ground terminal.
2. This is the voltage between two emitters of a multiple-emitter input transistor. This rating applies between the clock-2 input and the mode control input of the '95A.

3

TTL DEVICES

recommended operating conditions

	SN5495A MIN	SN5495A NOM	SN5495A MAX	SN7495A MIN	SN7495A NOM	SN7495A MAX	UNIT
Supply voltage, V_{CC}	4.5	5	5.5	4.75	5	5.25	V
High-level output current, I_{OH}			−800			−800	µA
Low-level output current, I_{OL}			16			16	mA
Clock frequency, f_{clock}	0		25	0		25	MHz
Width of clock pulse, $t_{w(clock)}$ (See Figure 1)	20			20			ns
Setup time, high-level or low-level data, t_{su} (See Figure 1)	15			15			ns
Hold time, high-level or low-level data, t_h (See Figure 1)	0			0			ns
Time to enable clock 1, $t_{enable\ 1}$ (See Figure 2)	15			15			ns
Time to enable clock 2 (See Figure 2)	15			15			ns
Time to inhibit clock 1, $t_{inhibit\ 1}$ (See Figure 2)	5			5			ns
Time to inhibit clock 2, $t_{inhibit\ 2}$ (See Figure 2)	5			5			ns
Operating free-air temperature, T_A	−55		125	0		70	C

electrical characteristics over recommended operating free-air temperature range (unless otherwise noted)

PARAMETER		TEST CONDITIONS[†]	SN5495A MIN	SN5495A TYP[‡]	SN5495A MAX	SN7495A MIN	SN7495A TYP[‡]	SN7495A MAX	UNIT
V_{IH}	High-level input voltage		2			2			V
V_{IL}	Low-level input voltage				0.8			0.8	V
V_{IK}	Input clamp voltage	V_{CC} = MIN, I_I = −12 mA			−1.5			−1.5	V
V_{OH}	High-level output voltage	V_{CC} = MIN, V_{IH} = 2 V, V_{IL} = 0.8 V, I_{OH} = −800 µA	2.4	3.4		2.4	3.4		V
V_{OL}	Low-level output voltage	V_{CC} = MIN, V_{IH} = 2 V, V_{IL} = 0.8 V, I_{OL} = 16 mA		0.2	0.4		0.2	0.4	V
I_I	Input current at maximum input voltage	V_{CC} = MAX, V_I = 5.5 V			1			1	mA
I_{IH}	High-level input current — Serial, A, B, C, D, Clock 1 or 2	V_{CC} = MAX, V_I = 2.4 V			40			40	µA
I_{IH}	High-level input current — Mode control	V_{CC} = MAX, V_I = 2.4 V			80			80	µA
I_{IL}	Low-level input current — Serial, A, B, C, D, Clock 1 or 2	V_{CC} = MAX, V_I = 0.4 V			−1.6			−1.6	mA
I_{IL}	Low-level input current — Mode control	V_{CC} = MAX, V_I = 0.4 V			−3.2			−3.2	mA
I_{OS}	Short-circuit output current[§]	V_{CC} = MAX	−18		−57	−18		−57	mA
I_{CC}	Supply current	V_{CC} = MAX, See Note 4		39	63		39	63	mA

[†] For conditions shown as MIN or MAX, use the appropriate value specified under recommended operating conditions.
[‡] All typical values are at V_{CC} = 5 V, T_A = 25°C.
[§] Not more than one output should be shorted at a time.
NOTE 4: I_{CC} is measured with all outputs and serial input open; A, B, C, and D inputs grounded; mode control at 4.5 V; and a momentary 3 V, then ground, applied to both clock inputs.

switching characteristics, V_{CC} = 5 V, T_A = 25°C

PARAMETER		TEST CONDITIONS	MIN	TYP	MAX	UNIT
f_{max}	Maximum clock frequency	C_L = 15 pF, R_L = 400 Ω, See Figure 1	25	36		MHz
t_{PLH}	Propagation delay time, low-to-high-level output from clock			18	27	ns
t_{PHL}	Propagation delay time, high-to-low-level output from clock			21	32	ns

3

TTL DEVICES

TEXAS INSTRUMENTS

recommended operating conditions

		SN54LS95B			SN74LS95B			UNIT
		MIN	NOM	MAX	MIN	NOM	MAX	
Supply voltage, V_{CC}		4.5	5	5.5	4.75	5	5.25	V
High-level output current, I_{OH}				−400			−400	μA
Low-level output current, I_{OL}				4			8	mA
Clock frequency, f_{clock}		0		25	0		25	MHz
Width of clock pulse, $t_{w(clock)}$ (see Figure 1)		20			20			ns
Setup time, high-level or low-level data, t_{su} (see Figure 1)		20			20			ns
Hold time, high-level or low-level data, t_h (see Figure 1)		20			10			ns
Time to enable clock 1, $t_{enable\ 1}$ (see Figure 2)		20			20			ns
Time to enable clock 2, $t_{enable\ 2}$ (see Figure 2)		20			20			ns
Time to inhibit clock 1, $t_{inhibit\ 1}$ (see Figure 2)		20			20			ns
Time to inhibit clock 2, $t_{inhibit\ 2}$ (see Figure 2)		20			20			ns
Operating free-air temperature, T_A		−55		125	0		70	°C

electrical characteristics over recommended operating free-air temperature range (unless otherwise noted)

PARAMETER		TEST CONDITIONS[†]		SN54LS95B			SN74LS95B			UNIT
				MIN	TYP[‡]	MAX	MIN	TYP[‡]	MAX	
V_{IH}	High-level input voltage			2			2			V
V_{IL}	Low-level input voltage					0.7			0.8	V
V_{IK}	Input clamp voltage	V_{CC} = MIN,	I_I'= −18 mA			−1.5			−1.5	V
V_{OH}	High-level output voltage	V_{CC} = MIN, V_{IL} = V_{IL} max,	V_{IH} = 2 V, I_{OH} = −400 μA	2.5	3.4		2.7	3.4		V
V_{OL}	Low-level output voltage	V_{CC} = MIN, V_{IH} = 2 V, V_{IL} = V_{IL} max	I_{OL} = 4 mA		0.25	0.4		0.25	0.4	V
			I_{OL} = 8 mA					0.35	0.5	
I_I	Input current at maximum input voltage	V_{CC} = MAX,	V_I = 7 V			0.1			0.1	mA
I_{IH}	High-level input current	V_{CC} = MAX,	V_I = 2.7 V			20			20	μA
I_{IL}	Low-level input current	V_{CC} = MAX,	V_I = 0.4 V			−0.4			−0.4	mA
I_{OS}	Short-circuit output current[§]	V_{CC} = MAX		−20		−100	−20		−100	mA
I_{CC}	Supply current	V_{CC} = MAX,	See Note 4		13	21		13	21	mA

†For conditions shown as MIN or MAX, use the appropriate value specified under recommended operating conditions.
‡All typical values are at V_{CC} = 5 V, T_A = 25°C.
§Not more than one output should be shorted at a time, and duration of the short-circuit should not exceed one second.
NOTE 4: I_{CC} is measured with all outputs and serial input open; A, B, C, and D inputs grounded; mode control at 4.5 V; and a momentary 3 V, then ground, applied to both clock inputs.

switching characteristics, V_{CC} = 5 V, T_A = 25°C

PARAMETER		TEST CONDITIONS	MIN	TYP	MAX	UNIT
f_{max}	Maximum clock frequency	C_L = 15 pF, R_L = 2 kΩ, See Figure 1	25	36		MHz
t_{PLH}	Propagation delay time, low-to-high-level output from clock			18	27	ns
t_{PHL}	Propagation delay time, high-to-low-level output from clock			21	32	ns

3

TTL DEVICES

TEXAS
INSTRUMENTS

TYPES SN5495A, SN54LS95B, SN7495A, SN74LS95B
4-BIT PARALLEL-ACCESS SHIFT REGISTERS

PARAMETER MEASUREMENT INFORMATION

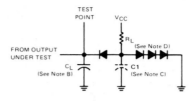

LOAD CIRCUIT

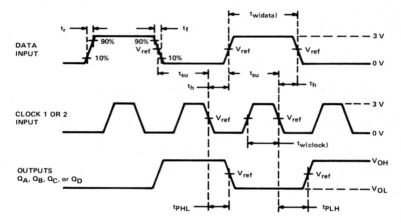

NOTES: A. Input pulses are supplied by a generator having the following characteristics: $t_r \leqslant 10$ ns, $t_f \leqslant 10$ ns, and $Z_{out} \approx 50 \, \Omega$. For the data pulse generator, PRR = 500 kHz; for the clock pulse generator, PRR = 1 MHz. When testing f_{max}, vary PRR. For '95A, $t_{w(data)} \geqslant 20$ ns; $t_{w(clock)} \geqslant 15$ ns. For 'LS95B, $t_{w(data)} \geqslant 20$ ns. For 'LS95B, $t_{w(data)} \geq 20$ ns, $t_{w(clock)} \geq 15$ ns.
B. C_L includes probe and jig capacitance.
D. All diodes are 1 N3064 equivalent.
E. For '95A, $V_{ref} = 1.5$ V; for 'LS95B, $V_{ref} = 1.3$ V.

VOLTAGE WAVEFORMS
FIGURE 1-SWITCHING TIMES

TEXAS INSTRUMENTS

PARAMETER MEASUREMENT INFORMATION

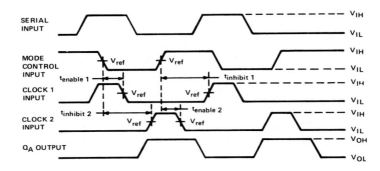

NOTES: A. Input A is at a low level.
B. For '95A, V_{ref} = 1.5 V; for 'LS95B, V_{ref} = 1.3 V.

VOLTAGE WAVEFORMS
FIGURE 2-CLOCK ENABLE/INHIBIT TIMES

3

TTL DEVICES

- N-Bit Serial-To-Parallel Converter
- N-Bit Parallel-To-Serial Converter
- N-Bit Storage Register

TYPE	TYPICAL PROPAGATION DELAY TIME	TYPICAL POWER DISSIPATION
'96	25 ns	240 mW
'LS96	25 ns	60 mW

SN5496, SN54LS96 ... J OR W PACKAGE
SN7496 ... J OR N PACKAGE
SN74LS96 ... D, J OR N PACKAGE
(TOP VIEW)

```
CLK [ 1    16 ] CLR
  A [ 2    15 ] QA
  B [ 3    14 ] QB
  C [ 4    13 ] QC
Vcc [ 5    12 ] GND
  D [ 6    11 ] QD
  E [ 7    10 ] QE
PRE [ 8     9 ] SER
```

**For chip carrier information on SN54LS96
and SN74LS96, contact the factory.**

description

These shift registers consist of five R-S master-slave flip-flops connected to perform parallel-to-serial or serial-to-parallel conversion of binary data. Since both inputs and outputs for all flip-flops are accessible, parallel-in/parallel-out or serial-in/serial-out operation may be performed.

All flip-flops are simultaneously set to a low output level by applying a low-level voltage to the clear input while the preset is inactive (low). Clearing is independent of the level of the clock input.

The register may be parallel loaded by using the clear input in conjunction with the preset inputs. After clearing all stages to low output levels, data to be loaded is applied to the individual preset inputs (A, B, C, D, and E) and a high-level load pulse is applied to the preset enable input. Presetting like clearing is independent of the level of the clock input.

Transfer of information to the outputs occurs on the positive-going edge of the clock pulse. The proper information must be set up at the R-S inputs of each flip-flop prior to the rising edge of the clock input waveform. The serial input provides this information to the first flip-flop, while the outputs of the subsequent flip-flops provide information for the remaining R-S inputs. The clear input must be high and the preset or preset enable inputs must be low when clocking occurs.

FUNCTION TABLE

CLEAR	PRESET ENABLE	PRESET A	B	C	D	E	CLOCK	SERIAL	Q_A	Q_B	Q_C	Q_D	Q_E
L	L	X	X	X	X	X	X	X	L	L	L	L	L
L	X	L	L	L	L	L	X	X	L	L	L	L	L
H	H	H	H	H	H	H	X	X	H	H	H	H	H
H	H	L	L	L	L	L	L	X	Q_{A0}	Q_{B0}	Q_{C0}	Q_{D0}	Q_{E0}
H	H	H	L	H	L	H	L	X	H	Q_{B0}	H	Q_{D0}	H
H	L	X	X	X	X	X	L	X	Q_{A0}	Q_{B0}	Q_{C0}	Q_{D0}	Q_{E0}
H	L	X	X	X	X	X	↑	H	H	Q_{An}	Q_{Bn}	Q_{Cn}	Q_{Dn}
H	L	X	X	X	X	X	↑	L	L	Q_{An}	Q_{Bn}	Q_{Cn}	Q_{Dn}

H = high level (steady state), L = low level (steady state)
X = irrelevant (any input, including transitions)
↑ = transition from low to high level
Q_{A0}, Q_{B0}, etc = the level of Q_A, Q_B, etc, respectively before the indicated steady-state input conditions were established.
Q_{An}, Q_{Bn}, etc = the level of Q_A, Q_B, etc, respectively before the most-recent ↑ transition of the clock.

TEXAS
INSTRUMENTS

TTL DEVICES

3

typical clear, shift, preset, and shift sequences

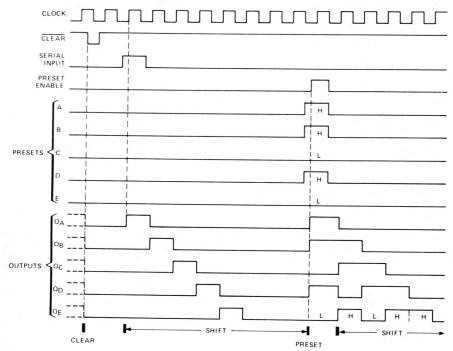

logic diagram

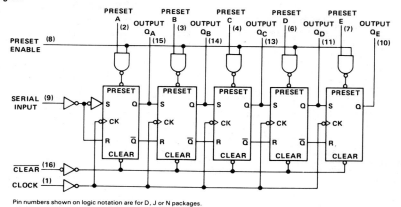

Pin numbers shown on logic notation are for D, J or N packages.

TEXAS INSTRUMENTS

schematics of inputs and outputs

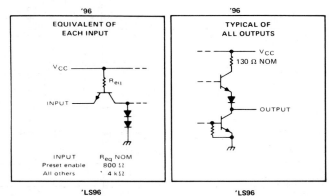

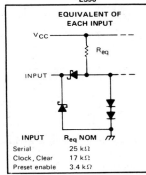

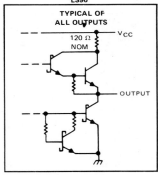

absolute maximum ratings over operating free-air temperature range (unless otherwise noted)

Supply voltage, V_{CC} (see Note 1) . . . . 7 V

Input voltage (see Note 2): '96 . . . . 5.5 V

'LS96 . . . . 7 V

Operating free-air temperature: SN54' . . . . −55°C to 125°C

SN74' . . . . 0°C to 70°C

Storage temperature range . . . . −65°C to 150°C

NOTES: 1. Voltage values are with respect to network ground terminal.
2. Input voltages must be zero or positive with respect to network ground terminal.

TTL DEVICES

3

TEXAS
INSTRUMENTS

recommended operating conditions

	SN5496			SN7496			UNIT
	MIN	NOM	MAX	MIN	NOM	MAX	
Supply voltage, V_{CC}	4.5	5	5.5	4.75	5	5.25	V
High-level output current, I_{OH}			−400			−400	μA
Low-level output current, I_{OL}			16			16	mA
Clock frequency, f_{clock}	0		10	0		10	MHz
Width of clock input pulse, $t_{w(clock)}$	35			35			ns
Width of preset and clear input pulse, t_w	30			30			ns
Serial input setup time, t_{su} (see Figure 1)	30			30			ns
Serial input hold time, t_h (see Figure 1)	0			0			ns
Operating free-air temperature, T_A	−55		125	0		70	°C

electrical characteristics over recommended operating free-air temperature range (unless otherwise noted)

PARAMETER		TEST CONDITIONS[†]	SN5496			SN7496			UNIT
			MIN	TYP[‡]	MAX	MIN	TYP[‡]	MAX	
V_{IH}	High-level input voltage		2			2			V
V_{IL}	Low-level input voltage				0.8			0.8	V
V_{OH}	High-level output voltage	V_{CC} = MIN, V_{IH} = 2 V, V_{IL} = 0.8 V, I_{OH} = −400 μA	2.4	3.4		2.4	3.4		V
V_{OL}	Low-level output voltage	V_{CC} = MIN, V_{IH} = 2 V, V_{IL} = 0.8 V, I_{OL} = 16 mA		0.2	0.4		0.2	0.4	V
I_I	Input current at maximum input voltage	V_{CC} = MAX, V_I = 5.5 V			1			1	mA
I_{IH}	High-level input current	any input except preset enable	V_{CC} = MAX, V_I = 2.4 V			40			40	μA
		preset enable				200			200	
I_{IL}	Low-level input current	any input except preset enable	V_{CC} = MAX, V_I = 0.4 V			−1.6			−1.6	mA
		preset enable				−8			−8	
I_{OS}	Short-circuit output current[§]	V_{CC} = MAX	−20		−57	−18		−57	mA
I_{CC}	Supply current	V_{CC} = MAX, See Note 3		48	68		48	79	mA

[†]For conditions shown at MIN or MAX, use the appropriate value specified under recommended operating conditions.
[‡]All typical values are at V_{CC} = 5 V, T_A = 25°C.
[§]Not more than one output should be shorted at a time.
NOTE 3: I_{CC} is measured with the clear input grounded and all other inputs and outputs open.

switching characteristics, V_{CC} = 5 V, T_A = 25°C

PARAMETER		TEST CONDITIONS	MIN	TYP	MAX	UNIT
t_{PLH}	Propagation delay time, low-to-high-level output from clock	C_L = 15 pF, R_L = 400 Ω, See Figure 1		25	40	ns
t_{PHL}	Propagation delay time, high-to-low-level output from clock			25	40	ns
t_{PLH}	Propagation delay time, low-to-high-level output from preset or preset enable			28	35	ns
t_{PHL}	Propagation delay time, high-to-low-level output from clear				55	ns

TEXAS
INSTRUMENTS

recommended operating conditions

	SN54LS96 MIN	NOM	MAX	SN74LS96 MIN	NOM	MAX	UNIT
Supply voltage, V_{CC}	4.5	5	5.5	4.75	5	5.25	V
High-level output current, I_{OH}			−400			−400	µA
Low-level output current, I_{OL}			4			8	mA
Clock frequency, f_{clock}	0		25	0		25	MHz
Width of clock input pulse, $t_{w(clock)}$	20			20			ns
Width of preset and clear input pulse, t_w	30			30			ns
Serial input setup time, t_{setup} (see Figure 1)	30			30			ns
Serial input hold time, t_{hold} (see Figure 1)	0			0			ns
Operating free-air temperature, T_A	−55		125	0		70	°C

electrical characteristics over recommended operating free-air temperature range (unless otherwise noted)

PARAMETER		TEST CONDITIONS[†]		SN54LS96 MIN	TYP[‡]	MAX	SN74LS96 MIN	TYP[‡]	MAX	UNIT
V_{IH} High-level input voltage				2			2			V
V_{IL} Low-level input voltage						0.7			0.8	V
V_{IK} Input clamp voltage		V_{CC} = MIN, I_I = −18 mA				−1.5			−1.5	V
V_{OH} High-level output voltage		V_{CC} = MIN, V_{IH} = 2 V, $V_{IL} = V_{IL}$ max, I_{OH} = −400 µA		2.5	3.5		2.7	3.5		V
V_{OL} Low-level output voltage		V_{CC} = MIN, V_{IH} = 2 V, $V_{IL} = V_{IL}$ max	I_{OL} = 4 mA		0.25	0.4		0.25	0.4	V
			I_{OL} = 8 mA					0.35	0.5	
I_I Input current at maximum input voltage	Preset enable	V_{CC} = MAX, V_I = 7 V				0.5			0.5	mA
	All others					0.1			0.1	
I_{IH} High-level input current	Preset enable	V_{CC} = MAX, V_I = 2.7 V				100			100	µA
	All others					20			20	
I_{IL} Low-level input current	Preset enable	V_{CC} = MAX, V_I = 0.4 V				−2			−2	mA
	All others					−0.4			−0.4	
I_{OS} Short-circuit output current [§]		V_{CC} = MAX		−20		−100	−20		−100	mA
I_{CC} Supply current		V_{CC} = MAX, See Note 3			12	20		12	20	mA

[†] For conditions shown at MIN or MAX, use the appropriate value specified under recommended operating conditions.
[‡] All typical values are at V_{CC} = 5 V, T_A = 25°C.
[§] Not more than one output should be shorted at a time, and duration of the short-circuit should not exceed one second.
NOTE 3: I_{CC} is measured with the clear input grounded and all other inputs and outputs open.

switching characteristics, V_{CC} = 5 V, T_A = 25°C

PARAMETER		TEST CONDITIONS	MIN	TYP	MAX	UNIT
t_{PLH}	Propagation delay time, low-to-high-level output from clock	C_L = 15 pF, R_L = 2 kΩ, See Figure 1		25	40	ns
t_{PHL}	Propagation delay time, high-to-low-level output from clock			25	40	ns
t_{PLH}	Propagation delay time, low-to-high-level output from preset or preset enable			28	35	ns
t_{PHL}	Propagation delay time, high-to-low-level output from clear				55	ns

TTL DEVICES

3

TYPES SN5496, SN54LS96, SN7496, SN74LS96
5-BIT SHIFT REGISTERS

PARAMETER MEASUREMENT INFORMATION

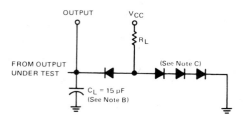

LOAD CIRCUIT

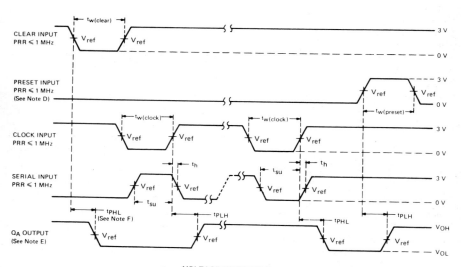

VOLTAGE WAVEFORMS

NOTES: A. Input pulses are supplied by pulse generators having the following characteristics: duty cycle ≤ 50%, $Z_{out} \approx 50\ \Omega$; for '96 $t_r \le 10$ ns, $t_f \le 10$ ns, and for 'LS96 $t_r = 15$ ns, $t_f = 6$ ns.
B. C_L includes probe and jig capacitance.
C. All diodes are 1N3064 or equivalent.
D. Preset may be tested by applying a high-level voltage to the individual preset inputs and pulsing the preset enable or by applying a high-level voltage to the preset enable and pulsing the individual preset inputs.
E. Q_A output is illustrated. Relationship of serial input to other Q outputs is illustrated in the typical shift sequence.
F. Outputs are set to the high level prior to the measurement of t_{PHL} from the clear input.
G. For '96, $V_{ref} = 1.5$ V; for 'LS96, $V_{ref} = 1.3$ V.

FIGURE 1—SWITCHING TIMES

3-302

TEXAS
INSTRUMENTS

3
TTL DEVICES

- Perform Fixed-Rate or Variable-Rate Frequency Division

- For Applications in Arithmetic, Radar, Digital-to-Analog (D/A), Analog-to-Digital (A/D), and other Conversion Operations

- Typical Maximum Clock Frequency . . . 32 Megahertz

SN5497 . . . J OR W PACKAGE
SN7497 . . . J OR N PACKAGE

(TOP VIEW)

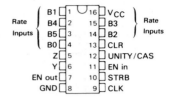

description

These monolithic, fully synchronous, programmable counters utilize Series 54/74 TTL circuitry to achieve 32-megahertz typical maximum operating frequencies. These six-bit serial binary counters feature buffered clock, clear, and enable inputs to control the operation of the counter, and a strobe input to enable or inhibit the rate input/decoding AND-OR-INVERT gates. The outputs have additional gating for cascading and transferring unity-count rates.

The counter is enabled when the clear, strobe, and enable inputs are low. With the counter enabled, the output frequency is equal to the input frequency multiplied by the rate input M and divided by 64, ie.:

$$f_{out} = \frac{M \cdot f_{in}}{64}$$

where: $M = F \cdot 2^5 + E \cdot 2^4 + D \cdot 2^3 + C \cdot 2^2 + B \cdot 2^1 + A \cdot 2^0$

When the rate input is binary 0 (all rate inputs low), Z remains high. In order to cascade devices to perform 12-bit multiplication, the enable output is connected to the enable and strobe inputs of the next stage, the Z output of each stage is connected to the unity/cascade input of the other stage, and the sub-multiple frequency is taken from the Y output.

The unity/cascade input, when connected to the clock input, may be utilized to pass the clock frequency (inverted) to the Y output when the rate input/decoding gates are inhibited by the strobe. The unity/cascade input may also be used as a control for the Y output.

schematics of inputs and outputs

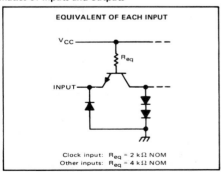

EQUIVALENT OF EACH INPUT

Clock input: R_{eq} = 2 kΩ NOM
Other inputs: R_{eq} = 4 kΩ NOM

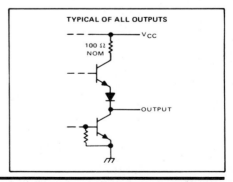

TYPICAL OF ALL OUTPUTS

TEXAS
INSTRUMENTS

3

TTL DEVICES

TYPES SN5497, SN7497
SYNCHRONOUS 6-BIT BINARY RATE MULTIPLIERS

description (continued)

STATE AND/OR RATE FUNCTION TABLE (See Note A)

	INPUTS			NUMBER OF CLOCK PULSES	UNITY/CASCADE	OUTPUTS			
			BINARY RATE			LOGIC LEVEL OR NUMBER OF PULSES			
CLEAR	ENABLE	STROBE	B5 B4 B3 B2 B1 B0			Y	Z	ENABLE	NOTES
H	X	H	X X X X X X	X	H	L	H	H	B
L	L	L	L L L L L L	64	H	L	H	1	C
L	L	L	L L L L L H	64	H	1	1	1	C
L	L	L	L L L L H L	64	H	2	2	1	C
L	L	L	L L L H L L	64	H	4	4	1	C
L	L	L	L L H L L L	64	H	8	8	1	C
L	L	L	L H L L L L	64	H	16	16	1	C
L	L	L	H L L L L L	64	H	32	32	1	C
L	L	L	H H H H H H	64	H	63	63	1	C
L	L	·L	H H H H H H	64	L	H	63	1	D
L	L	L	H L H L L L	64	H	40	40	1	E

NOTES: A. H = high level, L = low level, X = irrelevant. All remaining entries are numeric counts.

B. This is a simplified illustration of the clear function. The states of clock and strobe can affect the logic level of Y and Z. A low unity/cascade will cause output Y to remain high.

C. Each rate illustrated assumes a constant value at rate inputs; however, these illustrations in no way prohibit variable-rate inputs.

D. Unity/cascade is used to inhibit output Y.

E. $f_{out} = \dfrac{M \cdot f_{in}}{64} = \dfrac{(8 + 32) f_{in}}{64} = \dfrac{40 f_{in}}{64} = 0.625 f_{in}$

TEXAS
INSTRUMENTS

logic diagram

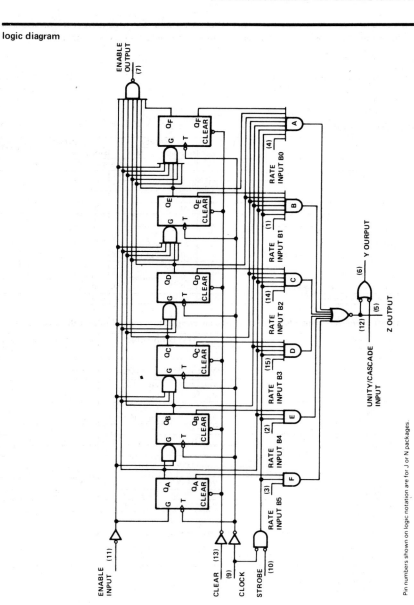

Pin numbers shown on logic notation are for J or N packages.

absolute maximum ratings over operating free-air temperature range (unless otherwise noted)

Supply voltage, V_{CC} (see Note 1) . . . . 7 V
Input voltage . . . . 5.5 V
Operating free-air temperature range: SN5497 (see Note 2) . . . . −55°C to 125°C
SN7497 . . . . 0°C to 70°C
Storage temperature range . . . . −65°C to 150°C

recommended operating conditions

		SN5497			SN7497			UNIT
		MIN	NOM	MAX	MIN	NOM	MAX	
Supply voltage, V_{CC}		4.5	5	5.5	4.75	5	5.25	V
High-level output current, I_{OH}				−400			−400	μA
Low-level output current, I_{OL}				16			16	mA
Clock frequency, f_{clock}		0		25	0		25	MHz
Width of clock pulse, $t_{w(clock)}$		20			20			ns
Width of clear pulse, $t_{w(clear)}$		15			15			ns
Enable setup time, t_{su}:	(See Figure 1)							
Before positive-going transition of clock pulse		25			25			ns
Before negative-going transition of previous clock pulse		0	$t_{w(clock)}$−10		0	$t_{w(clock)}$−10		
Enable hold time, t_h:	(See Figure 1)							
After positive-going transition of clock pulse		0	$t_{w(clock)}$−10		0	$t_{w(clock)}$−10		ns
After negative-going transition of previous clock pulse		20	t_{cp}−10		20	t_{cp}−10		
Operating free-air temperature, T_A (See Note 2)		−55		125	0		70	°C

electrical characteristics over recommended operating free-air temperature range (unless otherwise noted)

PARAMETER		TEST CONDITIONS[†]		MIN	TYP[‡]	MAX	UNIT
V_{IH}	High-level input voltage			2			V
V_{IL}	Low-level input voltage					0.8	V
V_{IK}	Input clamp voltage	V_{CC} = MIN,	I_I = −12 mA			−1.5	V
V_{OH}	High-level output voltage	V_{CC} = MIN, V_{IL} = 0.8 V,	V_{IH} = 2 V, I_{OH} = −400 μA	2.4	3.4		V
V_{OL}	Low-level output voltage	V_{CC} = MIN, V_{IL} = 0.8 V,	V_{IH} = 2 V, I_{OL} = 16 mA		0.2	0.4	V
I_I	Input current at maximum input voltage	V_{CC} = MAX,	V_I = 5.5 V			1	mA
I_{IH}	High-level input current	clock input	V_{CC} = MAX, V_I = 2.4 V			80	μA
		other inputs				40	
I_{IL}	Low-level input current	clock input	V_{CC} = MAX, V_I = 0.4 V			−3.2	mA
		other inputs				−1.6	
I_{OS}	Short circuit output current[§]	V_{CC} = MAX		−18		−55	mA
I_{CCH}	Supply current, outputs high	V_{CC} = MAX,	See Note 3		58		mA
I_{CCL}	Supply current, outputs low	V_{CC} = MAX,	See Note 4		80	120	mA

[†] For test conditions shown as MIN or MAX, use the appropriate value specified under recommended operating conditions.
[‡] All typical values are at V_{CC} = 5 V, T_A = 25°C.
[§] Not more than one output should be shorted at a time.

NOTES: 1. Voltage values are with respect to network ground terminal.
2. An SN5497 in the W package operating at free-air temperatures above 118°C requires a heat sink that provides a thermal resistance from case to free-air, $R_{\theta CA}$, of not more than 55°C/W.
3. I_{CCH} is measured with outputs open and all inputs grounded.
4. I_{CCL} is measured with outputs open and all inputs at 4.5 V.

3

TTL DEVICES

Texas Instruments

switching characteristics, V_{CC} = 5 V, T_A = 25°C, N = 10

PARAMETERS¶	FROM INPUT	TO OUTPUT	TEST CONDITIONS	MIN	TYP	MAX	UNIT
f_{max}				25	32		MHz
t_{PLH}	Enable	Enable			13	20	ns
t_{PHL}					14	21	
t_{PLH}	Strobe	Z			12	18	ns
t_{PHL}					15	23	
t_{PLH}	Clock	Y			26	39	ns
t_{PHL}					20	30	
t_{PLH}	Clock	Z			12	18	ns
t_{PHL}					17	26	
t_{PLH}	Rate	Z	C_L = 15 pF,		6	10	ns
t_{PHL}			R_L = 400 Ω,		9	14	
t_{PLH}	Unity/Cascade	Y	See Figure 1		9	14	ns
t_{PHL}					6	10	
t_{PLH}	Strobe	Y			19	30	ns
t_{PHL}					22	33	
t_{PLH}	Clock	Enable			19	30	ns
t_{PHL}					22	33	
t_{PLH}	Clear	Y			24	36	ns
t_{PHL}		Z			15	23	
t_{PLH}	Any Rate Input	Y			15	23	ns
t_{PHL}					15	23	

¶ f_{max} ≡ maximum clock frequency.
t_{PLH} ≡ propagation delay time, low-to-high-level output.
t_{PHL} ≡ propagation delay time, high-to-low-level output.

TYPICAL APPLICATION DATA

This application demonstrates how the '97 can be cascaded to perform 18-bit rate multiplication. This scheme is expandable to n-bits by extending the pattern illustrated.

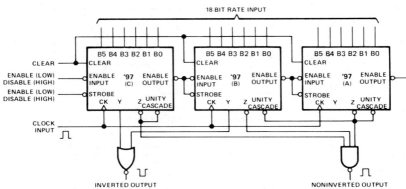

As illustrated, two of the 6-bit multipliers can be cascaded by connecting the Z output of unit A to the unity cascade input of unit B, in which case, a two-input NOR gate is used to cascade the remaining multipliers. Alternatively, all three Y outputs can be cascaded with a 3-input NOR gate. The three unused unity cascade inputs can be conveniently terminated by connecting each to its Z output.

TEXAS
INSTRUMENTS

TTL DEVICES

3

PARAMETER MEASUREMENT INFORMATION

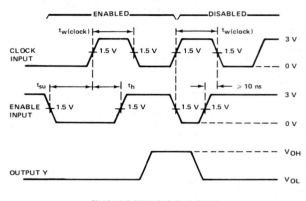

ENABLING FROM POSITIVE-GOING
TRANSITION OF CLOCK PULSE

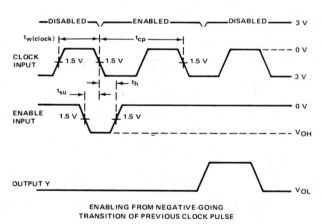

ENABLING FROM NEGATIVE-GOING
TRANSITION OF PREVIOUS CLOCK PULSE

1. Unity/Cascade and pin 2 (rate input), other inputs are low. Clear the counter and apply clock and enable pulse as illustrated.
2. Setup and hold times are illustrated for enabling a single clock pulse (count). Continued application of the enable function will enable subsequent clock pulse (counts) until disabling occurs (enable goes high). The total number of counts will be determined by the total number of positive-going clock transition enabled.

NOTES: A. The input pulse generator has the following characteristics: $t_{w(clock)}$ = 20 ns, t_{TLH} ≤ 10 ns, t_{THL} ≤ 10 ns, PRR = 1 MHz, Z_{out} ≈ 50 Ω.
      B. C_L includes probe and jig capacitance.
      C. All diodes are 1N3064 or equivalent.

FIGURE 1—SWITCHING TIMES

PARAMETER MEASUREMENT INFORMATION

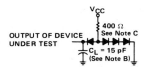

All three outputs are loaded during testing.

LOAD CIRCUIT

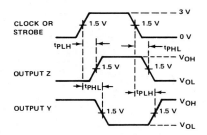

Unity/cascade and rate inputs are high, other inputs are low, and flip-flops are at any count other than maximum.

**PROPAGATION DELAY TIMES, CLOCK TO Z AND Y,
AND STROBE INPUT TO Z AND Y**

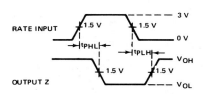

Flip-flops are at a count so that all other inputs to the gate under test are high and all other inputs, including other rate inputs, are low.

**PROPAGATION DELAY TIMES,
RATE INPUT TO Z**

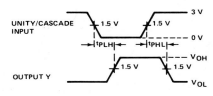

Output Z is high.

**PROPAGATION DELAY TIMES,
UNITY/CASCADE INPUT TO Y**

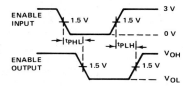

Flip-flops are at the maximum count. Other inputs are low.

**PROPAGATION DELAY TIMES,
ENABLE INPUT TO ENABLE OUTPUT**

NOTES: A. The input pulse generator has the following characteristics: $t_{w(clock)}$ = 20 ns, $t_{TLH} \leqslant$ 10 ns, $t_{THL} \leqslant$ 10 ns, PRR = 1 MHz, $Z_{out} \approx$ 50 Ω.
        B. C_L includes probe and jig capacitance.
        C. All diodes are 1N3064 or equivalent.

FIGURE 1—SWITCHING TIMES (CONTINUED)

**TEXAS
INSTRUMENTS**

3

TTL DEVICES

- **Package Options Include Both Plastic and Ceramic Chip Carriers in Addition to Plastic and Ceramic DIPs**

- **Dependable Texas Instruments Quality and Reliablity**

description

The '107 contain two independent J-K flip-flops with individual J-K, clock, and direct clear inputs. The '107 is a positive pulse-triggered flip-flop. The J-K input is loaded into the master while the clock is high and transferred to the slave on the high-to-low clock transition. For these devices the J and K inputs must be stable while the clock is high.

The 'LS107A contain two independent negative-edge-triggered flip-flops. The J and K inputs must be stable one setup time prior to the high-to-low clock transition for predictable operation. When the clear is low, it overrides the clock and data inputs forcing the Q output low and the $\overline{Q}$ output high.

The SN54107 and the SN54LS107A are characterized for operation over the full military temperature range of $-55\,°C$ to $125\,°C$. The SN74107 and the SN74LS107A are characterized for operation from $0\,°C$ to $70\,°C$.

SN54107, SN54LS107A . . . J PACKAGE
SN74107 . . . J OR N PACKAGE
SN74LS107A . . . D, J OR N PACKAGE
(TOP VIEW)

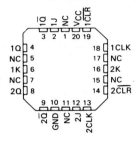

1J [1	14] V_CC
1Q̄ [2	13] 1CLR
1Q [3	12] 1CLK
1K [4	11] 2K
2Q [5	10] 2CLR
2Q̄ [6	9] 2CLK
GND [7	8] 2J

SN54LS107A . . . FK PACKAGE
SN74LS107A
(TOP VIEW)

NC - No internal connection

'107
FUNCTION TABLE

INPUTS				OUTPUTS	
$\overline{CLR}$	CLK	J	K	Q	$\overline{Q}$
L	X	X	X	L	H
H	⊓	L	L	Q_0	$\overline{Q}_0$
H	⊓	H	L	H	L
H	⊓	L	H	L	H
H	⊓	H	H	TOGGLE	

'LS107A
FUNCTION TABLE

INPUTS				OUTPUTS	
$\overline{CLR}$	CLK	J	K	Q	$\overline{Q}$
L	X	X	X	L	H
H	↓	L	L	Q_0	$\overline{Q}_0$
H	↓	H	L	H	L
H	↓	L	H	L	H
H	↓	H	H	TOGGLE	
H	H	X	X	Q_0	$\overline{Q}_0$

3

TTL DEVICES

TEXAS INSTRUMENTS

logic diagrams

'107

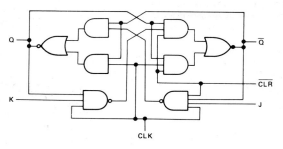

'LS107A

TEXAS INSTRUMENTS

logic symbols

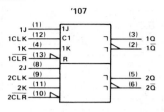

'107

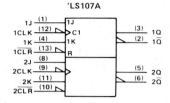

'LS107A

Pin numbers shown on logic notation are for D, J or N packages.

schematic of inputs and outputs

'107

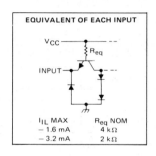

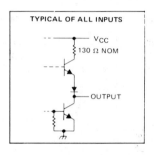

'LS107A

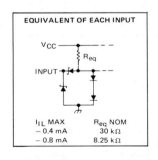

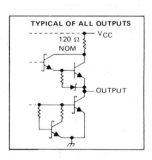

absolute maximum ratings over operating free-air temperature range (unless otherwise noted)

Supply voltage, V$_{CC}$ (see Note 1) . . . . 7 V
Input voltage: '107 . . . . 5.5 V
'LS107A . . . . 7 V
Operating free-air temperature range: SN54' . . . . −55°C to 125°C
SN74' . . . . 0°C to 70°C
Storage temperature range . . . . −65°C to 150°C

NOTE 1: Voltage values are with respect to network ground terminal.

3

TTL DEVICES

3-313

TYPES SN54107, SN74107
DUAL J-K FLIP-FLOPS WITH CLEAR

recommended operating conditions

			SN54107			SN74107			UNIT
			MIN	NOM	MAX	MIN	NOM	MAX	
V_{CC}	Supply voltage		4.5	5	5.5	4.75	5	5.25	V
V_{IH}	High-level input voltage		2			2			V
V_{IL}	Low-level input voltage				0.8			0.8	V
I_{OH}	High-level output current				−0.4			−0.4	mA
I_{OL}	Low-level output current				16			16	mA
t_w	Pulse duration	CLK high	20			20			
		CLK low	47			47			ns
		$\overline{CLR}$ low	25			25			
t_{su}	Input setup time before CLK↑		0			0			ns
t_h	Input hold time-data after CLK↑		0			0			ns
T_A	Operating free-air temperature		−55		125	0		70	°C

electrical characteristics over recommended operating free-air temperature range (unless otherwise noted)

PARAMETER		TEST CONDITIONS[†]		SN54107			SN74107			UNIT
				MIN	TYP[‡]	MAX	MIN	TYP[‡]	MAX	
V_{IK}		V_{CC} = MIN,	I_I = −12 mA			−1.5			−1.5	V
V_{OH}		V_{CC} = MIN, I_{OH} = −0.4 mA	V_{IH} = 2 V, V_{IL} = 0.8 V,	2.4	3.4		2.4	3.4		V
V_{OL}		V_{CC} = MIN, I_{OL} = 16 mA	V_{IH} = 2 V, V_{IL} = 0.8 V,		0.2	0.4		0.2	0.4	V
I_I		V_{CC} = MAX,	V_I = 5.5 V			1			1	mA
I_{IH}	J or K	V_{CC} = MAX,	V_I = 2.4 V			40			40	μA
	All other					80			80	
I_{IL}	J or K	V_{CC} = MAX,	V_I = 0.4 V			−1.6			−1.6	mA
	All other					−3.2			−3.2	
I_{OS}[§]		V_{CC} = MAX		−20		−57	−18		−57	mA
I_{CC} Supply Current (average per Flip-Flop)		V_{CC} = MAX,	See Note 2		10	20		10	20	mA

[†] For conditions shown as MIN or MAX, use the appropriate value specified under recommended operating conditions.
[‡] All typical values are at V_{CC} = 5 V, T_A = 25°C.
[§] Not more than one output should be shorted at a time.
NOTE 2: With all outputs open, I_{CC} is measured with the Q and $\overline{Q}$ outputs high in turn. At the time of measurement, the clock input is grounded.

switching characteristics, V_{CC} = 5 V, T_A = 25°C (see note 3)

PARAMETER	FROM (INPUT)	TO (OUTPUT)	TEST CONDITIONS		MIN	TYP	MAX	UNIT
f_{max}					15	20		MHz
t_{PLH}	$\overline{CLR}$	$\overline{Q}$	R_L = 400 Ω,	C_L = 15 pF		16	25	ns
t_{PHL}		Q				25	40	ns
t_{PLH}	CLK	Q or $\overline{Q}$				16	25	ns
t_{PHL}						25	40	ns

NOTE 3: See General Information Section for load circuits and voltage waveforms.

TEXAS
INSTRUMENTS

3

TTL DEVICES

recommended operating conditions

			SN54LS107A			SN74LS107A			UNIT
			MIN	NOM	MAX	MIN	NOM	MAX	
V_{CC}	Supply voltage		4.5	5	5.5	4.75	5	5.25	V
V_{IH}	High-level input voltage		2			2			V
V_{IL}	Low-level input voltage				0.7			0.8	V
I_{OH}	High-level output current				−0.4			0.4	mA
I_{OL}	Low-level output current				4			8	mA
f_{clock}	Clock frequency		0		30	0		30	MHz
t_w	Pulse duration	CLK high	20			20			ns
		$\overline{CLR}$ low	25			25			
t_{su}	Setup time before CLK↓	data high or low	20			20			ns
		$\overline{CLR}$ inactive	25			25			
t_h	Hold time-data after CLK↓		0			20			ns
T_A	Operating free-air temperature		−55		125	0		70	°C

electrical characteristics over recommended operating free-air temperature range (unless otherwise noted)

PARAMETER		TEST CONDITIONS†	SN54LS107A			SN74LS107A			UNIT
			MIN	TYP‡	MAX	MIN	TYP‡	MAX	
V_{IK}		V_{CC} = MIN, I_I = −18 mA			−1.5			−1.5	V
V_{OH}		V_{CC} = MIN, V_{IH} = 2 V, V_{IL} = MAX, I_{OH} = −0.4 mA	2.5	3.4		2.7	3.4		V
V_{OL}		V_{CC} = MIN, V_{IL} = MAX, V_{IH} = 2 V, I_{OL} = 4 mA		0.25	0.4		0.25	0.4	V
		V_{CC} = MIN, V_{IL} = MAX, V_{IH} = 2 V, I_{OL} = 8 mA					0.35	0.5	
I_I	J or K	V_{CC} = MAX, V_I = 7 V			0.1			0.1	mA
	CLR				0.3			0.3	
	CLK				0.4			0.4	
I_{IH}	J or K	V_{CC} = MAX, V_I = 2.7 V			20			20	μA
	CLR				60			60	
	CLK				80			80	
I_{IL}	J or K	V_{CC} = MAX, V_I = 0.4 V			−0.4			−0.4	mA
	CLR or CLK				−0.8			−0.8	
I_{OS}§		V_{CC} = MAX, See Note 4	−20		−100	−20		−100	mA
I_{CC}		V_{CC} = MAX, See Note 2		4	6		4	6	mA

†For conditions shown as MIN or MAX, use the appropriate value specified under recommended operating conditions.
‡ All typical values are at V_{CC} = 5 V, T_A = 25°C.
§Not more than one output should be shorted at a time, and the duration of the short circuit should not exceed one second.
NOTE 2: With all outputs open, I_{CC} is measured with the Q and $\overline{Q}$, outputs high in turn. At the time of measurement, the clock input is grounded.
NOTE 4: For certain devices where state commutation can be caused by shorting an output to ground, an equivalent test may be performed with V_O = 2.25 V and 2.125 V for the 54 family and the 74 family, respectively, with the minimum and maximum limits reduced to one half of their stated values.

switching characteristics, V_{CC} = 5 V, T_A = 25°C (see note 3)

PARAMETER	FROM (INPUT)	TO (OUTPUT)	TEST CONDITIONS		MIN	TYP	MAX	UNIT
f_{max}			R_L = 2 kΩ,	C_L = 15 pF	30	45		MHz
t_{PLH}	$\overline{CLR}$ or CLK	Q or $\overline{Q}$				15	20	ns
t_{PHL}						15	20	ns

NOTE 3: See General Information Section for load circuits and voltage waveforms.

3

TTL DEVICES

3

TTL DEVICES

- **Package Options Include Both Plastic and Ceramic Chip Carriers in Addition to Plastic and Ceramic DIPs.**

- **Dependable Texas Instruments Quality and Reliability**

description

These devices contain two independent J-K̄ positive-edge-triggered flip-flops. A low level at the preset or clear inputs sets or resets the outputs regardless of the levels of the other inputs. When preset and clear are inactive (high), data at the J and K̄ inputs meeting the setup time requirements are transferred to the outputs on the positive-going edge of the clock pulse. Clock triggering occurs at a voltage level and is not directly related to the rise time of the clock pulse. Following the hold time interval, data at the J and K̄ inputs may be changed without affecting the levels at the outputs. These versatile flip-flops can perform as toggle flip-flops by grounding K̄ and tying J high. They also can perform as D-type flip-flops if J and K̄ are tied together.

The SN54109 and SN54LS109A are characterized for operation over the full military temperature range of −55°C to 125°C. The SN74109 and SN74LS109A are characterized for operation from 0°C to 70°C.

FUNCTION TABLE (each flip-flop)

PRĒ	CLR̄	CLK	J	K̄	Q	Q̄
L	H	X	X	X	H	L
H	L	X	X	X	L	H
L	L	X	X	X	H†	H†
H	H	↑	L	L	L	H
H	H	↑	H	L	TOGGLE	
H	H	↑	L	H	Q₀	Q̄₀
H	H	↑	H	H	Q₀	L
H	H	L	X	X	Q₀	Q̄₀

The columns INPUTS (PRĒ, CLR̄, CLK, J, K̄) and OUTPUTS (Q, Q̄)

† The output levels in this configuration are not guaranteed to meet the minimum levels for V_{OH} if the lows at preset and clear are near V_{IL} maximum. Furthermore, this configuration is nonstable; that is, it will not persist when preset or clear return to their inactive (high) level.

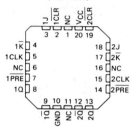

```
1CLR̄ [ 1   16 ] Vcc
  1J  [ 2   15 ] 2CLR̄
  1K̄  [ 3   14 ] 2J
1CLK  [ 4   13 ] 2K̄
1PRĒ [ 5   12 ] 2CLK
  1Q  [ 6   11 ] 2PRĒ
  1Q̄  [ 7   10 ] 2Q
 GND  [ 8    9 ] 2Q̄
```

SN54LS109A . . . FK PACKAGE
SN74LS109A

(TOP VIEW)

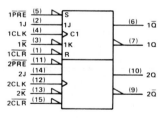

```
        1J 1CLR̄ NC Vcc 2CLR̄
         3   2   1  20  19
  1K̄ [ 4              18 ] 2J
1CLK [ 5              17 ] 2K̄
  NC [ 6              16 ] NC
1PRĒ[ 7              15 ] 2CLK
  1Q [ 8              14 ] 2PRĒ
         9  10  11  12  13
        1Q̄ GND  NC  2Q 2Q̄
```

logic symbol

```
1PRĒ (5)  ▷ S
  1J (2)     1J        (6)  1Q̄
1CLK (4)  ▷ C1
  1K̄ (3)     1K̄       (7)  1Q
1CLR̄ (1)  ▷ R
2PRĒ (11) ▷
  2J (14)              (10) 2Q
2CLK (12) ▷
  2K̄ (13)              (9)  2Q̄
2CLR̄ (15) ▷
```

Pin numbers shown on logic notation are for D, J or N packages.

TEXAS
INSTRUMENTS

3
TTL DEVICES

logic diagram

'109

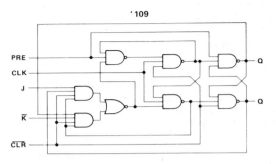

schematics of inputs and outputs

'109

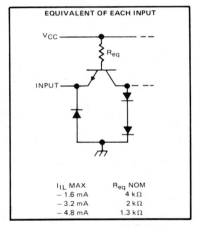

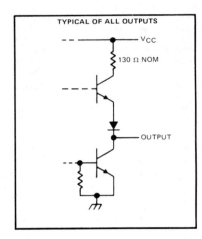

TEXAS
INSTRUMENTS

3
TTL DEVICES

schematic

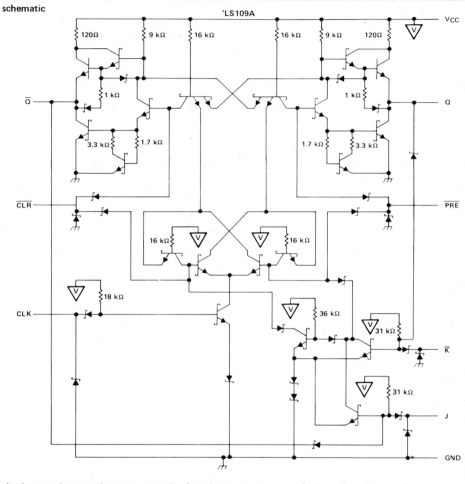

absolute maximum ratings over operating free-air temperature range (unless otherwise noted)

Supply voltage, V_{CC} (see Note 1) . . . . 7 V
Input voltage: '109 . . . . 5.5 V
'LS109A . . . . 7 V
Operating free-air temperature range: SN54' . . . . −55°C to 125°C
SN74' . . . . 0°C to 70°C
Storage temperature range . . . . −65°C to 150°C

NOTE 1: Voltage values are with respect to network ground terminal.

TTL DEVICES

recommended operating conditions

			SN54109			SN74109			UNIT
			MIN	NOM	MAX	MIN	NOM	MAX	
V_{CC}	Supply voltage		4.5	5	5.5	4.75	5	5.25	V
V_{IH}	High-level input voltage		2			2			V
V_{IL}	Low-level input voltage				0.8			0.8	V
I_{OH}	High-level output current				−0.8			−0.8	mA
I_{OL}	Low-level output current				16			16	mA
t_w	Pulse duration	CLK high or low	20			20			ns
		$\overline{PRE}$ or $\overline{CLR}$ low	20			20			
t_{su}	Input setup time before CLK↑		10			10			ns
t_h	Input hold time-data after CLK↑		6			6			ns
T_A	Operating free-air temperature		−55		125	0		70	°C

electrical characteristics over recommended operating free-air temperature range (unless otherwise noted)

PARAMETER		TEST CONDITIONS†		SN54109			SN74109			UNIT
				MIN	TYP‡	MAX	MIN	TYP‡	MAX	
V_{IK}		V_{CC} = MIN,	I_I = −12 mA			−1.5			−1.5	V
V_{OH}		V_{CC} = MIN, V_{IH} = 2 V, V_{IL} = −0.8 V, I_{OH} = −0.8 mA		2.4	3.4		2.4	3.4		V
V_{OL}		V_{CC} = MIN, V_{IH} = 2 V, V_{IL} = 0.8 V, I_{OL} = 16 mA			0.2	0.4		0.2	0.4	V
I_I		V_{CC} = MAX,	V_I = 5.5 V			1			1	mA
I_{IH}	J or $\overline{K}$	V_{CC} = MAX,	V_I = 2.4 V			40			40	μA
	$\overline{CLR}$					160			160	
	$\overline{PRE}$ or CLK					80			80	
I_{IL}	J or $\overline{K}$	V_{CC} = MAX,	V_I = 0.4 V			−1.6			−1.6	mA
	$\overline{CLR}$★					−4.8			−4.8	
	$\overline{PRE}$★					−3.2			−3.2	
	CLK					−3.2			−3.2	
I_{OS} §		V_{CC} = MAX		−30		−85	−30		−85	mA
I_{CC} Supply Current (average per Flip-Flop)		V_{CC} = MAX,	See Note 2		9	15		9	15	mA

† For conditions shown as MIN or MAX, use the appropriate value specified under recommended operating conditions.
‡ All typical values are at V_{CC} = 5 V, T_A = 25°C.
§ Not more than one output should be shorted at a time.
★ Clear is tested with preset high and preset is tested with clear high.
NOTE 2: With all outputs open, I_{CC} is measured with the Q and $\overline{Q}$ outputs high in turn. At the time of measurement, the clock input is grounded.

switching characteristics, V_{CC} = 5 V, T_A = 25°C (see note 3)

PARAMETER	FROM (INPUT)	TO (OUTPUT)	TEST CONDITIONS		MIN	TYP	MAX	UNIT
f_{max}					25	33		MHz
t_{PLH}	$\overline{PRE}$	Q				10	15	ns
t_{PHL}		$\overline{Q}$				23	35	ns
t_{PLH}	$\overline{CLR}$	$\overline{Q}$	R_L = 400 Ω, C_L = 15 pF			10	15	ns
t_{PHL}		Q				17	25	ns
t_{PLH}	CLK	Q or $\overline{Q}$				10	16	ns
t_{PHL}						18	28	ns

NOTE 3: See General Information Section for load circuits and voltage waveforms.

TEXAS
INSTRUMENTS

recommended operating conditions

		SN54LS109A MIN	NOM	MAX	SN74LS109A MIN	NOM	MAX	UNIT
V_{CC}	Supply voltage	4.5	5	5.5	4.75	5	5.25	V
V_{IH}	High-level input voltage	2			2			V
V_{IL}	Low-level input voltage			0.7			0.8	V
I_{OH}	High-level output current			−0.4			−0.4	mA
I_{OL}	Low-level output current			4			8	mA
f_{clock}	Clock frequency	0		25	0		25	MHz
t_w	Pulse duration	CLK high	25			25			ns
		$\overline{PRE}$ or $\overline{CLR}$ low	25			25			
t_{su}	Setup time before CLK ↑	High-level data	35			35			ns
		Low-level data	25			25			
t_h	Hold time-data after CLK ↑	5			5			ns
T_A	Operating free-air temperature	−55		125	0		70	°C

electrical characteristics over recommended operating free-air temperature range (unless otherwise noted)

PARAMETER		TEST CONDITIONS†	SN54LS109A MIN	TYP‡	MAX	SN74LS109A MIN	TYP‡	MAX	UNIT
V_{IK}		V_{CC} = MIN, I_I = −18 mA			−1.5			−1.5	V
V_{OH}		V_{CC} = MIN, V_{IH} = 2 V, V_{IL} = MAX, I_{OH} = −0.4 mA	2.5	3.4		2.7	3.4		V
V_{OL}		V_{CC} = MIN, V_{IL} = MAX, V_{IH} = 2 V, I_{OL} = 4 mA		0.25	0.4		0.25	0.4	V
		V_{CC} = MIN, V_{IL} = MAX, V_{IH} = 2 V, I_{OL} = 8 mA					0.35	0.5	
I_I	J, $\overline{K}$ or CLK	V_{CC} = MAX, V_I = 7 V			0.1			0.1	mA
	$\overline{CLR}$ or $\overline{PRE}$				0.2			0.2	
I_{IH}	J, $\overline{K}$ or CLK	V_{CC} = MAX, V_I = 2.7 V			20			20	μA
	$\overline{CLR}$ or $\overline{PRE}$				40			40	
I_{IL}	J, $\overline{K}$ or CLK	V_{CC} = MAX, V_I = 0.4 V			−0.4			−0.4	mA
	$\overline{CLR}$ or $\overline{PRE}$				−0.8			−0.8	
I_{OS}§		V_{CC} = MAX, See Note 4	−20		−100	−20		−100	mA
I_{CC}		V_{CC} = MAX, See Note 2		4	8		4	8	mA

† For conditions shown as MIN or MAX, use the appropriate value specified under recommended operating conditions.
‡ All typical values are at V_{CC} = 5 V, T_A = 25°C.
§ Not more than one output should be shorted at a time, and the duration of the short circuit should not exceed one second.
NOTE 2: With all outputs open, I_{CC} is measured wtih the Q and $\overline{Q}$ outputs high in turn. At the time of measurement, the clock input is grounded.
NOTE 4: For certain devices where state commutation can be caused by shorting an output to ground, an equivalent test may be performed with V_O = 2.25 V and 2.125 V for the 54 family and the 74 family, respectively with the minimum and maximum limits reduced to one half of their stated values.

switching characteristics, V_{CC} = 5 V, T_A = 25°C (see note 3)

PARAMETER	FROM (INPUT)	TO (OUTPUT)	TEST CONDITIONS	MIN	TYP	MAX	UNIT
f_{max}				25	33		MHz
t_{PLH}	$\overline{CLR}$, $\overline{PRE}$	Q or $\overline{Q}$	R_L = 2 kΩ, C_L = 15 pF		13	25	ns
t_{PHL}	or CLK				25	40	ns

NOTE 3: See General Information Section for load circuits and voltage waveforms.

3

TTL DEVICES

TTL DEVICES

- Package Options Include Plastic and Ceramic DIPs
- Dependable Texas Instruments Quality and Reliability

SN54111 . . . J OR W PACKAGE
SN74111 . . . J OR N PACKAGE
(TOP VIEW)

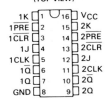

description

The SN54111 and SN74111 are d-c coupled, variable-skew, J-K flip-flops which utilize TTL circuitry to obtain 25-MHz performance typically. They are termed "variable-skew" because they allow the maximum clock skew in a system to be a direct function of the clock pulse width. The J and K inputs are enabled to accept data only during a short period (30 nanoseconds maximum hold time) starting with, and immediately following the rising edge of the clock pulse. After this, inputs may be changed while the clock is at the high level without affecting the state of the master. At the threshold level of the falling edge of the clock pulse, the data stored in the master will be transferred to the output. The effective allowable clock skew then is minimum propagation delay time minus hold time, plus clock pulse width. This means that the system designer can set the maximum allowable clock skew needed by varying the clock pulse width. Thus system design is made easier and the requirements for sophisticated clock distribution systems are minimized or, in some cases, entirely eliminated. These flip-flops have an additional feature-the synchronous input has reduced sensitivity to data change while the clock is high because the data need be present for only a short period of time and the system's susceptibility to noise is thereby effectively reduced.

The SN54111 is characterized for operation over the full military temperature range of $-55°C$ to $125°C$; the SN74111 is characterized for operation from $0°C$ to $70°C$.

logic symbol

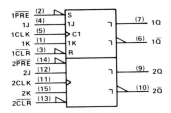

Pin numbers shown are for J and N packages.

FUNCTION TABLE

INPUTS					OUTPUTS	
$\overline{PRE}$	$\overline{CLR}$	CLK	J	K	Q	$\overline{Q}$
L	H	X	X	X	H	L
H	L	X	X	X	L	H
L	L	X	X	X	H†	H†
H	H	⊓	L	L	Q_0	$\overline{Q}_0$
H	H	⊓	H	L	H	L
H	H	⊓	L	H	L	H
H	H	⊓	H	H	TOGGLE	

† This configuration is non-stable; that is, it will not persist when preset or clear return to their inactive (high) level.

TEXAS INSTRUMENTS

3

TTL DEVICES

logic diagram

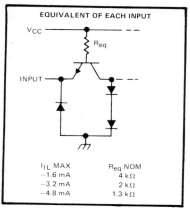

schematics of inputs and outputs

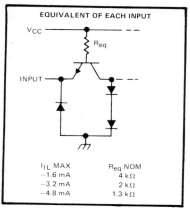
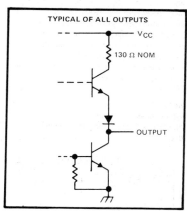

EQUIVALENT OF EACH INPUT

I_{IL} MAX	R_{eq} NOM
−1.6 mA	4 kΩ
−3.2 mA	2 kΩ
−4.8 mA	1.3 kΩ

TYPICAL OF ALL OUTPUTS

130 Ω NOM

absolute maximum ratings over operating free-air temperature range (unless otherwise noted)

Supply voltage, V_{CC} (see Note 1) . . . . 7 V
Input voltage . . . . 5.5 V
Operating free-air temperature range: SN54' . . . . −55°C to 125°C
                                        SN74' . . . . 0°C to 70°C
Storage temperature range . . . . −65°C to 150°C

NOTE 1: Voltage values are with respect to network ground terminal.

recommended operating conditions

			SN54111			SN74111			UNIT
			MIN	NOM	MAX	MIN	NOM	MAX	
V_{CC}	Supply voltage		4.5	5	5.5	4.75	5	5.25	V
V_{IH}	High-level input voltage		2			2			V
V_{IL}	Low-level input voltage				0.8			0.8	V
I_{OH}	High-level output current				−0.8			−0.8	mA
I_{OL}	Low-level output current				16			16	mA
t_w	Pulse duration	CLK high or low	25			25			ns
		$\overline{PRE}$ or $\overline{CLR}$ low	25			25			
t_{su}	Input setup time before CLK↑		0			0			ns
t_h	Input hold time data after CLK↑		30			30			ns
T_A	Operating free-air temperature		−55		125	0		70	°C

electrical characteristics over recommended operating free-air temperature range (unless otherwise noted)

PARAMETER		TEST CONDITIONS †			SN54111			SN74111			UNIT
					MIN	TYP‡	MAX	MIN	TYP‡	MAX	
V_{IK}		V_{CC} = MIN,	I_I = −12 mA				−1.5			−1.5	V
V_{OH}		V_{CC} = MIN,	V_{IH} = 2 V,	V_{IL} = 0.8 V, I_{OH} = −0.8 mA	2.4	3.4		2.4	3.4		V
V_{OL}		V_{CC} = MIN,	V_{IH} = 2 V,	V_{IL} = 0.8 V, I_{OL} = 16 mA		0.2	0.4		0.2	0.4	V
I_I		V_{CC} = MAX,	V_I = 5.5 V				1			1	mA
I_{IH}	J or K	V_{CC} = MAX, V_I = 2.4 V					40			40	μA
	$\overline{CLR}$ or $\overline{PRE}$						80			80	
	CLK						120			120	
I_{IL}	J or K	V_{CC} = MAX, V_I = 0.4 V					−1.6			−1.6	mA
	$\overline{CLR}$★						−3.2			−3.2	
	$\overline{PRE}$★						−3.2			−3.2	
	CLK						−4.8			−4.8	
I_{OS}§		V_{CC} = MAX			−20		−57	−18		−57	mA
I_{CC} Supply Current (average per Flip-Flop)		V_{CC} = MAX, See Note 2				14	20.5		14	20.5	mA

† For conditions shown as MIN or MAX, use the appropriate value specified under recommended operating conditions.
‡ All typical values are at V_{CC} = 5 V, T_A = 25°C.
§ Not more than one output should be shorted at a time.
★ Clear is tested with preset high and preset is tested with clear high.
NOTE 2: With all outputs open, I_{CC} is measured with the Q and $\overline{Q}$ outputs high in turn. At the time of measurement, the clock input is at 4.5 V.

switching characteristics, V_{CC} = 5 V, T_A = 25°C (see note 3)

PARAMETER	FROM (INPUT)	TO (OUTPUT)	TEST CONDITIONS		MIN	TYP	MAX	UNIT
f_{max}			R_L = 400 Ω,	C_L = 15 pF	20	25		MHz
t_{PLH}	$\overline{PRE}$ or $\overline{CLR}$	Q or $\overline{Q}$				12	18	ns
t_{PHL}						21	30	ns
t_{PLH}	CLK	Q or $\overline{Q}$				12	17	ns
t_{PHL}						20	30	ns

NOTE 3: See General Information Section for load circuits and voltage waveforms.

TEXAS
INSTRUMENTS

- Fully Buffered to Offer Maximum Isolation from External Disturbance

- Package Options Include Both Plastic and Ceramic Carriers in Addition to Plastic and Ceramic DIPs.

- Dependable Texas Instruments Quality and Reliability

description

These devices contain two independent J-K negative-edge-triggered flip-flops. A low level at the preset or clear inputs sets or resets the outputs regardless of the levels of the other inputs. When preset and clear are inactive (high), data at the J and K inputs meeting the setup time requirements are transferred to the outputs on the negative-going edge of the clock pulse. Clock triggering occurs at a voltage level and is not directly related to the rise time of the clock pulse. Following the hold time interval, data at the J and K inputs may be changed without affecting the levels at the outputs. These versatile flip-flops can perform as toggle flip-flops by tying J and K high.

The SN54LS112A and the SN54S112A are characterized for operation over the full military temperature range of −55°C to 125°C. The SN74LS112A and SN74S112A are characterized for operation from 0°C to 70°C.

SN54LS112A, SN54S112A ... J OR W PACKAGE
SN74LS112A, SN74S112A ... D, J OR N PACKAGE
(TOP VIEW)

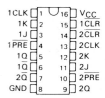

SN54LS112A, SN54S112A ... FK PACKAGE
SN74LS112A, SN74S112A
(TOP VIEW)

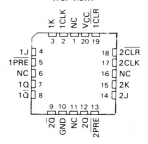

NC - No internal connection

FUNCTION TABLE (each flip-flop)

INPUTS					OUTPUTS	
$\overline{PRE}$	$\overline{CLR}$	CLK	J	K	Q	$\overline{Q}$
L	H	X	X	X	H	L
H	L	X	X	X	L	H
L	L	X	X	X	H†	H†
H	H	↓	L	L	Q_0	$\overline{Q}_0$
H	H	↓	H	L	H	L
H	H	↓	L	H	L	H
H	H	↓	H	H	TOGGLE	
H	H	H	X	X	Q_0	$\overline{Q}_0$

† The output levels in this configuration are not guaranteed to meet the minimum levels for V_{OH} if the lows at preset and clear are near V_{IL} maximum. Furthermore, this configuration is nonstable; that is, it will not persist when either preset or clear returns to its inactive (high) level.

logic symbol

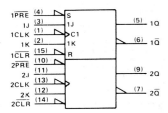

Pin numbers shown on logic notation are for D, J or N packages.

PRODUCTION DATA
This document contains information current as of publication date. Products conform to specifications per the terms of Texas Instruments standard warranty. Production processing does not necessarily include testing of all parameters.

TEXAS
INSTRUMENTS

logic diagrams

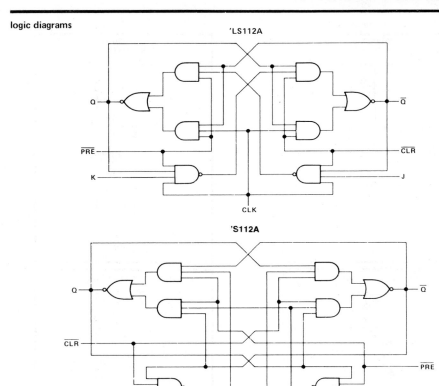

'LS112A

'S112A

TTL DEVICES

3

TYPES SN54LS112A, SN54S112A, SN74LS112A, SN74S112A
DUAL J-K NEGATIVE-EDGE-TRIGGERED
FLIP-FLOPS WITH PRESET AND CLEAR

schematics of inputs and outputs

'LS112A

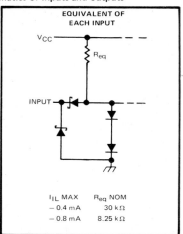

EQUIVALENT OF EACH INPUT

I_{IL} MAX	R_{eq} NOM
− 0.4 mA	30 kΩ
− 0.8 mA	8.25 kΩ

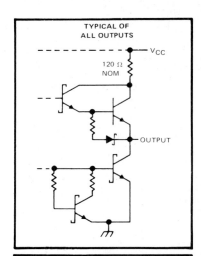

TYPICAL OF ALL OUTPUTS

120 Ω NOM

'S112A

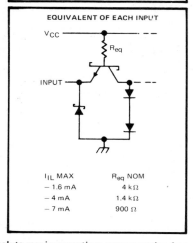

EQUIVALENT OF EACH INPUT

I_{IL} MAX	R_{eq} NOM
− 1.6 mA	4 kΩ
− 4 mA	1.4 kΩ
− 7 mA	900 Ω

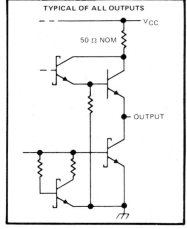

TYPICAL OF ALL OUTPUTS

50 Ω NOM

absolute maximum ratings over operating free-air temperature range (unless otherwise noted)

Supply voltage, V_{CC} (see Note 1)	7 V
Input voltage: 'LS112A	7 V
'S112A	5.5 V
Operating free-air temperature range: SN54'	− 55°C to 125°C
SN74'	0°C to 70°C
Storage temperature range	− 65°C to 150°C

NOTE 1: Voltage values are with respect to network ground terminal.

TEXAS INSTRUMENTS

recommended operating conditions

			SN54S112A			SN74S112A			UNIT
			MIN	NOM	MAX	MIN	NOM	MAX	
V_{CC}	Supply voltage		4.5	5	5.5	4.75	5	5.25	V
V_{IH}	High-level input voltage		2			2			V
V_{IL}	Low-level input voltage				0.8			0.8	V
I_{OH}	High-level output current				−1			−1	mA
I_{OL}	Low-level output current				20			20	mA
t_w	Pulse duration	CLK high	6			6			ns
		CLK low	6.5			6.5			
		$\overline{PRE}$ or $\overline{CLR}$ low	8			8			
t_{su}	Setup time before CLK↓	data high or low	7			7			ns
t_h	Hold time-data after CLK↓		0			0			ns
T_A	Operating free-air temperature		−55		125	0		70	°C

electrical characteristics over recommended free-air temperature range (unless otherwise noted)

PARAMETER		TEST CONDITIONS[†]		SN54S112A			SN74S112A			UNIT
				MIN	TYP[‡]	MAX	MIN	TYP[‡]	MAX	
V_{IK}		V_{CC} = MIN,	I_I = −18 mA			−1.2			−1.2	V
V_{OH}		V_{CC} = MIN, V_{IH} = 2 V, V_{IL} = 0.8 V, I_{OH} = −1 mA		2.5	3.4		2.7	3.4		V
V_{OL}		V_{CC} = MIN, V_{IH} = 2 V, V_{IL} = 0.8 V, I_{OL} = 20 mA				0.5			0.5	V
I_I		V_{CC} = MAX,	V_I = 5.5 V			1			1	mA
I_{IH}	J or K	V_{CC} = MAX,	V_I = 2.7 V			50			50	µA
	All other					100			100	
I_{IL}	J or K	V_{CC} = MAX,	V_I = 0.5 V			−1.6			−1.6	mA
	$\overline{CLR}$★					−7			−7	
	$\overline{PRE}$★					−7			−7	
	CLK					−4			−4	
I_{OS}§		V_{CC} = MAX		−40		−100	−40		−100	mA
I_{CC} Supply Current (average per Flip-Flop)		V_{CC} = MAX,	See Note 2		15	25		15	25	mA

† For conditions shown as MIN or MAX, use the appropriate value specified under recommended operating conditions.
‡ All typical values are at V_{CC} = 5 V, T_A = 25°C.
§ Not more than one output should be shorted at a time, and the duration of the short circuit should not exceed one second.
★ Clear is tested with preset high and preset is tested with clear high.
NOTE 2: With all outputs open, I_{CC} is measured with the Q and $\overline{Q}$ outputs high in turn. At the time of measurement, the clock input is grounded.

switching characteristics, V_{CC} = 5 V, T_A = 25°C (see note 3)

PARAMETER	FROM (INPUT)	TO (OUTPUT)	TEST CONDITIONS	MIN	TYP	MAX	UNIT
f_{max}				80	125		MHz
t_{PLH}	$\overline{PRE}$ or $\overline{CLR}$	Q or $\overline{Q}$			4	7	ns
t_{PHL}	$\overline{PRE}$ or $\overline{CLR}$ (CLK high)	$\overline{Q}$ or Q	R_L = 280 Ω, C_L = 15 pF		5	7	ns
	$\overline{PRE}$ or $\overline{CLR}$ (CLK low)	$\overline{Q}$ or Q			5	7	
t_{PLH}	CLK	Q or $\overline{Q}$			4	7	ns
t_{PHL}					5	7	

NOTE 3: See General Information Section for load circuits and voltage waveforms.

TEXAS
INSTRUMENTS

3

TTL DEVICES

recommended operating conditions

			SN54LS112A			SN74LS112A			UNIT
			MIN	NOM	MAX	MIN	NOM	MAX	
V_{CC}	Supply voltage		4.5	5	5.5	4.75	5	5.25	V
V_{IH}	High-level input voltage		2			2			V
V_{IL}	Low-level input voltage				0.7			0.8	V
I_{OH}	High-level output current				−0.4			−0.4	mA
I_{OL}	Low-level output current				4			8	mA
f_{clock}	Clock frequency		0		30	0		30	MHz
t_w	Pulse duration	CLK high	20			20			ns
		$\overline{PRE}$ or $\overline{CLR}$ low	25			25			
t_{su}	Setup time after CLK ↓	data high or low	20			20			ns
		$\overline{CLR}$ inactive	25			25			
		$\overline{PRE}$ inactive	20			20			
t_h	Hold time-data after CLK ↓		0			0			ns
T_A	Operating free-air temperature		−55		125	0		70	°C

electrical characteristics over recommended operating free-air temperature range (unless otherwise noted)

PARAMETER			TEST CONDITIONS†		SN54LS112A			SN74LS112A			UNIT
					MIN	TYP‡	MAX	MIN	TYP‡	MAX	
V_{IK}			V_{CC} = MIN,	I_I = −18 mA			−1.5			−1.5	V
V_{OH}			V_{CC} = MIN, V_{IH} = 2 V, V_{IL} = MAX, I_{OH} = −0.4 mA		2.5	3.4		2.7	3.4		V
V_{OL}			V_{CC} = MIN, V_{IL} = MAX, V_{IH} = 2 V, I_{OL} = 4 mA			0.25	0.4		0.25	0.4	V
			V_{CC} = MIN, V_{IL} = MAX, V_{IH} = 2 V, I_{OL} = 8 mA						0.35	0.5	
I_I	J or K		V_{CC} = MAX,	V_I = 7 V			0.1			0.1	mA
	$\overline{CLR}$ or $\overline{PRE}$						0.3			0.3	
	CLK						0.4			0.4	
I_{IH}	J or K		V_{CC} = MAX,	V_I = 2.7 V			20			20	μA
	$\overline{CLR}$ or $\overline{PRE}$						60			60	
	CLK						80			80	
I_{IL}	J or K		V_{CC} = MAX,	V_I = 0.4 V			−0.4			−0.4	mA
	All other						−0.8			−0.8	
I_{OS}§			V_{CC} = MAX,	See Note 4	−20		−100	−20		−100	mA
I_{CC}			V_{CC} = MAX,	See Note 2		4	6		4	6	mA

† For conditions shown as MIN or MAX, use the appropriate value specified under recommended operating conditions.
‡ All typical values are at V_{CC} = 5 V, T_A = 25°C.
§ Not more than one output should be shorted at a time, and the duration of the short circuit should not exceed one second.
NOTE 2: With all outputs open, I_{CC} is measured with the Q and $\overline{Q}$ outputs high in turn. At the time of measurement, the clock input is grounded.
NOTE 4: For certain devices where state commutation can be caused by shorting an output to ground, an equivalent test may be performed with V_O = 2.25 V and 2.125 V for the '54 family and the '74 family, respectively, with the minimum and maximum limits reduced to one half of their stated values.

switching characteristics, V_{CC} = 5 V, T_A = 25°C (see note 3)

PARAMETER	FROM (INPUT)	TO (OUTPUT)	TEST CONDITIONS		MIN	TYP	MAX	UNIT
f_{max}			R_L = 2 kΩ,	C_L = 15 pF	30	45		MHz
t_{PLH}	$\overline{CLR}$, $\overline{PRE}$ or CLK	Q or $\overline{Q}$				15	20	ns
t_{PHL}						15	20	ns

NOTE 3: See General Information Section for load circuits and voltage waveforms.

TEXAS
INSTRUMENTS

- **Fully Buffered to Offer Maximum Isolation from External Disturbance**
- **Package Options Include Both Plastic and Ceramic Carriers in Addition to Plastic and Ceramic DIPs.**
- **Dependable Texas Instruments Quality and Reliability**

description

These devices contain two independent J-K negative-edge-triggered flip-flops. A low level at the preset input sets the outputs regardless of the levels of the other inputs. When preset ($\overline{PRE}$) is inactive (high), data at the J and K inputs meeting the setup time requirements are transferred to the outputs on the negative-going edge of the clock pulse. Clock triggering occurs at a voltage level and is not directly related to the rise time of the clock pulse. Following the hold time interval, data at the J and K inputs may be changed without affecting the levels at the outputs. These versatile flip-flops can perform as toggle flip-flops by tying J and K high.

The SN54LS113A and SN54S113A are characterized for operation over the full military temperature range of −55°C to 125°C. The SN74LS113A and SN74S113A are characterized for operation from 0°C to 70°C.

SN54LS113A, SN54S113A ... J OR W PACKAGE
SN74LS113A, SN74S113A ... D, J OR N PACKAGE
(TOP VIEW)

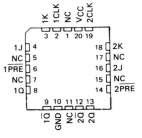

1CLK	1	14	V_{CC}
1K	2	13	2CLK
1J	3	12	2K
1$\overline{PRE}$	4	11	2J
1Q	5	10	2$\overline{PRE}$
1$\overline{Q}$	6	9	2Q
GND	7	8	2$\overline{Q}$

SN54LS113A, SN54S113A ... FK PACKAGE
SN74LS113A, SN74S113A
(TOP VIEW)

NC - No internal connection

FUNCTION TABLE (each flip-flop)

INPUTS				OUTPUTS	
$\overline{PRE}$	CLK	J	K	Q	$\overline{Q}$
L	X	X	X	H	L
H	↓	L	L	Q_0	$\overline{Q}_0$
H	↓	H	L	H	L
H	↓	L	H	L	H
H	↓	H	H	TOGGLE	
H	H	X	X	Q_0	$\overline{Q}_0$

logic symbol

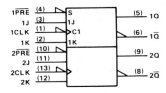

1$\overline{PRE}$	(4)	S	(5)	1Q
1J	(3)	1J		
1CLK	(1)	C1	(6)	1$\overline{Q}$
1K	(2)	1K		
2$\overline{PRE}$	(10)		(9)	2Q
2J	(11)			
2CLK	(13)		(8)	2$\overline{Q}$
2K	(12)			

Pin numbers shown on logic notation are for D, J or N packages.

TTL DEVICES — 3

TEXAS INSTRUMENTS

logic diagrams

'LS113A

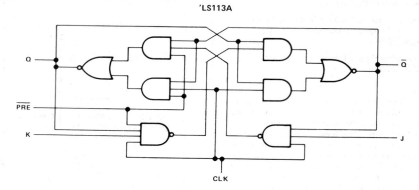

'S113A

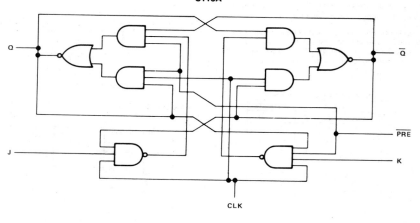

TEXAS INSTRUMENTS

schematics of inputs and outputs

'LS113A

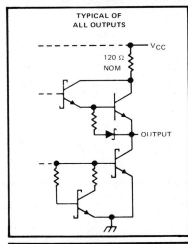

'S113A

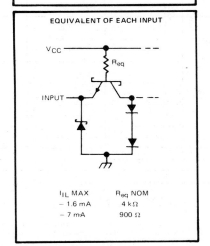

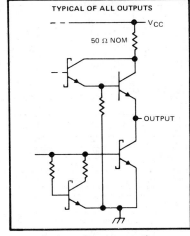

absolute maximum ratings over operating free-air temperature range (unless otherwise noted)

Supply voltage, V_{CC} (see Note 1) .... 7 V
Input voltage: 'LS113A .... 7 V
      'S113A .... 5.5 V
Operating free-air temperature range: SN54' .... -55°C to 125°C
             SN74' .... 0°C to 70°C
Storage temperature range .... -65°C to 150°C

NOTE 1: Voltage values are with respect to network ground terminal.

TEXAS
INSTRUMENTS

3

TTL DEVICES

recommended operating conditions

			SN54LS113A			SN74LS113A			UNIT
			MIN	NOM	MAX	MIN	NOM	MAX	
V_{CC}	Supply voltage		4.5	5	5.5	4.75	5	5.25	V
V_{IH}	High-level input voltage		2			2			V
V_{IL}	Low-level input voltage				0.7			0.8	V
I_{OH}	High-level output current				− 0.4			− 0.4	mA
I_{OL}	Low-level output current				4			8	mA
f_{clock}	Clock frequency		0		30	0		30	MHz
t_w	Pulse duration	CLK high	20			20			ns
		$\overline{PRE}$ or $\overline{CLR}$ low	25			25			
t_{su}	Setup time before CLK ↓	data high or low	20			20			ns
		$\overline{PRE}$ inactive	20			20			
t_h	Hold time-data after CLK ↓		0			20			ns
T_A	Operating free-air temperature		− 55		125	0		70	°C

electrical characteristics over recommended operating free-air temperature range (unless otherwise noted)

PARAMETER		TEST CONDITIONS†		SN54LS113A			SN74LS113A			UNIT
				MIN	TYP‡	MAX	MIN	TYP‡	MAX	
V_{IK}		V_{CC} = MIN,	I_I = − 18 mA			− 1.5			− 1.5	V
V_{OH}		V_{CC} = MIN, V_{IH} = 2 V, V_{IL} = MAX, I_{OH} = − 0.4 mA		2.5	3.4		2.7	3.4		V
V_{OL}		V_{CC} = MIN, V_{IL} = MAX, V_{IH} = 2 V, I_{OL} = 4 mA			0.25	0.4		0.25	0.4	V
		V_{CC} = MIN, V_{IL} = MAX, V_{IH} = 2 V, I_{OL} = 8 mA						0.35	0.5	
I_I	J or K	V_{CC} = MAX,	V_I = 7 V			0.1			0.1	mA
	$\overline{PRE}$					0.3			0.3	
	$\overline{CLK}$					0.4			0.4	
I_{IH}	J or K	V_{CC} = MAX,	V_I = 2.7 V			20			20	µA
	$\overline{PRE}$					60			60	
	CLK					80			80	
I_{IL}	J or K	V_{CC} = MAX,	V_I = 0.4 V			− 0.4			− 0.4	mA
	$\overline{PRE}$ or CLK					− 0.8			− 0.8	
I_{OS}§		V_{CC} = MAX,	see Note 4	− 20		− 100	− 20		− 100	mA
I_{CC}		V_{CC} = MAX,	see Note 2		4	6		4	6	mA

† For conditions shown as MIN or MAX, use the appropriate value specified under recommended operating conditions.
‡ All typical values are at V_{CC} = 5 V, T_A = 25°C.
§ Not more than one output should be shorted at a time, and the duration of the short circuit should not exceed one second.
NOTE 2: With all outputs open, I_{CC} is measured with the Q and $\overline{Q}$ outputs high in turn. At the time of measurement, the clock input is grounded.
NOTE 4: For certain devices where state commutation can be caused by shorting an output to ground, an equivalent test may be performed with V_O = 2.25 V and 2.125 V for the 54 family and the 74 family, respectively, with the minimum and maximum limits reduced to one half of their stated values.

switching characteristics, V_{CC} = 5 V, T_A = 25°C (see note 3)

PARAMETER	FROM (INPUT)	TO (OUTPUT)	TEST CONDITIONS		MIN	TYP	MAX	UNIT
f_{max}			R_L = 2 kΩ,	C_L = 15 pF	30	45		MHz
t_{PLH}	$\overline{PRE}$ or CLK	Q or $\overline{Q}$				15	20	ns
t_{PHL}						15	20	ns

NOTE 3: See General Information Section for load circuits and voltage waveforms.

TEXAS
INSTRUMENTS

recommended operating conditions

			SN54S113A			SN74S113A			UNIT
			MIN	NOM	MAX	MIN	NOM	MAX	
V_{CC}	Supply voltage		4.5	5	5.5	4.75	5	5.25	V
V_{IH}	High-level input voltage		2			2			V
V_{IL}	Low-level input voltage				0.8			0.8	V
I_{OH}	High-level output current				−1			−1	mA
I_{OL}	Low-level output current				20			20	mA
t_w	Pulse duration	CLK high	6			6			ns
		CLK low	6.5			6.5			
		$\overline{PRE}$ low	8			8			
t_{su}	Setup time before CLK ↓	data high or low	7			7			ns
t_h	Hold time-data after CLK ↓		0			0			ns
T_A	Operating free-air temperature		−55		125	0		70	°C

electrical characteristics over recommended operating free-air temperature range (unless otherwise noted)

PARAMETER		TEST CONDITIONS[†]			SN54S113A			SN74S113A			UNIT
					MIN	TYP[‡]	MAX	MIN	TYP[‡]	MAX	
V_{IK}		V_{CC} = MIN,	I_I = −18 mA				−1.2			−1.2	V
V_{OH}		V_{CC} = MIN,	V_{IH} = 2 V,	V_{IL} = 0.8 V,	2.5	3.4		2.7	3.4		V
		I_{OH} = −1 mA									
V_{OL}		V_{CC} = MIN,	V_{IH} = 2 V,	V_{IL} = 0.8 V,			0.5			0.5	V
		I_{OL} = 20 mA									
I_I		V_{CC} = MAX,	V_I = 5.5 V				1			1	mA
I_{IH}	J or K	V_{CC} = MAX,	V_I = 2.7 V				50			50	μA
	$\overline{PRE}$ or CLK						100			100	
I_{IL}	J or K	V_{CC} = MAX,	V_I = 0.5 V				−1.6			−1.6	mA
	$\overline{PRE}$						−7			−7	
	CLK						−4			−4	
I_{OS}[§]		V_{CC} = MAX			−40		−100	−40		−100	mA
I_{CC} Supply Current (average per Flip-Flop)		V_{CC} = MAX,	see Note 2			15	25		15	25	mA

[†] For conditions shown as MIN or MAX, use the appropriate value specified under recommended operating conditions.
[‡] All typical values are at V_{CC} = 5 V, T_A = 25°C.
[§] Not more than one output should be shorted at a time, and the duration of the short circuit should not exceed one second.
NOTE 2: With all outputs open, I_{CC} is measured with the Q and $\overline{Q}$ outputs high in turn. At the time of measurement, the clock input is grounded.

switching characteristics, V_{CC} = 5 V, T_A = 25°C (see note 3)

PARAMETER	FROM (INPUT)	TO (OUTPUT)	TEST CONDITIONS		MIN	TYP	MAX	UNIT
f_{max}					80	125		MHz
t_{PLH}	$\overline{PRE}$	Q or $\overline{Q}$	R_L = 280 Ω,	C_L = 15 pF		4	7	ns
t_{PHL}	$\overline{PRE}$ (CLK high)	$\overline{Q}$ or Q				5	7	ns
	$\overline{PRE}$ (CLK low)					5	7	
t_{PLH}	CLK	Q or $\overline{Q}$				4	7	ns
t_{PHL}						5	7	

NOTE 3: See General Information Section for load circuits and voltage waveforms.

TEXAS
INSTRUMENTS

3-335

TTL DEVICES 3

3

TTL DEVICES

TYPES SN54LS114A, SN54S114A, SN74LS114A, SN74S114A
DUAL J-K NEGATIVE-EDGE-TRIGGERED FLIP-FLOPS
WITH PRESET, COMMON CLEAR, AND COMMON CLOCK

REVISED DECEMBER 1983

- Fully Buffered to Offer Maximum Isolation from External Disturbance
- Package Options Include Both Plastic and Ceramic Carriers in Addition to Plastic and Ceramic DIPs.
- Dependable Texas Instruments Quality and Reliability

description

These devices contain two independent J-K negative-edge-triggered flip-flops. A low level at the preset and clear inputs sets or resets the outputs regardless of the levels of the other inputs. When preset and clear are inactive (high), data at the J and K inputs meeting the setup time requirements are transferred to the outputs on the negative-going edge of the clock pulse. Clock triggering occurs at a voltage level and is not directly related to the rise time of the clock pulse. Following the hold time interval, data at the J and K inputs may be changed without affecting the levels at the outputs. These versatile flip-flops can perform as toggle flip-flops by tying J and K high.

The SN54LS114A and SN54S114A are characterized for operation over the full military temperature range of −55°C to 125°C. The SN74LS114A and SN74S114A are characterized for operation from 0°C to 70°C.

FUNCTION TABLE

INPUTS					OUTPUTS	
$\overline{PRE}$	$\overline{CLR}$	CLK	J	K	Q	$\overline{Q}$
L	H	X	X	X	H	L
H	L	X	X	X	L	H
L	L	X	X	X	H†	H†
H	H	↓	L	L	Q₀	$\overline{Q}_0$
H	H	↓	H	L	H	L
H	H	↓	L	H	L	H
H	H	↓	H	H	TOGGLE	
H	H	H	X	X	Q₀	$\overline{Q}_0$

† The output levels in this configuration are not guaranteed to meet the minimum levels for V_{OH} if the lows at preset and clear are near V_{IL} minimum. Furthermore, this configuration is nonstable, that is, it will not persist when either preset or clear returns to its inactive (high) level.

SN54LS114A, SN54S114A ... J OR W PACKAGE
SN74LS114A, SN74S114A ... D, J OR N PACKAGE
(TOP VIEW)

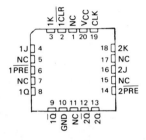

SN54LS114A, SN54S114A ... FK PACKAGE
SN74LS114A, SN74S114A
(TOP VIEW)

NC - No internal connection

logic symbol

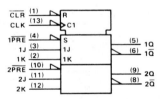

Pin numbers shown on logic notation are for D, J or N packages.

TEXAS
INSTRUMENTS

3 TTL DEVICES

3-337

logic diagram

'LS114A

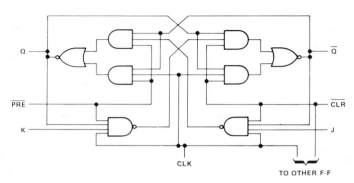

'S114A

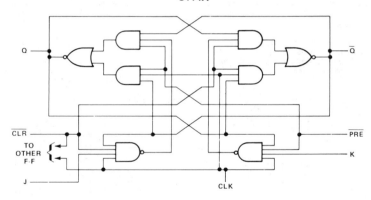

TEXAS
INSTRUMENTS

schematics of inputs and outputs

'LS114A

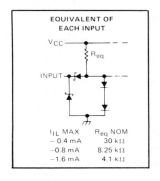

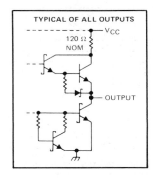

'S114A

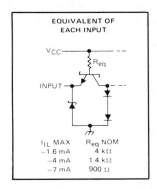

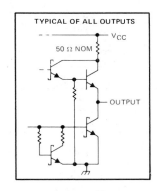

TTL DEVICES

3

absolute maximum ratings over operating free-air temperature range (unless otherwise noted)

Supply voltage, V_{CC} (see Note 1) . . . . 7 V
Input voltage: 'LS114A . . . . 7 V
              'S114A . . . . 5.5 V
Operating free-air temperature range: SN54' . . . . -55°C to 125°C
                             SN74' . . . . 0°C to 70°C
Storage temperature range . . . . -65°C to 150°C

NOTE 1: Voltage values are with respect to network ground terminal.

recommended operating conditions

			SN54LS114A			SN74LS114A			UNIT
			MIN	NOM	MAX	MIN	NOM	MAX	
V_{CC}	Supply voltage		4.5	5	5.5	4.75	5	5.25	V
V_{IH}	High-level input voltage		2			2			V
V_{IL}	Low-level input voltage				0.7			0.8	V
I_{OH}	High-level output current				− 0.4			− 0.4	mA
I_{OL}	Low-level output current				4			8	mA
f_{clock}	Clock frequency		0		30	0		30	MHz
t_w	Pulse duration	CLK	20			20			ns
		$\overline{PRE}$ or $\overline{CLR}$ low	25			25			
t_{su}	Set up time-before CLK↓	data high or low	20			20			ns
		$\overline{CLR}$ inactive	25			25			
		$\overline{PRE}$ inactive	20			20			
t_h	Hold time-data after CLK↓		0			0			ns
T_A	Operating free-air temperature		− 55		125	0		70	°C

electrical characteristics over recommended operating free-air temperature range (unless otherwise noted)

PARAMETER		TEST CONDITIONS†			SN54LS114A			SN74LS114A			UNIT
					MIN	TYP‡	MAX	MIN	TYP‡	MAX	
V_{IK}		V_{CC} = MIN,	I_I = − 18 mA				− 1.5			− 1.5	V
V_{OH}		V_{CC} = MIN, I_{OH} = − 0.4 mA	V_{IH} = 2 V,	V_{IL} = MAX,	2.5	3.4		2.7	3.4		V
V_{OL}		V_{CC} = MIN, I_{OL} = 4 mA	V_{IL} = MAX,	V_{IH} = 2 V,		0.25	0.4		0.25	0.4	V
		V_{CC} = MIN, I_{OL} = 8 mA	V_{IL} = MAX,	V_{IH} = 2 V,					0.35	0.5	
I_I	J or K	V_{CC} = MAX,	V_I = 7 V				0.1			0.1	mA
	$\overline{CLR}$						0.6			0.6	
	$\overline{PRE}$						0.3			0.3	
	CLK						0.8			0.8	
I_{IH}	J or K	V_{CC} = MAX,	V_I = 2.7 V				20			20	µA
	$\overline{CLR}$						120			120	
	$\overline{PRE}$						60			60	
	CLK						160			160	
I_{IL}	J or K	V_{CC} = MAX,	V_I = 0.4 V				− 0.4			− 0.4	mA
	$\overline{CLR}$						− 1.6			− 1.6	
	$\overline{PRE}$						− 0.8			− 0.8	
	CLK						− 1.6			− 1.6	
I_{OS}§		V_{CC} = MAX,	see Note 4		− 20		− 100	− 20		− 100	mA
I_{CC}		V_{CC} = MAX,	see Note 2			4	6		4	6	mA

† For conditions shown as MIN or MAX, use the appropriate value specified under recommended operating conditions.
‡ All typical values are at V_{CC} = 5 V, T_A = 25°C.
§ Not more than one output should be shorted at a time, and the duration of the short circuit should not exceed one second.
NOTE 2: With all outputs open, I_{CC} is measured with the Q and $\overline{Q}$ outputs high in turn. At the time of measurement, the clock input is grounded.
NOTE 4: For certain devices where state commutation can be caused by shorting an output to ground, an equivalent test may be performed with V_O = 2.25 V and 2.125 V for the '54 family and the '74 family, respectively, with the minimum and maximum limits reduced to one half of their stated values.

TEXAS
INSTRUMENTS

switching characteristics, V_{CC} = 5 V, T_A = 25°C (see note 3)

PARAMETER	FROM (INPUT)	TO (OUTPUT)	TEST CONDITIONS	MIN	TYP	MAX	UNIT
f_{max}			R_L = 2 kΩ, C_L = 15 pF	30	45		MHz
t_{PLH}	$\overline{CLR}$, $\overline{PRE}$ or CLK	Q or $\overline{Q}$			15	20	ns
t_{PHL}					15	20	ns

NOTE 3: See General Information Section for load circuits and voltage waveforms.

TYPES SN54S114A, SN74S114A
DUAL J-K NEGATIVE-EDGE-TRIGGERED FLIP-FLOPS
WITH PRESET, COMMON CLEAR, AND COMMON CLOCK

recommended operating conditions

			SN54S114A			SN74S114A			UNIT
			MIN	NOM	MAX	MIN	NOM	MAX	
V_{CC}	Supply voltage		4.5	5	5.5	4.75	5	5.25	V
V_{IH}	High-level input voltage		2			2			V
V_{IL}	Low-level input voltage				0.8			0.8	V
I_{OH}	High-level output current				−1			−1	mA
I_{OL}	Low-level output current				20			20	mA
t_w	Pulse duration	CLK high	6			6			ns
		CLK low	6.5			6.5			
		$\overline{CLR}$ or $\overline{PRE}$ low	8			8			
t_{su}	Setup time	data high or low	7			7			ns
t_h	Hold time-data after CLK↓		0			0			ns
T_A	Operating free-air temperature		−55		125	0		70	°C

electrical characteristics over recommended operating free-air temperature range (unless otherwise noted)

PARAMETER		TEST CONDITIONS[†]		SN54S114A			SN74S114A			UNIT
				MIN	TYP[‡]	MAX	MIN	TYP[‡]	MAX	
V_{IK}		V_{CC} = MIN,	I_I = −18 mA			−1.2			−1.2	V
V_{OH}		V_{CC} = MIN, V_{IH} = 2 V, V_{IL} = 0.8 V, I_{OH} = −1 mA		2.5	3.4		2.7	3.4		V
V_{OL}		V_{CC} = MIN, V_{IH} = 2 V, V_{IL} = 0.8 V, I_{OL} = 20 mA				0.5			0.5	V
I_I		V_{CC} = MAX,	V_I = 5.5 V			1			1	mA
I_{IH}	J or K	V_{CC} = MAX,	V_I = 2.7 V			50			50	μA
	$\overline{CLR}$					200			200	
	$\overline{PRE}$					100			100	
	CLK					200			200	
I_{IL}	J or K	V_{CC} = MAX,	V_I = 0.5 V			−1.6			−1.6	mA
	$\overline{CLR}$					−14			−14	
	$\overline{PRE}$					−7			−7	
	CLK					−8			−8	
I_{OS}[§]		V_{CC} = MAX		−40		−100	−40		−100	mA
I_{CC} Supply Current (average per Flip-Flop)		V_{CC} = MAX,	see Note 2		15	25		15	25	mA

† For conditions shown as MIN or MAX, use the appropriate value specified under recommended operating conditions.
‡ All typical values are at V_{CC} = 5 V, T_A = 25°C.
§ Not more than one output should be shorted at a time, and the duration of the short circuit should not exceed one second.
NOTE 2: With all outputs open, I_{CC} is measured with the Q and $\overline{Q}$ outputs high in turn. At the time of measurement, the clock input is grounded.

switching characteristics, V_{CC} = 5 V, T_A = 25°C (see note 3)

PARAMETER	FROM (INPUT)	TO (OUTPUT)	TEST CONDITIONS		MIN	TYP	MAX	UNIT
f_{max}					80	125		MHz
t_{PLH}	$\overline{PRE}$ or $\overline{CLR}$	Q or $\overline{Q}$	R_L = 280 Ω,	C_L = 15 pF		4	7	ns
t_{PHL}	$\overline{PRE}$ or $\overline{CLR}$ (CLK high)	$\overline{Q}$ or Q				5	7	ns
	$\overline{PRE}$ or $\overline{CLR}$ (CLK low)					5	7	
t_{PLH}	CLK	Q or $\overline{Q}$				4	7	ns
t_{PHL}						5	7	ns

NOTE 3: See General Information Section for load circuits and voltage waveforms.

3

TTL DEVICES

TEXAS
INSTRUMENTS

- Two Independent 4-Bit Latches in a Single Package
- Separate Clear Inputs Provide One-Step Clearing Operation
- Dual Gated Enable Inputs Simplify Cascading Register Implementations
- Compatible for Use with TTL Circuits
- Input Clamping Diodes Simplify System Design

SN54116 . . . J OR W PACKAGE
SN74116 . . . J OR N PACKAGE
(TOP VIEW)

$\overline{1CLR}$	1	24	V_{CC}
$1\overline{C}1$	2	23	2Q4
$1\overline{C}2$	3	22	2D4
1D1	4	21	2Q3
1Q1	5	20	2D3
1D2	6	19	2Q2
1Q2	7	18	2D2
1D3	8	17	2Q1
1Q3	9	16	2D1
1D4	10	15	$2\overline{C}2$
1Q4	11	14	$2\overline{C}1$
GND	12	13	$\overline{2CLR}$

description

These monolithic TTL circuits utlize D-type bistables to implement two independent four-bit latches in a single package. Each four-bit latch has an independent asynchronous clear input and a gated two-input enable circuit. When both enable inputs are low, the output levels will follow the data input levels. When either or both of the enable inputs are taken high, the outputs remain at the last levels setup at the inputs prior to the low-to-high-level transition at the enable input(s). After this, the data inputs are locked out.

The clear input is overriding and when taken low will reset all four outputs low regardless of the levels of the enable inputs.

The SN54116 is characterized for operation over the full military temperature range of $-55°C$ to $125°C$; the SN74116 is characterized for operation from $0°C$ to $70°C$.

FUNCTION TABLE
(EACH LATCH)

INPUTS				OUTPUT
CLEAR	ENABLE		DATA	Q
	$\overline{C1}$	$\overline{C2}$		
H	L	L	L	L
H	L	L	H	H
H	X	H	X	Q_0
H	H	X	X	Q_0
L	X	X	X	L

H   high level, L = low level, X = irrelevant
Q_0 - the level of Q before these input conditions were established.

3

TTL DEVICES

TEXAS
INSTRUMENTS

TYPES SN54116, SN74116
DUAL 4-BIT LATCHES WITH CLEAR

logic diagram

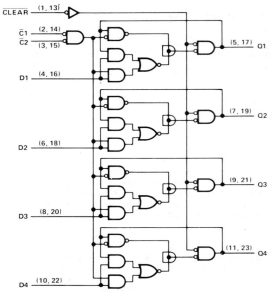

Pin numbers shown on logic notation are for J or N packages.

schematics of inputs and outputs

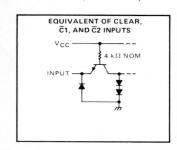

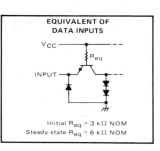

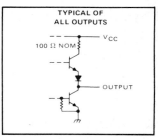

absolute maximum ratings over operating free-air temperature range (unless otherwise noted)

Supply voltage, V_{CC} (see Note 1) . . . . 7 V
Input voltage . . . . 5.5 V
Operating free-air temperature range: SN54116 Circuits . . . . −55°C to 125°C
                                        SN74116 Circuits . . . . 0°C to 70°C
Storage temperature range . . . . −65°C to 150°C

NOTE 1: Voltage values are with respect to network ground terminal.

TEXAS INSTRUMENTS

recommended operating conditions

		SN54116			SN74116			UNIT
		MIN	NOM	MAX	MIN	NOM	MAX	
Supply voltage, V_{CC}		4.5	5	5.5	4.75	5	5.25	V
High-level output current, I_{OH}				−800			−800	µA
Low-level output current, I_{OL}				16			16	mA
Input pulse width, t_w	$\overline{C}1, \overline{C}2$	18			18			ns
	$\overline{CLR}$	18			18			
Data setup time, t_{su}	High logic level	8			8			ns
	Low logic level	14			14			
Clear inactive-state setup time, t_{su}		8			8			ns
Data release time, high-level data, $t_{release}$				2			2	ns
Data hold time, low-level data, t_h		8			8			
Operating free-air temperature, T_A		−55		125	0		70	°C

electrical characteristics over recommended operating free-air temperature range (unless otherwise noted)

PARAMETER		TEST CONDITIONS[†]	MIN	TYP[‡]	MAX	UNIT
V_{IH} High-level input voltage			2			V
V_{IL} Low-level input voltage					0.8	V
V_{IK} Input clamp voltage		V_{CC} = MIN, I_I = −12 mA			−1.5	V
V_{OH} High-level output voltage		V_{CC} = MIN, V_{IH} = 2 V, V_{IL} = 0.8 V, I_{OH} = −800 µA	2.4	3.4		V
V_{OL} Low-level output voltage		V_{CC} = MIN, V_{IH} = 2 V, V_{IL} = 0.8 V, I_{OL} = 16 mA		0.2	0.4	V
I_I Input current at maximum input voltage		V_{CC} = MAX, V_I = 5.5 V			1	mA
I_{IH} High-level input current	$\overline{C}1, \overline{C}2$, or clear	V_{CC} = MAX, V_I = 2.4 V			40	µA
	Any D				60	
I_{IL} Low-level input current	$\overline{C}1, \overline{C}2$, or clear	V_{CC} = MAX, V_I = 0.4 V			−1.6	mA
	Any D, initial peak				−2.4	
	Any D, steady-state				−1.6	
I_{OS} Short-circuit output current[§]	SN54116	V_{CC} = MAX	−20		−57	mA
	SN74116		−18		−57	
I_{CC} Supply current	Condition A	V_{CC} = MAX, See Note 2		60	100	mA
	Condition B			40	70	

[†] For conditions shown as MIN or MAX, use the appropriate value specified under recommended operating conditions for the applicable device type.
[‡] All typical values are at V_{CC} = 5 V, T_A = 25°C.
[§] Not more than one output should be shorted at a time.
NOTE 2: With outputs open, I_{CC} is measured for the following conditions:
    A. All inputs grounded.
    B. All $\overline{C}$ inputs are grounded and all other inputs are at 4.5 V.

switching characteristics, V_{CC} = 5 V, T_A = 25°C

PARAMETER	FROM (INPUT)	TO (OUTPUT)	TEST CONDITIONS	MIN	TYP	MAX	UNIT
t_{PLH}	$\overline{C}1$ or $\overline{C}2$	Any Q	C_L = 15 pF, R_L = 400 Ω, See Figure 1		19	30	ns
t_{PHL}					15	22	
t_{PLH}	Data	Q			10	15	ns
t_{PHL}					12	18	
t_{PHL}	$\overline{CLR}$	Any Q			15	22	ns

TEXAS
INSTRUMENTS

3

TTL DEVICES

PARAMETER MEASUREMENT INFORMATION

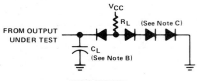

LOAD CIRCUIT

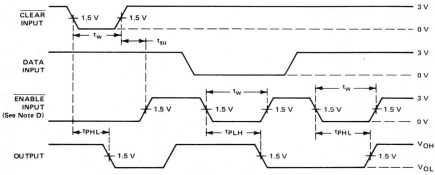

SWITCHING TIMES FROM CLEAR AND ENABLE INPUTS

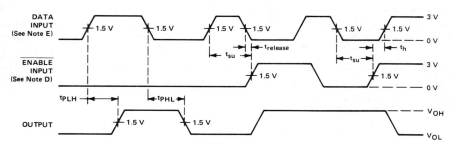

SWITCHING TIMES FROM DATA INPUTS

NOTES: A. Input pulses are supplied by generators having the following characteristics: $t_r \leqslant 10$ ns, $t_f \leqslant 10$ ns, PRR = 1 MHz, duty cycle $\leqslant$ 50%, $Z_{out} \approx 50\Omega$.
  B. C_L includes probe and jig capacitance.
  C. All diodes are 1N3064 or equivalent.
  D. The other enable input is low.
  E. Clear input is high.

FIGURE 1

- Generates Either a Single Pulse or Train of Pulses Synchronized with Control Functions

- Ideal for Implementing Sync-Control Circuits Similar to those Used in Oscilloscopes

- Latched Operation Ensures that Output Pulses Are Not Clipped

- High-Fan-Out Complementary Outputs Drive System Clock Lines Directly

- Internal Input Pull-Up Resistors Eliminate Need for External Components

- Diode-Clamped Inputs Simplify System Design

- Typical Propagation Delays:

  9 Nanoseconds through One Level
  16 Nanoseconds through Two Levels

SN54120 . . . J OR W PACKAGE
SN74120 . . . J OR N PACKAGE
(TOP VIEW)

```
        ___
1M  [ 1      16 ] VCC
1S̄1 [ 2      15 ] 2M
1S̄2 [ 3      14 ] 2S̄2
1R̄  [ 4      13 ] 2S̄1
1C  [ 5      12 ] 2R̄
1Y  [ 6      11 ] 2C
1Ȳ  [ 7      10 ] 2Y
GND [ 8       9 ] 2Ȳ
```

description

These monolithic pulse synchronizers are designed to synchronize an asynchronous or manual signal with a system clock. Reliable response is ensured as the input signals are latched up; therefore duration of logic input is not critical and the adverse effects of contact-bounce of a manual input are eliminated. The ability to pass output pulses is started and stopped by the levels or pulses applied to the latch inputs $\bar{S}1$, $\bar{S}2$, or $\bar{R}$ in accordance with the function table. High-speed circuitry is utilized throughout the clock paths to minimize skew with respect to the system clock.

After initiation, the mode control (M) input determines whether a series of pulses or only one pulse is passed. In the absence of a stop command, the clock driver will continue to pass clock pulses as long as the mode control input is low (see Figures 2 through 4). If the mode control input is high only a single clock pulse will be passed (see Figure 5).

When the mode control is set to pass a series of pulses, the last pulse out is determined by two general rules:

a. When pulses are terminated by the $\bar{S}$ or $\bar{R}$ inputs, conditions meeting the setup times (specified under recommended operating conditions) will dominate.

b. Low-to-high-level transitions at the mode control input should be avoided during the 20-nanosecond period immediately following the negative transition of the input clock pulse as transitions during this time period may or may not allow the next pulse to pass (see Figures 4 and 5). When pulses are terminated by the mode control input, a positive transition at the mode control input meeting the high-level setup time, t_{su} (H), (specified under recommended operating conditions) will pass that positive clock pulse then inhibit remaining clock pulses. The clock input (C) is latch-controlled ensuring that once initiated the output pulse will not be terminated until the full pulse has been passed.

FUNCTION TABLE

INPUTS			FUNCTION
$\bar{R}$	$\bar{S}1$	$\bar{S}2$	
X	L	X	Pass Output Pulses
X	X	L	Pass Output Pulses
L	H	H	Inhibit Output Pulses
H	↓	H	Start Output Pulses
H	H	↓	Start Output Pulses
↓	H	H	Stop Output Pulses
H	H	H	Continue†

H = high level (steady state)
L = low level (steady state)
↓ = transition from H to L
X = irrelevant
†Operation initiated by last ↓ transition continues.

TEXAS INSTRUMENTS

3

TTL DEVICES

description (continued)

This clock driver circuit is entirely compatible for use with either digital logic circuits or mechanical switches for input controls since all inputs, except the clock, have internal pull-up resistors. This eliminates the requirement to supply an external resistor to prevent the input from floating when the control switch is open. The internal resistor also means that these inputs may be left disconnected if unused.

Typical propagation delay time is 9 nanoseconds to the $\overline{Y}$ output and 16 nanoseconds to the Y output from the clock input. The outputs will drive 60 Series 54/74 loads at a high logic level and 30 loads at a low logic level. Typical power dissipation is 127 milliwatts per driver. The SN54120 is characterized for operation from -55°C to 125°C; the SN74120 is characterized for operation from 0°C to 70°C.

logic diagram (each driver)

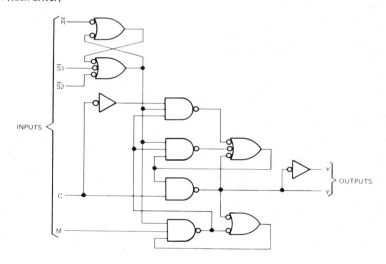

schematics of inputs and outputs

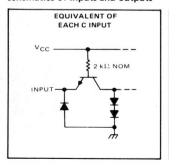

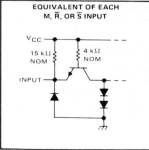

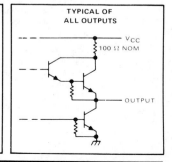

TEXAS
INSTRUMENTS

absolute maximum ratings over operating free-air temperature range (unless otherwise noted)

Supply voltage, V_{CC} (see Note 1)	7 V
Input voltage	5.5 V
Interemitter voltage (see Note 2)	5.5 V
Operating free-air temperature range: SN54120 Circuits	-55°C to 125°C
SN74120 Circuits	0°C to 70°C
Storage temperature range	-65°C to 150°C

NOTES: 1. Voltage values, except interemitter voltage, are with respect to network ground terminal.
2. This is the voltage between two emitters of a multiple-emitter transistor. For this circuit, this rating applies between the S1 and S2 inputs.

recommended operating conditions

			SN54120			SN74120			UNIT
			MIN	NOM	MAX	MIN	NOM	MAX	
Supply voltage, V_{CC}			4.5	5	5.5	4.75	5	5.25	V
High-level output current, I_{OH}					-2.4			2.4	mA
Low-level output current, I_{OL}					48			48	mA
Setup time (see Figures 2 thru 5)	Any input except mode control, t_{su}(H or L)		12			12			ns
	Mode control	t_{su}(H)	0			0			
		t_{su}(L)	12			12			
Hold time (see Figures 3 and 5)	Any input except mode control, t_h(H or L)		3			3			ns
	Mode control, t_h(H or L)		20			20			
Operating free-air temperature, T_A			-55		125	0		70	C

electrical characteristics over recommended operating free-air temperature range (unless otherwise noted)

PARAMETER			TEST CONDITIONS[†]	MIN	TYP[‡]	MAX	UNIT
V_{IH}	High-level input voltage			2			V
V_{IL}	Low-level input voltage					0.8	V
V_{IK}	Input clamp voltage		V_{CC} = MIN, I_I = -12 mA			1.5	V
V_{OH}	High-level output voltage		V_{CC} = MIN, V_{IH} = 2 V, V_{IL} = 0.8 V, I_{OH} = -2.4 mA	2.4	3.4		V
V_{OL}	Low-level output voltage		V_{CC} = MIN, V_{IH} = 2 V, V_{IL} = 0.8 V, I_{OL} = 48 mA		0.2	0.4	V
I_I	Input current at maximum input voltage		V_{CC} = MAX, V_I = 5.5 V			1	mA
I_{IH}	High-level input current	Clock input	V_{CC} = MAX, V_I = 2.4 V			80	µA
		Other inputs		0.12	0.2	0.36	mA
I_{IL}	Low-level input current	Clock input	V_{CC} = MAX, V_I = 0.4 V			3.2	mA
		Other inputs				2.1	
I_{OS}	Short-circuit output current[§]		V_{CC} = MAX	35		90	mA
I_{CC}	Supply current		V_{CC} = MAX See Note 3		51	90	mA

[†] For conditions shown as MIN or MAX, use the appropriate value specified under recommended operating conditions.
[‡] All typical values are at V_{CC} = 5 V, T_A = 25°C.
[§] Not more than one output should be shorted at a time.
NOTE 3: I_{CC} is measured with ground applied to all inputs except R which is at 4.5 V and all outputs open.

switching characteristics, V_{CC} = 5 V, T_A = 25°C

PARAMETER[¶]	FROM (INPUT)	TO (OUTPUT)	TEST CONDITIONS	MIN	TYP	MAX	UNIT
t_{PLH}	C	Y	C_L 45 pF, R_L 133 Ω, See Figure 1		14	22	ns
t_{PHL}					17	25	
t_{PLH}	C	$\overline{Y}$			10	16	ns
t_{PHL}					8	13	

[¶] t_{PLH} Propagation delay time, low-to-high-level output
t_{PHL} Propagation delay time, high-to-low-level output

TEXAS
INSTRUMENTS

3

TTL DEVICES

PARAMETER MEASUREMENT INFORMATION

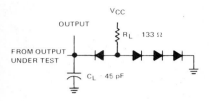

NOTES: A. The clock input pulse in figures 2 through 5 is supplied by a generator having the following characteristics: $t_{w(clock)} \approx 15\,ns$, $PRR \approx 1\,MHz$, and $Z_{out} \approx 50\,\Omega$.
B. C_L includes probe and jig capacitance.
C. All diodes are 1N3064 or equivalent.

FIGURE 1—LOAD CIRCUIT FOR SWITCHING TESTS

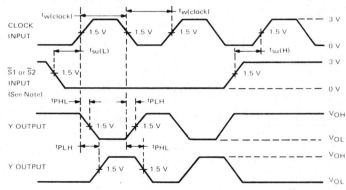

NOTE: Mode control and $\overline{R}$ inputs are low and unused $\overline{S}$ input is high.

FIGURE 2—INITIATING AND TERMINATING PULSE TRAIN FROM S INPUTS

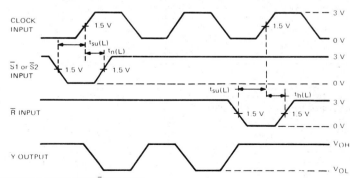

NOTE: Mode control input is low and unused $\overline{S}$ input is high.

FIGURE 3—INITIATING PULSE TRAIN FROM S AND TERMINATING WITH R INPUTS

PARAMETER MEASUREMENT INFORMATION

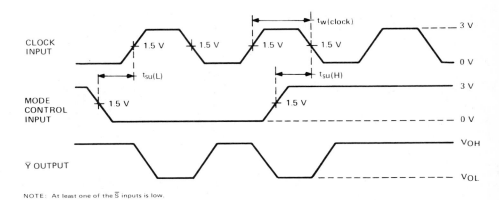

NOTE: At least one of the $\overline{S}$ inputs is low.

FIGURE 4—INITIATING AND TERMINATING PULSE TRAIN WITH MODE CONTROL INPUT

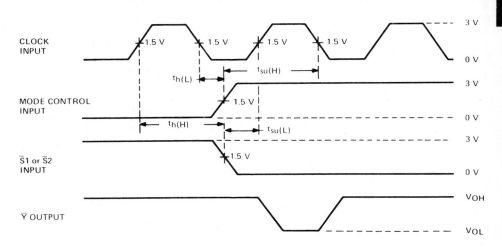

NOTE: Input $\overline{R}$ is low and the unused $\overline{S}$ input is high.

FIGURE 5—ENABLING SINGLE PULSE

TEXAS
INSTRUMENTS

TTL DEVICES

3

- Programmable Output Pulse Width
  With R_{int} . . . 35 ns Typ
  With R_{ext}/C_{ext} . . . 40 ns to 28 Seconds
- Internal Compensation for Virtual
  Temperature Independence
- Jitter-Free Operation up to 90%
  Duty Cycle
- Inhibit Capability

SN54121 . . . J OR W PACKAGE
SN74121 . . . J OR N PACKAGE

(TOP VIEW)

```
         ___  ___
 Q̄  □ 1 |   U   | 14 □ Vcc
 NC □ 2 |       | 13 □ NC
 A1 □ 3 |       | 12 □ NC
 A2 □ 4 |       | 11 □ Rext/Cext
 B  □ 5 |       | 10 □ Cext
 Q  □ 6 |       |  9 □ Rint
GND □ 7 |_____|  8 □ NC
```

NC - No internal connection.

FUNCTION TABLE

INPUTS			OUTPUTS	
A1	A2	B	Q	Q̄
L	X	H	L	H
X	L	H	L↑	H↑
X	X	L	L↑	H↑
H	H	X	L↑	H↑
H	↓	H	⊓	⊔
↓	H	H	⊓	⊔
↓	↓	H	⊓	⊔
L	X	↑	⊓	⊔
X	L	↑	⊓	⊔

For explanation of function table symbols, see page

† These lines of the function table assume that the indicated steady-state conditions at the A and B inputs have been setup long enough to complete any pulse started before the setup.

description

These multivibrators feature dual negative-transition-triggered inputs and a single positive-transition-triggered input which can be used as an inhibit input. Complementary output pulses are provided.

Pulse triggering occurs at a particular voltage level and is not directly related to the transition time of the input pulse. Schmitt-trigger input circuitry (TTL hysteresis) for the B input allows jitter-free triggering from inputs with transition rates as slow as 1 volt/second, providing the circuit with an excellent noise immunity of typically 1.2 volts. A high immunity to V_{CC} noise of typically 1.5 volts is also provided by internal latching circuitry.

Once fired, the outputs are independent of further transitions of the inputs and are a function only of the timing components. Input pulses may be of any duration relative to the output pulse. Output pulse length may be varied from 40 nanoseconds to 28 seconds by choosing appropriate timing components. With no external timing components (i.e., R_{int} connected to V_{CC}, C_{ext} and R_{ext}/C_{ext} open), an output pulse of typically 30 or 35 nanoseconds is achieved which may be used as a d-c triggered reset signal. Output rise and fall times are TTL compatible and independent of pulse length.

Pulse width stability is achieved through internal compensation and is virtually independent of V_{CC} and temperature. In most applications, pulse stability will only be limited by the accuracy of external timing components.

Jitter-free operation is maintained over the full temperature and V_{CC} ranges for more than six decades of timing capacitance (10 pF to 10 μF) and more than one decade of timing resistance (2 kΩ to 30 kΩ for the SN54121 and 2 kΩ to 40 kΩ for the SN74121). Throughout these ranges, pulse width is defined by the relationship $t_{w(out)} = C_{ext}R_T \ln 2 \approx 0.7\, C_{ext}R_T$. In circuits where pulse cutoff is not critical, timing capacitance up to 1000 μF and timing resistance as low as 1.4 kΩ may be used. Also, the range of jitter-free output pulse widths is extended if V_{CC} is held to 5 volts and free-air temperature is 25°C. Duty cycles as high as 90% are achieved when using maximum recommended R_T. Higher duty cycles are available if a certain amount of pulse-width jitter is allowed.

TEXAS
INSTRUMENTS

3-353

3
TTL DEVICES

logic diagram (positive logic)

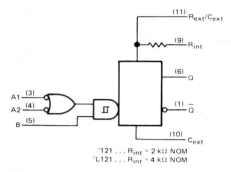

'121 . . . R_{int} = 2 kΩ NOM
'L121 . . . R_{int} = 4 kΩ NOM

Pin numbers shown on logic notation are for J or N packages.

NOTES: 1. An external capacitor may be connected between C_{ext} (positive) and R_{ext}/C_{ext}.
2. To use the internal timing resistor, connect R_{int} to V_{CC}. For improved pulse width accuracy and repeatability, connect an external resistor between R_{ext}/C_{ext} and V_{CC} with R_{int} open-circuited.

schematics of inputs and outputs

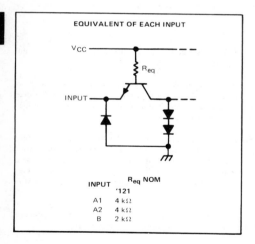

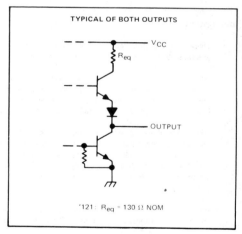

TEXAS
INSTRUMENTS

absolute maximum ratings over operating free-air temperature range (unless otherwise noted)

Supply voltage, V_{CC} (see Note 1) '121 . . . . 7 V

Input voltage: . . . . 5.5 V

Operating free-air temperature range: SN54121 . . . . -55°C to 125°C

SN74121 . . . . 0 C to 70 C

Storage temperature range . . . . -65°C to 150°C

NOTE 1: Voltage values are with respect to network ground terminal.

recommended operating conditions

			SN54121 SN74121			UNIT
			MIN	NOM	MAX	
V_{CC}	Supply voltage	54 Family	4.5	5	5.5	V
		74 Family	4.75	5	5.25	
I_{OH}	High-level output current				-0.4	mA
I_{OL}	Low-level output current				16	mA
dv/dt	Rate of rise or fall of input pulse	Schmitt input, B	1			V/s
		Logic inputs, A1, A2	1			V/μs
$t_{w(in)}$	Input pulse width		50			ns
R_{ext}	External timing capacitance	54 Family	1.4		30	kΩ
		74 Family	1.4		40	
C_{ext}	External timing capacitance		0		1000	μF
	Duty cycle	$R_T = 2$ kΩ			67	%
		$R_T = $ MAX R_{ext}			90	
T_A	Operating free-air termperature	54 Family	-55		125	$^\circ$C
		74 Family	0		70	

3

TTL DEVICES

electrical characteristics over recommended operating free-air temperature range (unless otherwise noted)

PARAMETER		TEST CONDITIONS[†]		SN54121 SN74121			UNIT
				MIN	TYP[‡]	MAX	
V_{T+}	Positive-going threshold voltage at A input	V_{CC} = MIN			1.4	2	V
V_{T-}	Negative-going threshold voltage at A input	V_{CC} = MIN		0.8	1.4		V
V_{T+}	Positive-going threshold voltage at B input	V_{CC} = MIN			1.55	2	V
V_{T-}	Negative-going threshold voltage at B input	V_{CC} = MIN		0.8	1.35		V
V_{IK}	Input clamp voltage	V_{CC} = MIN,	I_I = −12 mA			−1.5	V
V_{OH}	High-level output voltage	V_{CC} = MIN,	I_{OH} = MAX	2.4	3.4		V
V_{OL}	Low-level output voltage	V_{CC} = MIN,	I_{OL} = MAX		0.2	0.4	V
I_I	Input current at maximum input voltage	V_{CC} = MAX,	V_I = 5.5 V			1	mA
I_{IH}	High-level input current	V_{CC} = MAX, V_I = 2.4 V	A1 or A2			40	μA
			B			80	
I_{IL}	Low-level input current	V_{CC} = MAX, V_I = 0.4 V	A1 or A2			−1.6	mA
			B			−3.2	
I_{OS}	Short-circuit output current[♦]	V_{CC} = MAX	54 Family	−20		−55	mA
			74 Family	−18		−55	
I_{CC}	Supply current	V_{CC} = MAX	Quiescent		13	25	mA
			Triggered		23	40	

[†] For conditions shown as MIN or MAX, use the appropriate value specified under recommended operating conditions.
[‡] All typical values are at V_{CC} = 5 V, T_A = 25°C.
[♦] Not more than one output should be shorted at a time.

switching characteristics, V_{CC} = 5 V, T_A = 25°C

PARAMETER		TEST CONDITIONS		'121			UNIT
				MIN	TYP	MAX	
t_{PLH}	Propagation delay time, low-to-high-level Q output from either A input				45	70	ns
t_{PLH}	Propagation delay time, low-to-high-level Q output from B input		C_{ext} = 80 pF, R_{int} to V_{CC}		35	55	ns
t_{PHL}	Propagation delay time, high-to-low-level Q̄ output from either A input				50	80	ns
t_{PHL}	Propagation delay time, high-to-low-level Q̄ output from B input	C_L = 15 pF, R_L = 400 Ω for '121, See Note 2			40	65	ns
$t_{w(out)}$	Pulse width obtained using internal timing resistor		C_{ext} = 80 pF, R_{int} to V_{CC}	70	110	150	ns
$t_{w(out)}$	Pulse width obtained with zero timing capacitance		C_{ext} = 0, R_{int} to V_{CC}		30	50	ns
$t_{w(out)}$	Pulse width obtained using external timing resistor		C_{ext} = 100 pF, R_T = 10 kΩ	600	700	800	ns
			C_{ext} = 1 μF, R_T = 10 kΩ	6	7	8	ms

NOTE 2: See General Information Section for load circuits and voltage waveforms.

TEXAS INSTRUMENTS

TYPICAL CHARACTERISTICS§

DISTRIBUTION OF UNITS
for
OUTPUT PULSE WIDTH

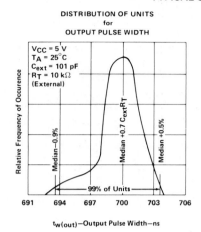

FIGURE 1

VARIATION IN INTERNAL TIMING RESISTOR VALUE
vs
FREE-AIR TEMPERATURE

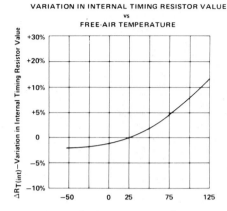

FIGURE 2

VARIATION IN OUTPUT PULSE WIDTH
vs
SUPPLY VOLTAGE

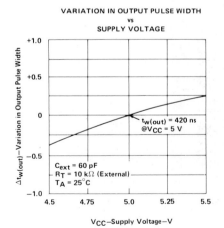

FIGURE 3

SCHMITT TRIGGER THRESHOLD VOLTAGE
vs
FREE-AIR TEMPERATURE

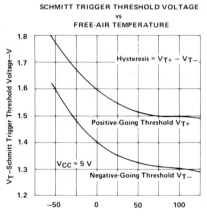

FIGURE 4

§Data for temperatures below $0°C$ and above $70°C$ are applicable for SN54121..

TYPICAL CHARACTERISTICS§ (continued)

VARIATION IN OUTPUT PULSE WIDTH
vs
FREE-AIR TEMPERATURE

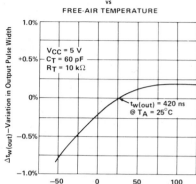

T$_A$—Free-Air Temperature—°C

FIGURE 5

OUTPUT PULSE WIDTH
vs
TIMING RESISTOR VALUE

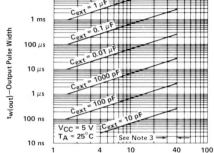

R$_T$—Timing Resistor Value-kΩ

FIGURE 6

OUTPUT PULSE WIDTH
vs
EXTERNAL CAPACITANCE

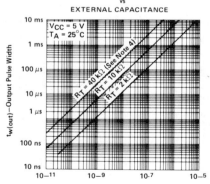

C$_{ext}$ —Timing Capacitance—F

FIGURE 7

NOTE 3: These values of resistance exceed the maximum recommended use over the full temperature range of the SN54LS121.
§Data for temperatures below 0°C and above 70°C are applicable for SN54121.

TEXAS INSTRUMENTS

SN54122, SN54123, SN54LS122, SN54LS123,
SN74122, SN74123, SN74LS122, SN74LS123
RETRIGGERABLE MONOSTABLE MULTIVIBRATORS

REVISED DECEMBER 1983

- **D-C Triggered from Active-High or Active-Low Gated Logic Inputs**
- **Retriggerable for Very Long Output Pulses, Up to 100% Duty Cycle**
- **Overriding Clear Terminates Output Pulse**
- **'122, 'L122, 'LS122 Have Internal Timing Resistors**

description

These d-c triggered multivibrators feature output pulse width control by three methods. The basic pulse time is programmed by selection of external resistance and capacitance values (see typical application data). The '122, and 'LS122 have internal timing resistors that allow the circuits to be used with only an external capacitor, if so desired. Once triggered, the basic pulse width may be extended by retriggering the gated low-level-active (A) or high-level-active (B) inputs, or be reduced by use of the overriding clear. Figure 1 illustrates pulse control by retriggering and early clear.

The 'LS122 and 'LS123 are provided enough Schmitt hysteresis to ensure jitter-free triggering from the B input with transition rates as slow as 0.1 millivolt per nanosecond.

The R_{int} is nominally 10 k ohms for '122, 'LS122.

SN54123, SN54LS123 ... J OR W PACKAGE
SN74123 ... J OR N PACKAGE
SN74LS123 ... D, J OR N PACKAGE
(TOP VIEW) (SEE NOTES 1 THRU 4)

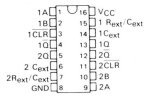

SN54LS122 ... FK PACKAGE
SN74LS122
(TOP VIEW) (SEE NOTES 1 THRU 4)

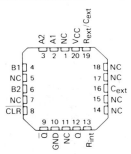

SN54LS123 ... FK PACKAGE
SN74LS123
(TOP VIEW) (SEE NOTES 1 THRU 4)

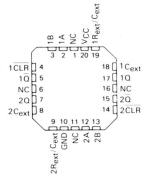

NC   No internal connection

SN54122, SN54LS122 ... J OR W PACKAGE
SN74122 ... J OR N PACKAGE
SN74LS122 ... D, J OR N PACKAGE
(TOP VIEW) (SEE NOTES 1 THRU 4)

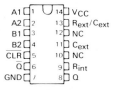

NOTES: 1. An external timing capacitor may be connected between C_{ext} and R_{ext}/C_{ext} (positive).
2. To use the internal timing resistor of '122, or 'LS122, connect R_{int} to V_{CC}.
3. For improved pulse width accuracy and repeatability, connect an external resistor between R_{ext}/C_{ext} and V_{CC} with R_{int} open-circuited.
4. To obtain variable pulse widths, connect an external variable resistance between R_{int} or R_{ext}/C_{ext} and V_{CC}.

TEXAS
INSTRUMENTS

3-359

TTL DEVICES

3

description (continued)

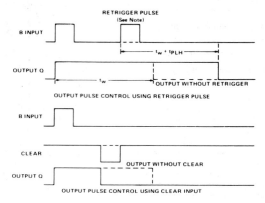

NOTE: Retrigger pulses starting before 0.22 C_{ext} (in picofrads) nanoseconds after the initial trigger pulse will be ignored and the output pulse will remain unchanged.

FIGURE 1—TYPICAL INPUT/OUTPUT PULSES

'122, 'LS122
FUNCTION TABLE

INPUTS					OUTPUTS	
CLEAR	A1	A2	B1	B2	Q	Q̄
L	X	X	X	X	L	H
X	H	H	X	X	L†	H†
X	X	X	L	X	L†	H†
X	X	X	X	L	L†	H†
H	L	X	↑	H	⊓	⊔
H	L	X	H	↑	⊓	⊔
H	X	L	↑	H	⊓	⊔
H	X	L	H	↑	⊓	⊔
H	H	↓	H	H	⊓	⊔
H	↓	↓	H	H	⊓	⊔
H	↓	H	H	H	⊓	⊔
↑	L	X	H	H	⊓	⊔
↑	X	L	H	H	⊓	⊔

See explanation of function tables on page
† These lines of the functional tables assume that the indicated steady-state conditons at the A and B inputs have
been set up long enough to complete any pulse started before the set up.

'123, 'LS123
FUNCTION TABLE

INPUTS			OUTPUTS	
CLEAR	A	B	Q	Q̄
L	X	X	L	H
X	H	X	L†	H†
X	X	L	L†	H†
H	L	↑	⊓	⊔
H	↓	H	⊓	⊔
↑	L	H	⊓	⊔

TEXAS
INSTRUMENTS

logic diagram

logic symbol

'122, 'LS122

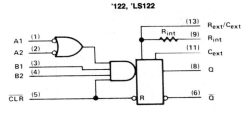

'122, 'LS122

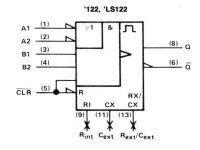

R_{int} is nominally 10 k ohms for '122, 'LS122.

logic diagram (each multivibrator)

logic symbol

'123, LS123

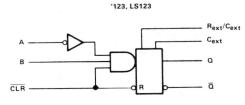

'123, 'LS123

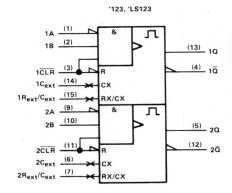

Pin numbers shown on logic notation are for D, J or N packages.

TTL DEVICES

3

SN54122, SN54123, SN54LS122, SN54LS123,
SN74122, SN74123, SN74LS122, SN74LS123
RETRIGGERABLE MONOSTABLE MULTIVIBRATORS

schematics of inputs and outputs

'122, '123, 'L123 CIRCUITS

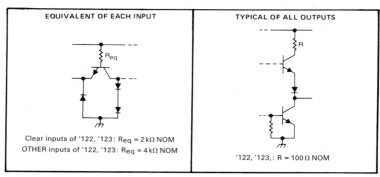

'LS122, 'LS123 CIRCUITS

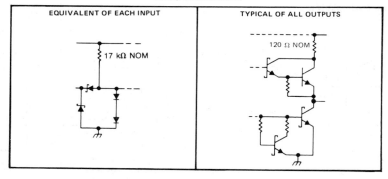

TEXAS
INSTRUMENTS

recommended operating conditions

	SN54' MIN	SN54' NOM	SN54' MAX	SN74' MIN	SN74' NOM	SN74' MAX	UNIT
Supply voltage, V_{CC}	4.5	5	5.5	4.75	5	5.25	V
High-level output current, I_{OH}			−800			−800	µA
Low-level output current, I_{OL}			16			16	mA
Pulse width, t_w	40			40			ns
External timing resistance, R_{ext}	5		25	5		50	kΩ
External capacitance, C_{ext}		No restriction			No restriction		
Wiring capacitance at R_{ext}/C_{ext} terminal			50			50	pF
Operating free-air temperature, T_A	−55		125	0		70	C

electrical characteristics over recommended free-air operating temperature range (unless otherwise noted)

PARAMETER		TEST CONDITIONS[†]	'122 MIN	'122 TYP[‡]	'122 MAX	'123, MIN	'123, TYP[‡]	'123, MAX	UNIT
V_{IH}	High-level input voltage		2			2			V
V_{IL}	Low-level input voltage				0.8			0.8	V
V_{IK}	Input clamp voltage	V_{CC} = MIN, I_I = −12 mA			−1.5			−1.5	V
V_{OH}	High-level output voltage	V_{CC} = MIN, I_{OH} = −800 µA, See Note 1	2.4	3.4		2.4	3.4		V
V_{OL}	Low-level output voltage	V_{CC} = MIN, I_{OL} = 16 mA, See Note 1		0.2	0.4		0.2	0.4	V
I_I	Input current at maximum input voltage	V_{CC} = MAX, V_I = 5.5 V			1			1	mA
I_{IH}	High-level input current	Data inputs	V_{CC} = MAX, V_I = 2.4 V		40			40	µA
		Clear input			80			80	
I_{IL}	Low-level input current	Data inputs	V_{CC} = MAX, V_I = 0.4 V		−1.6			−1.6	mA
		Clear input			−3.2			−3.2	
I_{OS}	Short-circuit output current[♦]	V_{CC} = MAX, See Note 5	−10		−40	−10		−40	mA
I_{CC}	Supply current (quiescent or triggered)	V_{CC} = MAX, See Notes 6 and 7		23	36		46	66	mA

[†] For conditions shown as MIN or MAX, use the value specified under recommended operating conditions.

[‡] All typical values are at V_{CC} = 5 V, T_A = 25°C.

[♦] Not more than one output should be shorted at a time.

NOTES: 5. Ground C_{ext} to measure V_{OH} at Q, V_{OL} at Q̄, or I_{OS} at Q. C_{ext} is open to measure V_{OH} at Q̄, V_{OL} at Q, or I_{OS} at Q̄.

6. Quiescent I_{CC} is measured (after clearing) with 2.4 V applied to all clear and A inputs, B inputs grounded, all outputs open, C_{ext} = 0.02 µF, and R_{ext} = 25 kΩ. R_{int} of '122 is open.

7. I_{CC} is measured in the triggered state with 2.4 V applied to all clear and B inputs, A inputs grounded, all outputs open, C_{ext} = 0.02 µF, and R_{ext} = 25 kΩ. R_{int} of '122 is open.

switching characteristics, V_{CC} = 5 V, T_A = 25°C, see note 8

PARAMETER[¶]	FROM (INPUT)	TO (OUTPUT)	TEST CONDITIONS	'122 MIN	'122 TYP	'122 MAX	'123 MIN	'123 TYP	'123 MAX	UNIT
t_{PLH}	A	Q			22	33		22	33	ns
	B				19	28		19	28	
t_{PHL}	A	Q̄	C_{ext} = 0, R_{ext} = 5 kΩ, C_L = 15 pF, R_L = 400 Ω		30	40		30	40	ns
	B				27	36		27	36	
t_{PHL}	Clear	Q			18	27		18	27	ns
t_{PLH}		Q̄			30	40		30	40	
t_{wQ} (min)	A or B	Q			45	65		45	65	ns
t_{wQ}	A or B	Q	C_{ext} = 1000 pF, R_{ext} = 10 kΩ, C_L = 15 pF, R_L = 400 Ω	3.08	3.42	3.76	2.76	3.03	3.37	µs

[¶] t_{PLH} ≡ propagation delay time, low-to-high-level output

t_{PHL} ≡ propagation delay time, high-to-low-level output

t_{wQ} ≡ width of pulse at output Q

NOTE 8: See General Information Section for load circuits and voltage waveforms.

TTL DEVICES **3**

TEXAS
INSTRUMENTS

TYPES SN54LS122, SN54LS123, SN74LS122, SN74LS123
RETRIGGERABLE MONOSTABLE MULTIVIBRATORS

recommended operating conditions

	SN54LS' MIN	SN54LS' NOM	SN54LS' MAX	SN74LS' MIN	SN74LS' NOM	SN74LS' MAX	UNIT
Supply voltage, V_{CC}	4.5	5	5.5	4.75	5	5.25	V
High-level output current, I_{OH}			−400			−400	μA
Low-level output current, I_{OL}			4			8	mA
Pulse width, t_w	40			40			ns
External timing resistance, R_{ext}	5		180	5		260	kΩ
External capacitance, C_{ext}	No restriction			No restriction			
Wiring capacitance at R_{ext}/C_{ext} terminal			50			50	pF
Operating free-air temperature, T_A	−55		125	0		70	°C

electrical characteristics over recommended operating free-air temperature range (unless otherwise noted)

PARAMETER		TEST CONDITIONS†		SN54LS' MIN	SN54LS' TYP‡	SN54LS' MAX	SN74LS' MIN	SN74LS' TYP‡	SN74LS' MAX	UNIT
V_{IH}	High-level input voltage			2			2			V
V_{IL}	Low-level input voltage					0.7			0.8	V
V_{IK}	Input clamp voltage	V_{CC} = MIN,	I_I = −18 mA			−1.5			−1.5	V
V_{OH}	High-level output voltage	V_{CC} = MIN, $V_{IL} = V_{IL}$max	V_{IH} = 2 V, I_{OH} = −400 μA	2.5	3.5		2.7	3.5		V
V_{OL}	Low-level output voltage	V_{CC} = MIN, $V_{IL} = V_{IL}$max	V_{IH} = 2 V, I_{OL} = 4 mA		0.25	0.4		0.25	0.4	V
			I_{OL} = 8 mA					0.35	0.5	
I_I	Input current at maximum input voltage	V_{CC} = MAX,	V_I = 7 V			0.1			0.1	mA
I_{IH}	High-level input current	V_{CC} = MAX,	V_I = 2.7 V			20			20	μA
I_{IL}	Low-level input current	V_{CC} = MAX,	V_I = 0.4 V			−0.4			−0.4	mA
I_{OS}	Short-circuit output current♦	V_{CC} = MAX		−20		−100	−20		−100	mA
I_{CC}	Supply current (quiescent or triggered)	V_{CC} = MAX, See Note 13	'LS122		6	11		6	11	mA
			'LS123		12	20		12	20	

†For conditions shown as MIN or MAX, use the appropriate value specified under recommended operating conditions.
‡All typical values are at V_{CC} = 5 V, T_A = 25°C.
♦Not more than one output should be shorted at a time and duration of the short-circuit should not exceed one second.
NOTES: 12. To measure V_{OH} at Q, V_{OL} at $\overline{Q}$, or I_{OS} at Q, ground R_{ext}/C_{ext}, apply 2 V to B and clear, and pulse A from 2 V to 0 V.
13. With all outputs open and 4.5 V applied to all data and clear inputs, I_{CC} is measured after a momentary ground, then 4.5 V, is applied to clock.

switching characteristics, V_{CC} = 5 V, T_A = 25°C (see note 8)

PARAMETER¶	FROM (INPUT)	TO (OUTPUT)	TEST CONDITIONS	MIN	TYP	MAX	UNIT
t_{PLH}	A	Q			23	33	ns
	B	Q			23	44	
t_{PHL}	A	$\overline{Q}$	C_{ext} = 0, R_{ext} = 5 kΩ, C_L = 15 pF, R_L = 2 kΩ		32	45	ns
	B	$\overline{Q}$			34	56	
t_{PHL}	Clear	Q			20	27	ns
t_{PLH}	Clear	$\overline{Q}$			28	45	
t_{wQ} (min)	A or B	Q			116	200	ns
t_{wQ}	A or B	Q	C_{ext} = 1000 pF, R_{ext} = 10 kΩ, C_L = 15 pF, R_L = 2 kΩ	4	4.5	5	μs

¶t_{PLH} = propagation delay time, low-to-high-level output
t_{PHL} = propagation delay time, high-to-low-level output
t_{wQ} = width of pulse at output Q
NOTE 8:   See General Information Section for load circuits and voltage waveforms.

3

TTL DEVICES

TEXAS
INSTRUMENTS

TYPICAL APPLICATION DATA FOR '122, '123

For pulse widths when $C_{ext} \leqslant 1000$ pF, See Figures 4 and 5.

The output pulse is primarily a function of the external capacitor and resistor. For $C_{ext} > 1000$ pF, the output pulse width (t_w) is defined as:

$$t_W = K \cdot R_T \cdot C_{ext} \left(1 + \frac{0.7}{R_T} \right)$$

where

K is 0.32 for '122, 0.28 for '123

R_T is in KΩ (internal or external timing resistance.)

C_{ext} is in pF

t_w is in nanoseconds

To prevent reverse voltage across C_{ext}, it is recommended that the method shown in Figure 2 be employed when using electrolytic capacitors and in applications utilizing the clear function. In all applications using the diode, the pulse width is:

$$t_W = K_D \cdot R_T \cdot C_{ext} \left(1 + \frac{0.7}{R_T} \right)$$

K_D is 0.28 for '122, 0.25 for '123

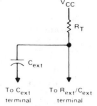

TIMING COMPONENT CONNECTIONS

FIGURE 3

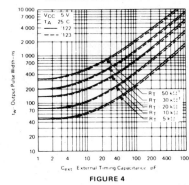

'122, '123, '130
TYPICAL OUTPUT PULSE WIDTH
vs
EXTERNAL TIMING CAPACITANCE

FIGURE 4

†These values of resistance exceed the maximum recommended for use over the full temperature range of the SN54' and SN54L' circuits.

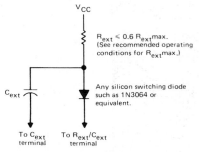

$R_{ext} \leqslant 0.6\,R_{ext}$max.
(See recommended operating conditions for R_{ext}max.)

Any silicon switching diode such as 1N3064 or equivalent.

TIMING COMPONENT CONNECTIONS WHEN
$C_{ext} > 1000$ pF AND CLEAR IS USED
FIGURE 2

Applications requiring more precise pulse widths (up to 28 seconds) and not requiring the clear feature can best be satisfied with the '121.

TYPES SN54LS122, SN54LS123, SN74LS122, SN74LS123
RETRIGGERABLE MONOSTABLE MULTIVIBRATORS

TYPICAL APPLICATION DATA FOR 'LS122, 'LS123

The basic output pulse width is essentially determined by the values of external capacitance and timing resistance. For pulse widths when $C_{ext} \leq 1000$ pF, use Figure 7, or may be defined as:

$$t_W \approx K \cdot R_T \cdot C_{ext}$$

When $C_{ext} \geq 1$ μF, the output pulse width is defined as:

$$t_W \approx 0.33 \cdot R_T \cdot C_{ext}$$

Where

    K is multiplier factor, see Figure 8
    R_T is in K ohms (internal or external
      timing resistance)
    C_{ext} is in pF
    t_W is in nanoseconds

For maximum noise immunity, system ground should be applied to the C_{ext} node, even though the C_{ext} node is already tied to the ground lead internally. Due to the timing scheme used by the 'LS122 and 'LS123, a switching diode is not required to prevent reverse biasing when using electrolytic capacitors.

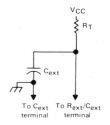

TIMING COMPONENT CONNECTIONS

FIGURE 6

'LS122, 'LS123
TYPICAL OUTPUT PULSE WIDTH
vs
EXTERNAL TIMING CAPACITANCE

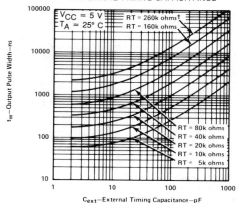

† This value of resistance exceeds the maximum recommended for use over the full temperature range of the SN54LS circuits.

FIGURE 7

TYPICAL APPLICATION DATA FOR 'LS122, 'LS123[†]

MULTIPLIER FACTOR
vs
EXTERNAL CAPACITOR

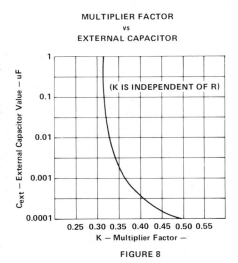

(K IS INDEPENDENT OF R)

C_{ext} – External Capacitor Value – uF

K – Multiplier Factor –

FIGURE 8

DISTRIBUTION OF UNITS
vs
OUTPUT PULSE WIDTH

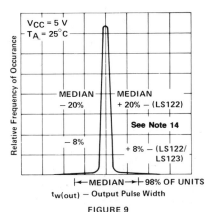

V_{CC} = 5 V
T_A = 25°C

Relative Frequency of Occurance

MEDIAN — MEDIAN
– 20%   + 20% – (LS122)

See Note 14

– 8%
+ 8% – (LS122/LS123)

|←MEDIAN→|98% OF UNITS

$t_{w(out)}$ – Output Pulse Width

FIGURE 9

VARIATION IN OUTPUT PULSE WIDTH
vs
SUPPLY VOLTAGE

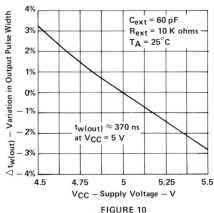

C_{ext} = 60 pF
R_{ext} = 10 K ohms
T_A = 25°C

$\Delta t_{w(out)}$ – Variation in Output Pulse Width

$t_{w(out)} \approx 370$ ns
at V_{CC} = 5 V

V_{CC} – Supply Voltage – V

FIGURE 10

VARIATION IN OUTPUT PULSE WIDTH
vs
FREE-AIR TEMPERATURE

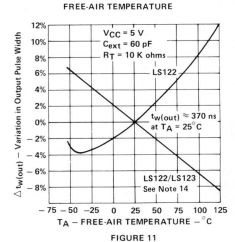

V_{CC} = 5 V
C_{ext} = 60 pF
R_T = 10 K ohms

LS122

$\Delta t_{w(out)}$ – Variation in Output Pulse Width

$t_{w(out)} \approx 370$ ns
at T_A = 25°C

LS122/LS123
See Note 14

T_A – FREE-AIR TEMPERATURE – °C

FIGURE 11

NOTE 14: For the 'LS122, the internal timing resistor, R_{int} was used. For the 'LS122/123, an external timing resistor was used for R_T.
[†]Data for temperatures below 0°C and above 70°C and for suply voltages below 4.75 V and above 5.25 V are applicable for SN54LS122 and SN54LS123 only.

TEXAS
INSTRUMENTS

3

TTL DEVICES

- Two Independent VCO's in a 16-Pin Package

- Output Frequency Set by Single External Component:
    Crystal for High-Stability Fixed-Frequency Operation
    Capacitor for Fixed- or Variable-Frequency Operation

- Separate Supply Voltage Pins for Isolation of Frequency Control Inputs and Oscillators from Output Circuitry

- Highly Stable Operation over Specified Temperature and/or Supply Voltage Ranges

- Typical f_{max} . . . . 85 MHz
  Typical Power Dissipation . . . . 525 mW

- Frequency Spectrum . . . 1 Hz to 60 MHz

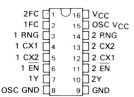

SN54S124 . . . J OR W PACKAGE
SN74S124 . . . D, J OR N PACKAGE
(TOP VIEW)

SN54S124 . . . FK PACKAGE
SN74S124
(TOP VIEW)

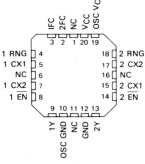

NC - No internal connection

description

The 'S124 features two independent voltage-controlled oscillators (VCO) in a single monolithic chip. The output frequency of each VCO is established by a single external component, either a capacitor or a crystal, in combination with two voltage-sensitive inputs, one for frequency range and one for frequency control. These inputs can be used to vary the output frequency as shown under typical characteristics. These highly stable oscillators can be set to operate at any frequency typically between 0.12 hertz and 85 megahertz. Under the conditions used in Figure 3, the output frequency can be approximated as follows:

$$f_O = \frac{5 \times 10 - 4}{CX}$$

where: f_O = output frequency in hertz

CX = external capacitance in farads.

logic

While the enable input is low, the output is enabled.
While the enable input is high, the output is high.

These devices can operate from a single 5-volt supply. However, one set of supply-voltage and ground pins (V_{CC} and GND) is provided for the enable, synchronization-gating, and output sections, and a separate set ($\ominus V_{CC}$ and $\ominus$ GND) is provided for the oscillator and associated frequency-control circuits so that effective isolation can be accomplished in the system.

The enable input of these devices starts or stops the output pulses when it is low or high, respectively. The internal oscillator of the 'S124 is started and stopped by the enable input. The enable input is one standard load; it and the buffered output operate at standard Schottky-clamped TTL levels.

The pulse synchronization-gating section ensures that the first output pulse is neither clipped nor extended. Duty cycle of the square-wave output is fixed at approximately 50 percent.

The SN54S124 is characterized for operation over the full military temperature range of $-55°C$ to $125°C$; the SN74S124 is characterized for operation from $0°C$ to $70°C$.

TEXAS INSTRUMENTS

TTL DEVICES

3

TYPES SN54S124, SN74S124
DUAL VOLTAGE-CONTROLLED OSCILLATORS

schematics of inputs and outputs

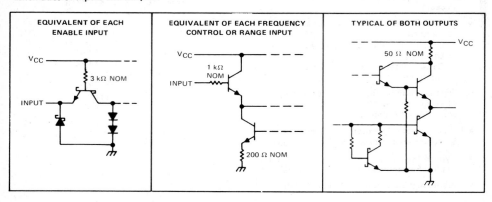

EQUIVALENT OF EACH ENABLE INPUT	EQUIVALENT OF EACH FREQUENCY CONTROL OR RANGE INPUT	TYPICAL OF BOTH OUTPUTS

absolute maximum ratings over operating free-air temperature range (unless otherwise noted)

Supply voltage, V_{CC} (See Notes 1 and 2) 7V
Input voltage . . . . 5.5 V
Operating free-air temperature range: SN54S124 . . . . $-55°$C to $125°$C
                              SN74S124 . . . . $0°$C to $70°$C
Storage temperature range . . . . $-65°$C to $150°$C

NOTES: 1. Voltage values are with respect to the appropriate ground terminal.
         2. Throughout this data sheet, the symbol V_{CC} is used for the voltage applied to both the V_{CC} and $\ominus V_{CC}$ terminals, unless otherwise noted.

TEXAS
INSTRUMENTS

recommended operating conditions

	SN54S124			SN74S124			UNIT
	MIN	NOM	MAX	MIN	NOM	MAX	
Supply voltage, V_{CC} (see Note 1)	4.5	5	5.5	4.75	5	5.25	V
Input voltage at frequency control or range input, $V_{I(freq)}$ or $V_{I(rng)}$	1		5	1		5	V
High-level output current, I_{OH}			−1			−1	mA
Low-level output current, I_{OL}			20			20	mA
Output frequency (enabled), f_o	1			1			Hz
			60			60	MHz
Operating free-air temperature, T_A	−55		125	0		70	C

electrical characteristics over recommended operating free-air temperature range (unless otherwise noted)

PARAMETER		TEST CONDITIONS[†]		MIN	TYP[‡]	MAX	UNIT
V_{IH} High-level input voltage at enable				2			V
V_{IL} Low-level input voltage at enable						0.8	V
V_{IK} Input clamp voltage at enable		V_{CC} = MIN, I_I = −18 mA				−1.2	V
V_{OH} High-level output voltage		V_{CC} = MIN, V_{IH} = 2 V, I_{OH} = −1 mA	SN54S'	2.5	3.4		V
			SN74S'	2.7	3.4		
V_{OL} Low-level output voltage		V_{CC} = MIN, V_{IL} = 0.8 V, I_{OL} = 20 mA				0.5	V
I_I Input current	Freq control or range	V_{CC} = MAX	V_I = 5 V		10	50	μA
			V_I = 1 V		1	15	
I_I Input current at maximum input voltage	Enable	V_{CC} = MAX, V_I = 5.5 V				1	mA
I_{IH} High-level input current	Enable	V_{CC} = MAX, V_I = 2.7 V				50	μA
I_{IL} Low-level input current	Enable	V_{CC} = MAX, V_I = 0.5 V				−2	mA
I_{OS} Short-circuit output current[§]		V_{CC} = MAX		−40		−100	mA
I_{CC} Supply current, total into V_{CC} and ⊖ V_{CC}		V_{CC} = MAX, See Note 3			105	150	mA
		V_{CC} = MAX, T_A = 125"C, See Note 3	W package only			110	

[†]For conditions shown as MIN or MAX, use the appropriate value specified under recommended operating conditions.
[‡]All typical values are at V_{CC} = 5 V, T_A = 25°C.
[§]Not more than one output should be shorted at a time and duration of the short-circuit should not exceed one second.
NOTE 3: I_{CC} is measured with the outputs disabled and open.

switching characteristics, V_{CC} = 5 V, R_L = 280 Ω, C_L = 15 pF, T_A = 25°C (see note 4)

PARAMETER		TEST CONDITIONS		MIN	TYP	MAX	UNIT
f_o Output frequency		CX = 2 pF	$V_{I(freq)}$ = 4 V, $V_{I(rng)}$ = 1 V	60	85		MHz
			$V_{I(freq)}$ = 1 V, $V_{I(rng)}$ = 5 V	25	40		
Output duty cycle		CX = 8.3 pF to 500 μF			50%		
t_{PHL} Propagation delay time, high-to-low-level output from enable		f_o = 1 Hz to 20 MHz			$\frac{1.4}{f_o(Hz)}$		s
		f_o = 20 MHz			70		ns

NOTE 4: See General Information Section for load circuits and voltage waveforms.

3 TTL DEVICES

TYPES SN54S124, SN74S124
DUAL VOLTAGE-CONTROLLED OSCILLATORS

TYPICAL APPLICATION DATA

free-running oscillator

Free-running oscillators can be implemented for most systems by setting the output frequency of the VCO with either a capacitor or a crystal. If excitation is provided with a capacitor the frequency control and/or range inputs can be used to vary the output frequency.

When the 'S124 is excited with a crystal, low-frequency response ($<$ 1 MHz) can be improved if a relatively small capacitor (5 to 15 pF) is paralleled with the crystal. When operated at the fundamental frequency of a crystal, the frequency control input should be high ($\approx$ 5 V) and the range input should be low (grounded) for maximum stability over temperature and supply voltage variations.

phase-locked loops

A basic crystal-controlled phase-locked loop is illustrated in Figure 1. This application can be used for implementation of:

    a. A highly stable fixed-frequency clock generator.
    b. A highly stable fixed- or variable-frequency synthesizer.
    c. A highly efficient "slave-clock" system for synchronizing off-card, remote, or data-interfacing clock systems

With fixed division rates for both M and N, the output frequency (f_O) will be stable at $f_O = \frac{N}{M} f_1$. Obviously, either M or N, or both, could be programmable counters in which case the output frequency (f_O) will be a variable frequency dependent on the instantaneous value of $\frac{N}{M} f_1$.

The crystal-controlled VCO can be operated up to 60 MHz with an accuracy that is dependent on the crystal. At the higher frequencies, response of the phase comparator can become a limiting factor and one of the following approaches may be necessary to extend the operating frequency range.

    a. Frequencies $\frac{f_1}{M}$ and $\frac{f}{N}$ can be divided equally by the same constant (K) also shown in Figure 1. The constant can be any value greater than unity (K $>$ 1), and should be selected to yield frequency ranges that can be handled adequately by the phase-comparator and filter. The output frequency (f_O) retains the same relationship as previously explained because now:

$$f_O = \frac{KN}{KM} f_1 = \frac{N}{M} f_1$$

    b. In another method, the comparison of $\frac{f_1}{M}$ and $\frac{f}{N}$ can be performed with either an SN54LS85/SN74LS85 or SN54S85/SN74S85. The resultant A $>$ B and A $<$ B outputs from the 'LS85 or 'S85 permit the detector to be simplified to a charge-pump circuit. See Figure 2.

TTL DEVICES

TEXAS
INSTRUMENTS

TYPICAL APPLICATION DATA

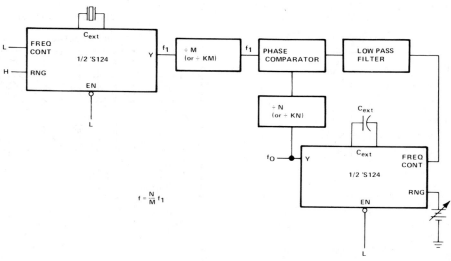

$$f = \frac{N}{M} f_1$$

FIGURE 1—PHASE-LOCKED LOOP

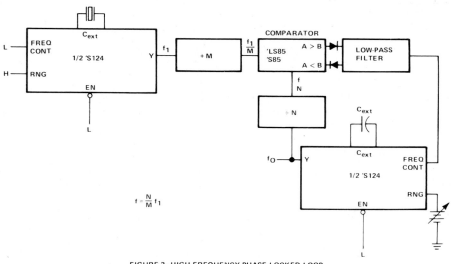

$$f = \frac{N}{M} f_1$$

FIGURE 2—HIGH-FREQUENCY PHASE-LOCKED LOOP

TEXAS
INSTRUMENTS

3

TTL DEVICES

TYPICAL CHARACTERISTICS

BASE OUTPUT FREQUENCY
vs
EXTERNAL CAPACITANCE

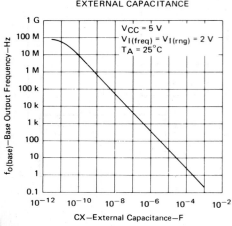

FIGURE 3

NORMALIZED OUTPUT FREQUENCY
vs
INPUT VOLTAGE

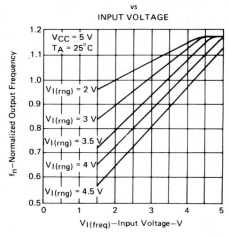

FIGURE 4

NOTE: $f_o = f_n \times f_{o(base)}$

TEXAS
INSTRUMENTS

- **Quad Bus Buffers**
- **3-State Outputs**
- **Separate Control for Each Channel**

description

These bus buffers feature three-state outputs that, when enabled, have the low impedence characteristics of a TTL output with additional drive capability at high logic levels to permit driving heavily loaded bus lines without external pull-up resistors, when disabled, both output transistors are turned off presenting a high-impedance state to the bus so the output will act neither as a significant load nor as a driver. The '125 and 'LS125A outputs are disabled when $\overline{G}$ is high. The '126 and 'LS126A outputs are disabled when G is low.

logic diagram (each gate)

'125, 'LS125A

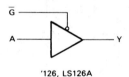

'126, LS126A

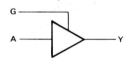

positive logic Y = A

SN54125, SN54126, SN54LS125A,
SN54LS126A . . . J OR W PACKAGE
SN74125, SN74126 . . . J OR N PACKAGE
SN74LS125A, SN74LS126A . . . D, J OR N PACKAGE
(TOP VIEW)

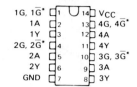

SN54LS125A, SN54LS126A . . . FK PACKAGE
SN74LS125A, SN74LS126A
(TOP VIEW)

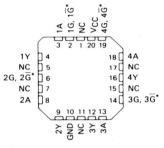

$^*\overline{G}$ on '125, 'LS125: G on 126, 'LS126

NC   No internal connection

absolute maximum ratings over operating free-air temperature range (unless otherwise noted)

Supply voltage, V_{CC} (see Note 1) . . . . 7 V
Input voltage: '125, '126 . . . . 5.5 V
              'LS125A, 'LS126A . . . . 7 V
Operating free-air temperature range: SN54' . . . . −55 C to 125 C
                              SN74' . . . . 0 C to 70 C
Storage temperature range . . . . −65 C to 150 C

NOTE 1: Voltage values are with respect to network ground terminal.

TTL DEVICES

3

TEXAS
INSTRUMENTS

schematics (each gate)

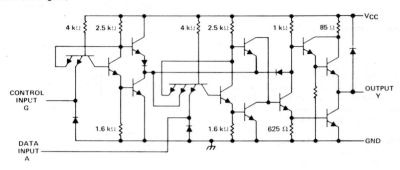

'125 CIRCUITS

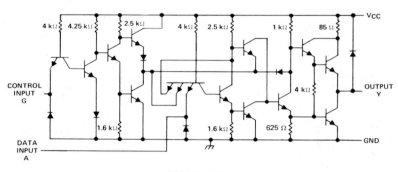

'126 CIRCUITS

Resistor values shown are nominal.

TEXAS
INSTRUMENTS

schematics (each gate)

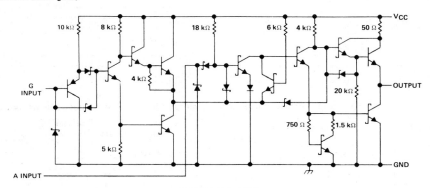

'LS125A CIRCUITS

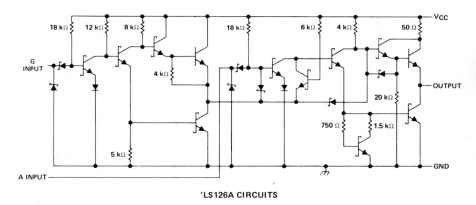

'LS126A CIRCUITS

Resistor values shown are nominal.

TTL DEVICES

3

recommended operating conditions

		SN54125, SN54126			SN74125, SN74126			UNIT
		MIN	NOM	MAX	MIN	NOM	MAX	
V_{CC}	Supply voltage	4.5	5	5.5	4.75	5	5.25	V
V_{IH}	High-level input voltage	2			2			V
V_{IL}	Low-level input voltage			0.8			0.8	V
I_{OH}	High-level output current			-2			-5.2	mA
I_{OL}	Low-level output current			16			16	mA
T_A	Operating free-air temperature	-55		125	0		70	°C

electrical characteristics over recommended operating free-air temperature range (unless otherwise noted)

PARAMETER	TEST CONDITIONS †			SN54125, SN54126			SN74125, SN74126			UNIT
				MIN	TYP‡	MAX	MIN	TYP‡	MAX	
V_{IK}	V_{CC} = MIN,	$I_I = -12$ mA				-1.5			-1.5	V
V_{OH}	V_{CC} = MIN, $V_{IH} = 2$ V,	$I_{OH} = -2$ V		2.4	3.3					V
	$V_{IL} = 0.8$ V	$I_{OH} = -5.2$ V					2.4	3.1		
V_{OL}	V_{CC} = MIN, $V_{IH} = 2$ V,	$V_{IL} = 0.8$ V,				0.4			0.4	V
	$I_{OL} = 16$ mA									
I_{OZ}	V_{CC} = MAX, $V_{IH} = 2$ V,	$V_O = 2.4$ V				40			40	µA
	$V_{IL} = 0.8$ V	$V_O = 0.4$ V				-40			-40	
I_I	V_{CC} = MAX,	$V_I = 5.5$ V				1			1	mA
I_{IH}	V_{CC} = MAX,	$V_I = 2.4$ V				40			40	µA
I_{IL}	V_{CC} = MAX,	$V_I = 0.4$ V				-1.6			-1.6	mA
I_{OS}§	V_{CC} = MAX			-30		-70	-28		-70	mA
I_{CC}	V_{CC} = MAX,	'125			32	54		32	54	mA
	(see Note 2)	'126			36	62		36	62	

† For condition shown as MIN or MAX, use the appropriate value specified under recommended operating conditions.
‡ All typical values are at $V_{CC} = 5$ V, $T_A = 25°$ C.
§ Not more than one output should be shorted at 2 time.
NOTE 2: Data inputs = 0 V; output control = 4.5 V for '125 and 0 V for '126.

switching characteristics, $V_{CC} = 5$ V, $T_A = 25°$C (see note 3)

PARAMETER	TEST CONDITIONS		SN54/74125			SN54/74126			UNIT
			MIN	TYP	MAX	MIN	TYP	MAX	
t_{PLH}				8	13		8	13	ns
t_{PHL}	$R_L = 400$ Ω,	$C_L = 50$ pF		12	18		12	18	ns
t_{PZH}				11	17		11	18	ns
t_{PZL}				16	25		16	25	ns
t_{PHZ}	$R_L = 400$ Ω,	$C_L = 5$ pF		5	8		10	16	ns
t_{PLZ}				7	12		12	18	ns

NOTE 3: See General Information Section for load circuits and voltage waveforms.

TEXAS
INSTRUMENTS

TYPES SN54LS125A, SN54LS126A, SN74LS125A, SN74LS126A
QUADRUPLE BUS BUFFERS WITH 3-STATE OUTPUTS

recommended operating conditions

		SN54LS125A SN54LS126A			SN74LS125A SN74LS126A			UNIT
		MIN	NOM	MAX	MIN	NOM	MAX	
V_{CC}	Supply voltage	4.5	5	5.5	4.75	5	5.25	V
V_{IH}	High-level input voltage	2			2			V
V_{IL}	Low-level input voltage			0.7			0.8	V
I_{OH}	High-level output current			−1			−2.6	mA
I_{OL}	Low-level output current			12			24	mA
T_A	Operating free-air temperature	−55		125	0		70	°C

electrical characteristics over recommended operating free-air temperature range (unless otherwise noted)

PARAMETER	TEST CONDITIONS†			SN54LS125A SN54LS126A			SN74LS125A SN74LS126A			UNIT
			MIN	TYP‡	MAX	MIN	TYP‡	MAX		
V_{IK}	V_{CC} = MIN,	I_I = −18 mA			−1.5			−1.5		V
V_{OH}	V_{CC} = MIN, V_{IH} = 2 V	V_{IL} = 0.7 V, I_{OH} = −1 mA	2.4							V
		V_{IL} = 0.8 V, I_{OH} = −2.6 mA				2.4				
V_{OL}	V_{CC} = MIN, V_{IH} = 2 V	V_{IL} = 0.7 V, I_{OL} = 12 mA		0.25	0.4					V
		V_{IL} = 0.8 V, I_{OL} = 12 mA					0.25	0.4		
		V_{IL} = 0.8 V, I_{OL} = 24 mA					0.35	0.5		
I_{OZ}	V_{CC} = MAX, V_{IH} = 2 V	V_{IL} = 0.7 V, V_O = 2.4 V			20					μA
		V_O = 0.4 V			−20					
		V_{IL} = 0.8 V, V_O = 2.4 V						20		
		V_O = 0.4 V						−20		
I_I	V_{CC} = MAX,	V_I = 7 V			0.1			0.1		mA
I_{IH}	V_{CC} = MAX,	V_I = 2.7 V			20			20		μA
I_{IL}	V_{CC} = MAX,	'LS125A-$\overline{G}$ inputs			−0.2			−0.2		mA
	V_I = 0.4 V	'LS125A-A inputs; 'LS126A-All inputs			−0.4			−0.4		
I_{OS}§	V_{CC} = MAX		−40		−225	−40		−225		mA
I_{CC}	V_{CC} = MAX, (see Note 2)	'LS125A		11	20		11	20		mA
		'LS126A		12	22		12	22		

† For conditions shown as MIN or MAX, use the appropriate value specified under recommended operating conditions.
‡ All typical values are at V_{CC} = 5 V, T_A = 25°C.
§ Not more than one output should be shorted at a time, and duration of the short circuit should not exceed one second.
NOTE 2: Data inputs = 0 V; Output controls = 4.5 V for 'LS125A and 0 V for 'LS126A.

switching characteristics, V_{CC} = 5 V, T_A = 25°C (see note 3)

PARAMETER	TEST CONDITIONS		SN54/74LS125A			SN54/74LS126A			UNIT
			MIN	TYP	MAX	MIN	TYP	MAX	
t_{PLH}	R_L = 667 Ω,	C_L = 45 pF		9	15		9	15	ns
t_{PHL}				7	18		8	18	ns
t_{PZH}				12	20		16	25	ns
t_{PZL}				15	25		21	35	ns
t_{PHZ}	R_L = 667 Ω,	C_L = 5 pF			20			25	ns
t_{PLZ}					20			25	ns

NOTE 3: See General Information Section for load circuits and voltage waveforms.

TEXAS INSTRUMENTS

- **Package Options Include Plastic and Ceramic DIPs**
- **Dependable Texas Instruments Quality and Reliability**

SN54128 . . . J OR W PACKAGE
SN74128 . . . J OR N PACKAGE
(TOP VIEW)

```
1Y  [ 1    14 ] VCC
1A  [ 2    13 ] 4Y
1B  [ 3    12 ] 4B
2Y  [ 4    11 ] 4A
2A  [ 5    10 ] 3Y
2B  [ 6     9 ] 3B
GND [ 7     8 ] 3A
```

description

These devices contain four independent 2-input-NOR line drivers. They perform the Boolean function $Y = \overline{A + B}$. The SN54128 is designed to drive 75 ohm lines. The SN74128 is designed to drive 50 ohm lines.

The SN54128 is characterized for operation over the full military temperature range of $-55°C$ to $125°C$. The SN74128 is characterized for operation from $0°C$ to $70°C$.

schematic (each driver)

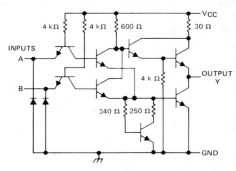

Resistor values shown are nominal.

logic diagram (each driver)

absolute maximum ratings over operating free-air temperature range (unless otherwise noted)

Supply voltage, V_{CC} (see Note 1) . . . . 7 V
Input voltage . . . . 5.5 V
Operating free-air temperature range: SN54' . . . . $-55°C$ to $125°C$
                                         SN74' . . . . $0°C$ to $70°C$
Storage temperature range . . . . $-65°C$ to $150°C$

NOTE 1: Voltage values are with respect to network ground terminal.

TEXAS
INSTRUMENTS

3

TTL DEVICES

recommended operating conditions

		SN54128			SN74128			UNIT
		MIN	NOM	MAX	MIN	NOM	MAX	
V_{CC}	Supply voltage	4.5	5	5.5	4.75	5	5.25	V
V_{IH}	High-level input voltage	2			2			V
V_{IL}	Low-level input voltage			0.8			0.8	V
I_{OH}	High-level output current			−29			−42.4	mA
I_{OL}	Low-level output current			48			48	mA
T_A	Operating free-air temperature	−55		125	0		70	°C

electrical characteristics over recommended operating free-air temperature range (unless otherwise noted)

PARAMETER	TEST CONDITIONS †			MIN	TYP‡	MAX	UNIT
V_{IK}	V_{CC} = MIN,	I_I = −12 mA				−1.5	V
V_{OH}	V_{CC} = MIN,	V_{IL} = 0.8 V,	I_{OH} = −2.4 mA	2.4	3.4		V
	V_{CC} = MIN,	V_{IL} = 0.4 V,	I_{OH} = −13.2 mA	2.4			
	V_{CC} = MIN,	V_{IL} = 0.4 V,	I_{OH} = MAX	2			
V_{OL}	V_{CC} = MIN,	V_{IH} = 2 V,	I_{OL} = 48 mA		0.26	0.4	V
I_I	V_{CC} = MAX,	V_I = 5.5 V				1	mA
I_{IH}	V_{CC} = MAX,	V_I = 2.4 V				40	µA
I_{IL}	V_{CC} = MAX,	V_I = 0.4 V				−1.6	mA
I_{OS}§	V_{CC} = MAX			−70		−180	mA
I_{CCH}	V_{CC} = MAX				12	21	mA
I_{CCL}	V_{CC} = MAX				33	57	mA

† For conditions shown as MIN or MAX, use the appropriate value specified under recommended operating conditions.
‡ All typical values are at V_{CC} = 5 V, T_A = 25°C.
§ Not more than one output should be shorted at a time.

switching characteristics, V_{CC} = 5 V, T_A = 25°C (see note 2)

PARAMETER	FROM (INPUT)	TO (OUTPUT)	TEST CONDITIONS		MIN	TYP	MAX	UNIT
t_{PLH}	A or B	Y	R_L = 133 Ω,	C_L = 50 pF		6	9	ns
t_{PHL}						8	12	ns
t_{PLH}			R_L = 133 Ω,	C_L = 150 pF		10	15	ns
t_{PHL}						12	18	ns

NOTE 2: See General Information Section for load circuits and voltage waveforms.

3

TTL DEVICES

TEXAS
INSTRUMENTS

TTL DEVICES

TYPES SN54132, SN54LS132, SN54S132, SN74132, SN74LS132, SN74S132
QUADRUPLE 2-INPUT POSITIVE-NAND SCHMITT TRIGGERS

REVISED DECEMBER 1983

- **Operation from Very Slow Edges**
- **Improved Line-Receiving Characteristics**
- **High Noise Immunity**

description

Each circuit functions as a 2-input NAND gate, but because of the Schmitt action, it has different input threshold levels for positive (V_{T+}) and for negative going (V_{T-}) signals.

These circuits are temperature-compensated and can be triggered from the slowest of input ramps and still give clear, jitter-free output signals.

The SN54132, SN54LS132, and SN54S132 are characterized for operation over the full military temperature range of $-55°C$ to $125°C$. The SN74132, SN74LS132, and SN74S132 are characterized for operation from $0°C$ to $70°C$.

SN54132, SN54LS132, SN54S132 . . . J OR W PACKAGE
SN74132 . . . J OR N PACKAGE
SN74LS132, SN74S132 . . . D, J OR N PACKAGE
(TOP VIEW)

SN54LS132, SN54S132 . . . FK PACKAGE
SN74LS132, SN74S132
(TOP VIEW)

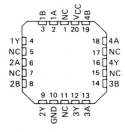

NC-No internal connection

logic diagram (each gate)

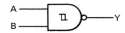

positive logic

$$Y = \overline{AB}$$

TTL DEVICES

3

TEXAS
INSTRUMENTS

schematics

'132 CIRCUITS

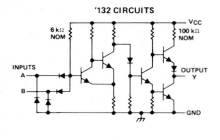

'LS132 CIRCUITS

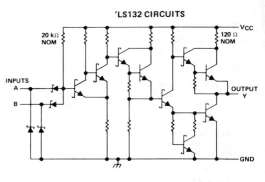

'S132 CIRCUITS

Resistor values shown are nominal.

absolute maximum ratings over operating free-air temperature range (unless otherwise noted)

Supply voltage, V_{CC} (see Note 1). . . . . 7 V

Input voltage: '132, 'S132 . . . . 5.5 V

　　　　　　　'LS132 . . . . 7 V

Operating free-air temperature: SN54'. . . . . -55°C to 125°C

　　　　　　　　　　　　　　　SN74'. . . . . 0°C to 70°C

Storage temperature range. . . . . -65°C to 150°C

NOTE 1: Voltages values are with respect to network ground terminal.

TEXAS
INSTRUMENTS

recommended operating conditions

		SN54132			SN74132			UNIT
		MIN	NOM	MAX	MIN	NOM	MAX	
V_{CC}	Supply voltage	4.5	5	5.5	4.75	5	5.25	V
I_{OH}	High-level output current			-0.8			-0.8	mA
I_{OL}	Low-level output current			16			16	mA
T_A	Operating free-air temperature	-55		125	0		70	°C

electrical characteristics over recommended operating free-air temperature range (unless otherwise noted)

PARAMETER	TEST CONDITIONS[†]			MIN	TYP[‡]	MAX	UNIT
V_{T+}	$V_{CC} = 5$ V			1.5	1.7	2	V
V_{T-}	$V_{CC} = 5$ V			0.6	0.9	1.1	V
Hysteresis $(V_{T+} - V_{T-})$	$V_{CC} = 5$ V			0.4	0.8		V
V_{IK}	$V_{CC} = $ MIN,	$I_I = -12$ mA				-1.5	V
V_{OH}	$V_{CC} = $ MIN,	$V_I = 0.6$ V,	$I_{OH} = -0.8$ mA	2.4	3.4		V
V_{OL}	$V_{CC} = $ MIN,	$V_I = 2$ V,	$I_{OL} = 16$ mA		0.2	0.4	V
I_{T+}	$V_{CC} = 5$ V,	$V_I = V_{T+}$			-0.43		mA
I_{T-}	$V_{CC} = 5$ V,	$V_I = V_{T-}$			-0.56		mA
I_I	$V_{CC} = $ MAX,	$V_I = 5.5$ V				1	mA
I_{IH}	$V_{CC} = $ MAX,	$V_I = 2.4$ V				40	µA
I_{IL}	$V_{CC} = $ MAX,	$V_{IL} = 0.4$ V			-0.8	-1.2	mA
I_{OS}[§]	$V_{CC} = $ MAX			-18		-55	mA
I_{CCH}	$V_{CC} = $ MAX				15	24	mA
I_{CCL}	$V_{CC} = $ MAX				26	40	mA

† For conditions shown as MIN or MAX, use the appropriate value specified under recommended operating conditions.
‡ All typical values are at $V_{CC} = 5$ V, $T_A = 25°$C.
§ Not more than one output should be shorted at a time.

switching characteristics, $V_{CC} = 5$ V, $T_A = 25°$C (see figure 1)

PARAMETER	FROM (INPUT)	TO (OUTPUT)	TEST CONDITIONS		MIN	TYP	MAX	UNIT
t_{PLH}	Any	Y	$R_L = 400$ Ω,	$C_L = 15$ pF		15	22	ns
t_{PHL}						15	22	ns

3

TTL DEVICES

recommended operating conditions

		SN54LS132			SN74LS132			UNIT
		MIN	NOM	MAX	MIN	NOM	MAX	
V_{CC}	Supply voltage	4.5	5	5.5	4.75	5	5.25	V
I_{OH}	High-level output current			−0.4			−0.4	mA
I_{OL}	Low-level output current			4			8	mA
T_A	Operating free-air temperature	−55		125	0		70	°C

electrical characteristics over recommended operating free-air temperature range (unless otherwise noted)

PARAMETER	TEST CONDITIONS†		SN54LS132			SN74LS132			UNIT
			MIN	TYP‡	MAX	MIN	TYP‡	MAX	
V_{T+}	$V_{CC} = 5$ V		1.4	1.6	1.9	1.4	1.6	1.9	V
V_{T-}	$V_{CC} = 5$ V		0.5	0.8	1	0.5	0.8	1	V
Hysteresis $(V_{T+} - V_{T-})$	$V_{CC} = 5$ V		0.4	0.8		0.4	0.8		V
V_{IK}	$V_{CC} = $ MIN, $I_I = -18$ mA				−1.5			−1.5	V
V_{OH}	$V_{CC} = $ MIN, $V_I = 0.5$ V, $I_{OH} = -0.4$ mA		2.5	3.4		2.7	3.4		V
V_{OL}	$V_{CC} = $ MIN, $V_I = 1.9$ V	$I_{OL} = 4$ mA		0.25	0.4		0.25	0.4	V
		$I_{OL} = 8$ mA					0.35	0.5	
I_{T+}	$V_{CC} = 5$ V, $V_I = V_{T+}$			−0.14			−0.14		mA
I_{T-}	$V_{CC} = 5$ V, $V_I = V_{T-}$			−0.18			−0.18		mA
I_I	$V_{CC} = $ MAX, $V_I = 7$ V				0.1			0.1	mA
I_{IH}	$V_{CC} = $ MAX, $V_I = 2.7$ V				20			20	μA
I_{IL}	$V_{CC} = $ MAX, $V_{IL} = 0.4$ V				−0.4			−0.4	mA
I_{OS} §	$V_{CC} = $ MAX		−20		−100	−20		−100	mA
I_{CCH}	$V_{CC} = $ MAX			5.9	11		5.9	11	mA
I_{CCL}	$V_{CC} = $ MAX			8.2	14		8.2	14	mA

† For conditions shown as MIN or MAX, use the appropriate value specified under recommended operating conditions.
‡ All typical values are at $V_{CC} = 5$ V, $T_A = 25°$C.
§ Not more than one output should be shorted at a time, and duration of the short-circuit should not exceed one second

switching characteristics, $V_{CC} = 5$ V, $T_A = 25°$C (see figure 1)

PARAMETER	FROM (INPUT)	TO (OUTPUT)	TEST CONDITIONS		MIN	TYP	MAX	UNIT
t_{PLH}	Any	Y	$R_L = 2$ kΩ,	$C_L = 15$ pF		15	22	ns
t_{PHL}						15	22	ns

TEXAS
INSTRUMENTS

recommended operating conditions

		SN54S132			SN74S132			UNIT
		MIN	NOM	MAX	MIN	NOM	MAX	
V_{CC}	Supply voltage	4.5	5	5.5	4.75	5	5.25	V
I_{OH}	High-level output current			−1			−1	mA
I_{OL}	Low-level output current			20			20	mA
T_A	Operating free-air temperature	−55		125	0		70	°C

electrical characteristics over recommended operating free-air temperature range (unless otherwise noted)

PARAMETER	TEST CONDITIONS[†]			SN54S132			SN74S132			UNIT
				MIN	TYP[‡]	MAX	MIN	TYP[‡]	MAX	
V_{T+}	V_{CC} = 5 V			1.6	1.77	1.9	1.6	1.77	1.9	V
V_{T-}	V_{CC} = 5 V			1.1	1.22	1.4	1.1	1.22	1.4	V
Hysteresis $(V_{T+} - V_{T-})$	V_{CC} = 5 V			0.2	0.55		0.2	0.55		V
V_{IK}	V_{CC} = MIN,	I_I = −18 mA				−1.2			−1.2	V
V_{OH}	V_{CC} = MIN,	V_I = 1.1 V,	I_{OH} = −1 mA	2.5	3.4		2.7	3.4		V
V_{OL}	V_{CC} = MIN,	V_I = 1.9 V,	I_{OL} = 20 mA			0.5			0.5	V
I_{T+}	V_{CC} = 5 V,	V_I = V_{T+}			−0.9			−0.9		mA
I_{T-}	V_{CC} = 5 V,	V_I = V_{T-}			−1.1			−1.1		mA
I_I	V_{CC} = MAX,	V_I = 5.5 V				1			1	mA
I_{IH}	V_{CC} = MAX,	V_I = 2.7 V				50			50	μA
I_{IL}	V_{CC} = MAX,	V_{IL} = 0.5 V				−2			−2	mA
I_{OS}[§]	V_{CC} = MAX			−40		−100	−40		−100	mA
I_{CCH}	V_{CC} = MAX				28	44		28	44	mA
I_{CCL}	V_{CC} = MAX				44	68		44	68	mA

† For conditions shown as MIN or MAX, use the appropriate value specified under recommended operating conditions.
‡ All typical values are at V_{CC} = 5 V, T_A = 25°C.
§ Not more than one output should be shorted at a time, and duration of the short-circuit should not exceed one second.

switching characteristics, V_{CC} = 5 V, T_A = 25°C (see figure 1)

PARAMETER	FROM (INPUT)	TO (OUTPUT)	TEST CONDITIONS		MIN	TYP	MAX	UNIT
t_{PLH}	A or B	Y	R_L = 280 Ω,	C_L = 15 pF		7	10.5	ns
t_{PHL}						8.5	13	ns

TEXAS INSTRUMENTS

3

TTL DEVICES

PARAMETER MEASUREMENT INFORMATION

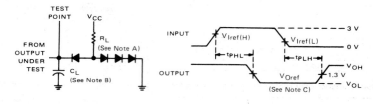

LOAD CIRCUIT **VOLTAGE WAVEFORMS**

NOTES: A. All diodes are 1N3064 or equivalent.
B. C_L includes probe and jig capacitance.
C. Generator characteristics and reference voltages are:

	Generator Characteristics				Reference Voltages		
	Z_{out}	PRR	t_r	t_f	$V_{I\,ref(H)}$	$V_{I\,ref(L)}$	$V_{O\,ref}$
SN54'/SN74'	50	1 MHz	10 ns	10 ns	1.7 V	0.9 V	1.5 V
SN54LS'/SN74LS'	50	1 MHz	15 ns	6 ns	1.6 V	0.8 V	1.3 V
'S132	50	1 MHz	2.5 ns	2.5 ns	1.8 V	1.2 V	1.5 V

FIGURE 1

TEXAS
INSTRUMENTS

TYPICAL CHARACTERISTICS OF '132 CIRCUITS

POSITIVE-GOING THRESHOLD VOLTAGE
vs
FREE-AIR TEMPERATURE

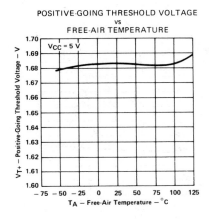

NEGATIVE-GOING THRESHOLD VOLTAGE
vs
FREE-AIR TEMPERATURE

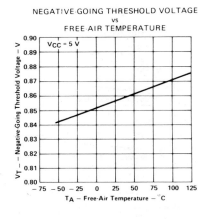

HYSTERESIS
vs
FREE-AIR TEMPERATURE

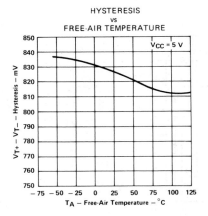

DISTRIBUTION OF UNITS
FOR HYSTERESIS

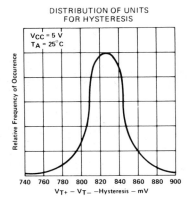

† Data for temperatures below 0°C and 70°C and supply below 4.75 V and above 5.25 V are applicable for SN54132 only.

TEXAS INSTRUMENTS

TTL DEVICES

3

TYPICAL CHARACTERISTICS OF '132 CIRCUITS

THRESHOLD VOLTAGES
vs
SUPPLY VOLTAGE

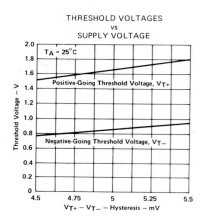

HYSTERESIS
vs
SUPPLY VOLTAGE

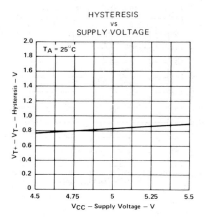

OUTPUT VOLTAGE
vs
INPUT VOLTAGE

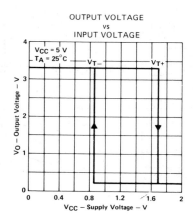

† Data for temperatures below 0"C and 70"C and supply below 4.75 V and above 5.25 V are applicable for SN54132 only.

TEXAS
INSTRUMENTS

TYPICAL CHARACTERISTICS OF 'LS132 CIRCUITS

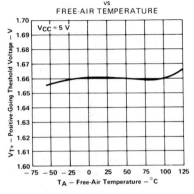

POSITIVE-GOING THRESHOLD VOLTAGE
vs
FREE-AIR TEMPERATURE

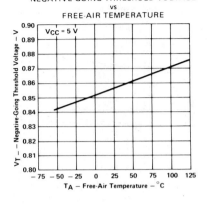

NEGATIVE-GOING THRESHOLD VOLTAGE
vs
FREE-AIR TEMPERATURE

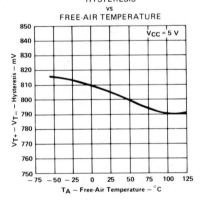

HYSTERESIS
vs
FREE-AIR TEMPERATURE

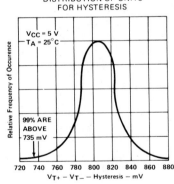

DISTRIBUTION OF UNITS
FOR HYSTERESIS

3

TTL DEVICES

† Data for temperatures below 0°C and above 70°C and supply voltages below 4.75 V and above 5.25 V are applicable for SN54LS132 only.

TEXAS
INSTRUMENTS

TYPICAL CHARACTERISTICS OF 'LS132 CIRCUITS

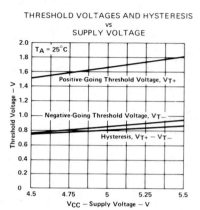

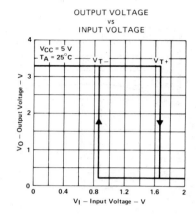

† Data for temperatures below 0°C and above 70°C and supply voltages below 4.75 V and above 5.25 V are applicable for SN54LS132 only.

Texas
Instruments

TYPICAL APPLICATION DATA

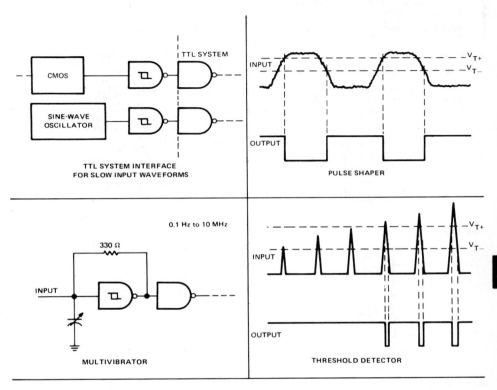

TTL SYSTEM INTERFACE
FOR SLOW INPUT WAVEFORMS

PULSE SHAPER

MULTIVIBRATOR

THRESHOLD DETECTOR

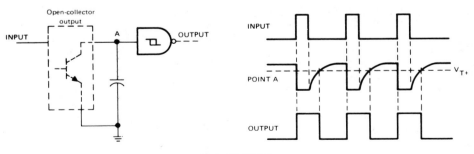

PULSE STRETCHER

- **Package Options Include Both Plastic and Ceramic Chip Carriers in Addition to Plastic and Ceramic DIPs**

- **Dependable Texas Instruments Quality and Reliability**

description

These devices contain a single 13-input NAND gate.

The SN54133 is characterized for operation over the full military temperature range of −55°C to 125°C. The SN74133 is characterized for operation from 0°C to 70°C.

SN54S133 . . . J OR W PACKAGE
SN74S133 . . . D, J OR N PACKAGE
(TOP VIEW)

SN54S133 . . . FK PACKAGE
SN74S133
(TOP VIEW)

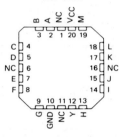

NC - No internal connection

FUNCTION TABLE

INPUTS A THRU M	OUTPUT Y
All inputs H	L
One or more inputs L	H

logic diagram

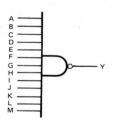

positive logic

$$Y = \overline{A \cdot B \cdot C \cdot D \cdot E \cdot F \cdot G \cdot H \cdot I \cdot J \cdot K \cdot L \cdot M} \text{ or}$$
$$Y = \overline{A} + \overline{B} + \overline{C} + \overline{D} + \overline{E} + \overline{F} + \overline{G} + \overline{H} + \overline{I} + \overline{J} + \overline{K} + \overline{L} + \overline{M}$$

3

TTL DEVICES

TEXAS INSTRUMENTS

schematic

'S133

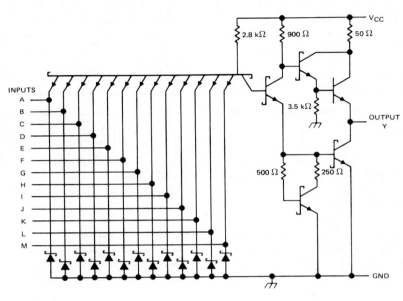

Resistor values shown are nominal.

absolute maximum ratings over operating free-air temperature range (unless otherwise noted)

Supply voltage, V_{CC} (see Note 1) . . . . 7 V

Input voltage . . . . 5.5 V

Operating free-air temperature range: SN54' . . . . − 55°C to 125°C

SN74' . . . . 0°C to 70°C

Storage temperature range . . . . − 65°C to 150°C

NOTE 1: Voltage values are with respect to network ground terminal.

recommended operating conditions

		SN54S133 MIN	NOM	MAX	SN74S133 MIN	NOM	MAX	UNIT
V_{CC}	Supply voltage	4.5	5	5.5	4.75	5	5.25	V
V_{IH}	High-level input voltage	2			2			V
V_{IL}	Low-level input voltage			0.8			0.8	V
I_{OH}	High-level output current			−1			−1	mA
I_{OL}	Low-level output current			20			20	mA
T_A	Operating free-air temperature	−55		125	0		70	°C

electrical characteristics over recommended operating free-air temperature range (unless otherwise noted)

PARAMETER	TEST CONDITIONS †	SN54S133 MIN	TYP‡	MAX	SN74S133 MIN	TYP‡	MAX	UNIT
V_{IK}	V_{CC} = MIN, I_I = −18 mA			−1.2			−1.2	V
V_{OH}	V_{CC} = MIN, V_{IL} = 0.8 V, I_{OH} = −1 mA	2.5	3.4		2.7	3.4		V
V_{OL}	V_{CC} = MIN, V_{IH} = 2 V, I_{OL} = 20 mA			0.5			0.5	V
I_I	V_{CC} = MAX, V_I = 5.5 V			1			1	mA
I_{IH}	V_{CC} = MAX, V_I = 2.7 V			50			50	μA
I_{IL}	V_{CC} = MAX, V_I = 0.5 V			−2			−2	mA
I_{OS} §	V_{CC} = MAX	−40		−100	−40		−100	mA
I_{CCH}	V_{CC} = MAX, V_I = 0 V		3	5		3	5	mA
I_{CCL}	V_{CC} = MAX, V_I = 4.5 V		5.5	10		5.5	10	mA

† For conditions shown as MIN or MAX, use the appropriate value specified under recommended operating conditions.
‡ All typical values are at V_{CC} = 5 V, T_A = 25°C.
§ Not more than one output should be shorted at a time, and the duration of the short-circuit should not exceed one second.

switching characteristics, V_{CC} = 5 V, T_A = 25°C (see note 2)

PARAMETER	FROM (INPUT)	TO (OUTPUT)	TEST CONDITIONS	MIN	TYP	MAX	UNIT
t_{PLH}			R_L = 280 Ω, C_L = 15 pF		4	6	ns
t_{PHL}	Any	Y	R_L = 280 Ω, C_L = 15 pF		4.5	7	ns
t_{PLH}			R_L = 280 Ω, C_L = 50 pF		5.5		ns
t_{PHL}			R_L = 280 Ω, C_L = 50 pF		6.5		ns

NOTE 2: See General Information Section for load circuits and voltage waveforms.

TEXAS
INSTRUMENTS

- **Package Options Include Both Plastic and Ceramic Chip Carriers in Addition to Plastic and Ceramic DIPs**

- **Dependable Texas Instruments Quality and Reliability**

description

The 'S134 feature three-state outputs that, when enabled, have the low impedance characteristics of a TTL output with additional drive capability at high logic levels to permit driving heavily loaded lines without external pull-up resistors. When disabled, both output transistors are turned off presenting a high-impedance state to the bus so the output will act neither as a significant load nor as a driver. The 'S134 outputs are diabled when G is high.

SN54S134 . . . J OR W PACKAGE
SN74S134 . . . D, J OR N PACKAGE
(TOP VIEW)

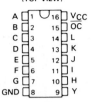

SN54S134 . . . FK PACKAGE
SN74S134

(TOP VIEW)

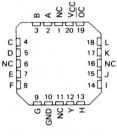

NC - No internal connection

logic diagram

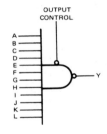

positive logic

$$Y = \overline{ABCDEFGHIJKL}$$

Output is off (disabled) when output control is high.

TEXAS INSTRUMENTS

3

TTL DEVICES

TYPES SN54S134, SN74S134
12-INPUT POSITIVE-NAND GATES WITH 3-STATE OUTPUTS

schematic

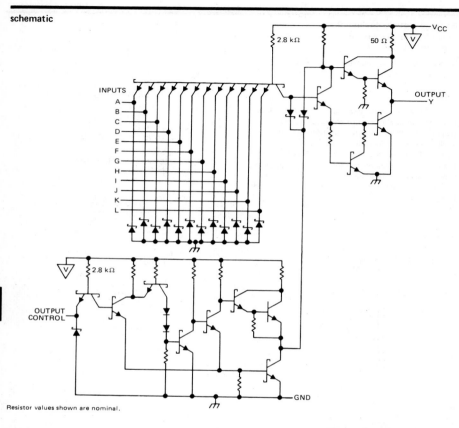

Resistor values shown are nominal.

absolute maximum ratings over operating free-air temperature range (unless otherwise noted)

Supply voltage, V_{CC} (see Note 1)	7 V
Input voltage	5.5 V
Voltage applied to a disabled 3-state output	5.5 V
Operating free-air temperature range: SN54'	−55°C to 125°C
SN74'	0°C to 70°C
Storage temperature range	−65°C to 150°C

NOTE 1: Voltage values are with respect to network ground terminal.

TEXAS
INSTRUMENTS

recommended operating conditions

		SN54S134			SN74S134			UNIT
		MIN	NOM	MAX	MIN	NOM	MAX	
V_{CC}	Supply voltage	4.5	5	5.5	4.75	5	5.25	V
V_{IH}	High-level input voltage	2			2			V
V_{IL}	Low-level input voltage			0.8			0.8	V
I_{OH}	High-level output current			-2			-6.5	mA
I_{OL}	Low-level output current			20			20	mA
T_A	Operating free-air temperature	-55		125	0		70	$^\circ$C

electrical characteristics over recommended operating free-air temperature range (unless otherwise noted)

PARAMETER	TEST CONDITIONS†			SN54S134			SN74S134			UNIT
				MIN	TYP‡	MAX	MIN	TYP‡	MAX	
V_{IK}	V_{CC} = MIN,	I_I = -18 mA				-1.2			-1.2	V
V_{OH}	V_{CC} = MIN, V_{IH} = 2 V	I_{OH} = -2 mA		2.4	3.4					V
	V_{IL} = 0.8 V	I_{OH} = -6.5 mA					2.4	3.2		
V_{OL}	V_{CC} = MIN, V_{IH} = 2 V,	V_{IL} = 0.8 V,				0.5			0.5	V
	I_{OL} = 20 mA									
I_{OZ}	V_{CC} = MAX, V_{IH} = 2 V,	V_O = 2.4 V				50			50	μA
	V_{IL} = 0.8 V	V_O = 0.5 V				-50			-50	
I_I	V_{CC} = MAX,	V_I = 5.5 V				1			1	mA
I_{IH}	V_{CC} = MAX,	V_I = 2.7 V				50			50	μA
I_{IL}	V_{CC} = MAX,	V_I = 0.5 V				-2			-2	mA
I_{OS}§	V_{CC} = MAX			-40		-100	-40		-100	mA
I_{CC}	V_{CC} = MAX	Outputs high			7	13		7	13	mA
		Outputs low			9	16		9	16	
		Outputs disabled			14	25		14	25	

† For conditions shown as MIN or MAX, use the appropriate value specified under recommended operating conditions
‡ All typical values are at V_{CC} = 5 V, T_A = 25°C.
§ Not more than one output should be shorted at a time, and duration of the short circuit should not exceed one second.

switching characteristics, V_{CC} = 5 V, T_A = 25°C (see note 2)

PARAMETER	TEST CONDITIONS		SN54S134			SN74S134			UNIT
			MIN	TYP	MAX	MIN	TYP	MAX	
t_{PLH}	R_L = 280 Ω,	C_L = 15 pF		4	6		4	6	ns
t_{PLH}	R_L = 280 Ω,	C_L = 50 pF		5.5			5.5		ns
t_{PHL}	R_L = 280 Ω,	C_L = 15 pF		5	7.5		5	7.5	ns
t_{PHL}	R_L = 280 Ω,	C_L = 50 pF		7			7		ns
t_{PZH}	R_L = 280 Ω,	C_L = 50 pF		13	19.5		13	19.5	ns
t_{PZL}				14	21		14	21	ns
t_{PHZ}	R_L = 280 Ω,	C_L = 5 pF		5.5	8.5		5.5	8.5	ns
t_{PLZ}				9	14		9	14	ns

NOTE 2: See General Information Section for load circuits and voltage waveforms.

TEXAS
INSTRUMENTS

3

TTL DEVICES

- Fully Compatible with Most TTL and TTL MSI Circuits

- Fully Schottky Clamping Reduces Delay Times . . . 8 ns Typical

- Can Operate as Exclusive-OR Gate (C Input Low) or as Exclusive-NOR Gate (C Input High)

SN54S135 . . . J OR W PACKAGE
SN74S135 . . . D, J OR N PACKAGE
(TOP VIEW)

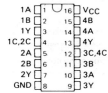

1A	1	16 VCC
1B	2	15 4B
1Y	3	14 4A
1C,2C	4	13 4Y
2A	5	12 3C,4C
2B	6	11 3B
2Y	7	10 3A
GND	8	9 3Y

FUNCTION TABLE

INPUTS			OUTPUT
A	B	C	Y
L	L	L	L
L	H	L	H
H	L	L	H
H	H	L	L
L	L	H	H
L	H	H	L
H	L	H	L
H	H	H	H

H = high level, L = low level

SN54S135 . . . FK PACKAGE
SN74S135
(TOP VIEW)

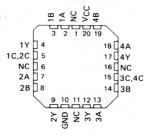

NC - No internal connection

logic diagram (one half)

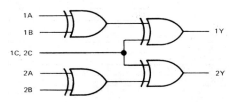

positive logic

$$Y = A \oplus B \oplus C = A\overline{B}\overline{C} + \overline{A}B\overline{C} + \overline{A}\overline{B}C + ABC$$

schematics of inputs and outputs

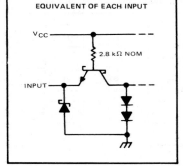

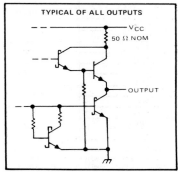

Resistor values shown are nominal.

TEXAS
INSTRUMENTS

TTL DEVICES

3

TYPES SN54S135, SN74S135
QUADRUPLE EXCLUSIVE-OR/NOR GATES

absolute maximum ratings over operating free-air temperature range (unless otherwise noted)

Supply voltage, V_{CC} (see Note 1) . . . . 7 V
Input voltage . . . . 5.5 V
Operating free-air temperature range: SN54S135 . . . . -55°C to 125°C
  SN74S135 . . . . 0°C to 70°C
Storage temperature range . . . . -65°C to 150°C

NOTE 1: Voltage values are with respect to network ground terminal.

recommended operating conditions

	SN54S135			SN74S135			UNIT
	MIN	NOM	MAX	MIN	NOM	MAX	
Supply voltage, V_{CC}	4.5	5	5.5	4.75	5	5.25	V
High-level output current, I_{OH}			-1			-1	mA
Low-level output current, I_{OL}			20			20	mA
Operating free-air temperature, T_A	-55		125	0		70	°C

electrical characteristics over recommended operating free-air temperature range (unless otherwise noted)

	PARAMETER	TEST CONDITIONS[†]		MIN	TYP[‡]	MAX	UNIT
V_{IH}	High-level input voltage			2			V
V_{IL}	Low-level input voltage					0.8	V
V_{IK}	Input clamp voltage	V_{CC} = MIN, $I_I = -18$ mA				-1.2	V
V_{OH}	High-level output voltage	V_{CC} = MIN, V_{IH} = 2 V,	SN54S'	2.5	3.4		V
		V_{IL} = 0.8 V, $I_{OH} = -1$ mA	SN74S'	2.7	3.4		
V_{OL}	Low-level output voltage	V_{CC} = MIN, V_{IH} = 2 V, V_{IL} = 0.8 V, I_{OL} = 20 mA				0.5	V
I_I	Input current at maximum input voltage	V_{CC} = MAX, V_I = 5.5 V				1	mA
I_{IH}	High-level input current	V_{CC} = MAX, V_I = 2.7 V				50	µA
I_{IL}	Low-level input current	V_{CC} = MAX, V_I = 0.5 V				-2	mA
I_{OS}	Short-circuit output current [§]	V_{CC} = MAX		-40		-100	mA
I_{CC}	Supply current	V_{CC} = MAX, See Note 2			65	99	mA

[†]For conditions shown as MIN or MAX, use the appropriate value specified under recommended operating conditions for the applicable type.
[‡]All typical values are at V_{CC} = 5 V, $T_A = 25^\circ$C.
[§]Not more than one output should be shorted at a time and duration of the short circuit should not exceed one second.
NOTE 2: I_{CC} is measured with the inputs grounded and the outputs open.

switching characteristics, V_{CC} = 5 V, $T_A = 25^\circ$C

PARAMETER[¶]	FROM (INPUT)	TEST CONDITIONS		MIN	TYP	MAX	UNIT
t_{PLH}	A or B	B or A = L, C = L			8.5	13	ns
t_{PHL}					11	15	
t_{PLH}	A or B	B or A = H, C = L			8	12	ns
t_{PHL}					9	13.5	
t_{PLH}	A or B	B or A = L, C = H	C_L = 15 pF, R_L = 280 Ω, See Note 3		10	15	ns
t_{PHL}					6.5	10	
t_{PLH}	A or B	B or A = H, C = H			8.5	12	ns
t_{PHL}					7	13	
t_{PLH}	C	A = B			8	12	ns
t_{PHL}					9.5	14.5	
t_{PLH}	C	A ≠ B			7.5	11.5	ns
t_{PHL}					8	12	

[¶]$t_{PLH} \equiv$ propagation delay time, low-to-high-level output
$t_{PHL} \equiv$ propagation delay time, high-to-low-level output
NOTE 3: See General Information Section for load circuits and voltage waveforms.

TEXAS
INSTRUMENTS

FUNCTION TABLE

INPUTS		OUTPUT
A	B	Y
L	L	L
L	H	H
H	L	H
H	H	L

H = high level, L = low level

SN54136, SN54LS136 . . . J OR W PACKAGE
SN74136 . . . J OR N PACKAGE
SN74LS136 . . . D, J OR N PACKAGE
(TOP VIEW)

```
        ___  ___
1A  [1        14]  VCC
1B  [2        13]  4B
1Y  [3        12]  4A
2A  [4        11]  4Y
2B  [5        10]  3B
2Y  [6         9]  3A
GND [7         8]  3Y
```

logic diagram (each gate)

SN54LS136 . . . FK PACKAGE
SN74LS136
(TOP VIEW)

```
         1B 1A NC VCC 4B
          3  2  1  20 19
1Y  [4              18]  4A
NC  [5              17]  NC
2A  [6              16]  4Y
NC  [7              15]  NC
2B  [8              14]  3B
          9 10 11 12 13
         2Y GND NC 3Y 3A
```

NC – No internal connection

positive logic

$$Y = A \oplus B = \overline{A}B + A\overline{B}$$

schematics of inputs and outputs

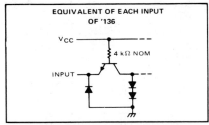

EQUIVALENT OF EACH INPUT
OF '136

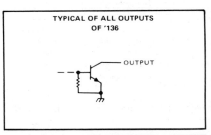

TYPICAL OF ALL OUTPUTS
OF '136

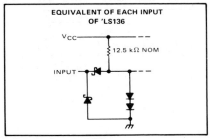

EQUIVALENT OF EACH INPUT
OF 'LS136

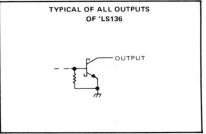

TYPICAL OF ALL OUTPUTS
OF 'LS136

Resistor values shown are nominal.

3

TTL DEVICES

TEXAS INSTRUMENTS

absolute maximum ratings over operating free-air temperature range (unless otherwise noted)

Supply voltage, V_{CC} (see Note 1)	7 V
Input voltage	5.5 V
Operating free-air temperature range: SN54136	$-55°C$ to $125°C$
SN74136	$0°C$ to $70°C$
Storage temperature range	$-65°C$ to $150°C$

NOTE 1: Voltage values are with respect to network ground terminal.

recommended operating conditions

	SN54136 MIN	NOM	MAX	SN74136 MIN	NOM	MAX	UNIT
Supply voltage, V_{CC}	4.5	5	5.5	4.75	5	5.25	V
High-level output voltage, V_{OH}			5.5			5.5	V
Low-level output current, I_{OL}			16			16	mA
Operating free-air temperature, T_A	-55		125	0		70	C

electrical characteristics over recommended operating free-air temperature range (unless otherwise noted)

PARAMETER		TEST CONDITIONS[†]		MIN	TYP[‡]	MAX	UNIT
V_{IH}	High-level input voltage			2			V
V_{IL}	Low-level input voltage					0.8	V
V_{IK}	Input clamp voltage	V_{CC} = MIN,	I_I = -8 mA			-1.5	V
I_{OH}	High-level output current	V_{CC} = MIN,\nV_{IL} = 0.8 V,	V_{IH} = 2 V,\nV_{OH} = 5.5 V			250	µA
V_{OL}	Low-level output voltage	V_{CC} = MIN,\nV_{IL} = 0.8 V,	V_{IH} = 2 V,\nI_{OL} = 16 mA		0.2	0.4	V
I_I	Input current at maximum input voltage	V_{CC} = MAX,	V_I = 5.5 V			1	mA
I_{IH}	High-level input current	V_{CC} = MAX,	V_I = 2.4 V			40	µA
I_{IL}	Low-level input current	V_{CC} = MAX,	V_I = 0.4 V			-1.6	mA
I_{CC}	Supply current, high-level output	V_{CC} = MAX, See Note 2	SN54136		30	43	mA
			SN74136		30	50	

[†]For conditions shown as MIN or MAX, use the appropriate value specified under recommended operating conditions for the applicable device type.
[‡]All typical values are at V_{CC} = 5 V, T_A = 25°C.
NOTE 2: I_{CC} is measured with one input of each gate at 4.5 V, the other inputs grounded, and the outputs open.

switching characteristics, V_{CC} = 5 V, T_A = 25°C

PARAMETER[¶]	FROM (INPUT)	TEST CONDITIONS		MIN	TYP	MAX	UNIT
t_{PLH}	A or B	Other input low	C_L = 15 pF,\nR_L = 400 Ω,\nSee Note 3		12	18	ns
t_{PHL}					39	50	
t_{PLH}	A or B	Other input high			14	22	ns
t_{PHL}					42	55	

[¶]t_{PLH} = propagation delay time, low-to-high-level output
t_{PHL} = propagation delay time, high-to-low-level output
NOTE 3: See General Information Section for load circuits and voltage waveforms.

3
TTL DEVICES

absolute maximum ratings over operating free-air temperature range (unless otherwise noted)

Supply voltage, V_{CC} (see Note 1) . . . . 7 V

Input voltage . . . . 7 V

Operating free-air temperature range: SN54LS136 . . . . −55°C to 125°C

SN74LS136 . . . . 0°C to 70°C

Storage temperature range . . . . −65°C to 150°C

NOTE 1: Voltage values are with respect to network ground terminal.

recommended operating conditions

	SN54LS136			SN74LS136			UNIT
	MIN	NOM	MAX	MIN	NOM	MAX	
Supply voltage, V_{CC}	4.5	5	5.5	4.75	5	5.25	V
High-level output voltage, V_{OH}			5.5			5.5	V
Low-level output current, I_{OL}			4			8	mA
Operating free-air temperature, T_A	−55		125	0		70	°C

electrical characteristics over recommended operating free-air temperature range (unless otherwise noted)

PARAMETER		TEST CONDITIONS[†]		SN54LS136			SN74LS136			UNIT
				MIN	TYP[‡]	MAX	MIN	TYP[‡]	MAX	
V_{IH}	High-level input voltage			2			2			V
V_{IL}	Low-level input voltage					0.7			0.8	V
V_{IK}	Input clamp voltage	V_{CC} = MIN,	I_I = −18 mA			−1.5			−1.5	V
I_{OH}	High-level output current	V_{CC} = MIN, V_{IH} = 2 V, $V_{IL} = V_{IL}$ max, V_{OH} = 5.5 V				100			100	μA
V_{OL} Low-level output voltage		V_{CC} = MIN, V_{IH} = 2 V, $V_{IL} = V_{IL}$ max	I_{OL} = 4 mA	0.25	0.4		0.25	0.4		V
			I_{OL} = 8 mA					0.35	0.5	
I_I	Input current at maximum input voltage	V_{CC} = MAX,	V_I = 7 V			0.2			0.2	mA
I_{IH}	High-level input current	V_{CC} = MAX,	V_I = 2.7 V			40			40	μA
I_{IL}	Low-level input current	V_{CC} = MAX,	V_I = 0.4 V			−0.8			−0.8	mA
I_{CC}	Supply current	V_{CC} = MAX,	See Note 2		6.1	10		6.1	10	mA

[†]For conditions shown as MIN or MAX, use the appropriate value specified under recommended operating conditions for the applicable type.
[‡]All typical values are at V_{CC} = 5 V, T_A = 25°C.
NOTE 2: I_{CC} is measured with one input of each gate at 4.5 V, the other inputs grounded, and the outputs open.

switching characteristics, V_{CC} = 5 V, T_A = 25°C

PARAMETER[¶]	FROM (INPUT)	TEST CONDITIONS		MIN	TYP	MAX	UNIT
t_{PLH}	A or B	Other input low	C_L = 15 pF, R_L = 2 kΩ, (See Note 3)		18	30	ns
t_{PHL}					18	30	
t_{PLH}	A or B	Other input high			18	30	ns
t_{PHL}					18	30	

[¶] t_{PLH} = propagation delay time, low-to-high-level output
t_{PHL} = propagation delay time, high-to-low-level output
NOTE 3: See General Information Section for load circuits and voltage waveforms.

3

TTL DEVICES

TEXAS
INSTRUMENTS

- **Combines Decoder and 3-Bit Address Latch**

- **Incorporates 2 Enable Inputs to Simplify Cascading**

- **Low Power Dissipation . . . 65 mW Typ**

SN54LS137 . . . J OR W PACKAGE
SN74LS137 . . . D, J OR N PACKAGE
(TOP VIEW)

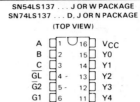

A	1	V_{CC} 16
B	2	Y0 15
C	3	Y1 14
$\overline{GL}$	4	Y2 13
$\overline{G2}$	5	Y3 12
G1	6	Y4 11
Y7	7	Y5 10
GND	8	Y6 9

description

The 'LS137 is a three-line to eight-line decoder/demultiplexer with latches on the three address inputs. When the latch-enable input ($\overline{GL}$) is low, the 'LS137 acts as a decoder/demultiplexer. When $\overline{GL}$ goes from low to high, the address present at the select inputs (A, B, and C) is stored in the latches. Further address changes are ignored as long as $\overline{GL}$ remains high. The output enable controls, G1 and $\overline{G2}$, control the state of the outputs independently of the select or latch-enable inputs. All of the outputs are high unless G1 is high and $\overline{G2}$ is low. The 'LS137 is ideally suited for implementing glitch-free decoders in strobed (stored-address) applications in bus-oriented systems.

SN54LS137 . . . FK PACKAGE
SN74LS137
(TOP VIEW)

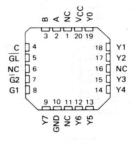

NC - No internal connection

schematics of inputs and outputs

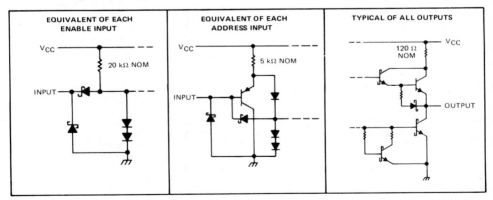

EQUIVALENT OF EACH ENABLE INPUT	EQUIVALENT OF EACH ADDRESS INPUT	TYPICAL OF ALL OUTPUTS
V_{CC} 20 kΩ NOM, INPUT	V_{CC} 5 kΩ NOM, INPUT	120 Ω NOM, V_{CC}, OUTPUT

TTL DEVICES

3

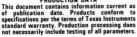

TEXAS INSTRUMENTS

TYPES SN54LS137, SN74LS137
3-LINE TO 8-LINE DECODERS/DEMULTIPLEXERS
WITH ADDRESS LATCHES

logic symbols

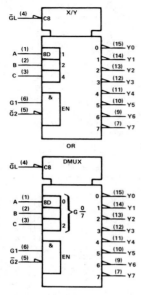

Pin numbers shown on logic notation are for D, J or N packages.

INPUTS						OUTPUTS							
ENABLE			SELECT										
$\overline{GL}$	G1	$\overline{G2}$	C	B	A	Y0	Y1	Y2	Y3	Y4	Y5	Y6	Y7
X	X	H	X	X	X	H	H	H	H	H	H	H	H
X	L	X	X	X	X	H	H	H	H	H	H	H	H
L	H	L	L	L	L	L	H	H	H	H	H	H	H
L	H	L	L	L	H	H	L	H	H	H	H	H	H
L	H	L	L	H	L	H	H	L	H	H	H	H	H
L	H	L	L	H	H	H	H	H	L	H	H	H	H
L	H	L	H	L	L	H	H	H	H	L	H	H	H
L	H	L	H	L	H	H	H	H	H	H	L	H	H
L	H	L	H	H	L	H	H	H	H	H	H	L	H
L	H	L	H	H	H	H	H	H	H	H	H	H	L
H	H	L	X	X	X	Output corresponding to stored address, L; all others, H							

H = high level, L = low level, X = irrelevant

TEXAS
INSTRUMENTS

logic diagram (positive logic)

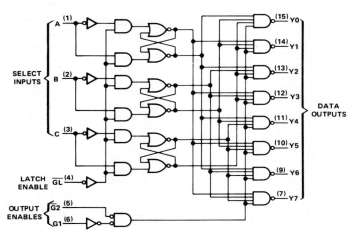

Pin numbers shown on logic notation are for D, J or N packages.

absolute maximum ratings over operating free-air temperature range (unless otherwise noted)

Supply voltage, V_{CC} (See Note 1) . . . . 7 V

Input voltage . . . . 7 V

Operating free-air temperature range: SN54LS137 . . . . $-55°$C to $125°$C

                                 SN74LS137 . . . . $0°$C to $70°$C

Storage temperature range . . . . $-65°$C to $150°$C

NOTE 1: Voltage values are with respect to network ground terminal.

3

TTL DEVICES

TYPES SN54LS137, SN74LS137
3-LINE TO 8-LINE DECODERS/DEMULTIPLEXERS
WITH ADDRESS LATCHES

recommended operating conditions

	SN54LS137			SN74LS137			UNIT
	MIN	NOM	MAX	MIN	NOM	MAX	
Supply voltage, V_{CC}	4.5	5	5.5	4.75	5	5.25	V
High-level output current, I_{OH}			−400			−400	μA
Low-level output current, I_{OL}			4			8	mA
Width of enabling pulse at $\overline{G}L$, t_w	15			15			ns
Setup time at A, B, and C inputs, t_{su}	10			10			ns
Hold time at A, B, and C inputs, t_h	10			10			ns
Operating free-air temperature, T_A	−55		125	0		70	C

electrical characteristics over recommended operating free-air temperature range (unless otherwise noted)

PARAMETER		TEST CONDITIONS[†]		SN54LS137			SN74LS137			UNIT
				MIN	TYP[‡]	MAX	MIN	TYP[‡]	MAX	
V_{IH}	High-level input voltage			2			2			V
V_{IL}	Low-level input voltage					0.7			0.8	V
V_{IK}	Input clamp voltage	V_{CC} = MIN,	I_I = −18 mA			−1.5			−1.5	V
V_{OH}	High-level output voltage	V_{CC} = MIN, V_{IH} = 2 V, V_{IL} = V_{IL} max, I_{OH} = −400 μA		2.5	3.5		2.7	3.5		V
V_{OL}	Low-level output voltage	V_{CC} = MIN, V_{IH} = 2 V, V_{IL} = V_{IL} max	I_{OL} = 4 mA		0.25	0.4		0.25	0.4	V
			I_{OL} = 8 mA					0.35	0.5	
I_I	Input current at maximum input voltage	V_{CC} = MAX,	V_I = 7 V			0.1			0.1	mA
I_{IH}	High-level input current	V_{CC} = MAX,	V_I = 2.7 V			20			20	μA
I_{IL}	Low-level input current	V_{CC} = MAX, V_I = 0.4 V	Enable			−0.4			−0.4	mA
			A, B, C			−0.2			−0.2	
I_{OS}	Short-circuit output current[§]	V_{CC} = MAX		−20		−100	−20		−100	mA
I_{CC}	Supply current	V_{CC} = MAX,	See Note 2		11	18		11	18	mA

[†] For conditions shown as MIN or MAX, use the appropriate value specified under recommended operating conditions.
[‡] All typical values are at V_{CC} = 5 V, T_A = 25°C.
[§] Not more than one output should be shorted at a time, and duration of the short-circuit should not exceed one second.
NOTE 2: I_{CC} is tested with all inputs grounded and all outputs open.

switching characteristics, V_{CC} = 5 V, T_A = 25°C, see note 3

PARAMETER	FROM (INPUT)	TO (OUTPUT)	LEVELS OF DELAY	TEST CONDITIONS	MIN	TYP	MAX	UNIT
t_{PLH}	A, B, C	Y	2			11	17	ns
t_{PHL}			4			25	38	
t_{PLH}	A, B, C	Y	3			16	24	ns
t_{PHL}			3			19	29	
t_{PLH}	Enable $\overline{G2}$	Y	2	C_L = 15 pF, R_L = 2 kΩ, See Note 3		13	21	ns
t_{PHL}			2			16	27	
t_{PLH}	Enable G1	Y	3			14	21	ns
t_{PHL}			3			18	27	
t_{PLH}	Enable $\overline{G}L$	Y	3			18	27	ns
t_{PHL}			4			25	38	

t_{PLH} = propagation delay time, low-to-high-level output.
t_{PHL} = propagation delay time, high-to-low-level output.

NOTE 3: See General Information Section for load circuits and voltage waveforms.

Texas
INSTRUMENTS

DECEMBER 1972 – REVISED APRIL 1985

- **Designed Specifically for High-Speed: Memory Decoders Data Transmission Systems**
- **3 Enable Inputs to Simplify Cascading and/or Data Reception**
- **Schottky-Clamped for High Performance**

description

These Schottky-clamped TTL MSI circuits are designed to be used in high-performance memory decoding or data-routing applications requiring very short propagation delay times. In high-performance memory systems these decoders can be used to minimize the effects of system decoding. When employed with high-speed memories utilizing a fast enable circuit the delay times of these decoders and the enable time of the memory are usually less than the typical access time of the memory. This means that the effective system delay introduced by the Schottky-clamped system decoder is negligible.

The 'LS138 and 'S138A decode one of eight lines dependent on the conditions at the three binary select inputs and the three enable inputs. Two active-low and one active-high enable inputs reduce the need for external gates or inverters when expanding. A 24-line decoder can be implemented without external inverters and a 32-line decoder requires only one inverter. An enable input can be used as a data input for demultiplexing applications.

All of these decoder/demultiplexers feature fully buffered inputs, each of which represents only one normalized load to its driving circuit. All inputs are clamped with high-performance Schottky diodes to suppress line-ringing and to simplify system design.

The SN54LS138 and SN54S138A are characterized for operation over the full military temperature range of −55°C to 125°C. The SN74LS138 and SN74S138A are characterized for operation from 0°C to 70°C.

SN54LS138, SN54S138A . . . J OR W PACKAGE
SN74LS138, SN74S138A . . . D, J OR N PACKAGE
(TOP VIEW)

SN54LS138, SN54S138A . . . FK PACKAGE
SN74LS138, SN74S138A
(TOP VIEW)

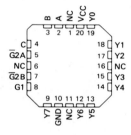

NC - No internal connection

logic symbols

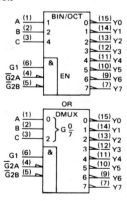

Pin numbers shown on logic notation are for D, J or N packages.

TEXAS INSTRUMENTS

TTL DEVICES

3

logic diagram and function table

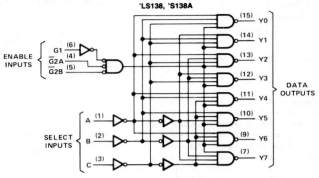

'LS138, 'S138A

Pin numbers shown on logic notation are for D, J or N packages.

'LS138, 'S138A
FUNCTION TABLE

INPUTS					OUTPUTS							
ENABLE		SELECT										
G1	Ḡ2*	C	B	A	Y0	Y1	Y2	Y3	Y4	Y5	Y6	Y7
X	H	X	X	X	H	H	H	H	H	H	H	H
L	X	X	X	X	H	H	H	H	H	H	H	H
H	L	L	L	L	L	H	H	H	H	H	H	H
H	L	L	L	H	H	L	H	H	H	H	H	H
H	L	L	H	L	H	H	L	H	H	H	H	H
H	L	L	H	H	H	H	H	L	H	H	H	H
H	L	H	L	L	H	H	H	H	L	H	H	H
H	L	H	L	H	H	H	H	H	H	L	H	H
H	L	H	H	L	H	H	H	H	H	H	L	H
H	L	H	H	H	H	H	H	H	H	H	H	L

*$\bar{G}2 = \bar{G}2A + \bar{G}2B$

H = high level, L = low level, X = irrelevant

schematics of inputs and outputs

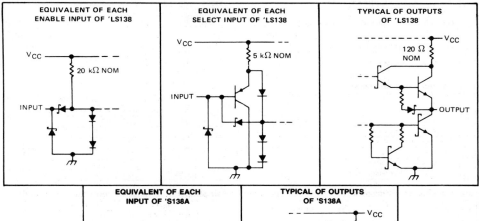

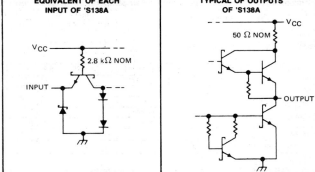

3

TTL DEVICES

absolute maximum ratings over operating free-air temperature range (unless otherwise noted)

Supply voltage, V_{CC} (see Note 1) .... 7 V
Input voltage .... 7 V
Operating free-air temperature range: SN54LS138 .... −55°C to 125°C
SN74LS138 .... 0°C to 70°C
Storage temperature range .... −65°C to 150°C

NOTE 1: Voltage values are with respect to network ground terminal.

recommended operating conditions

		SN54LS138			SN74LS138			UNIT
		MIN	NOM	MAX	MIN	NOM	MAX	
V_{CC}	Supply voltage	4.5	5	5.5	4.75	5	5.25	V
V_{IH}	High-level input voltage	2			2			V
V_{IL}	Low-level input voltage			0.7			0.8	V
I_{OH}	High-level output current			−0.4			−0.4	mA
I_{OL}	Low-level output current			4			8	mA
T_A	Operating free-air temperature	−55		125	0		70	°C

electrical characteristics over recommended operating free-air temperature range (unless otherwise noted)

PARAMETER	TEST CONDITIONS †		SN54LS138			SN74LS138			UNIT
			MIN	TYP‡	MAX	MIN	TYP‡	MAX	
V_{IK}	V_{CC} = MIN, I_I = −18 mA				−1.5			−1.5	V
V_{OH}	V_{CC} = MIN, V_{IH} = 2 V, V_{IL} = MAX, I_{OH} = −0.4 mA		2.5	3.4		2.7	3.4		V
V_{OL}	V_{CC} = MIN, V_{IH} = 2 V, V_{IL} = MAX	I_{OL} = 4 mA		0.25	0.4		0.25	0.4	V
		I_{OL} = 8 mA					0.35	0.5	
I_I	V_{CC} = MAX, V_I = 7 V				0.1			0.1	mA
I_{IH}	V_{CC} = MAX, V_I = 2.7 V				20			20	µA
I_{IL}	V_{CC} = MAX, V_I = 0.4 V	Enable			−0.4			−0.4	mA
		A, B, C			−0.2			−0.2	
I_{OS} §	V_{CC} = MAX		−20		−100	−20		−100	mA
I_{CC}	V_{CC} = MAX, Outputs enabled and open			6.3	10		6.3	10	mA

† For conditions shown as MIN or MAX, use the appropriate value specified under recommended operating conditions.
‡ All typical values are at V_{CC} = 5 V, T_A = 25°C.
§ Not more than one output should be shorted at a time.

switching characteristics, V_{CC} = 5 V, T_A = 25°C

PARAMETER¶	FROM (INPUT)	TO (OUTPUT)	LEVELS OF DELAY	TEST CONDITIONS	SN54LS138 SN74LS138			UNIT
					MIN	TYP	MAX	
t_{PLH}	Binary Select	Any	2	R_L = 2 kΩ, C_L = 15 pF, See Note 2		11	20	ns
t_{PHL}						18	41	ns
t_{PLH}			3			21	27	ns
t_{PHL}						20	39	ns
t_{PLH}	Enable	Any	2			12	18	ns
t_{PHL}						20	32	ns
t_{PLH}			3			14	26	ns
t_{PHL}						13	38	ns

¶ t_{PLH} = propagation delay time, low-to-high-level output; t_{PHL} = propagation delay time, high-to-low-level output.
NOTE 2: See General Information Section for load circuits and voltage waveforms.

TEXAS
INSTRUMENTS

absolute maximum ratings over operating free-air temperature range (unless otherwise noted)

Supply voltage, V_{CC} (see Note 1) .... 7 V

Input voltage .... 5.5 V

Operating free-air temperature range: SN54S138A .... −55°C to 125°C

SN74S138A .... 0°C to 70°C

Storage temperature range .... −65°C to 150°C

NOTE 1: Voltage values are with respect to network ground terminal.

recommended operating conditions

		SN54S138A			SN74S138A			UNIT
		MIN	NOM	MAX	MIN	NOM	MAX	
V_{CC}	Supply voltage	4.5	5	5.5	4.75	5	5.25	V
V_{IH}	High-level input voltage	2			2			V
V_{IL}	Low-level input voltage			0.8			0.8	V
I_{OH}	High-level output current			−1			−1	mA
I_{OL}	Low-level output current			20			20	mA
T_A	Operating free-air temperature	−55		125	0		70	°C

electrical characteristics over recommended operating free-air temperature range (unless otherwise noted)

PARAMETER	TEST CONDITIONS†		SN54S138A SN74S138A‡			UNIT
			MIN	TYP‡	MAX	
V_{IK}	V_{CC} = MIN, I_I = 18 mA				−1.2	V
V_{OH}	V_{CC} = MIN, V_{IH} = 2 V, V_{IL} = 0.8 V, I_{OH} = −1 mA	SN54S′	2.5	3.4		V
		SN74S′	2.7	3.4		
V_{OL}	V_{CC} = MIN, V_{IH} = 2 V, V_{IL} = 0.8 V, I_{OL} = 20 mA				0.5	V
I_I	V_{CC} = MAX, V_I = 5.5 V				1	mA
I_{IH}	V_{CC} = MAX, V_I = 2.7 V				50	µA
I_{IL}	V_{CC} = MAX, V_I = 0.5 V				−2	mA
I_{OS}§	V_{CC} = MAX		−40		−100	mA
I_{CC}	V_{CC} = MAX, Outputs enabled and open	SN54S′		49	74	mA
		SN74S′		49	74	

†For conditions shown as MIN or MAX, use the appropriate value specified under recommended operating conditions.

‡All typical values are at V_{CC} = 5 V, T_A = 25°C.

§Not more than one output should be shorted at a time, and duration of the short circuit test should not exceed one second.

switching characteristics, V_{CC} = 5 V, T_A = 25°C

PARAMETER¶	FROM (INPUT)	TO (OUTPUT)	LEVELS OF DELAY	TEST CONDITIONS	SN54S138A SN74S138A			UNIT
					MIN	TYP	MAX	
t_{PLH}	Binary Select	Any	2			4.5	7	ns
t_{PHL}						7	10.5	
t_{PLH}			3	R_L = 280 Ω, C_L = 15 pF, See Note 2		7.5	12	ns
t_{PHL}						8	12	
t_{PLH}	Enable	Any	2			5	8	ns
t_{PHL}						7	11	
t_{PLH}			3			7	11	ns
t_{PHL}						7	11	

¶ t_{PLH} = propagation delay time, low-to-high-level output

t_{PHL} = propagation delay time, high-to-low-level output

NOTE 2: See General Information Section for load circuits and voltage waveforms.

3

TTL DEVICES

- Designed Specifically for High-Speed:
  Memory Decoders
  Data Transmission Systems

- **Two Fully Independent 2-to-4-Line Decoders/Demultiplexers**

- **Schottky Clamped for High Performance**

description

These Schottky-clamped TTL MSI circuits are designed to be used in high-performance memory decoding or data-routing applications requiring very short propagation delay times. In high-performance memory systems these decoders can be used to minimize the effects of system decoding. When employed with high-speed memories utilizing a fast enable circuit the delay times of these decoders and the enable time of the memory are usually less than the typical access time of the memory. This means that the effective system delay introduced by the Schottky-clamped system decoder is negligible.

The circuit comprises two individual two-line to four-line decoders in a single package. The active-low enable input can be used as a data line in demultiplexing applications.

All of these decoders/demultiplexers feature fully buffered inputs, each of which represents only one normalized load to its driving circuit. All inputs are clamped with high-performance Schottky diodes to suppress line-ringing and to simplify system design. The SN54LS139A and the SN54S139A are characterized for operation range of −55°C to 125°C. The SN74LS139A and the SN74S139A are characterized for operation from 0°C to 70°C.

SN54LS139A, SN54S139A . . . J OR W PACKAGE
SN74LS139A, SN74S139A . . . D, J OR N PACKAGE
(TOP VIEW)

1G̅	1	16	V_{CC}
1A	2	15	2G̅
1B	3	14	2A
1Y0	4	13	2B
1Y1	5	12	2Y0
1Y2	6	11	2Y1
1Y3	7	10	2Y2
GND	8	9	2Y3

SN54LS139A, SN54S139A . . . FK PACKAGE
SN74LS139A, SN74S139A
(TOP VIEW)

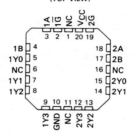

1B	4	18	2A
1Y0	5	17	2B
NC	6	16	NC
1Y1	7	15	2Y0
1Y2	8	14	2Y1

Top pins: 1A 1G̅ NC V_{CC} 2G̅ (3 2 1 20 19)
Bottom pins: 1Y3 GND NC 2Y3 2Y2 (9 10 11 12 13)

NC - No internal connection

logic diagram

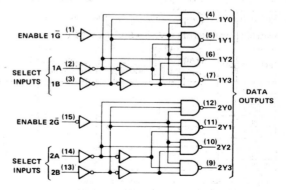

Pin numbers shown on logic notation are for D, J or N packages.

FUNCTION TABLE

INPUTS			OUTPUTS			
ENABLE	SELECT					
G̅	B	A	Y0	Y1	Y2	Y3
H	X	X	H	H	H	H
L	L	L	L	H	H	H
L	L	H	H	L	H	H
L	H	L	H	H	L	H
L	H	H	H	H	H	L

H = high level, L = low level, X = irrelevant

TEXAS
INSTRUMENTS

3
TTL DEVICES

schematics of inputs and outputs

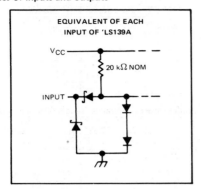

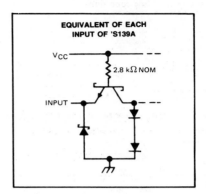

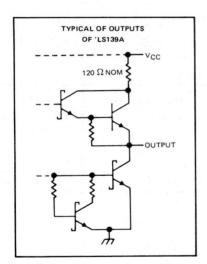

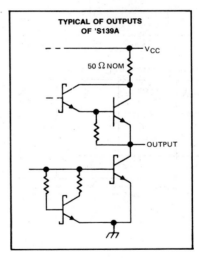

absolute maximum ratings over operating free-air temperature range (unless otherwise noted)

Supply voltage, V$_{CC}$ (see Note 1) . . . . 7 V
Input voltage: 'LS139A, 'LS139 . . . . 7 V
            'S139A . . . . 5.5 V
Operating free-air temperature range: SN54LS139A, SN54S139A . . . . −55°C to 125°C
                    SN74LS139A, SN54S139A . . . . 0°C to 70°C
Storage temperature range . . . . −65°C to 150°C

NOTE 1: Voltage values are with respect to network ground terminal.

TYPES SN54LS139A, SN74LS139A
DUAL 2-LINE TO 4-LINE DECODERS/DEMULTIPLEXERS

recommended operating conditions

		SN54LS139A			SN74LS139A			UNIT
		MIN	NOM	MAX	MIN	NOM	MAX	
V_{CC}	Supply voltage	4.5	5	5.5	4.75	5	5.25	V
V_{IH}	High-level input voltage	2			2			V
V_{IL}	Low-level input voltage			0.7			0.8	V
I_{OH}	High-level output current			-0.4			-0.4	mA
I_{OL}	Low-level output current			4			8	mA
T_A	Operating free-air temperature	-55		125	0		70	$^\circ$C

electrical characteristics over recommended operating free-air temperature range (unless otherwise noted)

PARAMETER	TEST CONDITIONS †			SN54LS139A			SN74LS139A			UNIT
				MIN	TYP‡	MAX	MIN	TYP‡	MAX	
V_{IK}	V_{CC} = MIN,	$I_I = -18$ mA				-1.5			-1.5	V
V_{OH}	V_{CC} = MIN,	V_{IH} = 2 V,	V_{IL} = MAX,	2.5	3.4		2.7	3.4		V
	$I_{OH} = -0.4$ mA									
V_{OL}	V_{CC} = MIN,	V_{IH} = 2 V,	I_{OL} = 4 mA		0.25	0.4		0.25	0.4	V
	V_{IL} = MAX		I_{OL} = 8 mA					0.35	0.5	
I_I	V_{CC} = MAX,	V_I = 7V				0.1			0.1	mA
I_{IH}	V_{CC} = MAX,	V_I = 2.7 V				20			20	μA
I_{IL}	V_{CC} = MAX,	V_I = 0.4 V				-0.4			-0.4	mA
I_{OS}	V_{CC} = MAX			-20		-100	-20		-100	mA
I_{CC}	V_{CC} = MAX,	Outputs enabled and open			6.8	11		6.8	11	mA

switching characteristics, V_{CC} = 5 V, T_A = 25°C (see note 2)

PARAMETER¶	FROM (INPUT)	TO (OUTPUT)	LEVELS OF DELAY	TEST CONDITIONS	SN54LS139A SN74LS139A			UNIT
					MIN	TYP	MAX	
t_{PLH}	Binary Select	Any	2	$R_L = 2$ kΩ, C_L = 15 pF		13	20	ns
t_{PHL}						22	33	ns
t_{PLH}			3			18	29	ns
t_{PHL}						25	38	ns
t_{PLH}	Enable	Any	2			16	24	ns
t_{PHL}						21	32	ns

¶ t_{PLH} = propagation delay time, low to high level output; t_{PHL} = propagation delay time, high-to-low-level output.
NOTE 2: See General Information Section for load circuits and voltage waveforms.

3

TTL DEVICES

TEXAS INSTRUMENTS

recommended operating conditions

		SN54S139A			SN74S139A			UNIT
		MIN	NOM	MAX	MIN	NOM	MAX	
V_{CC}	Supply voltage	4.5	5	5.5	4.75	5	5.25	V
V_{IH}	High-level input voltage	2			2			V
V_{IL}	Low-level input voltage			0.8			0.8	V
I_{OH}	High-level output current			−1			−1	mA
I_{OL}	Low-level output current			20			20	mA
T_A	Operating free-air temperature	−55		125	0		70	°C

electrical characteristics over recommended operating free-air temperature range (unless otherwise noted)

PARAMETER	TEST CONDITIONS†				SN54S139A SN74S139A			UNIT
					MIN	TYP‡	MAX	
V_{IK}	V_{CC} = MIN,	I_I = 18 mA					−1.2	V
V_{OH}	V_{CC} = MIN	V_{IH} = 2 V,	V_{IL} = 0.8 V,	SN54S'	2.5	3.4		V
	I_{OH} = −1 mA			SN74S'	2.7	3.4		
V_{OL}	V_{CC} = MIN,	V_{IH} = 2 V,	V_{IL} = 0.8 V,				0.5	V
	I_{OL} = 20 mA							
I_I	V_{CC} = MAX,	V_I = 5.5 V					1	mA
I_{IH}	V_{CC} = MAX,	V_I = 2.7 V					50	µA
I_{IL}	V_{CC} = MAX,	V_I = 0.5 V					−2	mA
I_{OS}§	V_{CC} = MAX				−40		−100	mA
I_{CC}	V_{CC} = MAX,	Outputs enabled and open		SN54S'		60	90	mA
				SN74S'		60	90	

†For conditions shown as MIN or MAX, use the appropriate value specified under recommended operating conditions.
‡All typical values are at V_{CC} = 5 V, T_A = 25°C.
§Not more than one output should be shorted at a time, and duration of the short circuit test should not exceed one second.

switching characteristics, V_{CC} = 5 V, T_A = 25°C (see note 2)

PARAMETER¶	FROM (INPUT)	TO (OUTPUT)	LEVELS OF DELAY	TEST CONDITIONS	SN54S139A SN74S139A			UNIT
					MIN	TYP	MAX	
t_{PLH}	Binary Select	Any	2			5	7.5	ns
t_{PHL}						6.5	10	ns
t_{PLH}			3	R_L = 280 Ω, C_L = 15 pF		7	12	ns
t_{PHL}						8	12	ns
t_{PLH}	Enable	Any	2			5	8	ns
t_{PHL}						6.5	10	ns

¶ t_{PLH} = propagation delay time, low to high-level output
t_{PHL} = propagation delay time, high to low-level output
NOTE 2: See General Information Section for load circuits and voltage waveforms.

3

TTL DEVICES

- **Package Options Include Both Plastic and Ceramic Chip Carriers in Addition to Plastic and Ceramic DIPs**

- **Dependable Texas Instruments Quality and Reliability**

description

These devices contain two independent 4-input positive-NAND 50-ohm line drivers. They perform the Boolean function $Y = \overline{ABCD}$.

The SN54S140 is characterized for operation over the full military temperature range of $-55°C$ to $125°C$. The SN74S140 is characterized for operation from $0°C$ to $70°C$.

logic diagram (each driver)

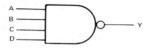

SN54S140 . . . J OR W PACKAGE
SN74S140 . . . D, J OR N PACKAGE
(TOP VIEW)

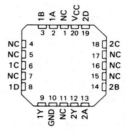

SN54S140 . . . FK PACKAGE
SN74S140

(TOP VIEW)

NC - No internal connection

TEXAS INSTRUMENTS

3

TTL DEVICES

schematic (each driver)

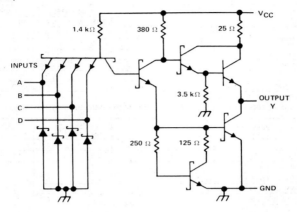

Resistor values shown are nominal.

absolute maximum ratings over operating free-air temperature range (unless otherwise noted)

Supply voltage, V_{CC} (see Note 1) .... 7 V
Input voltage .... 5.5 V
Operating free-air temperature range: SN54' .... -55°C to 125°C
　　　　　　　　　　　　　　　　　SN74' .... 0°C to 70°C
Storage temperature range .... -65°C to 150°C

NOTE 1: Voltage values are with respect to network ground terminal.

3

TTL DEVICES

TYPES SN54S140, SN74S140
DUAL 4-INPUT POSITIVE-NAND 50-OHM LINE DRIVERS

recommended operating conditions

		SN54S140			SN74S140			UNIT
		MIN	NOM	MAX	MIN	NOM	MAX	
V_{CC}	Supply voltage	4.5	5	5.5	4.75	5	5.25	V
V_{IH}	High-level input voltage	2			2			V
V_{IL}	Low-level input voltage			0.8			0.8	V
I_{OH}	High-level output current			-40			-40	mA
I_{OL}	Low-level output current			60			60	mA
T_A	Operating free-air temperature	-55		125	0		70	$^\circ$C

electrical characteristics over recommended operating free-air temperature range (unless otherwise noted)

PARAMETER	TEST CONDITIONS†			SN54S140			SN74S140			UNIT
			MIN	TYP‡	MAX	MIN	TYP‡	MAX		
V_{IK}	V_{CC} = MIN,	$I_I = -18$ mA			-1.2			-1.2		V
V_{OH}	V_{CC} = MIN,	V_{IL} = 0.8 V, $I_{OH} = -3$ mA	2.5	3.4		2.7	3.4			V
	V_{CC} = MIN,	V_{IL} = 0.5 V, R_O = 50 Ω to GND	2			2				
V_{OL}	V_{CC} = MIN,	V_{IH} = 2 V, I_{OL} = 60 mA			0.5			0.5		V
I_I	V_{CC} = MAX,	V_I = 5.5 V			1			1		mA
I_{IH}	V_{CC} = MAX,	V_{IH} = 2.7 V			0.1			0.1		mA
I_{IL}	V_{CC} = MAX,	V_{IL} = 0.5 V			-4			-4		mA
I_{OS} §	V_{CC} = MAX		-50		-225	-50		-225		mA
I_{CCH}	V_{CC} = MAX,	V_I = 0 V		10	18		10	18		mA
I_{CCL}	V_{CC} = MAX,	V_I = 4.5 V		25	44		25	44		mA

† For conditions shown as MIN or MAX, use the appropriate value specified under recommended operating conditions.
‡ All typical values are at V_{CC} = 5 V, T_A = 25°C.
§ Not more than one output should be shorted at a time, and the duration of the short circuit should not exceed 100 milliseconds.

switching characteristics, V_{CC} = 5 V, T_A = 25°C (see note 2)

PARAMETER	FROM (INPUT)	TO (OUTPUT)	TEST CONDITIONS		MIN	TYP	MAX	UNIT
t_{PLH}	Any	Y	R_L = 93 Ω,	C_L = 50 pF		4	6.5	ns
t_{PHL}						4	6.5	ns
t_{PLH}			R_L = 93 Ω,	C_L = 150 pF		6		ns
t_{PHL}						6		ns

NOTE 2: See General Information Section for load circuits and voltage waveforms.

TEXAS
INSTRUMENTS

3

TTL DEVICES

NOVEMBER 1971 – REVISED DECEMBER 1983

- **Choice of Driver Outputs:**

  SN54143 and SN74143 have 15 mA Constant-Current Outputs for Driving Common-Anode LED's such as TIL302 or TIL303 without Series Resistors

- **Universal Logic Capabilities:**

  Ripple Blanking of Extraneous Zeros
  Latch Outputs Can Drive Logic Processors Simultaneously

  Decimal Point Driver Is Included

- **Synchronous BCD Counter Capability Includes:**

  Cascadable to N-Bits

  Look-Ahead-Enable Techniques Minimize Speed Degradation When Cascaded for Large-Word Display

  Direct Clear Input

SN54143 ... J OR W PACKAGE
SN74143 ... J OR N PACKAGE
(TOP VIEW)

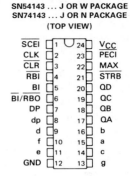

$\overline{SCEI}$	1	24	V_{CC}
CLK	2	23	PECI
$\overline{CLR}$	3	22	MAX
$\overline{RBI}$	4	21	$\overline{STRB}$
$\overline{BI}$	5	20	QD
$\overline{BI/RBO}$	6	19	QC
DP	7	18	QB
dp	8	17	QA
d	9	16	b
f	10	15	a
e	11	14	c
GND	12	13	g

description

These TTL MSI circuits contain the equivalent of 86 gates on a single chip. Logic inputs and outputs are completely TTL compatible. The buffered inputs are implemented with relatively large resistors in series with the bases of the input transistors to lower drive-current requirements to one-half of that required for a standard Series 54/74 input. The serial-count-enable, actually two internal emitters, is rated as one standard Series 54/74 load. The logic outputs, except $\overline{RBO}$, have active pull-ups.

The SN54143 and SN74143 driver outputs are designed specifically to maintain a relatively constant on-level sink current of approximately 15 milliamperes from output "a" through "g" and seven milliamperes from output "dp" over a voltage range from one to five volts. Any number of LED's in series may be driven as long as the output voltage rating is not exceeded.

All inputs are diode-clamped to minimize transmission-line effects, thereby simplifying system design. Maximum clock frequency is typically 18 megahertz and power dissipation is typically 280 milliwatts. The SN54143 is characterized for operation over the full military temperature range of –55°C to 125°C; the SN74143 is characterized for operation from 0°C to 70°C.

TEXAS INSTRUMENTS

3-423

3

TTL DEVICES

TYPES SN54143, SN74143
4-BIT COUNTER/LATCH, SEVEN-SEGMENT LED/LAMP DRIVERS

description (continued)

Functions of the inputs and outputs of these devices are as follows:

FUNCTION	PIN NO.	DESCRIPTION
CLEAR INPUT	3	When low, resets and holds counter at 0. Must be high for normal counting.
CLOCK INPUT	2	Each positive-going transition will increment the counter provided that the circuit is in the normal counting mode (serial and parallel count enable inputs low, clear input high).
PARALLEL COUNT ENABLE INPUT (PCEI)	23	Must be low for normal counting mode. When high, counter will be inhibited. Logic level must not be changed when the clock is low.
SERIAL COUNT ENABLE INPUT (SCEI)	1	Must be low for normal counting mode, also must be low to enable maximum count output to go low. When high, counter will be inhibited and maximum count output will be driven high. Logic level must not be changed when the clock is low.
MAXIMUM COUNT OUTPUT	22	Will go low when the counter is at 9 and serial count enable input is low. Will return high when the counter changes to 0 and will remain high during counts 1 through 8. Will remain high (inhibited) as long as serial count enable input is high.
LATCH STROBE INPUT	21	When low, data in latches follow the data in the counter. When high, the data in the latches are held constant, and the counter may be operated independently.
LATCH OUTPUTS (Q_A, Q_B, Q_C, Q_D)	17, 18, 19, 20	The BCD data that drives the decoder can be stored in the 4-bit latch and is available at these outputs for driving other logic and/or processors. The binary weights of the outputs are: $Q_A = 1$, $Q_B = 2$, $Q_C = 4$, $Q_D = 8$.
DECIMAL POINT INPUT	7	Must be high to display decimal point. The decimal point is not displayed when this input is low or when the display is blanked.
BLANKING INPUT ($\overline{BI}$)	5	When high, will blank (turn off) the entire display and force $\overline{RBO}$ low. Must be low for normal display. May be pulsed to implement intensity control of the display.
RIPPLE-BLANKING INPUT ($\overline{RBI}$)	4	When the data in the latches is BCD 0, a low input will blank the entire display and force the $\overline{RBO}$ low. This input has no effect if the data in the latches is other than 0.
RIPPLE-BLANKING OUTPUT ($\overline{RBO}$)	6	Supplies ripple blanking information for the ripple blanking input of the next decade. Provides a low if $\overline{BI}$ is high, or if $\overline{RBI}$ is low and the data in the latches in BCD 0; otherwise, this output is high. This pin has a resistive pull-up circuit suitable for performing a wire-AND function with any open-collector output. Whenever this pin is low the entire display will be blanked; therefore, this pin may be used as an active-low blanking input.
LED/LAMP DRIVER OUTPUTS (a, b, c, d, e, f, g, dp)	15, 16, 14, 9 11, 10, 13, 8	Outputs for driving seven-segment LED's or lamps and their decimal points. See segment identification and resultant displays on following page.

SEGMENT IDENTIFICATION

NUMERICAL DESIGNATIONS—RESULTANT DISPLAYS

3-424

logic diagram

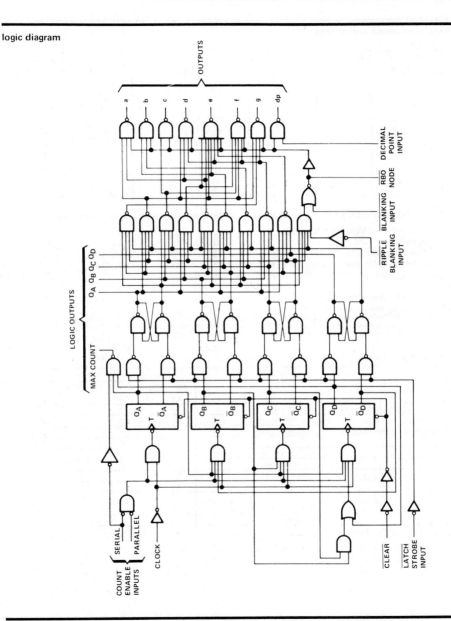

TEXAS
INSTRUMENTS

TTL DEVICES

3

schematic of inputs and outputs

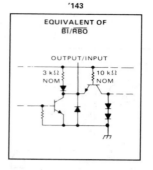

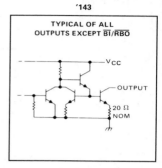

'143 — TYPICAL OF ALL OUTPUTS EXCEPT $\overline{BI}/\overline{RBO}$

absolute maximum ratings over operating free-air temperature range (unless otherwise noted)

Supply voltage, V_{CC} (see Note 1) .... 7 V
Input voltage .... 5.5 V
Off-state current at outputs "a" thru "g" and "dp", '143 .... 250 μA
Continuous total power dissipation at (or below) 70°C free-air temperature (see Note 2) . 1.4 W
Operating free-air temperature range: SN54' Circuits .... −55°C to 125°C
               SN74' Circuits .... 0°C to 70°C
Storage temperatur range .... −65°C to 150°C

NOTES: 1. Voltage values are with respect to network ground terminal.
     2. For the SN54143 in the N and W packages, this rating applies at (or below) 80°C free-air temperature. For operation above this temperature, derate linearly at the rate of 11,7 mW/°C for the W package and 14,7 mW/°C for the N package. No derating is required for these devices in the J package.

recommended operating conditions

		SN54143			SN74143			UNIT
		MIN	NOM	MAX	MIN	NOM	MAX	
Supply voltage, V_{CC}		4.5	5	5.5	4.75	5	5.25	V
On-state voltage at outputs a thru g and dp ('143 only)		1		5	1		5	V
High-level output current, I_{OH}	Q_A, Q_B, Q_C, Q_D			−240			−240	μA
	Maximum count			−560			−560	
	$\overline{RBO}$			−120			−120	
Low-level output current, I_{OL}	Q_A, Q_B, Q_C, Q_D, $\overline{RBO}$			4.8			4.8	mA
	Maximum count			11.2			11.2	
Clock pulse width, $t_{w(clock)}$	High logic level	25			25			ns
	Low logic level	55			55			
Clear pulse width, $t_{w(clear)}$		25			25			ns
Setup time, t_{su}	Serial and parallel carry	30†			30†			ns
	Clear inactive state	60†			60†			
Operating free-air temperature, T_A		−55		125	0		70	°C

† The arrow indicates that the rising edge of the clock pulse is used for reference.

TEXAS
INSTRUMENTS

electrical characteristics over recommended operating free-air temperature range (unless otherwise noted)

PARAMETER		TEST CONDITIONS[†]	SN54143, SN74143 MIN	TYP[*]	MAX	UNIT
V_{IH}	High-level input voltage		2			V
V_{IL}	Low-level input voltage				0.8	V
V_{IK}	Input clamp voltage	V_{CC} = MIN, I_I = 12 mA			1.5	V
V_{OH} High-level output voltage	$\overline{RBO}$	V_{CC} = MIN, V_{IH} = 2 V,	2.4			V
	Q_A, Q_B, Q_C, Q_D	V_{IL} = 0.8 V, I_{OH} = MAX				
	Maximum count					
V_{OL} Low-level output voltage	$Q_A, Q_B, Q_C, Q_D, \overline{RBO}$	V_{CC} = MIN, V_{IH} = 2 V,			0.4	V
	Maximum count	V_{IL} = 0.8 V, I_{OL} = MAX				
$V_{O (off)}$ Off-state output voltage	Outputs a thru g, dp	V_{CC} = MAX, I_{OH} = 250 μA	7			V
$V_{O (on)}$ On-state output voltage	Outputs a thru g, dp	V_{CC} = MIN				V
$I_{O (on)}$ On-state output current	Outputs a thru g	V_{CC} = MIN, V_O = 1 V	9	15		mA
		V_{CC} = 5 V, V_O = 2 V		15		
		V_{CC} = MAX, V_O = 5 V		15	22	
	Output dp	V_{CC} = MIN, V_O = 1 V	4.5	7		
		V_{CC} = 5 V, V_O = 2 V		7		
		V_{CC} = MAX, V_O = 5 V		7	12	
I_I	Input current at maximum input voltage	V_{CC} = MAX, V_I = 5.5 V			1	mA
I_{IH} High-level input current	Serial carry				40	μA
	$\overline{RBO}$ node	V_{CC} = MAX, V_I = 2.4 V	−0.12	−0.5		mA
	Other inputs				20	μA
I_{IL} Low-level input current	Serial carry				1.6	
	$\overline{RBO}$ node	V_{CC} = MAX, V_I = 0.4 V,		−1.5	−2.4	mA
	Other inputs	See Note 3			−0.8	
I_{OS} Short-circuit output current	Q_A, Q_B, Q_C, Q_D	V_{CC} = MAX	−9		27.5	mA
	Maximum count		−15		55	
I_{CC}	Supply current	V_{CC} = MAX, See Note 4		56	93	mA

[†] For conditions shown as MIN or MAX, use the appropriate value specified under recommended operating conditions for the applicable type.
[*] All typical values are at V_{CC} = 5 V, T_A = 25°C.
NOTES: 3. I_{IL} at $\overline{RBO}$ node is tested with $\overline{BI}$ grounded and RBI at 4.5 V.
       4. I_{CC} is measured after the following conditions are established:
         a) $\overline{Strobe}$ = $\overline{RBI}$ = DP = 4.5 V
         b) Parallel count enable = serial count enable = $\overline{BI}$ = GND
         c) Clear (⎍) then clock until all outputs are on (8)
         d) For '143, outputs "a" through "g" and "dp" = 2.5 V, all other outputs open.

switching characteristics, V_{CC} = 5 V, T_A = 25

PARAMETER[§]	FROM (INPUT)	TO (OUTPUT)	TEST CONDITIONS	MIN	TYP	MAX	UNIT
f_{max}				12	18		MHz
t_{PLH}	Serial look-ahead	Maximum count	C_L 15 pF, R_L 560 Ω, See Note 5		12	20	ns
t_{PHL}					23	35	
t_{PLH}	Clock	Maximum count			26	40	ns
t_{PHL}					29	45	
t_{PLH}	Clock	Q_A, Q_B, Q_C, Q_D	C_L 15 pF, R_L 1.2 kΩ, See Note 5		28	45	ns
t_{PHL}					38	60	
t_{PHL}	$\overline{Clear}$	Q_A, Q_B, Q_C, Q_D			57	90	ns

[§] f_{max} = Maximum clock frequency, t_{PLH} = Propagation delay time, low to high level output.
t_{PHL} = Propagation delay time, high to low level output.
NOTE 5: See General Information Section for load circuits and voltage waveforms.

TEXAS INSTRUMENTS

3

TTL DEVICES

TYPICAL APPLICATION DATA

This application demonstrates how the drivers may be cascaded for N-bit display applications. It features:

Synchronous, look-ahead counting

Ripple blanking of leading zeros; blanking of trailing zeros (not illustrated) can also be implemented

Overriding blanking for total suppression or intensity modulation of display

Direct parallel clear

Latch strobe permits counter to acquire next display while viewing current display

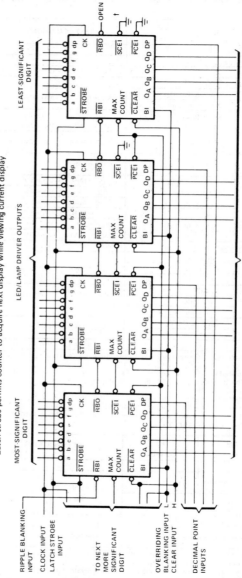

MOST SIGNIFICANT DIGIT

LEAST-SIGNIFICANT DIGIT

LED/LAMP DRIVER OUTPUTS

LATCH LOGIC OUTPUTS

RIPPLE BLANKING INPUT

CLOCK INPUT

LATCH STROBE INPUT

TO NEXT MORE SIGNIFICANT DIGIT

OVERRIDING BLANKING INPUT

CLEAR INPUT

DECIMAL POINT INPUTS

†The serial count-enable input of the least-significant digit is normally grounded; however, it may be used as a count-enable control for the entire counter (high to disable, low to count) provided the logic level on this pin is not changed while the clock line is low or false counting may result.

TEXAS
INSTRUMENTS

FUNCTION TABLE

FUNCTION	CLOCK PULSE	CLEAR	LATCH STROBE	RBI	BI	DECIMAL INPUT	SERIAL CARRY	PARALLEL CARRY	RBI/RBO	MAXIMUM COUNT OUTPUT	QD	QC	QB	QA	a	b	c	d	e	f	g	dp	TYPICAL DISPLAY	NOTES
Clear Ripple Blank		L	L	L	X	X	X	X	L	L	L	L	L	L	OFF	OFF	OFF	OFF	OFF	OFF	OFF	OFF	None	A, E
Blank		H	L	X	X	X	X	X	L	H	L	L	L	L	OFF	OFF	OFF	OFF	OFF	OFF	OFF	OFF	None	A, D, E
Decimal	0	H	L	H	L	H	L	L	H	H	L	L	L	L	ON	ON	ON	ON	ON	ON	OFF	ON	0.	B
	1	H	L	H	L	L	L	L	H	H	L	L	L	H	OFF	ON	ON	OFF	OFF	OFF	OFF	OFF	1	B
	2	H	L	H	L	L	L	L	H	H	L	L	H	L	ON	ON	OFF	ON	ON	OFF	ON	OFF	2	B
	3	H	L	H	L	L	L	L	H	H	L	L	H	H	ON	ON	ON	ON	OFF	OFF	ON	OFF	3	B
	4	H	L	H	L	L	L	L	H	H	L	H	L	L	OFF	ON	ON	OFF	OFF	ON	ON	OFF	4	B
	5	H	L	H	L	L	L	L	H	H	L	H	L	H	ON	OFF	ON	ON	OFF	ON	ON	OFF	5	B
	6	H	L	H	L	L	L	L	H	H	L	H	H	L	ON	OFF	ON	ON	ON	ON	ON	OFF	6	B
	7	H	L	H	L	L	L	L	H	H	L	H	H	H	ON	ON	ON	OFF	OFF	OFF	OFF	OFF	7	B, C
	8	H	L	H	L	L	L	L	H	H	H	L	L	L	ON	ON	ON	ON	ON	ON	ON	OFF	8	B
	9	H	L	H	L	L	L	L	H	L	H	L	L	H	ON	ON	ON	ON	OFF	ON	ON	OFF	9	B
	0	H	L	H	L	L	L	L	H	H	L	L	L	L	ON	ON	ON	ON	ON	ON	OFF	OFF	0	B
	1	H	L	H	L	L	L	L	H	H	L	L	L	H	OFF	ON	ON	OFF	OFF	OFF	OFF	OFF	1	B
	2	H	L	H	L	L	L	L	H	H	L	L	H	L	ON	ON	OFF	ON	ON	OFF	ON	OFF	2	B
	3	H	L	H	L	L	L	L	H	H	L	L	H	H	ON	ON	ON	ON	OFF	OFF	ON	OFF	3	B
	4	H	L	H	L	L	L	L	H	H	L	H	L	L	OFF	ON	ON	OFF	OFF	ON	ON	OFF	4	B
	5	H	L	H	L	L	L	L	H	H	L	H	L	H	ON	OFF	ON	ON	OFF	ON	ON	OFF	5	B
	6	H	L	H	L	L	L	L	H	H	L	H	H	L	ON	OFF	ON	ON	ON	ON	ON	OFF	6	B
Latch	7	H	H	H	L	L	L	L	H	H	L	H	H	H	ON	ON	ON	OFF	OFF	OFF	OFF	OFF	7	B
Latch	8	H	H	H	L	L	L	L	H	H	H	L	L	L	ON	ON	ON	ON	ON	ON	ON	OFF	8	B
	9	H	L	H	L	L	L	L	H	L	H	L	L	H	ON	ON	ON	ON	OFF	ON	ON	OFF	9	B
Ripple Blank	0	H	L	L	X	L	L	L	L	H	L	L	L	L	OFF	OFF	OFF	OFF	OFF	OFF	OFF	OFF	None	A, B, E

SEGMENT IDENTIFICATION

NOTES:
A. RBI/RBO is wire-AND logic serving as ripple blanking input (RBI) and/or ripple blanking output (RBO).
B. The blanking input (BI) must be low when functions DECIMAL/0 through 20/RIPPLE BLANK are desired.
C. The ripple-blanking input (RBI) must be open or high to display a zero during the decimal 0 input.
D. When a high logic level is applied directly to the blanking input (BI) all segment outputs are off regardless of any other input condition.
E. When the ripple-blanking input (RBI) and outputs Q_A through Q_D are at a low logic level, all segment outputs are off and the ripple-blanking output (RBO) goes to a low logic level (response condition).

FOR USE AS LAMP, RELAY, OR MOS DRIVERS

- Full Decoding of Input Logic
- SN54145, SN74145, and SN74LS145 Have 80-mA Sink-Current Capability
- All Outputs Are Off for Invalid BCD Input Conditions
- Low Power Dissipation of 'LS145 ... 35 mW Typical

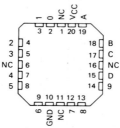

SN54145, SN54LS145 . . . J OR W PACKAGE
SN74145 . . . J OR N PACKAGE
SN74LS145 . . . D, J OR N PACKAGE
(TOP VIEW)

0	1	16	V_CC
1	2	15	A
2	3	14	B
3	4	13	C
4	5	12	D
5	6	11	9
6	7	10	8
GND	8	9	7

SN54LS145 . . . FK PACKAGE
SN74LS145
(TOP VIEW)

NC - No internal connection

logic

FUNCTION TABLE

NO.	INPUTS				OUTPUTS									
	D	C	B	A	0	1	2	3	4	5	6	7	8	9
0	L	L	L	L	L	H	H	H	H	H	H	H	H	H
1	L	L	L	H	H	L	H	H	H	H	H	H	H	H
2	L	L	H	L	H	H	L	H	H	H	H	H	H	H
3	L	L	H	H	H	H	H	L	H	H	H	H	H	H
4	L	H	L	L	H	H	H	H	L	H	H	H	H	H
5	L	H	L	H	H	H	H	H	H	L	H	H	H	H
6	L	H	H	L	H	H	H	H	H	H	L	H	H	H
7	L	H	H	H	H	H	H	H	H	H	H	L	H	H
8	H	L	L	L	H	H	H	H	H	H	H	H	L	H
9	H	L	L	H	H	H	H	H	H	H	H	H	H	L
INVALID	H	L	H	L	H	H	H	H	H	H	H	H	H	H
	H	L	H	H	H	H	H	H	H	H	H	H	H	H
	H	H	L	L	H	H	H	H	H	H	H	H	H	H
	H	H	L	H	H	H	H	H	H	H	H	H	H	H
	H	H	H	L	H	H	H	H	H	H	H	H	H	H
	H	H	H	H	H	H	H	H	H	H	H	H	H	H

H – high level (off), L = low level (on)

description

These monolithic BCD-to-decimal decoder/drivers consist of eight inverters and ten four-input NAND gates. The inverters are connected in pairs to make BCD input data available for decoding by the NAND gates. Full decoding of valid BCD input logic ensures that all outputs remain off for all invalid binary input conditions. These decoders feature high-performance, n-p-n output transistors designed for use as indicator/relay drivers or as open-collector logic-circuit drivers. Each of the high-breakdown output transistors (15 volts) of the SN54145, SN74145, or SN74LS145 will sink up to 80 milliamperes of current. Each input is one Series 54/74 or Series 54LS/74LS standard load, respectively. Inputs and outputs are entirely compatible for use with TTL or DTL logic circuits, and the outputs are compatible for interfacing with most MOS integrated circuits. Power dissipation is typically 215 milliwatts for the '145 and 35 milliwatts for the 'LS145.

logic diagram

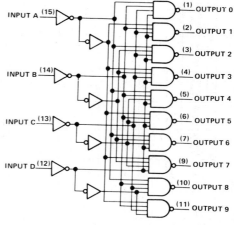

Pin numbers shown on logic notation are for D, J or N packages.

TEXAS
INSTRUMENTS

3
TTL DEVICES

absolute maximum ratings over operating free-air temperature range (unless otherwise noted)

Supply voltage, V_{CC} (see Note 1) . . . . 7 V
Input voltage . . . . 5.5 V
Maximum current into any output (off-state) . . . . 1 mA
Operating free-air temperature range: SN54145 . . . . −55°C to 125°C
SN74145 . . . . 0°C to 70°C
Storage temperature range . . . . −65°C to 150°C

NOTE 1: Voltage values are with respect to network ground terminal.

recommended operating conditions

	SN54145			SN74145			UNIT
	MIN	NOM	MAX	MIN	NOM	MAX	
Supply voltage, V_{CC}	4.5	5	5.5	4.75	5	5.25	V
Off-state output voltage, $V_{O(off)}$			15			15	V
Operating free-air temperature, T_A	−55		125	0		70	°C

electrical characteristics over recommended operating free-air temperature range (unless otherwise noted)

	PARAMETER	TEST CONDITIONS†		MIN	TYP‡	MAX	UNIT
V_{IH}	High-level input voltage			2			V
V_{IL}	Low-level input voltage					0.8	V
V_{IK}	Input clamp voltage	V_{CC} = MIN, I_I = −12 mA				−1.5	V
$I_{O(off)}$	Off-state output current	V_{CC} = MIN, V_{IH} = 2 V, V_{IL} = 0.8 V, $V_{O(off)}$ = 15 V				250	µA
$V_{O(on)}$	On-state output voltage	V_{CC} = MIN, V_{IH} = 2 V, V_{IL} = 0.8 V	$I_{O(on)}$ = 80 mA		0.5	0.9	V
			$I_{O(on)}$ = 20 mA			0.4	
I_I	Input current at maximum input voltage	V_{CC} = MAX, V_I = 5.5 V				1	mA
I_{IH}	High-level input current	V_{CC} = MAX, V_I = 2.4 V				40	µA
I_{IL}	Low-level input current	V_{CC} = MAX, V_I = 0.4 V				−1.6	mA
I_{CC}	Supply current	V_{CC} = MAX, See Note 2	SN54145		43	62	mA
			SN74145		43	70	

† For conditions shown as MIN or MAX, use the appropriate value specified under recommended operating conditions.
‡ All typical values are at V_{CC} = 5 V, T_A = 25 C.
NOTE 2: I_{CC} is measured with all inputs grounded and outputs open.

switching characteristics, V_{CC} = 5 V, T_A = 25°C

	PARAMETER	TEST CONDITIONS	MIN	MAX	UNIT
t_{PLH}	Propagation delay time, low-to-high-level output	C_L = 15 pF, R_L = 100 Ω, See Note 3		50	ns
t_{PHL}	Propagation delay time, high-to-low-level output			50	ns

NOTE 3: See General Information Section for load circuits and voltage waveforms.

schematics of inputs and outputs

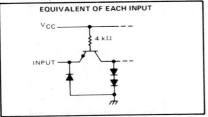

EQUIVALENT OF EACH INPUT

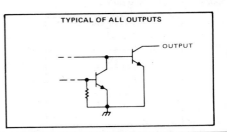

TYPICAL OF ALL OUTPUTS

TTL DEVICES

3

absolute maximum ratings over operating free-air temperature range (unless otherwise noted)

Supply voltage, V_{CC} (see Note 1) . . . . 7 V
Input voltage . . . . 7 V
Operating free-air temperature range: SN54LS145 . . . . -55°C to 125°C
                                   SN74LS145 . . . . 0°C to 70°C
Storage temperature range . . . . -65°C to 150°C

NOTE 1: Voltage values are with respect to network ground terminal.

recommended operating conditions

	SN54LS145			SN74LS145			UNIT
	MIN	NOM	MAX	MIN	NOM	MAX	
Supply voltage, V_{CC}	4.5	5	5.5	4.75	5	5.25	V
Off-state output voltage, $V_{O(off)}$			15			15	V
Operating free-air temperature, T_A	-55		125	0		70	$^\circ$C

electrical characteristics over recommended operating free-air temperature range (unless otherwise noted)

PARAMETER		TEST CONDITIONS†		SN54LS145			SN74LS145			UNIT
				MIN	TYP‡	MAX	MIN	TYP‡	MAX	
V_{IH}	High-level input voltage			2			2			V
V_{IL}	Low-level input voltage					0.7			0.8	V
V_{IK}	Input clamp voltage	V_{CC} = MIN,	I_I = -18 mA			-1.5			-1.5	V
$I_{O(off)}$	Off-state output current	V_{CC} = MIN, V_{IL} = V_{IL} max,	V_{IH} = 2 V, V_{OH} = 15 V			250			250	µA
$V_{O(on)}$	On-state output voltage	V_{CC} = MIN, V_{IH} = 2 V, V_{IL} = V_{IL} max	I_{OL} = 12 mA	0.25		0.4	0.25		0.4	V
			I_{OL} = 24 mA				0.35		0.5	
			I_{OL} = 80 mA					2.3	3	
I_I	Input current at maximum input voltage	V_{CC} = MAX,	V_I = 7 V			0.1			0.1	mA
I_{IH}	High-level input current	V_{CC} = MAX,	V_I = 2.7 V			20			20	µA
I_{IL}	Low-level input current	V_{CC} = MAX,	V_I = 0.4 V			-0.4			-0.4	mA
I_{CC}	Supply current	V_{CC} = MAX,	See Note 2	7		13	7		13	mA

†For conditions shown as MIN or MAX, use the appropriate value specified under recommended operating conditions.
‡All typical values are at V_{CC} = 5 V, T_A = 25°C.
NOTE 2: I_{CC} is measured with all inputs grounded and outputs open.

switching characteristics, V_{CC} = 5 V, T_A = 25°C

PARAMETER		TEST CONDITIONS	MIN	MAX	UNIT
t_{PLH}	Propagation delay time, low-to-high-level output	C_L = 45 pF, R_L = 665 Ω, See Note 3		50	ns
t_{PHL}	Propagation delay time, high-to-low-level output			50	ns

NOTE 3: See General Information Section for load circuits and voltage waveforms.

schematic of inputs and outputs

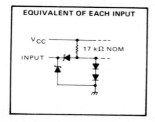

EQUIVALENT OF EACH INPUT

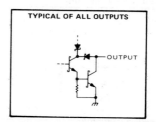

TYPICAL OF ALL OUTPUTS

3

TTL DEVICES

TEXAS
INSTRUMENTS

'147, 'LS147

- Encodes 10-Line Decimal to 4-Line BCD

- Applications Include:

  Keyboard Encoding
  Range Selection: '148, 'LS148

- Encodes 8 Data Lines to 3-Line Binary (Octal)

- Applications Include:

  N-Bit Encoding
  Code Converters and Generators

TYPE	TYPICAL DATA DELAY	TYPICAL POWER DISSIPATION
'147	10 ns	225 mW
'148	10 ns	190 mW
'LS147	15 ns	60 mW
'LS148	15 ns	60 mW

description

These TTL encoders feature priority decoding of the inputs to ensure that only the highest-order data line is encoded. The '147 and 'LS147 encode nine data lines to four-line (8-4-2-1) BCD. The implied decimal zero condition requires no input condition as zero is encoded when all nine data lines are at a high logic level. The '148 and 'LS148 encode eight data lines to three-line (4-2-1) binary (octal). Cascading circuitry (enable input EI and enable output EO) has been provided to allow octal expansion without the need for external circuitry. For all types, data inputs and outputs are active at the low logic level. All inputs are buffered to represent one normalized Series 54/74 or 54LS/74LS load, respectively.

SN54147, SN54LS147,
SN54148, SN54LS148 . . . J OR W PACKAGE
SN74147, SN74148 . . . J OR N PACKAGE
SN74LS147, SN74LS148 . . . D, J OR N PACKAGE
(TOP VIEW)

SN54LS147, SN54LS148 . . . FK PACKAGE
SN74LS147, SN74LS148
(TOP VIEW)

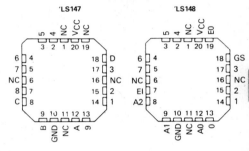

NC - No internal connection

'147, 'LS147
FUNCTION TABLE

INPUTS									OUTPUTS			
1	2	3	4	5	6	7	8	9	D	C	B	A
H	H	H	H	H	H	H	H	H	H	H	H	H
X	X	X	X	X	X	X	X	L	L	H	H	L
X	X	X	X	X	X	X	L	H	L	H	H	H
X	X	X	X	X	X	L	H	H	H	L	L	L
X	X	X	X	X	L	H	H	H	H	L	L	H
X	X	X	X	L	H	H	H	H	H	L	H	L
X	X	X	L	H	H	H	H	H	H	L	H	H
X	X	L	H	H	H	H	H	H	H	H	L	L
X	L	H	H	H	H	H	H	H	H	H	L	H
L	H	H	H	H	H	H	H	H	H	H	H	L

'148, 'LS148
FUNCTION TABLE

INPUTS									OUTPUTS				
EI	0	1	2	3	4	5	6	7	A2	A1	A0	GS	EO
H	X	X	X	X	X	X	X	X	H	H	H	H	H
L	H	H	H	H	H	H	H	H	H	H	H	H	L
L	X	X	X	X	X	X	X	L	L	L	L	L	H
L	X	X	X	X	X	X	L	H	L	L	H	L	H
L	X	X	X	X	X	L	H	H	L	H	L	L	H
L	X	X	X	X	L	H	H	H	L	H	H	L	H
L	X	X	X	L	H	H	H	H	H	L	L	L	H
L	X	X	L	H	H	H	H	H	H	L	H	L	H
L	X	L	H	H	H	H	H	H	H	H	L	L	H
L	L	H	H	H	H	H	H	H	H	H	H	L	H

H = high logic level, L = low logic level, X = irrelevant

TEXAS
INSTRUMENTS

3

TTL DEVICES

logic diagram

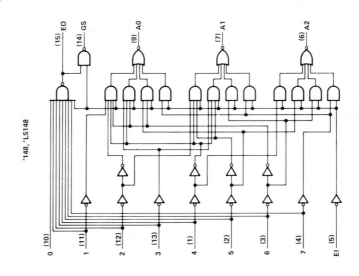

'148, 'LS148

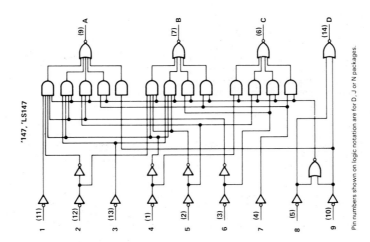

'147, 'LS147

Pin numbers shown on logic notation are for D, J or N packages.

3

TTL DEVICES

TEXAS
INSTRUMENTS

schematics of inputs and outputs

'147, '148

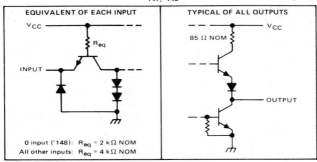

'LS147, 'LS148

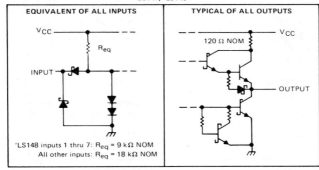

absolute maximum ratings over operating free-air temperature range (unless otherwise noted)

Supply voltage, V_{CC} (see Note 1) . . . . 7 V
Input voltage: '147, '148 . . . . 5.5 V
     'LS147, 'LS148 . . . . 7 V
Interemitter voltage: '148 only (see Note 2) . . . . 5.5 V
Operating free-air temperature range: SN54', SN54LS Circuits . . . . $-55°C$ to $125°C$
           SN74', SN74LS Circuits . . . . $0°C$ to $70°C$
Storage temperature range . . . . $-65°C$ to $150°C$

NOTES: 1. Voltage values, except interemitter voltage, are with respect to network ground terminal.
   2. This is the voltage between two emitters of a multiple-emitter transistor. For '148 circuits, this rating applies between any two of the eight data lines, 0 through 7.

recommended operating conditions

	SN54'			SN74'			SN54LS'			SN74LS'			UNIT
	MIN	NOM	MAX	MIN	NOM	MAX	MIN	NOM	MAX	MIN	NOM	MAX	
Supply voltage, V_{CC}	4.5	5	5.5	4.75	5	5.25	4.5	5	5.5	4.75	5	5.25	V
High-level output current, I_{OH}			−800			−800			−400			−400	μA
Low-level output current, I_{OL}			16			16			4			8	mA
Operating free-air temperature, T_A	−55		125	0		70	−55		125	0		70	C

TTL DEVICES 3

electrical characteristics over recommended operating free-air temperature range (unless otherwise noted)

PARAMETER		TEST CONDITIONS†	'147 MIN	'147 TYP‡	'147 MAX	'148 MIN	'148 TYP‡	'148 MAX	UNIT
V_{IH} High-level input voltage			2			2			V
V_{IL} Low-level input voltage					0.8			0.8	V
V_{IK} Input clamp voltage		V_{CC} = MIN, I_I = −12 mA			−1.5			−1.5	V
V_{OH} High-level output voltage		V_{CC} = MIN, V_{IH} = 2 V, V_{IL} = 0.8 V, I_{OH} = −800 μA	2.4	3.3		2.4	3.3		V
V_{OL} Low-level output voltage		V_{CC} = MIN, V_{IH} = 2 V, V_{IL} = 0.8 V, I_{OL} = 16 mA		0.2	0.4		0.2	0.4	V
I_I Input current at maximum input voltage		V_{CC} = MAX, V_I = 5.5 V			1			1	mA
I_{IH} High-level input current	0 input	V_{CC} = MAX, V_I = 2.4 V						40	μA
	Any input except 0				40			80	
I_{IL} Low-level input current	0 input	V_{CC} = MAX, V_I = 0.4 V						−1.6	mA
	Any input except 0				−1.6			−3.2	
I_{OS} Short-circuit output current §		V_{CC} = MAX	−35		−85	−35		−85	mA
I_{CC} Supply current		V_{CC} = MAX, Condition 1		50	70		40	60	mA
		See Note 3 Condition 2		42	62		35	55	mA

NOTE 3: For '147, I_{CC} (condition 1) is measured with input 7 grounded, other inputs and outputs open; I_{CC} (condition 2) is measured with all inputs and outputs open. For '148, I_{CC} (condition 1) is measured with inputs 7 and EI grounded, other inputs and outputs open; I_{CC} (condition 2) is measured with all inputs and outputs open.

†For conditions shown as MIN or MAX, use the appropriate value specified under recommended operating conditions.

‡All typical values are at V_{CC} = 5 V, T_A = 25°C.

§Not more than one output should be shorted at a time.

SN54147, SN74147 switching characteristics, V_{CC} = 5 V, T_A = 25°C

PARAMETER¶	FROM (INPUT)	TO (OUTPUT)	WAVEFORM	TEST CONDITIONS	MIN	TYP	MAX	UNIT
t_{PLH}	Any	Any	In-phase output	C_L = 15 pF, R_L = 400 Ω, See Note 4		9	14	ns
t_{PHL}						7	11	
t_{PLH}	Any	Any	Out-of-phase output			13	19	ns
t_{PHL}						12	19	

SN54148, SN74148 switching characteristics, V_{CC} = 5 V, T_A = 25°C

PARAMETER¶	FROM (INPUT)	TO (OUTPUT)	WAVEFORM	TEST CONDITIONS	MIN	TYP	MAX	UNIT
t_{PLH}	1 thru 7	A0, A1, or A2	In-phase output			10	15	ns
t_{PHL}						9	14	
t_{PLH}	1 thru 7	A0, A1, or A2	Out-of-phase output			13	19	ns
t_{PHL}						12	19	
t_{PLH}	0 thru 7	EO	Out-of-phase output			6	10	ns
t_{PHL}						14	25	
t_{PLH}	0 thru 7	GS	In-phase output	C_L = 15 pF, R_L = 400 Ω, See Note 4		18	30	ns
t_{PHL}						14	25	
t_{PLH}	EI	A0, A1, or A2	In-phase output			10	15	ns
t_{PHL}						10	15	
t_{PLH}	EI	GS	In-phase output			8	12	ns
t_{PHL}						10	15	
t_{PLH}	EI	EO	In-phase output			10	15	ns
t_{PHL}						17	30	

¶t_{PLH} ≡ propagation delay time, low-to-high-level output

t_{PHL} ≡ propagation delay time, high-to-low-level output

NOTE 4: See General Information Section for load circuits and voltage waveforms.

TEXAS
INSTRUMENTS

electrical characteristics over recommended operating free-air temperature range (unless otherwise noted)

PARAMETER		TEST CONDITIONS†		SN54LS' MIN	TYP‡	MAX	SN74LS' MIN	TYP‡	MAX	UNIT
V_{IH} High-level input voltage				2			2			V
V_{IL} Low-level input voltage						0.7			0.8	V
V_{IK} Input clamp voltage		V_{CC} = MIN,	I_I = −18 mA			−1.5			−1.5	V
V_{OH} High-level output voltage		V_{CC} = MIN, V_{IH} = 2 V, V_{IL} = 0.8 V,	I_{OH} = −400 µA	2.5	3.4		2.7	3.4		V
V_{OL} Low-level output voltage		V_{CC} = MIN, V_{IH} = 2 V,	I_{OL} = 4 mA		0.25	0.4		0.25	0.4	V
		V_{IL} = V_{IL}max	I_{OL} = 8 mA					0.35	0.5	
I_I Input current at maximum input voltage	'LS148 inputs 1 thru 7	V_{CC} = MAX,	V_I = 7 V			0.2			0.2	mA
	All other inputs					0.1			0.1	
I_{IH} High-level input current	'LS148 inputs 1 thru 7	V_{CC} = MAX,	V_I = 2.7 V			40			40	µA
	All other inputs					20			20	
I_{IL} Low-level input current	'LS148 inputs 1 thru 7	V_{CC} = MAX,	V_I = 0.4 V			−0.8			−0.8	mA
	All other inputs					−0.4			−0.4	
I_{OS} Short-circuit output current§		V_{CC} = MAX		−20		−100	−20		−100	mA
I_{CC} Supply current		V_{CC} = MAX, See Note 5	Condition 1		12	20		12	20	mA
			Condition 2		10	17		10	17	mA

NOTE 5: For 'LS147, I_{CC} (condition 1) is measured with input 7 grounded, other inputs and outputs open; I_{CC} (condition 2) is measured with all inputs and outputs open. For 'LS148, I_{CC} (condition 1) is measured with inputs 7 and EI grounded, other inputs and outputs open, I_{CC} (condition 2) is measured with all inputs and outputs open.

†For conditions shown as MIN or MAX, use the appropriate value specified under recommended operating conditions.

‡All typical values are at V_{CC} = 5 V, T_A = 25°C.

§Not more than one output should be shorted at a time.

SN54LS147, SN74LS147 switching characteristics, V_{CC} = 5 V, T_A = 25°C

PARAMETER¶	FROM (INPUT)	TO (OUTPUT)	WAVEFORM	TEST CONDITIONS	MIN	TYP	MAX	UNIT
t_{PLH}	Any	Any	In-phase output	C_L = 15 pF, R_L = 2 kΩ, See Note 4		12	18	ns
t_{PHL}						12	18	
t_{PLH}	Any	Any	Out-of-phase output			21	33	ns
t_{PHL}						15	23	

SN54LS148, SN74LS148 switching characteristics, V_{CC} = 5 V, T_A = 25°C

PARAMETER¶	FROM (INPUT)	TO (OUTPUT)	WAVEFORM	TEST CONDITIONS	MIN	TYP	MAX	UNIT
t_{PLH}	1 thru 7	A0, A1, or A2	In-phase output			14	18	ns
t_{PHL}						15	25	
t_{PLH}	1 thru 7	A0, A1, or A2	Out-of-phase output			20	36	ns
t_{PHL}						16	29	
t_{PLH}	0 thru 7	EO	Out-of-phase output			7	18	ns
t_{PHL}						25	40	
t_{PLH}	0 thru 7	GS	In-phase output	C_L = 15 pF, R_L = 2 kΩ, See Note 4		35	55	ns
t_{PHL}						9	21	
t_{PLH}	EI	A0, A1, or A2	In-phase output			16	25	ns
t_{PHL}						12	25	
t_{PLH}	EI	GS	In-phase output			12	17	ns
t_{PHL}						14	36	
t_{PLH}	EI	EO	In-phase output			12	21	ns
t_{PHL}						23	35	

¶t_{PLH} = propagation delay time, low-to-high-level output

t_{PHL} = propagation delay time, high-to-low-level output

NOTE 4: See General Information Section for load circuits and voltage waveforms.

3

TTL DEVICES

TEXAS
INSTRUMENTS

TYPICAL APPLICATION DATA

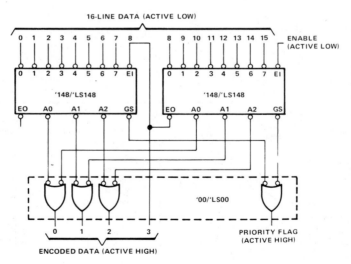

Since the '147/'LS147 and '148/'LS148 are combinational logic circuits, wrong addresses can appear during input transients. Moreover, for the '148/'LS148 a change from high to low at input EI can cause a transient low on the GS output when all inputs are high. This must be considered when strobing the outputs.

TEXAS
INSTRUMENTS

TYPES SN54150, SN54151A, SN54152A, SN54LS151, SN54LS152, SN54S151, SN74150, SN74151A, SN74LS151, SN74S151
DATA SELECTORS/MULTIPLEXERS

DECEMBER 1972–REVISED DECEMBER 1983

- '150 Selects One-of-Sixteen Data Sources
- Others Select One-of-Eight Data Sources
- Performs Parallel-to-Serial Conversion
- Permits Multiplexing from N Lines to One Line
- Also For Use as Boolean Function Generator
- Input-Clamping Diodes Simplify System Design
- Fully Compatible with Most TTL Circuits

TYPE	TYPICAL AVERAGE PROPAGATION DELAY TIME DATA INPUT TO W OUTPUT	TYPICAL POWER DISSIPATION
'150	13 ns	200 mW
'151A	8 ns	145 mW
'152A	8 ns	130 mW
'LS151	13 ns	30 mW
'LS152	13 ns	28 mW
'S151	4.5 ns	225 mW

SN54150 . . . J OR W PACKAGE
SN74150 . . . J OR N PACKAGE
(TOP VIEW)

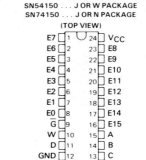

SN54151A, SN54LS151, SN54S151 . . . J OR W PACKAGE
SN74151A . . . J OR N PACKAGE
SN74LS151, SN74S151 . . . D, J OR N PACKAGE
(TOP VIEW)

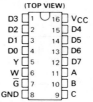

SN54LS151, SN54S151 . . . FK PACKAGE
SN74LS151, SN74S151
(TOP VIEW)

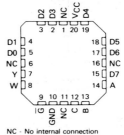

NC - No internal connection

SN54152A, SN54LS152 . . . W PACKAGE
(TOP VIEW)

D4 1 ⎿ 14 VCC
D3 2 13 D5
D2 3 12 D6
D1 4 11 D7
D0 5 10 A
W 6 9 B
GND 7 8 C

For SN54LS152 Chip Carrier Information, Contact The Factory.

description

These monolithic data selectors/multiplexers contain full on-chip binary decoding to select the desired data source. The '150 selects one-of-sixteen data sources; the '151A, '152A, 'LS151, 'LS152, and 'S151 select one-of-eight data sources. The '150, '151A, 'LS151, and 'S151 have a strobe input which must be at a low logic level to enable these devices. A high level at the strobe forces the W output high, and the Y output (as applicable) low.

The '151A, 'LS151, and 'S151 feature complementary W and Y outputs whereas the '150, '152A, and 'LS152 have an inverted (W) output only.

The '151A and '152A incorporate address buffers which have symmetrical propagation delay times through the complementary paths. This reduces the possibility of transients occurring at the output(s) due to changes made at the select inputs, even when the '151A outputs are enabled (i.e., strobe low).

TEXAS
INSTRUMENTS

3

TTL DEVICES

TYPES SN54150, SN54151A, SN54152A, SN54LS151, SN54LS152, SN54S151, SN74150, SN74151A, SN74LS151, SN74S151
DATA SELECTORS/MULTIPLEXERS

schematics of inputs and outputs

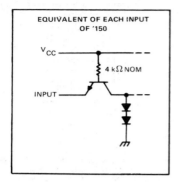

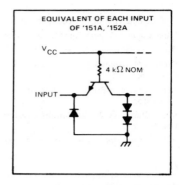

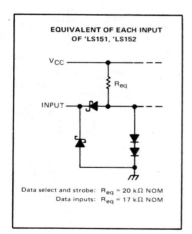

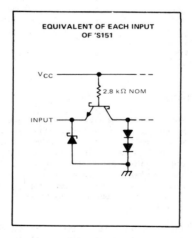

3

TTL DEVICES

schematics of inputs and outputs

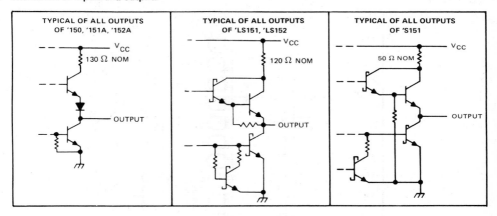

TYPICAL OF ALL OUTPUTS OF '150, '151A, '152A — V_CC, 130 Ω NOM, OUTPUT

TYPICAL OF ALL OUTPUTS OF 'LS151, 'LS152 — V_CC, 120 Ω NOM, OUTPUT

TYPICAL OF ALL OUTPUTS OF 'S151 — V_CC, 50 Ω NOM, OUTPUT

logic

'150
FUNCTION TABLE

INPUTS					OUTPUT
SELECT			STROBE	W
D	C	B	A	$\overline{G}$	
X	X	X	X	H	H
L	L	L	L	L	$\overline{E0}$
L	L	L	H	L	$\overline{E1}$
L	L	H	L	L	$\overline{E2}$
L	L	H	H	L	$\overline{E3}$
L	H	L	L	L	$\overline{E4}$
L	H	L	H	L	$\overline{E5}$
L	H	H	L	L	$\overline{E6}$
L	H	H	H	L	$\overline{E7}$
H	L	L	L	L	$\overline{E8}$
H	L	L	H	L	$\overline{E9}$
H	L	H	L	L	$\overline{E10}$
H	L	H	H	L	$\overline{E11}$
H	H	L	L	L	$\overline{E12}$
H	H	L	H	L	$\overline{E13}$
H	H	H	L	L	$\overline{E14}$
H	H	H	H	L	$\overline{E15}$

'151A, 'LS151, 'S151
FUNCTION TABLE

INPUTS				OUTPUTS	
SELECT			STROBE	Y	W
C	B	A	$\overline{G}$		
X	X	X	H	L	H
L	L	L	L	D0	$\overline{D0}$
L	L	H	L	D1	$\overline{D1}$
L	H	L	L	D2	$\overline{D2}$
L	H	H	L	D3	$\overline{D3}$
H	L	L	L	D4	$\overline{D4}$
H	L	H	L	D5	$\overline{D5}$
H	H	L	L	D6	$\overline{D6}$
H	H	H	L	D7	$\overline{D7}$

H = high level, L = low level, X = irrelevant
E0, E1 . . . E15 = the complement of the level of the respective E input
D0, D1 . . . D7 = the level of the D respective input

'152A, 'LS152
FUNCTION TABLE

SELECT INPUTS			OUTPUT
C	B	A	W
L	L	L	$\overline{D0}$
L	L	H	$\overline{D1}$
L	H	L	$\overline{D2}$
L	H	H	$\overline{D3}$
H	L	L	$\overline{D4}$
H	L	H	$\overline{D5}$
H	H	L	$\overline{D6}$
H	H	H	$\overline{D7}$

3

TTL DEVICES

logic diagrams

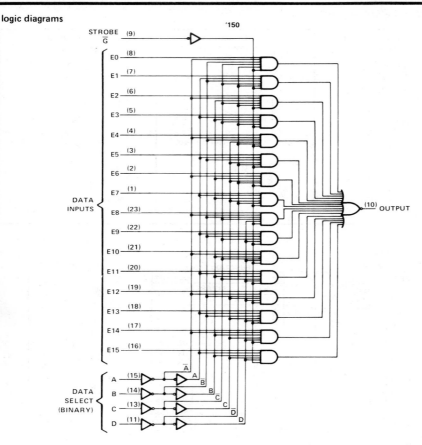

ADDRESS BUFFERS FOR '151A, '152A

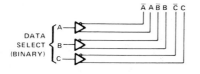

ADDRESS BUFFERS FOR 'LS151, 'S151, 'LS152

Pin numbers shown on logic notation are for D, J or N packages.

TEXAS
INSTRUMENTS

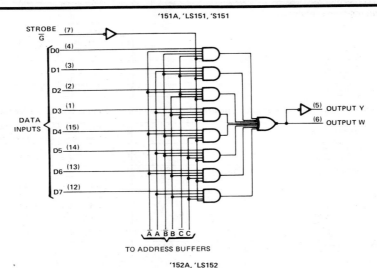

'151A, 'LS151, 'S151

TO ADDRESS BUFFERS

'152A, 'LS152

TO ADDRESS BUFFERS

Pin numbers shown on logic notation are for D, J or N packages.

absolute maximum ratings over operating free-air temperature range (unless otherwise noted)

Supply voltage, V_{CC} (see Note 1) . . . . 7 V
Input voltage (see Note 2): '150, '151A, 'S151, '152A . . . . 5.5 V
'LS151, 'LS152 . . . . 7 V
Operating free-air temperature range: SN54' . . . . -55°C to 125°C
SN74' . . . . 0°C to 70°C
Storage temperature range . . . . -65°C to 150°C

NOTES: 1. Voltage values are with respect to network ground terminal.
2. For the '150, input voltages must be zero or positive with respect to network ground terminal.

TEXAS
INSTRUMENTS

TYPES SN54150, SN54151A, SN54152A, SN74150, SN74151A
DATA SELECTORS/MULTIPLEXERS

recommended operating conditions

	SN54' MIN	SN54' NOM	SN54' MAX	SN74' MIN	SN74' NOM	SN74' MAX	UNIT
Supply voltage, V_{CC}	4.5	5	5.5	4.75	5	5.25	V
High-level output current, I_{OH}			−800			−800	μA
Low-level output current, I_{OL}			16			16	mA
Operating free-air temperature, T_A	−55		125	0		70	°C

electrical characteristics over recommended operating free-air temperature range (unless otherwise noted)

PARAMETER		TEST CONDITIONS[†]	'150 MIN	'150 TYP[‡]	'150 MAX	'151A, '152A MIN	'151A, '152A TYP[‡]	'151A, '152A MAX	UNIT
V_{IH}	High-level input voltage		2			2			V
V_{IL}	Low-level input voltage				0.8			0.8	V
V_{IK}	Input clamp voltage	V_{CC} = MIN, I_I = −8 mA						−1.5	V
V_{OH}	High-level output voltage	V_{CC} = MIN, V_{IH} = 2 V, V_{IL} = 0.8 V, I_{OH} = −800 μA	2.4	3.4		2.4	3.4		V
V_{OL}	Low-level output voltage	V_{CC} = MIN, V_{IH} = 2 V, V_{IL} = 0.8 V, I_{OL} = 16 mA		0.2	0.4		0.2	0.4	V
I_I	Input current at maximum input voltage	V_{CC} = MAX, V_I = 5.5 V			1			1	mA
I_{IH}	High-level input current	V_{CC} = MAX, V_I = 2.4 V			40			40	μA
I_{IL}	Low-level input current	V_{CC} = MAX, V_I = 0.4 V			−1.6			−1.6	mA
I_{OS}	Short-circuit output current [§]	V_{CC} = MAX SN54'	−20		−55	−20		−55	mA
		V_{CC} = MAX SN74'	−18		−55	−18		−55	
I_{CC}	Supply current	V_{CC} = MAX, See Note 3 '150		40	68				mA
		'151A					29	48	
		'152A					26	43	

[†]For conditions shown as MIN or MAX, use the appropriate value specified under recommended operating conditions for the applicable device type.
[‡]All typical values at V_{CC} = 5 V, T_A = 25°C.
[§]Not more than one output of the '151A should be shorted at a time.
NOTE 3: I_{CC} is measured with the strobe and data select inputs at 4.5 V, all other inputs and outputs open.

switching characteristics, V_{CC} = 5 V, T_A = 25°C

PARAMETER[¶]	FROM (INPUT)	TO (OUTPUT)	TEST CONDITIONS	'150 MIN	'150 TYP	'150 MAX	'151A, '152A MIN	'151A, '152A TYP	'151A, '152A MAX	UNIT
t_{PLH}	A, B, or C (4 levels)	Y						25	38	ns
t_{PHL}								25	38	
t_{PLH}	A, B, C, or D (3 levels)	W			23	35		17	26	ns
t_{PHL}					22	33		19	30	
t_{PLH}	Strobe $\overline{G}$	Y	C_L = 15 pF, R_L = 400 Ω, See Note 4					21	33	ns
t_{PHL}								22	33	
t_{PLH}	Strobe $\overline{G}$	W			15.5	24		14	21	ns
t_{PHL}					21	30		15	23	
t_{PLH}	D0 thru D7	Y						13	20	ns
t_{PHL}								18	27	
t_{PLH}	E0 thru E15, or D0 thru D7	W			8.5	14		8	14	ns
t_{PHL}					13	20		8	14	

[¶]t_{PLH} ≡ propagation delay time, low-to-high-level output
t_{PHL} ≡ propagation delay time, high-to-low-level output
NOTE 4: See General Information Section for load circuits and voltage waveforms.

TEXAS
INSTRUMENTS

recommended operating conditions

	SN54LS'			SN74LS'			UNIT
	MIN	NOM	MAX	MIN	NOM	MAX	
Supply voltage, V_{CC}	4.5	5	5.5	4.75	5	5.25	V
High-level output current, I_{OH}			−400			−400	μA
Low-level output current, I_{OL}			4			8	mA
Operating free-air temperature, T_A	−55		125	0		70	°C

electrical characteristics over recommended operating free-air temperature range (unless otherwise noted)

PARAMETER		TEST CONDITIONS[†]		SN54LS'			SN74LS'			UNIT
				MIN	TYP[‡]	MAX	MIN	TYP[‡]	MAX	
V_{IH}	High-level input voltage			2			2			V
V_{IL}	Low-level input voltage					0.7			0.8	V
V_{IK}	Input clamp voltage	V_{CC} = MIN, I_I = −18 mA				−1.5			−1.5	V
V_{OH}	High-level output voltage	V_{CC} = MIN, V_{IH} = 2 V, V_{IL} = V_{IL} max, I_{OH} = −400 μA		2.5	3.4		2.7	3.4		V
V_{OL}	Low-level output voltage	V_{CC} = MIN, V_{IH} = 2 V, V_{IL} = V_{IL} max	I_{OL} = 4 mA		0.25	0.4		0.25	0.4	V
			I_{OL} = 8 mA					0.35	0.5	
I_I	Input current at maximum input voltage	V_{CC} = MAX, V_I = 7 V				0.1			0.1	mA
I_{IH}	High-level input current	V_{CC} = MAX, V_I = 2.7 V				20			20	μA
I_{IL}	Low-level input current	V_{CC} = MAX, V_I = 0.4 V				−0.4			−0.4	mA
I_{OS}	Short-circuit output current[§]	V_{CC} = MAX		−20		−100	−20		−100	mA
I_{CC}	Supply current	V_{CC} = MAX, Outputs open, All inputs at 4.5 V	'LS151		6.0	10		6.0	10	mA
			'LS152		5.6	9				

[†]For conditions shown as MIN or MAX, use the appropriate value specified under recommended operating conditions for the applicable device type.
[‡]All typical values are at V_{CC} = 5 V, T_A = 25°C.
[§]Not more than one output should be shorted at a time and duration of short-circuit should not exceed one second.

switching characteristics, V_{CC} = 5 V, T_A = 25°C

PARAMETER[¶]	FROM (INPUT)	TO (OUTPUT)	TEST CONDITIONS	SN54LS', SN74LS'			UNIT
				MIN	TYP	MAX	
t_{PLH}	A, B, or C (4 levels)	Y			27	43	ns
t_{PHL}					18	30	
t_{PLH}	A, B, or C (3 levels)	W			14	23	ns
t_{PHL}					20	32	
t_{PLH}	Strobe $\overline{G}$	Y	C_L = 15 pF, R_L = 2 kΩ, See Note 4		26	42	ns
t_{PHL}					20	32	
t_{PLH}	Strobe $\overline{G}$	W			15	24	ns
t_{PHL}					18	30	
t_{PLH}	Any D	Y			20	32	ns
t_{PHL}					16	26	
t_{PLH}	Any D	W			13	21	ns
t_{PHL}					12	20	

[¶]t_{PLH} = propagation delay time, low-to-high-level output
t_{PHL} = propagation delay time, high-to-low-level output
NOTE 4:   See General Information Section for load circuits and voltage waveforms.

3

TTL DEVICES

TEXAS
INSTRUMENTS

recommended operating conditions

	SN54S151 MIN	SN54S151 NOM	SN54S151 MAX	SN74S151 MIN	SN74S151 NOM	SN74S151 MAX	UNIT
Supply voltage, V_{CC}	4.5	5	5.5	4.75	5	5.25	V
High-level output current, I_{OH}			−1			−1	mA
Low-level output current, I_{OL}			20			20	mA
Operating free-air temperature, T_A	−55		125	0		70	°C

electrical characteristics over recommended operating free-air temperature range (unless otherwise noted)

	PARAMETER	TEST CONDITIONS[†]		MIN	TYP[‡]	MAX	UNIT
V_{IH}	High-level input voltage			2			V
V_{IL}	Low-level input voltage					0.8	V
V_{IK}	Input clamp voltage	V_{CC} = MIN, I_I = −18 mA				−1.2	V
V_{OH}	High-level output voltage	V_{CC} = MIN, V_{IH} = 2 V, V_{IL} = 0.8 V, I_{OH} = −1 mA	SN54S'	2.5	3.4		V
			SN74S'	2.7	3.4		
V_{OL}	Low-level output voltage	V_{CC} = MIN, V_{IH} = 2 V, V_{IL} = 0.8 V, I_{OL} = 20 mA				0.5	V
I_I	Input current at maximum input voltage	V_{CC} = MAX, V_I = 5.5 V				1	mA
I_{IH}	High-level input current	V_{CC} = MAX, V_I = 2.7 V				50	µA
I_{IL}	Low-level input current	V_{CC} = MAX, V_I = 0.5 V				−2	mA
I_{OS}	Short-circuit output current[§]	V_{CC} = MAX		−40		−100	mA
I_{CC}	Supply current	V_{CC} = MAX, All inputs at 4.5 V, All outputs open			45	70	mA

[†]For conditions shown as MIN or MAX, use the appropriate value specified under recommended operating conditions for the applicable device type.
[‡]All typical values are at V_{CC} = 5 V, T_A = 25°C.
[§]Not more than one output should be shorted at a time, and duration of the short-circuit should not exceed one second.

switching characteristics, V_{CC} = 5 V, T_A = 25°C

PARAMETER[¶]	FROM (INPUT)	TO (OUTPUT)	TEST CONDITIONS	SN54S151, SN74S151 MIN	SN54S151, SN74S151 TYP	SN54S151, SN74S151 MAX	UNIT
t_{PLH}	A, B, or C	Y			12	18	ns
t_{PHL}	(4 levels)				12	18	
t_{PLH}	A, B, or C	W			10	15	ns
t_{PHL}	(3 levels)				9	13.5	
t_{PLH}	Any D	Y	C_L = 15 pF, R_L = 280 Ω, See Note 4		8	12	ns
t_{PHL}					8	12	
t_{PLH}	Any D	W			4.5	7	ns
t_{PHL}					4.5	7	
t_{PLH}	Strobe $\overline{G}$	Y			11	16.5	ns
t_{PHL}					12	18	
t_{PLH}	Strobe $\overline{G}$	W			9	13	ns
t_{PHL}					8.5	12	

[¶]t_{PLH} ≡ Propagation delay time, low-to-high-level output
t_{PHL} ≡ Propagation delay time, high-to-low-level output

NOTE 4: See General Information Section for load circuits and voltage waveforms.

3

TTL DEVICES

TEXAS
INSTRUMENTS

- Permits Multiplexing from N lines to 1 line
- Performs Parallel-to-Serial Conversion
- Strobe (Enable) Line Provided for Cascading (N lines to n lines)
- High-Fan-Out, Low-Impedance, Totem-Pole Outputs
- Fully Compatible with most TTL Circuits

SN54153, SN54LS153, SN54S153 . . . J OR W PACKAGE
SN74153 . . . J OR N PACKAGE
SN74LS153, SN74S153 . . . D, J OR N PACKAGE
(TOP VIEW)

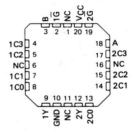

TYPE	TYPICAL AVERAGE PROPAGATION DELAY TIMES			TYPICAL POWER DISSIPATION
	FROM DATA	FROM STROBE	FROM SELECT	
'153	14 ns	17 ns	22 ns	180 mW
'LS153	14 ns	19 ns	22 ns	31 mW
'S153	6 ns	9.5 ns	12 ns	225 mW

SN54LS153, SN54S153 . . . FK PACKAGE
SN74LS153, SN74S153
(TOP VIEW)

NC – No internal connection

description

Each of these monolithic, data selectors/multiplexers contains inverters and drivers to supply fully complementary, on-chip, binary decoding data selection to the AND-OR gates. Separate strobe inputs are provided for each of the two four-line sections.

FUNCTION TABLE

SELECT INPUTS		DATA INPUTS				STROBE	OUTPUT
B	A	C0	C1	C2	C3	Ḡ	Y
X	X	X	X	X	X	H	L
L	L	L	X	X	X	L	L
L	L	H	X	X	X	L	H
L	H	X	L	X	X	L	L
L	H	X	H	X	X	L	H
H	L	X	X	L	X	L	L
H	L	X	X	H	X	L	H
H	H	X	X	X	L	L	L
H	H	X	X	X	H	L	H

Select inputs A and B are common to both sections.
H = high level, L = low level, X = irrelevant

absolute maximum ratings over operating free-air temperature range (unless otherwise noted)

Supply voltage, V_{CC} (see Note 1) . . . . 7 V
Input voltage : '153, 'S153 . . . . 5.5 V
'LS153 . . . . 7 V
Operating free-air temperature range: SN54' . . . . −55°C to 125°C
SN74' . . . . 0°C to 70°C
Storage temperature range . . . . −65°C to 150°C

NOTE 1: Voltage values are with respect to network ground terminal.

TEXAS
INSTRUMENTS

3

TTL DEVICES

logic symbol

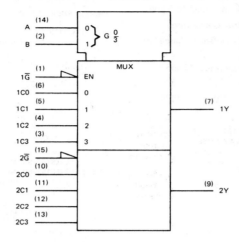

logic diagram

Pin numbers shown on logic notation are for D, J or N packages.

TEXAS
INSTRUMENTS

schematics of inputs and outputs

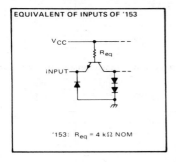

EQUIVALENT OF INPUTS OF '153

'153: R_{eq} = 4 kΩ NOM

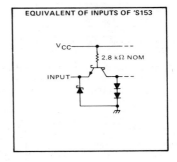

EQUIVALENT OF INPUTS OF 'S153

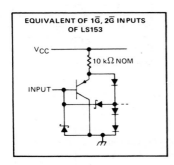

EQUIVALENT OF 1$\overline{G}$, 2$\overline{G}$ INPUTS
OF LS153

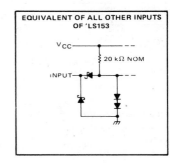

EQUIVALENT OF ALL OTHER INPUTS
OF 'LS153

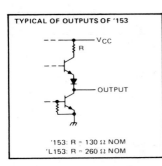

TYPICAL OF OUTPUTS OF '153

'153: R = 130 Ω NOM
'L153: R = 260 Ω NOM

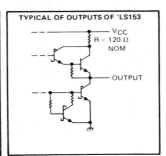

TYPICAL OF OUTPUTS OF 'LS153

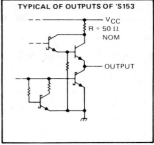

TYPICAL OF OUTPUTS OF 'S153

3

TTL DEVICES

TEXAS
INSTRUMENTS

3-449

recommended operating conditions

	SN54153 MIN	SN54153 NOM	SN54153 MAX	SN74153 MIN	SN74153 NOM	SN74153 MAX	UNIT
Supply voltage, V_{CC}	4.5	5	5.5	4.75	5	5.25	V
High-level output current, I_{OH}			−800			−800	µA
Low-level output current, I_{OL}			16			16	mA
Operating free-air temperature, T_A	−55		125	0		70	°C

electrical characteristics over recommended operating free-air temperature range (unless otherwise noted)

PARAMETER	TEST CONDITIONS[†]	SN54153 MIN	SN54153 TYP[‡]	SN54153 MAX	SN74153 MIN	SN74153 TYP[‡]	SN74153 MAX	UNIT
V_{IH} High-level input voltage		2			2			V
V_{IL} Low-level input voltage				0.8			0.8	V
V_{IK} Input clamp voltage	V_{CC} = MIN, I_I = −12 mA			−1.5			−1.5	V
V_{OH} High-level output voltage	V_{CC} = MIN, V_{IH} = 2 V, V_{IL} = 0.8 V, I_{OH} = −800 µA	2.4	3.4		2.4	3.4		V
V_{OL} Low-level output voltage	V_{CC} = MIN, V_{IH} = 2 V, V_{IL} = 0.8 V, I_{OL} = 16 mA		0.2	0.4		0.2	0.4	V
I_I Input current at maximum input voltage	V_{CC} = MAX, V_I = 5.5 V			1			1	mA
I_{IH} High-level input current	V_{CC} = MAX, V_I = 2.4 V			40			40	µA
I_{IL} Low-level input current	V_{CC} = MAX, V_I = 0.4 V			−1.6			−1.6	mA
I_{OS} Short-circuit output current[§]	V_{CC} = MAX	−20		−55	−18		−57	mA
I_{CCL} Supply current, output low	V_{CC} = MAX, See Note 2		36	52		36	60	mA

[†]For conditions shown as MIN or MAX, use the appropriate value specified under recommended operating conditions.
[‡]All typical values are at V_{CC} = 5 V, T_A = 25°C.
[§]Not more than one output should be shorted at a time.
NOTE 2: I_{CCL} is measured with the outputs open and all inputs grounded.

switching characteristics, V_{CC} = 5 V, T_A = 25°C

PARAMETER[¶]	FROM (INPUT)	TO (OUTPUT)	TEST CONDITIONS	MIN	TYP	MAX	UNIT
t_{PLH}	Data	Y			12	18	ns
t_{PHL}	Data	Y			15	23	ns
t_{PLH}	Select	Y	C_L = 30 pF, R_L = 400 Ω,		22	34	ns
t_{PHL}	Select	Y	See Note 3		22	34	ns
t_{PLH}	Strobe $\overline{G}$	Y			19	30	ns
t_{PHL}	Strobe $\overline{G}$	Y			15	23	ns

[¶]t_{PLH} = propagation delay time, low-to-high-level output
t_{PHL} = propagation delay time, high-to-low-level output
NOTE 3: See General Information Section for load circuits and voltage waveforms.

3

TTL DEVICES

TEXAS
INSTRUMENTS

recommended operating conditions

		SN54LS153			SN74LS153			UNIT
		MIN	NOM	MAX	MIN	NOM	MAX	
V_{CC}	Supply voltage	4.5	5	5.5	4.75	5	5.25	V
V_{IH}	High-level input voltage	2			2			V
V_{IL}	Low-level input voltage			0.7			0.8	V
I_{OH}	High-level output current			−0.4			−0.4	mA
I_{OL}	Low-level output current			4			8	mA
T_A	Operating free-air temperature	−55		125	0		70	°C

electrical characteristics over recommended operating free-air temperature range (unless otherwise noted)

PARAMETER	TEST CONDITIONS†		SN54LS153			SN74LS153			UNIT
			MIN	TYP‡	MAX	MIN	TYP‡	MAX	
V_{IK}	V_{CC} = MIN, I_I = −18 mA				−1.5			−1.5	V
V_{OH}	V_{CC} = MIN, V_{IH} = 2 V, V_{IL} = MAX I_{OH} = −0.4 mA		2.5	3.4		2.7	3.4		V
V_{OL}	V_{CC} = MIN, V_{IH} = 2 V,	I_{OL} = 4 mA		0.25	0.4		0.25	0.4	V
	V_{IL} = MAX,	I_{OL} = 8 mA					0.35	0.5	
I_I	V_{CC} = MAX, V_I = 7 V				0.1			0.1	mA
I_{IH}	V_{CC} = MAX, V_I = 2.7 V				20			20	μA
I_{IL} 1G, 2G	V_{CC} = MAX, V_I = 0.4 V				−0.2			−0.2	mA
All other					−0.4			−0.4	
I_{OS}§	V_{CC} = MAX		−20		−100	−20		−100	mA
I_{CCL}	V_{CC} = MAX, See Note 2			6.2	10		6.2	10	mA

† For conditions shown as MIN or MAX, use the appropriate value specified under recommended operating conditions.
‡ All typical values are at V_{CC} = 5 V, T_A = 25°C.
§ Not more than one output should be shorted at a time.
NOTE 2: I_{CCL} is measured with the outputs open and all inputs grounded.

switching characteristics, V_{CC} = 5 V, T_A = 25°C

PARAMETER¶	FROM (INPUT)	TO (OUTPUT)	TEST CONDITIONS	MIN	TYP	MAX	UNIT
t_{PLH}	Data	Y			10	15	ns
t_{PHL}	Data	Y	C_L = 15 pF,		17	26	ns
t_{PLH}	Select	Y	R_L = 2 kΩ,		19	29	ns
t_{PHL}	Select	Y	See Note 3		25	38	ns
t_{PLH}	Strobe $\overline{G}$	Y			16	24	ns
t_{PHL}	Strobe $\overline{G}$	Y			21	32	ns

¶ t_{PLH} = propagation delay time, low-to-high-level output
t_{PHL} = propagation delay time, high-to-low-level output
NOTE 3: See General Information Section for load circuits and voltage waveforms.

3

TTL DEVICES

TEXAS
INSTRUMENTS

recommended operating conditions

	SN54S153			SN74S153			UNIT
	MIN	NOM	MAX	MIN	NOM	MAX	
Supply voltage, V_{CC}	4.5	5	5.5	4.75	5	5.25	V
High-level output current, I_{OH}			−1			−1	mA
Low-level output current, I_{OL}			20			20	mA
Operating free-air temperature, T_A	−55		125	0		70	°C

electrical characteristics over recommended operating free-air temperature range (unless otherwise noted)

PARAMETER		TEST CONDITIONS[†]		MIN	TYP[‡]	MAX	UNIT
V_{IH}	High-level input voltage			2			V
V_{IL}	Low-level input voltage					0.8	V
V_{IK}	Input clamp voltage	V_{CC} = MIN, I_I = −18 mA				−1.2	V
V_{OH}	High-level output voltage	V_{CC} = MIN, V_{IH} = 2 V,	Series 54S	2.5	3.4		V
		V_{IL} = 0.8 V, I_{OH} = −1 mA	Series 74S	2.7	3.4		
V_{OL}	Low-level output voltage	V_{CC} = MIN, V_{IH} = 2 V, V_{IL} = 0.8 V, I_{OL} = 20 mA				0.5	V
I_I	Input current at maximum input voltage	V_{CC} = MAX, V_I = 5.5 V				1	mA
I_{IH}	High-level input current	V_{CC} = MAX, V_I = 2.7 V				50	µA
I_{IL}	Low-level input current	V_{CC} = MAX, V_I = 0.5 V				−2	mA
I_{OS}	Short-circuit output current[§]	V_{CC} = MAX		−40		−100	mA
I_{CCL}	Supply current, low-level output	V_{CC} = MAX, See Note 2			45	70	mA

[†] For conditions shown as MIN or MAX, use the appropriate value specified under recommended operating conditions.
[‡] All typical values are at V_{CC} = 5 V, T_A = 25°C.
[§] Not more than one output should be shorted at a time and duration of short-circuit should not exceed one second.
NOTE 2: I_{CCL} is measured with the outputs open and all inputs grounded.

switching characteristics, V_{CC} = 5 V, T_A = 25°C

PARAMETER[¶]	FROM (INPUT)	TO (OUTPUT)	TEST CONDITIONS	MIN	TYP	MAX	UNIT
t_{PLH}	Data	Y			6	9	ns
t_{PHL}	Data	Y			6	9	ns
t_{PLH}	Select	Y	C_L = 15 pF, R_L = 280 Ω, See Note 3		11.5	18	ns
t_{PHL}	Select	Y			12	18	ns
t_{PLH}	Strobe $\overline{G}$	Y			10	15	ns
t_{PHL}	Strobe $\overline{G}$	Y			9	13.5	ns

[¶] t_{PLH} = propagation delay time, low-to-high-level output
t_{PHL} = propagation delay time, high-to-low-level output
NOTE 3: See General Information Section for load circuits and voltage waveforms.

3
TTL DEVICES

TEXAS
INSTRUMENTS

DECEMBER 1972–REVISED DECEMBER 1983

- '154 is Ideal for High-Performance Memory Decoding
- Decodes 4 Binary-Coded Inputs into One of 16 Mutually Exclusive Outputs
- Performs the Demultiplexing Function by Distributing Data From One Input Line to Any One of 16 Outputs
- Input Clamping Diodes Simplify System Design
- High Fan-Out, Low-Impedance, Totem-Pole Outputs
- Fully Compatible with Most TTL and MSI Circuits

SN54154 . . . J OR W PACKAGE
SN74154 . . . J OR N PACKAGE
(TOP VIEW)

```
      0 [ 1    U  24 ] VCC
      1 [ 2       23 ] A
      2 [ 3       22 ] B
      3 [ 4       21 ] C
      4 [ 5       20 ] D
      5 [ 6       19 ] G2
      6 [ 7       18 ] G1
      7 [ 8       17 ] 15
      8 [ 9       16 ] 14
      9 [ 10      15 ] 13
     10 [ 11      14 ] 12
    GND [ 12      13 ] 11
```

TYPE	TYPICAL AVERAGE PROPAGATION DELAY		TYPICAL POWER DISSIPATION
	3 LEVELS OF LOGIC	STROBE	
'154	23 ns	19 ns	170 mW

description

Each of these monolithic, 4-line-to-16-line decoders utilizes TTL circuitry to decode four binary-coded inputs into one of sixteen mutually exclusive outputs when both the strobe inputs, G1 and G2, are low. The demultiplexing function is performed by using the 4 input lines to address the output line, passing data from one of the strobe inputs with the other strobe input low. When either strobe input is high, all outputs are high. These demultiplexers are ideally suited for implementing high-performance memory decoders. For ultra-high speed systems, SN54S138/SN74S138 and SN54S139/SN74S139 are recommended.

These circuits are fully compatible for use with most other TTL circuits. All inputs are buffered and input clamping diodes are provided to minimize transmission-line effects and thereby simplify system design.

The SN54154 is characterized for operation over the full military temperature range of −55°C to 125°C. The SN74154 is characterized for operation from 0°C to 70°C.

logic symbol

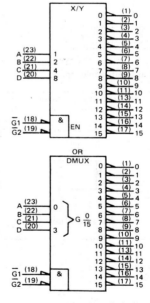

Pin numbers shown on logic notation are for J or N packages.

TEXAS
INSTRUMENTS

3-453

TTL DEVICES

3

TYPES SN54154, SN74154
4-LINE TO 16-LINE DECODERS/DEMULTIPLEXERS

FUNCTION TABLE

INPUTS						OUTPUTS															
$\overline{G1}$	$\overline{G2}$	D	C	B	A	0	1	2	3	4	5	6	7	8	9	10	11	12	13	14	15
L	L	L	L	L	L	L	H	H	H	H	H	H	H	H	H	H	H	H	H	H	H
L	L	L	L	L	H	H	L	H	H	H	H	H	H	H	H	H	H	H	H	H	H
L	L	L	L	H	L	H	H	L	H	H	H	H	H	H	H	H	H	H	H	H	H
L	L	L	L	H	H	H	H	H	L	H	H	H	H	H	H	H	H	H	H	H	H
L	L	L	H	L	L	H	H	H	H	L	H	H	H	H	H	H	H	H	H	H	H
L	L	L	H	L	H	H	H	H	H	H	L	H	H	H	H	H	H	H	H	H	H
L	L	L	H	H	L	H	H	H	H	H	H	L	H	H	H	H	H	H	H	H	H
L	L	L	H	H	H	H	H	H	H	H	H	H	L	H	H	H	H	H	H	H	H
L	L	H	L	L	L	H	H	H	H	H	H	H	H	L	H	H	H	H	H	H	H
L	L	H	L	L	H	H	H	H	H	H	H	H	H	H	L	H	H	H	H	H	H
L	L	H	L	H	L	H	H	H	H	H	H	H	H	H	H	L	H	H	H	H	H
L	L	H	L	H	H	H	H	H	H	H	H	H	H	H	H	H	L	H	H	H	H
L	L	H	H	L	L	H	H	H	H	H	H	H	H	H	H	H	H	L	H	H	H
L	L	H	H	L	H	H	H	H	H	H	H	H	H	H	H	H	H	H	L	H	H
L	L	H	H	H	L	H	H	H	H	H	H	H	H	H	H	H	H	H	H	L	H
L	L	H	H	H	H	H	H	H	H	H	H	H	H	H	H	H	H	H	H	H	L
L	H	X	X	X	X	H	H	H	H	H	H	H	H	H	H	H	H	H	H	H	H
H	L	X	X	X	X	H	H	H	H	H	H	H	H	H	H	H	H	H	H	H	H
H	H	X	X	X	X	H	H	H	H	H	H	H	H	H	H	H	H	H	H	H	H

H = high level, L = low level, X = irrelevant

schematics of inputs and outputs

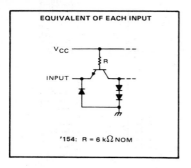

EQUIVALENT OF EACH INPUT

V_{CC}

R

INPUT

'154: R = 6 kΩ NOM

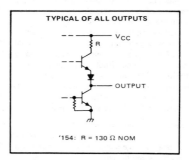

TYPICAL OF ALL OUTPUTS

V_{CC}

R

OUTPUT

'154: R = 130 Ω NOM

TEXAS
INSTRUMENTS

logic diagram

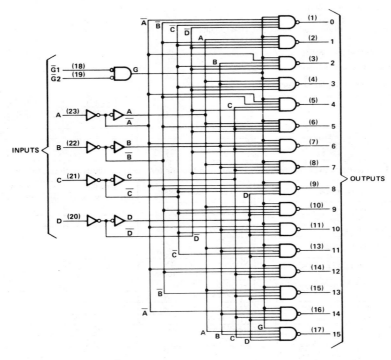

Pin numbers shown on logic notation are for J or N packages.

3

TTL DEVICES

absolute maximum ratings over operating free-air temperature range (unless otherwise noted)

Supply voltage, V_{CC} (see Note 1)	7 V
Input voltage	5.5 V
Operating free-air temperature range: SN54154 Circuits	$-55°C$ to $125°C$
SN74154 Circuits	$0°C$ to $70°C$
Storage temperature range	$-65°C$ to $150°C$

NOTE 1: Voltage values are with respect to network ground terminal.

recommended operating conditions

	SN54154			SN74154			UNIT
	MIN	NOM	MAX	MIN	NOM	MAX	
Supply voltage, V_{CC}	4.5	5	5.5	4.75	5	5.25	V
High-level output current, I_{OH}			−800			−800	µA
Low-level output current, I_{OL}			16			16	mA
Operating free-air temperature, T_A	−55		125	0		70	°C

electrical characteristics over recommended operating free-air temperature range (unless otherwise noted)

PARAMETER		TEST CONDITIONS†	SN54154			SN74154			UNIT
			MIN	TYP	MAX	MIN	TYP‡	MAX	
V_{IH}	High-level input voltage		2			2			V
V_{IL}	Low-level input voltage				0.8			0.8	V
V_{IK}	Input clamp voltage	V_{CC} = MIN, I_I = −12 mA			−1.5			−1.5	V
V_{OH}	High-level output voltage	V_{CC} = MIN, V_{IH} = 2 V, V_{IL} = 0.8 V, I_{OH} = −800 µA	2.4	3.4		2.4	3.4		V
V_{OL}	Low-level output voltage	V_{CC} = MIN, V_{IH} = 2 V, V_{IL} = 0.8 V, I_{OL} = 16 mA		0.2	0.4		0.2	0.4	V
I_I	Input current at maximum input voltage	V_{CC} = MAX, V_I = 5.5 V			1			1	mA
I_{IH}	High-level input current	V_{CC} = MAX, V_I = 2.4 V			40			40	µA
I_{IL}	Low-level input current	V_{CC} = MAX, V_I = 0.4 V			−1.6			−1.6	mA
I_{OS}	Short-circuit output current§	V_{CC} = MAX	−20		−55	−18		−57	mA
I_{CC}	Supply current	V_{CC} = MAX, See Note 2		34	49		34	56	mA

†For conditions shown as MIN or MAX, use the appropriate value specified under recommended operating conditions for the applicable type.
‡All typical values are at V_{CC} = 5 V, T_A = 25°C.
§Not more than one output should be shorted at a time.
NOTE 2: I_{CC} is measured with all inputs grounded and all outputs open.

switching characteristics, V_{CC} = 5 V, T_A = 25°C

PARAMETER		TEST CONDITIONS	MIN	TYP	MAX	UNIT
t_{PLH}	Propagation delay time, low-to-high-level output, from A, B, C, or D inputs through 3 levels of logic			24	36	ns
t_{PHL}	Propagation delay time, high-to-low-level output, from A, B, C, or D inputs through 3 levels of logic	C_L = 15 pF, R_L = 400 Ω, See Note 3		22	33	ns
t_{PLH}	Propagation delay time, low-to-high-level output, from either strobe input			20	30	ns
t_{PHL}	Propagation delay time, high-to-low-level output, from either strobe input			18	27	ns

NOTE 3: See General Information Section for load circuits and voltage waveforms.

3

TTL DEVICES

TEXAS INSTRUMENTS

TYPES SN54155, SN54156, SN54LS155A, SN54LS156, SN74155, SN74156, SN74LS155A, SN74LS156
DUAL 2-LINE TO 4-LINE DECODERS/DEMULTIPLEXERS

MARCH 1974–REVISED DECEMBER 1983

- **Applications:**
  - **Dual 2-to 4-Line Decoder**
  - **Dual 1-to 4-Line Demultiplexer**
  - **3-to 8-Line Decoder**
  - **1-to 8-Line Demultiplexer**

- **Individual Strobes Simplify Cascading for Decoding or Demultiplexing Larger Words**

- **Input Clamping Diodes Simplify System Design**

- **Choice of Outputs:**
  - **Totem Pole ('155, 'LS155A)**
  - **Open-Collector ('156, 'LS156)**

TYPES	TYPICAL AVERAGE PROPAGATION DELAY 3 GATE LEVELS	TYPICAL POWER DISSIPATION
'155, '156	21 ns	125 mW
'LS155A	18 ns	31 mW
'LS156	32 ns	31 mW

description

These monolithic transistor-transistor-logic (TTL) circuits feature dual 1-line-to-4-line demultiplexers with individual strobes and common binary-address inputs in a single 16-pin package. When both sections are enabled by the strobes, the common binary-address inputs sequentially select and route associated input data to the appropriate output of each section. The individual strobes permit activating or inhibiting each of the 4-bit sections as desired. Data applied to input 1C is inverted at its outputs and data applied at $2\overline{C}$ is not inverted through its outputs. The inverter following the 1C data input permits use as a 3-to-8-line decoder or 1-to-8-line demultiplexer without external gating. Input clamping diodes are provided on all of these circuits to minimize transmission-line effects and simplify system design.

Series 54 and 54LS are characterized for operation over the full military temperature range of -55°C to 125°C; Series 74 and 74LS are characterized for operation from 0°C to 70°C.

SN54155, SN54156, SN54LS155A,
SN54LS156 . . . J OR W PACKAGE
SN74155, SN74156 . . . J OR N PACKAGE
SN74LS155A, SN74LS156 . . . D, J OR N PACKAGE
(TOP VIEW)

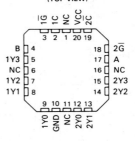

```
    1C  [ 1   16 ]  VCC
    1G  [ 2   15 ]  2C
     B  [ 3   14 ]  2G
   1Y3  [ 4   13 ]  A
   1Y2  [ 5   12 ]  2Y3
   1Y1  [ 6   11 ]  2Y2
   1Y0  [ 7   10 ]  2Y1
   GND  [ 8    9 ]  2Y0
```

SN54LS155A, SN54LS156 . . . FK PACKAGE
SN74LS155A, SN74LS156
(TOP VIEW)

NC - No internal connection

schematics of inputs and outputs

'155, '156

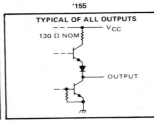

EQUIVALENT OF EACH INPUT
V_{CC} — 4 kΩ NOM — INPUT

'155

TYPICAL OF ALL OUTPUTS

V_{CC} — 130 Ω NOM — OUTPUT

'156

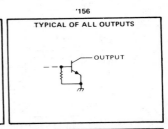

TYPICAL OF ALL OUTPUTS

OUTPUT

TEXAS INSTRUMENTS

3

TTL DEVICES

TYPES SN54155, SN54156, SN54LS155A, SN54LS156, SN74155, SN74156, SN74LS155A, SN74LS156
DUAL 2–LINE TO 4–LINE DECODERS/DEMULTIPLEXERS

schematics of inputs and outputs (continued)

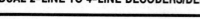

'LS155A, 'LS156	'LS155A	'LS156
EQUIVALENT OF EACH INPUT	TYPICAL OF ALL OUTPUTS	TYPICAL OF ALL OUTPUTS

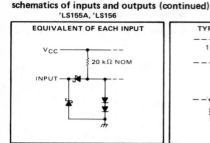
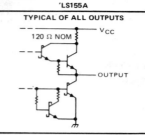
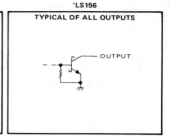

logic diagram

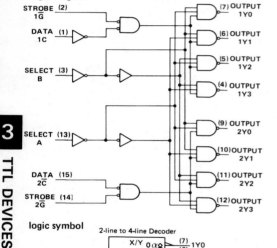

FUNCTION TABLES
2-LINE-TO-4-LINE DECODER
OR 1-LINE-TO-4-LINE DEMULTIPLEXER

INPUTS				OUTPUTS			
SELECT		STROBE	DATA	1Y0	1Y1	1Y2	1Y3
B	A	1G̅	1C				
X	X	H	X	H	H	H	H
L	L	L	H	L	H	H	H
L	H	L	H	H	L	H	H
H	L	L	H	H	H	L	H
H	H	L	H	H	H	H	L
X	X	X	L	H	H	H	H

INPUTS				OUTPUTS			
SELECT		STROBE	DATA	2Y0	2Y1	2Y2	2Y3
B	A	2G̅	2C̅				
X	X	H	X	H	H	H	H
L	L	L	L	L	H	H	H
L	H	L	L	H	L	H	H
H	L	L	L	H	H	L	H
H	H	L	L	H	H	H	L
X	X	X	H	H	H	H	H

logic symbol

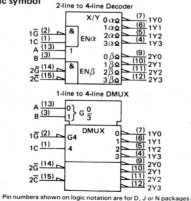

Pin numbers shown on logic notation are for D, J or N packages.

FUNCTION TABLE
3-LINE-TO-8-LINE DECODER
OR 1-LINE-TO-8-LINE DEMULTIPLEXER

INPUTS				OUTPUTS							
SELECT			STROBE OR DATA	(0)	(1)	(2)	(3)	(4)	(5)	(6)	(7)
C†	B	A	G̅‡	2Y0	2Y1	2Y2	2Y3	1Y0	1Y1	1Y2	1Y3
X	X	X	H	H	H	H	H	H	H	H	H
L	L	L	L	L	H	H	H	H	H	H	H
L	L	H	L	H	L	H	H	H	H	H	H
L	H	L	L	H	H	L	H	H	H	H	H
L	H	H	L	H	H	H	L	H	H	H	H
H	L	L	L	H	H	H	H	L	H	H	H
H	L	H	L	H	H	H	H	H	L	H	H
H	H	L	L	H	H	H	H	H	H	L	H
H	H	H	L	H	H	H	H	H	H	H	L

†C = inputs 1C and 2C̅ connected together
‡G = inputs 1G̅ and 2G̅ connected together
H = high level, L = low level, X = irrelevant

TEXAS INSTRUMENTS

absolute maximum ratings over operating free-air temperature range (unless otherwise noted)

Supply voltage, V_{CC} (see Note 1) . . . . 7 V

Input voltage: '155, '156 . . . . 5.5 V

            'LS155A, 'LS156 . . . . 7 V

Off-state output voltage: '156 . . . . 5.5 V

                'LS156 . . . . 7 V

Operating free-air temperature range: SN54', SN54LS' Circuits . . . . -55°C to 125°C

                         SN74', SN74LS' Circuits . . . . 0°C to 70°C

Storage temperature range . . . . -65°C to 150°C

NOTE 1: Voltage values are with respect to network ground terminal.

recommended operating conditions

	SN54155 MIN	SN54155 NOM	SN54155 MAX	SN74155 MIN	SN74155 NOM	SN74155 MAX	UNIT
Supply voltage, V_{CC}	4.5	5	5.5	4.75	5	5.25	V
High-level output current, I_{OH}			-800			-800	μA
Low-level output current, I_{OL}			16			16	mA
Operating free-air temperature, T_A	-55		125	0		70	$^{\circ}$C

electrical characteristics over recommended operating free-air temperature range (unless otherwise noted)

PARAMETER		TEST CONDITIONS[†]	SN54155 SN74155 MIN	TYP[‡]	MAX	UNIT
V_{IH}	High-level input voltage		2			V
V_{IL}	Low-level input voltage				0.8	V
V_{IK}	Input clamp voltage	V_{CC} = MIN, $I_I = -8$ mA			-1.5	V
V_{OH}	High-level output voltage	V_{CC} = MIN, V_{IH} = 2 V, V_{IL} = 0.8 V, $I_{OH} = -800$ μA	2.4	3.4		V
V_{OL}	Low-level output voltage	V_{CC} = MIN, V_{IH} = 2 V, V_{IL} = 0.8 V, I_{OL} = 16 mA		0.2	0.4	V
I_I	Input current at maximum input voltage	V_{CC} = MAX, V_I = 5.5 V			1	mA
I_{IH}	High-level input current	V_{CC} = MAX, V_I = 2.4 V			40	μA
I_{IL}	Low-level input current	V_{CC} = MAX, V_I = 0.4 V			-1.6	mA
I_{OS}	Short-circuit output current[§]	V_{CC} = MAX SN54155	-20		-55	mA
		SN74155	-18		-57	
I_{CC}	Supply current	V_{CC} = MAX, SN54155		25	35	mA
		See Note 2 SN74155		25	40	

[†] For conditions shown as MIN or MAX, use the appropriate value specified under recommended operating conditions.

[‡] All typical values are at V_{CC} = 5 V, $T_A = 25^{\circ}$C.

[§] Not more than one output should be shorted at a time.

NOTE 2: I_{CC} is measured with outputs open, A, B, and 1C inputs at 4.5 V, and 2C, 1G, and 2G inputs grounded.

switching characteristics, V_{CC} = 5 V, $T_A = 25^{\circ}$C

PARAMETER[¶]	FROM (INPUT)	TO (OUTPUT)	LEVELS OF LOGIC	TEST CONDITIONS	MIN	TYP	MAX	UNIT
t_{PLH}	A, B, 2$\overline{C}$, 1$\overline{G}$, or 2$\overline{G}$	Y	2			13	20	ns
t_{PHL}	A, B, 2$\overline{C}$, 1$\overline{G}$, or 2$\overline{G}$	Y	2	C_L = 15 pF, R_L = 400 Ω, See Note 3		18	27	ns
t_{PLH}	A or B	Y	3			21	32	ns
t_{PHL}	A or B	Y	3			21	32	ns
t_{PLH}	1C	Y	3			16	24	ns
t_{PHL}	1C	Y	3			20	30	ns

[¶] t_{PLH} ≡ propagation delay time, low-to-high-level output

  t_{PHL} ≡ propagation delay time, high-to-low-level output

NOTE 3: See General Information Section for load circuits and voltage waveforms.

TTL DEVICES   **3**

recommended operating conditions

	SN54156			SN74156			UNIT
	MIN	NOM	MAX	MIN	NOM	MAX	
Supply voltage, V_{CC}	4.5	5	5.5	4.75	5	5.25	V
High-level output voltage, V_{OH}			5.5			5.5	V
Low-level output current, I_{OL}			16			16	mA
Operating free-air temperature, T_A	−55		125	0		70	°C

electrical characteristics over recommended operating free-air temperature range (unless otherwise noted)

	PARAMETER	TEST CONDITIONS[†]	SN54156 SN74156			UNIT
			MIN	TYP[*]	MAX	
V_{IH}	High-level input voltage		2			V
V_{IL}	Low-level input voltage				0.8	V
V_{IK}	Input clamp voltage	V_{CC} = MIN, I_I = −8 mA			−1.5	V
I_{CH}	High-level output current	V_{CC} = MIN, V_{IH} = 2 V, V_{IL} = 0.8 V, V_{OH} = 5.5 V			250	μA
V_{OL}	Low-level output voltage	V_{CC} = MIN, V_{IH} = 2 V, V_{IL} = 0.8 V, I_{OL} = 16 mA		0.2	0.4	V
I_I	Input current at maximum input voltage	V_{CC} = MAX, V_I = 5.5 V			1	mA
I_{IH}	High-level input current	V_{CC} = MAX, V_I = 2.4 V			40	μA
I_{IL}	Low-level input current	V_{CC} = MAX, V_I = 0.4 V			−1.6	mA
I_{CC}	Supply current	V_{CC} = MAX, See Note 2 SN54156		25	35	mA
		SN74156		25	40	

[†] For conditions shown as MIN or MAX, use the appropriate value specified under recommended operating conditions.
[*] All typical values are at V_{CC} = 5 V, T_A = 25°C.
NOTE 2: I_{CC} is measured with outputs open, A, B, and 1C inputs at 4.5 V, and 2C, 1G, and 2G inputs grounded.

switching characteristics, V_{CC} = 5 V, T_A = 25°C

PARAMETER[*]	FROM (INPUT)	TO (OUTPUT)	LEVELS OF LOGIC	TEST CONDITIONS	MIN	TYP	MAX	UNIT
t_{PLH}	A, B, 2$\overline{C}$, 1$\overline{G}$, or 2$\overline{G}$	Y	2	C_L = 15 pF, R_L = 400 Ω, See Note 3		15	23	ns
t_{PHL}	A, B, 2$\overline{C}$, 1$\overline{G}$, or 2$\overline{G}$	Y	2			20	30	ns
t_{PLH}	A or B	Y	3			23	34	ns
t_{PHL}	A or B	Y	3			23	34	ns
t_{PLH}	1C	Y	3			18	27	ns
t_{PHL}	1C	Y	3			22	33	ns

[*] t_{PLH} = propagation delay time, low-to-high-level output
t_{PHL} = propagation delay time, high-to-low-level output
NOTE 3: See General information Section for load circuits and voltage waveforms.

TEXAS INSTRUMENTS

recommended operating conditions

	SN54LS155A			SN74LS155A			UNIT
	MIN	NOM	MAX	MIN	NOM	MAX	
Supply voltage, V_{CC}	4.5	5	5.5	4.75	5	5.25	V
High-level output current, I_{OH}			−400			−400	μA
Low-level output current, I_{OL}			4			8	mA
Operating free-air temperature, T_A	−55		125	0		70	°C

electrical characteristics over recommended operating free-air temperature range (unless otherwise noted)

PARAMETER		TEST CONDITIONS[†]		SN54LS155A			SN74LS155A			UNIT
				MIN	TYP[‡]	MAX	MIN	TYP[‡]	MAX	
V_{IH}	High-level input voltage			2			2			V
V_{IL}	Low-level input voltage					0.7			0.8	V
V_{IK}	Input clamp voltage	V_{CC} = MIN, I_I = −18 mA				−1.5			−1.5	V
V_{OH}	High-level output voltage	V_{CC} = MIN, V_{IH} = 2 V, $V_{IL} = V_{IL\,max}$, I_{OH} = −400 μA		2.5	3.4		2.7	3.4		V
V_{OL}	Low-level output voltage	V_{CC} = MIN, V_{IH} = 2 V, $V_{IL} = V_{IL\,max}$	I_{OL} = 4 mA		0.25	0.4		0.25	0.4	V
			I_{OL} = 8 mA					0.35	0.5	
I_I	Input current at maximum input voltage	V_{CC} = MAX, V_I = 7 V				0.1			0.1	mA
I_{IH}	High-level input current	V_{CC} = MAX, V_I = 2.7 V				20			20	μA
I_{IL}	Low-level input current	V_{CC} = MAX, V_I = 0.4 V				−0.4			−0.4	mA
I_{OS}	Short-circuit output current[§]	V_{CC} = MAX		−20		−100	−20		−100	mA
I_{CC}	Supply current	V_{CC} = MAX, See Note 2			6.1	10		6.1	10	mA

[†]For conditions shown as MIN or MAX, use the appropriate value specified under recommended operating conditions.
[‡]All typical values are at V_{CC} = 5 V, T_A = 25°C.
[§]Not more than one output should be shorted at a time.
NOTE 2: I_{CC} is measured with outputs open, A, B, and 1C inputs at 4.5 V, and 2C, 1G, and 2G inputs grounded.

switching characteristics, V_{CC} = 5 V, T_A = 25°C

PARAMETER[¶]	FROM (INPUT)	TO (OUTPUT)	LEVELS OF LOGIC	TEST CONDITIONS	SN54LS155A SN74LS155A			UNIT
					MIN	TYP	MAX	
t_{PLH}	A, B, 2$\overline{C}$, 1$\overline{G}$, or 2$\overline{G}$	Y	2			10	15	ns
t_{PHL}	A, B, 2$\overline{C}$, 1$\overline{G}$, or 2$\overline{G}$	Y	2	C_L = 15 pF, R_L = 2 kΩ, See Note 3		19	30	ns
t_{PLH}	A or B	Y	3			17	26	ns
t_{PHL}	A or B	Y	3			19	30	ns
t_{PLH}	1C	Y	3			18	27	ns
t_{PHL}	1C	Y	3			18	27	ns

[¶]t_{PLH} ≡ propagation delay time, low-to-high-level output
t_{PHL} ≡ propagation delay time, high-to-low-level output
NOTE 3: See General Information Section for load circuits and voltage waveforms.

3

TTL DEVICES

TEXAS
INSTRUMENTS

recommended operating conditions

	SN54LS156 MIN	NOM	MAX	SN74LS156 MIN	NOM	MAX	UNIT
Supply voltage, V_{CC}	4.5	5	5.5	4.75	5	5.25	V
High-level output voltage, V_{OH}			5.5			5.5	V
Low-level output current, I_{OL}			4			8	mA
Operating free-air temperature, T_A	−55		125	0		70	°C

electrical characteristics over recommended operating free-air temperature range (unless otherwise noted)

PARAMETER		TEST CONDITIONS[†]		SN54LS156 MIN	TYP[‡]	MAX	SN74LS156 MIN	TYP[‡]	MAX	UNIT
V_{IH}	High-level input voltage			2			2			V
V_{IL}	Low-level input voltage					0.7			0.8	V
V_{IK}	Input clamp voltage	V_{CC} = MIN,	I_I = −18 mA			−1.5			−1.5	V
I_{OH}	High-level output current	V_{CC} = MIN, V_{IH} = 2 V, $V_{IL} = V_{IL}$ max, V_{OH} = 5.5 V				100			100	µA
V_{OL}	Low-level output voltage	V_{CC} = MIN, V_{IH} = 2 V, $V_{IL} = V_{IL}$ max	I_{OL} = 4 mA	0.25		0.4	0.25		0.4	V
			I_{OL} = 8 mA				0.35		0.5	
I_I	Input current at maximum input voltage	V_{CC} = MAX,	V_I = 7 V			0.1			0.1	mA
I_{IH}	High-level input current	V_{CC} = MAX,	V_I = 2.7 V			20			20	µA
I_{IL}	Low-level input current	V_{CC} = MAX,	V_I = 0.4 V			−0.4			−0.4	mA
I_{CC}	Supply current	V_{CC} = MAX,	See Note 2		6.1	10		6.1	10	mA

[†]For conditions shown as MIN or MAX, use the appropriate value specified under recommended operating conditions.
[‡]All typical values are at V_{CC} = 5 V, T_A = 25°C.
NOTE 2: I_{CC} is measured with outputs open, A, B, and 1C inputs at 4.5 V, and 2C, 1G, and 2G inputs grounded.

switching characteristics, V_{CC} = 5 V, T_A = 25°C

PARAMETER[¶]	FROM (INPUT)	TO (OUTPUT)	LEVELS OF LOGIC	TEST CONDITIONS	SN54LS156 SN74LS156 MIN	TYP	MAX	UNIT
t_{PLH}	A, B, 2$\overline{C}$ 1$\overline{G}$, or 2$\overline{G}$	Y	2			25	40	ns
t_{PHL}	A, B, 2$\overline{C}$, 1$\overline{G}$, or 2$\overline{G}$	Y	2	C_L = 15 pF, R_L = 2 kΩ, See Note 3		34	51	ns
t_{PLH}	A or B	Y	3			31	46	ns
t_{PHL}	A or B	Y	3			34	51	ns
t_{PLH}	1C	Y	3			32	48	ns
t_{PHL}	1C	Y	3			32	48	ns

[¶]t_{PLH} ≡ propagation delay time, low-to-high-level output
t_{PHL} ≡ propagation delay time, high-to-low-level output
NOTE 3: See General Information Section for load circuits and voltage waveforms.

TEXAS
INSTRUMENTS

TYPES SN54157, SN54L157, SN54LS157, SN54LS158, SN54S157, SN54S158, SN74157, SN74LS157, SN74LS158, SN74S157, SN74S158
QUADRUPLE 2-LINE TO 1-LINE DATA SELECTORS/MULTIPLEXERS

MARCH 1974–REVISED DECEMBER 1983

- **Buffered Inputs and Outputs**
- **Three Speed/Power Ranges Available**

TYPES	TYPICAL AVERAGE PROPAGATION TIME	TYPICAL POWER DISSIPATION
'157	9 ns	150 mW
'L157	18 ns	75 mW
'LS157	9 ns	49 mW
'S157	5 ns	250 mW
'LS158	7 ns	24 mW
'S158	4 ns	195 mW

applications

- **Expand Any Data Input Point**
- **Multiplex Dual Data Buses**
- **Generate Four Functions of Two Variables (One Variable Is Common)**
- **Source Programmable Counters**

description

These monolithic data selectors/multiplexers contain inverters and drivers to supply full on-chip data selection to the four output gates. A separate strobe input is provided. A 4-bit word is selected from one of two sources and is routed to the four outputs. The '157, 'L157, 'LS157, and 'S157 present true data whereas the 'LS158 and 'S158 present inverted data to minimize propagation delay time.

SN54157, SN54LS157, SN54S157,
SN54LS158, SN54S158 . . . J OR W PACKAGE
SN54L157 . . . J PACKAGE
SN74157 . . . J OR N PACKAGE
SN74LS157, SN74S157,
SN74LS158, SN74S158 . . . D, J OR N PACKAGE
(TOP VIEW)

```
         ____  ____
$\overline{A}/B$ [ 1  U 16 ] VCC
   1A [ 2     15 ] $\overline{G}$
   1B [ 3     14 ] 4A
   1Y [ 4     13 ] 4B
   2A [ 5     12 ] 4Y
   2B [ 6     11 ] 3A
   2Y [ 7     10 ] 3B
  GND [ 8      9 ] 3Y
```

SN54LS157, SN54S157, SN54LS158
SN54S158, SN74LS157, SN74S157,
SN74LS158, SN74S158 . . . FK PACKAGE
(TOP VIEW)

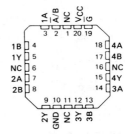

NC - No internal connection

FUNCTION TABLE

INPUTS				OUTPUT Y	
STROBE $\overline{G}$	SELECT $\overline{A}/B$	A	B	'157, 'L157, 'LS157,'S157	'LS158 'S158
H	X	X	X	L	H
L	L	L	X	L	H
L	L	H	X	H	L
L	H	X	L	L	H
L	H	X	H	H	L

H = high level, L = low level, X = irrelevant

absolute maximum ratings over operating free-air temperature range (unless otherwise noted)

Supply voltage, V_{CC} (see Note 1) . . . . 7 V
Input voltage: '157, 'L157, 'S158 . . . . 5.5 V
'LS157, 'LS158 . . . . 7 V
Operating free-air temperature range: SN54' . . . . −55°C to 125°C
SN74' . . . . 0°C to 70°C
Storage temperature range . . . . −65°C to 150°C

NOTE 1: Voltage values are with respect to network ground terminal.

3
TTL DEVICES

TEXAS
INSTRUMENTS

logic diagram

'157, 'L157

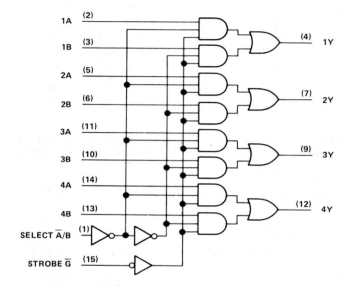

Pin numbers shown on logic notation are for D, J or N packages.

schematics of inputs and outputs

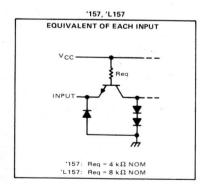

'157, 'L157
EQUIVALENT OF EACH INPUT

'157: R_{eq} = 4 kΩ NOM
'L157: R_{eq} = 8 kΩ NOM

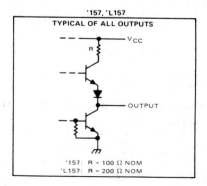

'157, 'L157
TYPICAL OF ALL OUTPUTS

'157: R = 100 Ω NOM
'L157: R = 200 Ω NOM

TEXAS
INSTRUMENTS

logic diagrams

schematics of inputs and outputs

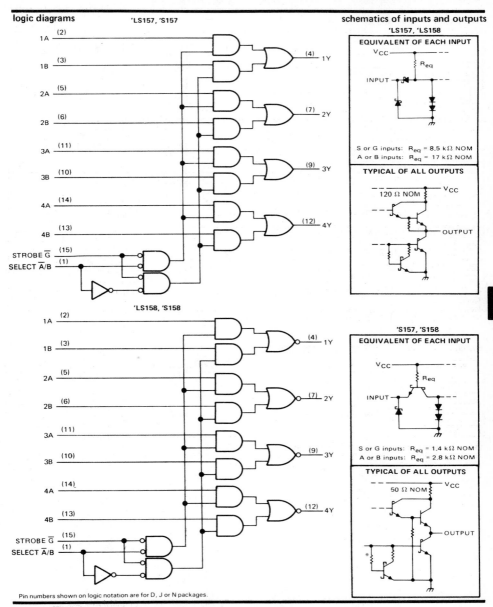

Pin numbers shown on logic notation are for D, J or N packages.

3

TTL DEVICES

recommended operating conditions

	SN54157 MIN	SN54157 NOM	SN54157 MAX	SN74157 MIN	SN74157 NOM	SN74157 MAX	UNIT
Supply voltage, V_{CC}	4.5	5	5.5	4.75	5	5.25	V
High-level output current, I_{OH}			−800			−800	μA
Low-level output current, I_{OL}			16			16	mA
Operating free-air temperature, T_A	−55		125	0		70	°C

electrical characteristics over recommended operating free-air temperature range (unless otherwise noted)

PARAMETER		TEST CONDITIONS[†]	SN54157 MIN	SN54157 TYP[‡]	SN54157 MAX	SN74157 MIN	SN74157 TYP[‡]	SN74157 MAX	UNIT
V_{IH}	High-level input voltage		2			2			V
V_{IL}	Low-level input voltage				0.8			0.8	V
V_{IK}	Input clamp voltage	V_{CC} = MIN, I_I = −12 mA			1.5			−1.5	V
V_{OH}	High-level output voltage	V_{CC} = MIN, V_{IH} = 2 V, V_{IL} = 0.8 V, I_{OH} = −800 μA	2.4	3.4		2.4	3.4		V
V_{OL}	Low-level output voltage	V_{CC} = MIN, V_{IH} = 2 V, V_{IL} = 0.8 V, I_{OL} = 16 mA		0.2	0.4		0.2	0.4	V
I_I	Input current at maximum input voltage	V_{CC} = MAX, V_I = 5.5 V			1			1	mA
I_{IH}	High-level input current	V_{CC} = MAX, V_I = 2.4 V			40			40	μA
I_{IL}	Low-level input current	V_{CC} = MAX, V_I = 0.4 V			−1.6			−1.6	mA
I_{OS}	Short-circuit output current[§]	V_{CC} = MAX	−20		−55	−18		−55	mA
I_{CC}	Supply current	V_{CC} = MAX, See Note 2		30	48		30	48	mA

[†]For conditions shown as MIN or MAX, use the appropriate value specified under recommended operating conditions.
[‡]All typical values are at V_{CC} = 5 V, T_A = 25°C.
[§]Not more than one output should be shorted at a time and duration of short-circuit should not exceed one second.
NOTE 2: I_{CC} is measured with 4.5 V applied to all inputs and all outputs open.

switching characteristics, V_{CC} = 5 V, T_A = 25°C

PARAMETER[¶]	FROM (INPUT)	TEST CONDITIONS	MIN	TYP	MAX	UNIT
t_{PLH}	Data			9	14	ns
t_{PHL}				9	14	
t_{PLH}	Strobe $\overline{G}$	C_L = 15 pF, R_L = 400 Ω, See Note 3		13	20	ns
t_{PHL}				14	21	
t_{PLH}	Select $\overline{A}/B$			15	23	ns
t_{PHL}				18	27	

[¶]t_{PLH} ≡ propagation delay time, low-to-high-level output
t_{PHL} ≡ propagation delay time, high-to-low-level output
NOTE 3: See General Information Section for load circuits and voltage waveforms.

TEXAS
INSTRUMENTS

recommended operating conditions

		MIN	NOM	MAX	UNIT
V_{CC}	Supply voltage	4.5	5	5.5	V
I_{OH}	High-level output current			−400	μA
I_{OL}	Low-level output current			8	mA
T_A	Operating free-air temperature	−55		125	C

electrical characteristics over recommended operating free-air temperature range (unless otherwise noted)

	PARAMETER	TEST CONDITIONS†	MIN	TYP‡	MAX	UNIT
V_{IH}	High-level input voltage		2			V
V_{IL}	Low-level input voltage				0.8	V
V_{IK}	Input clamp voltage	V_{CC} = MIN, I_I = −12 mA			−1.5	V
V_{OH}	High-level output voltage	V_{CC} = MIN, V_{IH} = 2 V, V_{IL} = 0.8 V, I_{OH} = −400 μA	2.4	3.4		V
V_{OL}	Low-level output voltage	V_{CC} = MIN, V_{IH} = 2 V, V_{IL} = 0.8 V, I_{OL} = 8 mA		0.2	0.4	V
I_I	Input current at maximum input voltage	V_{CC} = MAX, V_I = 5.5 V			1	mA
I_{IH}	High-level input current	V_{CC} = MAX, V_I = 2.4 V			20	μA
I_{IL}	Low-level input current	V_{CC} = MAX, V_I = 0.4 V			−0.8	mA
I_{OS}	Short-circuit output current§	V_{CC} = MAX	−9		−28	mA
I_{CC}	Supply current	V_{CC} = MAX, See Note 2		15	24	mA

†For conditions shown as MIN or MAX, use the appropriate value specified under recommended operating conditions.
‡All typical values are at V_{CC} = 5 V, T_A = 25°C.
§Not more than one output should be shorted at a time.
NOTE 2: I_{CC} is measured with 4.5 V applied to all inputs and all outputs open.

switching characteristics, V_{CC} = 5 V, T_A = 25°C

PARAMETER¶	FROM (INPUT)	TEST CONDITIONS	MIN	TYP	MAX	UNIT
t_{PLH}	Data			18	28	ns
t_{PHL}	Data			18	28	ns
t_{PLH}	Strobe $\overline{G}$	C_L = 15 pF, R_L = 800 Ω, See Note 3		26	40	ns
t_{PHL}	Strobe $\overline{G}$			28	42	ns
t_{PLH}	Select $\overline{A}$/B			30	46	ns
t_{PHL}	Select $\overline{A}$/B			36	54	ns

¶ t_{PLH} ≡ propagation delay time, low-to-high-level output
t_{PHL} ≡ propagation delay time, high-to-low-level output

NOTE 3: See General Information Section for load circuits and voltage waveforms.

3

TTL DEVICES

TEXAS
INSTRUMENTS

TYPES SN54LS157, SN54LS158, SN74LS157, SN74LS158
QUADRUPLE 2-LINE TO 1-LINE DATA SELECTORS/MULTIPLEXERS

recommended operating conditions

		SN54LS'			SN74LS'			UNIT
		MIN	NOM	MAX	MIN	NOM	MAX	
V_{CC}	Supply voltage	4.5	5	5.5	4.75	5	5.25	V
I_{OH}	High-level output current			−400			−400	μA
I_{OL}	Low-level output current			4			8	mA
T_A	Operating free-air temperature	−55		125	0		70	°C

electrical characteristics over recommended operating free-air temperature range (unless otherwise noted)

	PARAMETER		TEST CONDITIONS[†]		SN54LS'			SN74LS'			UNIT
					MIN	TYP[‡]	MAX	MIN	TYP[‡]	MAX	
V_{IH}	High-level input voltage				2			2			V
V_{IL}	Low-level input voltage						0.7			0.8	V
V_{IK}	Input clamp voltage		V_{CC} = MIN,	I_I = −18 mA			−1.5			−1.5	V
V_{OH}	High-level output voltage		V_{CC} = MIN, V_{IH} = 2 V, V_{IL} = MAX, I_{OH} = −400 μA		2.5	3.4		2.7	3.4		V
V_{OL}	Low-level output voltage		V_{CC} = MIN, V_{IH} = 2 V, V_{IL} = MAX	I_{OL} = 4 mA		0.25	0.4		0.25	0.4	V
				I_{OL} = 8 mA					0.35	0.5	
I_I	Input current at maximum input voltage	$\overline{A}/B$ or $\overline{G}$	V_{CC} = MAX,	V_I = 7 V			0.2			0.2	mA
		A or B					0.1			0.1	
I_{IH}	High-level input current	$\overline{A}/B$ or $\overline{G}$	V_{CC} = MAX,	V_I = 2.7 V			40			40	μA
		A or B					20			20	
I_{IL}	Low-level input current	$\overline{A}/B$ or $\overline{G}$	V_{CC} = MAX,	V_I = 0.4 V			−0.8			−0.8	mA
		A or B					−0.4			−0.4	
I_{OS}	Short-circuit output current[§]		V_{CC} = MAX		−20		−100	−20		−100	mA
I_{CC}	Supply current		V_{CC} = MAX, See Note 2	'LS157		9.7	16		9.7	16	mA
				'LS158		4.8	8		4.8	8	
			V_{CC} = MAX, All A inputs at 4.5 V, All other inputs at 0 V	'LS158		6.5	11		6.5	11	

[†]For conditions shown as MIN or MAX, use the appropriate value specified under recommended operating conditions.
[‡]All typical values are at V_{CC} = 5 V, T_A = 25°C.
[§]Not more than one output should be shorted at a time and duration of short-circuit should not exceed one second.
NOTE 2: I_{CC} is measured with 4.5 V applied to all inputs and all outputs open.

switching characteristics, V_{CC} = 5 V, T_A = 25°C

PARAMETER[¶]	FROM (INPUT)	TEST CONDITIONS	'LS157			'LS158			UNIT
			MIN	TYP	MAX	MIN	TYP	MAX	
t_{PLH}	Data			9	14		7	12	ns
t_{PHL}				9	14		10	15	
t_{PLH}	Strobe $\overline{G}$	C_L = 15 pF, R_L = 2 kΩ, See Note 3		13	20		11	17	ns
t_{PHL}				14	21		18	24	
t_{PLH}	Select $\overline{A}/B$			15	23		13	20	ns
t_{PHL}				18	27		16	24	

[¶]t_{PLH} ≡ propagation delay time, low-to-high-level output
t_{PHL} ≡ propagation delay time, high-to-low-level output
NOTE 3. See General Information Section for load circuits and voltage waveforms.

Texas
INSTRUMENTS

recommended operating conditions

	SN54S157 SN54S158			SN74S157 SN74S158			UNIT
	MIN	NOM	MAX	MIN	NOM	MAX	
Supply voltage, V_{CC}	4.5	5	5.5	4.75	5	5.25	V
High-level output current, I_{OH}			−1			−1	mA
Low-level output current, I_{OL}			20			20	mA
Operating free-air temperature, T_A	−55		125	0		70	°C

electrical characteristics over recommended operating free-air temperature range (unless otherwise noted)

PARAMETER		TEST CONDITIONS†		SN54S157 SN74S157			SN54S158 SN74S158			UNIT
				MIN	TYP‡	MAX	MIN	TYP‡	MAX	
V_{IH}	High-level input voltage			2			2			V
V_{IL}	Low-level input voltage					0.8			0.8	V
V_{IK}	Input clamp voltage	V_{CC} = MIN, I_I = −18 mA				−1.2			−1.2	V
V_{OH}	High-level output voltage	V_{CC} = MIN, V_{IH} = 2 V,	Series 54S	2.5	3.4		2.5	3.4		V
		V_{IL} = 0.8 V, I_{OH} = −1 mA	Series 74S	2.7	3.4		2.7	3.4		
V_{OL}	Low-level output voltage	V_{CC} = MIN, V_{IH} = 2 V, V_{IL} = 0.8 V, I_{OL} = 20 mA				0.5			0.5	V
I_I	Input current at maximum input voltage	V_{CC} = MAX, V_I = 5.5 V				1			1	mA
I_{IH}	High-level input current	$\overline{A}$/B or $\overline{G}$	V_{CC} = MAX, V_I = 2.7 V			100			100	μA
		A or B				50			50	
I_{IL}	Low-level input current	$\overline{A}$/B or $\overline{G}$	V_{CC} = MAX, V_I = 0.5 V			−4			−4	mA
		A or B				−2			−2	
I_{OS}	Short-circuit ouput current §	V_{CC} = MAX		−40		−100	−40		−100	mA
I_{CC}	Supply current	V_{CC} = MAX, All inputs at 4.5 V, See Note 2			50	78		39	61	mA
		V_{CC} = MAX, A inputs at 4.5 V, B,G,S, inputs at 0 V, See Note 2							81	

†For conditions shown as MIN or MAX, use the appropriate value specified under recommended operating conditions.
‡All typical values are at V_{CC} = 5 V, T_A = 25°C.
§Not more than one output should be shorted at a time, and duration of the short-circuit should not exceed one second.
Note 2: I_{CC} is measured with all outputs open.

switching characteristics, V_{CC} = 5 V, T_A = 25°C

PARAMETER¶	FROM (INPUT)	TEST CONDITIONS	SN54S157 SN74S157			SN54S158 SN74S158			UNIT
			MIN	TYP	MAX	MIN	TYP	MAX	
t_{PLH}	Data	C_L = 15 pF, R_L = 280 Ω, See Note 3		5	7.5		4	6	ns
t_{PHL}				4.5	6.5		4	6	
t_{PLH}	Strobe $\overline{G}$			8.5	12.5		6.5	11.5	ns
t_{PHL}				7.5	12		7	12	
t_{PLH}	Select $\overline{A}$/B			9.5	15		8	12	ns
t_{PHL}				9.5	15		8	12	

¶t_{PLH} ≡ propagation delay time, low-to-high-level output
t_{PHL} ≡ propagation delay time, high-to-low-level output
NOTE 3: See General Information Section for load circuits and voltage waveforms.

3

TTL DEVICES

TEXAS
INSTRUMENTS

- **Open-Collector Outputs for Interfacing with MOS or Memory Decoders/Drivers**

- **Decodes 4 Binary-Coded Inputs into One of 16 Mutually Exclusive Outputs**

- **Performs the Demultiplexing Function by Distributing Data from One Input Line to Any One of 16 Outputs**

- **Typical Average Propagation Delay Times:**
  24 ns through 3 levels of Logic
  19 ns from Strobe Input

- **Output Off-State Current is Less Than 50 μA**

- **Fully Compatible with Most TTL, and MSI Circuits**

SN54159 . . . J OR W PACKAGE
SN74159 . . . J OR N PACKAGE
(TOP VIEW)

0	1	24 V$_{CC}$
1	2	23 A
2	3	22 B
3	4	21 C
4	5	20 D
5	6	19 $\overline{G2}$
6	7	18 $\overline{G1}$
7	8	17 15
8	9	16 14
9	10	15 13
10	11	14 12
GND	12	13 11

description

Each of these monolithic, 4-line-to-16 line decoders utilizes TTL circuitry to decode four binary-coded inputs into one of sixteen mutually exclusive open-collector outputs when both the strobe inputs, $\overline{G1}$ and $\overline{G2}$, are low. The demultiplexing function is performed by using the 4 input lines to address the output line, passing data from one of the strobe inputs with the other strobe input low. When either strobe input is high, all outputs are high. These demultiplexers are ideally suited for implementing MOS memory decoding or for interfacing with discrete memory address drivers. For ultra-high-speed applications, the SN54S138/SN74S138 or SN54S139/SN74S139 is recommended.

These circuits are fully compatible for use with most other TTL circuits. Input clamping diodes are provided to minimize transmission-line effects and thereby simplify system design. Input buffers are used to lower the fan-in requirement to only one normalized Series 54/74 load. A fan-out to 10 normalized Series 54/74 loads in the low-level state is available from each of the sixteen outputs. Typical power dissipation is 170 mW.

The SN54159 is characterized for operation over the full military temperature range of $-55°C$ to $125°C$; the SN74159 is characterized for operation from $0°C$ to $70°C$.

function table

Same as SN54154, SN74154.

logic diagram

Same as SN54154, SN74154.

absolute maximum ratings over operating free-air temperature range (unless otherwise noted)

Supply voltage, V$_{CC}$ (see Note 1)	7 V
Input voltage	5.5 V
Off-state output voltage	5.5 V
Operating free-air temperature range: SN54159 Circuits	$-55°C$ to $125°C$
SN74159 Circuits	$0°C$ to $70°C$
Storage temperature range	$-65°C$ to $150°C$

NOTE 1: Voltage values are with respect to network ground terminal.

TEXAS
INSTRUMENTS

TTL DEVICES

3

recommended operating conditions

	SN54159			SN74159			UNIT
	MIN	NOM	MAX	MIN	NOM	MAX	
Supply voltage, V_{CC}	4.5	5	5.5	4.75	5	5.25	V
Low-level output current, I_{OL}			16			16	mA
Operating free-air temperature, T_A	−55		125	0		70	°C

electrical characteristics over recommended operating free-air temperature range (unless otherwise noted)

	PARAMETER	TEST CONDITIONS†	MIN	TYP‡	MAX	UNIT
V_{IH}	High-level input voltage		2			V
V_{IL}	Low-level input voltage				0.8	V
V_{IK}	Input clamp voltage	V_{CC} = MIN, I_I = −12 mA			−1.5	V
I_{OH}	High-level output current	V_{CC} = MIN, V_{IH} = 2 V, V_{IL} = 0.8 V, V_{OH} = 5.5 V			50	μA
V_{OL}	Low-level output voltage	V_{CC} = MIN, V_{IH} = 2 V, V_{IL} = 0.8 V, I_{OL} = 16 mA			0.4	V
I_I	Input current at maximum input voltage	V_{CC} = MAX, V_I = 5.5 V			1	mA
I_{IH}	High-level input current	V_{CC} = MAX, V_I = 2.4 V			40	μA
I_{IL}	Low-level input current	V_{CC} = MAX, V_I = 0.4 V			−1.6	mA
I_{CC}	Supply current	V_{CC} = MAX, All inputs grounded		34	56	mA

†For conditions shown as MIN or MAX, use the appropriate value specified under recommended operating conditions for the applicable type.
‡All typical values are at V_{CC} = 5 V, T_A = 25°C.

switching characteristics, V_{CC} = 5 V, T_A = 25°C

	PARAMETER	TEST CONDITIONS	MIN	TYP	MAX	UNIT
t_{PLH}	Propagation delay time, low-to-high-level output, from A, B, C, or D inputs through 3 levels of logic	C_L = 15 pF, R_L = 400 Ω, See Note 2		23	36	ns
t_{PHL}	Propagation delay time, high-to-low-level output, from A, B, C, or D inputs through 3 levels of logic			24	36	ns
t_{PLH}	Propagation delay time, low-to-high-level output, from either strobe input			15	25	ns
t_{PHL}	Propagation delay time, high-to-low-level output, from either strobe input			22	36	ns

NOTE 2: See General Information Section for load circuits and voltage waveforms.

schematics of inputs and outputs

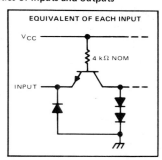

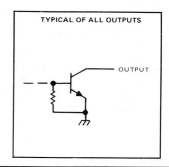

'160,'161,'LS160A,'LS161A . . . SYNCHRONOUS COUNTERS WITH DIRECT CLEAR
'162,'163,'LS162A,'LS163A,'S162,'S163 . . . FULLY SYNCHRONOUS COUNTERS

- **Internal Look-Ahead for Fast Counting**
- **Carry Output for n-Bit Cascading**
- **Synchronous Counting**
- **Synchronously Programmable**
- **Load Control Line**
- **Diode-Clamped Inputs**

SERIES 54', 54LS', 54S' . . . J OR W PACKAGE
SERIES 74' . . . J OR N PACKAGE
SERIES 74LS', 74S' . . . D, J OR N PACKAGE
(TOP VIEW)

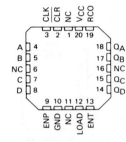

NC—No internal connection

SERIES 54LS', 54S' . . . FK PACKAGE
SERIES 74LS', 74S'
(TOP VIEW)

NC—No internal connection

TYPE	TYPICAL PROPAGATION TIME, CLOCK TO Q OUTPUT	TYPICAL MAXIMUM CLOCK FREQUENCY	TYPICAL POWER DISSIPATION
'160 thru '163	14 ns	32 MHz	305 mW
'LS162A thru 'LS163A	14 ns	32 MHz	93 mW
'S162 and 'S163	9 ns	70 MHz	475 mW

description

These synchronous, presettable counters feature an internal carry look-ahead for application in high-speed counting designs. The '160,'162,'LS160A,'LS162A, and 'S162 are decade counters and the '161,'163,'LS161A,'LS163A, and 'S163 are 4-bit binary counters. Synchronous operation is provided by having all flip-flops clocked simultaneously so that the outputs change coincident with each other when so instructed by the count-enable inputs and internal gating. This mode of operation eliminates the output counting spikes that are normally associated with asynchronous (ripple clock) counters. A buffered clock input triggers the four flip-flops on the rising edge of the clock input waveform.

These counters are fully programmable; that is, the outputs may be preset to either level. As presetting is synchronous, setting up a low level at the load input disables the counter and causes the outputs to agree with the setup data after the next clock pulse regardless of the levels of the enable inputs. Low-to-high transitions at the load input of the '160 thru '163 should be avoided when the clock is low if the enable inputs are high at or before the transition. This restriction is not applicable to the 'LS160A thru 'LS163A or 'S162 or 'S163. The clear function for the '160, '161,'LS160A, and 'LS161A is asynchronous and a low level at the clear input sets all four of the flip-flop outputs low regardless of the levels of clock, load, or enable inputs. The clear function for the '162,'163,'LS162A,'LS163A, 'S162, and 'S163 is synchronous and a low level at the clear input sets all four of the flip-flop outputs low after the next clock pulse, regardless of the levels of the enable inputs. This synchronous clear allows the count length to be modified easily as decoding the maximum count desired can be accomplished with one external NAND gate. The gate output is connected to the clear input to synchronously clear the counter to 0000 (LLLL). Low-to-high transitions at the clear input of the '162 and '163 should be avoided when the clock is low if the enable and load inputs are high at or before the transition.

TEXAS
INSTRUMENTS

TTL DEVICES

3

TYPES SN54160 THRU SN54163, SN54LS160A THRU SN54LS163A, SN54S162, SN54S163, SN74160 THRU SN74163, SN74LS160A THRU SN74LS163A, SN74S162, SN74S163 SYNCHRONOUS 4-BIT COUNTERS

The carry look-ahead circuitry provides for cascading counters for n-bit synchronous applications without additional gating. Instrumental in accomplishing this function are two count-enable inputs and a ripple carry output. Both count-enable inputs (P and T) must be high to count, and input T is fed forward to enable the ripple carry output. The ripple carry output thus enabled will produce a high-level output pulse with a duration approximately equal to the high-level portion of the Q_A output. This high-level overflow ripple carry pulse can be used to enable successive cascaded stages. High-to-low-level transitions at the enable P or T inputs of the '160 thru '163 should occur only when the clock input is high. Transitions at the enable P or T inputs of the 'LS160A thru 'LS163A or 'S162 and 'S163 are allowed regardless of the level of the clock input.

'LS160A thru 'LS163A, 'S162 and 'S163 feature a fully independent clock circuit. Changes at control inputs (enable P or T, or load) that will modify the operating mode have no effect until clocking occurs. The function of the counter (whether enabled, disabled, loading, or counting) will be dictated solely by the conditions meeting the stable setup and hold times.

The 'LS160A thru 'LS163A are completely new designs. Compared to the original 'LS160 thru 'LS163, they feature O-nanosecond minimium hold time and reduced input currents I_{IH} and I_{IL}.

N-BIT SYNCHRONOUS COUNTERS

This application demonstrates how the look-ahead carry circuit can be used to implement a high-speed n-bit counter. The '160, '162, 'LS160A, 'LS162A, or 'S162 will count in BCD and the '161, '163, 'LS161A, 'LS163A or 'S163 will count in binary. Virtually any count mode (modulo-N, N_1-to-N_2, N_1-to-maximum) can be used with this fast look-ahead circuit.

logic symbols

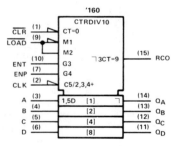

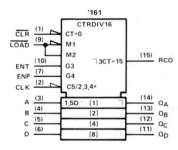

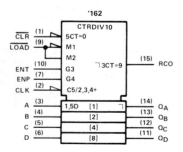

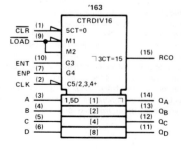

Pin numbers shown on logic notation are for D, J or N packages.

TEXAS
INSTRUMENTS

logic symbols (continued)

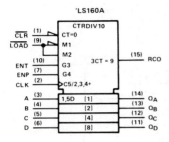

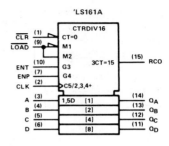

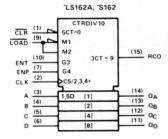

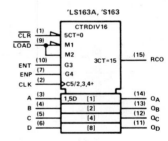

Pin numbers shown on logic notation are for D, J or N packages.

TTL DEVICES

3

logic diagram

SN54160, SN74160 SYNCHRONOUS DECADE COUNTERS

SN54162, SN74162 synchronous decade counters are similar; however the clear is synchronous as shown for the SN54163, SN74163 binary counters at right.

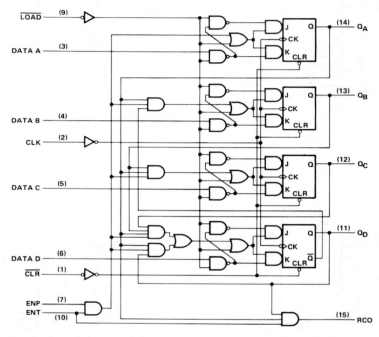

Pin numbers shown on logic notation are for D, J or N packages.

TEXAS
INSTRUMENTS

logic diagram

SN54163, SN74163 SYNCHRONOUS BINARY COUNTERS

SN54161, SN74161 synchronous binary counters are similar;
however, the clear is asynchronous as shown for the SN54160,
SN74160 decade counters at left.

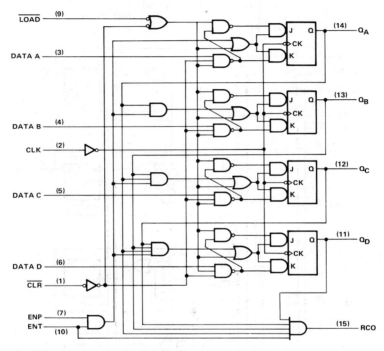

Pin numbers shown on logic notation are for D, J or N packages.

3

TTL DEVICES

logic diagram

SN54LS160A, SN74LS160A SYNCHRONOUS
DECADE COUNTERS

SN54LS162A, SN74LS162A synchronous decade
counters are similar; however the clear is synchronous
as shown for the SN54LS163A, SN74LS163A binary
counters at right.

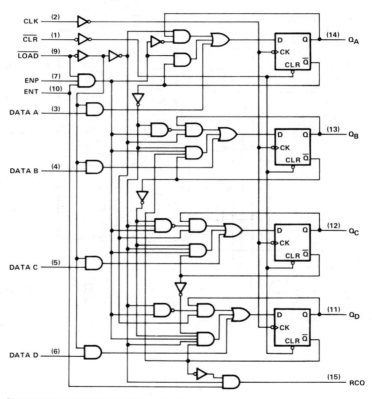

Pin numbers shown on logic notation are for D, J or N packages.

TEXAS
INSTRUMENTS

logic diagram

SN54LS163A, SN74LS163A SYNCHRONOUS
BINARY COUNTERS

SN54LS161A, SN74LS161A synchronous binary counters are similar; however, the clear is asynchronous as shown for the SN54LS160A, SN74LS160A decade counters at left.

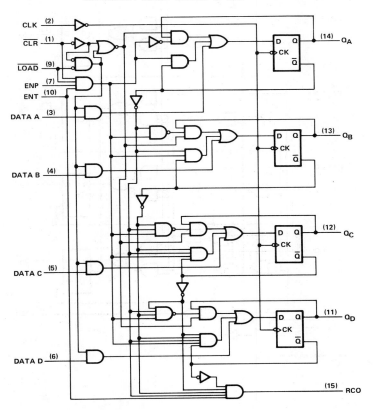

Pin numbers shown on logic notation are for D, J or N packages.

TEXAS
INSTRUMENTS

SN54S162, SN74S162
SYNCHRONOUS 4–BIT COUNTERS

logic diagram

SN54S162, SN74S162 SYNCHRONOUS DECADE COUNTER

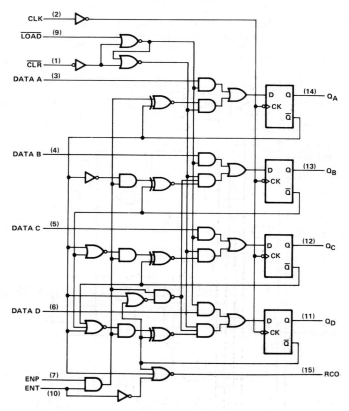

Pin numbers shown on logic notation are for D, J or N packages.

TEXAS
INSTRUMENTS

logic diagram

SN54S163, SN74S163 SYNCHRONOUS DECADE COUNTER

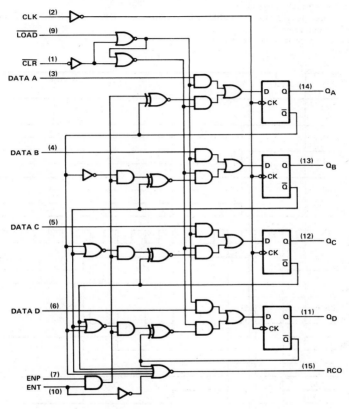

Pin numbers shown on logic notation are for D, J or N packages.

TEXAS
INSTRUMENTS

TYPES SN54160, SN54162, SN54LS160A, SN54LS162A, SN54S162, SN74160, SN74162, SN74LS160A, SN74LS162A, SN74S162
SYNCHRONOUS 4-BIT COUNTERS

'160, '162, 'LS160A, 'LS162A, 'S162 DECADE COUNTERS

typical clear, preset, count, and inhibit sequences

Illustrated below is the following sequence:

1. Clear outputs to zero ('160 and 'LS160A are asynchronous; '162, 'LS162A, and 'S162 are synchronous)
2. Preset to BCD seven
3. Count to eight, nine, zero, one, two, and three
4. Inhibit

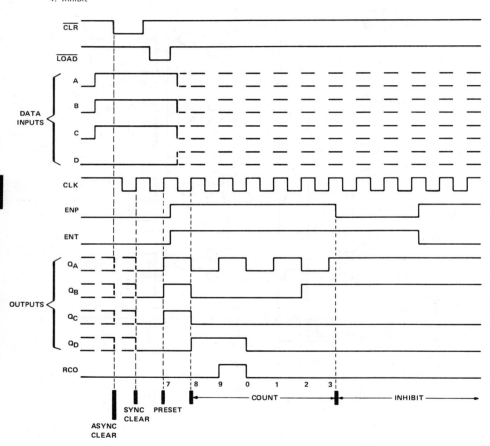

TEXAS INSTRUMENTS

'161, 'LS161A, '163, 'LS163A, 'S163 BINARY COUNTERS

typical clear, preset, count, and inhibit sequences

Illustrated below is the following sequence:

1. Clear outputs to zero ('161 and 'LS161A are asynchronous; '163, 'LS163A, and 'S163 are synchronous)
2. Preset to binary twelve
3. Count to thirteen, fourteen fifteen, zero, one, and two
4. Inhibit

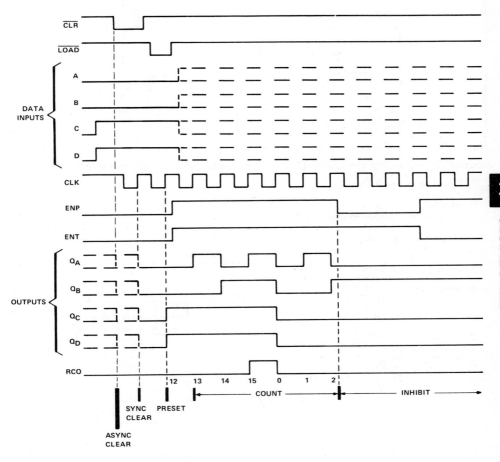

TTL DEVICES

3

SN54160 THRU SN54163, SN74160 THRU SN74163
SYNCHRONOUS 4-BIT COUNTERS

schematics of inputs and outputs

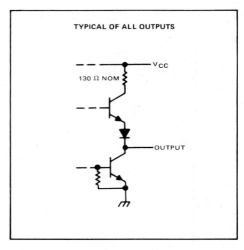

EQUIVALENT OF EACH INPUT

V_{CC}

R_{eq}

INPUT

CLK: R_{eq} = 2.8 kΩ NOM
ENT: R_{eq} = 2 kΩ NOM
$\overline{CLR}$, ENP: R_{eq} = 4 kΩ NOM
A, B, C, D: R_{eq} = 6 kΩ NOM

TYPICAL OF ALL OUTPUTS

V_{CC}

130 Ω NOM

OUTPUT

absolute maximum ratings over operating free-air temperature range (unless otherwise noted)

Supply voltage, V_{CC} (see Note 1) . . . . 7 V
Input voltage . . . . 5.5 V
Interemitter voltage (see Note 2) . . . . 5.5 V
Operating free-air temperature range: SN54' Circuits . . . . −55°C to 125°C
  SN74' Circuits . . . . 0°C to 70°C
Storage temperature range . . . . −65°C to 150°C

NOTES: 1. Voltage values, except interemitter voltage, are with respect to network ground terminal.
2. This is the voltage between two emitters of a multiple-emitter transistor. For these circuits, this rating applies between the count enable inputs P and T.

recommended operating conditions

		SN54160, SN54161 SN54162, SN54163			SN74160, SN74161 SN74162, SN74163			UNIT
		MIN	NOM	MAX	MIN	NOM	MAX	
Supply voltage, V_{CC}		4.5	5	5.5	4.75	5	5.25	V
High-level output current, I_{OH}				−800			−800	μA
Low-level output current, I_{OL}				16			16	mA
Clock frequency, f_{clock}		0		25	0		25	MHz
Width of clock pulse, $t_{w(clock)}$		25			25			ns
Width of clear pulse, $t_{w(clear)}$		20			20			ns
Setup time, t_{su} (see Figures 1 and 2)	Data inputs A, B, C, D	20			20			ns
	ENP	20			20			
	$\overline{LOAD}$	25			25			
	CLR †	20			20			
Hold time at any input, t_h		0			0			ns
Operating free-air temperature, T_A		−55		125	0		70	°C

†This applies only for '162 and '163, which have synchronous clear inputs.

TEXAS INSTRUMENTS

electrical characteristics over recommended operating free-air temperature range (unless otherwise noted)

	PARAMETER		TEST CONDITIONS†	SN54160, SN54161 SN54162, SN54163			SN74160, SN74161 SN74162, SN74163			UNIT
				MIN	TYP‡	MAX	MIN	TYP‡	MAX	
V_{IH}	High-level input voltage			2			2			V
V_{IL}	Low-level input voltage					0.8			0.8	V
V_{IK}	Input clamp voltage		V_{CC} = MIN, I_I = −12 mA			−1.5			−1.5	V
V_{OH}	High-level output voltage		V_{CC} = MIN, V_{IH} = 2 V, V_{IL} = 0.8 V, I_{OH} = −800 μA	2.4	3.4		2.4	3.4		V
V_{OL}	Low-level output voltage		V_{CC} = MIN, V_{IH} = 2 V, V_{IL} = 0.8 V, I_{OL} = 16 mA		0.2	0.4		0.2	0.4	V
I_I	Input current at maximum input voltage		V_{CC} = MAX, V_I = 5.5 V			1			1	mA
I_{IH}	High-level input current	CLK or ENT	V_{CC} = MAX, V_I = 2.4 V			80			80	μA
		Other inputs				40			40	
I_{IL}	Low-level input current	CLK or ENT	V_{CC} = MAX, V_I = 0.4 V			−3.2			−3.2	mA
		Other inputs				−1.6			−1.6	
I_{OS}	Short-circuit output current §		V_{CC} = MAX	−20		−57	−18		−57	mA
I_{CCH}	Supply current, all outputs high		V_{CC} = MAX, See Note 3		59	85		59	94	mA
I_{CCL}	Supply current, all outputs low		V_{CC} = MAX, See Note 4		63	91		63	101	mA

†For conditions shown as MIN or MAX, use the appropriate value specified under recommended operating conditions.
‡All typical values are at V_{CC} = 5 V, T_A = 25°C.
§Not more than one output should be shorted at a time.
NOTES: 3. I_{CCH} is measured with the load input high, then again with the load input low, with all other inputs high and all outputs open.
   4. I_{CCL} is measured with the clock input high, then again with the clock input low, with all other inputs low and all outputs open.

switching characteristics, V_{CC} = 5 V, T_A = 25°C

PARAMETER¶	FROM (INPUT)	TO (OUTPUT)	TEST CONDITIONS	MIN	TYP	MAX	UNIT
f_{max}				25	32		MHz
t_{PLH}	CLK	RCO			23	35	ns
t_{PHL}					23	35	
t_{PLH}	CLK	Any	C_L = 15 pF,		13	20	ns
t_{PHL}	(LOAD input high)	Q	R_L = 400 Ω,		15	23	
t_{PLH}	CLK	Any	See Figures 1 and 2		17	25	ns
t_{PHL}	(LOAD input low)	Q	and Note 5		19	29	
t_{PLH}	ENT	RCO			11	16	ns
t_{PHL}					11	16	
t_{PHL}	CLR	Any Q			26	38	ns

¶f_{max} = Maximum clock frequency
t_{PLH} = propagation delay time, low-to-high-level output
t_{PHL} = propagation delay time, high-to-low-level output
NOTE 5: Propagation delay for clearing is measured from the clear input for the '160 and '161 or from the clock input transition for the '162 and '163.

3

TTL DEVICES

TEXAS INSTRUMENTS

SN54LS160A THRU SN54LS163A, SN74LS160A THRU SN74LS163A
SYNCHRONOUS 4-BIT COUNTERS

schematics of inputs and outputs

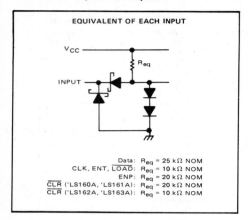

EQUIVALENT OF EACH INPUT

V_{CC}

R_{eq}

INPUT

Data: R_{eq} = 25 kΩ NOM
CLK, ENT, $\overline{LOAD}$: R_{eq} = 10 kΩ NOM
ENP: R_{eq} = 20 kΩ NOM
$\overline{CLR}$ ('LS160A, 'LS161A): R_{eq} = 20 kΩ NOM
$\overline{CLR}$ ('LS162A, 'LS163A): R_{eq} = 10 kΩ NOM

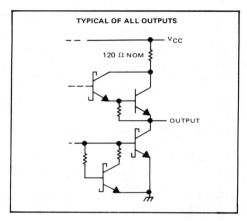

TYPICAL OF ALL OUTPUTS

V_{CC}

120 Ω NOM

OUTPUT

absolute maximum ratings over operating free-air temperature range (unless otherwise noted)

Supply voltage, V_{CC} (see Note 7) . . . . 7 V
Input voltage . . . . 7 V
Operating free-air temperature range: SN54LS' Circuits . . . . −55 °C to 125 °C
SN74LS' Circuits . . . . 0 °C to 70 °C
Storage temperature range . . . . −65 °C to 150 °C

NOTE 7: Voltage values are with respect to network ground terminal.

recommended operating conditions

		SN54LS'			SN74LS'			UNIT
		MIN	NOM	MAX	MIN	NOM	MAX	
V_{CC}	Supply voltage	4.5	5	5.5	4.75	5	5.25	V
I_{OH}	High-level output current			−400			−400	µA
I_{OL}	Low-level output current			4			8	mA
f_{clock}	Clock frequency	0		25	0		25	MHz
$t_{w(clock)}$	Width of clock pulse	25			25			ns
$t_{w(clear)}$	Width of clear pulse	20			20			ns
t_{su}	Setup time, (see Figures 1 and 2)	Data inputs A, B, C, D	20			20			ns
		ENP or ENT	20			20		
		$\overline{LOAD}$	20			20		
		$\overline{LOAD}$ inactive state	20			20		
		$\overline{CLR}$†	20			20		
		$\overline{CLR}$ inactive state	25			25		
t_h	Hold time at any input	9			3			ns
T_A	Operating free-air temperature	−55		125	0		70	°C

† This applies only for 'LS162 and 'LS163, which have synchronous clear inputs.

TEXAS INSTRUMENTS

3 TTL DEVICES

electrical characteristics over recommended operating free-air temperature range (unless otherwise noted)

PARAMETER		TEST CONDITIONS†	SN54LS' MIN	SN54LS' TYP‡	SN54LS' MAX	SN74LS' MIN	SN74LS' TYP‡	SN74LS' MAX	UNIT
V_{IH} High-level input voltage			2			2			V
V_{IL} Low-level input voltage					0.7			0.8	V
V_{IK} Input clamp voltage		V_{CC} = MIN, I_I = −18 mA			−1.5			−1.5	V
V_{OH} High-level output voltage		V_{CC} = MIN, V_{IH} = 2 V, V_{IL} = V_{IL} max, I_{OH} = −400 µA	2.5	3.4		2.7	3.4		V
V_{OL} Low-level output voltage		V_{CC} = MIN, V_{IH} = 2 V, V_{IL} = V_{IL} max, I_{OL} = 4 mA		0.25	0.4		0.25	0.4	V
		I_{OL} = 8 mA					0.35	0.5	
I_I Input current at maximum input voltage	Data or ENP	V_{CC} = MAX, V_I = 7 V			0.1			0.1	mA
	$\overline{LOAD}$, CLK, or ENT				0.2			0.2	
	$\overline{CLR}$ ('LS160A, 'LS161A)				0.1			0.1	
	$\overline{CLR}$ ('LS162A, 'LS163A)				0.2			0.2	
I_{IH} High-level input current	Data or ENP	V_{CC} = MAX, V_I = 2.7 V			20			20	µA
	$\overline{LOAD}$, CLK, or ENT				40			40	
	$\overline{CLR}$ ('LS160A, 'LS161A)				20			20	
	$\overline{CLR}$ ('LS162A, 'LS163A)				40			40	
I_{IL} Low-level input current	Data or ENP	V_{CC} = MAX, V_I = 0.4 V			−0.4			−0.4	mA
	$\overline{LOAD}$, CLK, or ENT				−0.8			−0.8	
	$\overline{CLR}$ ('LS160A, 'LS161A)				−0.4			−0.4	
	$\overline{CLR}$ ('LS162A, 'LS163A)				−0.8			−0.8	
I_{OS} Short-circuit output current§		V_{CC} = MAX	−20		−100	−20		−100	mA
I_{CCH} Supply current, all outputs high		V_{CC} = MAX, See Note 3		18	31		18	31	mA
I_{CCL} Supply current, all outputs low		V_{CC} = MAX, See Note 4		19	32		19	32	mA

†For conditions shown as MIN or MAX, use the appropriate value specified under recommended operating conditions.
‡All typical values are at V_{CC} = 5 V, T_A = 25°C.
§Not more than one output should be shorted at a time, and duration of the short-circuit should not exceed one second.
NOTES: 3. I_{CCH} is measured with the load input high, then again with the load input low, with all other inputs high and all outputs open.
 4. I_{CCL} is measured with the clock input high, then again with the clock input low, with all other inputs low and all outputs open.

switching characteristics, V_{CC} = 5 V, T_A = 25°C

PARAMETER¶	FROM (INPUT)	TO (OUTPUT)	TEST CONDITIONS	MIN	TYP	MAX	UNIT
f_{max}				25	32		MHz
t_{PLH}	CLK	RCO			20	35	ns
t_{PHL}					18	35	
t_{PLH}	CLK	Any Q	C_L = 15 pF, R_L = 2 kΩ, See figures 1 and 2 and Note 8		13	24	ns
t_{PHL}	($\overline{LOAD}$ input high)				18	27	
t_{PLH}	CLK	Any Q			13	24	ns
t_{PHL}	($\overline{LOAD}$ input low)				18	27	
t_{PLH}	ENT	RCO			9	14	ns
t_{PHL}					9	14	
t_{PHL}	$\overline{CLR}$	Any Q			20	28	ns

¶f_{max} = Maximum clock frequency
t_{PLH} = propagation delay time, low-to-high-level output.
t_{PHL} = propagation delay time, high-to-low-level output.
NOTE 8: Propagation delay for clearing is measured from the clear input for the 'LS160A and 'LS161A or from the clock transition for the 'LS162A and 'LS163A.

TEXAS
INSTRUMENTS

SN54S162, SN54S163, SN74S162, SN74S163
SYNCHRONOUS 4-BIT COUNTERS

schematics of inputs and outputs

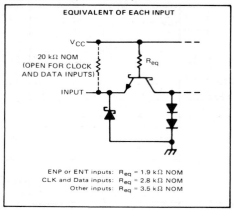

EQUIVALENT OF EACH INPUT

V_{CC}

20 kΩ NOM
(OPEN FOR CLOCK
AND DATA INPUTS)

R_{eq}

INPUT

ENP or ENT inputs: R_{eq} = 1.9 kΩ NOM
CLK and Data inputs: R_{eq} = 2.8 kΩ NOM
Other inputs: R_{eq} = 3.5 kΩ NOM

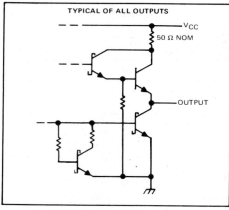

TYPICAL OF ALL OUTPUTS

V_{CC}

50 Ω NOM

OUTPUT

absolute maximum ratings over operating free-air temperature range (unless otherwise noted)

Supply voltage, V_{CC} (see Note 1) . . . . 7 V
Input voltage . . . . 5.5 V
Interemitter voltage (see Note 2) . . . . 5.5 V
Operating free-air temperature range: SN54S162, SN54S163 (see Note 10) . . . . $-55°$C to $125°$C
                               SN74S162, SN74S163 . . . . $0°$C to $70°$C
Storage temperature range . . . . $-65°$C to $150°$C

recommended operating conditions

		SN54S162, SN54S163			SN74S162, SN74S163			UNIT
		MIN	NOM	MAX	MIN	NOM	MAX	
Supply voltage, V_{CC}		4.5	5	5.5	4.75	5	5.25	V
High-level output current, I_{OH}				-1			-1	mA
Low-level output current, I_{OL}				20			20	mA
Clock frequency, f_{clock}		0		40	0		40	MHz
Width of clock pulse, $t_{w(clock)}$ (high or low)		10			10			ns
Width of clear pulse, $t_{w(clear)}$		10			10			ns
Setup time, t_{su} (see Figure 4)	Data inputs, A, B, C, D	4			4			ns
	ENP or ENT	12			12			
	$\overline{LOAD}$	14			14			
	$\overline{CLR}$	14			14			
	$\overline{LOAD}$ inactive-state	12			12			
	$\overline{CLR}$ inactive-state	12			12			
Release time, $t_{release}$ (see Figure 4)	ENP or ENT			4			4	ns
Hold time, t_h (see Figure 4)	Data inputs A, B, C, D	3			3			ns
	$\overline{LOAD}$	0			0			
	$\overline{CLR}$	0			0			
Operating free-air temperature, T_A (see Note 10)		-55		125	0		70	°C

NOTES: 1. Voltage values, except interemitter voltage, are with respect to network ground terminal.
       2. This is the voltage between two emitters of a multiple emitter transistor. For these circuits, this rating applies between the count enable inputs P and T.
   10. An SN54S162 or SN54S163 in the W package operating at free air temperatures above 91°C requires a heat sink that provides a thermal resistance from case to free-air, $R_{\theta CA}$, of not more than 26°C/W.

TEXAS INSTRUMENTS

electrical characteristics over recommended operating free-air temperature range (unless otherwise noted)

PARAMETER		TEST CONDITIONS†	SN54S162 SN54S163			SN74S162 SN74S163			UNIT
			MIN	TYP‡	MAX	MIN	TYP‡	MAX	
V_{IH}	High-level input voltage		2			2			V
V_{IL}	Low-level input voltage				0.8			0.8	V
V_{IK}	Input clamp voltage	V_{CC} = MIN, I_I = −18 mA			−1.2			−1.2	V
V_{OH}	High-level output voltage	V_{CC} = MIN, V_{IH} = 2 V, V_{IL} = 0.8 V, I_{OH} = −1 mA	2.5	3.4		2.7	3.4		V
V_{OL}	Low-level output voltage	V_{CC} = MIN, V_{IH} = 2 V, V_{IL} = 0.8 V, I_{OL} = 20 mA			0.5			0.5	V
I_I	Input current at maximum input voltage		V_{CC} = MAX, V_I = 5.5 V			1			1	mA
I_{IH}	High-level input current	CLK and data inputs	V_{CC} = MAX, V_I = 2.7 V			50			50	μA
		Other inputs		−10		−200	−10		−200	
I_{IL}	Low-level input current	ENT	V_{CC} = MAX, V_I = 0.5 V			−4			−4	mA
		Other inputs				2			2	
I_{OS}	Short-circuit output current§		V_{CC} = MAX	−40		−100	−40		100	mA
I_{CC}	Supply current		V_{CC} = MAX		95	160		95	160	mA

†For conditions shown as MIN or MAX, use the appropriate value specified under recommended operating conditions.
‡All typical values are at V_{CC} = 5 V, T_A = 25 C.
§Not more than one output should be shorted at a time, and duration of the short-circuit should not exceed one second.

switching characteristics, V_{CC} = 5 V, T_A = 25°C

PARAMETER¶	FROM (INPUT)	TO (OUTPUT)	TEST CONDITIONS	MIN	TYP	MAX	UNIT
f_{max}				40	70		MHz
t_{PLH}	CLK	RCO	C_L = 15 pF, R_L = 280 Ω, See Figures 1, 3, and 4		14	25	ns
t_{PHL}					17	25	
t_{PLH}	CLK	Any Q			8	15	ns
t_{PHL}					10	15	
t_{PLH}	ENT	RCO			10	15	ns
t_{PHL}					10	15	

¶ f_{max} ≡ maximum clock frequency
t_{PLH} ≡ propagation delay time, low-to-high-level output
t_{PHL} ≡ propagation delay time, high-to-low-level output

TTL DEVICES

3

TEXAS
INSTRUMENTS

SN54160 THRU SN54163, SN54LS160A THRU SN54LS163A, SN54S162, SN54S163, SN74160 THRU SN74163, SN74LS160A THRU SN74LS163A, SN74S162, SN74S163 SYNCHRONOUS 4-BIT COUNTERS

PARAMETER MEASUREMENT INFORMATION

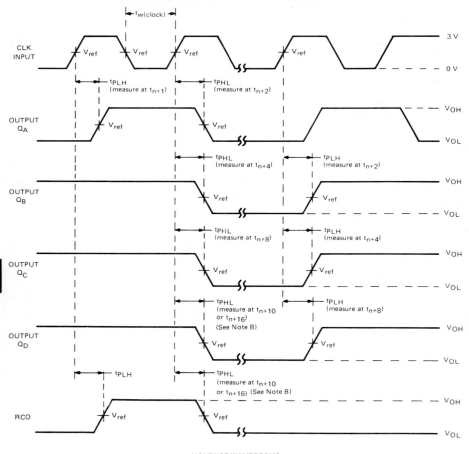

VOLTAGE WAVEFORMS

NOTES: A. The input pulses are supplied by a generator having the following characteristics: PRR ≤ 1 MHz, duty cycle ≤ 50%, $Z_{out} \approx 50\ \Omega$; for '160 thru '163, t_r ≤ 10 ns, t_f ≤ 10 ns; for 'LS160A thru 'LS163A, t_r ≤ 15 ns, t_f ≤ 6 ns; and for 'S162, 'S163, t_r ≤ 2.5 ns, t_f ≤ 2.5 ns. Vary PRR to measure f_{max}.
B. Outputs Q_D and carry are tested at t_{n+10} for '160, '162, 'LS160A, 'LS162A, and 'S162, and at t_{n+16} for '161, '163, 'LS161A, 'LS163A, and 'S163, where t_n is the bit time when all outputs are low.
C. For '160 thru '163, 'S162, and 'S163, V_{ref} = 1.5 V; for 'LS160A thru 'LS163A, V_{ref} = 1.3 V.

FIGURE 1—SWITCHING TIMES

3-490

TEXAS
INSTRUMENTS

PARAMETER MEASUREMENT INFORMATION

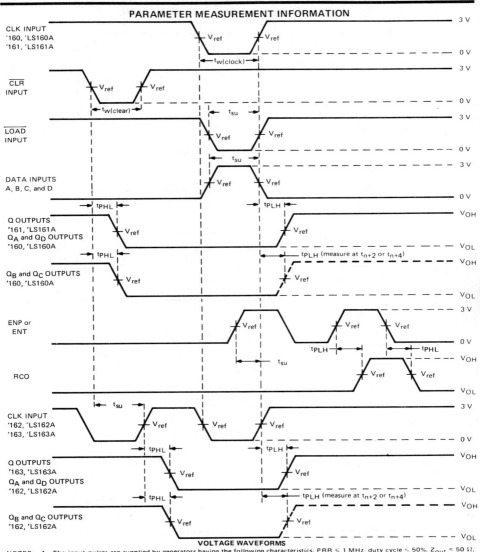

3

TTL DEVICES

VOLTAGE WAVEFORMS

NOTES: A. The input pulses are supplied by generators having the following characteristics: PRR ≤ 1 MHz, duty cycle ≤ 50%, $Z_{out} \approx 50\ \Omega$; for '160 thru '163, $t_r \le 10$ ns, $t_f \le 10$ ns; and for 'LS160A thru 'LS163A, $t_r \le 15$ ns, $t_f \le 6$ ns.
B. Enable P and enable T setup times are measured at t_{n+0}.
C. For '160 thru '163, $V_{ref} = 1.5$ V; for 'LS160A thru 'LS163A, $V_{ref} = 1.3$ V.

FIGURE 2—SWITCHING TIMES

TYPES SN54S162, SN54S163, SN74S162, SN74S163
SYNCHRONOUS 4-BIT COUNTERS

PARAMETER MEASUREMENT INFORMATION

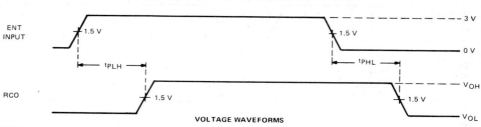

NOTES: A. The input pulse is supplied by a generator having the following characteristics: $t_r \approx 2.5$ ns, $t_f \approx 2.5$ ns, PRR ≈ 1 MHz, duty cycle $\leqslant 50\%$, $Z_{out} \approx 50\ \Omega$.

B. t_{PLH} and t_{PHL} from enable T input to carry output assume that the counter is at the maximum count (Q_A and Q_D high for 'S162, all Q outputs high for 'S163).

FIGURE 3—PROPAGATION DELAY TIMES FROM ENABLE T INPUT TO CARRY OUTPUT

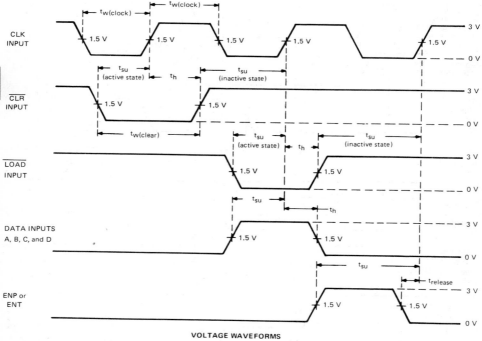

NOTE A: The input pulses are supplied by generators having the following characteristics: $t_r \approx 2.5$ ns, $t_f \approx 2.5$ ns, PRR ≈ 1 MHz, duty cycle $\leqslant 50\%$, $Z_{out} \approx 50\ \Omega$.

FIGURE 4—PULSE WIDTHS, SETUP TIMES, HOLD TIMES, AND RELEASE TIME

TYPICAL APPLICATION DATA

This application demonstrates how the ripple mode carry circuit (Figure 1) and the carry-look-ahead circuit (Figure 2) can be used to implement a high-speed N-bit counter. The '160, '162, 'LS160A, 'LS162A, or 'S162 will count in BCD and the '161, '163, 'LS161A, 'LS163A, or 'S163 will count in binary. When additional stages are added the f_{MAX} decreases in Figure 1, but remains unchanged in Figure 2.

N-BIT SYNCHRONOUS COUNTERS

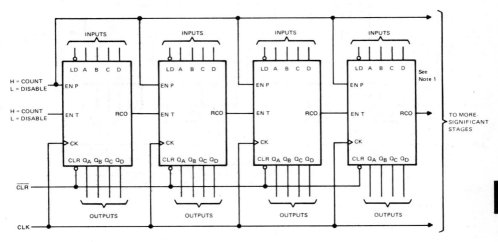

$$f_{MAX} = 1/(CLK \text{ to } RCO \, t_{PLH}) + (ENT \text{ to } RCO \, t_{PLH})(N-2) + (ENT \, t_{su})$$

FIGURE 1

3

TTL DEVICES

TYPICAL APPLICATION DATA

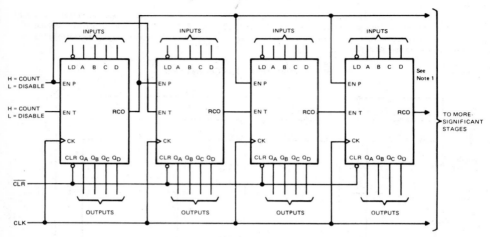

$$f_{MAX} = 1/(CLK \text{ to } RCO \ t_{PLH}) + (ENP \ t_{su})$$

FIGURE 2

TEXAS
INSTRUMENTS

- **Gated Serial Inputs**
- **Fully Buffered Clock and Serial Inputs**
- **Asynchronous Clear**

TYPE	TYPICAL MAXIMUM CLOCK FREQUENCY	TYPICAL POWER DISSIPATION
'164	36 MHz	21 mW per bit
'LS164	36 MHz	10 mW per bit

description

These 8-bit shift registers feature gated serial inputs and an asynchronous clear. The gated serial inputs (A and B) permit complete control over incoming data as a low at either input inhibits entry of the new data and resets the first flip-flop to the low level at the next clock pulse. A high-level input enables the other input which will then determine the state of the first flip-flop. Data at the serial inputs may be changed while the clock is high or low, but only information meeting the setup-time requirements will be entered. Clocking occurs on the low-to-high-level transition of the clock input. All inputs are diode-clamped to minimize transmission-line effects.

The SN54164 and SN54LS164 are characterized for operation over the full military temperature range of −55°C to 125°C. The SN74164 and SN74LS164 are characterized for operation from 0°C to 70°C.

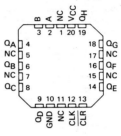

SN54164, SN54LS164 . . . J OR W PACKAGE
SN74164 . . . J OR N PACKAGE
SN74LS164 . . . D, J OR N PACKAGE
(TOP VIEW)

SN54LS164 . . . FK PACKAGE
SN74LS164
(TOP VIEW)

NC — No internal connection

FUNCTION TABLE

INPUTS				OUTPUTS		
$\overline{CLEAR}$	CLOCK	A	B	Q_A	$Q_B \cdots$	Q_H
L	X	X	X	L	L	L
H	L	X	X	Q_{A0}	Q_{B0}	Q_{H0}
H	↑	H	H	H	Q_{An}	Q_{Gn}
H	↑	L	X	L	Q_{An}	Q_{Gn}
H	↑	X	L	L	Q_{An}	Q_{Gn}

H = high level (steady state), L = low level (steady state)
X = irrelevant (any input, including transitions)
↑ = transition from low to high level.
Q_{A0}, Q_{B0}, Q_{H0} = the level of Q_A, Q_B, or Q_H, respectively, before the indicated steady-state input conditions were established.
Q_{An}, Q_{Gn} = the level of Q_A or Q_G before the most-recent ↑ transition of the clock; indicates a one-bit shift.

schematics of inputs and outputs

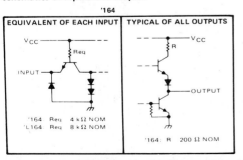

'164

| EQUIVALENT OF EACH INPUT | TYPICAL OF ALL OUTPUTS |

'164 Req 4 kΩ NOM
'L164 Req 8 kΩ NOM

'164: R 200 Ω NOM

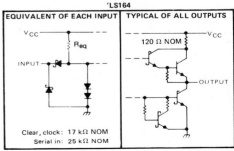

'LS164

| EQUIVALENT OF EACH INPUT | TYPICAL OF ALL OUTPUTS |

120 Ω NOM

Clear, clock: 17 kΩ NOM
Serial in: 25 kΩ NOM

TEXAS
INSTRUMENTS

3

TTL DEVICES

TYPES SN54164, SN54LS164, SN74164, SN74LS164
8-BIT PARALLEL-OUT SERIAL SHIFT REGISTERS

typical clear, shift, and clear sequences

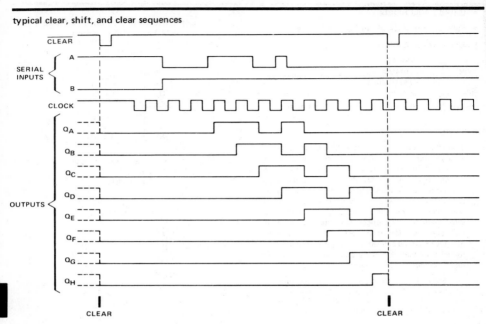

TEXAS
INSTRUMENTS

logic diagram

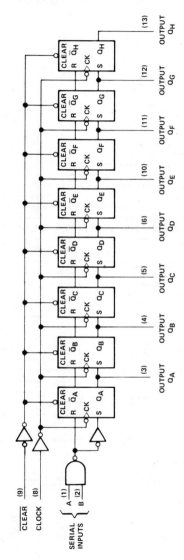

Pin numbers shown on logic notation are for D, J or N packages.

TTL DEVICES

3

absolute maximum ratings over operating free-air temperature range (unless otherwise noted)

Supply voltage, V_{CC} (see Note 1)	7 V
Input voltage	5.5 V
Operating free-air temperature range: SN54164	-55°C to 125°C
SN74164	0°C to 70°C
Storage temperature range	-65°C to 150°C

NOTE 1: Voltage values are with respect to network ground terminal.

recommended operating conditions

	SN54164			SN74164			UNIT
	MIN	NOM	MAX	MIN	NOM	MAX	
Supply voltage, V_{CC}	4.5	5	5.5	4.75	5	5.25	V
High-level output current, I_{OH}			−400			−400	μA
Low-level output current, I_{OL}			8			8	mA
Clock frequency, f_{clock}	0		25	0		25	MHz
Width of clock or clear input pulse, t_w	20			20			ns
Data setup time, t_{su} (see Figure 1)	15			15			ns
Data hold time, t_h (see Figure 1)	5			5			ns
Operating free-air temperature, T_A	−55		125	0		70	°C

electrical characteristics over recommended operating free-air temperature range (unless otherwise noted)

PARAMETER		TEST CONDITIONS†		SN54164			SN74164			UNIT
				MIN	TYP‡	MAX	MIN	TYP‡	MAX	
V_{IH}	High-level input voltage	*		2			2			V
V_{IL}	Low-level input voltage					0.8			0.8	V
V_{IK}	Input clamp voltage	V_{CC} = MIN,	I_I = −12 mA			−1.5			−1.5	V
V_{OH}	High-level output voltage	V_{CC} = MIN, V_{IH} = 2 V, V_{IL} = 0.8 V, I_{OH} = −400 μA		2.4	3.2		2.4	3.2		V
V_{OL}	Low-level output voltage	V_{CC} = MIN, V_{IH} = 2 V, V_{IL} = 0.8 V, I_{OL} = 8 mA			0.2	0.4		0.2	0.4	V
I_I	Input current at maximum input voltage	V_{CC} = MAX, V_I = 5.5 V,				1			1	mA
I_{IH}	High-level input current	V_{CC} = MAX, V_I = 2.4 V				40			40	μA
I_{IL}	Low-level input current	V_{CC} = MAX, V_I = 0.4 V				−1.6			−1.6	mA
I_{OS}	Short-circuit output current §	V_{CC} = MAX		−10		−27.5	−9		−27.5	mA
I_{CC}	Supply current	V_{CC} = MAX, See Note 2	$V_{I(clock)}$ = 0.4 V		30			30		mA
			$V_{I(clock)}$ = 2.4 V		37	54		37	54	

† For conditions shown at MIN or MAX, use the appropriate value specified under recommended operating conditions.
‡ All typical values are at V_{CC} = 5 V, T_A = 25°C.
§ Not more than two outputs should be shorted at a time.
NOTE 2: I_{CC} is measured with outputs open, serial inputs grounded, and a momentary ground, then 4.5 V, applied to clear.

switching characteristics, V_{CC} = 5 V, T_A = 25°C

PARAMETER		TEST CONDITIONS		MIN	TYP	MAX	UNIT
f_{max}	Maximum clock frequency		C_L = 15 pF	25	36		MHz
t_{PHL}	Propagation delay time, high-to-low-level Q outputs from clear input	R_L = 800 Ω, See Figure 1	C_L = 15 pF		24	36	ns
			C_L = 50 pF		28	42	
t_{PLH}	Propagation delay time, low-to-high-level Q outputs from clock input		C_L = 15 pF	8	17	27	ns
			C_L = 50 pF	10	20	30	
t_{PHL}	Propagation delay time, high-to-low-level Q outputs from the clock input		C_L = 15 pF	10	21	32	ns
			C_L = 50 pF	10	25	37	

absolute maximum ratings over operating free-air temperature range (unless otherwise noted)

Supply voltage, V_{CC} (see Note 1) . . . . 7 V
Input voltage . . . . 7 V
Operating free-air temperature range: SN54LS164 . . . . −55°C to 125°C
　　　　　　　　　　　　　　　　　　　　SN74LS164 . . . . 0°C to 70°C
Storage temperature range . . . . −65°C to 150°C

NOTE 1: Voltage values are with respect to network ground terminal.

recommended operating conditions

		SN54LS164			SN74LS164			UNIT
		MIN	NOM	MAX	MIN	NOM	MAX	
V_{CC}	Supply voltage	4.5	5	5.5	4.75	5	5.25	V
V_{IH}	High-level input voltage	2			2			V
V_{IL}	Low-level input voltage			0.7			0.8	V
I_{OH}	High-level output current			− 0.4			− 0.4	mA
I_{OL}	Low-level output current			4			8	mA
f_{clock}	Clock frequency	0		25	0		25	MHz
t_w	Width of clock or clear input pulse	20			20			ns
t_{su}	Data setup time (See Figure 1)	15			15			ns
t_{su}	Clear inactive setup time (See Figure 1)	15			15			ns
t_h	Data hold time (See Figure 1)	5			5			ns
T_A	Operating free-air temperature	− 55		125	0		70	°C

electrical characteristics over recommended operating free-air temperature range (unless otherwise noted)

PARAMETER	TEST CONDITIONS†		SN54LS164			SN74LS164			UNIT
			MIN	TYP‡	MAX	MIN	TYP‡	MAX	
V_{IK}	V_{CC} = MIN, I_I = − 18 mA				− 1.5			− 1.5	V
V_{OH}	V_{CC} = MIN, V_{IH} = 2 V, V_{IL} = MAX I_{OH} = − 0.4 μA		2.5	3.5		2.7	3.5		V
V_{OL}	V_{CC} = MIN, V_{IH} = 2 V, V_{IL} = MAX	I_{OL} = 4 mA	0.25			0.25	0.4		V
		I_{OL} = 8 mA				0.35	0.5		
I_I	V_{CC} = MAX, V_I = 7 V				0.1			0.1	mA
I_{IH}	V_{CC} = MAX, V_I = 2.7 V				20			20	μA
I_{IL}	V_{CC} = MAX, V_I = 0.4 V				− 0.4			− 0.4	mA
I_{OS}	V_{CC} = MAX		− 20		− 100	− 20		− 100	mA
I_{CC}	V_{CC} = MAX, See Note 3			16	27		16	27	mA

† For conditions shown as MIN or MAX, use the appropriate value specified under recommended operating conditions.
‡ All typical values are at V_{CC} = 5 V, T_A = 25°C.
§ Not more than one output should be shorted at a time, and duration of the short-circuit should not exceed one second.
NOTE 3: I_{CC} is measured with outputs open, serial inputs grounded, the clock input at 2.4 V, and a momentary ground, then 4.5 V applied to clear.

switching characteristics, V_{CC} = 5 V, T_A = 25°C

PARAMETER		TEST CONDITIONS	MIN	TYP	MAX	UNIT
f_{max}	Maximum clock frequency		25	36		MHz
t_{PHL}	Propagation delay time, high-to-low-level Q outputs from clear input	R_L = 2 kΩ, C_L = 15 pF,		24	36	ns
t_{PLH}	Propagation delay time, low-to-high-level Q outputs from clock input	See Figure 1		17	27	ns
t_{PHL}	Propagation delay time, high-to-low-level Q outputs from clock input			21	32	ns

3

TTL DEVICES

TYPES SN54164, SN54LS164, SN74164, SN74LS164
8-BIT PARALLEL-OUT SERIAL SHIFT REGISTERS

PARAMETER MEASUREMENT INFORMATION

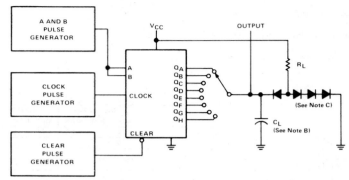

TEST CIRCUIT

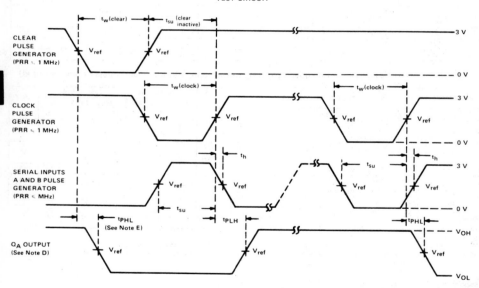

VOLTAGE WAVEFORMS

NOTES: A. The pulse generators have the following characteristics: duty cycle ≤ 50%, $Z_{out} \approx 50\ \Omega$; for '164, $t_r \le 10$ ns, $t_f \le 10$ ns, and for 'LS164, $t_r \le 15$ ns, $t_f \le 6$ ns.
  B. C_L includes probe and jig capacitance.
  C. All diodes are 1N3064 or equivalent.
  D. Q_A output is illustrated. Relationship of serial input A and B data to other Q outputs is illustrated in the typical shift sequence.
  E. Outputs are set to the high level prior to the measurement of t_{PHL} from the clear input.
  F. For '164, $V_{ref} = 1.5$ V; for 'LS164, $V_{ref} = 1.3$ V.

FIGURE 1—SWITCHING TIMES

TEXAS
INSTRUMENTS

OCTOBER 1976 - REVISED APRIL 1985

- **Complementary Outputs**
- **Direct Overriding Load (Data) Inputs**
- **Gated Clock Inputs**
- **Parallel-to-Serial Data Conversion**

TYPE	TYPICAL MAXIMUM CLOCK FREQUENCY	TYPICAL POWER DISSIPATION
'165	26 MHz	210 mW
'LS165A	35 MHz	90 mW

SN54165, SN54LS165A . . . J OR W PACKAGE
SN74165 . . . J OR N PACKAGE
SN74LS165A . . . D, J OR N PACKAGE
(TOP VIEW)

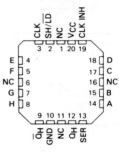

SN54LS165A . . . FK PACKAGE
SN74LS165A
(TOP VIEW)

description

The '165 and 'LS165A are 8-bit serial shift registers that shift the data in the direction of Q_A toward Q_H when clocked. Parallel-in access to each stage is made available by eight individual direct data inputs that are enabled by a low level at the shift/load input. These registers also feature gated clock inputs and complementary outputs from the eighth bit. All inputs are diode-clamped to minimize transmission-line effects, thereby simplifying system design.

Clocking is accomplished through a 2-input positive-NOR gate, permitting one input to be used as a clock-inhibit function. Holding either of the clock inputs high inhibits clocking and holding either clock input low with the shift/load input high enables the other clock input. The clock-inhibit input should be changed to the high level only while the clock input is high. Parallel loading is inhibited as long as the shift/load input is high. Data at the parallel inputs are loaded directly into the register while the shift/load input is low independently of the levels of the clock, clock inhibit, or serial inputs.

FUNCTION TABLE

INPUTS					INTERNAL OUTPUTS		OUTPUT
SHIFT/ LOAD	CLOCK INHIBIT	CLOCK	SERIAL	PARALLEL A . . . H	Q_A	Q_B	Q_H
L	X	X	X	a . . . h	a	b	h
H	L	L	X	X	Q_{A0}	Q_{B0}	Q_{H0}
H	L	↑	H	X	H	Q_{An}	Q_{Gn}
H	L	↑	L	X	L	Q_{An}	Q_{Gn}
H	H	X	X	X	Q_{A0}	Q_{B0}	Q_{H0}

TEXAS
INSTRUMENTS

3

TTL DEVICES

TYPES SN54165, SN54LS165A, SN74165, SN74S165A
PARALLEL-LOAD 8-BIT SHIFT REGISTERS

schematics of inputs and outputs

'165

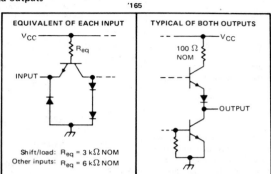

'LS165A

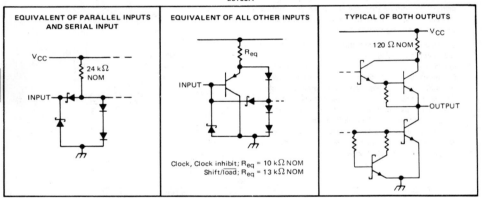

TEXAS INSTRUMENTS

logic diagram (positive logic)

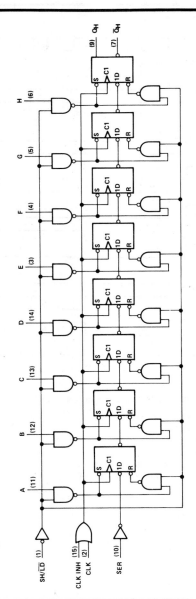

Pin numbers shown on logic notation are for D, J or N packages.

TTL DEVICES

3

TYPES SN54165, SN54LS165A, SN74165, SN74LS165A
PARALLEL-LOAD 8-BIT SHIFT REGISTERS

typical shift, load, and inhibit sequences

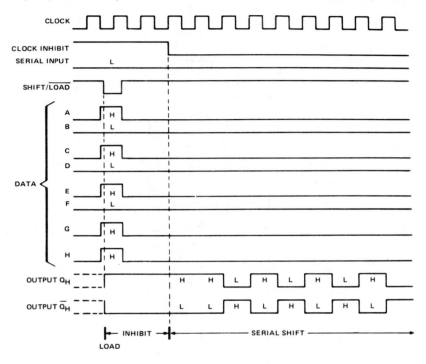

absolute maximum ratings over operating free-air temperature range (unless otherwise noted)

Supply voltage, V_{CC} (see Note 1) . . . . 7 V
Input voltage: SN54165, SN74165 . . . . 5.5 V
            SN54LS165A, SN74LS165A . . . . 7 V
Interemitter voltage (see Note 2) . . . . 5.5 V
Operating free-air temperature range: SN54165, SN54LS165A . . . . -55°C to 125°C
                                   SN74165, SN74LS165A . . . . 0°C to 70°C
Storage temperature range . . . . -65°C to 150°C

NOTES 1. Voltage values, except interemitter voltage, are with respect to network ground terminal.
      2. This is the voltage between two emitters of a multiple-emitter transistor. This rating applies for the '165 to the shift/load input in
          conjunction with the clock-inhibit inputs.

TEXAS
INSTRUMENTS

recommended operating conditions

		SN54165			SN74165			UNIT
		MIN	NOM	MAX	MIN	NOM	MAX	
Supply voltage, V_{CC}		4.5	5	5.5	4.75	5	5.25	V
High-level output current, I_{OH}				−800			−800	μA
Low-level output current, I_{OL}				16			16	mA
Clock frequency, f_{clock}		0		20	0		20	MHz
Width of clock input pulse, $t_{w(clock)}$		25			25			ns
Width of load input pulse, $t_{w(load)}$		15			15			ns
Clock-enable setup time, t_{su} (see Figure 1)		30			30			ns
Parallel input setup time, t_{su} (see Figure 1)		10			10			ns
Serial input setup time, t_{su} (see Figure 2)		20			20			ns
Shift setup time, t_{su} (see Figure 2)		45			45			ns
Hold time at any input, t_h		0			0			ns
Operating free-air temperature, T_A		−55		125	0		70	°C

electrical characteristics over recommended operating free-air temperature range (unless otherwise noted)

PARAMETER		TEST CONDITIONS[†]	SN54165			SN74165			UNIT
			MIN	TYP[‡]	MAX	MIN	TYP[‡]	MAX	
V_{IH}	High-level input voltage		2			2			V
V_{IL}	Low-level input voltage				0.8			0.8	V
V_{IK}	Input clamp voltage	V_{CC} = MIN, I_I = −12 mA			−1.5			−1.5	V
V_{OH}	High-level output voltage	V_{CC} = MIN, V_{IH} = 2 V, V_{IL} = 0.8 V, I_{OH} = −800 μA	2.4	3.4		2.4	3.4		V
V_{OL}	Low-level output voltage	V_{CC} = MIN, V_{IH} = 2 V, V_{IL} = 0.8 V, I_{OL} = 16 mA		0.2	0.4		0.2	0.4	V
I_I	Input current at maximum input voltage	V_{CC} = MAX, V_I = 5.5 V			1			1	mA
I_{IH}	High-level input current — Shift/load	V_{CC} = MAX, V_I = 2.4 V			80			80	μA
	High-level input current — Other inputs				40			40	
I_{IL}	Low-level input current — Shift/load	V_{CC} = MAX, V_I = 0.4 V			3.2			3.2	mA
	Low-level input current — Other inputs				−1.6			−1.6	
I_{OS}	Short-circuit output current§	V_{CC} = MAX	−20		−55	18		55	mA
I_{CC}	Supply current	V_{CC} = MAX, See Note 3		42	63		42	63	mA

NOTE 3: With the outputs open, clock inhibit and clock at 4.5 V, and a clock pulse applied to the shift/load input, I_{CC} is measured first with the parallel inputs at 4.5 V, then with the parallel inputs grounded.

[†]For conditions shown as MIN or MAX, use the appropriate value specified under recommended operating conditions.

[‡]All typical values are at V_{CC} = 5 V, T_A = 25°C.

§Not more than one output should be shorted at a time.

switching characteristics, V_{CC} = 5 V, T_A = 25°C

PARAMETER¶	FROM (INPUT)	TO (OUTPUT)	TEST CONDITIONS	MIN	TYP	MAX	UNIT
f_{max}				20	26		MHz
t_{PLH}	Load	Any			21	31	ns
t_{PHL}					27	40	
t_{PLH}	Clock	Any	C_L = 15 pF, R_L = 400 Ω, See figures 1 thru 3		16	24	ns
t_{PHL}					21	31	
t_{PLH}	H	Q_H			11	17	ns
t_{PHL}					24	36	
t_{PLH}	H	$\overline{Q}_H$			18	27	ns
t_{PHL}					18	27	

¶f_{max} ≡ maximum clock frequency

t_{PLH} ≡ propagation delay time, low-to-high-level output

t_{PHL} ≡ propagation delay time, high-to-low-level output

3

TTL DEVICES

TEXAS
INSTRUMENTS

recommended operating conditions

			SN54LS165A			SN74LS165A			UNIT
			MIN	NOM	MAX	MIN	NOM	MAX	
V_{CC}	Supply voltage		4.5	5	5.5	4.75	5	5.25	V
V_{IH}	High-level input voltage		2			2			V
V_{IL}	Low-level input voltage				0.7			0.8	V
I_{OH}	High-level output current				−0.4			−0.4	mA
I_{OL}	Low-level output current				4			8	mA
f_{clock}	Clock frequency		0		25	0		25	MHz
t_w(clock)	Width of clock input pulse (See Figure 1)	clock high	15			15			ns
		clock low	25			25			
t_w(load)	Width of load input pulse	clock high	25			25			ns
		clock low	17			17			
t_{su}	Clock-enable setup time (See Figure 1)		30			30			ns
t_{su}	Parallel input setup time (See Figure 1)		10			10			ns
t_{su}	Serial input setup time (See Figure 2)		20			20			ns
t_{su}	Shift setup time (See Figure 2)		45			45			ns
t_h	Hold time at any input		0			0			ns
T_A	Operating free-air temperature		−55		125	0		70	°C

electrical characteristics over recommended operating free-air temperature range (unless otherwise noted)

PARAMETER	TEST CONDITIONS		SN54LS165A			SN74LS165A			UNIT
			MIN	TYP‡	MAX	MIN	TYP‡	MAX	
V_{IK}	V_{CC} = MIN, I_I = −18 mA				−1.5			−1.5	V
V_{OH}	V_{CC} = MIN, V_{IH} = 2 V, V_{IL} = MAX, I_{OH} = −0.4 mA		2.5	3.5		2.7	3.5		V
V_{OL}	V_{CC} = MIN V_{IH} = 2 V V_{IL} = MAX,	I_{OL} = 4 mA		0.25	0.4		0.25	0.4	V
		I_{OL} = 8 mA					0.35	0.5	
I_I	V_{CC} = MAX, V_I = 7 V				0.1			0.1	mA
I_{IH}	V_{CC} = MAX, V_I = 2.7 V				20			20	µA
I_{IL}	V_{CC} = MAX, V_I = 0.4 V				−0.4			−0.4	mA
I_{OS}§	V_{CC} = MAX		−20		−100	−20		−100	mA
I_{CC}	V_{CC} = MAX, See Note 3			18	30		18	30	mA

NOTE 3: With the outputs open, clock inhibit and clock at 4.5 V, and a clock pulse applied to the shift-load input, I_{CC} is measured first with the parallel inputs at 4.5 V, then with the parallel inputs grounded.
† For conditions shown as MIN or MAX, use the appropriate value specified under recommended operating conditions.
‡ All typical values are at V_{CC} = 5 V, T_A = 25°C.
§ Not more than one output should be shorted at a time, and the duration of the short-circuit should not exceed one second.

switching characteristics, V_{CC} = 5 V, T_A = 25°C

PARAMETER¶	FROM (INPUT)	TO (OUTPUT)	TEST CONDITIONS	MIN	TYP	MAX	UNIT
f_{max}				25	35		MHz
t_{PLH}	Load	Any			21	35	ns
t_{PHL}					26	35	
t_{PLH}	Clock	Any	R_L = 2 kΩ, C_L = 15 pF See Figures 1 thru 3		14	25	ns
t_{PHL}					16	25	
t_{PLH}	H	Q_H			13	25	ns
t_{PHL}					24	30	
t_{PLH}	H	$\bar{Q}_H$			19	30	ns
t_{PHL}					17	25	

¶ f_{max} = maximum clock frequency
t_{PLH} = propagation delay time, low-to-high-level output
t_{PHL} = propagation delay time, high-to-low-level output

TEXAS
INSTRUMENTS

PARAMETER MEASUREMENT INFORMATION

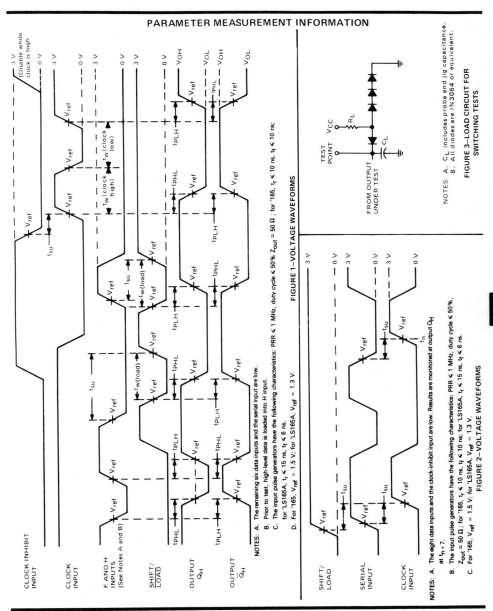

FIGURE 1–VOLTAGE WAVEFORMS

FIGURE 2–VOLTAGE WAVEFORMS

FIGURE 3–LOAD CIRCUIT FOR SWITCHING TESTS

NOTES: A. The remaining six data inputs and the serial input are low.
B. Prior to test, high-level data is loaded into H input.
C. The input pulse generators have the following characteristics: PRR ≤ 1 MHz, duty cycle ≤ 50% Z_out = 50 Ω ; for '165, t_r ≤ 10 ns, t_f ≤ 10 ns; for 'LS165A, t_r ≤ 15 ns, t_f ≤ 6 ns.
D. For '165, V_ref = 1.5 V; for 'LS165A, V_ref = 1.3 V.

NOTES: A. The eight data inputs and the clock-inhibit input are low. Results are monitored at output Q_H at t_n + 7.
B. The input pulse generators have the following characteristics: PRR ≤ 1 MHz, duty cycle ≤ 50%, Z_out = 50 Ω ; for '165, t_r ≤ 10 ns; for 'LS165A, t_r ≤ 15 ns, t_f ≤ 6 ns.
C. For '165, V_ref = 1.5 V; for 'LS165A, V_ref = 1.3 V.

NOTES: A. C_L includes probe and jig capacitance.
B. All diodes are IN3064 or equivalent.

3

TTL DEVICES

TYPES SN54166, SN54LS166A, SN74166, SN74LS166A
PARALLEL-LOAD 8-BIT SHIFT REGISTERS

OCTOBER 1976–REVISED DECEMBER 1983

- **Synchronous Load**
- **Direct Overriding Clear**
- **Parallel to Serial Conversion**

TYPE	TYPICAL MAXIMUM CLOCK FREQUENCY	TYPICAL POWER DISSIPATION
'166	35 MHz	360 mW
'LS166A	35 MHz	100 mW

description

The '166 and 'LS166A 8-bit shift registers are compatible with most other TTL logic families. All '166 and 'LS166A inputs are buffered to lower the drive requirements to one Series 54/74 or Series 54LS/74LS standard load, respectively. Input clamping diodes minimize switching transients and simplify system design.

These parallel-in or serial-in, serial-out shift registers have a complexity of 77 equivalent gates on a monolithic chip. They feature gated clock inputs and an overriding clear input. The parallel-in or serial-in modes are established by the shift/load input. When high, this input enables the serial data input and couples the eight flip-flops for serial shifting with each clock pulse. When low, the parallel (broadside) data inputs are enabled and synchronous loading occurs on the next clock pulse. During parallel loading, serial data flow is inhibited. Clocking is accomplished on the low-to-high-level edge of the clock pulse through a two-input positive NOR gate permitting one input to be used as a clock-enable or clock-inhibit function. Holding either of the clock inputs high inhibits clocking; holding either low enables the other clock input. This, of course, allows the system clock to be free-running and the register can be stopped on command with the other clock input. The clock inhibit input should be changed to the high level only while the clock input is high. A buffered, direct clear input overrides all other inputs, including the clock, and sets all flip-flops to zero.

SN54166, SN54LS166A . . . J OR W PACKAGE
SN74166 . . . J OR N PACKAGE
SN74LS166A . . . D, J OR N PACKAGE
(TOP VIEW)

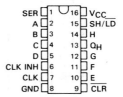

SN54LS166A . . . FK PACKAGE
SN74LS166A
(TOP VIEW)

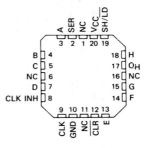

NC - No internal connection

FUNCTION TABLE

INPUTS						INTERNAL OUTPUTS		OUTPUT
CLEAR	SHIFT/ LOAD	CLOCK INHIBIT	CLOCK	SERIAL	PARALLEL A...H	Q_A	Q_B	Q_H
L	X	X	X	X	X	L	L	L
H	X	L	L	X	X	Q_{A0}	Q_{B0}	Q_{H0}
H	L	L	↑	X	a...h	a	b	h
H	H	L	↑	H	X	H	Q_{An}	Q_{Gn}
H	H	L	↑	L	X	L	Q_{An}	Q_{Gn}
H	X	H	↑	X	X	Q_{A0}	Q_{B0}	Q_{H0}

TEXAS INSTRUMENTS

3

TTL DEVICES

typical clear, shift, load, inhibit, and shift sequences

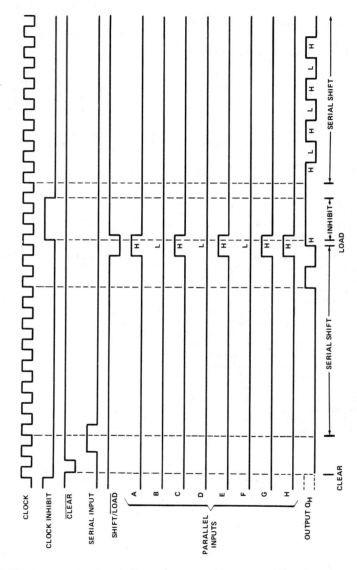

TEXAS
INSTRUMENTS

schematics of inputs and outputs

'166

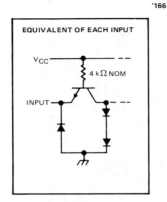

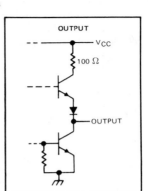

'LS166A

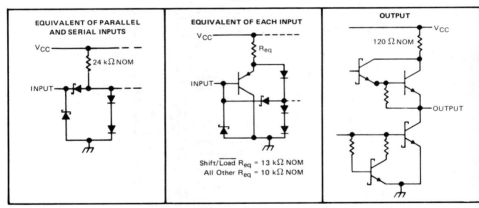

3

TTL DEVICES

logic diagram

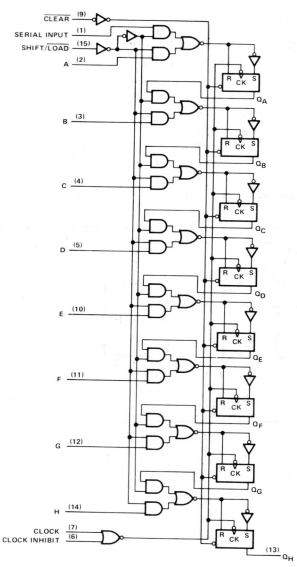

Pin numbers shown on logic notation are for D, J or N packages.

TEXAS
INSTRUMENTS

absolute maximum ratings over operating free-air temperature range (unless otherwise noted)

Supply voltage, V_{CC} (see Note 1) . . . . 7 V
Input voltage . . . . 5.5 V
Operating free-air temperature range: SN54166 (see Note 2) . . . . −55°C to 125°C
SN74166 . . . . 0°C to 70°C
Storage temperature range . . . . −65°C to 150°C

recommended operating conditions

	SN54166			SN74166			UNIT
	MIN	NOM	MAX	MIN	NOM	MAX	
Supply voltage, V_{CC}	4.5	5	5.5	4.75	5	5.25	V
High-level output current, I_{OH}			−800			−800	μA
Low-level output current, I_{OL}			16			16	mA
Clock frequency, f_{clock}	0		25	0		25	MHz
Width of clock or clear pulse, t_W (see Figure 1)	20			20			ns
Mode-control setup time, t_{su}	30			30			ns
Data setup time, t_{su} (see Figure 1)	20			20			ns
Hold time at any input, t_h (see Figure 1)	0			0			ns
Operating free-air temperature, T_A (see Note 2)	−55		125	0		70	°C

electrical characteristics over recommended operating free-air temperature range (unless otherwise noted)

PARAMETER		TEST CONDITIONS†	SN54166			SN74166			UNIT
			MIN	TYP‡	MAX	MIN	TYP‡	MAX	
V_{IH}	High-level input voltage		2			2			V
V_{IL}	Low-level input voltage				0.8			0.8	V
V_{IK}	Input clamp voltage	V_{CC} = MIN, I_I = −12 mA			−1.5			−1.5	V
V_{OH}	High-level output voltage	V_{CC} = MIN, V_{IH} = 2 V, V_{IL} = 0.8 V, I_{OH} = −800 μA	2.4	3.4		2.4	3.4		V
V_{OL}	Low-level output voltage	V_{CC} = MIN, V_{IH} = 2 V, V_{IL} = 0.8 V, I_{OL} = 16 mA		0.2	0.4		0.2	0.4	V
I_I	Input current at maximum input voltage	V_{CC} = MAX, V_I = 5.5 V			1			1	mA
I_{IH}	High-level input current	V_{CC} = MAX, V_I = 2.4 V			40			40	μA
I_{IL}	Low-level input current	V_{CC} = MAX, V_I = 0.4 V			−1.6			−1.6	mA
I_{OS}	Short-circuit output current§	V_{CC} = MAX	−20		−57	−18		−57	mA
I_{CC}	Supply current	V_{CC} = MAX, See Note 3		90	127		90	127	mA

†For conditions shown as MIN or MAX, use the appropriate value specified under recommended operating conditions.
‡All typical values are at V_{CC} = 5 V, T_A = 25°C.
§Not more than one output should be shorted at a time.
NOTES: 1. Voltage values are with respect to network ground terminal.
2. An SN54166 in the W package operating at free-air temperatures above 113°C requires a heat sink that provides a thermal resistance from case to free air, $R_{\theta CA}$, of not more than 48°C/W.
3. With all outputs open, 4.5 V applied to the serial input, all other inputs except the clock grounded, I_{CC} is measured after a momentary ground, then 4.5 V, is applied to the clock.

switching characteristics, V_{CC} = 5 V, T_A = 25°C

PARAMETER		TEST CONDITIONS	MIN	TYP	MAX	UNIT
f_{max}	Maximum clock frequency		25	35		MHz
t_{PHL}	Propagation delay time, high-to-low-level output from clear	C_L = 15 pF, R_L = 400 Ω, See Figure 1		23	35	ns
t_{PHL}	Propagation delay time, high-to-low-level output from clock			20	30	ns
t_{PLH}	Propagation delay time, low-to-high-level output from clock			17	26	ns

TEXAS
INSTRUMENTS

TTL DEVICES

3

absolute maximum ratings over operating free-air temperature range (unless otherwise noted)

Supply voltage, V_{CC} (see Note 1) .... 7 V
Input voltage .... 7 V
Operating free-air temperature range: SN54LS166A .... -55°C to 125°C
SN74LS166A .... 0°C to 70°C
Storage temperature range .... -65°C to 150°C

NOTE 1: Voltage values are with respect to network ground terminal.

recommended operating conditions

			SN54LS166A			SN74LS166A			UNIT
			MIN	TYP	MAX	MIN	TYP	MAX	
V_{CC}	Supply voltage		4.5	5	5.5	4.75	5	5.25	V
V_{IH}	High-level input voltage		2			2			V
V_{IL}	Low-level input voltage				0.7			0.8	V
I_{OH}	High-level output current				-0.4			-0.4	mA
I_{OL}	Low-level output current				4			8	mA
f_{clock}	Clock frequency		0		25	0		25	MHz
t_w	Width of clear pulse (See Figure 1)		20			20			ns
t_w	Width of clock pulse (See Figure 1)	High	15			15			ns
		Low	25			25			
t_{su}	Mode-control setup time		30			30			ns
t_{su}	Data setup time (See Figure 1)		20			20			ns
t_h	Hold time at any input (See Figure 1 and Note 4)		0			0			ns
T_A	Operating free air temperature		-55		125	0		70	$^\circ$C

NOTE 4: The hold time limit of 0 ns applies only if the rise time is less than or equal to 10 ns.

electrical characteristics over recommended operating free-air temperature range (unless otherwise noted)

PARAMETER	TEST CONDITIONS†		SN54LS166A			SN74LS166A			UNIT
			MIN	TYP‡	MAX	MIN	TYP‡	MAX	
V_{IK}	V_{CC} = MIN,	I_I = -18 mA			-1.5			-1.5	V
V_{OH}	V_{CC} = MIN, V_{IH} = 2 V, V_{IL} = MAX, I_{OH} = -0.4 mA		2.5	3.4		2.7	3.4		V
V_{OL}	V_{CC} = MIN, V_{IH} = 2 V, V_{IL} = MAX	I_{OL} = 4 mA		0.25	0.4		0.25	0.4	V
		I_{OL} = 8 mA					0.35	0.5	
I_I	V_{CC} = MAX,	V_I = 7 V			0.1			0.1	mA
I_{IH}	V_{CC} = MAX,	V_I = 2.7 V			20			20	μA
I_{IL}	V_{CC} = MAX,	V_I = 0.4 V			-0.4			-0.4	mA
I_{OS}§	V_{CC} = MAX		-20		-100	-20		-100	mA
I_{CC}	V_{CC} = MAX,	See Note 5		20	32		20	32	mA

†For conditions shown as MIN or MAX, use the appropriate value specified under recommended operating conditions.
‡All typical values are at V_{CC} = 5 V, T_A = 25°C.
§Not more than one output should be shorted at a time, and duration for short-circuit should not exceed one second.
NOTE 5: With all outputs open, 4.5 V applied to the serial input and all other inputs except the clock grounded, I_{CC} is measured after a momentary ground, than 4.5 V. is applied to clock.

switching characteristics, V_{CC} = 5 V, T_A = 25°C

PARAMETER		TEST CONDITIONS	MIN	TYP	MAX	UNIT
f_{max}	Maximum clock frequency		25	35		MHz
t_{PHL}	Propagation delay time, high-to-low-level output from clear			19	30	ns
t_{PHL}	Propagation delay time, high-to-low-level output from clock	C_L = 15 pF, R_L = 2 kΩ, See Figure 1	7	14	25	ns
t_{PLH}	Propagation delay time, low-to-high-level output from clock		5	11	20	ns

TEXAS
INSTRUMENTS

PARAMETER MEASUREMENT INFORMATION

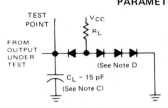

LOAD FOR OUTPUT UNDER TEST

TEST TABLE FOR SYNCHRONOUS INPUTS

DATA INPUT FOR TEST	SHIFT/$\overline{LOAD}$	OUTPUT TESTED (SEE NOTE F)
H	0 V	Q_H at t_{n+1}
Serial Input	4.5 V	Q_H at t_{n+8}

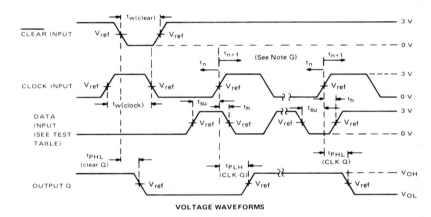

VOLTAGE WAVEFORMS

NOTE: A. All pulse generators have the following characteristics: $Z_{out} \approx 50\Omega$; for '166, $t_r \leqslant 7$ ns and $t_f \leqslant 7$ ns; for 'LS166A, $t_r \leqslant 15$ ns and $t_f \leqslant 6$ ns.

B. The clock pulse has the following characteristics: $t_{w(clock)} \leqslant 20$ ns and PRR = 1 MHz. The clear pulse has the following characteristics: $t_{w(clear)} \leqslant 20$ ns and $t_{hold} = 0$ ns. When testing f_{max}, vary the clock PRR.

C. C_L includes probe and jig capacitance.

D. All diodes are 1N3064, 1N916, or equivalent.

E. A clear pulse is applied prior to each test.

F. Propagation delay times (t_{PLH} and t_{PHL}) are measured at t_{n+1}. Proper shifting of data is verified at t_{n+8} with a functional test.

G. t_n = bit time before clocking transition

t_{n+1} = bit time after one clocking transition

t_{n+8} = bit time after eight clocking transitions

H. For '166 V_{ref} = 1.5 V; for 'LS166A V_{ref} = 1.3 V.

FIGURE 1

TEXAS
INSTRUMENTS

3

TTL DEVICES

3

TTL DEVICES

- **Perform Fixed-Rate or Variable-Rate Frequency Division**

- **For Applications in Arithmetic, Radar, Digital-to-Analog (D/A), Analog-to-Digital (A/D), and other Conversion Operations**

- **Typical Maximum Clock Frequency . . . 32 MHz**

SN54167 . . . J OR W PACKAGE
SN74167 . . . J OR N PACKAGE
(TOP VIEW)

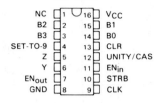

NC—No internal connection

description

These monolithic, fully synchronous, programmable counters utilize Series 54/74 TTL circuitry to achieve 32-megahertz typical maximum operating frequencies. These decade counters feature buffered clock, clear, enable and set-to-nine inputs to control the operation of the counter, and a strobe input to enable or inhibit the rate input/decoding AND-OR-INVERT gates. The outputs have additional gating for cascading and transferring unity-count rates.

The counter is enabled when the clear, strobe set-to-nine, and enable inputs are low. With the counter enabled, the output frequency is equal to the input frequency multiplied by the rate input M and divided by 10, ie.:

$$f_{out} = \frac{M \cdot f_{in}}{10}$$

where: $M = B3 \cdot 2^3 + B2 \cdot 2^2 + B1 \cdot 2^1 + B0 \cdot 2^0$ for decimal zero through nine.

When the rate input is binary 0 (all rate inputs low), Z remains high. In order to cascade devices to perform two-decade rate multiplication (0-99), the enable output is connected to the enable and strobe inputs of the next stage, the Z output of each stage is connected to the unity/cascade input of the other stage, and the sub-multiple frequency is taken from the Y output. For longer words, see typical application data, Figure 1.

The unity/cascade input, when connected to the clock input, may be utilized to pass the clock frequency (inverted) to the Y output when the rate input/decoding gates are inhibited by the strobe. The unity/cascade input may also be used as a control for the Y output.

All of the inputs of these counters are diode-clamped, and each input, except the clock input, represents one normalized Series 54/74 load. The buffered clock input, used with the strobe gate, is only two Series 54/74 loads. Full fan-out to 10 Series 54/74 loads is available from each of the output. These devices are completely compatible with most TTL and DTL families. Typical dissipation is 270 milliwatts. The SN54167 is characterized for operation over the full military temperature range of $-55°C$ to $125°C$, and the SN74167 is characterized for operation from $0°C$ to $70°C$.

3

TTL DEVICES

Texas
INSTRUMENTS

TYPES SN54167, SN74167
SYNCHRONOUS DECADE RATE MULTIPLIERS

STATE AND/OR RATE FUNCTION TABLE (See Note A)

INPUTS									**OUTPUTS**				
									LOGIC LEVEL OR NUMBER OF PULSES			
			BCD RATE				**NUMBER OF**	**UNITY/**				
CLEAR	**ENABLE**	**STROBE**	**B3**	**B2**	**B1**	**B0**	**CLOCK PULSES**	**CASCADE**	**Y**	**Z**	**ENABLE**	**NOTES**
H	X	H	X	X	X	X	X	H	L	H	H	B
L	L	L	L	L	L	L	10	H	L	H	1	C
L	L	L	L	L	L	H	10	H	1	1	1	C
L	L	L	L	L	H	L	10	H	2	2	1	C
L	L	L	L	L	H	H	10	H	3	3	1	C
L	L	L	L	H	L	L	10	H	4	4	1	C
L	L	L	L	H	L	H	10	H	5	5	1	C
L	L	L	L	H	H	L	10	H	6	6	1	C
L	L	L	L	H	H	H	10	H	7	7	1	C
L	L	L	H	L	L	L	10	H	8	8	1	C
L	L	L	H	L	L	H	10	H	9	9	1	C
L	L	L	H	L	H	L	10	H	8	8	1	C, D
L	L	L	H	L	H	H	10	H	9	9	1	C, D
L	L	L	H	H	L	L	10	H	8	8	1	C, D
L	L	L	H	H	L	H	10	H	9	9	1	C, D
L	L	L	H	H	H	L	10	H	8	8	1	C, D
L	L	L	H	H	H	H	10	H	9	9	1	C, D
L	L	L	H	L	L	H	10	L	H	9	1	E

NOTES:
A. H = high level, L = low level, X = irrelevant. All remaining entries are numeric counts.
B. This is a simplified illustration of the clear function. The states of clock and strobe can affect the logic level of Y and Z. A low unity/cascade will cause output Y to remain high.
C. Each rate illustrated assumes a constant value at rate inputs; however, these illustrations in no way prohibit variable-rate inputs.
D. These input conditions exceed the range of the decimal rate inputs.
E. Unity/cascade can be used to inhibit output Y.

schematics of inputs and outputs

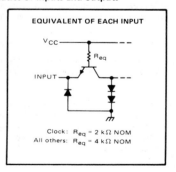

EQUIVALENT OF EACH INPUT

V_{CC}

R_{eq}

INPUT

Clock: R_{eq} = 2 kΩ NOM
All others: R_{eq} = 4 kΩ NOM

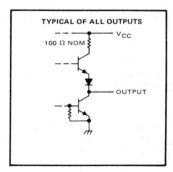

TYPICAL OF ALL OUTPUTS

V_{CC}

100 Ω NOM

OUTPUT

TEXAS INSTRUMENTS

logic diagram

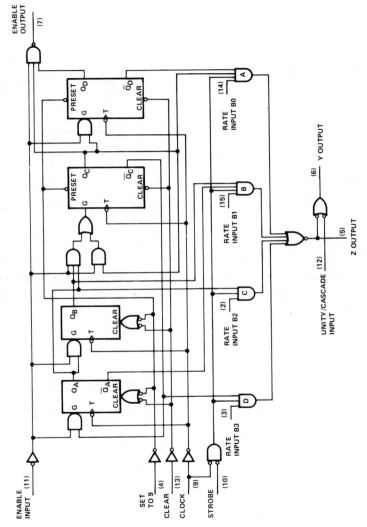

Pin numbers shown on logic notation are for J or N packages.

3

TTL DEVICES

absolute maximum ratings over operating free-air temperature range (unless otherwise noted)

Supply voltage, V_{CC} (see Note 1) . . . . 7 V

Input voltage . . . . 5.5 V

Operating free-air temperature range: SN54167 . . . . −55°C to 125°C

SN74167 . . . . 0°C to 70°C

Storage temperature range . . . . −65°C to 150°C

NOTE 1: Voltage values are with respect to network ground terminal.

recommended operating conditions

		SN54167			SN74167			
		MIN	NOM	MAX	MIN	NOM	MAX	UNIT
Supply voltage, V_{CC}		4.5	5	5.5	4.75	5	5.25	V
High-level output current, I_{OH}				−400			−400	µA
Low-level output current, I_{OL}				16			16	mA
Clock frequency, f_{clock}		0		25	0		25	MHz
Width of clock pulse, $t_{w(clock)}$		20			20			ns
Width of clear pulse, $t_{w(clear)}$		15			15			ns
Width of set-to-nine pulse $t_{w(set-to-9)}$		15			15			ns
Enable setup time, t_{su}: (See Note 2)								
From positive-going transition of clock pulse		25			25			ns
From negative-going transition of previous clock pulse		0	$t_{w(clock)}-10$		0	$t_{w(clock)}-10$		ns
Enable hold time, t_h: (See Note 2)								
From positive-going transition of clock pulse		0	$t_{w(clock)}-10$		0	$t_{w(clock)}-10$		ns
From negative-going transition of previous clock pulse		20	$t_{cp}-10$		20	$t_{cp}-10$		ns
Operating free-air temperature, T_A		−55		125	0		70	°C

NOTE 2: $t_{w(clock)}$ is the interval in which the clock is high. t_{cp} is the total clock cycle starting with a negative transition. See Figure 1 on SN5497, SN7497 data sheet.

electrical characteristics over recommended operating free-air temperature range (unless otherwise noted)

PARAMETER		TEST CONDITIONS[†]		MIN	TYP[‡]	MAX	UNIT
V_{IH}	High-level input voltage			2			V
V_{IL}	Low-level input voltage					0.8	V
V_I	Input clamp voltage	V_{CC} = MIN,	I_I = −12 mA			−1.5	V
V_{OH}	High-level output voltage	V_{CC} = MIN, V_{IH} = 2 V, V_{IL} = 0.8 V,	I_{OH} = −400 µA	2.4	3.4		V
V_{OL}	Low-level output voltage	V_{CC} = MIN, V_{IH} = 2 V, V_{IL} = 0.8 V,	I_{OL} = 16 mA		0.2	0.4	V
I_I	Input current at maximum input voltage	V_{CC} = MAX,	V_I = 5.5 V			1	mA
I_{IH}	High-level input current	clock input	V_{CC} = MAX, V_I = 2.4 V			80	µA
		other inputs				40	
I_{IL}	Low-level input current	clock inputs	V_{CC} = MAX, V_I = 0.4 V			−3.2	mA
		other inputs				−1.6	
I_{OS}	Short circuit output current[§]	V_{CC} = MAX		−18		−55	mA
I_{CCH}	Supply current, output high	V_{CC} = MAX,	See Note 3		43		mA
I_{CCL}	Supply current, output low	V_{CC} = MAX,	See Note 4		65	99	mA

NOTES: 3. I_{CCH} is measured with outputs open and all inputs low.

4. I_{CCL} is measured with outputs open and all inputs high except the set-to-nine input which is low.

[†]For test conditions shown as MIN or MAX, use the appropriate value specified under recommended operating conditions for the applicable device type.

[‡]All typical values are at V_{CC} = 5 V, T_A = 25°C.

[§]Not more than one output should be shorted at a time.

3

TTL DEVICES

TEXAS
INSTRUMENTS

switching characteristics, $V_{CC} = 5$ V, $T_A = 25°C$

PARAMETERS[†]	FROM INPUT	TO OUTPUT	TEST CONDITIONS	MIN	TYP	MAX	UNIT
f_{max}				25	32		MHz
t_{PLH}	Enable	Enable			13	20	ns
t_{PHL}					14	21	
t_{PLH}	Strobe	Z			12	18	ns
t_{PHL}					15	23	
t_{PLH}	Clock	Y			26	39	ns
t_{PHL}					20	30	
t_{PLH}	Clock	Z			12	18	ns
t_{PHL}					17	26	
t_{PLH}	Rate	Z	$C_L = 15$ pF, $R_L = 400$ Ω, See Note 5		9	14	ns
t_{PHL}					6	10	
t_{PLH}	Unity/Cascade	Y			9	14	ns
t_{PHL}					6	10	
t_{PLH}	Strobe	Y			19	30	ns
t_{PHL}					22	33	
t_{PLH}	Clock	Enable			19	30	ns
t_{PHL}					22	33	
t_{PLH}	Clear	Y			24	36	ns
t_{PHL}		Z			15	23	
t_{PHL}	Set-to-9	Enable			18	27	ns
t_{PLH}	Any Rate Input	Y			15	23	ns
t_{PHL}					15	23	

[†] f_{max} is maximum clock frequency.
t_{PLH} is propagation delay time, low-to-high-level output.
t_{PHL} is propagation delay time, high-to-low-level output.
NOTE 5: Load circuit, voltage waveforms, and input conditions for measuring switching characteristics are the same as those for the SN5497 and SN7497.

3

TTL DEVICES

TEXAS
INSTRUMENTS

TYPICAL APPLICATION DATA

This application demonstrates how the decimal-rate multipliers may be cascaded for longer words. Three decades are illustrated (0.999 to 999) although longer words can be implemented by using the pattern shown. The output is decoded either from output Y with a NOR gate or from output Z with a NAND gate. Either method of decoding produces the complement of the output used.

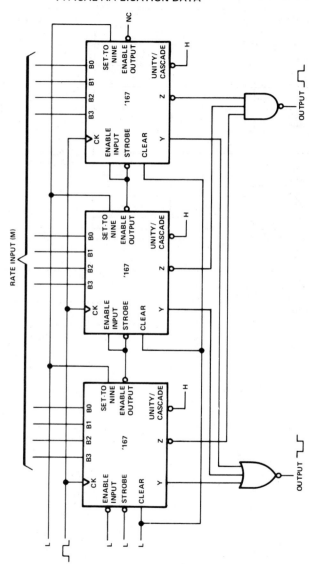

TEXAS INSTRUMENTS

'LS169B, 'S169 ... SYNCHRONOUS UP/DOWN BINARY COUNTERS

- **Programmable Look-Ahead Up/Down Binary/Decade Counters**
- **Fully Synchronous Operation for Counting and Programming**
- **Internal Look-Ahead for Fas Counting**
- **Carry Output for n-Bit Cascading**
- **Fully Independent Clock Circuit**

SN54LS169B, SN54S169 ... J OR W PACKAGE
SN74LS169B, SN74S169 ... D, J OR N PACKAGE
(TOP VIEW)

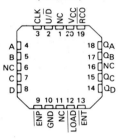

SN54LS169B, SN54S169 ... FK PACKAGE
SN74LS169B, SN74S169
(TOP VIEW)

NC — No internal connection

description

These synchronous presettable counters feature an internal carry look-ahead for cascading in high speed counting applications. The 'LS169B and 'S169 are 4-bit binary counters. Synchronous operation is provided by having all flip-flops clocked simultaneously so that the outputs change coincident with each other when so instructed by the count-enable inputs and internal gating. This mode of operation helps eliminate the output counting spikes that are normally associated with asynchronous (ripple-clock) counters. A buffered clock input triggers the four master-slave flip-flops on the rising (positive-going) edge of the clock waveform.

These counters are fully programmable; that is, the outputs may each be preset to either level. The load input circuitry allows loading with the carry-enable output of cascaded counters. As loading is synchronous, setting up a low level at the load input disables the counter and causes the outputs to agree with the data inputs after the next clock pulse.

TYPE	TYPICAL MAXIMUM CLOCK FREQUENCY		TYPICAL POWER DISSIPATION
	COUNTING UP	COUNTING DOWN	
'LS169B	35 MHz	35 MHz	100 mW
'S169	70 MHz	55 MHz	500 mW

The carry look-ahead circuitry provides for cascading counters for n-bit synchronous applications without additional gating. Instrumental in accomplishing this function are two count-enable inputs and a carry output. Both count enable inputs ($\overline{ENP}$, $\overline{ENT}$) must be low to count. The direction of the count is determined by the level of the up/down input. When the input is high, the counter counts up; when low, it counts down. Input $\overline{ENT}$ is fed forward to enable the carry output. The carry output thus enabled will produce a low-level output pulse with a duration approximately equal to the high portion of the Q_A output when counting up and approximately equal to the low portion of the Q_A output when counting down. This low-level overflow carry pulse can be used to enable successive cascaded stages. Transitions at the $\overline{ENP}$ or $\overline{ENT}$ inputs are allowed regardless of the level of the clock input. All inputs are diode-clamped to minimize transmission-line effects, thereby simplifying system design.

These counters feature a fully independent clock circuit. Changes at control inputs ($\overline{ENP}$, $\overline{ENT}$, $\overline{LOAD}$, U/$\overline{D}$) that will modify the operating mode have no effect until clocking occurs. The function of the counter (whether enabled, disabled, loading, or counting) will be dictated solely by the conditions meeting the stable setup and hold times.

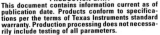

TTL DEVICES

3

TYPES SN54LS169B, SN54S169, SN74LS169B, SN74S169 SYNCHRONOUS 4-BIT UP/DOWN COUNTERS

Logic symbols

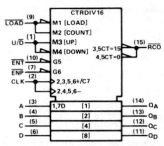

'LS169B, 'S169

Pin numbers shown on logic notation are for D, J or N packages.

Texas
Instruments

logic diagram

SN54LS169B, SN74LS169B BINARY COUNTERS

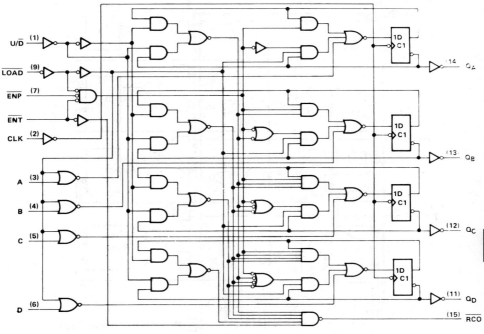

Pin numbers shown on logic notation are for D, J or N packages.

logic diagram

SN54S169, SN74S169 BINARY COUNTERS

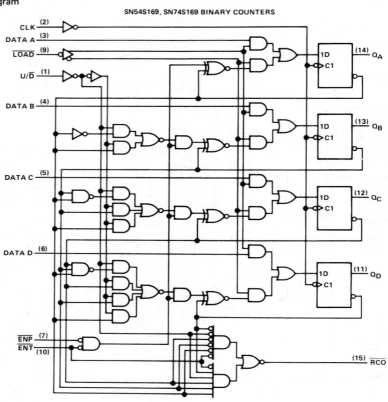

Pin numbers shown on logic notation are for D, J or N packages.

TEXAS
INSTRUMENTS

'LS169B, 'S169 BINARY COUNTERS

typical load, count, and inhibit sequences

Illustrated below is the following sequence:

1. Load (preset) to binary thirteen
2. Count up to fourteen, fifteen (maximum), zero, one, and two
3. Inhibit
4. Count down to one, zero (minimum), fifteen, fourteen, and thirteen

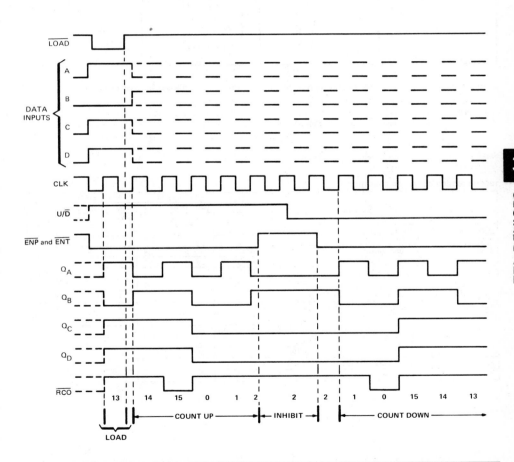

TYPES SN54LS169B, SN74LS169B
SYNCHRONOUS 4-BIT UP/DOWN COUNTERS

schematics of inputs and outputs

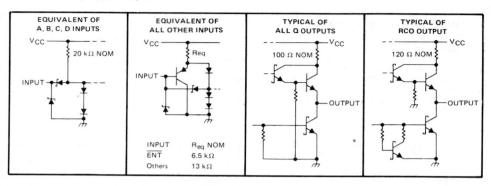

INPUT	R_{eq} NOM
$\overline{ENT}$	6.5 kΩ
Others	13 kΩ

absolute maximum ratings over operating free-air temperature range (unless otherwise noted)

Supply voltage, V_{CC} (see Note 1) . . . . 7 V
Input voltage . . . . 7 V
Operating free-air temperature range: SN54LS169B . . . . −55°C to 125°C
$\quad$ SN74LS169B . . . . 0°C to 70°C
Storage temperature range . . . . −65°C to 150°C

NOTE 1: Voltage values are with respect to network ground terminal.

recommended operating conditions

			SN54LS169B			SN74LS169B			UNIT
			MIN	NOM	MAX	MIN	NOM	MAX	
V_{CC}	Supply voltage		4.5	5	5.5	4.75	5	5.25	V
V_{IH}	High-level-input voltage		2			2			V
V_{IL}	Low-level input voltage				0.7			0.8	V
I_{OH}	High-level output current	$\overline{RCO}$			−0.4			−0.4	mA
		Any Q			−1.2			−1.2	mA
I_{OL}	Low-level output current	$\overline{RCO}$			4			8	mA
		Any Q			12			24	mA
f_{clock}	Clock frequency		0			0			MHz
$t_{w(clock)}$	Width of clock pulse (high or low) (see Figure 1)		25			25			ns
t_{su}	Setup time, (see Figure 1)	Data inputs A, B, C, D	30			30			ns
		$\overline{ENP}$ or $\overline{ENT}$	30			30			
		Load	35			35			
		Up/Down	35			35			
t_h	Hold time at any input with respect to clock (see Figure 1)		0			0			ns
T_A	Operating free-air temperature		−55		125	0		70	°C

TEXAS
INSTRUMENTS

electrical characteristics over recommended operating free-air temperature range (unless otherwise noted)

PARAMETER	TEST CONDITIONS†				SN54LS169B			SN74LS169B			UNIT
					MIN	TYP‡	MAX	MIN	TYP‡	MAX	
V_{IK}	V_{CC} = MIN,	I_I = − 18 mA					− 1.5			− 1.5	V
V_{OH}	V_{CC} = MIN,	V_{IH} = 2 V,	$\overline{RCO}$	I_{OH} = − 0.4 mA	2.5	3.4		2.7	3.4		V
	V_{IL} = MAX		Any Q	I_{OH} = − 1.2 mA	2.4	3.2		2.4	3.2		
V_{OL}	V_{CC} = MIN,	V_{IH} = 2 V,	$\overline{RCO}$	I_{OL} = 4 mA		0.25	0.4		0.25	0.4	V
				I_{OL} = 8 mA					0.35	0.5	
	V_{IL} = MAX		Any Q	I_{OL} = 12 mA		0.25	0.4		0.25	0.4	
				I_{OL} = 24 mA					0.35	0.5	
I_I	V_{CC} = MAX,	V_I = 7 V					0.1			0.1	mA
I_{IH}	V_{CC} = MAX,	V_I = 2.7 V					20			20	μA
I_{IL}	V_{CC} = MAX,	V_I = 0.4 V	U/$\overline{D}$, LOAD, $\overline{ENP}$, CLK				− 0.2			− 0.2	mA
			All other inputs				− 0.4			− 0.4	
I_{OS}§	V_{CC} = MAX,	V_O = 0 V	$\overline{RCO}$		− 20		− 100	− 20		− 100	mA
			Any Q		− 30		− 130	− 30		− 130	
I_{CC}	V_{CC} = MAX,	See Note 2				28	45		28	45	mA

†For conditions shown as MIN or MAX, use the appropriate value specified under recommended operating conditions.
‡All typical values are at V_{CC} = 5 V, T_A = 25°C.
§Not more than one output should be shorted at a time, and duration of the short-circuit should not exceed one second.
NOTE 2: I_{CC} is measured after applying a momentary 4.5 V, then ground, to the clock input with all other inputs grounded and the outputs open.

switching characteristics, V_{CC} = 5 V, T_A = 25°C (see note 3)

PARAMETER¶	FROM (INPUT)	TO (OUTPUT)	TEST CONDITIONS		'LS169B			UNIT
					MIN	TYP	MAX	
f_{max}					20	35		MHz
t_{PLH}	CLK	$\overline{RCO}$				26	40	ns
t_{PHL}						17	25	
t_{PLH}	$\overline{ENT}$	$\overline{RCO}$	R_L = 2 kΩ,	C_L = 15 pF		15	25	ns
t_{PHL}						11	20	
t_{PLH}	U/$\overline{D}$	$\overline{RCO}$				23	35	ns
t_{PHL}						15	25	
t_{PLH}	CLK	Any Q	R_L = 667 Ω,	C_L = 45 pF		16	25	ns
t_{PHL}						17	25	

¶ Propagation delay time from up/down to ripple carry must be measured with the counter at either a minimum or a maximum count. As the logic level of the up/down input is changed, the ripple carry output will follow. If the count is minimum (0), the ripple carry output transition will be in phase. If the count is maximum (15), the ripple carry output will be out of phase.
NOTE 3: See General Information Section for load circuits and voltage waveforms.

3

TTL DEVICES

schematics of inputs and outputs

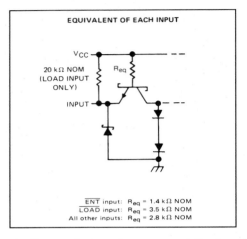

EQUIVALENT OF EACH INPUT

$\overline{ENT}$ input: R_{eq} = 1.4 kΩ NOM
$\overline{LOAD}$ input: R_{eq} = 3.5 kΩ NOM
All other inputs: R_{eq} = 2.8 kΩ NOM

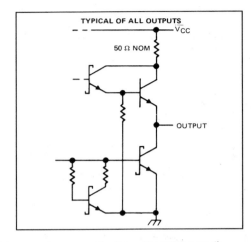

TYPICAL OF ALL OUTPUTS

absolute maximum ratings over operating free-air temperature range (unless otherwise noted)

Supply voltage, V_{CC} (see Note 4) .... 7 V
Input voltage .... 5.5 V
Interemitter voltage (see Note 5) .... 5.5 V
Operating free-air temperature range: SN54S169 (see Note 6) .... −55°C to 125°C
SN74S169 .... 0°C to 70°C
Storage temperature range .... −65°C to 150°C

recommended operating conditions

		SN54S169			SN74S169			UNIT
		MIN	NOM	MAX	MIN	NOM	MAX	
Supply voltage, V_{CC}		4.5	5	5.5	4.75	5	5.25	V
High-level output current, I_{OH}				−1			−1	mA
Low-level output current, I_{OL}				20			20	mA
Clock frequency, f_{clock}		0		40	0		40	MHz
Width of clock pulse, $t_{w(clock)}$ (high or low) (see Figure 1)		10			10			ns
Setup time, t_{su} (see Figure 1)	Data inputs A, B, C, D	4			4			ns
	$\overline{ENP}$ or $\overline{ENT}$	14			14			
	$\overline{Load}$	6			6			
	Up/Down	20			20			
Hold time at any input with respect to clock, t_h (see Figure 1)		1			1			ns
Operating free-air temperature, T_A (see Note 6)		−55		125	0		70	°C

NOTES: 4. Voltage values, except interemitter voltage, are with respect to network ground terminal.
5. This is the voltage between two emitters of a multiple-emitter transistor. For these circuits, this rating applies between the count enable inputs $\overline{ENP}$ and $\overline{ENT}$.
6. A SN54S169 in the W package operating at free-air temperatures above 91°C requires a heat sink that provides a thermal resistance from case to free-air, $R_{\theta CA}$, of not more than 26°C/W.

TEXAS
INSTRUMENTS

electrical characteristics over recommended operating free-air temperature range (unless otherwise noted)

PARAMETER		TEST CONDITIONS†	SN54S169 MIN	TYP*	MAX	SN74S169 MIN	TYP*	MAX	UNIT
V_{IH} High-level input voltage			2			2			V
V_{IL} Low-level input voltage					0.8			0.8	V
V_{IK} Input clamp-voltage		V_{CC} = MIN, I_I = −18 mA			−1.2			−1.2	V
V_{OH} High-level output voltage		V_{CC} = MIN, V_{IH} = 2 V, V_{IL} = 0.8 V, I_{OH} = −1 mA	2.5	3.5		2.7	3.4		V
V_{OL} Low-level output voltage		V_{CC} = MIN, V_{IH} = 2 V, V_{IL} = 0.8 V, I_{OL} = 20 mA			0.5			0.5	V
I_I Input current at maximum input voltage		V_{CC} = MAX, V_I = 5.5 V			1			1	mA
I_{IH} High-level input current	$\overline{ENT}$	V_{CC} = MAX, V_I = 2.7 V			100			100	μA
	Load		−10		−200	−10		−200	
	Other inputs				50			50	
I_{IL} Low-level input current	$\overline{ENT}$	V_{CC} = MAX, V_I = 0.5 V			−4			−4	mA
	Other inputs				−2			−2	
I_{OS} Short-circuit output current§		V_{CC} = MAX	−40		−100	−40		−100	mA
I_{CC} Supply current		V_{CC} = MAX, See Note 2		100	160		100	160	mA

† For conditions shown as MIN or MAX, use the appropriate value specified under recommended operating conditions.
* All typical values are at V_{CC} = 5 V, T_A = 25°C.
§ Not more than one output should be shorted at a time, and duration of the short-circuit should not exceed one second.
NOTE 2: I_{CC} is measured after applying a momentary 4.5 V, then ground to the clock input with all other inputs grounded and the outputs open.

switching characteristics, V_{CC} = 5 V, T_A = 25°C

PARAMETER*	FROM (INPUT)	TO (OUTPUT)	TEST CONDITIONS	UP/DOWN = HIGH MIN	TYP	MAX	UP/DOWN = LOW MIN	TYP	MAX	UNIT
f_{max}				40	70		40	55		MHz
t_{PLH}	CLK	$\overline{RCO}$	C_L = 15 pF, R_L = 280 Ω, See Figures 2 and 3		14	21		14	21	ns
t_{PHL}					20	28		20	28	
t_{PLH}	CLK	Any Q			8	15		8	15	ns
t_{PHL}					11	15		11	15	
t_{PLH}	$\overline{ENT}$	$\overline{RCO}$			7.5	11		6	12	ns
t_{PHL}					15	22		15	25	
t_{PLH}◊	U/$\overline{D}$	$\overline{RCO}$			9	15		8	15	ns
t_{PHL}◊					10	15		16	22	

* f_{max} = maximum clock frequency
t_{PLH} = propagation delay time, low-to-high-level output
t_{PHL} = propagation delay time, high-to-low-level output
◊ Propagation delay time from up/down to ripple carry must be measured with the counter at either a minimum or a maximum count. As the logic level of the up/down input is changed, the ripple carry output will follow. If the count is minimum (0), the ripple carry output transition will be in phase. If the count is maximum (15 for 'S169), the ripple carry output will be out of phase.
NOTE 3: See General Information Section for load circuits and voltage waveforms.

3

TTL DEVICES

TEXAS INSTRUMENTS

PARAMETER MEASUREMENT INFORMATION

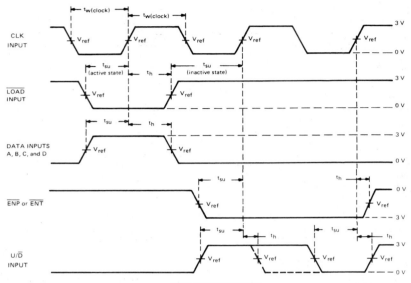

VOLTAGE WAFEFORMS

NOTES: A. The input pulses are supplied by a generator having the following characteristics: PRR ≤ 1 MHz, duty cycle ≤ 50%, $Z_{out} ≈$
50 Ω; for 'LS169B, t_r ≤ 15 ns, t_f ≤ 6 ns, and for 'S169, t_r ≤ 2.5 ns, t_f ≤ 2.5 ns.
B. For 'LS169B, V_{ref} = 1.3 V; for 'S169, V_{ref} = 1.5 V.

FIGURE 1.   PULSE WIDTHS, SETUP TIMES, HOLD TIMES

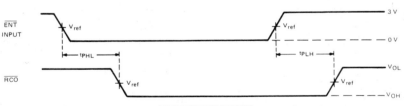

VOLTAGE WAVEFORMS

NOTES: A. The input pulses are supplied by a generator having the following characteristics: PRR ≤ 1 MHz, duty cycle ≤ 50%, $Z_{out} ≈$
50 Ω; for 'LS169B, t_r ≤ 15 ns, t_f ≤ 6 ns; and for 'S169, t_r ≤ 2.5 ns, t_f ≤ 2.5 ns.
B. t_{PLH} and t_{PHL} from enable T input to ripple carry output assume that the counter is at the maximum count (all Q outputs high for
'LS169B and 'S169).
C. For 'LS169B, V_{ref} = 1.3 V; for 'S169, V_{ref} = 1.5 V.
D. Propagation delay time from up/down to ripple carry must be measured with the counter at either a minimum or a maximum
count. As the logic level of the up/downn inputs is changed, the ripple carry output will follow. If the count is minimum (0) the
ripple carry output transition will be in phase. If the count is maximum (15 for 'LS169B and 'S169), the ripple carry output will be
out of phase.

FIGURE 2.   PROPAGATION DELAY TIMES TO CARRY OUTPUT

3

TTL DEVICES

PARAMETER MEASAUREMENT INFORMATION

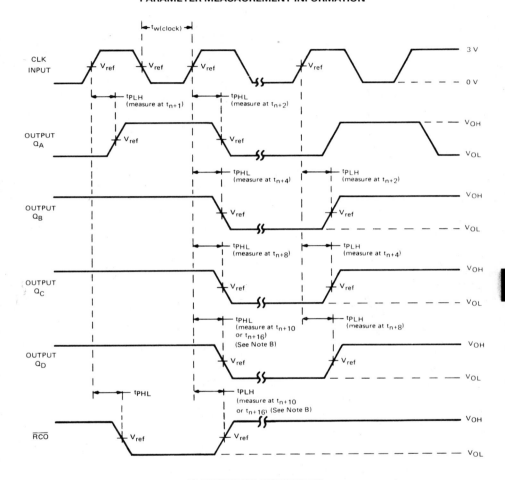

UP-COUNT VOLTAGE WAFEFORMS

NOTES: A. The input pulses are supplied by a generator having the following characteristics: PRR ≤ 1 MHz, duty cycle ≤ 50%, Z_{out} ≈ 50 Ω; for 'LS169B, t_r ≤ 15 ns, t_f ≤ 6 ns; and for 'S169, t_r ≤ 2.5 ns, t_f ≤ 2.5 ns. Vary PRR to measure f_{max}.
B. Outputs Q_D and carry are tested at t_{n+16} for the 'LS169B and 'S169, where t_n is the bit-time when all outputs are low.
C. For 'LS169B, V_{ref} = 1.3 V; for 'S169, V_{ref} = 1.5 V.

FIGURE 3.   PROPAGATION DELAY TIMES FROM CLOCK

3

- Separate Read/Write Addressing Permits Simultaneous Reading and Writing

- Fast Access Times . . . Typically 20 ns

- Organized as 4 Words of 4 Bits

- Expandable to 1024 Words of n-Bits

- For Use as:
  Scratch-Pad Memory
  Buffer Storage between Processors
  Bit Storage in Fast Multiplication Designs

- Open-Collector Outputs with Low Maximum Off-State Current:
  '170 . . . 30 μA
  'LS170 . . . 20 μA

- SN54LS670 and SN74LS670 Are Similar But Have 3-State Outputs

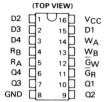

SN54170, SN54LS170 . . . J OR W PACKAGE
SN74170 . . . J OR N PACKAGE
SN74LS170 . . . D, J OR N PACKAGE
(TOP VIEW)

D2	1	16	V_{CC}
D3	2	15	D1
D4	3	14	W_A
R_B	4	13	W_B
R_A	5	12	$\overline{G}_W$
Q4	6	11	$\overline{G}_R$
Q3	7	10	Q1
GND	8	9	Q2

SN54LS170 . . . FK PACKAGE
SN74LS170
(TOP VIEW)

NC - No internal connection

description

The '170 and 'LS170 MSI 16-bit TTL register files incorporate the equivalent of 98 gates. The register file is organized as 4 words of 4 bits each and separate on-chip decoding is provided for addressing the four word locations to either write-in or retrieve data. This permits simultaneous writing into one location and reading from another word location.

Four data inputs are available which are used to supply the 4-bit word to be stored. Location of the word is determined by the write-address inputs A and B in conjunction with a write-enable signal. Data applied at the inputs should be in its true form. That is, if a high-level signal is desired from the output, a high level is applied at the data input for that particular bit location. The latch inputs are arranged so that new data will be accepted only if both internal address gate inputs are high. When this condition exists, data at the D input is transferred to the latch output. When the write-enable input, $\overline{G}_W$, is high, the data inputs are inhibited and their levels can cause no change in the information stored in the internal latches. When the read-enable input, $\overline{G}_R$, is high, the data outputs are inhibited and remain high.

The individual address lines permit direct acquisition of data stored in any four of the latches. Four individual decoding gates are used to complete the address for reading a word. When the read address is made in conjunction with the read-enable signal, the word appears at the four outputs.

This arrangement—data-entry addressing separate from data-read addressing and individual sense line—eliminates recovery times, permits simultaneous reading and writing, and is limited in speed only by the write time (30 nanoseconds typical) and the read time (25 nanoseconds typical). The register file has a nondestructive readout in that data is not lost when addressed.

All '170 inputs and all inputs except the read enable and write enable of the 'LS170 are buffered to lower the drive requirements to one Series 54/74 or Series 54LS/74LS standard load, respectively. Input-clamping diodes minimize switching transients to simplify system design. High-speed, double-ended AND-OR-INVERT gates are employed for the read-address function and drive high-sink-current, open-collector outputs. Up to 256 of these outputs may be wire-AND connected for increasing the capacity up to 1024 words. Any number of these registers may be paralleled to provide n-bit word length.

The SN54170 and SN54LS170 are characterized for operation over the full military temperature range of −55°C to 125°C; the SN74170 and SN74LS170 are characterized for operation from 0°C to 70°C.

TEXAS
INSTRUMENTS

TTL DEVICES

3

logic diagram

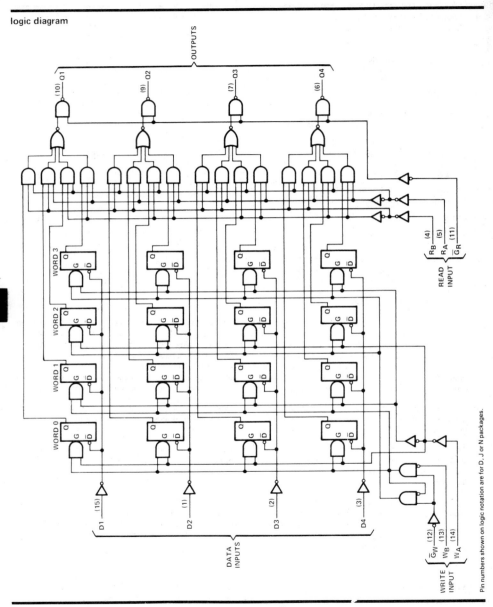

3

TTL DEVICES

TEXAS
INSTRUMENTS

logic diagram

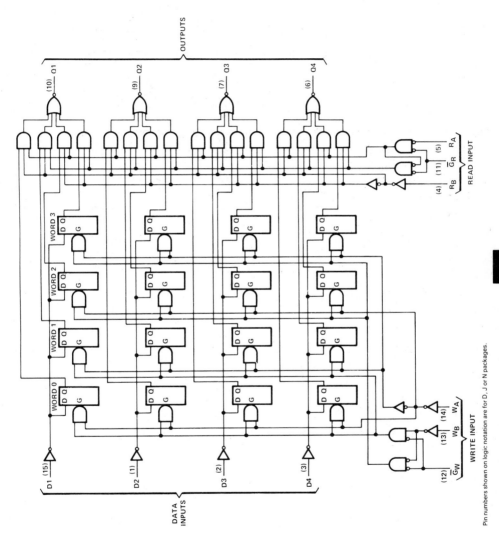

Pin numbers shown on logic notation are for D, J or N packages.

TTL DEVICES

3

logic

WRITE FUNCTION TABLE (SEE NOTES A, B, AND C)

WRITE INPUTS			WORD			
W_B	W_A	$\overline{G}_W$	0	1	2	3
L	L	L	Q = D	Q_0	Q_0	Q_0
L	H	L	Q_0	Q = D	Q_0	Q_0
H	L	L	Q_0	Q_0	Q = D	Q_0
H	H	L	Q_0	Q_0	Q_0	Q = D
X	X	H	Q_0	Q_0	Q_0	Q_0

READ FUNCTION TABLE (SEE NOTES A AND D)

READ INPUTS			OUTPUTS			
R_B	R_A	$\overline{G}_R$	Q1	Q2	Q3	Q4
L	L	L	W0B1	W0B2	W0B3	W0B4
L	H	L	W1B1	W1B2	W1B3	W1B4
H	L	L	W2B1	W2B2	W2B3	W2B4
H	H	L	W3B1	W3B2	W3B3	W3B4
X	X	H	H	H	H	H

NOTES: A. H = high level, L = low level, X = irrelevant.
          B. (Q = D) = The four selected internal flip-flop outputs will assume the states applied to the four external data inputs.
          C. Q_0 = the level of Q before the indicated input conditions were established.
          D. W0B1 = The first bit of word 0, etc.

absolute maximum ratings over operating free-air temperature range (unless otherwise noted)

Supply voltage, V_{CC} (see Note 1) . . . . 7 V
Input voltage: '170 . . . . 5.5 V
              'LS170 . . . . 7 V
Off-state output voltage: '170 . . . . 5.5 V
                  'LS170 . . . . 7 V
Operating free-air temperature range: SN54170, SN54LS170 (see Note 2) . . . . $-55°C$ to $125°C$
                           SN74170, SN74LS170 . . . . $0°C$ to $70°C$
Storage temperature range . . . . $-65°C$ to $150°C$

NOTES: 1. Voltage values are with respect to network ground terminal.
          2. An SN54170 in the W package operating at free-air temperatures above $105°C$ requires a heat sink that provides a thermal
             resistance from case to free-air, $R_{\theta CA}$, of not more than $38°C/W$

3

TTL DEVICES

TEXAS
INSTRUMENTS

recommended operating conditions

		SN54170 MIN	SN54170 NOM	SN54170 MAX	SN74170 MIN	SN74170 NOM	SN74170 MAX	UNIT
Supply voltage, V_{CC}		4.5	5	5.5	4.75	5	5.25	V
High-level output voltage, V_{OH}				5.5			5.5	V
Low-level output current, I_{OL}				16			16	mA
Width of write-enable or read-enable pulse, t_w		25			25			ns
Setup times, high- or low-level data (see Figure 2)	Data input with respect to write enable, $t_{su(D)}$	10			10			ns
	Write select with respect to write enable, $t_{su(W)}$	15			15			ns
Hold times, high- or low-level data (see Note 3 and Figure 2)	Data input with respect to write enable, $t_{h(D)}$	15			15			ns
	Write select with respect to write enable, $t_{h(W)}$	5			5			ns
Latch time for new data, t_{latch} (see Note 4)		25			25			ns
Operating free-air temperature range, T_A (see Note 2)		−55		125	0		70	°C

NOTES: 2. An SN54170 in the W package operating at free-air temperatures above 105°C requires a heat sink that provides a thermal resistance from case to free-air, $R_{\theta CA}$, of not more than 38°C/W.
  3. Write select setup time will protect the data written into the previous address. If protection of data in the previous address is not required, $t_{su(W)}$ can be ignored as any address selection sustained for the final 30 ns of the write-enable pulse and during $t_{h(W)}$ will result in data being written into that location. Depending on the duration of the input conditions, one or a number of previous addresses may have been written into.
  4. Latch time is the time allowed for the internal output of the latch to assume the state of new data. See Figure 2. This is important only when attempting to read from a location immediately after that location has received new data.

electrical characteristics over recommended operating free-air temperature range (unless otherwise noted)

PARAMETER	TEST CONDITIONS†	MIN	TYP‡	MAX	UNIT
V_{IH} High-level input voltage		2			V
V_{IL} Low-level input voltage				0.8	V
V_{IK} Input clamp voltage	V_{CC} = MIN, I_I = −12 mA			−1.5	V
I_{OH} High-level output current	V_{CC} = MIN, V_{OH} = 5.5 V, V_{IH} = 2 V, V_{IL} = 0.8 V			30	µA
V_{OL} Low-level output voltage	V_{CC} = MIN, V_{IH} = 2 V, V_{IL} = 0.8 V, I_{OL} = 16 mA		0.2	0.4	V
I_I Input current at maximum input voltage	V_{CC} = MAX, V_I = 5.5 V			1	mA
I_{IH} High-level input current	V_{CC} = MAX, V_I = 2.4 V			40	µA
I_{IL} Low-level input current	V_{CC} = MAX, V_I = 0.4 V			−1.6	mA
I_{CC} Supply current	V_{CC} = MAX, See Note 5 SN54170		127§	140	mA
	SN74170		127§	150	

†For conditions shown as MIN or MAX, use the appropriate value specified under recommended operating conditions.
‡All typical values are at V_{CC} = 5 V, T_A = 25°C.
§Typical supply current shown is an average for 50% duty cycle.
NOTE 5: Maximum I_{CC} is guaranteed for the following worst-case conditions: 4.5 V is applied to all data inputs and both enable inputs, all address inputs are grounded, and all outputs are open.

TTL DEVICES

3

TEXAS
INSTRUMENTS

switching characteristics, V_{CC} = 5 V, T_A = 25°C

PARAMETER¶	FROM (INPUT)	TO (OUTPUT)	TEST CONDITIONS	MIN	TYP	MAX	UNIT
t_{PLH}	Read enable	Any Q	C_L = 15 pF, R_L = 400 Ω, See Figures 1 and 2		10	15	ns
t_{PHL}	Read enable	Any Q			20	30	
t_{PLH}	Read Select	Any Q			23	35	ns
t_{PHL}	Read Select	Any Q			30	40	
t_{PLH}	Write enable	Any Q	C_L = 15 pF, R_L = 400 Ω, See Figures 1 and 3		25	40	ns
t_{PHL}	Write enable	Any Q			34	45	
t_{PLH}	Data	Any Q			20	30	ns
t_{PHL}	Data	Any Q			30	45	

¶ t_{PLH} ≡ propagation delay time, low-to-high-level output
t_{PHL} ≡ propagation delay time, high-to-low-level output

schematics of inputs and outputs

'170

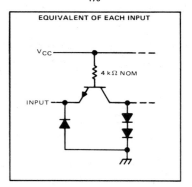

EQUIVALENT OF EACH INPUT

'170

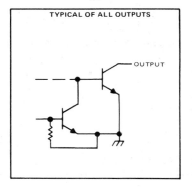

TYPICAL OF ALL OUTPUTS

TEXAS
INSTRUMENTS

recommended operating conditions

		SN54LS170			SN74LS170			UNIT
		MIN	NOM	MAX	MIN	NOM	MAX	
Supply voltage, V_{CC}		4.5	5	5.5	4.75	5	5.25	V
High-level output voltage, V_{OH}				5.5			5.5	V
Low-level output current, I_{OL}				4			8	mA
Width of write-enable or read-enable pulse, t_w		25			25			ns
Setup times, high- or low-level data (see Figure 2)	Data input with respect to write enable, $t_{su(D)}$	10			10			ns
	Write select with respect to write enable, $t_{su(W)}$	15			15			ns
Hold times, high- or low-level data (see Note 3 and Figure 2)	Data input with respect to write enable, $t_{h(D)}$	15			15			ns
	Write select with respect to write enable, $t_{h(W)}$	5			5			ns
Latch time for new data, t_{latch} (see Note 4)		25			25			ns
Operating free-air temperature range, T_A		−55		125	0		70	°C

NOTES: 3. Write-select setup time will protect the data written into the previous address. If protection of data in the previous address is not required, $t_{su(W)}$ can be ignored as any address selection sustained for the final 30 ns of the write-enable pulse and during $t_{h(W)}$ will result in data being written into that location. Depending on the duration of the input conditions, one or a number of previous addresses may have been written into.

4. Latch time is the time allowed for the internal output of the latch to assume the state of new data. See Figure 2. This is important only when attempting to read from a location immediately after that location has received new data.

electrical characteristics over recommended operating free-air temperature range (unless otherwise noted)

PARAMETER		TEST CONDITIONS†	SN54LS170			SN74LS170			UNIT
			MIN	TYP‡	MAX	MIN	TYP‡	MAX	
V_{IH}	High-level input voltage		2			2			V
V_{IL}	Low-level input voltage				0.7			0.8	V
V_{IK}	Input clamp voltage	V_{CC} = MIN, I_I = −18 mA			−1.5			−1.5	V
I_{OH}	High-level output current	V_{CC} = MIN, V_{OH} = 5.5 V, $V_{IL} = V_{IL}$ max, V_{IH} = 2 V			100			100	µA
V_{OL}	Low-level output voltage	V_{CC} = MIN, V_{IH} = 2 V, $V_{IL} = V_{IL}$ max / I_{OL} = 4 mA	0.25		0.4		0.25	0.4	V
		/ I_{OL} = 8 mA					0.35	0.5	
I_I	Input current at maximum input voltage	Any D, R, or W / V_{CC} = MAX, V_I = 7 V			0.1			0.1	mA
		$\overline{G}_R$ or $\overline{G}_W$			0.2			0.2	
I_{IH}	High-level input current	Any D, R, or W / V_{CC} = MAX, V_I = 2.7 V			20			20	µA
		$\overline{G}_R$ or $\overline{G}_W$			40			40	
I_{IL}	Low-level input current	Any D, R, or W / V_{CC} = MAX, V_I = 0.4 V			−0.4			−0.4	mA
		$\overline{G}_R$ or $\overline{G}_W$			−0.8			−0.8	
I_{CC}	Supply current	V_{CC} = MAX, See Note 5		25	40		25	40	mA

†For conditions shown as MIN or MAX, use the appropriate value specified under recommended operating conditions.
‡All typical values are at V_{CC} = 5 V, T_A = 25°C.
NOTE 5: I_{CC} is measured under the following worst-case conditions: 4.5 V is applied to all data inputs and both enable inputs, all address inputs are ground, and all outputs are open.

TEXAS
INSTRUMENTS

TTL DEVICES

3

switching characteristics, V_{CC} = 5 V, T_A = 25°C

PARAMETER[¶]	FROM (INPUT)	TO (OUTPUT)	TEST CONDITIONS	MIN	TYP	MAX	UNIT
t_{PLH}	Read enable	Any Q	C_L = 15 pF, R_L = 2 kΩ, See Figures 1 and 2		20	30	ns
t_{PHL}					20	30	
t_{PLH}	Read select	Any Q			25	40	ns
t_{PHL}					24	40	
t_{PLH}	Write enable	Any Q	C_L = 15 pF, R_L = 2 kΩ, See Figures 1 and 3		30	45	ns
t_{PHL}					26	40	
t_{PLH}	Data	Any Q			30	45	ns
t_{PHL}					22	35	

[¶] t_{PLH} propagation delay time, low-to-high-level output
t_{PHL} propagation delay time, high-to-low-level output

schematics of inputs and outputs

'LS170

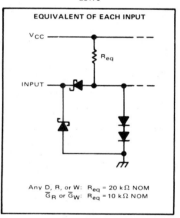

EQUIVALENT OF EACH INPUT

Any D, R, or W: R_{eq} = 20 kΩ NOM
$\overline{G}_R$ or $\overline{G}_W$: R_{eq} = 10 kΩ NOM

'LS170

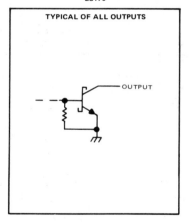

TYPICAL OF ALL OUTPUTS

TEXAS
INSTRUMENTS

PARAMETER MEASUREMENT INFORMATION

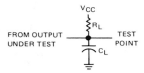

C_L includes probe and jig capacitance

LOAD CIRCUIT

FIGURE 1

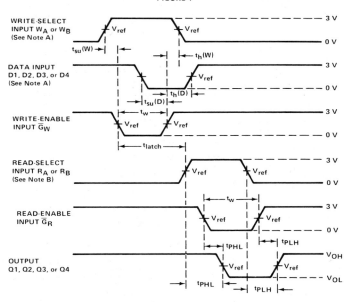

VOLTAGE WAVEFORMS

FIGURE 2

NOTES: A. High-level input pulses at the select and data inputs are illustrated in Figure 2; however, times associated with low-level pulses are measured from the same reference points.
B. When measuring delay times from a read-select input, the read-enable input is low. When measuring delay times from the read-enable input, both read-select inputs have been established at steady states.
C. In Figure 3, each select address is tested. Prior to the start of each of the above tests, both write and read address inputs are stablized with $W_A = R_A$ and $W_B = R_B$. During the test G_R is low.
D. Input waveforms are supplied by generators having the following characteristics: PRR ≤ 1 MHz, $Z_{out} \approx$ 50 Ω, duty cycle ≤ 50%, t_r ≤ 10 ns and t_f ≤ 10 ns for '170, and t_r ≤ 15 ns and t_f ≤ 6 ns for 'LS170.
E. For '170, V_{ref} = 1.5 V; for 'LS170, V_{ref} = 1.3 V.

3

TTL DEVICES

PARAMETER MEASUREMENT INFORMATION

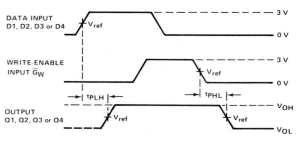

VOLTAGE WAVEFORM 1

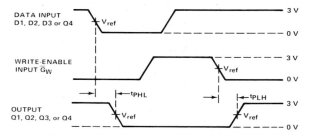

VOLTAGE WAVEFORM 2

FIGURE 3

NOTES: A. High-level input pulses at the select and data inputs are illustrated in Figure 2; however, times associated with low-level pulses are
measured from the same reference points.
B. When measuring delay times from a read-select input, the read-enable input is low. When measuring delay times from the
read-enable input, both read-select inputs have been established at steady states.
C. In Figure 3, each select address is tested. Prior to the start of each of the above tests, both write and read address inputs are
stabilized with $W_A = R_A$ and $W_B = R_B$. During the test G_R is low.
D. Input waveforms are supplied by generators having the following characteristics: PRR $\leqslant$ 1 MHz, $Z_{out} \approx$ 50 Ω, duty cycle $\leqslant$ 50%,
$t_r \leqslant$ 10 ns and $t_f \leqslant$ 10 ns for '170, and $t_r \leqslant$ 15 ns and $t_f \leqslant$ 6 ns for 'LS170.
E. For '170, V_{ref} = 1.5 V; for 'LS170, V_{ref} = 1.3 V.

TEXAS INSTRUMENTS

- **Contains Four Flip-Flops with Double Rail Outputs**
- **Buffered Clock and Clear Inputs**
- **Individual Data Inputs to Each Flip-Flop**

description

These monolithic, positive-edge triggered flip-flops utilize the latest low-power Schottky circuitry to implement D-type flip-flop logic. They have a direct clear input and complementary outputs from each flip-flop.

Information at the D inputs meeting the setup time requirements is transferred to the Q outputs on the positive-going edge of the clock pulse. Clock triggering occurs at a particular voltage level and is not directly related to the transition time of the positive going pulse. When the clock input is at either the high or low level, the D input signal has no effect at the output.

logic diagram

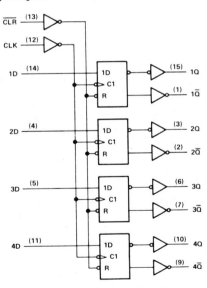

Pin numbers shown on logic notation are for D, J or N packages.

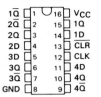

SN54LS171 . . . J OR W PACKAGE
SN74LS171 . . . D, J OR N PACKAGE
(TOP VIEW)

SN54LS171 . . . FK PACKAGE
SN74LS171
(TOP VIEW)

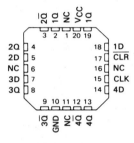

NC-No internal connection

FUNCTION TABLE
(EACH FLIP-FLOP)

INPUTS			OUTPUTS	
$\overline{CLR}$	CLK	D	Q	$\overline{Q}$
L	X	X	L	H
H	↑	H	H	L
H	↑	L	L	H
H	L	X	Q_O	$\overline{Q}_O$

3

TTL DEVICES

TEXAS INSTRUMENTS

schematics of inputs and outputs

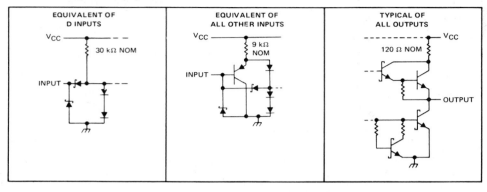

absolute maximum ratings over operating free-air temperature range (unless otherwise noted)

Supply voltage, V_{CC} (See Note 1) .... 7 V
Input voltage .... 7 V
Operating free-air temperature range: SN54LS171 Circuits .... $-55°C$ to $125°C$
                                        SN74LS171 Circuits .... $0°C$ to $70°C$
Storage temperature range .... $-65°C$ to $150°C$

NOTE 1: Voltage values are with respect to network ground terminal.

recommended operating conditions

			SN54LS171			SN74LS171			UNIT
			MIN	NOM	MAX	MIN	NOM	MAX	
V_{CC}	Supply voltage		4.5	5	5.5	4.75	5	5.25	V
V_{IH}	High-level input voltage		2			2			V
V_{IL}	Low-level input voltage				0.7			0.8	V
I_{OH}	High-level output current				−0.4			−0.4	mA
I_{OL}	Low-level output current				4			8	mA
f_{clock}	Clock frequency		0		20	0		20	MHz
t_w	Width of clock or clear pulse		20			20			ns
t_{su}	Setup time	Data input	20			20			ns
		Clear inactive-state	25			25			
t_h	Data hold time		5			5			ns
T_A	Operating free-air temperature		−55		125	0		70	°C

3

TTL DEVICES

electrical characteristics over recommended operating free-air temperature range (unless otherwise noted)

PARAMETER		TEST CONDITIONS†			SN54LS171 MIN	SN54LS171 TYP‡	SN54LS171 MAX	SN74LS171 MIN	SN74LS171 TYP‡	SN74LS171 MAX	UNIT
V_{IK}	Input clamp voltage	V_{CC} = MIN,	I_I = −18 mA				−1.5			−1.5	V
V_{OH}	High-level output voltage	V_{CC} = MIN, V_{IL} = MAX	V_{IH} = 2 V,	I_{OH} = −1 mA	2.5	3.4		2.7	3.4		V
V_{OL}	Low-level output voltage	V_{CC} = MIN, V_{IL} = MAX	V_{IH} = 2 V,	I_{OL} = 4 mA		0.25	0.4		0.25	0.4	V
				I_{OL} = 8 mA					0.35	0.5	V
I_I	Input current at maximum input voltage	V_{CC} = MAX,	V_I = 7 V				0.1			0.1	mA
I_{IH}	High-level input current	V_{CC} = MAX,	V_I = 2.7 V				20			20	μA
I_{IL}	Low-level input current — D inputs	V_{CC} = MAX,	V_I = 0.4 V				−0.4			−0.4	mA
	Low-level input current — All others						−0.2			−0.2	mA
I_{OS}§	Short-circuit output current	V_{CC} = MAX,	V_O = 0 V		−20		−100	−20		−100	mA
I_{CC}	Supply current	V_{CC} = MAX,	See Note 1			14	25		14	25	mA

† For conditions shown as MIN or MAX, use the appropriate value specified under recommended operating conditions.
‡ All typical values are at V_{CC} = 5 V, T_A = 25°C.
§ Not more than one output should be shorted at a time and the duration of the short-circuit should not exceed one second.
NOTE 1: I_{CC} is measured with all inputs grounded and all outputs open.

switching characteristics, V_{CC} = 5 V, T_A = 25°C (see note 2)

PARAMETER	FROM (INPUT)	TO (OUTPUT)	TEST CONDITIONS		'LS171 MIN	'LS171 TYP	'LS171 MAX	UNIT
f_{max}					20	30		MHz
t_{PLH}	CLK	Q, $\overline{Q}$	R_L = 2 kΩ,	C_L = 15 pF		15	25	ns
t_{PHL}						18	30	ns
t_{PLH}	$\overline{CLR}$	Q				18	30	ns
t_{PHL}						24	40	ns

NOTE 2: See General Information Section for load circuits and voltage waveforms.

3

TTL DEVICES

TEXAS
INSTRUMENTS

TTL DEVICES

- Independent Read/Write Addressing Permits Simultaneous Reading and Writing

- Organized as Eight Words of Two Bits Each

- Fast Access Times:
  From Read Enable . . . 15 ns Typical
  From Read Select . . . 33 ns Typical

- 3-State Outputs Simplify Use in Bus-Organized Systems

- Applications:
  Stacked Data Registers
  Scratch-Pad Memory
  Buffer Storage Between Processors
  Fast Multiplication Schemes

SN74172 . . . J OR N PACKAGE
(TOP VIEW)

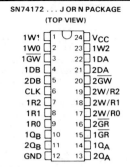

1W1	1	24 VCC
1W0	2	23 1W2
1GW	3	22 1DA
1DB	4	21 2DA
2DB	5	20 2GW
CLK	6	19 2W/R2
1R2	7	18 2W/R1
1R1	8	17 2W/R0
1R0	9	16 2GR
1QB	10	15 1GR
2QB	11	14 1QA
GND	12	13 2QA

description

The SN74172, containing the equivalent of 201 gates on a monolithic chip, is a high-performance 16-bit register file organized as eight words of two bits each.

Multiple address decoding circuitry is used so that the read and write operation can be performed independently on two word locations. This provides a true simultaneous read/write capability. Basically, the file consists of two distenct sections (see Figure 1).

Section 1 permits the writing of data into any two-bit word location while reading two bits of data from another location simultaneously. To provide this flexibility, independent decoding is incorporated.

Section 2 of the register file is similar to section 1 with the exception that common read/write address circuitry is employed. This means that section 2 can be utilized in one of three modes:

1) Writing new data into two bits
2) Reading from two bits
3) Writing into and simultaneously reading from the same two bits.

Regardless of the mode, the operation of section 2 is entirely independent of section 1.

schematics of inputs and outputs

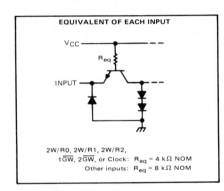

EQUIVALENT OF EACH INPUT

2W/R0, 2W/R1, 2W/R2, 1$\overline{GW}$, 2$\overline{GW}$, or Clock: R_{eq} = 4 kΩ NOM
Other inputs: R_{eq} = 8 kΩ NOM

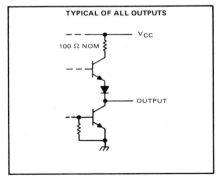

TYPICAL OF ALL OUTPUTS

100 Ω NOM

3

TTL DEVICES

TEXAS INSTRUMENTS

description (continued)

The three-state outputs of this register file permit connection of up to 129 compatible outputs and one Series 54/74 high-logic-level load to a common system bus. The outputs are controlled by the read-enable circuitry so that they operate as standard TTL totem-pole outputs when the appropriate read-enable input is low or they are placed in a high-impedance state when the associated read-enable input is at a high logic level. To minimize the possibility that two outputs from separate register files will attempt to take a common bus to opposite logic levels, the read-enable circuitry is designed such that disable times are shorter than enable times.

All inputs are buffered to lower the drive requirements of the clock, read/write address, and write-enable inputs to one normalized Series 54/74 load, and of all other inputs to one-half of one normalized Series 54/74 load.

Functions of the inputs and outputs of the SN74172 are as shown in the following table.

FUNCTION	SECTION 1	SECTION 2	DESCRIPTION
Write Address	1W0, 1W1, 1W2	2W/R0, 2W/R1, 2W/R2	Binary write address selects one of eight two-bit word locations.
Write Enable	1$\overline{\text{GW}}$	2$\overline{\text{GW}}$	When low, permits the writing of new data into the selected word location on a positive transition of the clock input.
Data Inputs	1DA, 1DB	2DA, 2DB	Data at these inputs is entered on a positive transition of the clock input into the location selected by the write address inputs if the write enable input is low. Since the two sections are independent, it is possible for both write functions to be activated with both write addresses selecting the same word location. If this occurs and the information at the data inputs is not the same for both sections (i.e., 1DA $\neq$ 2DA and/or 1DB $\neq$ 2DB) the low-level data will predominate in each bit and be stored.
Read Address	1R0, 1R1, 1R2	Common with write address	Binary write address selects one of eight two-bit word locations.
Read Enable	1$\overline{\text{GR}}$	2$\overline{\text{GR}}$	When read enable is low, the outputs assume the levels of the data stored in the location selected by read address inputs. When read enable is high, the associated outputs remain in the high-impedance state and neither significantly load nor drive the lines to which they are connected.
Data Outputs	1$Q_{\ddot{A}}$, 1Q_B	2Q_A, 2Q_B	
Clock	CK		The positive-going transition of the clock input will enter new data into the addressed location if the write enable input is low. The clock is common to both sections.

TEXAS
INSTRUMENTS

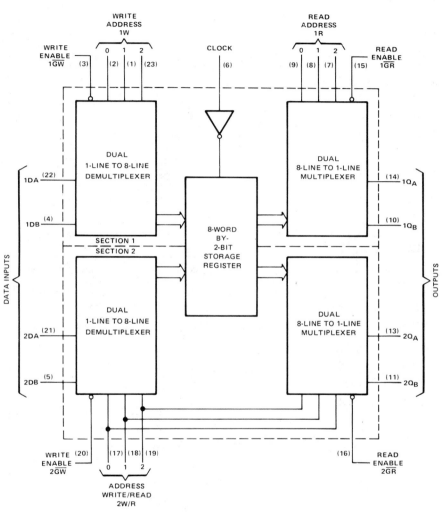

FIGURE 1

TTL DEVICES

3

absolute maximum ratings over operating free-air temperature range (unless otherwise noted)

Supply voltage (see Note 1) . . . . 7 V
Input voltage . . . . 5.5 V
Output voltage (see Note 2) . . . . 5.5 V
Operating free-air temperature range . . . . 0°C to 70°C
Storage temperature . . . . −65°C to 150°C

NOTES: 1. Voltage values are with respect to network ground terminal.
2. This is the maximum voltage which should be applied to any output when it is in the high-impedance state.

recommended operating conditions

		MIN	NOM	MAX	UNIT
Supply voltage, V_{CC}		4.75	5	5.25	V
High-level output current, I_{OH}				−5.2	mA
Low-level output current, I_{OL}				16	mA
Clock frequency, f_{clock}		0		20	MHz
Width of clock pulse, $t_{w(clock)}$		25			ns
Setup time, t_{su} (see Figure 1)	Write select	$t_{w(clock)}+10$			ns
	High-level data	30			
	Low-level data	45			
	Write enable	35			
Hold time, t_h (see Figure 1)	Write select	0			ns
	Write enable	0			
Data release time, $t_{release}$ (see Figure 1)	High-level data	0			ns
	Low-level data	0			
Operating free-air temperature, T_A		0		70	°C

electrical characteristics over recommended operating free-air temperature range (unless otherwise noted)

PARAMETER		TEST CONDITIONS†		MIN	TYP‡	MAX	UNIT
V_{IH}	High-level input voltage			2			V
V_{IL}	Low-level input voltage					0.8	V
V_{IK}	Input clamp voltage	V_{CC} = MIN,	I_I = −12 mA			−1.5	V
V_{OH}	High-level output voltage	V_{CC} = MIN, V_{IH} = 2 V, V_{IL} = 0.8 V, I_{OH} = −5.2 mA		2.4	3		V
V_{OL}	Low-level output voltage	V_{CC} = MIN, V_{IH} = 2 V, V_{IL} = 0.8 V, I_{OL} = 16 mA			0.2	0.4	V
$I_{O(off)}$	Off-state (high-impedance state) output current	V_{CC} = MAX, V_O = 2.4 V				40	μA
		V_{CC} = MAX, V_O = 0.4 V				−40	
I_I	Input current at maximum input voltage	V_{CC} = MAX, V_I = 5.5 V				1	mA
I_{IH}	High-level input current	V_{CC} = MAX, V_I = 2.4 V				40	μA
I_{IL}	Low-level input current	2W/R0, 2W/R1, 2W/R2, 1$\overline{GW}$, 2$\overline{GW}$, or clock	V_{CC} = MAX, V_I = 0.4 V			−1.6	mA
		Any other input				−0.8	
I_{OS}	Short-circuit output current §	V_{CC} = MAX		−18		−55	mA
I_{CC}	Supply current	V_{CC} = MAX, All inputs at 4.5 V, Outputs open			112	170	mA

†For conditions shown as MIN or MAX, use the appropriate value specified under recommended operating conditions.
‡All typical values are at V_{CC} = 5 V, T_A = 25°C.
§Not more than one output should be shorted at a time.

TEXAS
INSTRUMENTS

switching characteristics, V_{CC} = 5 V, T_A = 25°C, R_L = 400 Ω

PARAMETER		TEST CONDITIONS	MIN	TYP	MAX	UNIT
f_{max}	Maximum clock frequency		20			MHz
t_{PLH}	Propagation delay time, low-to-high-level output from read select			33	45	ns
t_{PHL}	Propagation delay time, high-to-low-level output from read select	C_L = 50 pF, See Figure 2		30	45	
t_{PLH}	Propagation delay time, low-to-high-level output from clock			35	50	ns
t_{PHL}	Propagation delay time, high-to-low-level output from clock			35	50	
t_{PZH}	Output enable time to high level			14	30	ns
t_{PZL}	Output enable time to low level			16	30	
t_{PHZ}	Output disable time from high level	C_L = 5 pF, See Figure 2		6	20	ns
t_{PLZ}	Output disable time from low level			11	20	

PARAMETER MEASUREMENT INFORMATION

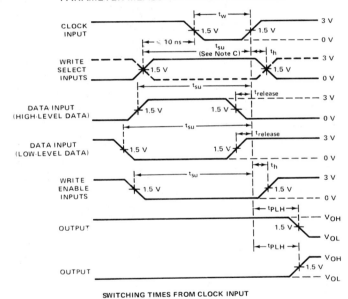

SWITCHING TIMES FROM CLOCK INPUT

VOLTAGE WAVEFORMS
FIGURE 2

PARAMETER MEASUREMENT INFORMATION

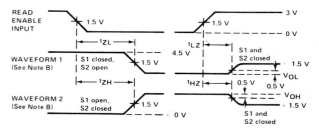

ENABLE AND DISABLE TIMES FROM READ ENABLE

NOTES: A. Input waveforms are supplied by pulse generators
having the following characteristics: $t_r \leqslant$ 7 ns,
$t_f \leqslant$ ns, PRR = 1 MHz, $Z_{out} \approx$ 50 Ω.
B. Waveform 1 is for an output with internal conditions
such that the output is low except when disabled.
Waveform 2 is for an output with internal conditions
such that the output is high except when disabled.
C. Write select setup time, as specified, will protect data
written into previous address.
D. Load circuit is shown on page .

VOLTAGE WAVEFORMS
FIGURE 2 (continued)

TEXAS
INSTRUMENTS

OCTOBER 1976—REVISED APRIL 1985

- **3-State Outputs Interface Directly with System Bus**
- **Gated Output-Control Lines for Enabling or Disabling the Outputs**
- **Fully Independent Clock Virtually Elimi-nates Restrictions for Operating in One of of Two Modes:**

  Parallel Load
  Do Nothing (Hold)

- **For application as Bus Buffer Registers**

SN54173, SN54LS173A . . . J OR W PACKAGE
SN74173 . . . J OR N PACKAGE
SN74LS173A . . . D, J OR N PACKAGE
(TOP VIEW)

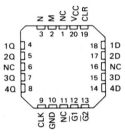

SN54LS173A . . . FK PACKAGE
SN74LS173A
(TOP VIEW)

NC - No internal connection

TYPE	TYPICAL PROPAGATION DELAY TIME	MAXIMUM CLOCK FREQUENCY	TYPICAL POWER DISSIPATION
'173	23 ns	35 MHz	250 mW
'LS173A	18 ns	50 MHz	95 mW

description

The '173 and 'LS173A four-bit registers include D-type flip-flops featuring totem-pole three-state outputs capable of driving highly capacitive or relatively low-impedance loads. The high-impedance third state and increased high-logic-level drive provide these flip-flops with the capability of being connected directly to and driving the bus lines in a bus-organized system without need for interface or pull-up components. Up to 128 of the SN74173 or SN74LS173A outputs may be connected to a common bus and still drive two Series 54/74 or 54LS/74LS TTL normalized loads, respectively. Similarly, up to 49 of the SN54173 or SN54LS173A outputs can be connected to a common bus and drive one additional Series 54/74 or 54LS/74LS TTL normalized load, respectively. To minimize the possibility that two outputs will attempt to take a common bus to opposite logic levels, the output control circuitry is designed so that the average output disable times are shorter than the average output enable times.

FUNCTION TABLE

INPUTS					OUTPUT
		DATA ENABLE		DATA	
CLEAR	CLOCK	$\overline{G1}$	$\overline{G2}$	D	Q
H	X	X	X	X	L
L	L	X	X	X	Q_0
L	↑	H	X	X	Q_0
L	↑	X	H	X	Q_0
L	↑	L	L	L	L
L	↑	L	L	H	H

When either M or N (or both) is (are) high the output is disabled to the high-impedance state; however sequential operation of the flip-flops is not affected.

Gated enable inputs are provided on these devices for controlling the entry of data into the flip-flops. When both data-enable inputs are low, data at the D inputs are loaded into their respective flip-flops on the next positive transition of the buffered clock input. Gate output control inputs are also provided. When both are low, the normal logic states (high or low levels) of the four outputs are available for driving the loads or bus lines. The outputs are disabled independently from the level of the clock by a high logic level at either output control input. The outputs then present a high impedance and neither load nor drive the bus line. Detailed operation is given in the function table.

TYPE SN54173, SN54LS173A, SN74173, SN74LS173A
4-BIT D-TYPE REGISTERS WITH 3-STATE OUTPUTS

absolute maximum ratings over operating free-air temperature range (unless otherwise noted)

Supply voltage, V_{CC} (see Note 1)	....	7 V
Input voltage: '173	....	5.5 V
'LS173A	....	7 V
Off-state output voltage	....	5.5 V
Operating free-air temperature range: SN54173, SN54LS173A	....	−55°C to 125°C
SN74173, SN74LS173A	....	0°C to 70°C
Storage temperature range	....	−65°C to 150°C

NOTE 1: Voltage values are with respect to network ground terminals.

logic diagram

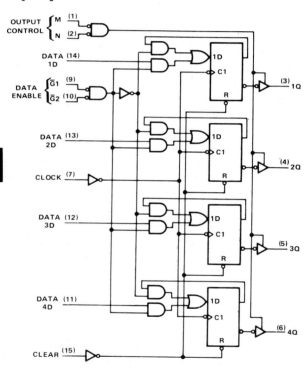

Pin numbers shown on logic notation are for D, J or N packages.

schematics of inputs and outputs

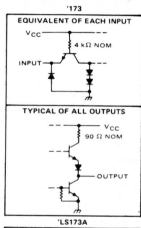

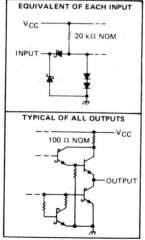

3

TTL DEVICES

TEXAS INSTRUMENTS

recommended operating conditions

		SN54173 MIN	SN54173 NOM	SN54173 MAX	SN74173 MIN	SN74173 NOM	SN74173 MAX	UNIT
Supply voltage, V_{CC}		4.5	5	5.5	4.75	5	5.25	V
High-level output current, I_{OH}				−2			−5.2	mA
Low-level output current, I_{OL}				16			16	mA
Input clock frequency, f_{clock}		0		25	0		25	MHz
Width of clock or clear pulse, t_w		20			20			ns
Setup time, t_{su}	Data enable	17			17			ns
	Data	10			10			
	Clear inactive state	10			10			
Hold time, t_h	Data enable	2			2			ns
	Data	10			10			
Operating free-air temperature, T_A		−55		125	0		70	°C

electrical characteristics over recommended operating free-air temperature range (unless otherwise noted)

	PARAMETER	TEST CONDITIONS[†]		MIN	TYP[‡]	MAX	UNIT
V_{IH}	High-level input voltage			2			V
V_{IL}	Low-level input voltage					0.8	V
V_{IK}	Input clamp voltage	V_{CC} = MIN,	I_I = −12 mA			−1.5	V
V_{OH}	High-level output voltage	V_{CC} = MIN, V_{IH} = 2 V, V_{IL} = 0.8 V, I_{OH} = MAX		2.4			V
V_{OL}	Low-level output voltage	V_{CC} = MIN, V_{IH} = 2 V, V_{IL} = 0.8 V, I_{OL} .6 mA				0.4	V
$I_{O(off)}$	Off-state (high-impedance state) output current	V_{CC} = MAX, V_{IH} = 2 V	V_O = 2.4 V			40	μA
			V_O = 0.4 V			−40	
I_I	Input current at maximum input voltage	V_{CC} = MAX,	V_I = 5.5 V			1	mA
I_{IH}	High-level input current	V_{CC} = MAX,	V_I = 2.4 V			40	μA
I_{IL}	Low-level input current	V_{CC} = MAX,	V_I = 0.4 V			−1.6	mA
I_{OS}	Short-circuit output current[§]	V_{CC} = MAX		−30		−70	mA
I_{CC}	Supply current	V_{CC} = MAX,	See Note 2		50	72	mA

[†] For conditions shown as MIN or MAX, use the appropriate value specified under recommended operating conditions.
[‡] All typical values are at V_{CC} = 5 V, T_A = 25°C.
[§] Not more than one output should be shorted at a time.
NOTE 2: I_{CC} is measured with all outputs open; clear grounded following momentary connection to 4.5 V; N, G1, G2, and all data inputs grounded; and the clock input and M at 4.5 V.

switching characteristics, V_{CC} = 5 V, T_A = 25°C, R_L = 400 Ω

	PARAMETER	TEST CONDITIONS	MIN	TYP	MAX	UNIT
f_{max}	Maximum clock frequency		25	35		MHz
t_{PHL}	Propagation delay time, high-to-low-level output from clear input			18	27	ns
t_{PLH}	Propagation delay time, low-to-high-level output from clock input	C_L = 50 pF, See Note 3		28	43	ns
t_{PHL}	Propagation delay time, high-to-low-level output from clock input			19	31	
t_{PZH}	Output enable time to high level		7	16	30	ns
t_{PZL}	Output enable time to low level		7	21	30	
t_{PHZ}	Output disable time from high level	C_L = 5 pF, See Note 3	3	5	14	ns
t_{PLZ}	Output disable time from low level		3	11	20	

NOTE 3: See General Information Section for load circuits and voltage waveforms.

TEXAS INSTRUMENTS

3

TTL DEVICES

recommended operating conditions

		SN54LS173A MIN	SN54LS173A NOM	SN54LS173A MAX	SN74LS173A MIN	SN74LS173A NOM	SN74LS173A MAX	UNIT
Supply voltage, V_{CC}		4.5	5	5.5	4.75	5	5.25	V
High-level output current, I_{OH}				−1			−2.6	mA
Low-level output current, I_{OL}				12			24	mA
Input clock frequency, f_{clock}		0		30	0		30	MHz
Width of clock or clear pulse, t_w		25			25			ns
Setup time, t_{su}	Data enable	35			35			ns
	Data	17			17			
	Clear inactive state	10			10			
Hold time, t_h	Data enable	0			0			ns
	Data	3			3			
Operating free-air temperature, T_A		−55		125	0		70	°C

electrical characteristics over recommended operating free-air temperature range (unless otherwise noted)

PARAMETER		TEST CONDITIONS[†]	SN54LS173A MIN	SN54LS173A TYP[‡]	SN54LS173A MAX	SN74LS173A MIN	SN74LS173A TYP[‡]	SN74LS173A MAX	UNIT
V_{IH}	High-level input voltage		2			2			V
V_{IL}	Low-level input voltage				0.7			0.8	V
V_{IK}	Input clamp voltage	V_{CC} = MIN, I_I = −18 mA			−1.5			−1.5	V
V_{OH}	High-level output voltage	V_{CC} = MIN, V_{IH} = 2 V, V_{IL} = V_{IL}max, I_{OH} = MAX	2.4	3.4		2.4	3.1		V
V_{OL}	Low-level output voltage	V_{CC} = MIN, I_{OL} = 12 mA, V_{IL} = 0.8 V, I_{OL} = 24 mA		0.25	0.4		0.25	0.4	V
							0.35	0.5	
$I_{O(off)}$	Off-state (high-impedance state) output current	V_{CC} = MAX, V_{IH} = 2 V, V_O = 2.7 V, V_O = 0.4 V			20 −20			20 −20	μA
I_I	Input current at maximum input voltage	V_{CC} = MAX, V_I = 7 V			0.1			0.1	mA
I_{IH}	High-level input current	V_{CC} = MAX, V_I = 2.7 V			20			20	μA
I_{IL}	Low-level input current	V_{CC} = MAX, V_I = 0.4 V			−0.4			−0.4	mA
I_{OS}	Short-circuit output current[§]	V_{CC} = MAX	−30		−130	−30		−130	mA
I_{CC}	Supply current	V_{CC} = MAX, See Note 2		19	30		19	24	mA

[†] For conditions shown as MIN or MAX, use the appropriate value specified under recommended operating conditions.
[‡] All typical values are at V_{CC} = 5 V, T_A = 25°C.
[§] Not more than one output should be shorted at a time.
NOTE 2: I_{CC} is measured with all outputs open; clear grounded following momentary connection to 4.5 V; N, G1, G2, and all data inputs grounded; and the clock input and M at 4.5 V.

switching characteristics, V_{CC} = 5 V, T_A = 25°C, R_L = 667 Ω

PARAMETER		TEST CONDITIONS	MIN	TYP	MAX	UNIT
f_{max}	Maximum clock frequency		30	50		MHz
t_{PHL}	Propagation delay time, high-to-low-level output from clear input	C_L = 45 pF, See Note 3		26	35	ns
t_{PLH}	Propagation delay time, low-to-high-level output from clock input			17	25	ns
t_{PHL}	Propagation delay time, high-to-low-level output from clock input			22	30	
t_{PZH}	Output enable time to high level			15	23	ns
t_{PZL}	Output enable time to low level			18	27	
t_{PHZ}	Output disable time from high level	C_L = 5 pF, See Note 3		11	20	ns
t_{PLZ}	Output disable time from low level			11	17	

NOTE 3: See General Information Section for load circuits and voltage waveforms.

3-558

TEXAS
INSTRUMENTS

3
TTL DEVICES

TYPES SN54174, SN54175, SN54LS174, SN54LS175, SN54S174, SN54S175, SN74174, SN74175, SN74LS174, SN74LS175, SN74S174, SN74S175
HEX/QUADRUPLE D-TYPE FLIP-FLOPS WITH CLEAR

DECEMBER 1972—REVISED DECEMBER 1983

'174, 'LS174, 'S174 . . . HEX D-TYPE FLIP-FLOPS
'175, 'LS175, 'S175 . . . QUADRUPLE D-TYPE FLIP-FLOPS

- '174, 'LS174, 'S174 Contain Six Flip-Flops with Single-Rail Outputs
- '175, 'LS175, 'S175 Contain Four Flip-Flops with Double-Rail Outputs
- Three Performance Ranges Offered: See Table Lower Right
- Buffered Clock and Direct Clear Inputs
- Individual Data Input to Each Flip-Flop
- Applications include:
  Buffer/Storage Registers
  Shift Registers
  Pattern Generators

description

These monolithic, positive-edge-triggered flip-flops utilize TTL circuitry to implement D-type flip-flop logic. All have a direct clear input, and the '175, 'LS175, and 'S175 feature complementary outputs from each flip-flop.

Information at the D inputs meeting the setup time requirements is transferred to the Q outputs on the positive-going edge of the clock pulse. Clock triggering occurs at a particular voltage level and is not directly related to the transition time of the positive-going pulse. When the clock input is at either the high or low level, the D input signal has no effect at the output.

These circuits are fully compatible for use with most TTL circuits.

FUNCTION TABLE
(EACH FLIP-FLOP)

INPUTS			OUTPUTS	
CLEAR	CLOCK	D	Q	$\bar{Q}$ †
L	X	X	L	H
H	↑	H	H	L
H	↑	L	L	H
H	L	X	Q_0	$\bar{Q}_0$

H = high level (steady state)
L = low level (steady state)
X = irrelevant
↑ = transition from low to high level
Q_0 = the level of Q before the indicated steady-state input conditions were established.
† = '175, 'LS175, and 'S175 only.

TYPES	TYPICAL MAXIMUM CLOCK FREQUENCY	TYPICAL POWER DISSIPATION PER FLIP-FLOP
'174, '175	35 MHz	38 mW
'LS174, 'LS175	40 MHz	14 mW
'S174, 'S175	110 MHz	75 mW

SN54174, SN54LS174, SN54S174 . . . J OR W PACKAGE
SN74174 . . . J OR N PACKAGE
SN74LS174, SN74S174 . . . D, J OR N PACKAGE
(TOP VIEW)

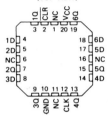

$\overline{CLR}$	1	16 V_{CC}
1Q	2	15 6Q
1D	3	14 6D
2D	4	13 5D
2Q	5	12 5Q
3D	6	11 4D
3Q	7	10 4Q
GND	8	9 CLK

SN54LS174, SN54S174 . . . FK PACKAGE
SN74LS174, SN74S174
(TOP VIEW)

Pins (top): 1Q, $\overline{CLR}$, NC, V_{CC}, 6Q (3 2 1 20 19)

1D	4	18 6D
2D	5	17 5D
NC	6	16 NC
2Q	7	15 5Q
3D	8	14 4D

Pins (bottom): 3Q, GND, NC, CLK, 4Q (9 10 11 12 13)

SN54175, SN54LS175, SN54S175 . . . J OR W PACKAGE
SN74175 . . . J OR N PACKAGE
SN74LS175, SN74S175 . . . D, J OR N PACKAGE
(TOP VIEW)

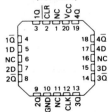

$\overline{CLR}$	1	16 V_{CC}
1Q	2	15 4Q
1$\overline{Q}$	3	14 4$\overline{Q}$
1D	4	13 4D
2D	5	12 3D
2$\overline{Q}$	6	11 3$\overline{Q}$
2Q	7	10 3Q
GND	8	9 CLK

SN54LS175, SN54S175 . . . FK PACKAGE
SN74LS175, SN74S175
(TOP VIEW)

Pins (top): 1Q, $\overline{CLR}$, NC, V_{CC}, 4Q (3 2 1 20 19)

1$\overline{Q}$	4	18 4$\overline{Q}$
1D	5	17 4D
NC	6	16 NC
2D	7	15 3D
2Q	8	14 3$\overline{Q}$

Pins (bottom): 2$\overline{Q}$, GND, NC, CLK, 3Q (9 10 11 12 13)

NC — No internal connection

TTL DEVICES — 3

TEXAS INSTRUMENTS

TYPES SN54174, SN54175, SN54LS174, SN54LS175, SN54S174, SN54S175, SN74174, SN74175, SN74LS174, SN74LS175, SN74S174, SN74S175
HEX/QUADRUPLE D-TYPE FLIP-FLOPS WITH CLEAR

logic diagrams

'174, 'LS174, 'S174

'175, 'LS175, 'S175

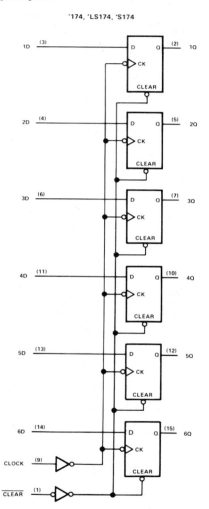

Pin numbers shown on logic notation are for D, J or N packages.

TEXAS
INSTRUMENTS

schematics of inputs and outputs

SN54174, SN54175, SN74174, SN74175

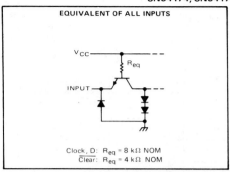

EQUIVALENT OF ALL INPUTS

Clock, D: R_{eq} = 8 kΩ NOM
$\overline{\text{Clear}}$: R_{eq} = 4 kΩ NOM

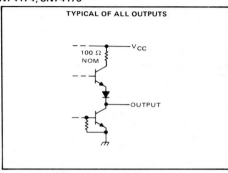

TYPICAL OF ALL OUTPUTS

SN54LS174, SN54LS175, SN74LS174, SN74LS175

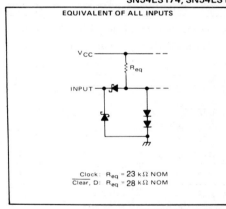

EQUIVALENT OF ALL INPUTS

$\overline{\text{Clock}}$: R_{eq} = 23 kΩ NOM
$\overline{\text{Clear}}$, D: R_{eq} = 28 kΩ NOM

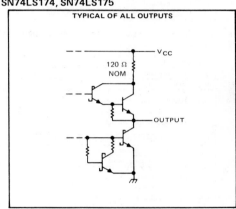

TYPICAL OF ALL OUTPUTS

SN54S174, SN54S175, SN74S174, SN74S175

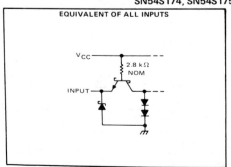

EQUIVALENT OF ALL INPUTS

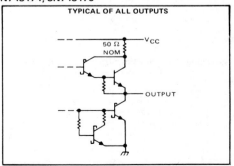

TYPICAL OF ALL OUTPUTS

TEXAS
INSTRUMENTS

TTL DEVICES

3

absolute maximum ratings over operating free-air temperature range (unless otherwise noted)

Supply voltage, V_{CC} (see Note 1) . . . . 7 V
Input voltage . . . . 5.5 V
Operating free-air temperature range: SN54174, SN54175 Circuits . . . . −55°C to 125°C
             SN74174, SN74175 Circuits . . . . 0°C to 70°C
Storage temperature range . . . . −65°C to 150°C
NOTE 1: Voltage values are with respect to network ground terminal.

recommended operating conditions

		SN54174, SN54175			SN74174, SN74175			UNIT
		MIN	NOM	MAX	MIN	NOM	MAX	
Supply voltage, V_{CC}		4.5	5	5.5	4.75	5	5.25	V
High-level output current, I_{OH}				−800			−800	μA
Low-level output current, I_{OL}				16			16	mA
Clock frequency, f_{clock}		0		25	0		25	MHz
Width of clock or clear pulse, t_w		20			20			ns
Setup time, t_{su}	Data input	20			20			ns
	Clear inactive-state	25			25			ns
Data hold time, t_h		5			5			ns
Operating free-air temperature, T_A		−55		125	0		70	°C

electrical characteristics over recommended operating free-air temperature range (unless otherwise noted)

PARAMETER		TEST CONDITIONS[†]		MIN	TYP[‡]	MAX	UNIT
V_{IH}	High-level input voltage			2			V
V_{IL}	Low-level input voltage					0.8	V
V_{IK}	Input clamp voltage	V_{CC} = MIN,	I_I = −12 mA			−1.5	V
V_{OH}	High-level output voltage	V_{CC} = MIN, V_{IL} = 0.8 V,	V_{IH} = 2 V, I_{OH} = −800 μA	2.4	3.4		V
V_{OL}	Low-level output voltage	V_{CC} = MIN, V_{IL} = 0.8 V,	V_{IH} = 2 V, I_{OL} = 16 mA		0.2	0.4	V
I_I	Input current at maximum input voltage	V_{CC} = MAX,	V_I = 5.5 V			1	mA
I_{IH}	High-level input current	V_{CC} = MAX,	V_I = 2.4 V			40	μA
I_{IL}	Low-level input current	V_{CC} = MAX,	V_I = 0.4 V			−1.6	mA
I_{OS}	Short-circuit output current[§]	V_{CC} = MAX	SN54'	−20		−57	mA
			SN74'	−18		−57	
I_{CC}	Supply current	V_{CC} = MAX, See Note 2	'174		45	65	mA
			'175		30	45	

[†] For conditions shown as MIN or MAX, use the appropriate value specified under recommended operating conditions for the applicable device type.

[‡] All typical values are at V_{CC} = 5 V, T_A = 25°C.

[§] Not more than one output should be shorted at a time.

NOTE 2: With all outputs open and 4.5 V applied to all data and clear inputs, I_{CC} is measured after a momentary ground, then 4.5 V, is applied to clock.

switching characteristics, V_{CC} = 5 V, T_A = 25°C

PARAMETER		TEST CONDITIONS	MIN	TYP	MAX	UNIT
f_{max}	Maximum clock frequency	C_L = 15 pF, R_L = 400 Ω, See Note 3	25	35		MHz
t_{PLH}	Propagation delay time, low-to-high-level output from clear (SN54175, SN74175 only)			16	25	ns
t_{PHL}	Propagation delay time, high-to-low-level output from clear			23	35	ns
t_{PLH}	Propagation delay time, low-to-high-level output from clock			20	30	ns
t_{PHL}	Propagation delay time, high-to-low-level output from clock			24	35	ns

NOTE 3: See General Information Section for load circuits and voltage waveforms.

TEXAS INSTRUMENTS

absolute maximum ratings over operating free-air temperature range (unless otherwise noted)

Supply voltage, V_{CC} (see Note 1)	7 V
Input voltage	7 V
Operating free-air temperature range: SN54LS174, SN54LS175 Circuits	$-55°$C to $125°$C
SN74LS174, SN74LS175 Circuits	$0°$C to $70°$C
Storage temperature range	$-65°$C to $150°$C

NOTE 1: Voltage values are with respect to network ground terminal.

recommended operating conditions

		SN54LS174 SN54LS175			SN74LS174 SN74LS175			UNIT
		MIN	NOM	MAX	MIN	NOM	MAX	
Supply voltage, V_{CC}		4.5	5	5.5	4.75	5	5.25	V
High-level output current, I_{OH}				-400			-400	μA
Low-level output current, I_{OL}				4			8	mA
Clock frequency, f_{clock}		0		30	0		30	MHz
Width of clock or clear pulse, t_w		20			20			ns
Setup time, t_{su}	Data input	20			20			ns
	Clear inactive-state	25			25			ns
Data hold time, t_h		5			5			ns
Operating free-air temperature, T_A		-55		125	0		70	$°$C

electrical characteristics over recommended operating free-air temperature range (unless otherwise noted)

PARAMETER		TEST CONDITIONS[†]		SN54LS174 SN54LS175			SN74LS174 SN74LS175			UNIT
				MIN	TYP[‡]	MAX	MIN	TYP[‡]	MAX	
V_{IH}	High-level input voltage			2			2			V
V_{IL}	Low-level input voltage					0.7			0.8	V
V_{IK}	Input clamp voltage	V_{CC} = MIN, I_I = -18 mA				-1.5			-1.5	V
V_{OH}	High-level output voltage	V_{CC} = MIN, V_{IH} = 2 V, V_{IL} = V_{IL}max, I_{OH} = -400 μA		2.5	3.5		2.7	3.5		V
V_{OL}	Low-level output voltage	V_{CC} = MIN, V_{IH} = 2 V, V_{IL} = V_{IL} max	I_{OL} = 4 mA		0.25	0.4		0.25	0.4	V
			I_{OL} = 8 mA					0.35	0.5	
I_I	Input current at maximum input voltage	V_{CC} = MAX, V_I = 7 V				0.1			0.1	mA
I_{IH}	High-level input current	V_{CC} = MAX, V_I = 2.7 V				20			20	μA
I_{IL}	Low-level input current	V_{CC} = MAX, V_I = 0.4 V				-0.4			-0.4	mA
I_{OS}	Short-circuit output current[§]	V_{CC} = MAX		-20		-100	-20		-100	mA
I_{CC}	Supply current	V_{CC} = MAX, See Note 2	'LS174		16	26		16	26	mA
			'LS175		11	18		11	18	

[†]For conditions shown as MIN or MAX, use the appropriate value specified under recommended operating conditions.
[‡]All typical values are at V_{CC} = 5 V, T_A = 25°C.
[§]Not more than one output should be shorted at a time, and duration of the short-circuit should not exceed one second.
NOTE 2: With all outputs open and 4.5 V applied to all data and clear inputs, I_{CC} is measured after a momentary ground, then 4.5 V, is applied to clock.

switching characteristics, V_{CC} = 5 V, T_A = 25°C

PARAMETER	TEST CONDITIONS	'LS174			'LS175			UNIT
		MIN	TYP	MAX	MIN	TYP	MAX	
f_{max} Maximum clock frequency	C_L = 15 pF, R_L = 2 kΩ, See Note 3	30	40		30	40		MHz
t_{PLH} Propagation delay time, low-to-high-level output from clear						20	30	ns
t_{PHL} Propagation delay time, high-to-low-level output from clear			23	35		20	30	ns
t_{PLH} Propagation delay time, low-to-high-level output from clock			20	30		13	25	ns
t_{PHL} Propagation delay time, high-to-low-level output from clock			21	30		16	25	ns

NOTE 3: See General Information Section for load circuits and voltage waveforms.

3

TTL DEVICES

TYPES SN54S174, SN54S175, SN74S174, SN74S175
HEX/QUADRUPLE D-TYPE FLIP-FLOPS WITH CLEAR

absolute maximum ratings over operating free-air temperature range (unless otherwise noted)

Supply voltage, V_{CC} (see Note 1)	7 V
Input voltage	5.5 V
Operating free-air temperature range: SN54S174, SN54S175 Circuits	-55°C to 125°C
SN74S174, SN74S175 Circuits	0°C to 70°C
Storage temperature range	-65°C to 150°C

NOTE 1: Voltage values are with respect to network ground terminal.

recommended operating conditions

			SN54S174, SN54S175			SN74S174, SN74S175			UNIT
			MIN	NOM	MAX	MIN	NOM	MAX	
Supply voltage, V_{CC}			4.5	5	5.5	4.75	5	5.25	V
High-level output current, I_{OH}					-1			-1	mA
Low-level output current, I_{OL}					20			20	mA
Clock frequency, f_{clock}			0		75	0		75	MHz
Pulse width, t_w	Clock		7			7			ns
	Clear		10			10			
Setup time, t_{su}	Data input		5			5			ns
	Clear inactive-state		5			5			
Data hold time, t_h			3			3			ns
Operating free-air temperature, T_A			-55		125	0		70	$^{\circ}$C

electrical characteristics over recommended operating free-air temperature range (unless otherwise noted)

PARAMETER		TEST CONDITIONS[†]		MIN	TYP[‡]	MAX	UNIT
V_{IH}	High-level input voltage			2			V
V_{IL}	Low-level input voltage					0.8	V
V_{IK}	Input clamp voltage	V_{CC} = MIN, $I_I = -18$ mA				-1.2	V
V_{OH}	High-level output voltage	V_{CC} = MIN, V_{IH} = 2 V,	SN54S'	2.5	3.4		V
		V_{IL} = 0.8 V, $I_{OH} = -1$ mA	SN74S'	2.7	3.4		
V_{OL}	Low-level output voltage	V_{CC} = MIN, V_{IH} = 2 V, V_{IL} = 0.8 V, I_{OL} = 20 mA				0.5	V
I_I	Input current at maximum input voltage	V_{CC} = MAX, V_I = 5.5 V				1	mA
I_{IH}	High-level input current	V_{CC} = MAX, V_I = 2.7 V				50	μA
I_{IL}	Low-level input current	V_{CC} = MAX, V_I = 0.5 V				-2	mA
I_{OS}	Short-circuit output current[§]	V_{CC} = MAX		-40		-100	mA
I_{CC}	Supply current	V_{CC} = MAX, See Note 2	'174		90	144	mA
			'175		60	96	

[†]For conditions shown as MIN or MAX, use the appropriate value specified under recommended operating conditions for the applicable device type.
[‡]All typical values are at V_{CC} = 5 V, $T_A = 25^{\circ}$C.
[§]Not more than one output should be shorted at a time, and duration of the short-circuit should not exceed one second.
NOTE 2: With all outputs open and 4.5 V applied to all data and clear inputs, I_{CC} is measured after a momentary ground, then 4.5 V, is applied to clock.

switching characteristics, V_{CC} = 5 V, $T_A = 25^{\circ}$C

PARAMETER		TEST CONDITIONS	MIN	TYP	MAX	UNIT
f_{max}	Maximum clock frequency		75	110		MHz
t_{PLH}	Propagation delay time, low-to-high-level Q output from clear (SN54S175, SN74S175 only)	C_L = 15 pF, R_L = 280 Ω, See Note 3		10	15	ns
t_{PHL}	Propagation delay time, high-to-low-level Q output from clear			13	22	ns
t_{PLH}	Propagation delay time, low-to-high-level output from clock			8	12	ns
t_{PHL}	Propagation time, high-to-low-level output from clock			11.5	17	ns

NOTE 3: See General Information Section for load circuits and voltage waveforms.

TEXAS
INSTRUMENTS

- Reduced-Power Versions of SN54196, SN54197, SN74196, and SN74197 50-MHz Counters

- D-C Coupled Counters Designed to Replace Signetics 8280, 8281, 8290, and 8291 Counters in Most Applications

- Performs BCD, Bi-Quinary, or Binary Counting

- Fully Programmable

- Fully Independent Clear Input

- Guaranteed to Count at Input Frequencies from 0 to 35 MHz

- Input Clamping Diodes Simplify System Design

SN54176, SN54177 . . . J OR W PACKAGE
SN74176, SN74177 . . . J OR N PACKAGE
(TOP VIEW)

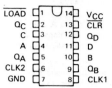

$\overline{\text{LOAD}}$	1	V_{CC}
Q_C	2	$\overline{\text{CLR}}$
C	3	Q_D
A	4	D
Q_A	5	B
CLK2	6	Q_B
GND	7	CLK1

description

These high-speed monolithic counters consist of four d-c coupled master-slave flip-flops which are internally interconnected to provide either a divide-by-two and a divide-by-five counter (SN54176, SN74176) or a divide-by-two and a divide-by-eight counter (SN54177, SN74177). These counters are fully programmable; that is, the outputs may be preset to any state by placing a low on the count/load input and entering the desired data at the data inputs. The outputs will change to agree with the data inputs independent of the state of the clocks.

These counters may also be used as 4-bit latches by using the count/load input as the strobe and entering data at the data inputs. The outputs will directly follow the data inputs when the count/load is low, but will remain unchanged when the count/load is high and the clock inputs are inactive.

These high-speed counters will accept count frequencies of 0 to 35 megahertz at the clock-1 input and 0 to 17.5 megahertz at the clock-2 input. During the count operation, transfer of information to the outputs occurs on the negative-going edge of the clock pulse. The counters feature a direct clear which when taken low sets all outputs low regardless of the states of the clocks.

All inputs are diode-clamped to minimize transmission-line effects and simplify system design. The circuits are compatible with most TTL logic families. Typical power dissipation is 150 milliwatts. The SN54176 and SN54177 circuits are characterized for operation over the full military temperature range of -55°C to 125°C; the SN74176 and SN74177 circuits are characterized for operation from 0°C to 70°C.

TTL DEVICES

3

TEXAS INSTRUMENTS

typical count configurations

SN54176 and SN74176

The output of flip-flop A is not internally connected to the succeeding flip-flops; therefore, the count may be operated in three independent modes:

1. When used as a binary-coded-decimal decade counter, the clock-2 input must be externally connected to the Q_A output. The clock-1 input receives the incoming count, and a count sequence is obtained in accordance with the BCD count sequence function table shown at right.

2. If a symmetrical divide-by-ten count is desired for frequency synthesizers (or other applications requiring division of a binary count by a power of ten), the Q_D output must be externally connected to the clock-1 input. The input count is then applied at the clock-2 input and a divide-by-ten square wave is obtained at output Q_A in accordance with the bi-quinary function table.

FUNCTION TABLES
SN54176, SN74176

DECADE (BCD)
(See Note A)

COUNT	OUTPUT			
	Q_D	Q_C	Q_B	Q_A
0	L	L	L	L
1	L	L	L	H
2	L	L	H	L
3	L	L	H	H
4	L	H	L	L
5	L	H	L	H
6	L	H	H	L
7	L	H	H	H
8	H	L	L	L
9	H	L	L	H

BI-QUINARY (5-2)
(See Note B)

COUNT	OUTPUT			
	Q_A	Q_D	Q_C	Q_B
0	L	L	L	L
1	L	L	L	H
2	L	L	H	L
3	L	L	H	H
4	L	H	L	L
5	H	L	L	H
6	H	L	L	H
7	H	L	H	L
8	H	L	H	H
9	H	H	L	L

H = high level, L = low level

NOTES: A. Output Q_A connected to clock-2 input.
B. Output Q_D connected to clock-1 input.

3. For operation as a divide-by-two counter and a divide-by-five counter, no external interconnections are required. Flip-flop A is used as a binary element for the divide-by-two function. The clock-2 input is used to obtain binary divide-by-five operation at the Q_B, Q_C, and Q_D outputs. In this mode, the two counters operate independently; however, all four flip-flops are loaded and cleared simultaneously.

SN54177 and SN74177

The output of flip-flop A is not internally connected to the succeeding flip-flops, therefore the counter may be operated in two independent modes:

1. When used as a high-speed 4-bit ripple-through counter, output Q_A must be externally connected to the clock-2 input. The input count pulses are applied to the clock-1 input. Simultaneous divisions by 2, 4, 8, and 16 are performed at the Q_A, Q_B, Q_C, and Q_D outputs as shown in the function table at right.

2. When used as a 3-bit ripple-through counter, the input count pulses are applied to the clock-2 input. Simultaneous frequency divisions by 2, 4, and 8 are available at the Q_B, Q_C, and Q_D outputs. Independent use of flip-flop A is available if the load and clear functions coincide with those of the 3-bit ripple-through counter.

FUNCTION TABLE
SN54177, SN74177
(See Note A)

COUNT	OUTPUT			
	Q_D	Q_C	Q_B	Q_A
0	L	L	L	L
1	L	L	L	H
2	L	L	H	L
3	L	L	H	H
4	L	H	L	L
5	L	H	L	H
6	L	H	H	L
7	L	H	H	H
8	H	L	L	L
9	H	L	L	H
10	H	L	H	L
11	H	L	H	H
12	H	H	L	L
13	H	H	L	H
14	H	H	H	L
15	H	H	H	H

H = high level, L = low level

NOTE A: Output Q_A connected to clock-2 input.

TEXAS INSTRUMENTS

3

TTL DEVICES

logic diagrams

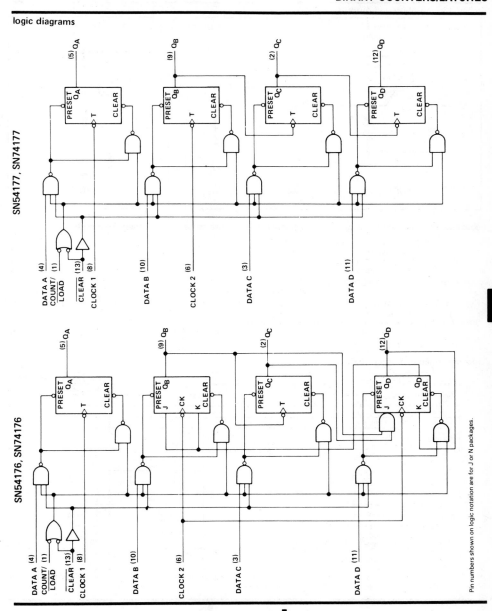

SN54177, SN74177

SN54176, SN74176

Pin numbers shown on logic notation are for J or N packages.

3

TTL DEVICES

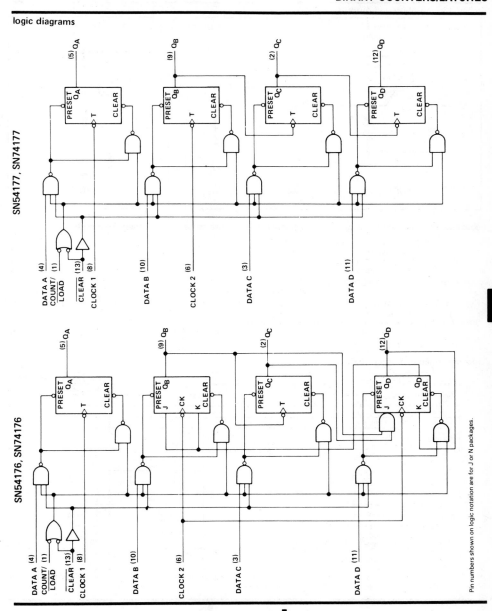

TEXAS
INSTRUMENTS

TYPES SN54176, SN54177, SN74176, SN74177
35-MHz PRESETTABLE DECADE AND
BINARY COUNTERS/LATCHES

schematics of inputs and outputs

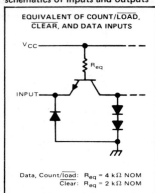

EQUIVALENT OF COUNT/LOAD, CLEAR, AND DATA INPUTS

Data, Count/load: R_{eq} = 4 kΩ NOM
Clear: R_{eq} = 2 kΩ NOM

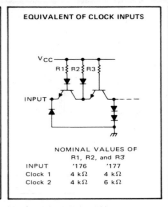

EQUIVALENT OF CLOCK INPUTS

NOMINAL VALUES OF
R1, R2, and R3

INPUT	'176	'177
Clock 1	4 kΩ	4 kΩ
Clock 2	4 kΩ	6 kΩ

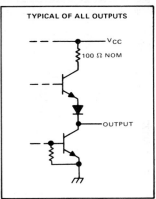

TYPICAL OF ALL OUTPUTS

absolute maximum ratings over operating free-air temperature range (unless otherwise noted)

Supply voltage, V_{CC} (see Note 1) . . . . 7 V
Input voltage . . . . 5.5 V
Interemitter voltage (see Note 2) . . . . 5.5 V
Operating free-air temperature range: SN54176, SN54177 Circuits . . . . −55°C to 125°C
                                     SN74176, SN74177 Circuits . . . . 0°C to 70°C
Storage temperature range . . . . −65°C to 150°C

NOTES: 1. Voltage values are with respect to network ground terminal.
        2. This is the voltage between two emitters of a multiple-emitter transistor. For this circuit, this rating applies between the clear and count/load inputs.

recommended operating conditions

		MIN	NOM	MAX	UNIT
Supply voltage, V_{CC}	SN54'	4.5	5	5.5	V
	SN74'	4.75	5	5.25	
High-level output current, I_{OH}				−800	μA
Low-level output current, I_{OL}				16	mA
Count frequency (see Figure 1)	Clock-1 input	0		35	MHz
	Clock-2 input	0		17.5	
Pulse width, t_W (see Figure 1)	Clock-1 input	14			ns
	Clock-2 input	28			
	Clear	20			
	Load	25			
Input hold time, t_h (see Figure 1)	High-level data	$t_{W(load)}$			ns
	Low-level data	$t_{W(load)}$			
Input setup time, t_{su} (see Figure 1)	High-level data	15			ns
	Low-level data	20			
Count enable time, t_{enable} (see Note 3 and Figure 1)		25			ns
Operating free-air temperature, T_A	SN54'	−55		125	°C
	SN74'	0		70	

NOTE 3: Minimum count enable time is the interval immediately preceding the negative-going edge of the clock pulse during which interval the count/load and clear inputs must both be high to ensure counting.

TEXAS
INSTRUMENTS

electrical characteristics over recommended operating free-air temperature range (unless otherwise noted)

PARAMETER		TEST CONDITIONS†		SN54176, SN74176			SN54177, SN74177			UNIT
				MIN	TYP‡	MAX	MIN	TYP‡	MAX	
V_{IH}	High-level input voltage			2			2			V
V_{IL}	Low-level input voltage					0.8			0.8	V
V_{IK}	Input clamp voltage	V_{CC} = MIN, I_I = −12 mA				−1.5			−1.5	V
V_{OH}	High-level output voltage	V_{CC} = MIN, V_{IH} = 2 V, V_{IL} = 0.8 V, I_{OH} = −800 µA		2.4	3.4		2.4	3.4		V
V_{OL}	Low-level output voltage	V_{CC} = MIN, V_{IH} = 2 V, V_{IL} = 0.8 V, I_{OL} = 16 mA¶			0.2	0.4		0.2	0.4	V
I_I	Input current at maximum input voltage	V_{CC} = MAX, V_I = 5.5 V				1			1	mA
I_{IH}	High-level input current	Data, count/load	V_{CC} = MAX, V_I = 2.4 V			40			40	µA
		Clear, clock 1				80			80	
		Clock 2				120			80	
I_{IL}	Low-level input current	Data, count/load	V_{CC} = MAX, V_I = 0.4 V			−1.6			−1.6	mA
		Clear				−3.2			−3.2	
		Clock 1				−4.8			−4.8	
		Clock 2				−4.8			−3.2	
I_{OS}	Short-circuit output current §	V_{CC} = MAX	SN54'	−20		−57	−20		−57	mA
			SN74'	−18		−57	−18		−57	
I_{CC}	Supply current	V_{CC} = MAX, See Note 4			30	48		30	48	mA

† For conditions shown as MIN or MAX, use the appropriate value specified under recommended operation conditions.
‡ All typical values are at V_{CC} = 5 V, T_A = 25°C.
¶ Q_A outputs are tested at I_{OL} = 16 mA plus the limit value of I_{IL} for the clock-2 input. This permits driving the clock-2 input while fanning out to 10 Series 54/74 loads.
§ Not more than one output should be shorted at a time.
NOTE 4: I_{CC} is measured with all inputs grounded and all outputs open.

switching characteristics, V_{CC} = 5 V, R_L = 400 Ω, C_L = 15 pF, T_A = 25°C, see figure 1

PARAMETER	FROM (INPUT)	TO (OUTPUT)	SN54176, SN74176			SN54177, SN74177			UNIT
			MIN	TYP	MAX	MIN	TYP	MAX	
f_{max}	Clock 1	Q_A	35	50		35	50		MHz
t_{PLH}	Clock 1	Q_A		8	13		8	13	ns
t_{PHL}				11	17		11	17	
t_{PLH}	Clock 2	Q_B		11	17		11	17	ns
t_{PHL}				17	26		17	26	
t_{PLH}	Clock 2	Q_C		27	41		27	41	ns
t_{PHL}				34	51		34	51	
t_{PLH}	Clock 2	Q_D		13	20		44	66	ns
t_{PHL}				17	26		50	75	
t_{PLH}	A, B, C, D	Q_A, Q_B, Q_C, Q_D		19	29		19	29	ns
t_{PHL}				31	46		31	46	
t_{PLH}	Load	Any		29	43		29	43	ns
t_{PHL}				32	48		32	48	
t_{PHL}	Clear	Any		32	48		32	48	ns

f_{max} ≡ maximum count frequency
t_{PLH} ≡ propagation delay time, low-to-high-level output
t_{PHL} ≡ propagation delay time, high-to-low-level output

3

TTL DEVICES

TEXAS
INSTRUMENTS

PARAMETER MEASUREMENT INFORMATION

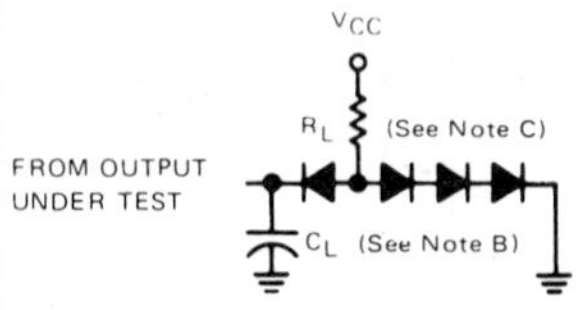
VCC
RL (See Note C)
FROM OUTPUT
UNDER TEST
CL (See Note B)

LOAD CIRCUIT

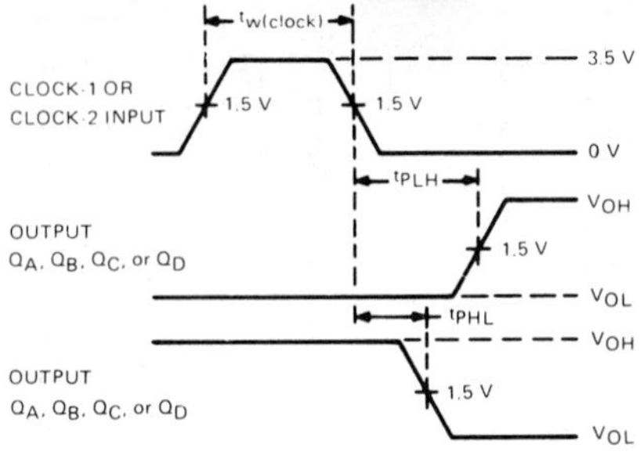
tw(clock)
CLOCK-1 OR
CLOCK-2 INPUT
1.5 V
1.5 V
3.5 V
0 V
tPLH
OUTPUT
QA, QB, QC, or QD
1.5 V
VOH
VOL
tPHL
OUTPUT
QA, QB, QC, or QD
1.5 V
VOH
VOL

CLOCK-MODE VOLTAGE WAVEFORMS

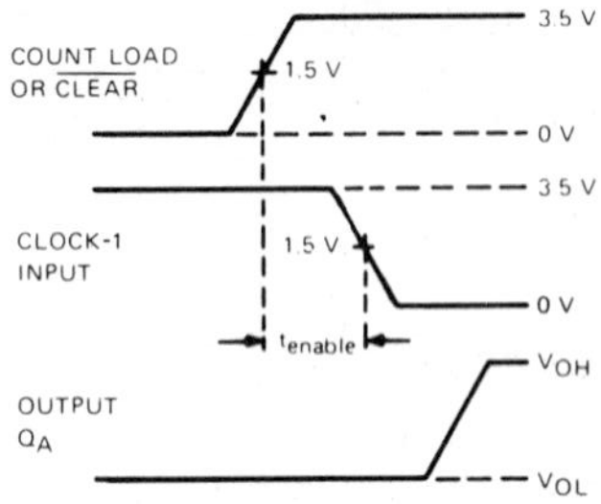
COUNT LOAD
OR CLEAR
1.5 V
3.5 V
0 V
CLOCK-1
INPUT
1.5 V
3.5 V
0 V
tenable
OUTPUT
QA
VOH
VOL

CLOCK ENABLE TIME VOLTAGE WAVEFORMS

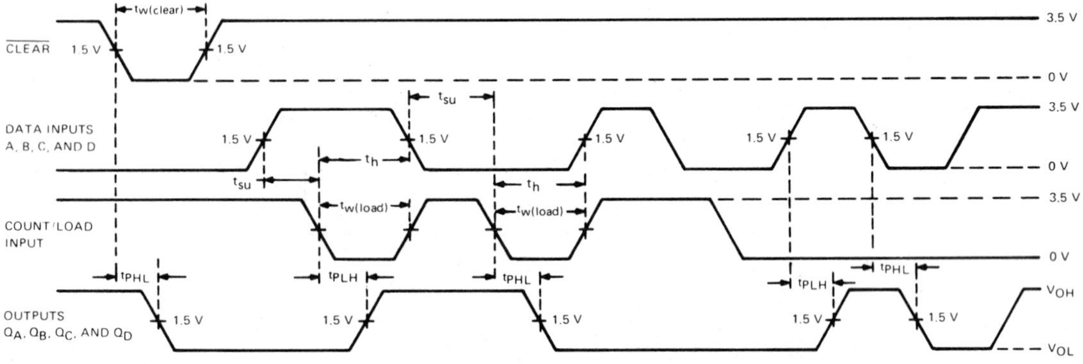
tw(clear)
CLEAR
1.5 V
1.5 V
3.5 V
0 V
tsu
DATA INPUTS
A, B, C, AND D
1.5 V
th
tsu
th
3.5 V
0 V
COUNT/LOAD
INPUT
tw(load)
tw(load)
3.5 V
0 V
tPHL
tPLH
tPHL
tPLH
tPHL
OUTPUTS
QA, QB, QC, AND QD
1.5 V
VOH
VOL

CLEAR AND LOAD VOLTAGE WAVEFORMS

FIGURE 1

NOTES: A. The input pulse is supplied by a generator having the following characteristics: PRR ⩽ 1 MHz, duty cycle ⩽ 50%, t_r < 5 ns, and unless specified, t_f < 5 ns. When testing f_{max}, vary PRR.

B. C_L includes probe and jig capacitance.

C. All diodes are 1N3064 or equivalent.

D. Unless otherwise specified, Q_A is connected to clock 2.

DECEMBER 1972 – REVISED DECEMBER 1983

- **Typical Maximum Clock Frequency ... 39 MHz**
- **Three Operating Modes:**
  Synchronous Parallel Load
  Right Shift
  Hold (Do Nothing)
- **Negative-Edge-Triggered Clocking**
- **D-C Coupling Symplifies System Designs**

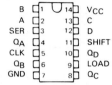

SN54178 ... J OR W PACKAGE
SN74178 ... J OR N PACKAGE
(TOP VIEW)

```
         ___  ___
  B   [ 1  \_/ 14 ] V_CC
  A   [ 2      13 ] C
 SER  [ 3      12 ] D
  QA  [ 4      11 ] SHIFT
 CLK  [ 5      10 ] QD
  QB  [ 6       9 ] LOAD
 GND  [ 7       8 ] QC
```

description

These shift registers utilize d-c coupled storage elements and feature synchronous parallel inputs and parallel outputs.

Parallel loading is accomplished by taking the shift input low, applying the four bits of data, and taking the load input high. The data is loaded into the associated flip-flop synchronously and appears at the outputs after a high-to-low transition of the clock. During loading, serial data flow is inhibited.

Shift right is also accomplished on the falling edge of the clock pulse when the shift input is high regardless of the level of the load input. Serial data for this mode is entered at the serial data input.

When both the shift and load inputs are low, clocking of the register can continue; however, data appearing at each output is fed back to the flip-flop input creating a mode in which the data is held unchanged. Thus, the system clock may be left free-running without changing the contents of the register.

'178
FUNCTION TABLE

INPUTS								OUTPUTS			
SHIFT	LOAD	CLOCK	SERIAL	PARALLEL				Q_A	Q_B	Q_C	Q_D
				A	B	C	D				
X	X	H	X	X	X	X	X	Q_{A0}	Q_{B0}	Q_{C0}	Q_{D0}
L	L	↓	X	X	X	X	X	Q_{A0}	Q_{B0}	Q_{C0}	Q_{D0}
L	H	↓	X	a	b	c	d	a	b	c	d
H	X	↓	H	X	X	X	X	H	Q_{An}	Q_{Bn}	Q_{Cn}
H	X	↓	L	X	X	X	X	L	Q_{An}	Q_{Bn}	Q_{Cn}

H = high level (steady state), L = low level (steady state)
X = irrelevant (any input, including transitions)
↓ = transition from high to low level
a, b, c, d = the level of steady state input at inputs A, B, C, or D, respectively.
Q_{A0}, Q_{B0}, Q_{C0}, Q_{D0} = the level of Q_A, Q_B, Q_C, or $\overline{Q}_D$, respectively, before the indicated steady-state input conditions were established.
Q_{An}, Q_{Bn}, Q_{Cn} = the level of Q_A, Q_B, or Q_C, respectively, before the most-recent ↓ transition of the clock.

TEXAS
INSTRUMENTS

3-571

logic diagram ('178)

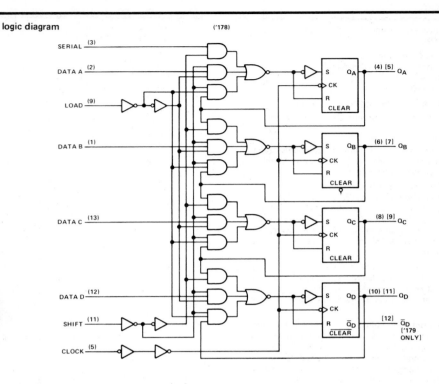

Pin numbers shown on logic notation are for J or N packages.

schematics of inputs and outputs

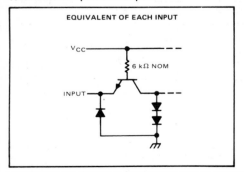

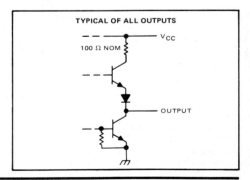

TEXAS
INSTRUMENTS

absolute maximum ratings over operating free-air temperature range (unless otherwise noted)

Supply voltage, V_{CC} (see Note 1) .... 7 V
Input voltage .... 5.5 V
Operating free-air temperature range: SN54178 Circuit .... −55°C to 125°C
SN74178 Circuit .... 0°C to 70°C
Storage temperature range .... −65°C to 150°C

NOTE 1: Voltage values are with respect to network ground terminal.

recommended operating conditions

		SN54178 MIN	SN54178 NOM	SN54178 MAX	SN74178 MIN	SN74178 NOM	SN74178 MAX	UNIT
Supply voltage, V_{CC}		4.5	5	5.5	4.75	5	5.25	V
High-level output current, I_{OH}				−800			−800	μA
Low-level output current, I_{OL}				16			16	mA
Clock frequency, f_{clock}		0		25	0		25	MHz
Width of clock or clear pulse, t_w (see Figure 1)		20			20			ns
Setup time, t_{su} (see Figure 1)	Shift (H or L) or load	35			35			ns
	Data	30			30			
	$\overline{\text{Clear}}$-inactive-state	15			15			
Hold time at any input, t_h		5			5			ns
Operating free-air temperature, T_A		−55		125	0		70	°C

electrical characteristics over recommended operating free-air temperature range (unless otherwise noted)

PARAMETER	TEST CONDITIONS[†]	SN54178 MIN	SN54178 TYP[*]	SN54178 MAX	SN74178 MIN	SN74178 TYP[*]	SN74178 MAX	UNIT
V_{IH} High-level input voltage		2			2			V
V_{IL} Low-level input voltage				0.8			0.8	V
V_{IK} Input clamp voltage	V_{CC} = MIN, I_I = −12 mA			−1.5			−1.5	V
V_{OH} High-level output voltage	V_{CC} = MIN, V_{IH} = 2 V, V_{IL} = 0.8 V, I_{OH} = −800μA	2.4	3.4		2.4	3.4		V
V_{OL} Low-level output voltage	V_{CC} = MIN, V_{IH} = 2 V, V_{IL} = 0.8 V, I_{OL} = 16 mA		0.2	0.4		0.2	0.4	V
I_I Input current at maximum input voltage	V_{CC} = MAX, V_I = 5.5 V			1			1	mA
I_{IH} High-level input current	V_{CC} = MAX, V_I = 2.4 V			40			40	μA
I_{IL} Low-level input current	V_{CC} = MAX, V_I = 0.4 V			−1.6			−1.6	mA
I_{OS} Short-circuit output current[§]	V_{CC} = MAX	−20		−57	−18		−57	mA
I_{CC} Supply current	V_{CC} = MAX, See Note 2		46	70		46	75	mA

[†] For conditions shown as MIN or MAX, use the appropriate value specified under recommended operating conditions for the applicable device type.
[*] All typical values are at V_{CC} = 5 V, T_A = 25°C.
[§] Not more than one output should be shorted at a time.
NOTE 2: I_{CC} is measured as follows:
     a) 4.5 V is applied to serial inputs, load, shift, and $\overline{\text{clear}}$.
     b) Parallel inputs A through D are grounded.
     c) 4.5 V is momentarily applied to clock which is then grounded.

3

TTL DEVICES

TEXAS INSTRUMENTS

switching characteristics, $V_{CC} = 5$ V, $T_A = 25°C$

PARAMETER¶	FROM (INPUT)	TO (OUTPUT)	TEST CONDITIONS	MIN	TYP	MAX	UNIT
f_{max}				25	39		MHz
t_{PLH}	$\overline{Clear}$	$\overline{Q_D}$	$C_L = 15$ pF, $R_L = 400$ Ω, See Figure 1		15	23	ns
t_{PHL}		Q_A, Q_B, Q_C, Q_D			24	36	
t_{PLH}	Clock	Any output			17	26	ns
t_{PHL}					23	35	

¶ f_{max} ≡ Maximum clock frequency

t_{PHL} ≡ Propagation delay time, high-to-low-level output

t_{PLH} ≡ Propagation delay time, low-to-high-level output

PARAMETER MEASUREMENT INFORMATION

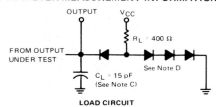

LOAD CIRCUIT

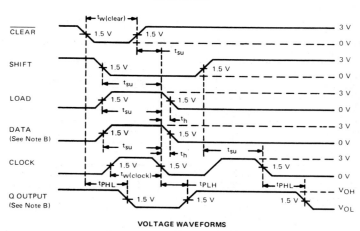

VOLTAGE WAVEFORMS

NOTES: A. Input pulses are supplied by generators having the following characteristics: $t_{TLH} \leqslant 10$ ns, $t_{THL} \leqslant 10$ ns, PRR $\leqslant 1$ MHz, $Z_{out} \approx 50$ Ω.

B. Data input and Q output are any related pair. Serial and other data inputs are at GND. Serial data input is tested in conjunction with Q_A output in the shift mode.

C. C_L includes probe and jig capacitance.

D. All diodes are 1N3064 or equivalent.

FIGURE 1—SWITCHING TIMES

3

TTL DEVICES

FUNCTION TABLE

INPUTS			OUTPUTS	
Σ OF H's AT A THRU H	EVEN	ODD	Σ EVEN	Σ ODD
EVEN	H	L	H	L
ODD	H	L	L	H
EVEN	L	H	L	H
ODD	L	H	H	L
X	H	H	L	L
X	L	L	H	H

H = high level, L = low level, X = irrelevant

SN54180 . . . J OR W PACKAGE
SN74180 . . . J OR N PACKAGE
(TOP VIEW)

G	1	14	V_CC
H	2	13	F
EVEN	3	12	E
ODD	4	11	D
ΣEVEN	5	10	C
ΣODD	6	9	B
GND	7	8	A

description

These universal, monolithic, 9-bit (8 data bits plus 1 parity bit) parity generators/checkers, utilize familiar Series 54/74 TTL circuitry and feature odd/even outputs and control inputs to facilitate operation in either odd or even-parity applications. Depending on whether even or odd parity is being generated or checked, the even or odd inputs can be utilized as the parity or 9th-bit input. The word-length capability is easily expanded by cascading.

The SN54180/SN74180 are fully compatible with other TTL or DTL circuits. Input buffers are provided so that each data input represents only one normalized series 54/74 load. A full fan-out to 10 normalized series 54/74 loads is available from each of the outputs at a low logic level. A fan-out to 20 normalized loads is provided at a high logic level to facilitate the connection of unused inputs to used inputs. Typical power dissipation is 170 mW.

The SN54180 is characterized for operation over the full military temperature range of $-55°C$ to $125°C$; and the SN74180 is characterized for operation from $0°C$ to $70°C$.

absolute maximum ratings over operating free-air temperature range (unless otherwise noted)

Supply voltage, V_{CC} (see Note 1) . . . . 7 V
Input voltage . . . . 5.5 V
Operating free-air temperature range: SN54180 Circuits . . . . $-55°C$ to $125°C$
SN74180 Circuits . . . . $0°C$ to $70°C$
Storage temperature range . . . . $-65°C$ to $150°C$

NOTE 1: Voltage values are with respect to network ground terminal.

recommended operating conditions

	SN54180			SN74180			UNIT
	MIN	NOM	MAX	MIN	NOM	MAX	
Supply voltage, V_{CC}	4.5	5	5.5	4.75	5	5.25	V
High-level output current, I_{OH}			−800			−800	μA
Low-level output current, I_{OL}			16			16	mA
Operating free-air temperature, T_A	−55		125	0		70	°C

3

TTL DEVICES

electrical characteristics over recommended operating free-air temperature range (unless otherwise noted)

PARAMETER		TEST CONDITIONS†	SN54180 MIN	SN54180 TYP‡	SN54180 MAX	SN74180 MIN	SN74180 TYP‡	SN74180 MAX	UNIT
V_{IH}	High-level input voltage		2			2			V
V_{IL}	Low-level input voltage				0.8			0.8	V
V_{IK}	Input clamp voltage	V_{CC} = MIN, I_I = −12 mA			−1.5			−1.5	V
V_{OH}	High-level output voltage	V_{CC} = MIN, V_{IH} = 2 V, V_{IL} = 0.8 V, I_{OH} = −800 µA	2.4	3.3		2.4	3.3		V
V_{OL}	Low-level output voltage	V_{CC} = MIN, V_{IH} = 2 V, V_{IL} = 0.8 V, I_{OL} = 16 mA		0.2	0.4		0.2	0.4	V
I_I	Input current at maximum input voltage	V_{CC} = MAX, V_I = 5.5 V			1			1	mA
I_{IH}	High-level input current — Any data input	V_{CC} = MAX, V_I = 2.4 V			40			40	µA
I_{IH}	High-level input current — Even or odd input				80			80	µA
I_{IL}	Low-level input current — Any data input	V_{CC} = MAX, V_I = 0.4 V			−1.6			−1.6	mA
I_{IL}	Low-level input current — Even or odd input				−3.2			−3.2	mA
I_{OS}	Short-circuit output current§	V_{CC} = MAX	−20		−55	−18		−55	mA
I_{CC}	Supply current	V_{CC} = MAX, See Note 2		34	49		34	56	mA

NOTE 2: I_{CC} is measured with even and odd inputs at 4.5 V, all other inputs and outputs open.

† For conditions shown as MIN or MAX, use the appropriate value specified under recommended operating conditions for the applicable type.

‡ All typical values are at V_{CC} = 5 V, T_A = 25°C.

§ Not more than one output should be shorted at a time.

switching characteristics, V_{CC} = 5 V, T_A = 25°C

PARAMETER¶	FROM (INPUT)	TO (OUTPUT)	TEST CONDITIONS	MIN	TYP	MAX	UNIT
t_{PLH}	Data	Σ Even	C_L = 15 pF, R_L = 400 Ω, Odd input grounded, See Note 3		40	60	ns
t_{PHL}					45	68	
t_{PLH}	Data	Σ Odd			32	48	ns
t_{PHL}					25	38	
t_{PLH}	Data	Σ Even	C_L = 15 pF, R_L = 400 Ω, Even input grounded, See Note 3		32	48	ns
t_{PHL}					25	38	
t_{PLH}	Data	Σ Odd			40	60	ns
t_{PHL}					45	68	
t_{PLH}	Even or Odd	Σ Even or Σ Odd	C_L = 15 pF, R_L = 400 Ω, See Note 3		13	20	ns
t_{PHL}					7	10	

NOTE 3: See General Information Section for load circuits and voltage waveforms.

TEXAS
INSTRUMENTS

3

TTL DEVICES

schematics of inputs and outputs

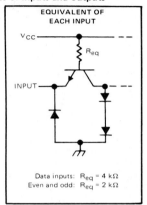

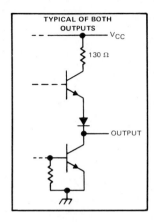

logic diagram

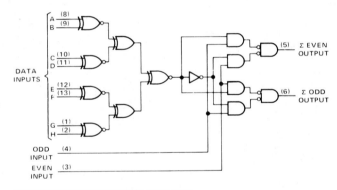

Pin numbers shown on logic notation are for J or N packages.

TTL DEVICES

3

TEXAS
INSTRUMENTS

TTL DEVICES

- **Full Look-Ahead for High-Speed Operations on Long Words**
- **Input Clamping Diodes Minimize Transmission-Line Effects**
- **Darlington Outputs Reduce Turn-Off Time**
- **Arithmetic Operating Modes:**
  Addition
  Subtraction
  Shift Operand A One Position
  Magnitude Comparison
  Plus Twelve Other Arithmetic
  Operations
- **Logic Function Modes:**
  Exclusive-OR
  Comparator
  AND, NAND, OR, NOR
  Plus Ten Other Logic Operations

SN54LS181, SN54S181 ... J OR W PACKAGE
SN74LS181, SN74S181 ... DW, J OR N PACKAGE
(TOP VIEW)

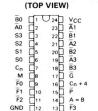

SN54LS181, SN54S181 ... FK PACKAGE
SN74LS181, SN74S181
(TOP VIEW)

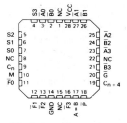

NC – No internal connection

TYPICAL ADDITION TIMES

NUMBER OF BITS	ADDITION TIMES		PACKAGE COUNT		CARRY METHOD BETWEEN ALU's
	USING 'LS181 AND '182	USING 'S181 AND '182	ARITHMETIC/ LOGIC UNITS	LOOK-AHEAD CARRY GENERATORS	
1 to 4	24 ns	11 ns	1		NONE
5 to 8	40 ns	18 ns	2		RIPPLE
9 to 16	44 ns	19 ns	3 or 4	1	FULL LOOK-AHEAD
17 to 64	68 ns	28 ns	5 to 16	2 to 5	FULL LOOK-AHEAD

description

The 'LS181 and 'S181 are arithmetic logic units (ALU)/function generators that have a complexity of 75 equivalent gates on a monolithic chip. These circuits perform 16 binary arithmetic operations on two 4-bit words as shown in Tables 1 and 2. These operations are selected by the four function-select lines (S0, S1, S2, S3) and include addition, subtraction, decrement, and straight transfer. When performing arithmetic manipulations, the internal carries must be enabled by applying a low-level voltage to the mode control input (M). A full carry look-ahead scheme is made available in these devices for fast, simultaneous carry generation by means of two cascade-outputs (pins 15 and 17) for the four bits in the package. When used in conjunction with the SN54S182 or SN74S182, full carry look-ahead circuits, high speed arithmetic operations can be performed. The typical addition times shown above illustrate the little additional time required for addition of longer words when full carry look-ahead is employed. The method of cascading 'S182 circuits with these ALU's to provide multi-level carry look-ahead is illustrated under typical applications data for the 'S182.

If high speed is not of importance, a ripple-carry input (C_n) and a ripple-carry output (C_{n+4}) are available. However, the ripple-carry delay has also been minimized so that arithmetic manipulations for small word lengths can be performed without external circuitry.

TTL DEVICES

TYPES SN54LS181, SN54S181, SN74LS181, SN74S181
ARITHMETIC LOGIC UNITS/FUNCTION GENERATORS

description (continued)

The 'LS181 and 'S181 will accommodate active-high or active-low data if the pin designations are interpreted as follows:

PIN NUMBER	2	1	23	22	21	20	19	18	9	10	11	13	7	16	15	17
Active-low data (Table 1)	$\overline{A}_0$	$\overline{B}_0$	$\overline{A}_1$	$\overline{B}_1$	$\overline{A}_2$	$\overline{B}_2$	$\overline{A}_3$	$\overline{B}_3$	$\overline{F}_0$	$\overline{F}_1$	$\overline{F}_2$	$\overline{F}_3$	C_n	C_{n+4}	$\overline{P}$	$\overline{G}$
Active-high data (Table 2)	A_0	B_0	A_1	B_1	A_2	B_2	A_3	B_3	F_0	F_1	F_2	F_3	$\overline{C}_n$	$\overline{C}_{n+4}$	X	Y

Subtraction is accomplished by 1's complement addition where the 1's complement of the subtrahend is generated internally. The resultant output is A−B−1, which requires an end-around or forced carry to provide A−B.

The 'LS181 or 'S181 can also be utilized as a comparator. The A = B outputs, is internally decoded from the function outputs (F0, F1, F2, F3) so that when two words of equal magnitude are applied at the A and B inputs, it will assume a high level to indicate equality (A = B). The ALU must be in the subtract mode with C_n = H when performing this comparison. The A = B output is open-collector so that it can be wire-AND connected to give a comparison for more than four bits. The carry output (C_{n+4}) can also be used to supply relative magnitude information. Again, the ALU must be placed in the subtract mode by placing the function select inputs S3, S2, S1, S0 at L, H, H, L respectively.

INPUT C_n	OUTPUT C_{n+4}	ACTIVE-LOW DATA (FIGURE 1)	ACTIVE-HIGH DATA (FIGURE 2)
H	H	$A \geq B$	$A \leq B$
H	L	$A < B$	$A > B$
L	H	$A > B$	$A < B$
L	L	$A \leq B$	$A \geq B$

These circuits have been designed to not only incorporate all of the designer's requirements for arithmetic operations, but also to provide 16 possible functions of two Boolean variables without the use of external circuitry. These logic functions are selected by use of the four function-select inputs (S0, S1, S2, S3) with the mode-control input (M) at a high level to disable the internal carry. The 16 logic functions are detailed in Tables 1 and 2 and include exclusive-OR, NAND, AND, NOR, and OR functions.

Series 54, 54LS, and 54S devices are characterized for operation over the full military temperature range of −55°C to 125°C; Series 74, 74LS, and 74S devices are characterized for operation from 0°C to 70°C.

signal designations

The 'LS181 and 'S181 together with the 'S182 can be used with the signal designations of either Figure 1 or Figure 2. The inversion indicators (O) and the bars over the terminal letter symbols (e.g., $\overline{C}$) each indicate that the associated input or output is active with respect to the selected function of the device when that input or output is low. That is, a low at $\overline{C}$ means "do carry" while a high means "do not carry".

The logic functions and arithmetic operations obtained with signal designations of Figure 1 are given in Table 1; those obtained with signal designations of Figure 2 are given in Table 2.

TEXAS
INSTRUMENTS

signal designations (continued)

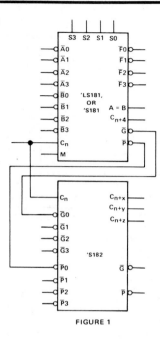

FIGURE 1

TABLE 1

SELECTION				ACTIVE-LOW DATA		
				M = H	M = L; ARITHMETIC OPERATIONS	
S3	S2	S1	S0	LOGIC FUNCTIONS	C_n = L (no carry)	C_n = H (with carry)
L	L	L	L	F = $\overline{A}$	F = A MINUS 1	F = A
L	L	L	H	F = $\overline{AB}$	F = AB MINUS 1	F = AB
L	L	H	L	F = $\overline{A}$ + B	F = $A\overline{B}$ MINUS 1	F = $A\overline{B}$
L	L	H	H	F = 1	F = MINUS 1 (2's COMP)	F = ZERO
L	H	L	L	F = $\overline{A + B}$	F = A PLUS (A + $\overline{B}$)	F = A PLUS (A + $\overline{B}$) PLUS 1
L	H	L	H	F = $\overline{B}$	F = AB PLUS (A + $\overline{B}$)	F = AB PLUS (A + $\overline{B}$) PLUS 1
L	H	H	L	F = A $\oplus$ B	F = A MINUS B MINUS 1	F = A MINUS B
L	H	H	H	F = A + $\overline{B}$	F = A + $\overline{B}$	F = (A + $\overline{B}$) PLUS 1
H	L	L	L	F = $\overline{A}B$	F = A PLUS (A + B)	F = A PLUS (A + B) PLUS 1
H	L	L	H	F = A $\oplus$ B	F = A PLUS B	F = A PLUS B PLUS 1
H	L	H	L	F = B	F = $A\overline{B}$ PLUS (A + B)	F = $A\overline{B}$ PLUS (A + B) PLUS 1
H	L	H	H	F = A + B	F = (A + B)	F = (A + B) PLUS 1
H	H	L	L	F = 0	F = A	F = A PLUS A PLUS 1
H	H	L	H	F = $A\overline{B}$	F = AB PLUS A	F = AB PLUS A PLUS 1
H	H	H	L	F = AB	F = $A\overline{B}$ PLUS A	F = $A\overline{B}$ PLUS A PLUS 1
H	H	H	H	F = A	F = A	F = A PLUS 1

TEXAS INSTRUMENTS

3-581

3

TTL DEVICES

signal designations (continued)

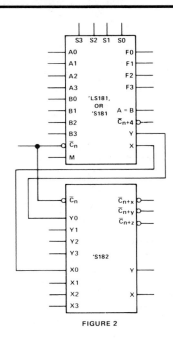

FIGURE 2

TABLE 2

SELECTION				ACTIVE-HIGH DATA		
				M = H	M = L; ARITHMETIC OPERATIONS	
S3	S2	S1	S0	LOGIC FUNCTIONS	$\overline{C}_n = H$ (no carry)	$\overline{C}_n = L$ (with carry)
L	L	L	L	$F = \overline{A}$	$F = A$	$F = A$ PLUS 1
L	L	L	H	$F = \overline{A + B}$	$F = A + B$	$F = (A + B)$ PLUS 1
L	L	H	L	$F = \overline{A}B$	$F = A + \overline{B}$	$F = (A + \overline{B})$ PLUS 1
L	L	H	H	$F = 0$	$F = $ MINUS 1 (2's COMPL)	$F = $ ZERO
L	H	L	L	$F = \overline{AB}$	$F = A$ PLUS $A\overline{B}$	$F = A$ PLUS $A\overline{B}$ PLUS 1
L	H	L	H	$F = \overline{B}$	$F = (A + B)$ PLUS $A\overline{B}$	$F = (A + B)$ PLUS $A\overline{B}$ PLUS 1
L	H	H	L	$F = A \oplus B$	$F = A$ MINUS B MINUS 1	$F = A$ MINUS B
L	H	H	H	$F = A\overline{B}$	$F = A\overline{B}$ MINUS 1	$F = A\overline{B}$
H	L	L	L	$F = \overline{A} + B$	$F = A$ PLUS AB	$F = A$ PLUS AB PLUS 1
H	L	L	H	$F = \overline{A \oplus B}$	$F = A$ PLUS B	$F = A$ PLUS B PLUS 1
H	L	H	L	$F = B$	$F = (A + \overline{B})$ PLUS AB	$F = (A + \overline{B})$ PLUS AB PLUS 1
H	L	H	H	$F = AB$	$F = AB$ MINUS 1	$F = AB$
H	H	L	L	$F = 1$	$F = A$ PLUS A	$F = A$ PLUS A PLUS 1
H	H	L	H	$F = A + \overline{B}$	$F = (A + B)$ PLUS A	$F = (A + B)$ PLUS A PLUS 1
H	H	H	L	$F = A + B$	$F = (A + \overline{B})$ PLUS A	$F = (A + \overline{B})$ PLUS A PLUS 1
H	H	H	H	$F = A$	$F = A$ MINUS 1	$F = A$

TEXAS
INSTRUMENTS

logic diagram

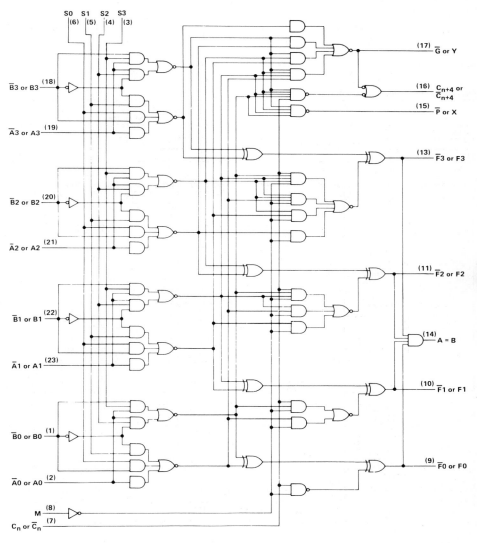

Pin numbers shown on logic notation are for DW, J or N packages.

3

TTL DEVICES

TYPES SN54LS181, SN74LS181
ARITHMETIC LOGIC UNITS/FUNCTION GENERATORS

absolute maximum ratings over recommended operating free-air temperature range (unless otherwise noted)

Supply voltage, V_{CC} (see Note 1)	7 V
Input voltage	5.5 V
Interemitter voltage (see Note 2)	5.5 V
Operating free-air temperature range: SN54LS181	−55°C to 125°C
SN74LS181	0°C to 70°C
Storage temperature range	−65°C to 150°C

NOTES: 1. Voltage values, except interemitter voltage, are with respect to network ground terminal.
2. This is the voltage between two emitters of a multiple-emitter transistor. For this circuit, this rating applies to each $\overline{A}$ input in conjunction with inputs S2 or S3, and to each $\overline{B}$ input in conjunction with inputs S0 or S3.

recommended operating conditions

	SN54LS181			SN74LS181			UNIT
	MIN	NOM	MAX	MIN	NOM	MAX	
Supply voltage, V_{CC}	4.5	5	5.5	4.75	5	5.25	V
High-level output current, I_{OH} (All outputs except A = B)			−400			−400	μA
Low-level output current, I_{OL}			4			8	mA
Operating free-air temperature, T_A	−55		125	0		70	°C

electrical characteristics over recommended operating free-air temperature range (unless otherwise noted)

PARAMETER		TEST CONDITIONS†		SN54LS181			SN74LS181			UNIT
				MIN	TYP‡	MAX	MIN	TYP‡	MAX	
V_{IH}	High-level input voltage			2			2			V
V_{IL}	Low-level input voltage					0.7			0.8	V
V_{IK}	Input clamp voltage	V_{CC} = MIN, I_I = −18 mA				−1.5			−1.5	V
V_{OH}	High-level output voltage, any output except A = B	V_{CC} = MIN, V_{IH} = 2 V, V_{IL} = V_{IL} max, I_{OH} = −400 μA		2.5	3.4		2.7	3.4		V
I_{OH}	High-level output current, A = B output only	V_{CC} = MIN, V_{IH} = 2 V, V_{IL} = V_{IL} max, V_{OH} = 5.5 V				100			100	μA
V_{OL}	Low-level output voltage	All outputs	V_{CC} = MIN, V_{IH} = 2 V, V_{IL} = V_{IL} max	I_{OL} = 4 mA	0.25	0.4		0.25	0.4	V
				I_{OL} = 8 mA				0.35	0.5	
		Output $\overline{G}$		I_{OL} = 16 mA	0.47	0.7		0.47	0.7	
		Output $\overline{P}$		I_{OL} = 8 mA	0.35	0.6		0.35	0.5	
I_I	Input current at max. input voltage	Mode input	V_{CC} = MAX, V_I = 5.5 V				0.1			0.1	mA
		Any $\overline{A}$ or $\overline{B}$ input					0.3			0.3	
		Any S input					0.4			0.4	
		Carry input					0.5			0.5	
I_{IH}	High-level input current	Mode input	V_{CC} = MAX, V_I = 2.7 V				20			20	μA
		Any $\overline{A}$ or $\overline{B}$ input					60			60	
		Any S input					80			80	
		Carry input					100			100	
I_{IL}	Low-level input current	Mode input	V_{CC} = MAX, V_I = 0.4 V				−0.4			−0.4	mA
		Any $\overline{A}$ or $\overline{B}$ input					−1.2			−1.2	
		Any S input					−1.6			−1.6	
		Carry input					−2			−2	
I_{OS}	Short-circuit output current, any output except A = B §	V_{CC} = MAX		−6		−40	−5		−42	mA
I_{CC}	Supply current	V_{CC} = MAX, See Note 3	Condition A		20	32		20	34	mA
			Condition B		21	35		21	37	

†For conditions shown as MIN or MAX, use the appropriate value specified under recommended operating conditions.
‡All typical values are at V_{CC} = 5 V, T_A = 25°C.
§Not more than one output should be shorted at a time.
NOTE 3: With outputs open, I_{CC} is measured for the following conditions:
A. S0 through S3, M, and $\overline{A}$ inputs are at 4.5 V, all other inputs are grounded.
B. S0 through S3 and M are at 4.5 V, all other inputs are grounded.

TEXAS
INSTRUMENTS

3 TTL DEVICES

switching characteristics, V_{CC} = 5 V, T_A = 25°C, (C_L = 15 pF, R_L = 2 kΩ, see note 4)

PARAMETER¶	FROM (INPUT)	TO (OUTPUT)	TEST CONDITIONS	MIN	TYP	MAX	UNIT
t_{PLH}	C_n	C_{n+4}			18	27	ns
t_{PHL}					13	20	
t_{PLH}	Any $\overline{A}$ or $\overline{B}$	C_{n+4}	M = 0 V, S0 = S3 = 4.5 V,		25	38	ns
t_{PHL}			S1 = S2 = 0 V ($\overline{SUM}$ mode)		25	38	
t_{PLH}	Any $\overline{A}$ or $\overline{B}$	C_{n+4}	M = 0 V, S0 = S3 = 0 V		27	41	ns
t_{PHL}			S1 = S2 = 4.5 V ($\overline{DIFF}$ mode)		27	41	
t_{PLH}	C_n	Any $\overline{F}$	M = 0 V		17	26	ns
t_{PHL}			($\overline{SUM}$ or $\overline{DIFF}$ mode)		13	20	
t_{PLH}	Any $\overline{A}$ or $\overline{B}$	$\overline{G}$	M = 0 V, S0 = S3 = 4.5 V,		19	29	ns
t_{PHL}			S1 = S2 = 0 V ($\overline{SUM}$ mode)		15	23	
t_{PLH}	Any $\overline{A}$ or $\overline{B}$	$\overline{G}$	M = 0 V, S0 = S3 = 0 V,		21	32	ns
t_{PHL}			S1 = S2 = 4.5 V ($\overline{DIFF}$ mode)		21	32	
t_{PLH}	Any $\overline{A}$ or $\overline{B}$	$\overline{P}$	M = 0 V, S0 = S3 = 4.5 V,		20	30	ns
t_{PHL}			S1 = S2 = 0 V ($\overline{SUM}$ mode)		20	30	
t_{PLH}	Any $\overline{A}$ or $\overline{B}$	$\overline{P}$	M = 0 V, S0 = S3 = 0 V,		20	30	ns
t_{PHL}			S1 = S2 = 4.5 V ($\overline{DIFF}$ mode)		22	33	
t_{PLH}	$\overline{A}_i$ or $\overline{B}_i$	$\overline{F}_i$	M = 0 V, S0 = S3 = 4.5 V,		21	32	ns
t_{PHL}			S1 = S2 = 0 V (SUM mode)		13	20	
t_{PLH}	$\overline{A}_i$ or $\overline{B}_i$	$\overline{F}_i$	M = 0 V, S0 = S3 = 0 V,		21	32	ns
t_{PHL}			S1 = S2 = 4.5 V ($\overline{DIFF}$ mode)		21	32	
t_{PLH}	$\overline{A}_i$ or $\overline{B}_i$	$\overline{F}_i$	M = 4.5 V (logic mode)		22	33	ns
t_{PHL}					26	38	
t_{PLH}	Any $\overline{A}$ or $\overline{B}$	A = B	M = 0 V, S0 = S3 = 0 V,		33	50	ns
t_{PHL}			S1 = S2 = 4.5 V ($\overline{DIFF}$ mode)		41	62	

¶ t_{PLH} ≡ propagation delay time, low-to-high-level output
t_{PHL} ≡ propagation delay time, high-to-low-level output
NOTE 4: See General Information Section for load circuits and voltage waveforms.

schematics of inputs and outputs

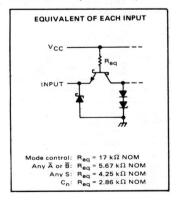

EQUIVALENT OF EACH INPUT

V_{CC}

R_{eq}

INPUT

Mode control: R_{eq} = 17 kΩ NOM
Any $\overline{A}$ or $\overline{B}$: R_{eq} = 5.67 kΩ NOM
Any S: R_{eq} = 4.25 kΩ NOM
C_n: R_{eq} = 2.86 kΩ NOM

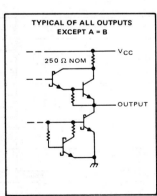

TYPICAL OF ALL OUTPUTS
EXCEPT A = B

V_{CC}

250 Ω NOM

OUTPUT

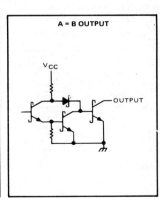

A = B OUTPUT

V_{CC}

OUTPUT

TEXAS
INSTRUMENTS

absolute maximum ratings over operating free-air temperature range (unless otherwise noted)

Supply voltage, V_{CC} (see Note 1)	7 V
Input voltage	5.5 V
Interemitter voltage (see Note 2)	5.5 V
Operating free-air temperature: SN54S181	-55°C to 125°C
SN74S181	0°C to 70°C
Storage temperature range	-65°C to 150°C

NOTES: 1. Voltage values, except interemitter voltage, are with respect to network ground terminal.
2. This is the voltage between two emitters of a multiple emitter transistor. For this circuit, this rating applies to each $\overline{A}$ input in conjunction with inputs S2 or S3, and to each $\overline{B}$ input in conjunction with inputs S0 or S3.

recommended operating conditions

	SN54S181			SN74S181			UNIT
	MIN	NOM	MAX	MIN	NOM	MAX	
Supply voltage, V_{CC}	4.5	5	5.5	4.75	5	5.25	V
High-level output current, I_{OH} (All outputs except A = B)			-1			-1	mA
Low-level output current, I_{OL}			20			20	mA
Operating free-air temperature, T_A	-55		125	0		70	$^{\circ}$C

electrical characteristics over recommended operating free-air temperature range (unless otherwise noted)

PARAMETER		TEST CONDITIONS†		SN54S181			SN74S181			UNIT
				MIN	TYP‡	MAX	MIN	TYP‡	MAX	
V_{IH}	High-level input voltage			2			2			V
V_{IL}	Low-level input voltage					0.8			0.8	V
V_{IK}	Input clamp voltage	V_{CC} = MIN,	$I_I = -18$ mA			-1.2			-1.2	V
V_{OH}	High-level output voltage, any output except A = B	V_{CC} = MIN, V_{IL} = 0.8 V,	V_{IH} = 2 V, $I_{OH} = -1$ mA	2.5	3.4		2.7	3.4		V
I_{OH}	High-level output current, A = B output only	V_{CC} = MIN, V_{IL} = 0.8 V,	V_{IH} = 2 V, V_{OH} = 5.5 V			250			250	μA
V_{OL}	Low-level output voltage	V_{CC} = MIN, V_{IL} = 0.8 V,	V_{IH} = 2 V, I_{OL} = 20 mA			0.5			0.5	V
I_I	Input current at maximum input voltage	V_{CC} = MAX,	V_I = 5.5 V			1			1	mA
I_{IH}	High-level input current	Mode input				50			50	μA
		Any $\overline{A}$ or $\overline{B}$ input	V_{CC} = MAX, V_I = 2.5 V			150			150	
		Any S input				200			200	
		Carry input				250			250	
I_{IL}	Low-level input current	Mode input				-2			-2	mA
		Any $\overline{A}$ or $\overline{B}$ input	V_{CC} = MAX, V_I = 0.5 V			-6			-6	
		Any S input				-8			-8	
		Carry input				-10			-10	
I_{OS}	Short-circuit output current, any output except A = B§	V_{CC} = MAX		-40		-100	-40		-100	mA
I_{CC}	Supply current	V_{CC} = MAX, T_A = 125°C, See Note 3	W package only		195					mA
		V_{CC} = MAX, See Note 3	All packages		120	220		120	220	

†For conditions shown as MIN or MAX, use the appropriate value specified under recommended operating conditions.
‡All typical values are at V_{CC} = 5 V, T_A = 25°C.
§Not more than one output should be shorted at a time.
NOTE 3: I_{CC} is measured for the following conditions (the typical and maximum values apply to both):
A. S0 through S3, M, and $\overline{A}$ inputs are at 4.5 V, all other inputs are grounded, and all outputs are open.
B. S0 through S3 and M are at 4.5 V, all other inputs grounded, and all outputs are open.

3

TTL DEVICES

TEXAS
INSTRUMENTS

switching characteristics, V_{CC} = 5 V, T_A = 25°C (C_L = 15 pF, R_L = 280 Ω, see note 4)

PARAMETER¶	FROM (INPUT)	TO (OUTPUT)	TEST CONDITIONS		MIN	TYP	MAX	UNIT
t_{PLH}	C_n	C_{n+4}				7	10.5	ns
t_{PHL}						7	10.5	
t_{PLH}	Any $\overline{A}$ or $\overline{B}$	C_{n+4}	M = 0 V, S0 - S3 = 4.5 V,			12.5	18.5	ns
t_{PHL}			S1 = S2 = 0 V ($\overline{SUM}$ mode)			12.5	18.5	
t_{PLH}	Any $\overline{A}$ or $\overline{B}$	C_{n+4}	M = 0 V, S0 - S3 = 0 V,			15.5	23	ns
t_{PHL}			S1 = S2 = 4.5 V ($\overline{DIFF}$ mode)			15.5	23	
t_{PLH}	C_n	Any $\overline{F}$	M = 0 V			7	12	ns
t_{PHL}			($\overline{SUM}$ or $\overline{DIFF}$ mode)			7	12	
t_{PLH}	Any $\overline{A}$ or $\overline{B}$	$\overline{G}$	M = 0 V, S0 - S3 = 4.5 V,			8	12	ns
t_{PHL}			S1 = S2 = 0 V ($\overline{SUM}$ mode)			7.5	12	
t_{PLH}	Any $\overline{A}$ or $\overline{B}$	$\overline{G}$	M = 0 V, S0 - S3 = 0 V,			10.5	15	ns
t_{PHL}			S1 = S2 = 4.5 V ($\overline{DIFF}$ mode)			10.5	15	
t_{PLH}	Any $\overline{A}$ or $\overline{B}$	$\overline{P}$	M = 0 V, S0 - S3 = 4.5 V,			7.5	12	ns
t_{PHL}			S1 = S2 = 0 V ($\overline{SUM}$ mode)			7.5	12	
t_{PLH}	Any $\overline{A}$ or $\overline{B}$	$\overline{P}$	M = 0 V, S0 - S3 = 0 V,			10.5	15	ns
t_{PHL}			S1 = S2 = 4.5 V ($\overline{DIFF}$ mode)			10.5	15	
t_{PLH}	$\overline{A}_i$ or $\overline{B}_i$	$\overline{F}_i$	M = 0 V, S0 - S3 = 4.5 V,			11	16.5	ns
t_{PHL}			S1 = S2 = 0 V ($\overline{SUM}$ mode)			11	16.5	
t_{PLH}	$\overline{A}_i$ or $\overline{B}_i$	$\overline{F}_i$	M = 0 V, S0 - S3 = 0 V,			14	20	ns
t_{PHL}			S1 = S2 = 4.5 V ($\overline{DIFF}$ mode)			14	22	
t_{PLH}	$\overline{A}_i$ or $\overline{B}_i$	$\overline{F}_i$	M = 4.5 V (logic mode)			14	20	ns
t_{PHL}						14	22	
t_{PLH}	Any $\overline{A}$ or $\overline{B}$	A = B	M = 0 V, S0 - S3 = 0 V,			15	23	ns
t_{PHL}			S1 = S2 = 4.5 V ($\overline{DIFF}$ mode)			20	30	

¶ t_{PLH} $\equiv$ propagation delay time, low-to-high-level output
   t_{PHL} $\equiv$ propagation delay time, high-to-low-level output
NOTE 4: See General Information Section for load circuits and voltage waveforms.

schematics of inputs and outputs

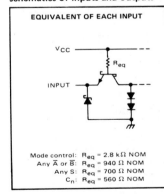

EQUIVALENT OF EACH INPUT

Mode control: R_{eq} = 2.8 kΩ NOM
Any $\overline{A}$ or $\overline{B}$: R_{eq} = 940 Ω NOM
Any S: R_{eq} = 700 Ω NOM
C_n: R_{eq} = 560 Ω NOM

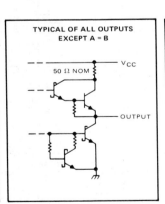

TYPICAL OF ALL OUTPUTS
EXCEPT A = B

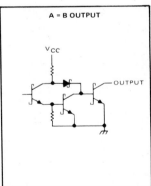

A = B OUTPUT

TEXAS
INSTRUMENTS

PARAMETER MEASUREMENT INFORMATION

SUM MODE TEST TABLE
FUNCTION INPUTS: S0 = S3 = 4.5 V, S1 = S2 = M = 0 V

PARAMETER	INPUT UNDER TEST	OTHER INPUT SAME BIT		OTHER DATA INPUTS		OUTPUT UNDER TEST	OUTPUT WAVEFORM (See Note 4)
		APPLY 4.5 V	APPLY GND	APPLY 4.5 V	APPLY GND		
t_{PLH} / t_{PHL}	$\overline{A}_i$	$\overline{B}_i$	None	Remaining $\overline{A}$ and $\overline{B}$	C_n	$\overline{F}_i$	In-Phase
t_{PLH} / t_{PHL}	$\overline{B}_i$	$\overline{A}_i$	None	Remaining $\overline{A}$ and $\overline{B}$	C_n	$\overline{F}_i$	In-Phase
t_{PLH} / t_{PHL}	$\overline{A}_i$	$\overline{B}_i$	None	None	Remaining $\overline{A}$ and $\overline{B}$, C_n	$\overline{P}$	In-Phase
t_{PLH} / t_{PHL}	$\overline{B}_i$	$\overline{A}_i$	None	None	Remaining $\overline{A}$ and $\overline{B}$, C_n	$\overline{P}$	In-Phase
t_{PLH} / t_{PHL}	$\overline{A}_i$	None	$\overline{B}_i$	Remaining $\overline{B}$	Remaining $\overline{A}$, C_n	$\overline{G}$	In-Phase
t_{PLH} / t_{PHL}	$\overline{B}_i$	None	$\overline{A}_i$	Remaining $\overline{B}$	Remaining $\overline{A}$, C_n	$\overline{G}$	In-Phase
t_{PLH} / t_{PHL}	C_n	None	None	All $\overline{A}$	All $\overline{B}$	Any $\overline{F}$ or C_{n+4}	In-Phase
t_{PLH} / t_{PHL}	$\overline{A}_i$	None	$\overline{B}_i$	Remaining $\overline{B}$	Remaining $\overline{A}$, C_n	C_{n+4}	Out-of-Phase
t_{PLH} / t_{PHL}	$\overline{B}_i$	None	$\overline{A}_i$	Remaining $\overline{B}$	Remaining $\overline{A}$, C_n	C_{n+4}	Out-of-Phase

DIFF MODE TEST TABLE
FUNCTION INPUTS: S1 = S2 = 4.5 V, S0 = S3 = M = 0 V

PARAMETER	INPUT UNDER TEST	OTHER INPUT SAME BIT		OTHER DATA INPUTS		OUTPUT UNDER TEST	OUTPUT WAVEFORM (See Note 4)
		APPLY 4.5 V	APPLY GND	APPLY 4.5 V	APPLY GND		
t_{PLH} / t_{PHL}	$\overline{A}_i$	None	$\overline{B}_i$	Remaining $\overline{A}$	Remaining $\overline{B}$, C_n	$\overline{F}_i$	In-Phase
t_{PLH} / t_{PHL}	$\overline{B}_i$	$\overline{A}_i$	None	Remaining $\overline{A}$	Remaining $\overline{B}$, C_n	$\overline{F}_i$	Out-of-Phase
t_{PLH} / t_{PHL}	$\overline{A}_i$	None	$\overline{B}_i$	None	Remaining $\overline{A}$ and $\overline{B}$, C_n	$\overline{P}$	In-Phase
t_{PLH} / t_{PHL}	$\overline{B}_i$	$\overline{A}_i$	None	None	Remaining $\overline{A}$ and $\overline{B}$, C_n	$\overline{P}$	Out-of-Phase
t_{PLH} / t_{PHL}	$\overline{A}_i$	$\overline{B}_i$	None	None	Remaining $\overline{A}$ and $\overline{B}$, C_n	$\overline{G}$	In-Phase
t_{PLH} / t_{PHL}	$\overline{B}_i$	None	$\overline{A}_i$	None	Remaining $\overline{A}$ and $\overline{B}$, C_n	$\overline{G}$	Out-of-Phase
t_{PLH} / t_{PHL}	$\overline{A}_i$	None	$\overline{B}_i$	Remaining $\overline{A}$	Remaining $\overline{B}$, C_n	$A \cdot B$	In-Phase
t_{PLH} / t_{PHL}	$\overline{B}_i$	$\overline{A}_i$	None	Remaining $\overline{A}$	Remaining $\overline{B}$, C_n	$A \cdot B$	Out-of-Phase
t_{PLH} / t_{PHL}	C_n	None	None	All $\overline{A}$ and $\overline{B}$	None	C_{n+4} or any $\overline{F}$	In-Phase
t_{PLH} / t_{PHL}	$\overline{A}_i$	$\overline{B}_i$	None	None	Remaining $\overline{A}$, $\overline{B}$, C_n	C_{n+4}	Out-of-Phase
t_{PLH} / t_{PHL}	$\overline{B}_i$	None	$\overline{A}_i$	None	Remaining $\overline{A}$, $\overline{B}$, C_n	C_{n+4}	In-Phase

LOGIC MODE TEST TABLE
FUNCTION INPUTS: S1 = S2 = M = 4.5 V, S0 = S3 = 0 V

PARAMETER	INPUT UNDER TEST	OTHER INPUT SAME BIT		OTHER DATA INPUTS		OUTPUT UNDER TEST	OUTPUT WAVEFORM (See Note 4)
		APPLY 4.5 V	APPLY GND	APPLY 4.5 V	APPLY GND		
t_{PLH} / t_{PHL}	$\overline{A}_i$	$\overline{B}_i$	None	None	Remaining $\overline{A}$ and $\overline{B}$, C_n	$\overline{F}_i$	Out-of-Phase
t_{PLH} / t_{PHL}	$\overline{B}_i$	$\overline{A}_i$	None	None	Remaining $\overline{A}$ and $\overline{B}$, C_n	$\overline{F}_i$	Out-of-Phase

NOTE 4: See General Information Section for load circuits and voltage waveforms.

TEXAS INSTRUMENTS

● **Directly Compatible for Use With:**
  SN54LS181/SN74LS181,
  SN54S281/SN74S281, SN54S381/SN74S381,
  SN54S481/SN74S481

PIN DESIGNATIONS

ALTERNATIVE DESIGNATIONS[†]		PIN NOS.	FUNCTION
$\overline{G0}, \overline{G1}, \overline{G2}, \overline{G3}$	G0, G1, G2, G3	3, 1, 14, 5	CARRY GENERATE INPUTS
$\overline{P0}, \overline{P1}, \overline{P2}, \overline{P3}$	P0, P1, P2, P3	4, 2, 15, 6	CARRY PROPAGATE INPUTS
C_n	$\overline{C_n}$	13	CARRY INPUT
$C_{n+x}, C_{n+y}, C_{n+z}$	$\overline{C}_{n+x}, \overline{C}_{n+y}, \overline{C}_{n+z}$	12, 11, 9	CARRY OUTPUTS
$\overline{G}$	y	10	CARRY GENERATE OUTPUT
$\overline{P}$	x	7	CARRY PROPAGATE OUTPUT
V_{CC}		16	SUPPLY VOLTAGE
GND		8	GROUND

*Interpretations are illustrated in the 'LS181, 'S181 data sheet.

logic symbol[†]

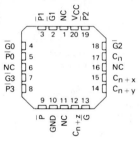

SN54182, SN54S182 . . . J OR W PACKAGE
SN74182 . . . J OR N PACKAGE
SN74S182 . . . D J OR N PACKAGE
(TOP VIEW)

$\overline{G1}$	1	16 V_{CC}
$\overline{P1}$	2	15 $\overline{P2}$
$\overline{G0}$	3	14 $\overline{G2}$
$\overline{P0}$	4	13 C_n
$\overline{G3}$	5	12 C_{n+x}
$\overline{P3}$	6	11 C_{n+y}
$\overline{P}$	7	10 $\overline{G}$
GND	8	9 C_{n+z}

SN54S182 . . . FK PACKAGE
SN74S182
(TOP VIEW)

Pin numbers shown on logic notation are for D, J or N packages.

NC - No internal connection

description

The SN54S182 and SN74S182 are high-speed, look-ahead carry generators capable of anticipating a carry across four binary adders or group of adders. They are cascadable to perform full look-ahead across n-bit adders. Carry, generate-carry, and propagate-carry functions are provided as enumerated in the pin designation table above.

When used in conjunction with the 'LS181 or 'S181 arithmetic logic unit (ALU), these generators provide high-speed carry look-ahead capability for any word length. The 'S182 generates the look-ahead (anticipated carry) across a group of four ALU's and in addition, other carry look-ahead circuits may be employed to anticipate carry across sections of four look-ahead packages up to n-bits. The method of cascading 'S182 circuits to perform multi-level look-ahead is illustrated under typical application data.

The carry functions (inputs, outputs, generate, and propagate) of the look-ahead generators are implemented in the compatible forms for direct connection to the ALU. Reinterpretations of carry functions as explained on the 'LS181 and 'S181 data sheet are also applicable to and compatible with the look-ahead generator. Logic equations for the 'S182 is:

$C_{n+x} = G0 + P0\, C_n$

$C_{n+y} = G1 + P1\, G0 + P1\, P0\, C_n$

$C_{n+z} = G2 + P2\, G1 + P2\, P1\, G0 + P2\, P1\, P0\, C_n$ or

$\overline{G} = \overline{G3 + P3\, G2 + P3\, P2\, G1 + P3\, P2\, P1\, G0}$

$\overline{P} = \overline{P3\, P2\, P1\, P0}$

$\overline{C}_{n+x} = \overline{Y0\,(X0 + \overline{C_n})}$

$\overline{C}_{n+y} = \overline{Y1\,[X1 + Y0\,(X0 + \overline{C_n})]}$

$\overline{C}_{n+z} = \overline{Y2\,\{X2 + Y1\,[X1 + Y0\,(X0 + \overline{C_n})]\}}$

$Y = Y3\,(X3 + Y2)\,(X3 + X2 + Y1)\,(X3 + X2 + X1 + Y0)$

$X = X3 + X2 + X1 + X0$

3

TTL DEVICES

TEXAS INSTRUMENTS

logic

FUNCTION TABLE FOR $\bar{G}$ OUTPUT

INPUTS							OUTPUT
$\bar{G}3$	$\bar{G}2$	$\bar{G}1$	$\bar{G}0$	$\bar{P}3$	$\bar{P}2$	$\bar{P}1$	$\bar{G}$
L	X	X	X	X	X	X	L
X	L	X	X	L	X	X	L
X	X	L	X	L	L	X	L
X	X	X	L	L	L	L	L
All other combinations							H

FUNCTION TABLE FOR $\bar{P}$ OUTPUT

INPUTS				OUTPUT
$\bar{P}3$	$\bar{P}2$	$\bar{P}1$	$\bar{P}0$	$\bar{P}$
L	L	L	L	L
All other combinations				H

FUNCTION TABLE FOR C_{n+x} OUTPUT

INPUTS			OUTPUT
$\bar{G}0$	$\bar{P}0$	Cn	C_{n+x}
L	X	X	H
X	L	H	H
All other combinations			L

FUNCTION TABLE FOR C_{n+y} OUTPUT

INPUTS					OUTPUT
$\bar{G}1$	$\bar{G}0$	$\bar{P}1$	$\bar{P}0$	Cn	C_{n+y}
L	X	X	X	X	H
X	L	L	X	X	H
X	X	L	L	H	H
All other combinations					L

FUNCTION TABLE FOR C_{n+z} OUTPUT

INPUTS							OUTPUT
$\bar{G}2$	$\bar{G}1$	$\bar{G}0$	$\bar{P}2$	$\bar{P}1$	$\bar{P}0$	Cn	C_{n+z}
L	X	X	X	X	X	X	H
X	L	X	L	X	X	X	H
X	X	L	L	L	X	X	H
X	X	X	L	L	L	H	H
All other combinations							L

H = high level, L = low level, X = irrelevant
Any inputs not shown in a given table are irrelevant with respect to that output.

logic diagram

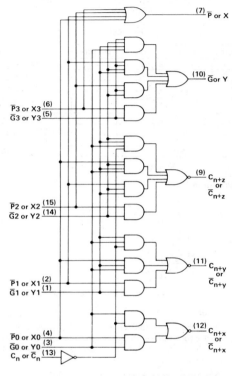

$\bar{P}3$ or X3 (6)
$\bar{G}3$ or Y3 (5)
$\bar{P}2$ or X2 (15)
$\bar{G}2$ or Y2 (14)
$\bar{P}1$ or X1 (2)
$\bar{G}1$ or Y1 (1)
$\bar{P}0$ or X0 (4)
$\bar{G}0$ or Y0 (3)
Cn or $\bar{C}n$ (13)

(7) $\bar{P}$ or X
(10) $\bar{G}$ or Y
(9) C_{n+z} or $\bar{C}_{n+z}$
(11) C_{n+y} or $\bar{C}_{n+y}$
(12) C_{n+x} or $\bar{C}_{n+x}$

Pin numbers shown on logic notation are for D, J or N packages.

absolute maximum ratings over operating free-air temperature range (unless otherwise noted)

Supply voltage, V_{CC} (see Note 1) . . . . 7 V
Input voltage . . . . 5.5 V
Interemitter voltage (see Note 2) . . . . 5.5 V
Operating free-air temperature range: SN54', SN54S' Circuits . . . . $-55°C$ to $125°C$
　　　　　　　　　　　　　　　　SN74', SN74S' Circuits . . . . $0°C$ to $70°C$
Storage temperature range . . . . $-65°C$ to $150°C$

NOTES: 1. Voltage values, except interemitter voltage, are with respect to network ground terminal.
2. This is the voltage between two emitters of a multiple-emitter input transistor. For these circuits, this rating applies to each $\bar{G}$ input in conjunction with any other $\bar{G}$ input or in conjunction with any $\bar{P}$ input.

TEXAS INSTRUMENTS

3
TTL DEVICES

TYPES SN54S182, SN74S182
LOOK-AHEAD CARRY GENERATORS

recommended operating conditions

		SN54S182			SN74S182			UNIT
		MIN	NOM	MAX	MIN	NOM	MAX	
Supply voltage, V_{CC}		4.5	5	5.5	4.75	5	5.25	V
High-level output current, I_{OH}				−1			−1	mA
Low-level output current, I_{OL}				20			20	mA
Operating free-air temperature, T_A		−55		125	0		70	°C

electrical characteristics over recommended operating free-air temperature range (unless otherwise noted)

PARAMETER		TEST CONDITIONS[†]	SN54S182			SN74S182			UNIT
			MIN	TYP[‡]	MAX	MIN	TYP[‡]	MAX	
V_{IH}	High-level input voltage		2			2			V
V_{IL}	Low-level input voltage				0.8			0.8	V
V_{IK}	Input clamp voltage	V_{CC} = MIN, I_I = −18 mA			−1.2			−1.2	V
V_{OH}	High-level output voltage	V_{CC} = MIN, V_{IH} = 2 V, V_{IL} = 0.8 V, I_{OH} = −1 mA	2.5	3.4		2.7	3.4		V
V_{OL}	Low-level output voltage	V_{CC} = MIN, V_{IH} = 2 V, V_{IL} = 0.8 V, I_{OL} = 20 mA			0.5			0.5	V
I_I	Input current at maximum input voltage	V_{CC} = MAX, V_I = 5.5 V			1			1	mA
I_{IH}	High-level input current	C_n input	V_{CC} = MAX, V_I = 2.7 V			50			50	µA
		$\overline{P}3$ input				100			100	
		$\overline{P}2$ input				150			150	
		$\overline{P}0, \overline{P}1,$ or $\overline{G}3$ input				200			200	
		$\overline{G}0$ or $\overline{G}2$ input				350			350	
		$\overline{G}1$ input				400			400	
I_{IL}	Low-level input current	C_n input	V_{CC} = MAX, V_I = 0.5 V			−2			−2	mA
		$\overline{P}3$ input				−4			−4	
		$\overline{P}2$ input				−6			−6	
		$\overline{P}0, \overline{P}1,$ or $\overline{G}3$ input				−8			−8	
		$\overline{G}0$ or $\overline{G}2$ input				−14			−14	
		$\overline{G}1$ input				−16			−16	
I_{OS}	Short-circuit output current[§]	V_{CC} = MAX	−40		−100	−40		−100	mA
I_{CCH}	Supply current, all outputs high	V_{CC} = 5 V, See Note 3		35	70		35	70	mA
I_{CCL}	Supply current, all outputs low	V_{CC} = MAX, See Note 4		69	99		69	109	mA

[†]For conditions shown as MIN or MAX, use the appropriate value specified under recommended operating conditions for the applicable type.
[‡]All typical values are at V_{CC} = 5 V, T_A = 25°C.
[§]Not more than one output should be shorted at a time and duration of the short-circuit test should not exceed one second.
NOTES: 3. I_{CCH} is measured with all outputs open, inputs $\overline{P}3$ and $\overline{G}3$ at 4.5 V, and all other inputs grounded.
4. I_{CCL} is measured with all outputs open; inputs $\overline{G}0, \overline{G}1,$ and $\overline{G}2$ at 4.5 V; and all other inputs grounded.

switching characteristics, V_{CC} = 5 V, T_A = 25°C

PARAMETER[¶]	FROM (INPUT)	TO (OUTPUT)	TEST CONDITIONS	MIN	TYP	MAX	UNIT
t_{PLH}	$\overline{G}0, \overline{G}1, \overline{G}2, \overline{G}3,$ P0, P1, P2, P3	$C_{n+x}, C_{n+y},$ or C_{n+z}			4.5	7	ns
t_{PHL}					4.5	7	
t_{PLH}	$\overline{G}0, \overline{G}1, \overline{G}2, \overline{G}3,$ P1, P2, or P3	$\overline{G}$	R_L = 280 Ω, C_L = 15 pF, See Note 5		5	7.5	ns
t_{PHL}					7	10.5	
t_{PLH}	$\overline{P}0, \overline{P}1, \overline{P}2,$ or $\overline{P}3$	$\overline{P}$			4.5	6.5	ns
t_{PHL}					6.5	10	
t_{PLH}	C_n	$C_{n+x}, C_{n+y},$ or C_{n+z}			6.5	10	ns
t_{PHL}					7	10.5	

[¶]$t_{PLH} \equiv$ propagation delay time, low-to-high-level output
$t_{PHL} \equiv$ propagation delay time, high-to-low-level output
NOTE 5: See General Information Section for load circuits and voltage waveforms.

TEXAS INSTRUMENTS

3

TTL DEVICES

schematics of inputs and outputs

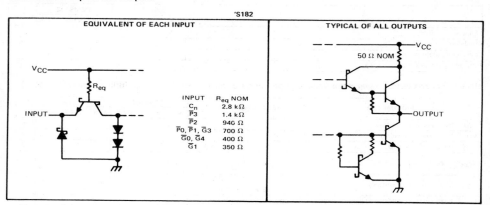

'S182

| EQUIVALENT OF EACH INPUT | TYPICAL OF ALL OUTPUTS |

INPUT	R_{eq} NOM
C_n	2.8 kΩ
$\overline{P}3$	1.4 kΩ
$\overline{P}2$	940 Ω
$\overline{P}0, \overline{P}1, \overline{G}3$	700 Ω
$\overline{G}0, \overline{G}4$	400 Ω
$\overline{G}1$	350 Ω

TEXAS
INSTRUMENTS

TYPICAL APPLICATION DATA

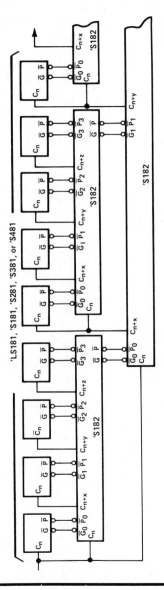

64-BIT ALU, FULL-CARRY LOOK-AHEAD IN THREE LEVELS

Remaining inputs and outputs of 'LS181, 'S181, 'S281, 'S381, and 'S481 are not shown.

3

TTL DEVICES

TEXAS
INSTRUMENTS

3

BULLETIN NO. DL-S 7711848, OCTOBER 1976 — REVISED OCTOBER 1983

- For Use in High-Speed Wallace-Tree Summing Networks
- High-Speed, High-Fan-Out Darlington Outputs
- Input Clamping Diodes Simplify System Design

TYPES	TYPICAL AVERAGE PROPAGATION DELAY TIME	TYPICAL POWER DISSIPATION
'LS183	15 ns	23 mW per bit

SN54LS183 . . . J OR W PACKAGE
SN74LS183 . . . D, J OR N PACKAGE
(TOP VIEW)

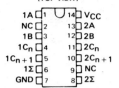

SN54LS183 . . . FK PACKAGE
SN74LS183
(TOP VIEW)

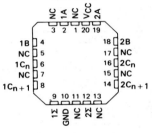

NC – No internal connection

logic diagram (each adder)

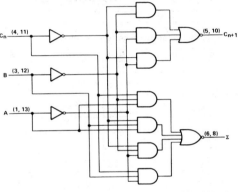

Pin numbers shown on logic notation are for D, J or N packages.

FUNCTION TABLE
(EACH ADDER)

INPUTS			OUTPUTS	
C_n	B	A	Σ	C_{n+1}
L	L	L	L	L
L	L	H	H	L
L	H	L	H	L
L	H	H	L	H
H	L	L	H	L
H	L	H	L	H
H	H	L	L	H
H	H	H	H	H

H = high level, L = low level

schematics of inputs and outputs

'LS183

EQUIVALENT OF EACH INPUT	TYPICAL OF ALL OUTPUTS
V_{CC} 6 kΩ NOM INPUT	V_{CC} 120 Ω NOM OUTPUT

TEXAS INSTRUMENTS

TTL DEVICES

3

TYPES SN54LS183, SN74LS183
DUAL CARRY-SAVE FULL ADDERS

absolute maximum ratings over operating free-air temperature range (unless otherwise noted)

Supply voltage V_{CC} (see Note 1)	7 V
Input voltage	7 V
Operating free-air temperature range: SN54LS183 Circuits	−55°C to 125°C
SN74LS183 Circuits	0°C to 70°C
Storage temperature range	−65°C to 150°C

NOTE 1: Voltage values, except interemitter voltage, are with respect to network ground terminal.

recommended operating conditions

	SN54LS183			SN74LS183			UNIT
	MIN	NOM	MAX	MIN	NOM	MAX	
Supply voltage, V_{CC}	4.5	5	5.5	4.75	5	5.25	V
High-level output current, I_{OH}			−400			−400	μA
Low-level output current, I_{OL}			4			8	mA
Operating free-air temperature, T_A	−55		125	0		70	°C

electrical characteristics over recommended operation free-air temperature range (unless otherwise noted)

	PARAMETER	TEST CONDITIONS†	MIN	TYP‡	MAX	MIN	TYP‡	MAX	UNIT
V_{IH}	High-level input voltage		2			2			V
V_{IL}	Low-level input voltage				0.7			0.8	V
V_{IK}	Input clamp voltage	V_{CC} = MIN, I_I = −18 mA			−1.5			−1.5	V
V_{OH}	High-level output voltage	V_{CC} = MIN, V_{IH} = 2 V, V_{IL} = V_{IL}max, I_{OH} = −400 μA	2.5	3.4		2.7	3.4		V
V_{OL}	Low-level output voltage	V_{CC} = MIN, V_{IH} = 2 V, V_{IL} = V_{IL}max, I_{OL} = 4 mA		0.25	0.4		0.25	0.4	V
		I_{OL} = 8 mA					0.35	0.5	
I_I	Input current at maximum input voltage	V_{CC} = MAX, V_I = 7 V			0.3			0.3	mA
I_{IH}	High-level input current	V_{CC} = MAX, V_I = 2.7 V			60			60	μA
I_{IL}	Low-level input current	V_{CC} = MAX, V_I = 0.4 V			−1.2			−1.2	mA
I_{OS}	Short-circuit output current§	V_{CC} = MAX	−20		−100	−20		−100	mA
I_{CCL}	Supply current, all outputs low	V_{CC} = MAX, See Note 3		10	17		10	17	mA
I_{CCH}	Supply current, all outputs high	V_{CC} = MAX, See Note 4		8	14		8	14	mA

† For conditions shown as MIN or MAX, use the appropriate value specified under recommended operating conditions for the applicable type.
‡All typical values are at V_{CC} = 5 V, T_A = 25°C.
§Not more than one output should be shorted at a time, and duration of the short circuit should not exceed one second.
NOTES: 3. I_{CCL} is measured with all outputs open and all inputs grounded.
　　　　 4. I_{CCH} is measured with all outputs open and all inputs at 4.5 V.

switching characteristics, V_{CC} = 5 V, T_A = 25°C

PARAMETER	TEST CONDITIONS	MIN	TYP	MAX	UNIT
t_{PLH} Propagation delay time, low-to-high-level output	C_L = 15 pF, R_L = 2 kΩ, See Note 5		9	15	ns
t_{PHL} Propagation delay time, high-to-low-level output			20	33	ns

NOTE 5:   See General Information Section for load circuits and voltage waveforms.

TEXAS
INSTRUMENTS

- **Counts 8-4-2-1 BCD or Binary**
- **Single Down/Up Count Control Line**
- **Count Enable Control Input**
- **Ripple Clock Output for Cascading**
- **Asynchronously Presettable with Load Control**
- **Parallel Outputs**
- **Cascadable for n-Bit Applications**

TYPE	AVERAGE PROPAGATION DELAY	TYPICAL MAXIMUM CLOCK FREQUENCY	TYPICAL POWER DISSIPATION
'190,'191	20ns	25MHz	325mW
'LS190,'LS191	20ns	25MHz	100mW

SN54190, SN54191, SN54LS190,
SN54LS191 . . . J OR W PACKAGE
SN74190, SN74191 . . . J OR N PACKAGE
SN74LS190, SN74LS191 . . . D, J OR N PACKAGE
(TOP VIEW)

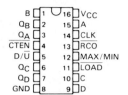

SN54LS190, SN54LS191 . . . FK PACKAGE
SN74LS190, SN74LS191
(TOP VIEW)

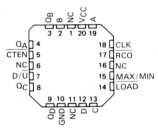

NC - No internal connection

description

The '190, 'LS190, '191, and 'LS191 are synchronous, reversible up/down counters having a complexity of 58 equivalent gates. The '191 and 'LS191 are 4-bit binary counters and the '190 and 'LS190 are BCD counters. Synchronous operation is provided by having all flip-flops clocked simultaneously so that the outputs change coincident with each other when so instructed by the steering logic. This mode of operation eliminates the output counting spikes normally associated with asynchronous (ripple clock) counters.

The outputs of the four master-slave flip-flops are triggered on a low-to-high transition of the clock input if the enable input is low. A high at the enable input inhibits counting. Level changes at the enable input should be made only when the clock input is high. The direction of the count is determined by the level of the down/up input. When low, the counter count up and when high, it counts down. A false clock may occur if the down/up input changes while the clock is low. A false ripple carry may occur if both the clock and enable are low and the down/up input is high during a load pulse.

These counters are fully programmable; that is, the outputs may be preset to either level by placing a low on the load input and entering the desired data at the data inputs. The output will change to agree with the data inputs independently of the level of the clock input. This feature allows the counters to be used as modulo-N dividers by simply modifying the count length with the preset inputs.

The clock, down/up, and load inputs are buffered to lower the drive requirement which significantly reduces the number of clock drivers, etc., required for long parallel words.

Two outputs have been made available to perform the cascading function: ripple clock and maximum/minimum count. The latter output produces a high-level output pulse with a duration approximately equal to one complete cycle of the clock when the counter overflows or underflows. The ripple clock output produces a low-level output pulse equal in width to the low-level portion of the clock input when an overflow or underflow condition exists. The counters can be easily cascaded by feeding the ripple clock output to the enable input of the succeeding counter if parallel clocking is used, or to the clock input if parallel enabling is used. The maximum/minimum count output can be used to accomplish look-ahead for high-speed operation.

Series 54' and 54LS' are characterized for operation over the full military temperature range of 55 C to 125 C; Series 74' and 74LS' are characterized for operation from 0°C to 70°C.

TEXAS INSTRUMENTS

3

TTL DEVICES

logic symbols

'190, 'LS190

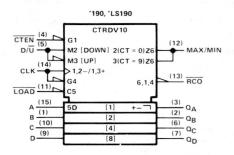

'191, 'LS191

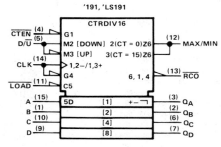

Pin numbers shown on logic notation are for D, J or N packages.

TEXAS INSTRUMENTS

logic diagram

'190, 'LS190 DECADE COUNTERS

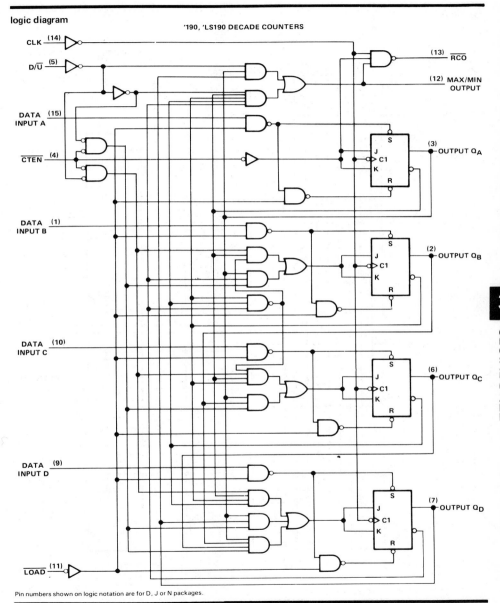

Pin numbers shown on logic notation are for D, J or N packages.

TYPES SN54191, SN54LS191, SN74191, SN74LS191
SYNCHRONOUS UP/DOWN COUNTERS WITH DOWN/UP MODE CONTROL

logic diagram

'191, 'LS191 BINARY COUNTERS

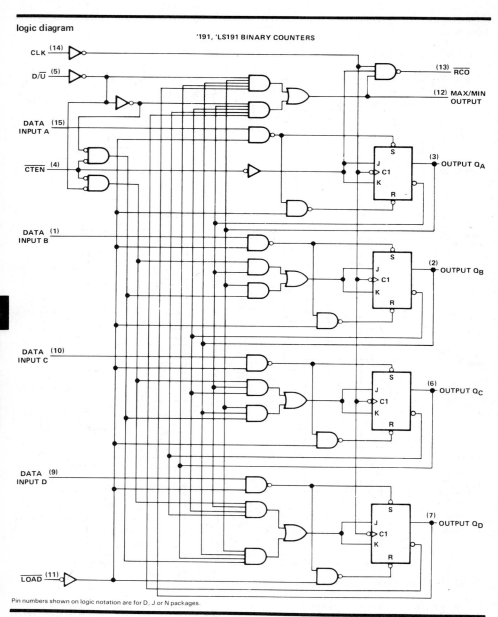

Pin numbers shown on logic notation are for D, J or N packages.

'190, 'LS190 DECADE COUNTERS

typical load, count, and inhibit sequences

Illustrated below is the following sequence:

1. Load (preset) to BCD seven.
2. Count up to eight, nine (maximum), zero, one, and two.
3. Inhibit.
4. Count down to one, zero (minimum), nine, eight, and seven.

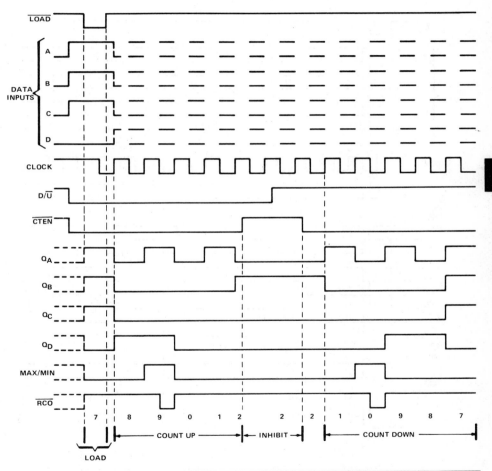

3

TTL DEVICES

'191, 'LS191 BINARY COUNTERS

typical load, count, and inhibit sequences

Illustrated below is the following sequence:

1. Load (preset) to binary thirteen.
2. Count up to fourteen, fifteen (maximum), zero, one, and two.
3. Inhibit.
4. Count down to one, zero (minimum), fifteen, fourteen, and thirteen.

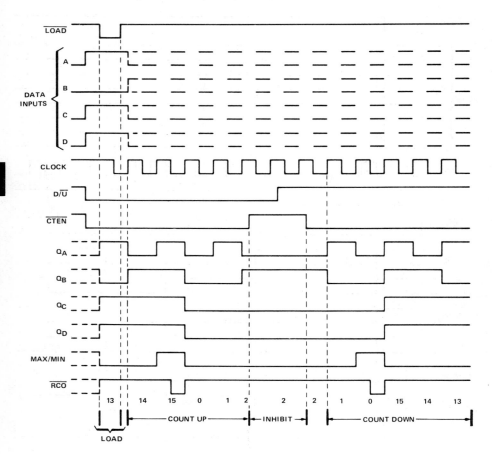

Texas
Instruments

absolute maximum ratings over operating free-air temperature range (unless otherwise noted)

Supply voltage, V_{CC} (see Note 1) . . . . 7 V
Input voltage: SN54', SN74' Circuits . . . . 5.5 V
SN54LS', SN74LS' Circuits . . . . 7 V
Operating free-air temperature range: SN54', SN54LS' Circuits . . . . -55°C to 125°C
SN74', SN74LS' Circuits . . . . 0°C to 70°C
Storage temperature range . . . . -65°C to 150°C

NOTE 1: Voltage values are with respect to network ground terminal.

recommended operating conditions

		SN54190, SN54191			SN74190, SN74191			UNIT
		MIN	NOM	MAX	MIN	NOM	MAX	
V_{CC}	Supply voltage	4.5	5	5.5	4.75	5	5.25	V
I_{OH}	High-level output current			-0.8			-0.8	mA
I_{OL}	Low-level output current			16			16	mA
f_{clock}	Input clock frequency	0		20	0		20	MHz
$t_{w(clock)}$	Width of clock input pulse	25			25			ns
$t_{w(load)}$	Width of load input pulse	35			35			ns
t_{su}	Setup time	Data, high or low (See Figure 1 and 2)	20			20			ns
		Load inactive state	20			20			
t_{hold}	Data hold time	0			0			ns
T_A	Operating free-air temperature	-55		125	0		70	$^{\circ}$C

electrical characteristics over recommended operating free-air temperature range (unless otherwise noted)

PARAMETER		TEST CONDITIONS[†]	SN54190, SN54191			SN74190, SN74191			UNIT
			MIN	TYP[‡]	MAX	MIN	TYP[‡]	MAX	
V_{IH}	High-level input voltage	V_{CC} = MIN	2			2			V
V_{IL}	Low-level input voltage	V_{CC} = MIN			0.8			0.8	V
V_{IK}	Input clamp voltage	V_{CC} = MIN, $I_I = -12$ mA			-1.5			-1.5	V
V_{OH}	High-level output voltage	V_{CC} = MIN, V_{IH} = 2 V, V_{IL} = 0.8 V, $I_{OH} = -0.8$ mA	2.4	3.4		2.4	3.4		V
V_{OL}	Low-level output voltage	V_{CC} = MIN, V_{IH} = 2 V, V_{IL} = 0.8 V, I_{OL} = 16 mA		0.2	0.4		0.2	0.4	V
I_I	High-level input current at maximum input voltage	V_{CC} = MAX, V_I = 5.5 V			1			1	mA
I_{IH}	High-level input current at any input except enable	V_{CC} = MAX, V_I = 2.4 V			40			40	μA
I_{IH}	High-level input current at enable input				120			120	μA
I_{IL}	Low-level input current at any input except enable	V_{CC} = MAX, V_I = 0.4 V			-1.6			-1.6	mA
I_{IL}	Low-level input current at enable input				-4.8			-4.8	mA
I_{OS}	Short-circuit output current [§]	V_{CC} = MAX	-20		-65	-18		-65	mA
I_{CC}	Supply current	V_{CC} = MAX, See Note 2		65	99		65	105	mA

[†] For conditions shown as MAX or MIN, use appropriate value specified under recommended operating conditions.
[‡] All typical values are at V_{CC} = 5 V, $T_A = 25^{\circ}$C.
[§] Not more than one output should be shorted at a time.
NOTE 2: I_{CC} is measured with all inputs grounded and all outputs open.

3

TTL DEVICES

TEXAS
INSTRUMENTS

switching characteristics, $V_{CC} = 5$ V, $T_A = 25°C$

PARAMETER[◄]	FROM (INPUT)	TO (OUTPUT)	TEST CONDITIONS	'190, '191 MIN	'190, '191 TYP	'190, '191 MAX	UNIT
f_{max}				20	25		MHz
t_{PLH}	$\overline{Load}$	Q_A, Q_B, Q_C, Q_D			22	33	ns
t_{PHL}					33	50	
t_{PLH}	Data A, B, C, D	Q_A, Q_B, Q_C, Q_D			14	22	ns
t_{PHL}					35	50	
t_{PLH}	CLK	$\overline{RCO}$	$C_L = 15\,pF$, $R_L = 400\,\Omega$,		13	20	ns
t_{PHL}			See Figures 1 and 3 thru 7		16	24	
t_{PLH}	CLK	Q_A, Q_B, Q_C, Q_D			16	24	ns
t_{PHL}					24	36	
t_{PLH}	CLK	Max/Min			28	42	ns
t_{PHL}					37	52	
t_{PLH}	$D/\overline{U}$	$\overline{RCO}$			30	45	ns
t_{PHL}					30	45	
t_{PLH}	$D/\overline{U}$	Max/Min			21	33	ns
t_{PHL}					22	33	

◄ f_{max} maximum clock frequency
t_{PLH} propagation delay time, low-to-high-level output
t_{PHL} propagation delay time, high-to-low-level output

schematics of inputs and outputs

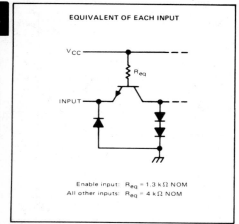

EQUIVALENT OF EACH INPUT

Enable input: $R_{eq} = 1.3\,k\Omega$ NOM
All other inputs: $R_{eq} = 4\,k\Omega$ NOM

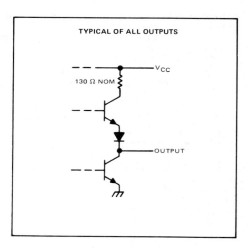

TYPICAL OF ALL OUTPUTS

130 Ω NOM

TEXAS INSTRUMENTS

recommended operating conditions

		SN54LS190 SN54LS191			SN74LS190 SN74LS191			UNIT
		MIN	NOM	MAX	MIN	NOM	MAX	
V_{CC}	Supply voltage	4.5	5	5.5	4.75	5	5.25	V
I_{OH}	High-level output current			−0.4			−0.4	mA
I_{OL}	Low-level output current			4			8	mA
f_{clock}	Clock frequency	0		20	0		20	MHz
$t_{w(clock)}$	Width of clock input pulse	25			25			ns
$t_{w(load)}$	Width of load input pulse	35			35			ns
t_{su}	Data setup time (See Figures 1 and 2)	20			20			ns
t_{su}	Load inactive state setup time	30			30			ns
t_h	Data hold time	5			5			ns
t_h	Enable hold time	0			0			ns
t_{enable}	Count enable time (see Note 3)	40			40			ns
T_A	Operating free-air temperature	−55		125	0		70	°C

electrical characteristics over recommended operating free-air temperature range (unless otherwise noted)

PARAMETER		TEST CONDITIONS[†]		SN54LS190 SN54LS191			SN74LS190 SN74LS191			UNIT
				MIN	TYP[‡]	MAX	MIN	TYP[‡]	MAX	
V_{IH}	High-level input voltage			2			2			V
V_{IL}	Low-level input voltage					0.7			0.8	V
V_{IK}	Input clamp voltage	V_{CC} = MIN,	I_I = −18 mA			−1.5			−1.5	V
V_{OH}	High-level output voltage	V_{CC} = MIN, V_{IH} = 2 V, V_{IL} = V_{IL} max, I_{OH} = −400 μA		2.5	3.4		2.7	3.4		V
V_{OL}	Low-level output voltage	V_{CC} = MIN, V_{IH} = 2 V, V_{IL} = V_{IL} max	I_{OL} = 4 mA		0.25	0.4		0.25	0.4	V
			I_{OL} = 8 mA					0.35	0.5	
I_I	High-level input current at maximum input voltage	Enable	V_{CC} = MAX, V_I = 7 V			0.3			0.3	mA
		Others				0.1			0.1	
I_{IH}	High-level input current	Enable	V_{CC} = MAX, V_I = 2.7 V			60			60	μA
		Others				20			20	
I_{IL}	Low-level input current	Enable	V_{CC} = MAX, V_I = 0.4 V			−1.2			−1.2	mA
		Others				−0.4			−0.4	
I_{OS}	Short-circuit output current[§]	V_{CC} = MAX,		−20		−100	−20		−100	mA
I_{CC}	Supply current	V_{CC} = MAX,	See Note 2		20	35		20	35	mA

[†]For conditions shown as MAX or MIN, use appropriate value specified under recommended operating conditions for the applicable device type.

[‡]All typical values are at V_{CC} = 5 V, T_A = 25°C.

[§]Not more than one output should be shorted at a time, and duration of the short-circuit should not exceed one second.

NOTES: 2. I_{CC} is measured with all inputs grounded and all outputs open.

3. Minimum count enable time is the interval immediately preceeding the rising edge of the clock pulse during which interval the count enable input must be low to ensure counting.

3

TTL DEVICES

TEXAS
INSTRUMENTS

switching characteristics, V_{CC} = 5 V, T_A = 25°C

PARAMETER[¶]	FROM (INPUT)	TO (OUTPUT)	TEST CONDITIONS	'LS190, 'LS191 MIN	TYP	MAX	UNIT
f_{max}				20	25		MHz
t_{PLH}	$\overline{Load}$	Q_A, Q_B, Q_C, Q_D			22	33	ns
t_{PHL}					33	50	
t_{PLH}	Data A, B, C, D	Q_A, Q_B, Q_C, Q_D			20	32	ns
t_{PHL}					27	40	
t_{PLH}	CLK	$\overline{RCO}$	C_L = 15 pF, R_L = 2 kΩ, See Figures 1 and 3 thru 7		13	20	ns
t_{PHL}					16	24	
t_{PLH}	CLK	Q_A, Q_B, Q_C, Q_D			16	24	ns
t_{PHL}					24	36	
t_{PLH}	CLK	Max/Min			28	42	ns
t_{PHL}					37	52	
t_{PLH}	D/$\overline{U}$	$\overline{RCO}$			30	45	ns
t_{PHL}					30	45	
t_{PLH}	D/$\overline{U}$	Max/Min			21	33	ns
t_{PHL}					22	33	
t_{PLH}	$\overline{CTEN}$	$\overline{RCO}$			21	33	ns
t_{PHL}					22	33	

¶f_{max} ≡ maximum clock frequency
t_{PLH} ≡ propagation delay time, low-to-high-level output
t_{PHL} ≡ propagation delay time, high-to-low-level output

schematics of inputs and outputs

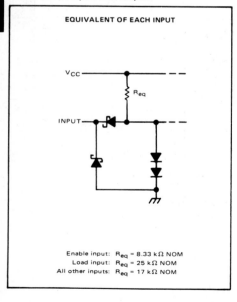

EQUIVALENT OF EACH INPUT

Enable input: R_{eq} = 8.33 kΩ NOM
Load input: R_{eq} = 25 kΩ NOM
All other inputs: R_{eq} = 17 kΩ NOM

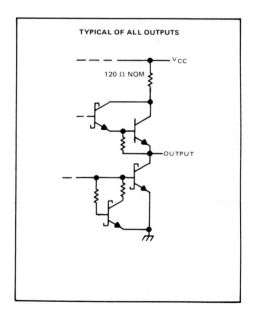

TYPICAL OF ALL OUTPUTS

TEXAS
INSTRUMENTS

PARAMETER MEASUREMENT INFORMATION

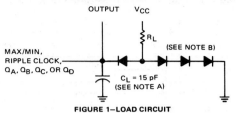

FIGURE 1—LOAD CIRCUIT
FOR SWITCHING TIME MEASUREMENT

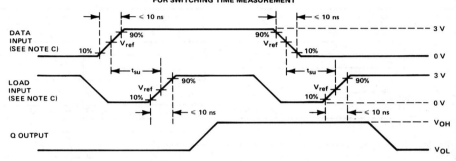

FIGUTE 2-DATA SETUP TIME VOLTAGE WAVEFORMS

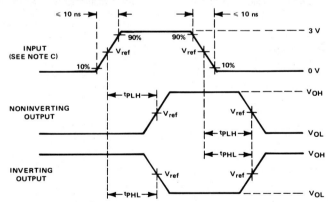

See waveform sequences in figures 4 through 7 for propagation times from a specific input to a specific output. For simplication, pulse rise times, reference levels, etc., have not been shown in figures 4 through 7.

FIGURE 3-GENERAL VOLTAGE WAVEFORMS FOR PROPAGATION TIMES

NOTES: A. C_L includes probe and jig capacitance.
B. All diodes are 1N3064 or equivalent.
C. The input pulses are supplied by generators having the following characteristics: Z_{out} = 50 Ω, duty cycle ≤ 50%, PRR ≤ 1 MHz.
D. V_{ref} = 1.5 V for '190 and '191; 1.3 V for 'LS190 and 'LS191.

TEXAS
INSTRUMENTS

TTL DEVICES

3

TYPES SN54190, SN54191, SN54LS190, SN54LS191,
SN74190, SN74191, SN74LS190, SN74LS191
SYNCHRONOUS UP/DOWN COUNTERS WITH DOWN/UP MODE CONTROL

PARAMETER MEASUREMENT INFORMATION (continued)

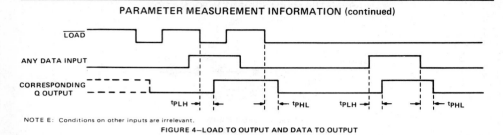

NOTE E: Conditions on other inputs are irrelevant.

FIGURE 4—LOAD TO OUTPUT AND DATA TO OUTPUT

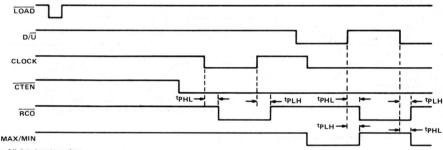

NOTE F: All data inputs are low.

FIGURE 5—ENABLE TO RIPPLE CLOCK, CLOCK TO RIPPLE CLOCK, DOWN/UP TO RIPPLE CLOCK, AND DOWN/UP TO MAX/MIN

TEXAS
INSTRUMENTS

PARAMETER MEASUREMENT INFORMATION (continued)

switching characteristics (continued)

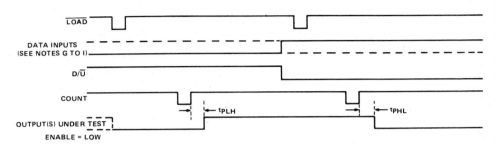

NOTES: G. To test Q_A, Q_B, and Q_C outputs of '190 and 'LS190: Data inputs A, B, and C are shown by the solid line. Data input D is shown by the dashed line.
H. To test Q_D output of '190 and 'LS190: Data inputs A and D are shown by the solid line. Data inputs B and C are held at the low logic level.
I. To test Q_A, Q_B, Q_C, and Q_D outputs of '191 and 'LS191: All four data inputs are shown by the solid line.

FIGURE 6-CLOCK TO OUTPUT

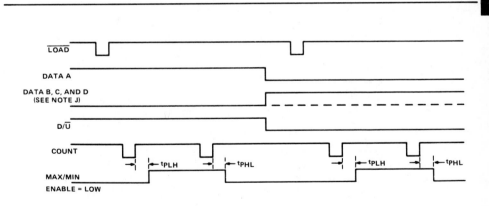

NOTE J: Data inputs B and C are shown by the dashed line for the '190 and 'LS190 and the solid line for the '191 and 'LS191: Data input D is shown by the solid line for both devices.

FIGURE 7-CLOCK TO MAX/MIN

TEXAS
INSTRUMENTS

3-609

3

TTL DEVICES

3

TYPES SN54192, SN54193, SN54LS192, SN54LS193
SN74192, SN74LS193, SN74LS192, SN74LS193
SYNCHRONOUS 4-BIT UP/DOWN COUNTERS (DUAL CLOCK WITH CLEAR)

DECEMBER 1972–REVISED DECEMBER 1983

- **Cascading Circuitry Provided Internally**
- **Synchronous Operation**
- **Individual Preset to Each Flip-Flop**
- **Fully Independent Clear Input**

TYPES	TYPICAL MAXIMUM COUNT FREQUENCY	TYPICAL POWER DISSIPATION
'192,'193	32 MHz	325 mW
'LS192,'LS193	32 MHz	95 mW

SN54192, SN54193, SN54LS192, SN54LS193 ... J OR W PACKAGE
SN74192, SN74193 ... J OR N PACKAGE
SN74LS192, SN74LS193 ... D, J OR N PACKAGE
(TOP VIEW)

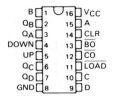

SN54LS192, SN54LS193 ... FK PACKAGE
SN74LS192, SN74LS193
(TOP VIEW)

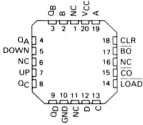

NC · No internal connection

description

These monolithic circuits are synchronous reversible (up/down) counters having a complexity of 55 equivalent gates. The '192 and 'LS192 circuits are BCD counters and the '193 and 'LS193 are 4-bit binary counters. Synchronous operation is provided by having all flip-flops clocked simultaneously so that the outputs change coincidently with each other when so instructed by the steering logic. This mode of operation eliminates the output counting spikes which are normally associated with asynchronous (ripple-clock) counters.

The outputs of the four master-slave flip-flops are triggered by a low-to-high-level transition of either count (clock) input. The direction of counting is determined by which count input is pulsed while the other count input is high.

All four counters are fully programmable; that is, each output may be preset to either level by entering the desired data at the data inputs while the load input is low. The output will change to agree with the data inputs independently of the count pulses. This feature allows the counters to be used as modulo-N dividers by simply modifying the count length with the preset inputs.

A clear input has been provided which forces all outputs to the low level when a high level is applied. The clear function is independent of the count and load inputs. The clear, count, and load inputs are buffered to lower the drive requirements. This reduces the number of clock drivers, etc., required for long words.

These counters were designed to be cascaded without the need for external circuitry. Both borrow and carry outputs are available to cascade both the up- and down-counting functions. The borrow output produces a pulse equal in width to the count-down input when the counter underflows. Similarly, the carry output produces a pulse equal in width to the count-up input when an overflow condition exists. The counters can then be easily cascaded by feeding the borrow and carry outputs to the count-down and count-up inputs respectively of the succeeding counter.

absolute maximum ratings over operating free-air temperature range (unless otherwise noted)

	SN54'		SN54LS'	SN74'	SN74LS'	UNIT
Supply voltage, V_{CC} (see Note 1)	7		7	7	7	V
Input voltage	5.5		7	5.5	7	V
Operating free-air temperature range		−55 to 125		0 to 70		C
Storage temperature range		−65 to 150		−65 to 150		C

NOTE 1: Voltage values are with respect to network ground terminal.

TEXAS
INSTRUMENTS

TTL DEVICES

3

logic diagram

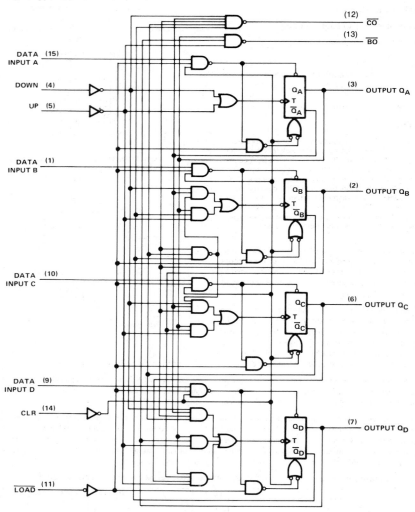

Pin numbers shown on logic notation are for D, J or N packages.

logic diagram

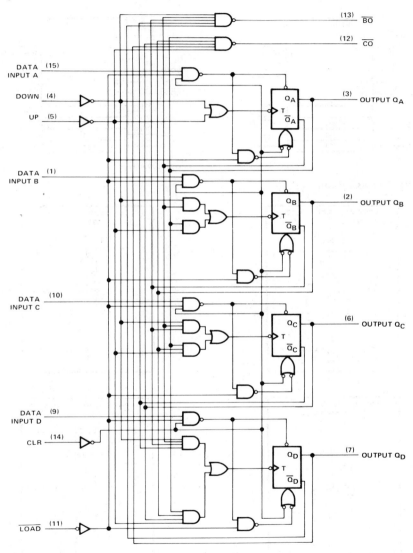

Pin numbers shown on logic notation are for D, J or N packages.

TEXAS
INSTRUMENTS

TTL DEVICES

3

TYPES SN54192, SN54193, SN54LS192, SN54LS193,
SN74192, SN74LS193, SN74LS192, SN74LS193
SYNCHRONOUS 4-BIT UP/DOWN COUNTERS (DUAL CLOCK WITH CLEAR)

logic symbols

'192

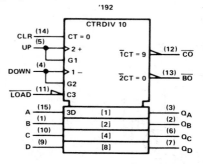

'193

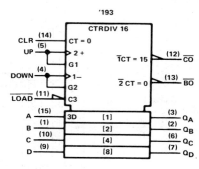

Pin numbers shown on logic notation are for D, J or N packages.

schematics of inputs and outputs

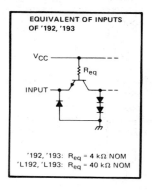

EQUIVALENT OF INPUTS
OF '192, '193

'192, '193: R_{eq} = 4 kΩ NOM
'L192, 'L193: R_{eq} = 40 kΩ NOM

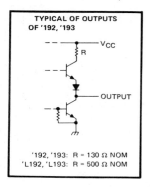

TYPICAL OF OUTPUTS
OF '192, '193

'192, '193: R = 130 Ω NOM
'L192, 'L193: R = 500 Ω NOM

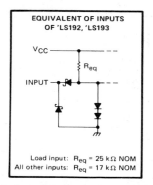

EQUIVALENT OF INPUTS
OF 'LS192, 'LS193

Load input: R_{eq} = 25 kΩ NOM
All other inputs: R_{eq} = 17 kΩ NOM

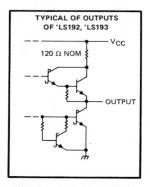

TYPICAL OF OUTPUTS
OF 'LS192, 'LS193

120 Ω NOM

TEXAS
INSTRUMENTS

'192, 'LS192 DECADE COUNTERS

typical clear, load, and count sequences

Illustrated below is the following sequence:

1. Clear outputs to zero.
2. Load (preset) to BCD seven.
3. Count up to eight, nine, carry, zero, one, and two.
4. Count down to one, zero, borrow, nine, eight, and seven.

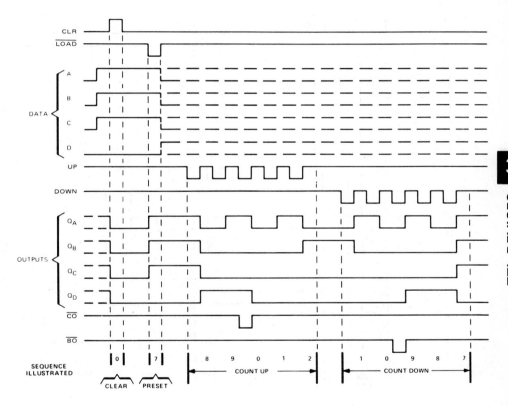

NOTES: A. Clear overrides load, data, and count inputs.
       B. When counting up, count-down input must be high; when counting down, count-up input must be high.

TEXAS
INSTRUMENTS

3

TTL DEVICES

TYPES SN54193, SN54LS193, SN74193, SN74LS193
SYNCHRONOUS 4-BIT UP/DOWN COUNTERS (DUAL CLOCK WITH CLEAR)

'193, 'LS193 BINARY COUNTERS

typical clear, load, and count sequences

Illustrated below is the following sequence:

1. Clear outputs to zero.
2. Load (preset) to binary thirteen.
3. Count up to fourteen, fifteen, carry, zero, one, and two.
4. Count down to one, zero, borrow, fifteen, fourteen, and thirteen.

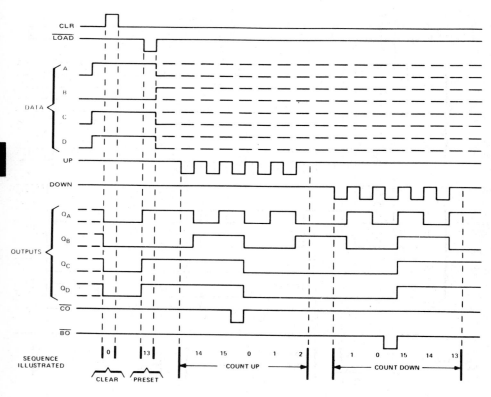

NOTES: A. Clear overrides load, data, and count inputs.

B. When counting up, count-down input must be high; when counting down, count-up input must be high.

recommended operating conditions

			SN54192 SN54193			SN74192 SN74193			UNIT
			MIN	NOM	MAX	MIN	NOM	MAX	
V_{CC}	Supply voltage		4.5	5	5.5	4.75	5	5.25	V
I_{OH}	High-level output current				−0.4			−0.4	mA
I_{OL}	Low-level output current				16			16	mA
f_{clock}	Clock frequency		0		25	0		25	MHz
t_w	Width of any input pulse		20			20			ns
t_{su}	Data setup time, (see Figure 1)		20			20			ns
t_h	Hold time	Data, high or low	0			0			ns
		$\overline{LOAD}$	3			3			
T_A	Operating free-air temperature		−55		125	0		70	°C

electrical characteristics over recommended operating free-air temperature range (unless otherwise noted)

PARAMETER		TEST CONDITIONS[†]	SN54192 SN54193			SN74192 SN74193			UNIT
			MIN	TYP[‡]	MAX	MIN	TYP[‡]	MAX	
V_{IH}	High-level input voltage		2			2			V
V_{IL}	Low-level input voltage				0.8			0.8	V
V_{IK}	Input clamp voltage	V_{CC} = MIN, I_I = −12 mA			−1.5			−1.5	V
V_{OH}	High-level output voltage	V_{CC} = MIN, V_{IH} = 2 V, V_{IL} = 0.8 V, I_{OH} = −0.4 mA	2.4	3.4		2.4	3.4		V
V_{OL}	Low-level output voltage	V_{CC} = MIN, V_{IH} = 2 V V_{IL} = 0.8 V, I_{OL} = 16 mA		0.2	0.4		0.2	0.4	V
I_I	Input current at maximum input voltage	V_{CC} = MAX, V_I = 5.5 V			1			1	mA
I_{IH}	High-level input current	V_{CC} = MAX, V_I = 2.4 V			40			40	µA
I_{IL}	Low-level input current	V_{CC} = MAX, V_I = 0.4 V			−1.6			−1.6	mA
I_{OS}	Short-circuit output current[§]	V_{CC} = MAX	−20		−65	−18		−65	mA
I_{CC}	Supply current	V_{CC} = MAX, See Note 2		65	89		65	102	mA

[†]For conditions shown as MIN or MAX, use the appropriate value specified under recommended operating conditions for the applicable type.
[‡]All typical values are at V_{CC} = 5 V, T_A = 25°C.
[§]Not more than one output should be shorted at a time.
NOTE 2: I_{CC} is measured with all outputs open, clear and load inputs grounded, and all other inputs at 4.5 V.

switching characteristics, V_{CC} = 5 V, T_A = 25°C

PARAMETER[¶]	FROM INPUT	TO OUTPUT	TEST CONDITIONS	MIN	TYP	MAX	UNIT
f_{max}				25	32		MHz
t_{PLH}	UP	$\overline{CO}$			17	26	ns
t_{PHL}					16	24	
t_{PLH}	DOWN	$\overline{BO}$	C_L = 15 pF,		16	24	ns
t_{PHL}			R_L = 400 Ω,		16	24	
t_{PLH}	UP OR DOWN	Q	See Figures 1 and 2		25	38	ns
t_{PHL}					31	47	
t_{PLH}	$\overline{LOAD}$	Q			27	40	ns
t_{PHL}					29	40	
t_{PHL}	CLR	Q			22	35	ns

[¶]f_{max} ≡ maximum clock frequency
t_{PLH} ≡ propagation delay time, low-to-high-level output
t_{PHL} ≡ propagation delay time, high-to-low-level output

TEXAS INSTRUMENTS

3

TTL DEVICES

recommended operating conditions

		SN54LS192 SN54LS193			SN74LS192 SN74LS193			UNIT
		MIN	NOM	MAX	MIN	NOM	MAX	
V_{CC}	Supply voltage	4.5	5	5.5	4.75	5	5.25	V
I_{OH}	High-level output current			−400			−400	μA
I_{OL}	Low-level output current			4			8	mA
f_{clock}	Clock frequency	0		25	0		25	MHz
t_w	Width of any input pulse	20			20			ns
t_{su}	Clear inactive-state setup time	15			15			ns
	Load inactive-state setup time	15			15			ns
	Data setup time (see Figure 1)	20			20			ns
t_h	Data hold time	5			5			ns
T_A	Operating free-air temperature range	−55		125	0		70	°C

electrical characteristics over recommended operating free-air temperature range (unless otherwise noted)

PARAMETER		TEST CONDITIONS[†]		SN54LS192 SN54LS193			SN74LS192 SN74LS193			UNIT
				MIN	TYP[‡]	MAX	MIN	TYP[‡]	MAX	
V_{IH}	High-level input voltage			2			2			V
V_{IL}	Low-level input voltage					0.7			0.8	V
V_{IK}	Input clamp voltage	V_{CC} = MIN,	I_I = −18 mA			−1.5			−1.5	V
V_{OH}	High-level output voltage	V_{CC} = MIN, V_{IH} = 2 V, $V_{IL} = V_{IL}$ max, I_{OH} = −400 μA		2.5	3.4		2.7	3.4		V
V_{OL}	Low-level output voltage	V_{CC} = MIN, V_{IH} = 2 V, $V_{IL} = V_{IL}$ max	I_{OL} = 4 mA	0.25	0.4		0.15	0.4		V
			I_{OL} = 8 mA				0.35	0.5		
I_I	Input current at maximum input voltage	V_{CC} = MAX,	V_I = 7 V			0.1			0.1	mA
I_{IH}	High-level input current	V_{CC} = MAX,	V_I = 2.7 V			20			20	μA
I_{IL}	Low-level input current	V_{CC} = MAX,	V_I = 0.4 V			−0.4			−0.4	mA
I_{OS}	Short-circuit output current[§]	V_{CC} = MAX		−20		−100	−20		−100	mA
I_{CC}	Supply current	V_{CC} = MAX,	See Note 2		19	34		19	34	mA

[†]For conditions shown as MIN or MAX, use the appropriate value specified under recommended operating conditions for the applicable type.
[‡]All typical values are at V_{CC} = 5 V, T_A = 25°C.
[§]Not more than one output should be shorted at a time ,and duration of the short-circuit should not exceed one second.
NOTE 2: I_{CC} is measured with all outputs open, clear and load inputs grounded, and all other inputs at 4.5 V.

switching characteristics, V_{CC} = 5 V, T_A = 25°C

PARAMETER	FROM INPUT	TO OUTPUT	TEST CONDITIONS	MIN	TYP	MAX	UNIT
f_{max}				25	32		MHz
t_{PLH}	UP	$\overline{CO}$			17	26	ns
t_{PHL}					18	24	
t_{PLH}	DOWN	$\overline{BO}$	C_L = 15 pF,		16	24	ns
t_{PHL}			R_L = 2 kΩ,		15	24	
t_{PLH}	UP OR DOWN	Q	See Figures 1 and 2		27	38	ns
t_{PHL}					30	47	
t_{PLH}	$\overline{LOAD}$	Q			24	40	ns
t_{PHL}					25	40	
t_{PHL}	CLR	Q			23	35	ns

TEXAS
INSTRUMENTS

3
TTL DEVICES

PARAMETER MEASUREMENT INFORMATION

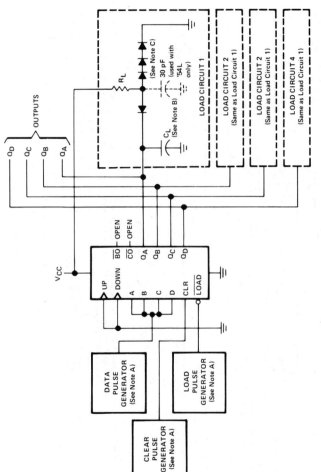

TEST CIRCUIT

FIGURE 1A – CLEAR, SETUP AND LOAD TIMES

NOTES: A. The pulse generators have the following characteristics: $Z_{out} \approx 50\ \Omega$ and for the data pulse generator PRR ≤ 500 kHz, duty cycle = 50%; for the load pulse generator PRR is two times data PRR, duty cycle = 50%.
B. C_L includes probe and jig capacitance.
C. Diodes are 1N3064 or equivalent.
D. t_r and t_f ≤ 7 ns for '192, '193, 'LS192, and 'LS193.
E. V_{ref} is 1.5 volts for '192 and '193; 'LS192, and LS193.

TTL DEVICES

3

PARAMETER MEASUREMENT INFORMATION

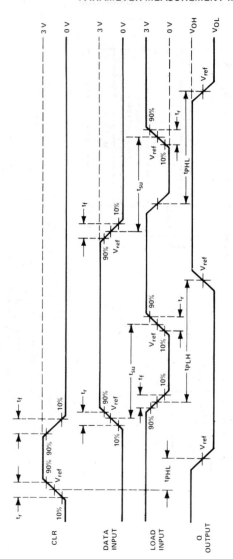

VOLTAGE WAVEFORMS

FIGURE 1B – CLEAR, SETUP, AND LOAD TIMES

NOTES: A. The pulse generators have the following characteristics: $Z_{out} \approx 50\ \Omega$ and for the data pulse generator PRR $\leq$ 500 kHz, duty cycle = 50%; for the load pulse generator PRR is two times data PRR, duty cycle = 50%.
B. C_L includes probe and jig capacitance.
C. Diodes are 1N3064 or equivalent.
D. t_r and $t_f \leq 7$ ns for '192, '193, 'LS192, and 'LS193.
E. V_{ref} is 1.5 volts for '192 and '193; 'LS192, and 'LS193.

TEXAS INSTRUMENTS

PARAMETER MEASUREMENT INFORMATION

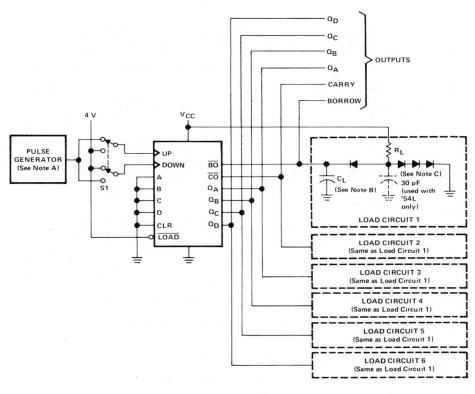

TEST CIRCUIT

NOTES: A. The pulse generator has the following characteristics: PRR ≤ 1 MHz, $Z_{out} \approx 50\ \Omega$, duty cycle = 50%.
      B. C_L includes probe and jig capacitance.
      C. Diodes are 1N3064 or equivalent.
      D. Count-up and count-down pulse shown are for the '193, and 'LS193 binary counters. Count cycle for '192, and 'LS192 decade counters is 1 through 10.
      E. Waveforms for outputs Q_A, Q_B, and Q_C are omitted to simplify the drawing.
      F. t_r and $t_f \leq 7$ ns for '192, '193, 'LS192, and 'LS193.
      G. V_{ref} is 1.5 volts for '192 and '193; 'LS192, and 'LS193.

FIGURE 2A – PROPAGATION DELAY TIMES

3

TTL DEVICES

TYPES SN54192, SN54193, SN54LS192, SN54LS193
SN74192, SN74193, SN74LS192, SN74LS193
SYNCHRONOUS 4-BIT UP/DOWN COUNTERS (DUAL CLOCK WITH CLEAR)

PARAMETER MEASUREMENT INFORMATION

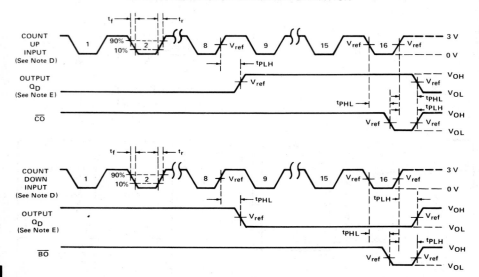

VOLTAGE WAVEFORMS

NOTES: A. The pulse generator has the following characteristics: PRR ≤ 1 MHz, $Z_{out} \approx 50\ \Omega$, duty cycle = 50%.
          B. C_L includes probe and jig capacitance.
          C. Diodes are 1N3064 or equivalent.
          D. Count-up and count-down pulse shown are for the '193, and 'LS193 binary counters. Count cycle for '192,
             and 'LS192 decade counters is 1 through 10.
          E. Waveforms for outputs Q_A, Q_B, and Q_C are omitted to simplify the drawing.
          F. t_r and $t_f \leqslant 7$ ns for '192, '193, 'LS192, and 'LS193.
          G. V_{ref} is 1.5 volts for '192 and '193; 'LS192, and 'LS193.

FIGURE 2B – PROPAGATION DELAY TIMES

3

TTL DEVICES

TEXAS
INSTRUMENTS

- Parallel Inputs and Outputs
- Four Operating Modes:
  - Synchronous Parallel Load
  - Right Shift
  - Left Shift
  - Do Nothing
- Positive Edge-Triggered Clocking
- Direct Overriding Clear

SN54194, SN54LS194A, SN54S194 . . . J OR W PACKAGE
SN74194 . . . J OR N PACKAGE
SN74LS194A, SN74S194 . . . D, J OR N PACKAGE
(TOP VIEW)

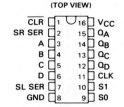

TYPE	TYPICAL MAXIMUM CLOCK FREQUENCY	TYPICAL POWER DISSIPATION
'194	36 MHz	195 mW
'LS194A	36 MHz	75 mW
'S194	105 MHz	425 mW

SN54LS194A, SN54S194 . . . FK PACKAGE
SN74LS194A, SN74S194
(TOP VIEW)

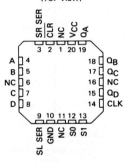

NC - No internal connection

description

These bidirectional shift registers are designed to incorporate virtually all of the features a system designer may want in a shift register. The circuit contains 46 equivalent gates and features parallel inputs, parallel outputs, right-shift and left-shift serial inputs, operating-mode-control inputs, and a direct overriding clear line. The register has four distinct modes of operation, namely:

  Inhibit clock (do nothing)
  Shift right (in the direction Q_A toward Q_D)
  Shift left (in the direction Q_D toward Q_A)
  Parallel (broadside) load

Synchronous parallel loading is accomplished by applying the four bits of data and taking both mode control inputs, S0 and S1, high. The data are loaded into the associated flip-flops and appear at the outputs after the positive transition of the clock input. During loading, serial data flow is inhibited.

Shift right is accomplished synchronously with the rising edge of the clock pulse when S0 is high and S1 is low. Serial data for this mode is entered at the shift-right data input. When S0 is low and S1 is high, data shifts left synchronously and new data is entered at the shift-left serial input.

Clocking of the shift register is inhibited when both mode control inputs are low. The mode controls of the SN54194/SN74194 should be changed only while the clock input is high.

TEXAS
INSTRUMENTS

3

TTL DEVICES

TYPES SN54194, SN54LS194A, SN54S194, SN74194, SN74LS194A, SN74S194
4-BIT BIDIRECTIONAL UNIVERSAL SHIFT REGISTERS

FUNCTION TABLE

CLEAR	MODE S1	MODE S0	CLOCK	SERIAL LEFT	SERIAL RIGHT	PARALLEL A	PARALLEL B	PARALLEL C	PARALLEL D	Q_A	Q_B	Q_C	Q_D
L	X	X	X	X	X	X	X	X	X	L	L	L	L
H	X	X	L	X	X	X	X	X	X	Q_{A0}	Q_{B0}	Q_{C0}	Q_{D0}
H	H	H	↑	X	X	a	b	c	d	a	b	c	d
H	L	H	↑	X	H	X	X	X	X	H	Q_{An}	Q_{Bn}	Q_{Cn}
H	L	H	↑	X	L	X	X	X	X	L	Q_{An}	Q_{Bn}	Q_{Cn}
H	H	L	↑	H	X	X	X	X	X	Q_{Bn}	Q_{Cn}	Q_{Dn}	H
H	H	L	↑	L	X	X	X	X	X	Q_{Bn}	Q_{Cn}	Q_{Dn}	L
H	L	L	X	X	X	X	X	X	X	Q_{A0}	Q_{B0}	Q_{C0}	Q_{D0}

H = high level (steady state)
L = low level (steady state)
X = irrelevant (any input, including transitions)
↑ = transition from low to high level
a, b, c, d = the level of steady-state input at inputs A, B, C, or D, respectively.
Q_{A0}, Q_{B0}, Q_{C0}, Q_{D0} = the level of Q_A, Q_B, Q_C, or Q_D, respectively, before the indicated steady-state input conditions were established.
Q_{An}, Q_{Bn}, Q_{Cn}, Q_{Dn} = the level of Q_A, Q_B, Q_C, respectively, before the most-recent ↑ transition of the clock.

schematics of inputs and outputs

'194

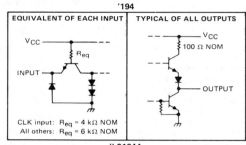

'LS194A

'S194

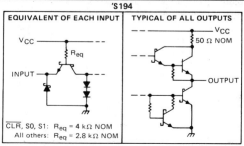

TEXAS
INSTRUMENTS

logic diagrams

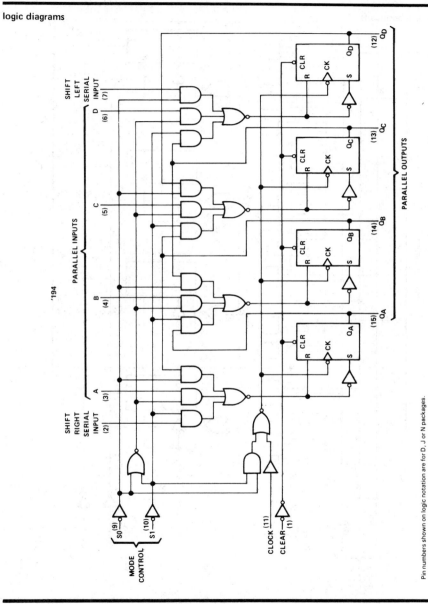

Pin numbers shown on logic notation are for D, J or N packages.

TEXAS
INSTRUMENTS

logic diagrams (continued)

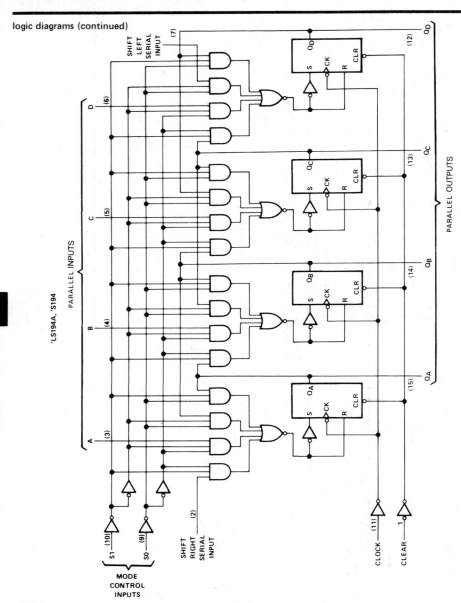

TEXAS
INSTRUMENTS

typical clear, load, right-shift, left-shift, inhibit, and clear sequences

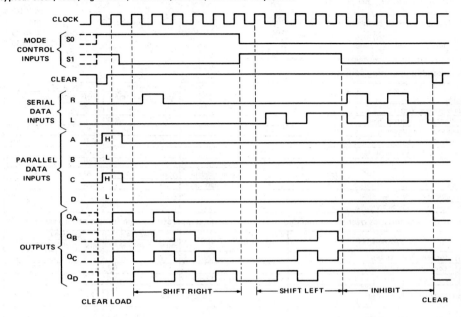

TTL DEVICES

3

absolute maximum ratings over operating free-air temperature range (unless otherwise noted)

Supply voltage, V_{CC} (see Note 1) . . . . 7 V
Input voltage . . . . 5.5 V
Operating free-air temperature range: SN54194 . . . . −55°C to 125°C
                                    SN74194 . . . . 0°C to 70°C
Storage temperature range . . . . −65°C to 150°C

NOTE 1: Voltage values are with respect to network ground terminal.

recommended operating conditions

		SN54194			SN74194			UNIT
		MIN	NOM	MAX	MIN	NOM	MAX	
Supply voltage, V_{CC}		4.5	5	5.5	4.75	5	5.25	V
High-level output current, I_{OH}				−800			−800	μA
Low-level output current, I_{OL}				16			16	mA
Clock frequency, f_{clock}		0		25	0		25	MHz
Width of clock or clear pulse, t_w		20			20			ns
Setup time, t_{su}	Mode control	30			30			ns
	Serial and parallel data	20			20			ns
	Clear inactive-state	25			25			ns
Hold time at any input, t_h		0			0			ns
Operating free-air temperature, T_A		−55		125	0		70	°C

electrical characteristics over recommended operating free-air temperature range (unless otherwise noted)

PARAMETER		TEST CONDITIONS†	SN54194			SN74194			UNIT
			MIN	TYP‡	MAX	MIN	TYP‡	MAX	
V_{IH}	High-level input voltage		2			2			V
V_{IL}	Low-level input voltage				0.8			0.8	V
V_{IK}	Input clamp voltage	V_{CC} = MIN, I_I = −12 mA			−1.5			−1.5	V
V_{OH}	High-level output voltage	V_{CC} = MIN, V_{IH} = 2 V, V_{IL} = 0.8 V, I_{OH} = −800 μA	2.4	3.4		2.4	3.4		V
V_{OL}	Low-level output voltage	V_{CC} = MIN, V_{IH} = 2 V, V_{IL} = 0.8 V, I_{OL} = 16 mA		0.2	0.4		0.2	0.4	V
I_I	Input current at maximum input voltage	V_{CC} = MAX, V_I = 5.5 V			1			1	mA
I_{IH}	High-level input current	V_{CC} = MAX, V_I = 2.4 V			40			40	μA
I_{IL}	Low-level input current	V_{CC} = MAX, V_I = 0.4 V			−1.6			−1.6	mA
I_{OS}	Short-circuit output current§	V_{CC} = MAX	−20		−57	−18		−57	mA
I_{CC}	Supply current	V_{CC} = MAX, See Note 2		39	63		39	63	mA

†For conditions shown as MIN or MAX, use the appropriate value specified under recommended operating conditions.
‡All typical values are at V_{CC} = 5 V, T_A = 25°C.
§Not more than one output should be shorted at a time.
NOTE 2: With all outputs open, inputs A through D grounded, and 4.5 V applied to S0, S1, clear, and the serial inputs, I_{CC} is tested with a momentary GND, then 4.5 V applied to clock.

switching characteristics, V_{CC} = 5 V, T_A = 25°C

PARAMETER		TEST CONDITIONS	MIN	TYP	MAX	UNIT
f_{max}	Maximum clock frequency	C_L = 15 pF, R_L = 400 Ω, See Figure 1	25	36		MHz
t_{PHL}	Propagation delay time, high-to-low-level output from clear			19	30	ns
t_{PLH}	Propagation delay time, low-to-high-level output from clock			14	22	ns
t_{PHL}	Propagation delay time, high-to-low-level output from clock			17	26	ns

TEXAS
INSTRUMENTS

absolute maximum ratings over operating free-air temperature range (unless otherwise noted)

Supply voltage, V_{CC} (see Note 1) . . . . 7 V
Input voltage . . . . 7 V
Operating free-air temperature range: SN54LS194A . . . . −55°C to 125°C
                       SN74LS194A . . . . 0°C to 70°C
Storage temperature range . . . . −65°C to 150°C

NOTE 1: Voltage values are with respect to network ground terminal.

recommended operating conditions

			SN54LS194A			SN74LS194A			UNIT
			MIN	NOM	MAX	MIN	NOM	MAX	
Supply voltage, V_{CC}			4.5	5	5.5	4.75	5	5.25	V
High-level output current, I_{OH}					−400			−400	μA
Low-level output current, I_{OL}					4			8	mA
Clock frequency, f_{clock}			0		25	0		25	MHz
Width of clock or clear pulse, t_w			20			20			ns
Setup time, t_{su}	Mode control		30			30			ns
	Serial and parallel data		20			20			ns
	Clear inactive-state		25			25			ns
Hold time at any input, t_h			0			0			ns
Operating free-air temperature, T_A			−55		125	0		70	°C

electrical characteristics over recommended operating free-air temperature range (unless otherwise noted)

PARAMETER		TEST CONDITIONS†		SN54LS194A			SN74LS194A			UNIT
				MIN	TYP‡	MAX	MIN	TYP‡	MAX	
V_{IH}	High-level input voltage			2			2			V
V_{IL}	Low-level input voltage					0.7			0.8	V
V_I	Input clamp voltage	V_{CC} = MIN, I_I = −18 mA				−1.5			−1.5	V
V_{OH}	High-level output voltage	V_{CC} = MIN, V_{IH} = 2 V, V_{IL} = V_{IL} max, I_{OH} = −400 μA		2.5	3.5		2.7	3.5		V
V_{OL}	Low-level output voltage	V_{CC} = MIN, V_{IH} = 2 V, V_{IL} = V_{IL} max	I_{OL} = 4 mA		0.25	0.4		0.25	0.4	V
			I_{OL} = 8 mA					0.35	0.5	
I_I	Input current at maximum input voltage	V_{CC} = MAX, V_I = 7 V				0.1			0.1	mA
I_{IH}	High-level input current	V_{CC} = MAX, V_I = 2.7 V				20			20	μA
I_{IL}	Low-level input current	V_{CC} = MAX, V_I = 0.4 V				−0.4			−0.4	mA
I_{OS}	Short-circuit output current§	V_{CC} = MAX		−20		−100	−20		−100	mA
I_{CC}	Supply current	V_{CC} = MAX, See Note 2			15	23		15	23	mA

†For conditions shown as MIN or MAX, use the appropriate value specified under recommended operating conditions.
‡All typical values are at V_{CC} = 5 V, T_A = 25°C
§Not more than one output should be shorted at a time, and duration of the short-circuit should not exceed one second.
NOTE 2: With all outputs open, inputs A through D grounded, and 4.5 V applied to S0, S1, clear, and the serial inputs, I_{CC} is tested with a momentary GND, then 4.5 V, applied to clock.

switching characteristics, V_{CC} = 5 V, T_A = 25°C

PARAMETER		TEST CONDITIONS	MIN	TYP	MAX	UNIT
f_{max}	Maximum clock frequency	C_L = 15 pF, R_L = 2 kΩ, See Figure 1	25	36		MHz
t_{PHL}	Propagation delay time, high-to-low-level output from clear			19	30	ns
t_{PLH}	Propagation delay time, low-to-high-level output from clock			14	22	ns
t_{PHL}	Propagation delay time, high-to-low-level output from clock			17	26	ns

3

TTL DEVICES

TEXAS
INSTRUMENTS

absolute maximum ratings over operating free-air temperature range (unless otherwise noted)

Supply voltage, V_{CC} (see Note 1)	7 V
Input voltage	5.5 V
Operating free-air temperature range: SN54S194	-55°C to 125°C
SN74S194	0°C to 70°C
Storage temperature range	-65°C to 150°C

NOTE 1: Voltage values are with respect to network ground terminal.

recommended operating conditions

		SN54S194			SN74S194			UNIT
		MIN	NOM	MAX	MIN	NOM	MAX	
Supply voltage, V_{CC}		4.5	5	5.5	4.75	5	5.25	V
High-level output current, I_{OH}				-1			-1	mA
Low-level output current, I_{OL}				20			20	mA
Clock frequency, f_{clock}		0		70	0		70	MHz
Width of clock pulse, $t_{w(clock)}$		7			7			ns
Width of clear pulse, $t_{w(clear)}$		12			12			ns
Setup time, t_{su}	Mode control	11			11			ns
	Serial and parallel data	5			5			ns
	Clear inactive-state	9			9			ns
Hold time at any input, t_h		3			3			ns
Operating free-air temperature, T_A		-55		125	0		70	$^\circ$C

electrical characteristics over recommended operating free-air temperature range (unless otherwise noted)

PARAMETER		TEST CONDITIONS[†]	SN54S194			SN74S194			UNIT
			MIN	TYP[‡]	MAX	MIN	TYP[‡]	MAX	
V_{IH}	High-level input voltage		2			2			V
V_{IL}	Low-level input voltage				0.8			0.8	V
V_{IK}	Input clamp voltage	V_{CC} = MIN, I_I = -18 mA			-1.2			-1.2	V
V_{OH}	High-level output voltage	V_{CC} = MIN, V_{IH} = 2 V, V_{IL} = 0.8 V, I_{OH} = -1 mA	2.5	3.4		2.7	3.4		V
V_{OL}	Low-level output voltage	V_{CC} = MIN, V_{IH} = 2 V, V_{IL} = 0.8 V, I_{OL} = 20 mA			0.5			0.5	V
I_I	Input current at maximum input voltage	V_{CC} = MAX, V_I = 5.5 V			1			1	mA
I_{IH}	High-level input current	V_{CC} = MAX, V_I = 2.7 V			50			50	μA
I_{IL}	Low-level input current	V_{CC} = MAX, V_I = 0.5 V			-2			-2	mA
I_{OS}	Short-circuit output current[§]	V_{CC} = MAX	-40		-100	-40		-100	mA
I_{CC}	Supply current	V_{CC} = MAX, See Note 2		85	135		85	135	mA
		V_{CC} = MAX, T_A = 125°C, W package See Note 2		110					

[†] For conditions shown as MIN or MAX, use the appropriate value specified under recommended operating conditions.
[‡] All typical values are at V_{CC} = 5 V, T_A = 25°C.
[§] Not more than one output should be shorted at a time, and duration of the short-circuit should not exceed one second.
NOTE 2: With all outputs open, inputs A through D grounded, and 4.5 V applies to S0, S1, clear, and the serial inputs, I_{CC} is tested with a momemtary GND, then 4.5 V, applied to clock.

switching characteristics, V_{CC} = 5 V, T_A = 25°C

PARAMETER		TEST CONDITIONS	MIN	TYP	MAX	UNIT
f_{max}	Maximum clock frequency	C_L = 15 pF, R_L = 280 Ω, See Figure 1	70	105		MHz
t_{PHL}	Propagation delay time, high-to-low-level output from clear			12.5	18.5	ns
t_{PLH}	Propagation delay time, low-to-high-level output from clock		4	8	12	ns
t_{PHL}	Propagation delay time, high-to-low-level output from clock		4	11	16.5	ns

TEXAS
INSTRUMENTS

PARAMETER MEASUREMENT INFORMATION

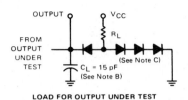

LOAD FOR OUTPUT UNDER TEST

TEST TABLE FOR SYNCHRONOUS INPUTS

DATA INPUT FOR TEST	S1	S0	OUTPUT TESTED (SEE NOTE E)
A	4.5 V	4.5 V	Q_A at t_{n+1}
B	4.5 V	4.5 V	Q_B at t_{n+1}
C	4.5 V	4.5 V	Q_C at t_{n+1}
D	4.5 V	4.5 V	Q_D at t_{n+1}
L Serial Input	4.5 V	0 V	Q_A at t_{n+4}
R Serial Input	0 V	4.5 V	Q_D at t_{n+4}

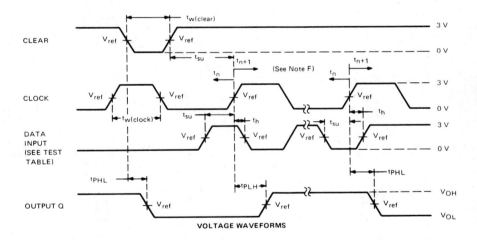

VOLTAGE WAVEFORMS

3 — **TTL DEVICES**

NOTES: A. The clock pulse generator has the following characteristics: $Z_{out} \approx 50\ \Omega$ and PRR ≤ 1 MHz, For '194, t_r ≤ 7 ns and t_f ≤ 7 ns.
For 'LS194A, t_r ≤ 15 ns and t_f ≤ 6 ns. For 'S194, t_r ≤ 2.5 ns and t_f ≤ 2.5 ns. When testing f_{max}, vary PRR.
B. C_L includes probe and jig capacitance.
C. All diodes are 1N3064 or 1N916.
D. A clear pulse is applied prior to each test.
E. For '194 and 'S194, V_{ref} = 1.5 V; for 'LS194A, V_{ref} = 1.3 V.
F. Propagation delay times (t_{PLH} and t_{PHL}) are measured at t_{n+1}. Proper shifting of data is verified at t_{n+4} with a functional test.
G. t_n = bit time before clocking transition.
t_{n+1} = bit time after one clocking transition.
t_{n+4} = bit time after four clocking transitions.

FIGURE 1—SWITCHING TIMES

- **Synchronous Parallel Load**
- **Positive-Edge-Triggered Clocking**
- **Parallel Inputs and Outputs from Each Flip-Flop**
- **Direct Overriding Clear**
- **J and K̄ Inputs to First Stage**
- **Complementary Outputs from Last Stage**
- **For Use in High Performance: Accumulators/Processors Serial-to-Parallel, Parallel-to-Serial Converters**

SN54195, SN54LS195A, SN54S195 . . . J OR W PACKAGE
SN74195 . . . J OR N PACKAGE
SN74LS195A, SN74S195 . . . D, J OR N PACKAGE
(TOP VIEW)

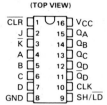

SN54LS195, SN54S195 . . . FK PACKAGE
SN74LS195, SN74S195
(TOP VIEW)

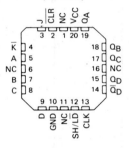

NC - No internal connection

description

These 4-bit registers feature parallel inputs, parallel outputs, J-K̄ serial inputs, shift/load control input, and a direct overriding clear. All inputs are buffered to lower the input drive requirements. The registers have two modes of operation:

Parallel (broadside) load
Shift (in the direction Q_A toward Q_D)

Parallel loading is accomplished by applying the four bits of data and taking the shift/load control input low. The data is loaded into the associated flip-flop and appears at the outputs after the positive transition of the clock input. During loading, serial data flow is inhibited.

Shifting is accomplished synchronously when the shift/load control input is high. Serial data for this mode is entered at the J-K̄ inputs. These inputs permit the first stage to perform as a J-K̄, D-, or T-type flip-flop as shown in the function table.

The high-performance 'S195, with a 105-megahertz typical maximum shift-frequency, is particularly attractive for very-high-speed data processing systems. In most cases existing systems can be upgraded merely by using this Schottky-clamped shift register.

TYPE	TYPICAL MAXIMUM CLOCK FREQUENCY	TYPICAL POWER DISSIPATION
'195	39 MHz	195 mW
'LS195A	39 MHz	70 mW
'S195	105 MHz	350 mW

FUNCTION TABLE

INPUTS								OUTPUTS				
CLEAR	SHIFT/ LOAD	CLOCK	SERIAL		PARALLEL				Q_A	Q_B	Q_C	Q_D	$\bar{Q}_D$
			J	K̄	A	B	C	D					
L	X	X	X	X	X	X	X	X	L	L	L	L	H
H	L	↑	X	X	a	b	c	d	a	b	c	d	d̄
H	H	L	X	X	X	X	X	X	Q_{A0}	Q_{B0}	Q_{C0}	Q_{D0}	$\bar{Q}_{D0}$
H	H	↑	L	H	X	X	X	X	Q_{A0}	Q_{A0}	Q_{Bn}	Q_{Cn}	$\bar{Q}_{Cn}$
H	H	↑	L	L	X	X	X	X	L	Q_{An}	Q_{Bn}	Q_{Cn}	$\bar{Q}_{Cn}$
H	H	↑	H	H	X	X	X	X	H	Q_{An}	Q_{Bn}	Q_{Cn}	$\bar{Q}_{Cn}$
H	H	↑	H	L	X	X	X	X	$\bar{Q}_{An}$	Q_{An}	Q_{Bn}	Q_{Cn}	$\bar{Q}_{Cn}$

H = high level (steady state)
L = low level (steady state)
X = irrelevant (any input, including transitions)
↑ = transition from low to high level
a, b, c, d = the level of steady-state input at A, B, C, or D, respectively
Q_{A0}, Q_{B0}, Q_{C0}, Q_{D0} = the level of Q_A, Q_B, Q_C, or Q_D, respectively, before the indicated steady-state input conditions were established
Q_{An}, Q_{Bn}, Q_{Cn} = the level of Q_A, Q_B, or Q_C, respectively, before the most-recent transition of the clock

TEXAS INSTRUMENTS

3-633

TTL DEVICES

3

logic diagram

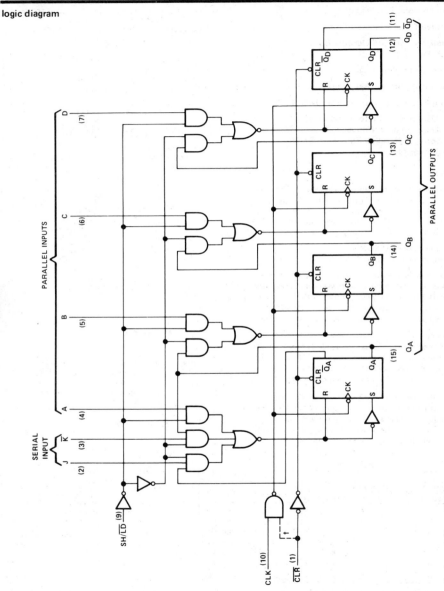

†This connection is made on '195 only.
Pin numbers shown on logic notation are for D, J or N packages.

TEXAS
INSTRUMENTS

typical clear, shift, and load sequences

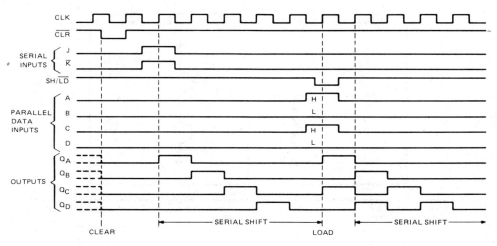

3

TTL DEVICES

TYPES SN54195, SN54LS195A, SN54S195, SN74195, SN74LS195A, SN74S195
4-BIT PARALLEL-ACCESS SHIFT REGISTERS

schematics of inputs and outputs

'195

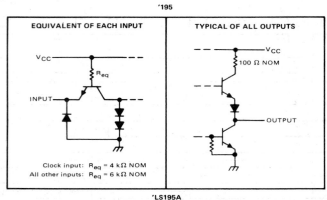

EQUIVALENT OF EACH INPUT

TYPICAL OF ALL OUTPUTS

Clock input: R_{eq} = 4 kΩ NOM
All other inputs: R_{eq} = 6 kΩ NOM

'LS195A

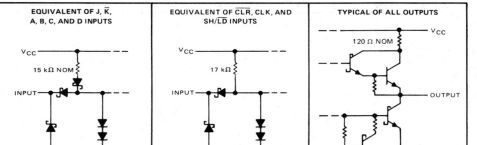

EQUIVALENT OF J, $\overline{K}$, A, B, C, AND D INPUTS

EQUIVALENT OF $\overline{CLR}$, CLK, AND SH/$\overline{LD}$ INPUTS

TYPICAL OF ALL OUTPUTS

'S195

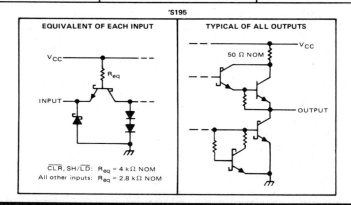

EQUIVALENT OF EACH INPUT

TYPICAL OF ALL OUTPUTS

$\overline{CLR}$, SH/$\overline{LD}$: R_{eq} = 4 kΩ NOM
All other inputs: R_{eq} = 2.8 kΩ NOM

TEXAS
INSTRUMENTS

absolute maximum ratings over operating free-air temperature range (unless otherwise noted)

Supply voltage, V_{CC} (see Note 1) . . . . 7 V
Input voltage . . . . 5.5 V
Operating free-air temperature range: SN54195 . . . . -55°C to 125°C
SN74195 . . . . 0°C to 70°C
Storage temperature range . . . . -65°C to 150°C

NOTE 1: Voltage values are with respect to network ground terminal.

recommended operating conditions

		SN54195 MIN	NOM	MAX	SN74195 MIN	NOM	MAX	UNIT
Supply voltage, V_{CC}		4.5	5	5.5	4.75	5	5.25	V
High-level output current, I_{OH}				−800			−800	µA
Low-level output current, I_{OL}				16			16	mA
Clock frequency, f_{clock}		0		30	0		30	MHz
Width of clock input pulse, $t_{w(clock)}$		16			16			ns
Width of clear input pulse, $t_{w(clear)}$		12			12			ns
Setup time, t_{su} (see Figure 1)	Shift/load	25			25			ns
	Serial and parallel data	20			20			
	Clear inactive-state	25			25			
Shift/load release time, $t_{release}$ (see Figure 1)				20			10	ns
Serial and parallel data hold time, t_h (see Figure 1)		0			0			ns
Operating free-air temperature, T_A		−55		125	0		70	°C

electrical characteristics over recommended operating free-air temperature range (unless otherwise noted)

PARAMETER		TEST CONDITIONS[†]	MIN	TYP[‡]	MAX	UNIT
V_{IH}	High-level input voltage		2			V
V_{IL}	Low-level input voltage				0.8	V
V_{IK}	Input clamp voltage	V_{CC} = MIN, I_I = −12 mA			−1.5	V
V_{OH}	High-level output voltage	V_{CC} = MIN, V_{IH} = 2 V, V_{IL} = 0.8 V, I_{OH} = −800 µA	2.4	3.4		V
V_{OL}	Low-level output voltage	V_{CC} = MIN, V_{IH} = 2 V, V_{IL} = 0.8 V, I_{OL} = 16 mA		0.2	0.4	V
I_I	Input current at maximum input voltage	V_{CC} = MAX, V_I = 5.5 V			1	mA
I_{IH}	High-level input current	V_{CC} = MAX, V_I = 2.4 V			40	µA
I_{IL}	Low-level input current	V_{CC} = MAX, V_I = 0.4 V			1.6	mA
I_{OS}	Short-circuit output current[§]	V_{CC} = MAX SN54195	−20		−57	mA
		SN74195	−18		−57	
I_{CC}	Supply current	V_{CC} = MAX, See Note 2		39	63	mA

[†]For conditions shown as MIN or MAX, use the appropriate value specified under recommended operating conditions.
[‡]All typical values are at V_{CC} = 5 V, T_A = 25°C.
[§]Not more than one output should be shorted at a time.
NOTE 2: With all outputs open, shift/load grounded, and 4.5 V applied to the J, $\overline{K}$, and data inputs, I_{CC} is measured by applying a momentary ground, followed by 4.5 V, to clear and then applying a momentary ground, followed by 4.5 V, to clock.

switching characteristics, V_{CC} = 5 V, T_A = 25°C

PARAMETER		TEST CONDITIONS	MIN	TYP	MAX	UNIT
f_{max}	Maximum clock frequency	C_L = 15 pF, R_L = 400 Ω, See Figure 1	30	39		MHz
t_{PHL}	Propagation delay time, high-to-low-level output from clear			19	30	ns
t_{PLH}	Propagation delay time, low-to-high-level output from clock			14	22	ns
t_{PHL}	Propagation delay time, high-to-low-level output from clock			17	26	ns

3

TTL DEVICES

TEXAS
INSTRUMENTS

TYPES SN54LS195A, SN74LS195A
4-BIT PARALLEL-ACCESS SHIFT REGISTERS

absolute maximum ratings over operating free-air temperature range (unless otherwise noted)

Supply voltage, V_{CC} (see Note 1) . . . . 7 V
Input voltage . . . . 7 V
Operating free-air temperature range: SN54LS195A . . . . −55°C to 125°C
                                 SN74LS195A . . . . 0°C to 70°C
Storage temperature range . . . . −65°C to 150°C

NOTE 1: Voltage values are with respect to network ground terminal.

recommended operating conditions

		SN54LS195A MIN	NOM	MAX	SN74LS195A MIN	NOM	MAX	UNIT
Supply voltage, V_{CC}		4.5	5	5.5	4.75	5	5.25	V
High-level output current, I_{OH}				−400			−400	μA
Low-level output current, I_{OL}				4			8	mA
Clock frequency, f_{clock}		0		30	0		30	MHz
Width of clock or clear pulse, $t_{w(clock)}$		16			16			ns
Width of clear input pulse, $t_{w(clear)}$		12			12			ns
Setup time, t_{su} (see Figure 1)	Shift/load	25			25			ns
	Serial and parallel data	15			15			
	Clear inactive-state	25			25			
Shift/load release time, $t_{release}$ (see Figure 1)				20			20	ns
Serial and parallel data hold time, t_h (see Figure 1)		0			0			ns
Operating free-air temperature, T_A		−55		125	0		70	°C

electrical characteristics over recommended operating free-air temperature range (unless otherwise noted)

PARAMETER		TEST CONDITIONS[†]	SN54LS195A MIN	TYP[‡]	MAX	SN74LS195A MIN	TYP[‡]	MAX	UNIT
V_{IH}	High-level input voltage		2			2			V
V_{IL}	Low-level input voltage				0.7			0.8	V
V_{IK}	Input clamp voltage	V_{CC} = MIN, I_I = −18 mA			−1.5			−1.5	V
V_{OH}	High-level output voltage	V_{CC} = MIN, V_{IH} = 2 V, V_{IL} = V_{IL} max, I_{OH} = −400 μA	2.5	3.4		2.7	3.4		V
V_{OL}	Low-level output voltage	V_{CC} = MIN, V_{IH} = 2 V, V_{IL} = V_{IL} max I_{OL} = 4 mA		0.25	0.4		0.25	0.4	V
		I_{OL} = 8 mA					0.35	0.5	
I_I	Input current at maximum input voltage	V_{CC} = MAX, V_I = 7 V			0.1			0.1	mA
I_{IH}	High-level input current	V_{CC} = MAX, V_I = 2.7 V			20			20	μA
I_{IL}	Low-level input current	V_{CC} = MAX, V_I = 0.4 V			−0.4			−0.4	mA
I_{OS}	Short-circuit output current[§]	V_{CC} = MAX	−20		−100	−20		−100	mA
I_{CC}	Supply current	V_{CC} = MAX, See Note 2		14	21		14	21	mA

[†]For conditions shown as MIN or MAX, use the appropriate value specified under recommended operating conditions.
[‡]All typical values are at V_{CC} = 5 V, T_A = 25°C.
[§]Not more than one output should be shorted at a time, and duration of the short-circuit should not exceed one second.
NOTE 2: With all outputs open, shift/load grounded, and 4.5 V applied to the J, K, and data inputs, I_{CC} is measured by applying a momentary ground, followed by 4.5 V, to clear and then applying a momentary ground, followed by 4.5 V, to clock

switching characteristics, V_{CC} = 5 V, T_A = 25°C

PARAMETER	TEST CONDITIONS	MIN	TYP	MAX	UNIT
f_{max} Maximum clock frequency	C_L = 15 pF, R_L = 2 kΩ, See Figure 1	30	39		MHz
t_{PHL} Propagation delay time, high-to-low-level output from clear			19	30	ns
t_{PLH} Propagation delay time, low-to-high-level output from clock			14	22	ns
t_{PHL} Propagation delay time, high-to-low-level output from clock			17	26	ns

TEXAS
INSTRUMENTS

3

TTL DEVICES

absolute maximum ratings over operating free-air temperature range (unless otherwise noted)

Supply voltage, V_{CC} (see Note 1) . . . . 7 V
Input voltage . . . . 5.5 V
Operating free-air temperature range: SN54S195 . . . . $-55°C$ to $125°C$
                                     SN74S195 . . . . $0°C$ to $70°C$
Storage temperature range . . . . $-65°C$ to $150°C$

NOTE 1: Voltage values are with respect to network ground terminal.

recommended operating conditions

		SN54S195			SN74S195			UNIT
		MIN	NOM	MAX	MIN	NOM	MAX	
Supply voltage, V_{CC}		4.5	5	5.5	4.75	5	5.25	V
High-level output current, I_{OH}				-1			-1	mA
Low-level output current, I_{OL}				20			20	mA
Clock frequency, f_{clock}		0		70	0		70	MHz
Width of clock input pulse, $t_{w(clock)}$		7			7			ns
Width of clear input pulse, $t_{w(clear)}$		12			12			ns
Setup time, t_{su} (see Figure 1)	Shift/load	11			11			ns
	Serial and parallel data	5			5			
	Clear inactive-state	9			9			
Shift/load release time, $t_{release}$ (see Figure 1)				6			6	ns
Serial and parallel data hold time, t_h (see Figure 1)		3			3			ns
Operating free-air temperature, T_A		-55		125	0		70	$°C$

electrical characteristics over recommended operating free-air temperature range (unless otherwise noted)

PARAMETER		TEST CONDITIONS[†]		MIN	TYP[‡]	MAX	UNIT
V_{IH}	High-level input voltage			2			V
V_{IL}	Low-level input voltage					0.8	V
V_{IK}	Input clamp voltage	V_{CC} = MIN,	$I_I = -18$ mA			-1.2	V
V_{OH}	High-level output voltage	V_{CC} = MIN, V_{IH} = 2 V,	SN54S195	2.5	3.4		V
		V_{IL} = 0.8 V, $I_{OH} = -1$ mA	SN74S195	2.7	3.4		
V_{OL}	Low-level output voltage	V_{CC} = MIN, V_{IH} = 2 V, V_{IL} = 0.8 V, I_{OL} = 20 mA				0.5	V
I_I	Input current at maximum input voltage	V_{CC} = MAX,	V_I = 5.5 V			1	mA
I_{IH}	High-level input current	V_{CC} = MAX,	V_I = 2.7 V			50	µA
I_{IL}	Low-level input current	V_{CC} = MAX,	V_I = 0.5 V			-2	mA
I_{OS}	Short-circuit output current[§]	V_{CC} = MAX		-40		-100	mA
I_{CC}	Supply current	V_{CC} = MAX, See Note 2	SN54S195		70	99	mA
			SN74S195		70	109	

[†] For conditions shown as MIN or MAX, use the appropriate value specified under recommended operating conditions.
[‡] All typical values are at V_{CC} = 5 V, $T_A = 25°C$.
[§] Not more than one output should be shorted at a time, and duration of the short-circuit should not exceed one second.
NOTE 2: With all outputs open, shift/load grounded, and 4.5 V applied to the J, $\overline{K}$, and data inputs, I_{CC} is measured by applying a momentary ground, followed by 4.5 V, to clear, and then applying a momentary ground, followed by 4.5 V, to clock.

switching characteristics, V_{CC} = 5 V, $T_A = 25°C$

PARAMETER		TEST CONDITIONS	MIN	TYP	MAX	UNIT
f_{max}	Maximum clock frequency	C_L = 15 pF, R_L = 280 Ω, See Figure 1	70	105		MHz
t_{PHL}	Propagation delay time, high-to-low-level output from clear			12.5	18.5	ns
t_{PLH}	Propagation delay time, low-to-high-level output from clock			8	12	ns
t_{PHL}	Propagation delay time, high-to-low-level output from clock			11	16.5	ns

TEXAS
INSTRUMENTS

3

TTL DEVICES

PARAMETER MEASUREMENT INFORMATION

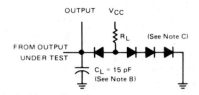

LOAD FOR OUTPUT UNDER TEST

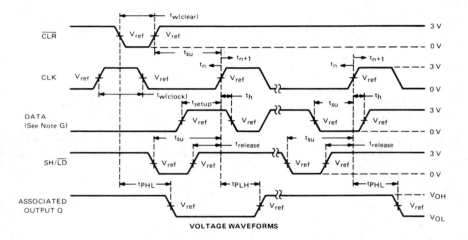

VOLTAGE WAVEFORMS

NOTES: A. The clock pulse generator has the following characteristics: $Z_{out} \approx 50\ \Omega$ and PRR $\leqslant$ 1 MHz. For '195, $t_r \leqslant$ 7 ns and $t_f \leqslant$ 7 ns.
   For 'LS195A, $t_r \leqslant$ 15 ns and $t_f \leqslant$ 6 ns. For 'S195, t_r = 2.5 ns and t_f = 2.5 ns. When testing f_{max}, vary the clock PRR.
B. C_L includes probe and jig capacitance.
C. All diodes are 1N3064 or equivalent.
D. A clear pulse is applied prior to each test.
E. For '195 and 'S195, V_{ref} = 1.5 V; for 'LS195A, V_{ref} = 1.3 V.
F. Propagation delay times (t_{PLH} and t_{PHL}) are measured at t_{n+1}. Proper shifting of data is verified at t_{n+4} with a functional test.
G. J and K inputs are tested the same as data A, B, C, and D inputs except that shift/load input remains high.
H. t_n = bit time before clocking transition.
    t_{n+1} = bit time after one clocking transition.
    t_{n+4} = bit time after four clocking transitions.

FIGURE 1—SWITCHING TIMES

TYPES SN54196, SN54197, SN54LS196, SN54LS197, SN54S196, SN54S197, SN74196, SN74197, SN74LS196, SN74LS197, SN74S196, SN74S197
50/30/100-MHz PRESETTABLE DECADE OR BINARY COUNTERS/LATCHES

OCTOBER 1976 – REVISED APRIL 1985

- Performs BCD, Bi-Quinary, or Binary Counting
- Fully Programmable
- Fully Independent Clear Input
- Input Clamping Diodes Simplify System Design
- Output Q_A Maintains Full Fan-out Capability In Addition to Driving Clock-2 Input

TYPES	GUARANTEED COUNT FREQUENCY		TYPICAL POWER DISSIPATION
	CLOCK 1	CLOCK 2	
'196, '197	0-50 MHz	0-25 MHz	240 mW
'LS196, 'LS197	0-30 MHz	0-15 MHz	80 mW
'S196, 'S197	0-100 MHz	0-50 MHz	375 mW

description

These high-speed monolithic counters consist of four d-c coupled, master-slave flip-flops, which are internally interconnected to provide either a divide-by-two and a divide-by-five counter ('196, 'LS196, 'S196) or a divide-by-two and a divide-by-eight counter ('197, 'LS197, 'S197). These four counters are fully programmable; that is, the outputs may be preset to any state by placing a low on the count/load input and entering the desired data at the data inputs. The outputs will change to agree with the data inputs independent of the state of the clocks.

During the count operation, transfer of information to the outputs occurs on the negative-going edge of the clock pulse. These counters feature a direct clear which when taken low sets all outputs low regardless of the states of the clocks.

These counters may also be used as 4-bit latches by using the count/load input as the strobe and entering data at the data inputs. The outputs will directly follow the data inputs when the count/load is low, but will remain unchanged when the count/load is high and the clock inputs are inactive.

All inputs are diode-clamped to minimize transmission-line effects and simplify system design. These circuits are compatible with most TTL logic families. Series 54, 54LS, and 54S circuits are characterized for operation over the full military temperature range of $-55°C$ to $125°C$; Series 74, 74LS, and 74S circuits are characterized for operation from $0°C$ to $70°C$.

SN54196, SN54LS196, SN54S196,
SN54197, SN54LS197, SN54S197 . . . J OR W PACKAGE
SN74196, SN74197 . . . J OR N PACKAGE
SN74LS196, SN74S196,
SN74LS197, SN74S197 . . . D, J OR N PACKAGE
(TOP VIEW)

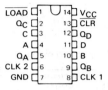

```
LOAD [1    14] VCC
  QC [2    13] CLR
   C [3    12] QD
   A [4    11] D
  QA [5    10] B
CLK 2 [6    9] QB
 GND [7    8] CLK 1
```

SN54LS196, SN54S196, SN54LS197,
SN54S197, SN74LS196, SN74S196
SN74LS197, SN74S197 . . . FK PACKAGE
(TOP VIEW)

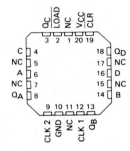

NC - No internal connection

logic symbols†

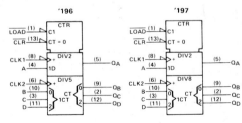

†Pin numbers shown on logic notation are for D, J or N packages.

TTL DEVICES

3

TEXAS
INSTRUMENTS

typical count configurations

'196, 'LS196, and 'S196 typical count configurations and function tables are the same as those for '176.
'197, 'LS197, and 'S197 typical count configurations and function tables are the same as those for '177.

logic diagrams

'196, 'LS196, and 'S196 logic diagrams are the same as those for '176.
'197, 'LS197, and 'S197 logic diagrams are the same as those for '177.

schematics of inputs and outputs

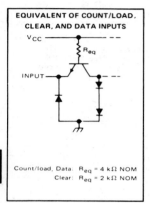

EQUIVALENT OF COUNT/LOAD, CLEAR, AND DATA INPUTS

Count/load, Data: R_{eq} = 4 kΩ NOM
Clear: R_{eq} = 2 kΩ NOM

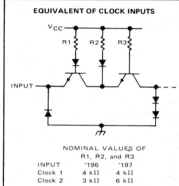

EQUIVALENT OF CLOCK INPUTS

NOMINAL VALUES OF
R1, R2, and R3

INPUT	'196	'197
Clock 1	4 kΩ	4 kΩ
Clock 2	3 kΩ	6 kΩ

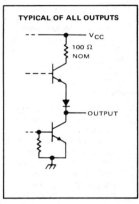

TYPICAL OF ALL OUTPUTS

100 Ω NOM

3

TTL DEVICES

TEXAS
INSTRUMENTS

absolute maximum ratings over operating free-air temperature range (unless otherwise noted)

Supply voltage, V_{CC} (see Note 1) . . . . 7 V
Input voltage . . . . 5.5 V
Interemitter voltage (see Note 2) . . . . 5.5 V
Operating free-air temperature range: SN54196, SN54197 Circuits . . . . −55°C to 125°C
　　　　　　　　　　　　　　　　　　SN74196, SN74197 Circuits . . . . 0°C to 70°C
Storage temperature range . . . . −65°C to 150°C

NOTES: 1. Voltage values are with respect to network ground terminal.
　　　　 2. This is the voltage between two emitters of a multiple-emitter transistor. For this circuit, this rating applies between the clear and
　　　　　　count/load inputs.

recommended operating conditions

		SN54196, SN54197			SN74196, SN74197			UNIT
		MIN	NOM	MAX	MIN	NOM	MAX	
Supply voltage, V_{CC}		4.5	5	5.5	4.75	5	5.25	V
High-level output current, I_{OH}				−800			−800	μA
Low-level output current, I_{OL}				16			16	mA
Count frequency	Clock-1 input	0		50	0		50	MHz
	Clock-2 input	0		25	0		25	
Pulse width, t_w	Clock-1 input	10			10			ns
	Clock-2 input	20			20			
	Clear	15			15			
	Load	20			20			
Input hold time, t_h	High-level data	t_w(load)			t_w(load)			ns
	Low-level data	t_w(load)			t_w(load)			
Input setup time, t_{su} (see Note 4)	High-level data	10			10			ns
	Low-level data	15			15			
Count enable time, t_{en} (see Note 3)		20			20			ns
Operating free-air temperature, T_A		−55		125	0		70	°C

NOTES: 3. Minimum count enable time is the interval immediately preceding the negative-going edge of the clock pulse during which interval the count/load
　　　　　　and clear inputs must both be high to ensure counting.
　　　　 4. t_{su} is measured with respect to load input.

3 TTL DEVICES

TEXAS
INSTRUMENTS

TYPES SN54196, SN54197, SN74196, SN74197
50-MHz PRESETTABLE DECADE OR BINARY COUNTERS/LATCHES

electrical characteristics over recommended operating free-air temperature range (unless otherwise noted)

PARAMETER		TEST CONDITIONS†	SN54196, SN74196 MIN	TYP‡	MAX	SN54197, SN74197 MIN	TYP‡	MAX	UNIT
V_{IH} High-level input voltage			2			2			V
V_{IL} Low-level input voltage					0.8			0.8	V
V_{IK} Input clamp voltage		V_{CC} = MIN, I_I = −12 mA			−1.5			−1.5	V
V_{OH} High-level output voltage		V_{CC} = MIN, V_{IH} = 2 V, V_{IL} = 0.8 V, I_{OH} = −800 µA	2.4	3.4		2.4	3.4		V
V_{OL} Low-level output voltage		V_{CC} = MIN, V_{IH} = 2 V, V_{IL} = 0.8 V, I_{OL} = 16 mA¶		0.2	0.4		0.2	0.4	V
I_I Input current at maximum input voltage		V_{CC} = MAX, V_I = 5.5 V			1			1	mA
I_{IH} High-level input current	Data, count/load	V_{CC} = MAX, V_I = 2.4 V			40			40	µA
	Clear, clock 1				80			80	
	Clock 2				120			80	
I_{IL} Low-level input current	Data, count/load	V_{CC} = MAX, V_I = 0.4 V			−1.6			−1.6	mA
	Clear				−3.2			−3.2	
	Clock 1				−4.8			−4.8	
	Clock 2				−6.4			−3.2	
I_{OS} Short-circuit output current§	SN54'	V_{CC} = MAX	−20		−57	−20		−57	mA
	SN74'		−18		−57	−18		−57	
I_{CC} Supply current		V_{CC} = MAX, See Note 5		48	59		48	59	mA

NOTE 5: I_{CC} is measured with all inputs grounded and all outputs open.

†For conditions shown as MIN or MAX, use the appropriate value specified under recommended operating conditions.

‡All typical values are at V_{CC} = 5 V, T_A = 25°C.

¶Q_A outputs are tested at I_{OL} = 16 mA plus the limit value of I_{IL} for the clock 2 input. This permits driving the clock-2 input while fanning out to 10 Series 54/74 loads.

§Not more than one output should be shorted at a time.

switching characteristics, V_{CC} = 5 V, T_A = 25°C

PARAMETER◊	FROM (INPUT)	TO (OUTPUT)	TEST CONDITIONS	SN54196 SN74196 MIN	TYP	MAX	SN54197 SN74197 MIN	TYP	MAX	UNIT
f_{max}	Clock 1	Q_A		50	70		50	70		MHz
t_{PLH}	Clock 1	Q_A			7	12		7	12	ns
t_{PHL}					10	15		10	15	
t_{PLH}	Clock 2	Q_B			12	18		12	18	ns
t_{PHL}					14	21		14	21	
t_{PLH}	Clock 2	Q_C	C_L = 15 pF, R_L = 400 Ω, See Note 6		24	36		24	36	ns
t_{PHL}					28	42		28	42	
t_{PLH}	Clock 2	Q_D			14	21		36	54	ns
t_{PHL}					12	18		42	63	
t_{PLH}	A, B, C, D	Q_A, Q_B, Q_C, Q_D			16	24		16	24	ns
t_{PHL}					25	38		25	38	
t_{PLH}	Load	Any			22	33		22	33	ns
t_{PHL}					24	36		24	36	
t_{PHL}	Clear	Any			25	37		25	37	ns

◊f_{max} ≡ maximum count frequency.

t_{PLH} ≡ propagation delay time, low-to-high-level output.

t_{PHL} ≡ propagation delay time, high-to-low-level output.

NOTE 6: Load circuit, input conditions, and voltage waveforms are the same as those shown for the '176, '177 except that testing f_{max}, V_{IL} = 0.3 V.

3-644

TEXAS
INSTRUMENTS

schematics of inputs and outputs

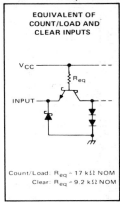

EQUIVALENT OF
COUNT/LOAD AND
CLEAR INPUTS

Count/Load: R_{eq} ~ 17 kΩ NOM
Clear: R_{eq} = 9.2 kΩ NOM

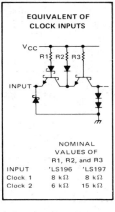

EQUIVALENT OF
CLOCK INPUTS

NOMINAL
VALUES OF
R1, R2, and R3

INPUT	'LS196	'LS197
Clock 1	8 kΩ	8 kΩ
Clock 2	6 kΩ	15 kΩ

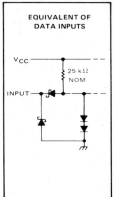

EQUIVALENT OF
DATA INPUTS

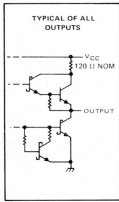

TYPICAL OF ALL
OUTPUTS

absolute maximum ratings over operating free-air temperature range (unless otherwise noted)

Supply voltage, V_{CC} (see Note 1) . . . . 7 V
Input voltage . . . . 5.5 V
Interemitter voltage (see Note 2). . . . . 5.5 V
Operating free-air temperature range: SN54LS196, SN54LS197 Circuits . . . . −55°C to 125°C
SN74LS196, SN74LS197 Circuits . . . . 0°C to 70°C
Storage temperature range . . . . −65°C to 150°C

NOTES: 1. Voltage values are with respect to network ground terminal.
2. This is the voltage between two emitters of a multiple-emitter transistor. For this circuit, this rating applies between the clear and count/load inputs.

recommended operating conditions

			SN54LS196, SN54LS197			SN74LS196, SN74LS197			UNIT
			MIN	NOM	MAX	MIN	NOM	MAX	
V_{CC}	Supply voltage		4.5	5	5.5	4.75	5	5.25	V
I_{OH}	High-level output current				−400			−400	µA
I_{OL}	Low-level output current				4			8	mA
	Count frequency	Clock-1 input	0		30	0		30	MHz
		Clock-2 input	0		15	0		15	
t_w	Pulse width	Clock-1 input	20			20			ns
		Clock-2 input	30			30			
		Clear	15			15			
		Load	20			20			
t_h	Input hold time	High-level data	10			10			ns
		Low-level data	10			10			
t_{su}	Input setup time	High-level data	10			10			ns
		Low-level data	15			15			
t_{enable}	Count enable time (see Note 3)	Clock 1	30			30			ns
		Clock 2	50			50			
T_A	Operating free-air temperature		−55		125	0		70	°C

NOTE 3: Minimum count enable time is the interval immediately preceding the negative-going edge of the clock pulse during which interval the count/load and clear inputs must both be high to ensure counting.

TEXAS
INSTRUMENTS

3

TTL DEVICES

electrical characteristics over recommended operating free-air temperature range (unless otherwise noted)

PARAMETER		TEST CONDITIONS[†]		SN54LS196 SN54LS197 MIN	TYP[‡]	MAX	SN74LS196 SN74LS197 MIN	TYP[‡]	MAX	UNIT
V_{IH} High-level input voltage				2			2			V
V_{IL} Low-level input voltage						0.7			0.8	V
V_{IK} Input clamp voltage		V_{CC} = MIN, I_I = −18 mA				−1.5			−1.5	V
V_{OH} High-level output voltage		V_{CC} = MIN, V_{IH} = 2 V, $V_{IL} = V_{IL\,max}$, I_{OH} = −400 μA		2.5	3.4		2.7	3.4		V
V_{OL} Low-level output voltage		V_{CC} = MIN, V_{IH} = 2 V, $V_{IL} = V_{IL\,max}$	I_{OL} = 4 mA[¶]		0.25	0.4		0.25	0.4	V
			I_{OL} = 8 mA[¶]					0.35	0.5	
I_I Input current at maximum input voltage	Data, count/load	V_{CC} = MAX, V_I = 5.5 V				0.1			0.1	mA
	Clear, clock 1					0.2			0.2	
	Clock 2 of 'LS196					0.4			0.4	
	Clock 2 of 'LS197					0.2			0.2	
I_{IH} High-level input current	Data, count/load	V_{CC} = MAX, V_I = 2.7 V				20			20	μA
	Clear, clock 1					40			40	
	Clock 2 of 'LS196					80			80	
	Clock 2 of 'LS197					40			40	
I_{IL} Low-level Input current	Data, count/load	V_{CC} = MAX, V_I = 0.4 V				−0.4			−0.4	mA
	Clear					−0.8			−0.8	
	Clock 1					−2.4			−2.4	
	Clock 2 of 'LS196					−2.8			−2.8	
	Clock 2 of 'LS197					−1.3			−1.3	
I_{OS} Short-circuit output current[§]		V_{CC} = MAX		−20		−100	−20		−100	mA
I_{CC} Supply current		V_{CC} = MAX, See Note 4			16	27		16	27	mA

[†]For conditions shown as MIN or MAX, use the appropriate value specified under recommended operating conditions.
[‡]All typical values are at V_{CC} = 5 V, T_A = 25°C.
[§]Not more than one output should be shorted at a time, and duration of the short-circuit should not exceed one second.
[¶]Q_A outputs are tested at specified I_{OL} plus the limit value of I_{IL} for the clock 2 input. This permits driving the clock 2 input while maintaining full fan-out capability.
NOTE 4: I_{CC} is measured with all inputs grounded and all outputs open.

switching characteristics, V_{CC} = 5 V, T_A = 25°C

PARAMETER	FROM (INPUT)	TO (OUTPUT)	TEST CONDITIONS	SN54LS196 SN74LS196 MIN	TYP	MAX	SN54LS197 SN74LS197 MIN	TYP	MAX	UNIT
f_{max}	Clock 1	Q_A		30	40		30	40		MHz
t_{PLH}	Clock 1	Q_A			8	15		8	15	ns
t_{PHL}					13	20		14	21	
t_{PLH}	Clock 2	Q_B			16	24		12	19	ns
t_{PHL}					22	33		23	35	
t_{PLH}	Clock 2	Q_C	C_L = 15 pF, R_L = 2 kΩ, See Note 5		38	57		34	51	ns
t_{PHL}					41	62		42	63	
t_{PLH}	Clock 2	Q_D			12	18		55	78	ns
t_{PHL}					30	45		63	95	
t_{PLH}	A, B, C, D	$Q_A, Q_B, Q_C Q_D$			20	30		18	27	ns
t_{PHL}					29	44		29	44	
t_{PLH}	Load	Any			27	41		26	39	ns
t_{PHL}					30	45		30	45	
t_{PHL}	Clear	Any			34	51		34	51	ns

f_{max} ≡ maximum count frequency

t_{PLH} ≡ propagation delay time, low-to-high-level output, t_{PHL} ≡ propagation delay time, high-to-low-level output
NOTE 5: Load circuit, input conditions, and voltage waveforms are the same as those shown for the '176, '177 except that t_r ≤ 15 ns, t_f ≤ 6 ns, and V_{ref} = 1.3 V (as opposed to 1.5 V)

3

TTL DEVICES

TEXAS INSTRUMENTS

schematics of inputs and outputs

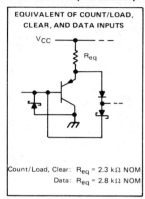

EQUIVALENT OF COUNT/LOAD, CLEAR, AND DATA INPUTS

Count/Load, Clear: R_{eq} = 2.3 kΩ NOM
Data: R_{eq} = 2.8 kΩ NOM

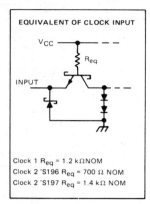

EQUIVALENT OF CLOCK INPUT

Clock 1 R_{eq} = 1.2 kΩ NOM
Clock 2 'S196 R_{eq} = 700 Ω NOM
Clock 2 'S197 R_{eq} = 1.4 kΩ NOM

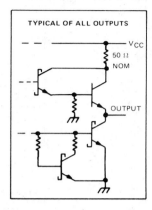

TYPICAL OF ALL OUTPUTS

50 Ω NOM

absolute maximum ratings over operating free-air temperature range (unless otherwise noted)

Supply voltage, V_{CC} (see Note 1) . . . . 7 V
Input voltage . . . . 5.5 V
Operating free-air temperature range: SN54S196, SN54S197 Circuits . . . . −55°C to 125°C
SN74S196, SN74S197 Circuits . . . . 0°C to 70°C
Storage temperature range . . . . −65°C to 150°C

NOTE 1: Voltage values are with respect to network ground terminal.

recommended operating conditions

		SN54S196, SN54S197			SN74S196, SN74S197			UNIT
		MIN	NOM	MAX	MIN	NOM	MAX	
Supply voltage, V_{CC}		4.5	5	5.5	4.75	5	5.25	V
High-level output current, I_{OH}				−1			−1	mA
Low-level output current, I_{OL}				20			20	mA
Clock frequency	Clock-1 input	0		100	0		100	MHz
	Clock-2 input	0		50	0		50	
Pulse width, t_W	Clock-1 input	5			5			ns
	Clock-2 input	10			10			
	Clear	30			30			
	Load	5			5			
Input hold time, t_h	High-level data	3↑			3↑			ns
	Low-level data	3↑			3↑			
Input setup time, t_{su} (see Note 6)	High-level data	6↑			6↑			ns
	Low-level data	6↑			6↑			
Count enable time, t_{en} (see Note 2)		12			12			ns
Operating free-air temperature, T_A		−55		125	0		70	°C

NOTES: 2. Minimum count enable time is the interval immediately preceding the negative-going edge of the clock pulse during which interval the count/load and clear inputs are both high to permit counting.
6. t_{su} is measured with respect to load input.

TEXAS
INSTRUMENTS

3

TTL DEVICES

electrical characteristics over recommended operating free-air temperature range (unless otherwise noted)

PARAMETER		TEST CONDITIONS †		SN54S196, SN74S196			SN54S197, SN74S197			UNIT
				MIN	TYP‡	MAX	MIN	TYP‡	MAX	
V_{IH}				2			2			V
V_{IL}						0.8			0.8	V
V_{IK}		V_{CC} = MIN,	I_I = −18 mA			−1.2			−1.2	V
V_{OH}		V_{CC} = MIN, V_{IH} = 2 V,	54S	2.5	3.4		2.5	3.4		V
		V_{IL} = 0.8 V, I_{OH} = −1 mA	74S	2.7	3.4		2.7	3.4		
V_{OL}		V_{CC} = MIN, V_{IH} = 2 V, V_{IL} = 0.8 V, I_{OL} = 20 mA ¶				0.5			0.5	V
I_I		V_{CC} = MAX,	V_I = 5.5 V			1			1	mA
I_{IH}	Clock 1, clock 2	V_{CC} = MAX,	V_I = 2.7 V			150			150	μA
	All other inputs					50			50	
I_{IL}	Data, count/load Clear	V_{CC} = MAX,	V_I = 0.5V			−0.75			−0.75	mA
	Clock 1					−8			−8	mA
	Clock 2					−10			−6	mA
I_{OS} §		V_{CC} = MAX		−30		−110	−30		−110	mA
I_{CC}		V_{CC} = MAX, See Note 3	54S		75	110		75	110	mA
			74S		75	120		75	120	

† For conditions shown as MIN or MAX, use the appropriate value specified under recommended operating conditions.
‡ All typical values are at V_{CC} = 5 V, T_A = 25°C.
¶ Q_A outputs are tested at I_{OL} = 20 mA plus the limit value of I_{IL} for the clock-2 input. This permits driving the clock-2 input while fanning out to 10 Series 54S/74S loads.
§ Not more than one output should be shorted at a time, and duration of the short-circuit should not exceed one second.
NOTE 3: I_{CC} is measured with all inputs grounded and all outputs open.

switching characteristics, V_{CC} = 5 V, T_A = 25°C

PARAMETER◊	(FROM (INPUT)	TO (OUTPUT)	TEST CONDITIONS	SN54S196, SN74S196			SN54S197, SN74S197			UNIT
				MIN	TYP	MAX	MIN	TYP	MAX	
f_{max}	Clock 1	Q_A		100	140		100	140		MHz
t_{PLH}	Clock 1	Q_A			5	10		5	10	ns
t_{PHL}					6	10		6	10	
t_{PLH}	Clock 2	Q_B			5	10		5	10	ns
t_{PHL}					8	12		8	12	
t_{PLH}	Clock 2	Q_C	R_L = 280 Ω, C_L = 15 pF,		12	18		12	18	ns
t_{PHL}			See Note 4		16	24		15	22	
t_{PLH}	Clock 2	Q_D			5	10		18	27	ns
t_{PHL}					8	12		22	33	
t_{PLH}	A,B,C,D	Q_A,Q_B,Q_C,Q_D			7	12		7	12	ns
t_{PHL}					12	18		12	18	
t_{PLH}	Load	Any			10	18		10	18	ns
t_{PHL}					12	18		12	18	
t_{PHL}	Clear	Any			26	37		26	37	ns

◊ f_{max} = maximum input county frequency.
t_{PLH} = propagation delay time, low-to-high-level output.
t_{PHL} = propagation delay time, high-to-low-level output.
NOTE 4: See General Information Section for load circuits and voltage waveforms.

3

TTL DEVICES

TEXAS
INSTRUMENTS

description

These 8-bit shift registers are compatible with most other TTL and MSI logic families. All inputs are buffered to lower the drive requirements to one normalized Series 54/74 load, and input clamping diodes minimize switching transients to simplify system design. Maximum input clock frequency is typically 35 megahertz and power dissipation is typically 360 mW.

Series 54 devices are characterized for operation over the full military temperature range of $-55°C$ to $125°C$; Series 74 devices are characterized for operation from $0°C$ to $70°C$.

SN54198 . . . J OR W PACKAGE
SN74198 . . . J OR N PACKAGE
(TOP VIEW)

S0	1	24	V_{CC}
SR SER	2	23	S1
A	3	22	SL SER
Q_A	4	21	H
B	5	20	Q_H
Q_B	6	19	G
C	7	18	Q_G
Q_C	8	17	F
D	9	16	Q_F
Q_D	10	15	E
CLK	11	14	Q_E
GND	12	13	$\overline{CLR}$

SN54198 and SN74198

These bidirectional registers are designed to incorporate virtually all of the features a system designer may want in a shift register. These circuits contain 87 equivalent gates and feature parallel inputs, parallel outputs, right-shift and left-shift serial inputs, operating-mode-control inputs, and a direct overriding clear line. The register has four distinct modes of operation, namely:

Inhibit Clock (Do nothing)
Shift Right (In the direction Q_A toward Q_H)
Shift Left (In the direction Q_H toward Q_A)
Parallel (Broadside) Load

Synchronous parallel loading is accomplished by applying the eight bits of data and taking both mode control inputs, S0 and S1, high. The data is loaded into the associated flip-flop and appears at the outputs after the positive transition of the clock input. During loading, serial data flow is inhibited.

Shift right is accomplished synchronously with the rising edge of the clock pulse when S0 is high and S1 is low. Serial data for this mode is entered at the shift-right data input. When S0 is low and S1 is high, data shifts left synchronously and new data is entered at the shift-left serial input.

Clocking of the flip-flop is inhibited when both mode control inputs are low. The mode controls should be changed only while the clock input is high.

'198
FUNCTION TABLE

INPUTS							OUTPUTS			
CLEAR	MODE		CLOCK	SERIAL		PARALLEL	Q_A	Q_B ...	Q_G	Q_H
	S_1	S_0		LEFT	RIGHT	A ... H				
L	X	X	X	X	X	X	L	L	L	L
H	X	X	L	X	X	X	Q_{A0}	Q_{B0}	Q_{G0}	Q_{H0}
H	H	H	↑	X	X	a ... h	a	b	g	h
H	L	H	↑	X	H	X	H	Q_{An}	Q_{Fn}	Q_{Gn}
H	L	H	↑	X	L	X	L	Q_{An}	Q_{Fn}	Q_{Gn}
H	H	L	↑	H	X	X	Q_{Bn}	Q_{Cn}	Q_{Hn}	H
H	H	L	↑	L	X	X	Q_{Bn}	Q_{Cn}	Q_{Hn}	L
H	L	L	X	X	X	X	Q_{A0}	Q_{B0}	Q_{G0}	Q_{H0}

H = high level (steady state), L = low level (steady state)
X = irrelevant (any input, including transitions)
↑ = transition from low to high level
a . . . h = the level of steady-state input at inputs A thru H, respectively.
Q_{A0}, Q_{B0}, Q_{G0}, Q_{H0} = the level of Q_A, Q_B, Q_G, or Q_H, respectively, before the indicated steady-state input conditions were established.
Q_{An}, Q_{Bn}, etc. = the level of Q_A, Q_B, etc., respectively, before the most-recent ↑ transition of the clock.

TEXAS
INSTRUMENTS

TTL DEVICES 3

SN54199 and SN74199

These registers feature parallel inputs, parallel outputs, J-$\overline{K}$ serial inputs, shift/load control input, a direct overriding clear line, and gated clock inputs. The register has three modes of operation:

> Inhibit Clock (Do nothing)
> Shift (In the direction Q_A toward Q_H)
> Parallel (Broadside) Load

Parallel loading is accomplished by applying the eight bits of data and taking the shift/load control input low when the clock input is not inhibited. The data is loaded into the associated flip-flop and appears at the outputs after the positive transition of the clock input. During loading, serial data flow is inhibited.

SN54199 . . . J OR W PACKAGE
SN74199 . . . J OR N PACKAGE
(TOP VIEW)

```
         ___
    K  [ 1   U  24 ]  VCC
           ____
    J  [ 2      23 ]  SH/LD
    A  [ 3      22 ]  H
   QA  [ 4      21 ]  QH
    B  [ 5      20 ]  G
   QB  [ 6      19 ]  QG
    C  [ 7      18 ]  F
   QC  [ 8      17 ]  QF
    D  [ 9      16 ]  E
   QD  [10      15 ]  QE
                       ___
CLK INH [11     14 ]  CLR
  GND  [12      13 ]  CLK
```

Shifting is accomplished synchronously when shift/load is high and the clock input is not inhibited. Serial data for this mode is entered at the J-$\overline{K}$ inputs. See the function table for levels required to enter serial data into the first flip-flop.

Both of the clock inputs are identical in function and may be used interchangeably to serve as clock or clock-inhibit inputs. Holding either high inhibits clocking, but when one is held low, a clock input applied to the other input is passed to the eight flip-flops of the register. The clock-inhibit input should be changed to the high level only while the clock input is high.

These shift registers contain the equivalent of 79 TTL gates. Average power dissipation per gate is typically 4.55 mW.

'199
FUNCTION TABLE

INPUTS							OUTPUTS			
CLEAR	SHIFT/ LOAD	CLOCK INHIBIT	CLOCK	SERIAL J	SERIAL $\overline{K}$	PARALLEL A...H	Q_A	Q_B	Q_C ...	Q_H
L	X	X	X	X	X	X	L	L	L	L
H	X	L	L	X	X	X	Q_{A0}	Q_{B0}	Q_{C0}	Q_{H0}
H	L	L	↑	X	X	a...h	a	b	c	h
H	H	L	↑	L	L	X	Q_{A0}	Q_{An}	Q_{Bn}	Q_{Gn}
H	H	L	↑	L	H	X	L	Q_{An}	Q_{Bn}	Q_{Gn}
H	H	L	↑	H	H	X	H	Q_{An}	Q_{Bn}	Q_{Gn}
H	H	L	↑	H	L	X	$\overline{Q}_{An}$	Q_{An}	Q_{Bn}	Q_{Gn}
H	X	H	↑	X	X	X	Q_{A0}	Q_{B0}	Q_{B0}	Q_{H0}

schematics of inputs and outputs

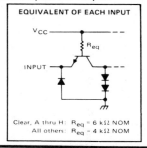

EQUIVALENT OF EACH INPUT

Clear, A thru H: R_{eq} = 6 kΩ NOM
All others: R_{eq} = 4 kΩ NOM

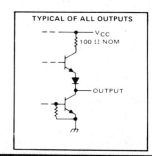

TYPICAL OF ALL OUTPUTS

TEXAS INSTRUMENTS

3
TTL DEVICES

logic diagram

'198

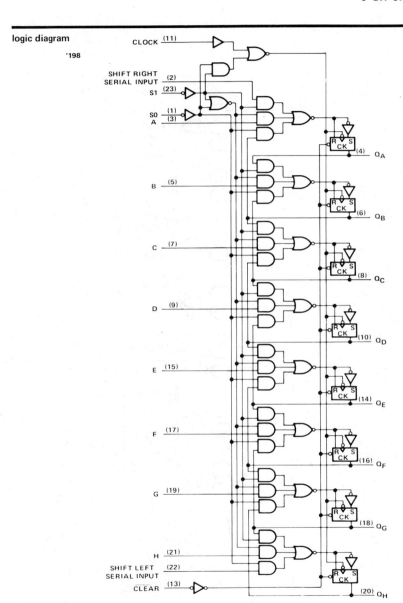

Pin numbers shown on logic notation are for J or N packages.

logic diagram

'199

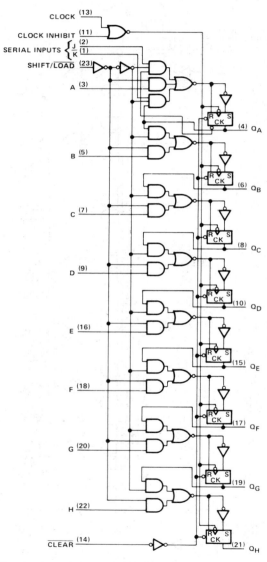

Pin numbers shown on logic notation are for J or N packages.

TEXAS
INSTRUMENTS

SN54198, SN74198

typical clear, load, right-shift, left-shift, inhibit, and clear sequences

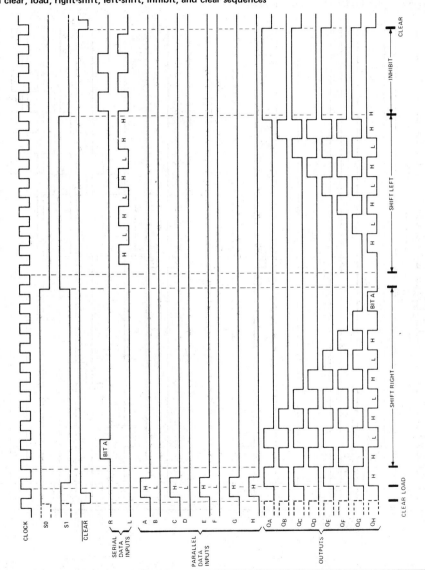

TTL DEVICES

3

SN54199, SN74199

typical clear, shift, load, and inhibit sequences

3 TTL DEVICES

CLOCK

CLOCK INHIBIT

CLEAR

SERIAL INPUTS J

K̄

SHIFT/LOAD

PARALLEL DATA INPUTS — A B C D E F G H

OUTPUT — Q_A Q_B Q_C Q_D Q_E Q_F Q_G Q_H

SERIAL SHIFT

INHIBIT

LOAD

SERIAL SHIFT

CLEAR

TEXAS
INSTRUMENTS

absolute maximum ratings over operating free-air temperature range (unless otherwise noted)

Supply voltage, V_{CC} (see Note 1)	7 V
Input voltage	5.5 V
Operating free-air temperature range: SN54' Circuits	-55°C to 125°C
SN74' Circuits	0°C to 70°C
Storage temperature range	-65°C to 150°C

NOTE 1: Voltage values are with respect to network ground terminal.

recommended operating conditions

	SN54198 SN54199			SN74198 SN74199			UNIT
	MIN	NOM	MAX	MIN	NOM	MAX	
Supply voltage, V_{CC}	4.5	5	5.5	4.75	5	5.25	V
High-level output current, I_{OH}			-800			-800	μA
Low-level output current, I_{OL}			16			16	mA
Clock frequency, f_{clock}	0		25	0		25	MHz
Width of clock or clear pulse, t_w (see Figure 1)	20			20			ns
Mode-control setup time, t_{su}	30			30			ns
Data setup time, t_{su} (see Figure 1)	20			20			ns
Hold time at any input, t_h (see Figure 1)	0			0			ns
Operating free-air temperature, T_A	-55		125	0		70	$^\circ$C

electrical characteristics over recommended operating free-air temperature range (unless otherwise noted)

PARAMETER		TEST CONDITIONS[†]	SN54198 SN54199			SN74198 SN74199			UNIT
			MIN	TYP[‡]	MAX	MIN	TYP[‡]	MAX	
V_{IH}	High-level input voltage		2			2			V
V_{IL}	Low-level input voltage				0.8			0.8	V
V_{IK}	Input clamp voltage	V_{CC} = MIN, I_I = -12 mA			-1.5			-1.5	V
V_{OH}	High-level output voltage	V_{CC} = MIN, V_{IH} = 2 V, V_{IL} = 0.8 V, I_{OH} = -800 μA	2.4	3.4		2.4	3.4		V
V_{OL}	Low-level output voltage	V_{CC} = MIN, V_{IH} = 2 V, V_{IL} = 0.8 V, I_{OL} = 16 mA		0.2	0.4		0.2	0.4	V
I_I	Input current at maximum input voltage	V_{CC} = MAX, V_I = 5.5 V			1			1	mA
I_{IH}	High-level input current	V_{CC} = MAX, V_I = 2.4 V			40			40	μA
I_{IL}	Low-level input current	V_{CC} = MAX, V_I = 0.4 V			-1.6			-1.6	mA
I_{OS}	Short-circuit output current[§]	V_{CC} = MAX	-20		-57	-18		-57	mA
I_{CC}	Supply current	V_{CC} = MAX, See Table Below		90	127		90	127	mA

[†] For conditions shown as MIN or MAX, use the appropriate value specified under recommended operating conditions.

[‡] All typical values are at V_{CC} = 5 V, T_A = 25°C.

[§] Not more than one output should be shorted at a time.

TEST CONDITIONS FOR I_{CC}
(ALL OUTPUTS ARE OPEN)

TYPE	APPLY 4.5 V	FIRST GROUND, THEN APPLY 4.5 V	GROUND
SN54198, SN74198	Serial Input, S_0, S_1	Clock	$\overline{\text{Clear}}$, Inputs A thru H
SN54199, SN74199	J, $\overline{K}$, Inputs A thru H	Clock	Clock inhibit, Clear, Shift/Load

TEXAS
INSTRUMENTS

3

TTL DEVICES

switching characteristics, V_{CC} = 5 V, T_A = 25°C

	PARAMETER	TEST CONDITIONS	MIN	TYP	MAX	UNIT
f_{max}	Maximum clock frequency		25	35		MHz
t_{PHL}	Propagation delay time, high-to-low-level output from clear	C_L = 15 pF, R_L = 400 Ω, See Figure 1		23	35	ns
t_{PHL}	Propagation delay time, high-to-low-level output from clock			20	30	ns
t_{PLH}	Propagation delay time, low-to-high-level output from clock			17	26	ns

3

TTL DEVICES

PARAMETER MEASUREMENT INFORMATION

SN54198, SN74198
TEST TABLE FOR SYNCHRONOUS INPUTS

DATA INPUT FOR TEST	S1	S0	OUTPUT TESTED (SEE NOTE E)
A	4.5 V	4.5 V	Q_A at t_{n+1}
B	4.5 V	4.5 V	Q_B at t_{n+1}
C	4.5 V	4.5 V	Q_C at t_{n+1}
D	4.5 V	4.5 V	Q_D at t_{n+1}
E	4.5 V	4.5 V	Q_E at t_{n+1}
F	4.5 V	4.5 V	Q_F at t_{n+1}
G	4.5 V	4.5 V	Q_G at t_{n+1}
H	4.5 V	4.5 V	Q_H at t_{n+1}
L Serial Input	4.5 V	0 V	Q_A at t_{n+8}
R Serial Input	0 V	4.5 V	Q_H at t_{n+8}

SN54199, SN74199
TEST TABLE FOR SYNCHRONOUS INPUTS

DATA INPUT FOR TEST	SHIFT/$\overline{LOAD}$	OUTPUT TESTED (SEE NOTE E)
A	0 V	Q_A at t_{n+1}
B	0 V	Q_B at t_{n+1}
C	0 V	Q_C at t_{n+1}
D	0 V	Q_D at t_{n+1}
E	0 V	Q_E at t_{n+1}
F	0 V	Q_F at t_{n+1}
G	0 V	Q_G at t_{n+1}
H	0 V	Q_H at t_{n+1}
J and $\overline{K}$	4.5 V	Q_H at t_{n+8}

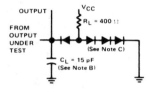

LOAD FOR OUTPUT UNDER TEST

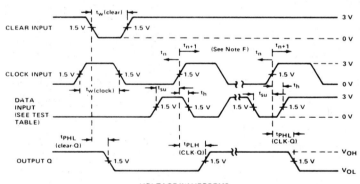

VOLTAGE WAVEFORMS

NOTES:
A. The clock pulse has the following characteristics: $t_{w(clock)} \geq$ 20 ns and PRR = 1 MHz. The clear pulse has the following characteristics: $t_{w(clear)} \geq$ 20 ns and t_{hold} = 0 ns. When testing f_{max}, vary the clock PRR.
B. C_L includes probe and jig capacitance.
C. All diodes are 1N3064.
D. A clear pulse is applied prior to each test.
E. Propagation delay times (t_{PLH} and t_{PHL}) are measured at t_{n+1}. Proper shifting of data is verified at t_{n+8} with a functional test.
F. t_n = bit time before clocking transition
  t_{n+1} = bit time after one clocking transition
  t_{n+8} = bit time after eight clocking transitions

FIGURE 1

- **SN54221, SN54LS221, SN74221 and SN74LS221 Are Dual Versions of Highly Stable SN54121, SN74121 One-Shots on a Monolithic Chip**

- **SN54221 and SN74221 Demonstrate Electrical and Switching Characteristics That Are Virtually Identical to the SN54121, SN74121 One-Shots**

- **Pin-Out Is Identical to the SN54123, SN74123, SN54LS123, SN74LS123**

- **Overriding Clear Terminates Output Pulse**

TYPE	TYPICAL POWER DISSIPATION	MAXIMUM OUTPUT PULSE LENGTH
SN54221	130 mW	21 s
SN74221	130 mW	28 s
SN54LS221	23 mW	49 s
SN74LS221	23 mW	70 s

SN54221, SN54LS221 . . . J OR W PACKAGE
SN74221 . . . J OR N PACKAGE
SN74LS221 . . . D, J OR N PACKAGE
(TOP VIEW)

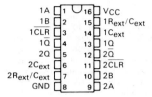

SN54LS221 . . . FK PACKAGE
SN74LS221
(TOP VIEW)

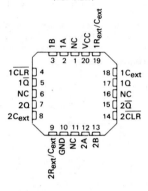

description

The '221 and 'LS221 are monolithic dual multivibrators with performance characteristics virtually identical to those of the '121. Each multivibrator features a negative-transition-triggered input and a positive-transition-triggered input either of which can be used as an inhibit input.

Pulse triggering occurs at a particular voltage level and is not directly related to the transition time of the input pulse. Schmitt-trigger input circuitry (TTL hysteresis) for B input allows jitter-free triggering from inputs with transition rates as slow as 1 volt/second, providing the circuit with excellent noise immunity of typically 1.2 volts. A high immunity to V_{CC} noise of typically 1.5 volts is also provided by internal latching circuitry.

Once fired, the outputs are independent of further transitions of the A and B inputs and are a function of the timing components, or the output pulses can be terminated by the overriding clear. Input pulses may be of any duration relative to the output pulse. Output pulse length may be varied from 35 nanoseconds to the maximums shown in the above table by choosing appropriate timing components. With $R_{ext} = 2 k\Omega$ and $C_{ext} = 0$, an output pulse of typically 30 nanoseconds is achieved which may be used as a d-c-triggered reset signal. Output rise and fall times are TTL compatible and independent of pulse length. Typical triggering and clearing sequences are illustrated as a part of the switching characteristics waveforms.

FUNCTION TABLE
(EACH MONOSTABLE)

INPUTS			OUTPUTS	
CLEAR	A	B	Q	Q̄
L	X	X	L	H
X	H	X	L	H
X	X	L	L	H
H	L	↑	⊓	⊔
H	↓	H	⊓	⊔
↑ *	L	H	⊓	⊔

Also see description and switching characteristics

* This condition is true only if the output of the latch formed by the two NAND gates has been conditioned to the logical "1" state prior to CLR going high. This latch is conditioned by taking either A high or B low which $\overline{CLR}$ is in the inactive state.

TEXAS
INSTRUMENTS

3

TTL DEVICES

description (continued)

Pulse width stability is achieved through internal compensation and is virtually independent of V_{CC} and temperature. In most applications, pulse stability will only be limited by the accuracy of external timing components.

Jitter-free operation is maintained over the full temperature and V_{CC} ranges for more than six decades of timing capacitance (10 pF to 10 μF) and more than one decade of timing resistance (2 kΩ to 30 kΩ for the SN54221, 2 kΩ to 40 kΩ for the SN74221, 2 kΩ to 70 kΩ for the SN54LS221, and 2 kΩ to 100 kΩ for the SN74LS221). Throughout these ranges, pulse width is defined by the relationship: $t_{w(out)} = C_{ext}R_{ext}$ $ln2 \approx 0.7$ $C_{ext}R_{ext}$. In circuits where pulse cutoff is not critical, timing capacitance up to 1000 μF and timing resistance as low as 1.4 kΩ may be used. Also, the range of jitter-free output pulse widths is extended if V_{CC} is held to 5 volts and free-air temperature is 25°C. Duty cycles as high as 90% are achieved when using maximum recommended R_T. Higher duty cycles are available if a certain amount of pulse-width jitter is allowed.

The variance in output pulse width from device to device is typically less than ± 0.5% for given external timing components. An example of this distribution for the '221 is shown in Figure 2. Variations in output pulse width versus supply voltage and temperature for the '221 are shown in Figure 3 and 4, respectively.

Pin assignments for these devices are identical to those of the SN54123/SN74123 or SN54LS123/SN74LS123 so that the '221 or 'LS221 can be substituted for those products in systems not using the retrigger by merely changing the value of R_{ext} and/or C_{ext}, however the polarity of the capacitor will have to be changed.

TIMING COMPONENT CONNECTIONS

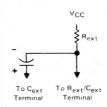

V_CC

R_ext

To C_ext Terminal   To R_ext/C_ext Terminal

NOTE: Due to the internal circuit, the R_{ext}/C_{ext} pin will never be more positive than the C_{ext} pin.
Pin numbers shown on logic notation are for D, J or N packages.

LOGIC SYMBOL

1A	(1)	
1B	(2)	&
1CLR	(3)	R
1C_ext	(14)	CX
1R_ext/C_ext	(15)	RX/CX
		(13) 1Q
		(4) 1Q̄
2A	(9)	
2B	(10)	&
2CLR	(11)	R
2C_ext	(6)	CX
2R_ext/C_ext	(7)	RX/CX
		(5) 2Q
		(12) 2Q̄

schematics of inputs and outputs

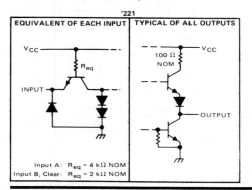

'221

EQUIVALENT OF EACH INPUT

V_CC
R_eq
INPUT

TYPICAL OF ALL OUTPUTS

100 Ω NOM
V_CC
OUTPUT

Input A: R_{eq} = 4 kΩ NOM
Input B, Clear: R_{eq} = 2 kΩ NOM

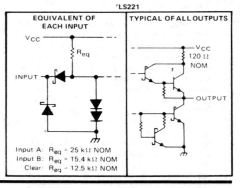

'LS221

EQUIVALENT OF EACH INPUT

V_CC
R_eq
INPUT

TYPICAL OF ALL OUTPUTS

V_CC
120 Ω NOM
OUTPUT

Input A: R_{eq} = 25 kΩ NOM
Input B: R_{eq} = 15.4 kΩ NOM
Clear: R_{eq} = 12.5 kΩ NOM

TEXAS INSTRUMENTS

3

TTL DEVICES

recommended operating conditions

		SN54221			SN74221			UNIT
		MIN	NOM	MAX	MIN	NOM	MAX	
Supply voltage, V_{CC}		4.5	5	5.5	4.75	5	5.25	V
High-level output current, I_{OH}				−800			−800	μA
Low-level output current, I_{OL}				16			16	mA
Rate of rise or fall of input pulse, dv/dt	Schmitt input, B	1			1			V/s
	Logic input, A	1			1			V/μs
Input pulse width	A or B, $t_{w(in)}$	50			50			ns
	Clear, $t_{w(clear)}$	20			20			
Clear-inactive-state setup time, t_{su}		15			15			ns
External timing resistance, R_{ext}		1.4		30	1.4		40	kΩ
External timing capacitance, C_{ext}		0		1000	0		1000	μF
Output duty cycle	$R_{ext} = 2\ k\Omega$			67			67	%
	$R_{ext} = MAX\ R_{ext}$			90			90	
Operating free-air temperature, T_A		−55		125	0		70	°C

electrical characteristics over recommended operating free-air temperature range (unless otherwise noted)

	PARAMETER	TEST CONDITIONS[†]		MIN	TYP[‡]	MAX	UNIT
V_{T+}	Positive-going threshold voltage at A input	$V_{CC} = MIN$			1.4	2	V
V_{T-}	Negative-going threshold voltage at A input	$V_{CC} = MIN$		0.8	1.4		V
V_{T+}	Positive-going threshold voltage at B input	$V_{CC} = MIN$			1.55	2	V
V_{T-}	Negative-going threshold voltage at B input	$V_{CC} = MIN$		0.8	1.35		V
V_{IK}	Input clamp voltage	$V_{CC} = MIN$, $I_I = -12\ mA$				−1.5	V
V_{OH}	High-level output voltage	$V_{CC} = MIN$, $I_{OH} = -800\ \mu A$		2.4	3.4		V
V_{OL}	Low-level output voltage	$V_{CC} = MIN$, $I_{OL} = 16\ mA$			0.2	0.4	V
I_I	Input current at maximum input voltage	$V_{CC} = MAX$, $V_I = 5.5\ V$				1	mA
I_{IH}	High-level input current	$V_{CC} = MAX$, $V_I = 2.4\ V$	Input A			40	μA
			Input B, Clear			80	
I_{IL}	Low-level input current	$V_{CC} = MAX$, $V_I = 0.4\ V$	Input A			−1.6	mA
			Input B, Clear			−3.2	
I_{OS}	Short-circuit output current[§]	$V_{CC} = MAX$	SN54221	−20		−55	mA
			SN74221	−18		−55	
I_{CC}	Supply current	$V_{CC} = MAX$	Quiescent		26	50	mA
			Triggered		46	80	

[†]For conditions shown as MIN or MAX, use the appropriate value specified under recommended operating conditions.
[‡]All typical values are at $V_{CC} = 5\ V$, $T_A = 25°C$.
[§]Not more than one output should be shorted at a time.

switching characteristics, $V_{CC} = 5\ V$, $T_A = 25°C$

PARAMETER[¶]	FROM (INPUT)	TO (OUTPUT)	TEST CONDITIONS		MIN	TYP	MAX	UNIT
t_{PLH}	A	Q				45	70	ns
	B	Q				35	55	
t_{PHL}	A	$\overline{Q}$	$C_{ext} = 80\ pF$, $R_{ext} = 2\ k\Omega$			50	80	ns
	B	$\overline{Q}$				40	65	
t_{PHL}	Clear	Q	$C_L = 15\ pF$,				27	ns
t_{PLH}	Clear	$\overline{Q}$	$R_L = 400\ \Omega$, See Figure 1				40	ns
$t_{w(out)}$	A or B	Q or $\overline{Q}$	and Note 2	$C_{ext} = 80\ pF$, $R_{ext} = 2\ k\Omega$	70	110	150	ns
				$C_{ext} = 0$, $R_{ext} = 2\ k\Omega$	20	30	50	
				$C_{ext} = 100\ pF$, $R_{ext} = 10\ k\Omega$	650	700	750	
				$C_{ext} = 1\ \mu F$, $R_{ext} = 10\ k\Omega$	6.5	7	7.5	ms

[¶]$t_{PLH} \equiv$ Propagation delay time, low-to-high-level output
$t_{PHL} \equiv$ Propagation delay time, high-to-low-level output
$t_{w(out)} \equiv$ Output pulse width
NOTE 2: See General Information Section for load circuits and voltage waveforms.

TEXAS
INSTRUMENTS

TTL DEVICES

3

recommended operating conditions

		SN54LS221			SN74LS221			UNIT
		MIN	NOM	MAX	MIN	NOM	MAX	
Supply voltage, V_{CC}		4.5	5	5.5	4.75	5	5.25	V
High-level output current, I_{OH}				−400			−400	μA
Low-level output current, I_{OL}				4			8	mA
Rate of rise or fall of input pulse, dv/dt	Schmitt, B	1			1			V/s
	Logic input, A	1			1			V/μs
Input pulse width	A or B, $t_{w(in)}$	50			50			ns
	Clear, $t_{w(clear)}$	40			40			
Clear-inactive-state setup time, t_{su}		15			15			ns
External timing resistance, R_{ext}		1.4		70	1.4		100	kΩ
External timing capacitance, C_{ext}		0		1000	0		1000	μF
Output duty cycle	R_T = 2 kΩ			50			50	%
	R_T = MAX R_{ext}			90			90	
Operating free-air temperature, T_A		−55		125	0		70	°C

electrical characteristics over recommended operating free-air temperature range (unless otherwise noted)

PARAMETER		TEST CONDITIONS[†]		SN54LS221			SN74LS221			UNIT
				MIN	TYP[‡]	MAX	MIN	TYP[‡]	MAX	
V_{T+}	Positive-going threshold voltage at A input	V_{CC} = MIN			1.0	2		1.0	2	V
V_{T-}	Negative-going threshold voltage at A input	V_{CC} = MIN		0.7	1.0		0.8	1.0		V
V_{T+}	Positive-going threshold voltage at B input	V_{CC} = MIN			1.0	2		1.0	2	V
V_{T-}	Negative-going threshold voltage at B input	V_{CC} = MIN		0.7	0.9		0.8	0.9		V
V_{IK}	Input clamp voltage	V_{CC} = MIN, I_I = −18 mA				−1.5			−1.5	V
V_{OH}	High-level output voltage	V_{CC} = MIN, I_{OH} = −400 μA		2.5	3.4		2.7	3.4		V
V_{OL}	Low-level output voltage	V_{CC} = MIN	I_{OL} = 4 mA		0.25	0.4		0.25	0.4	V
			I_{OL} = 8 mA					0.35	0.5	
I_I	Input current at maximum input voltage	V_{CC} = MAX, V_I = 7 V				0.1			0.1	mA
I_{IH}	High-level input current	V_{CC} = MAX, V_I = 2.7 V				20			20	μA
I_{IL}	Low-level input current	Input A	V_{CC} = MAX, V_I = 0.4 V			−0.4			−0.4	mA
		Input B				−0.8			−0.8	
		Clear				−0.8			−0.8	
I_{OS}	Short-circuit output current[§]	V_{CC} = MAX		−20		−100	−20		−100	mA
I_{CC}	Supply current	V_{CC} = MAX	Quiescent		4.7	11		4.7	11	mA
			Triggered		19	27		19	27	

[†]For conditions shown as MIN or MAX, use the appropriate value specified under recommended operating conditions.
[‡]All typical values are at V_{CC} = 5 V, T_A = 25°C.
[§]Not more than one output should be shorted at a time and duration of the short-circuit should not exceed one second.

TEXAS
INSTRUMENTS

switching characteristics, V_{CC} = 5 V, T_A = 25°C

PARAMETER[¶]	FROM (INPUT)	TO (OUTPUT)	TEST CONDITIONS		MIN	TYP	MAX	UNIT
t_{PLH}	A	Q	C_L = 15 pF, R_L = 2 kΩ, See Figure 1 and Note 3	C_{ext} = 80 pF, R_{ext} = 2 kΩ		45	70	ns
	B	Q				35	55	
t_{PHL}	A	$\overline{Q}$				50	80	ns
	B	$\overline{Q}$				40	65	
t_{PHL}	Clear	Q				35	55	ns
t_{PLH}	Clear	$\overline{Q}$				44	65	ns
$t_{w(out)}$	A or B	Q or $\overline{Q}$		C_{ext} = 80 pF, R_{ext} = 2 kΩ	70	120	150	ns
				C_{ext} = 0, R_{ext} = 2 kΩ	20	47	70	
				C_{ext} = 100 pF, R_{ext} = 10 kΩ	670	740	810	
				C_{ext} = 1 μF, R_{ext} = 10 kΩ	6	6.9	7.5	ms

[¶] t_{PLH} ≡ Propagation delay time, low-to-high-level output
t_{PHL} ≡ Propagation delay time, high-to-low-level output
$t_{w(out)}$ ≡ Output pulse width

NOTE 3: See General Information Section for load circuits and voltage waveforms.

3

PARAMETER MEASUREMENT INFORMATION

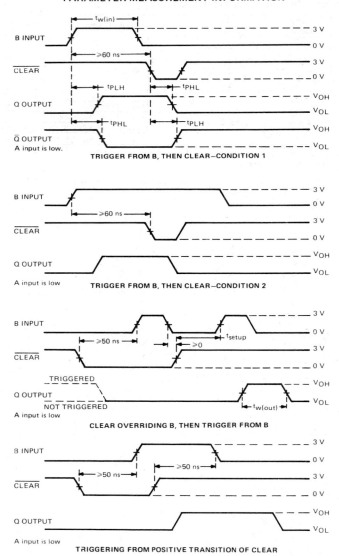

TRIGGER FROM B, THEN CLEAR—CONDITION 1

TRIGGER FROM B, THEN CLEAR—CONDITION 2

CLEAR OVERRIDING B, THEN TRIGGER FROM B

TRIGGERING FROM POSITIVE TRANSITION OF CLEAR

FIGURE 1—SWITCHING CHARACTERISTICS

TEXAS
INSTRUMENTS

PARAMETER MEASUREMENT INFORMATION

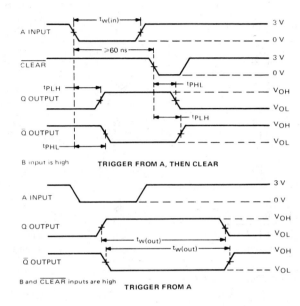

TRIGGER FROM A, THEN CLEAR

B input is high

TRIGGER FROM A

B and CLEAR inputs are high

3

TTL DEVICES

NOTES: A. Input pulses are supplied by generators having the following characteristics: PRR ≤ 1 MHz, $Z_{out} \approx 50\ \Omega$; for '221, $t_r \le 7$ ns, $t_f \le 7$ ns, for 'LS221, $t_r \le 15$ ns, $t_f \le 6$ ns.
B. All measurements are made between the 1.5 V points of the indicated transitions for the '221 or between the 1.3 V points for the 'LS221.

FIGURE 1—SWITCHING CHARACTERISTICS (CONTINUED)

TEXAS
INSTRUMENTS

TYPICAL CHARACTERISTICS ('221 ONLY)†

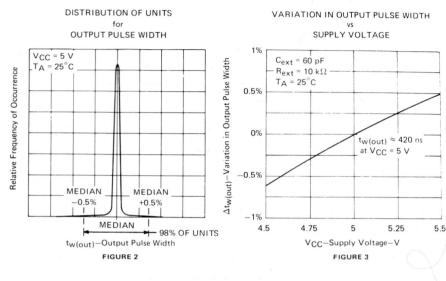

DISTRIBUTION OF UNITS
for
OUTPUT PULSE WIDTH

FIGURE 2

VARIATION IN OUTPUT PULSE WIDTH
vs
SUPPLY VOLTAGE

FIGURE 3

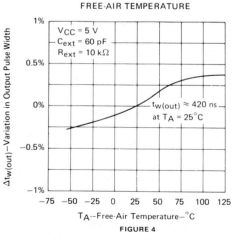

VARIATION IN OUTPUT PULSE WIDTH
vs
FREE-AIR TEMPERATURE

FIGURE 4

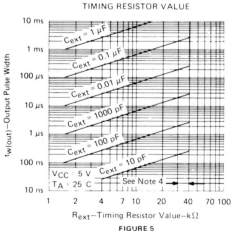

OUTPUT PULSE WIDTH
vs
TIMING RESISTOR VALUE

FIGURE 5

NOTE 4: These values of resistance exceed the maximum recommended for use over the full temperature range of the SN54221

†Data for temperatures below 0°C and above 70°C, and for supply voltages below 4.75 V and above 5.25 V are applicable for the SN54221 only.

TEXAS
INSTRUMENTS

TYPES SN54LS240, SN54LS241, SN54LS244, SN54S240, SN54S241, SN54S244, SN74LS240, SN74LS241, SN74LS244, SN74S240, SN74S241, SN74S244
OCTAL BUFFERS AND LINE DRIVERS WITH 3-STATE OUTPUTS

REVISED APRIL 1985

- **3-State Outputs Drive Bus Lines or Buffer Memory Address Registers**
- **PNP Inputs Reduce D-C Loading**
- **Hysteresis at Inputs Improves Noise Margins**

description

These octal buffers and line drivers are designed specifically to improve both the performance and density of three-state memory address drivers, clock drivers, and bus-oriented receivers and transmitters. The designer has a choice of selected combinations of inverting and noninverting outputs, symmetrical $\overline{G}$ (active-low output control) inputs, and complementary G and $\overline{G}$ inputs. These devices feature high fan-out, improved fan-in, and 400-mV noise-margin. The SN74LS' and SN74S' can be used to drive terminated lines down to 133 ohms.

The SN54' family is characterized for operation over the full military temperature range of $-55°C$ to $125°C$. The SN74' family is characterized for operation from $0°C$ to $70°C$.

SN54LS', SN54S' . . . J PACKAGE
SN74LS', SN74S' . . . DW, J OR N PACKAGE
(TOP VIEW)

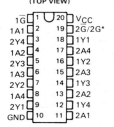

SN54LS', SN54S' . . . FK PACKAGE
SN74LS', SN74S'
(TOP VIEW)

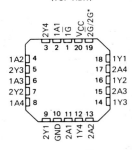

*2G for 'LS241 and 'S241 or $\overline{2G}$ for all other drivers.

schematics of inputs and outputs

'LS240, 'LS241, 'LS244	'S240, 'S241, 'S244	
EQUIVALENT OF EACH INPUT	EQUIVALENT OF EACH INPUT	TYPICAL OF ALL OUTPUTS

G and $\overline{G}$ inputs: $R_{eq} = 2$ kΩ NOM
A inputs: $R_{eq} = 2.8$ kΩ NOM

'LS240, 'LS241, 'LS244;
R = 50 Ω NOM
'S240, 'S241, 'S244
R = 25 Ω NOM

TEXAS INSTRUMENTS

TTL DEVICES

3

TYPES SN54LS240, SN54LS241, SN54LS244, SN54S240, SN54S241, SN54S244, SN74LS240, SN74LS241, SN74LS244, SN74S240, SN74S241, SN74S244
OCTAL BUFFERS AND LINE DRIVERS WITH 3-STATE OUTPUTS

logic symbols

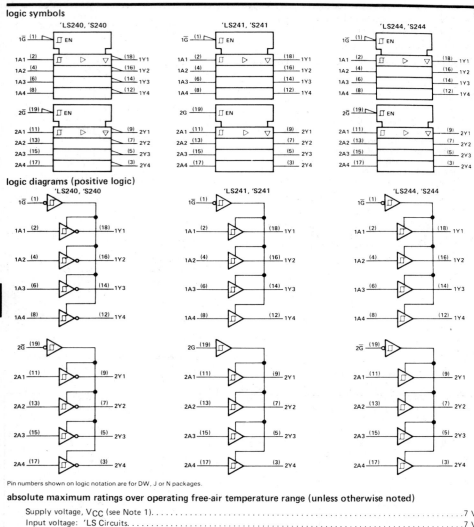

logic diagrams (positive logic)

Pin numbers shown on logic notation are for DW, J or N packages.

absolute maximum ratings over operating free-air temperature range (unless otherwise noted)

Supply voltage, V_{CC} (see Note 1)... 7 V
Input voltage: 'LS Circuits... 7 V
'S Circuits... 5.5 V
Off-state output voltage... 5.5 V
Operating free-air temperature range: SN54LS', SN54S' Circuits............................... −55°C to 125°C
SN74LS', SN74S' Circuits............................... 0°C to 70°C
Storage temperature range... −65°C to 150°C

NOTE 1: Voltage values are with respect to network ground terminal.

TYPES SN54LS240, SN54LS241, SN54LS244, SN74LS240, SN74LS241, SN74LS244
OCTAL BUFFERS AND LINE DRIVERS WITH 3-STATE OUTPUTS

recommended operating conditions

PARAMETER		SN54LS' MIN	SN54LS' NOM	SN54LS' MAX	SN74LS' MIN	SN74LS' NOM	SN74LS' MAX	UNIT
V_{CC}	Supply voltage (see Note 1)	4.5	5	5.5	4.75	5	5.25	V
V_{IH}	High-level input voltage	2			2			V
V_{IL}	Low-level input voltage			0.7			0.8	V
I_{OH}	High-level output current			-12			-15	mA
I_{OL}	Low-level output current			12			24	mA
T_A	Operating free-air temperature	-55		125	0		70	°C

NOTE 1: Voltage values are with respect to network ground terminal.

electrical characteristics over recommended operating free-air temperature range (unless otherwise noted)

PARAMETER		TEST CONDITIONS†			SN54LS' MIN	SN54LS' TYP‡	SN54LS' MAX	SN74LS' MIN	SN74LS' TYP‡	SN74LS' MAX	UNIT
V_{IK}		V_{CC} = MIN,	$I_I = -18$ mA				-1.5			-1.5	V
Hysteresis $(V_{T+} - V_{T-})$		V_{CC} = MIN			0.2	0.4		0.2	0.4		V
V_{OH}		V_{CC} = MIN, $I_{OH} = -3$ mA	V_{IH} = 2 V,	V_{IL} = MAX,	2.4	3.4		2.4	3.4		V
		V_{CC} = MIN, I_{OH} = MAX	V_{IH} = 2 V,	V_{IL} = 0.5 V,	2			2			
V_{OL}		V_{CC} = MIN, V_{IL} = MAX	V_{IH} = 2 V,	$I_{OL} = 12$ mA			0.4			0.4	V
				$I_{OL} = 24$ mA						0.5	
I_{OZH}		V_{CC} = MAX, V_{IL} = MAX	V_{IH} = 2 V,	$V_O = 2.7$ V			20			20	µA
I_{OZL}				$V_O = 0.4$ V			-20			-20	
I_I		V_{CC} = MAX,	$V_I = 7$ V				0.1			0.1	mA
I_{IH}		V_{CC} = MAX,	$V_I = 2.7$ V				20			20	µA
I_{IL}		V_{CC} = MAX,	$V_{IL} = 0.4$ V				-0.2			-0.2	mA
I_{OS}§		V_{CC} = MAX			-40		-225	-40		-225	mA
I_{CC}	Outputs high	V_{CC} = MAX, Output open	All			17	27		17	27	mA
	Outputs low		'LS240			26	44		26	44	
			'LS241, 'LS244			27	46		27	46	
	All outputs disabled		'LS240			29	50		29	50	
			'LS241, 'LS244			32	54		32	54	

† For conditions shown as MIN or MAX, use the appropriate value specified under recommended operating conditions.
‡ All typical values are at V_{CC} = 5 V, T_A = 25°C.
§ Not more than one output should be shorted at a time, and duration of the short-circuit should not exceed one second.

switching characteristics, V_{CC} = 5 V, T_A = 25°C

PARAMETER	TEST CONDITIONS		'LS240 MIN	'LS240 TYP	'LS240 MAX	'LS241, 'LS244 MIN	'LS241, 'LS244 TYP	'LS241, 'LS244 MAX	UNIT
t_{PLH}	$R_L = 667\ \Omega$, See Note 2	$C_L = 45$ pF,		9	14		12	18	ns
t_{PHL}				12	18		12	18	ns
t_{PZL}				20	30		20	30	ns
t_{PZH}				15	23		15	23	ns
t_{PLZ}	$R_L = 667\ \Omega$, See Note 2	$C_L = 5$ pF,		10	20		10	20	ns
t_{PHZ}				15	25		15	25	ns

NOTE 2: See General Information Section for load circuits and voltage waveforms.

TEXAS
INSTRUMENTS

recommended operating conditions

PARAMETER		SN54S' MIN	SN54S' NOM	SN54S' MAX	SN74S' MIN	SN74S' NOM	SN74S' MAX	UNIT
V_{CC}	Supply voltage, (see Note 1)	4.5	5	5.5	4.75	5	5.25	V
V_{IH}	High-level input voltage	2			2			V
V_{IL}	Low-level input voltage			0.8			0.8	V
I_{OH}	High-level output current			−12			−15	mA
I_{OL}	Low-level output current			48			64	mA
	External resistance between any input and V_{CC} or ground			40			40	kΩ
T_A	Operating free-air temperature (see Note 3)	−55		125	0		70	°C

NOTES: 1. Voltage values are with respect to network ground terminal.
3. An SN54S241J operating at free-air temperature above 116°C requires a heat sink that provides a thermal resistance from case to free-air $R_{\theta CA}$, of not more than 40°C/W.

electrical characteristics over recommended operating free-air temperature range (unless otherwise noted)

PARAMETER		TEST CONDITIONS†			SN54S' MIN	SN54S' TYP‡	SN54S' MAX	SN74S' MIN	SN74S' TYP‡	SN74S' MAX	UNIT
V_{IK}		V_{CC} = MIN,	I_I = −18 mA				−1.2			−1.2	V
Hysteresis $(V_{T+} - V_{T-})$		V_{CC} = MIN			0.2	0.4		0.2	0.4		V
V_{OH}		V_{CC} = MIN, I_{OH} = −1 mA	V_{IH} = 2 V,	V_{IL} = 0.8 V,					2.7		V
		V_{CC} = MIN, I_{OH} = −3 mA	V_{IH} = 2 V,	V_{IL} = 0.8 V,	2.4	3.4		2.4	3.4		
		V_{CC} = MIN, I_{OH} = MAX	V_{IH} = 2 V,	V_{IL} = 0.5 V,	2			2			
V_{OL}		V_{CC} = MIN, I_{OL} = MAX	V_{IH} = 2 V,	V_{IL} = 0.8 V,			0.55			0.55	V
I_{OZH}		V_{CC} = MAX,	V_{IH} = 2 V,	V_O = 2.4 V			50			50	μA
I_{OZL}		V_{IL} = 0.8 V,		V_O = 0.5 V			−50			−50	
I_I		V_{CC} = MAX,	V_I = 5.5 V				1			1	mA
I_{IH}		V_{CC} = MAX,	V_I = 2.7 V				50			50	μA
I_{IL}	Any A	V_{CC} = MAX,	V_I = 0.5 V				−400			−400	μA
	Any G						−2			−2	mA
I_{OS}§		V_{CC} = MAX			−50		−225	−50		−225	mA
I_{CC}	Outputs high	V_{CC} = MAX, Outputs open		'S240		80	123		80	135	mA
				'S241, 'S244		95	147		95	160	
	Outputs low			'S240		100	145		100	150	
				'S241, 'S244		120	170		120	180	
	Outputs disabled			'S240		100	145		100	150	
				'S241, 'S244		120	170		120	180	

† For conditions shown as MIN or MAX, use the appropriate value specified under recommended operating conditions.
‡ All typical values are at V_{CC} = 5 V, T_A = 25°C.
§ Not more than one output should be shorted at a time, and duration of the short-circuit should not exceed one second.

3

TTL DEVICES

TEXAS
INSTRUMENTS

switching characteristics, V_{CC} = 5 V, T_A = 25°C

PARAMETER	TEST CONDITIONS		'S240			'S241, 'S244			UNIT
			MIN	TYP	MAX	MIN	TYP	MAX	
t_{PLH}	R_L = 90 Ω, C_L = 50 pF, See Note 4			4.5	7		6	9	ns
t_{PHL}				4.5	7		6	9	ns
t_{PZL}				10	15		10	15	ns
t_{PZH}				6.5	10		8	12	ns
t_{PLZ}	R_L = 90 Ω, C_L = 5 pF, See Note 4			10	15		10	15	ns
t_{PHZ}				6	9		6	9	ns

NOTE 4: See General Information Section for load circuits and voltage waveforms.

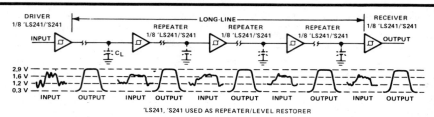

'LS241, 'S241 USED AS REPEATER/LEVEL RESTORER

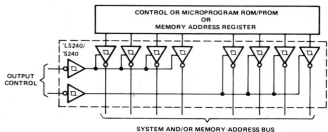

'LS240/'S240 USED AS SYSTEM AND/OR MEMORY BUS DRIVER—4-BIT
ORGANIZATION CAN BE APPLIED TO HANDLE BINARY OR BCD

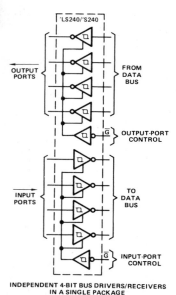

INDEPENDENT 4-BIT BUS DRIVERS/RECEIVERS
IN A SINGLE PACKAGE

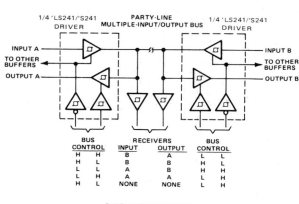

BUS CONTROL		RECEIVERS		BUS CONTROL	
		INPUT	OUTPUT		
H	H	B	A	L	L
H	L	B	B	H	L
L	L	A	B	H	H
L	H	A	A	L	H
H	L	NONE	NONE	L	H

PARTY-LINE BUS SYSTEM
WITH MULTIPLE INPUTS, OUTPUTS, AND RECEIVERS

**TEXAS
INSTRUMENTS**

- **Two-Way Asynchronous Communication Between Data Buses**
- **PNP Inputs Reduce D-C Loading**
- **Hysteresis (Typically 400 mV) at Inputs Improves Noise Margin**

description

These four-data-line transceivers are designed for asynchronous two-way communications between data buses. The SN74LS' can be used to drive terminated lines down to 133 ohms.

The SN54' family is characterized for operation over the full military temperature range of −55°C to 125°C. The SN74' family is characterized for operation from 0°C to 70°C.

SN54LS242, SN54LS243 . . . J OR W PACKAGE
SN74LS242, SN74LS243 . . . D, J OR N PACKAGE
(TOP VIEW)

```
         ┌────┐ ┌────┐
 GAB  [ 1   U    14 ]  VCC
 NC   [ 2         13 ]  GBA
 A1   [ 3         12 ]  NC
 A2   [ 4         11 ]  B1
 A3   [ 5         10 ]  B2
 A4   [ 6          9 ]  B3
 GND  [ 7          8 ]  B4
         └─────────────┘
```

SN54LS242, SN54LS243 . . . FK PACKAGE
SN74LS242, SN74LS243
(TOP VIEW)

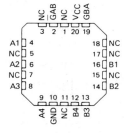

NC-No internal connection

FUNCTION TABLE (EACH TRANSCEIVER)

INPUTS		'LS242	'LS243
$\overline{\text{GAB}}$	GBA		
L	L	$\overline{\text{A}}$ to B	A to B
H	H	$\overline{\text{B}}$ to A	B to A
H	L	Isolation	Isolation
L	H	Latch A and B (A = $\overline{\text{B}}$)	Latch A and B (A = B)

schematics of inputs and outputs

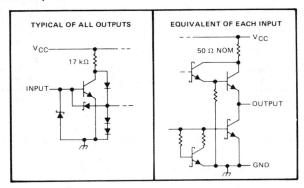

TEXAS INSTRUMENTS

TTL DEVICES

3

TYPES SN54LS242, SN54LS243, SN74LS242, SN74LS243
QUADRUPLE BUS TRANSCEIVERS

logic symbols

'LS242

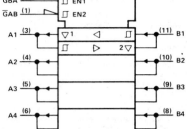

'LS243

logic diagrams (positive logic)

'LS242

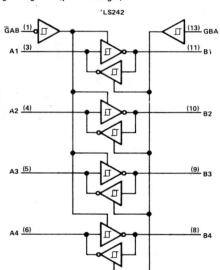

'LS243

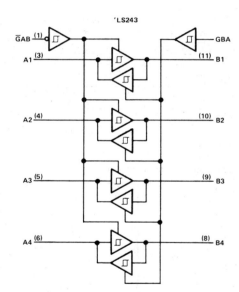

Pin numbers shown on logic notation are for D, J or N packages.

absolute maximum ratings over operating free-air temperature range (unless otherwise noted)

Supply voltage, V_{CC} (see Note 1) . . . . 7 V

Input voltage . . . . 7 V

Off-state output voltage . . . . 5.5 V

Operating free-air temperature range: SN54LS' . . . . $-55°C$ to $125°C$

SN74LS' . . . . $0°C$ to $70°C$

Storage temperature range . . . . $-65°C$ to $150°C$

NOTE 1: Voltage values are with respect to network ground terminal.

TEXAS INSTRUMENTS

recommended operating conditions

		SN54LS'			SN74LS'			UNIT
		MIN	NOM	MAX	MIN	NOM	MAX	
V_{CC}	Supply voltage, (see Note 1)	4.5	5	5.5	4.75	5	5.25	V
V_{IH}	High-level input voltage	2			2			V
V_{IL}	Low-level input voltage			0.7			0.8	V
I_{OH}	High-level output current			-12			-15	mA
I_{OL}	Low-level output current			12			24	mA
T_A	Operating free-air temperature	-55		125	0		70	°C

electrical characteristics over recommended operating free-air temperature range (unless otherwise noted)

PARAMETER		TEST CONDITIONS†		SN54LS'			SN74LS'			UNIT
				MIN	TYP‡	MAX	MIN	TYP‡	MAX	
V_{IK}	A or B	V_{CC} = MIN,	$I_I = -18$ mA			-1.5			-1.5	V
Hysteresis $(V_{T+} - V_{T-})$		V_{CC} = MIN		0.2	0.4		0.2	0.4		V
V_{OH}		V_{CC} = MIN, V_{IH} = 2 V, V_{IL} = MAX, $I_{OH} = -3$ mA		2.4	3.1		2.4	3.1		V
		V_{CC} = MIN, V_{IH} = 2 V, V_{IL} = 0.5 V, I_{OH} = MAX		2			2			
V_{OL}		V_{CC} = MIN, V_{IH} = 2 V, V_{IL} = MAX	I_{OL} = 12 mA		0.25	0.4		0.25	0.4	V
			I_{OL} = 24 mA					0.35	0.5	
I_{OZH}		V_{CC} = MAX, V_{IH} = 2 V,	V_O = 2.7 V			40			40	μA
I_{OZL}		V_{IL} = MAX	V_O = 0.4 V			-200			-200	μA
I_I	A or B	V_{CC} = MAX,	V_I = 5.5 V			0.1			0.1	mA
	$\overline{GAB}$ or GBA		V_I = 7 V			0.1			0.1	
I_{IH}		V_{CC} = MAX, V_I = 2.7 V				20			20	μA
I_{IL}	A inputs	V_{CC} = MAX, V_I = 0.4 V, GAB and GBA at 0 V				-0.2			-0.2	mA
	B inputs	V_{CC} = MAX, V_I = 0.4 V, GAB and GBA at 4.5 V				-0.2			-0.2	
	$\overline{GAB}$ or GBA	V_{CC} = MAX, V_I = 0.4 V				-0.2			-0.2	
I_{OS}§		V_{CC} = MAX		-40		-225	-40		-225	mA
I_{CC}	Outputs high	V_{CC} = MAX, Outputs open, See Note 2	'LS242, 'LS243		22	38		22	38	mA
	Outputs low		'LS242, 'LS243		29	50		29	50	
	All outputs disabled		'LS242		29	50		29	50	
			'LS243		32	54		32	54	

† For conditions shown as MIN or MAX, use the appropriate value specified under recommended operating conditions.
‡ All typical values are at V_{CC} = 5 V, T_A = 25°C.
§ Not more than one output should be shorted at a time, and duration of the short-circuit should not exceed one second.
NOTE 2: I_{CC} is measured with transceivers enabled in one direction only, or with all transceivers disabled.

switching characteristics, V_{CC} = 5 V, T_A = 25°C

PARAMETER		TEST CONDITIONS		'LS242			'LS243			UNIT
				MIN	TYP	MAX	MIN	TYP	MAX	
t_{PLH}		R_L = 667 Ω, See Note 3	C_L = 45 pF,		9	14		12	18	ns
t_{PHL}					12	18		12	18	ns
t_{PZL}					20	30		20	30	ns
t_{PZH}					15	23		15	23	ns
t_{PLZ}		R_L = 667 Ω, See Note 3	C_L = 5 pF,		10	20		10	20	ns
t_{PHZ}					15	25		15	25	ns

NOTE 3: See General Information Section for load circuits and voltage waveforms.

TEXAS
INSTRUMENTS

3

TTL DEVICES

3

TTL DEVICES

- **Bi-directional Bus Transceiver in a High-Density 20-Pin Package**

- **3-State Outputs Drive Bus Lines Directly**

- **PNP Inputs Reduce D-C Loading on Bus Lines**

- **Hysteresis at Bus Inputs Improve Noise Margins**

- **Typical Propagation Delay Times, Port-to-Port . . . 8 ns**

TYPE	I_{OL} (SINK CURRENT)	I_{OH} (SOURCE CURRENT)
SN54LS245	12 mA	–12 mA
SN74LS245	24 mA	–15 mA

description

These octal bus transceivers are designed for asynchronous two-way communication between data buses. The control function implementation minimizes external timing requirements.

The devices allow data transmission from the A bus to the B bus or from the B bus to the A bus depending upon the logic level at the direction control (DIR) input. The enable input ($\overline{G}$) can be used to disable the device so that the buses are effectively isolated.

The SN54LS245 is characterized for operation over the full military temperature range of $-55°C$ to $125°C$. The SN74LS245 is characterized for operation from $0°C$ to $70°C$.

schematics of inputs and outputs

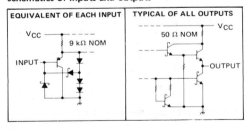

EQUIVALENT OF EACH INPUT

TYPICAL OF ALL OUTPUTS

SN54LS245 . . . J PACKAGE
SN74LS245 . . . DW, J OR N PACKAGE
(TOP VIEW)

DIR	1	20	V_{CC}
A1	2	19	$\overline{G}$
A2	3	18	B1
A3	4	17	B2
A4	5	16	B3
A5	6	15	B4
A6	7	14	B5
A7	8	13	B6
A8	9	12	B7
GND	10	11	B8

SN54LS245 . . . FK PACKAGE
SN74LS245
(TOP VIEW)

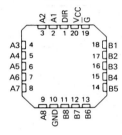

FUNCTION TABLE

ENABLE $\overline{G}$	DIRECTION CONTROL DIR	OPERATION
L	L	B data to A bus
L	H	A data to B bus
H	X	Isolation

H = high level, L = low level, X = irrelevant

3

TTL DEVICES

TEXAS
INSTRUMENTS

TYPES SN54LS245, SN74LS245
OCTAL BUS TRANSCEIVERS WITH 3-STATE OUTPUTS

logic symbol

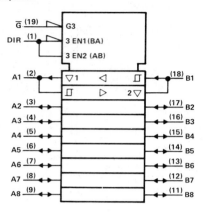

logic diagram (positive logic)

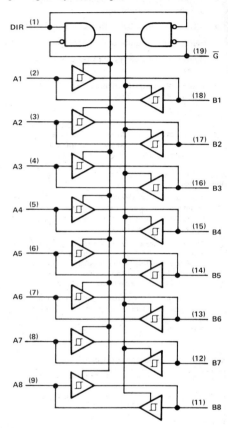

Pin numbers shown on logic notation are for DW, J or N packages.

absolute maximum ratings over operating free-air temperature range (unless otherwise noted)

Supply voltage, V_{CC} (see Note 1)	7 V
Input voltage	7 V
Off-state output voltage	5.5 V
Operating free-air temperature range: SN54LS'	$-55°C$ to $125°C$
SN74LS'	$0°C$ to $70°C$
Storage temperature range	$-65°C$ to $150°C$

NOTE 1: Voltage values are with respect to network ground terminal.

TEXAS
INSTRUMENTS

recommended operating conditions

PARAMETER	SN54LS245 MIN	SN54LS245 NOM	SN54LS245 MAX	SN74LS245 MIN	SN74LS245 NOM	SN74LS245 MAX	UNIT
Supply voltage, V_{CC}	4.5	5	5.5	4.75	5	5.25	V
High-level output current, I_{OH}			−12			−15	mA
Low-level output current, I_{OL}			12			24	mA
Operating free-air temperature, T_A	−55		125	0		70	°C

electrical characteristics over recommended operating free-air temperature range (unless otherwise noted)

PARAMETER		TEST CONDITIONS†		SN54LS245 MIN	SN54LS245 TYP‡	SN54LS245 MAX	SN74LS245 MIN	SN74LS245 TYP‡	SN74LS245 MAX	UNIT
V_{IH}	High-level input voltage			2			2			V
V_{IL}	Low-level input voltage					0.7			0.8	V
V_{IK}	Input clamp voltage	V_{CC} = MIN,	I_I = −18 mA			−1.5			−1.5	V
	Hysteresis $(V_{T+} - V_{T-})$A or B input	V_{CC} = MIN		0.2	0.4		0.2	0.4		V
V_{OH}	High-level output voltage	V_{CC} = MIN, V_{IH} = 2 V, V_{IL} = V_{IL} max	I_{OH} = −3 mA	2.4	3.4		2.4	3.4		V
			I_{OH} = MAX	2			2			
V_{OL}	Low-level output voltage	V_{CC} = MIN, V_{IH} = 2 V, V_{IL} = V_{IL} max	I_{OL} = 12 mA			0.4			0.4	V
			I_{OL} = 24 mA						0.5	
I_{OZH}	Off-state output current, high-level voltage applied	V_{CC} = MAX, $\overline{G}$ at 2 V	V_O = 2.7 V			20			20	µA
I_{OZL}	Off-state output current, low-level voltage applied		V_O = 0.4 V			−200			−200	
I_I	Input current at maximum input voltage	A or B	V_{CC} = MAX,	V_I = 5.5 V			0.1			0.1	mA
		DIR or $\overline{G}$		V_I = 7 V			0.1			0.1	
I_{IH}	High-level input current	V_{CC} = MAX,	V_{IH} = 2.7 V			20			20	µA
I_{IL}	Low-level input current	V_{CC} = MAX,	V_{IL} = 0.4 V			−0.2			−0.2	mA
I_{OS}	Short-circuit output current¶	V_{CC} = MAX		−40		−225	−40		−225	mA
I_{CC}	Supply current	Total, outputs high	V_{CC} = MAX, Outputs open		48	70		48	70	mA
		Total, outputs low			62	90		62	90	
		Outputs at Hi-Z			64	95		64	95	

†For conditions shown as MIN or MAX, use the appropriate value specified under recommended operating conditions.
‡All typical values are at V_{CC} = 5 V, T_A = 25°C.
¶Not more than one output should be shorted at a time, and duration of the short-circuit should not exceed one second.

switching characteristics, V_{CC} = 5 V, T_A = 25°C

PARAMETER		TEST CONDITIONS	MIN	TYP	MAX	UNIT
t_{PLH}	Propagation delay time, low-to-high-level output	C_L = 45 pF, R_L = 667 Ω, See Note 2		8	12	ns
t_{PHL}	Propagation delay time, high-to-low-level output			8	12	ns
t_{PZL}	Output enable time to low level			27	40	ns
t_{PZH}	Output enable time to high level			25	40	ns
t_{PLZ}	Output disable time from low level	C_L = 5 pF, R_L = 667 Ω, See Note 2		15	25	ns
t_{PHZ}	Output disable time from high level			15	28	ns

NOTE 2: See General Information Section for load circuits and voltage waveforms.

TEXAS
INSTRUMENTS

TTL DEVICES

3

TTL DEVICES

TYPES SN54247, SN54LS247, SN54LS248
SN74247, SN74LS247, SN74LS248
BCD-TO-SEVEN-SEGMENT DECODERS/DRIVERS

MARCH 1974 – REVISED DECEMBER 1983

'247, 'LS247 feature

- **Open-Collector Outputs Drive Indicators Directly**
- **Lamp-Test Provision**
- **Leading/Trailing Zero Suppression**

'LS248 feature

- **Internal Pull-Ups Eliminate Need for External Resistors**
- **Lamp-Test Provision**
- **Leading/Trailing Zero Suppression**

- **All Circuit Types Feature Lamp Intensity Modulation Capability**

TYPE	DRIVER OUTPUTS				TYPICAL POWER DISSIPATION	PACKAGES
	ACTIVE LEVEL	OUTPUT CONFIGURATION	SINK CURRENT	MAX VOLTAGE		
SN54247	low	open-collector	40 mA	15 V	320 mW	J, W
SN54LS247	low	open-collector	12 mA	15 V	35 mW	J, W
SN54LS248	high	2-kΩ pull-up	2 mA	5.5 V	125 mW	J, W
SN74247	low	open-collector	40 mA	15 V	320 mW	J, N
SN74LS247	low	open-collector	24 mA	15 V	35 mW	J, N
SN74LS248	high	2-kΩ pull-up	6 mA	5.5 V	125 mW	J, N

SN54247
SN54LS247, SN54LS248 ... J OR W PACKAGE
SN74247 ... J OR N PACKAGE
SN74LS247, SN74LS248 ... D, J OR N PACKAGE
(TOP VIEW)

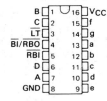

SN54LS247, SN54LS248 ... FK PACKAGE
SN74LS247, SN74LS248
(TOP VIEW)

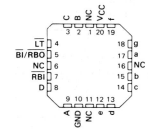

NC – No internal connection

description

The '247 is electrically and functionally identical to the SN5447A/SN7447A, and have the same pin assignment. Also the 'LS247 and 'LS248 are electrically and functionally identical to the SN54LS47/SN74LS47 and SN54LS48/SN74LS48, respectively, and have the same pin assignments as their equivalents. They can be used interchangeably in present or future designs to offer designers a choice between two indicator fonts. The '46A, '47A, '48, 49, 'LS47, and 'LS48 compose the 6 and the 5 without tails and the '247, 'LS247, and 'LS248 compose the 5 and the 9 with tails. Composition of all other characters, including display patterns, for BCD inputs above nine, is identical. The '247, and 'LS247 feature active-low outputs designed for driving indicators directly, and the 'LS248 feature active-high outputs for driving lamp buffers. All of the circuits have full ripple-blanking input/output controls and a lamp test input. Segment identification and resultant displays are shown below. Display patterns for BCD input counts above 9 are unique symbols to authenticate input conditions.

TEXAS INSTRUMENTS

3
TTL DEVICES

TYPES SN54247, SN54LS247, SN54LS248, SN74247, SN74LS247, SN74LS248
BCD-TO-SEVEN-SEGMENT DECODERS/DRIVERS

description (continued)

All of these circuits incorporate automatic leading and/or trailing-edge zero-blanking control ($\overline{RBI}$ and $\overline{RBO}$). Lamp test ($\overline{LT}$) of these types may be performed at any time when the $\overline{BI}/\overline{RBO}$ node is at a high level. All types contain an overriding blanking input (BI) which can be used to control the lamp intensity by pulsing or to inhibit the outputs. Inputs and outputs are entirely compatible for use with TTL logic outputs.

Series 54 and Series 54LS devices are characterized for operation over the full military temperature range of $-55°$C to $125°$C; Series 74 and Series 74LS devices are characterized for operation from $0°$C to $70°$C.

SEGMENT
IDENTIFICATION

NUMERICAL DESIGNATIONS AND RESULTANT DISPLAYS

'247, 'LS247
FUNCTION TABLE

DECIMAL OR FUNCTION	INPUTS						BI/RBO†	OUTPUTS							NOTE
	LT	RBI	D	C	B	A		a	b	c	d	e	f	g	
0	H	H	L	L	L	L	H	ON	ON	ON	ON	ON	ON	OFF	
1	H	X	L	L	L	H	H	OFF	ON	ON	OFF	OFF	OFF	OFF	
2	H	X	L	L	H	L	H	ON	ON	OFF	ON	ON	OFF	ON	
3	H	X	L	L	H	H	H	ON	ON	ON	ON	OFF	OFF	ON	
4	H	X	L	H	L	L	H	OFF	ON	ON	OFF	OFF	ON	ON	
5	H	X	L	H	L	H	H	ON	OFF	ON	ON	OFF	ON	ON	
6	H	X	L	H	H	L	H	ON	OFF	ON	ON	ON	ON	ON	
7	H	X	L	H	H	H	H	ON	ON	ON	OFF	OFF	OFF	OFF	
8	H	X	H	L	L	L	H	ON	ON	ON	ON	ON	ON	ON	1
9	H	X	H	L	L	H	H	ON	ON	ON	OFF	OFF	ON	ON	
10	H	X	H	L	H	L	H	OFF	OFF	OFF	ON	ON	OFF	ON	
11	H	X	H	L	H	H	H	OFF	OFF	ON	ON	OFF	OFF	ON	
12	H	X	H	H	L	L	H	OFF	ON	OFF	OFF	OFF	ON	ON	
13	H	X	H	H	L	H	H	ON	OFF	OFF	ON	OFF	ON	ON	
14	H	X	H	H	H	L	H	OFF	OFF	OFF	ON	ON	ON	ON	
15	H	X	H	H	H	H	H	OFF	OFF	OFF	OFF	OFF	OFF	OFF	
$\overline{BI}$	X	X	X	X	X	X	L	OFF	OFF	OFF	OFF	OFF	OFF	OFF	2
$\overline{RBI}$	H	L	L	L	L	L	L	OFF	OFF	OFF	OFF	OFF	OFF	OFF	3
$\overline{LT}$	L	X	X	X	X	X	H	ON	ON	ON	ON	ON	ON	ON	4

H = high level, L = low level, X = irrelevant

NOTES: 1. The blanking input ($\overline{BI}$) must be open or held at a high logic level when output functions 0 through 15 are desired. The ripple-blanking input ($\overline{RBI}$) must be open or high if blanking of a decimal zero is not desired.

2. When a low logic level is applied directly to the blanking input ($\overline{BI}$), all segment outputs are off regardless of the level of any other input.

3. When ripple-blanking input ($\overline{RBI}$) and inputs A, B, C, and D are at a low level with the lamp test input high, all segment outputs go off and the ripple-blanking output ($\overline{RBO}$) goes to a low level (response condition).

4. When the blanking input/ripple blanking output ($\overline{BI}/\overline{RBO}$) is open or held high and a low is applied to the lamp-test input, all segment outputs are on.

†$\overline{BI}/\overline{RBO}$ is wire AND logic serving as blanking input ($\overline{BI}$) and/or ripple-blanking output ($\overline{RBO}$).

3

TTL DEVICES

TEXAS
INSTRUMENTS

'LS248
FUNCTION TABLE

DECIMAL OR FUNCTION	INPUTS						$\overline{BI}/\overline{RBO}$†	OUTPUTS							NOTE
	$\overline{LT}$	$\overline{RBI}$	D	C	B	A		a	b	c	d	e	f	g	
0	H	H	L	L	L	L	H	H	H	H	H	H	H	L	1
1	H	X	L	L	L	H	H	L	H	H	L	L	L	L	1
2	H	X	L	L	H	L	H	H	H	L	H	H	L	H	
3	H	X	L	L	H	H	H	H	H	H	H	L	L	H	
4	H	X	L	H	L	L	H	L	H	H	L	L	H	H	
5	H	X	L	H	L	H	H	H	L	H	H	L	H	H	
6	H	X	L	H	H	L	H	H	L	H	H	H	H	H	
7	H	X	L	H	H	H	H	H	H	H	L	L	L	L	1
8	H	X	H	L	L	L	H	H	H	H	H	H	H	H	
9	H	X	H	L	L	H	H	H	H	H	H	L	H	H	
10	H	X	H	L	H	L	H	L	L	L	H	H	L	H	
11	H	X	H	L	H	H	H	L	L	H	H	L	L	H	
12	H	X	H	H	L	L	H	L	H	L	L	L	H	H	
13	H	X	H	H	L	H	H	H	L	L	H	L	H	H	
14	H	X	H	H	H	L	H	L	L	L	H	H	H	H	
15	H	X	H	H	H	H	H	L	L	L	L	L	L	L	
$\overline{BI}$	X	X	X	X	X	X	L	L	L	L	L	L	L	L	2
$\overline{RBI}$	H	L	L	L	L	L	L	L	L	L	L	L	L	L	3
$\overline{LT}$	L	X	X	X	X	X	H	H	H	H	H	H	H	H	4

H = high level, L = low level, X = irrelevant

NOTES: 1. The blanking input ($\overline{BI}$) must be open or held at a high logic level when output functions 0 through 15 are desired. The ripple-blanking input ($\overline{RBI}$) must be open or high if blanking of a decimal zero is not desired.
2. When a low logic level is applied directly to the blanking input ($\overline{BI}$), all segment outputs are low regardless of the level of any other input.
3. When ripple-blanking input ($\overline{RBI}$) and inputs A, B, C, and D are at a low level with the lamp test input high, all segment outputs go low and the ripple-blanking output ($\overline{RBO}$) goes to a low level (response condition).
4. When the blanking input/ripple-blanking output ($\overline{BI}/\overline{RBO}$) is open or held high and a low is applied to the lamp-test input, all segment outputs are high.

†$\overline{BI}/\overline{RBO}$ is wire-AND logic serving as blanking input ($\overline{BI}$) and/or ripple-blanking output ($\overline{RBO}$).

3

TTL DEVICES

logic diagram

'247, 'LS247

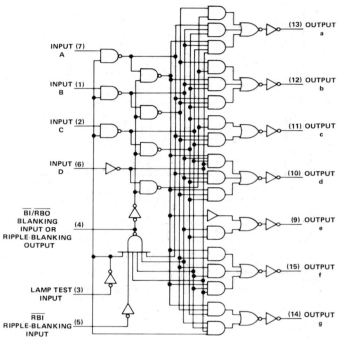

Pin numbers shown on logic notation are for D, J or N packages.

TEXAS
INSTRUMENTS

logic diagram

'LS248

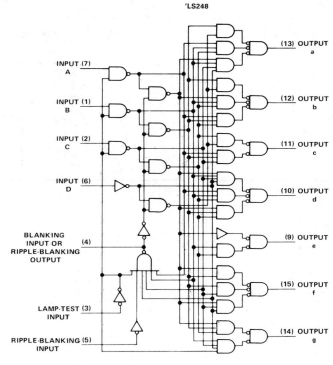

Pin numbers shown on logic notation are for D, J or N packages.

3

TTL DEVICES

schematics of inputs and outputs

'247

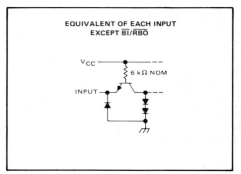

'247

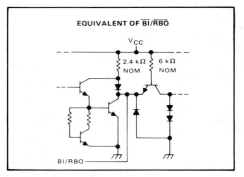

'247

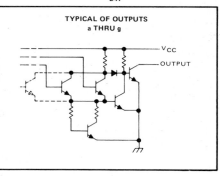

schematics of inputs and outputs

'LS247, 'LS248

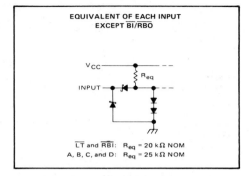

'LS247, 'LS248

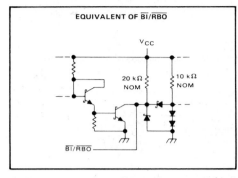

'LS247

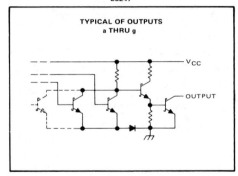

'LS248

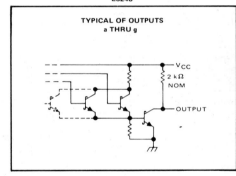

3

TTL DEVICES

TYPES SN54247, SN74247
BCD-TO-SEVEN-SEGMENT DECODERS/DRIVERS

absolute maximum ratings over operating free-air temperature range (unless otherwise noted)

Supply voltage, V_{CC} (see Note 1) . . . . 7 V
Input voltage . . . . 5.5 V
Current forced into any output in the off state . . . . 1 mA
Operating free-air temperature range: SN54247 . . . . -55°C to 125°C
                                 SN74247 . . . . 0°C to 70°C
Storage temperature range . . . . -65°C to 150°C

NOTE 1: Voltage values are with respect to network ground terminal.

recommended operating conditions

		SN54247			SN74247			UNIT
		MIN	NOM	MAX	MIN	NOM	MAX	
Supply voltage, V_{CC}		4.5	5	5.5	4.75	5	5.25	V
Off-state output voltage, $V_{O(off)}$	a thru g			15			15	V
On-state output current, $I_{O(on)}$	a thru g			40			40	mA
High-level output current, I_{OH}	$\overline{BI}/\overline{RBO}$			-200			-200	μA
Low-level output current, I_{OL}	$\overline{BI}/\overline{RBO}$			8			8	mA
Operating free-air temperature, T_A		-55		125	0		70	$^{\circ}$C

electrical characteristics over recommended operating free-air temperature range (unless otherwise noted)

	PARAMETER		TEST CONDITIONS[†]	MIN	TYP[‡]	MAX	UNIT
V_{IH}	High-level input voltage			2			V
V_{IL}	Low-level input voltage					0.8	V
V_{IK}	Input clamp voltage		V_{CC} = MIN, $I_I = -12$ mA			1.5 V	V
V_{OH}	High-level output voltage	$\overline{BI}/\overline{RBO}$	V_{CC} = MIN, V_{IH} = 2 V, V_{IL} = 0.8 V, $I_{OH} = -200 \mu$A	2.4	3.7		V
V_{OL}	Low-level output voltage	$\overline{BI}/\overline{RBO}$	V_{CC} = MIN, V_{IH} = 2 V, V_{IL} = 0.8 V, I_{OL} = 8 mA		0.27	0.4	V
$I_{O(off)}$	Off-state output current	a thru g	V_{CC} = MAX, V_{IH} = 2 V, V_{IL} = 0.8 V, $V_{O(off)}$ = MAX			250	μA
$V_{O(on)}$	On-state output voltage	a thru g	V_{CC} = MIN, V_{IH} = 2 V, V_{IL} = 0.8 V, $I_{O(on)}$ = 40 mA		0.3	0.4	V
I_I	Input current at maximum input voltage	Any input except $\overline{BI}/\overline{RBO}$	V_{CC} = MAX, V_I = 5.5 V			1	mA
I_{IH}	High-level input current	Any input except $\overline{BI}/\overline{RBO}$	V_{CC} = MAX, V_I = 2.4 V			40	μA
I_{IL}	Low-level input current	Any input except $\overline{BI}/\overline{RBO}$	V_{CC} = MAX, V_I = 0.4 V			-1.6	mA
		$\overline{BI}/\overline{RBO}$				-4	
I_{OS}	Short-circuit output current	$\overline{BI}/\overline{RBO}$	V_{CC} = MAX			-4	mA
I_{CC}	Supply current		V_{CC} = MAX, See Note 2		64	103	mA

[†]For conditions shown as MIN or MAX, use the appropriate value specified under recommended operating conditions.
[‡]All typical values are at V_{CC} = 5 V, $T_A = 25^{\circ}$C.
NOTE 2: I_{CC} is measured with all outputs open and all inputs at 4.5 V.

switching characteristics, V_{CC} = 5 V, $T_A = 25^{\circ}$C

	PARAMETER	TEST CONDITIONS	MIN	TYP	MAX	UNIT
t_{off}	Turn-off time from A input	C_L = 15 pF, R_L = 120 Ω, See Note 3			100	ns
t_{on}	Turn-on time from A input				100	
t_{off}	Turn-off time from $\overline{RBI}$ input				100	ns
t_{on}	Turn-on time from $\overline{RBI}$ input				100	

NOTE 3: See General Information Section for load circuits and voltage waveforms.

TEXAS
INSTRUMENTS

absolute maximum ratings over operating free-air temperature range (unless otherwise noted)

Supply voltage, V_{CC} (see Note 1)	7 V
Input voltage	7 V
Peak output current ($t_w \leqslant 1$ ms, duty cycle $\leqslant$ 10%)	200 mA
Current forced into any output in the off state	1 mA
Operating free-air temperature range: SN54LS247	-55°C to 125°C
SN74LS247	0°C to 70°C
Storage temperature range	-65°C to 150°C

NOTE 1: Voltage values are with respect to network ground terminal.

recommended operating conditions

		SN54LS247			SN74LS247			UNIT
		MIN	NOM	MAX	MIN	NOM	MAX	
Supply voltage, V_{CC}		4.5	5	5.5	4.75	5	5.25	V
Off-state output voltage, $V_{O(off)}$	a thru g			15			15	V
On-state output current, $I_{O(on)}$	a thru g			12			24	mA
High-level output current, I_{OH}	$\overline{BI}/\overline{RBO}$			-50			-50	μA
Low-level output current, I_{OL}	$\overline{BI}/\overline{RBO}$			1.6			3.2	mA
Operating free-air temperature, T_A		-55		125	0		70	$^\circ$C

electrical characteristics over recommended operating free-air temperature range (unless otherwise noted)

PARAMETER		TEST CONDITIONS[†]		SN54LS247			SN74LS247			UNIT
				MIN	TYP[‡]	MAX	MIN	TYP[‡]	MAX	
V_{IH}	High-level input voltage			2			2			V
V_{IL}	Low-level input voltage					0.7			0.8	V
V_{IK}	Input clamp voltage	$V_{CC} =$ MIN,	$I_I = -18$ mA			-1.5			-1.5	V
V_{OH}	High-level output voltage $\overline{BI}/\overline{RBO}$	$V_{CC} =$ MIN, $V_{IL} = V_{IL}$ max,	$V_{IH} = 2$ V, $I_{OH} = -50$ μA	2.4	4.2		2.4	4.2		V
V_{OL}	Low-level output voltage $\overline{BI}/\overline{RBO}$	$V_{CC} =$ MIN, $V_{IH} = 2$ V, $V_{IL} = V_{IL}$ max	$I_{OL} = 1.6$ mA		0.25	0.4		0.25	0.4	V
			$I_{OL} = 3.2$ mA					0.35	0.5	
$I_{O(off)}$	Off-state output current a thru g	$V_{CC} =$ MIN, $V_{IL} = V_{IL}$ max,	$V_{IH} = 2$ V, $V_{O(off)} = 15$ V			250			250	μA
$V_{O(on)}$	On-state output voltage a thru g	$V_{CC} =$ MIN, $V_{IH} = 2$ V, $V_{IL} = V_{IL}$ max	$I_{O(on)} = 12$ mA		0.25	0.4		0.25	0.4	V
			$I_{O(on)} = 24$ mA					0.35	0.5	
I_I[4]	Input current at maximum input voltage	$V_{CC} =$ MAX,	$V_I = 7$ V			0.1			0.1	mA
I_{IH}[4]	High-level input current	$V_{CC} =$ MAX,	$V_I = 2.7$ V			20			20	μA
I_{IL}	Low-level input current	Any input except $\overline{BI}/\overline{RBO}$ $V_{CC} =$ MAX,	$V_I = 0.4$ V			-0.4			-0.4	mA
		$\overline{BI}/\overline{RBO}$				-1.2			-1.2	
I_{OS}	Short-circuit output current $\overline{BI}/\overline{RBO}$	$V_{CC} =$ MAX		-0.3		-2	-0.3		-2	mA
I_{CC}	Supply current	$V_{CC} =$ MAX,	See Note 2		7	13		7	13	mA

[†]For conditions shown as MIN or MAX, use the appropriate value specified under recommended operating conditions.
[‡]All typical values are at $V_{CC} = 5$ V, $T_A = 25^\circ$C.
NOTE 2: I_{CC} is measured with all outputs open and all inputs at 4.5 V.

switching characteristics, $V_{CC} = 5$ V, $T_A = 25^\circ$C

PARAMETER		TEST CONDITIONS	MIN	TYP	MAX	UNIT
t_{off}	Turn-off time from A input				100	ns
t_{on}	Turn-on time from A input	$C_L = 15$ pF, $R_L = 665$ Ω, See Note 3			100	
t_{off}	Turn-off time from $\overline{RBI}$ input				100	ns
t_{on}	Turn-on time from $\overline{RBI}$ input				100	

NOTE 3: See General Information Section for load circuits and voltage waveforms.   NOTE 4: Any input except $\overline{BI}/\overline{RBO}$

TEXAS INSTRUMENTS

3

TTL DEVICES

absolute maximum ratings over operating free-air temperature range (unless otherwise noted)

Supply voltage, V_{CC} (see Note 1) . . . . 7 V
Input voltage . . . . 7 V
Operating free-air temperature range: SN54LS248 . . . . -55°C to 125°C
  SN74LS248 . . . . 0°C to 70°C
Storage temperature range . . . . -65°C to 150°C

NOTE 1: Voltage values are with respect to network ground terminal.

recommended operating conditions

		SN54LS248			SN74LS248			UNIT
		MIN	NOM	MAX	MIN	NOM	MAX	
Supply voltage, V_{CC}		4.5	5	5.5	4.75	5	5.25	V
High-level output current, I_{OH}	a thru g			-100			-100	μA
	$\overline{BI}/\overline{RBO}$			-50			-50	
Low-level output current, I_{OL}	a thru g			2			6	mA
	$\overline{BI}/\overline{RBO}$			1.6			3.2	
Operating free-air temperature, T_A		-55		125	0		70	$^{\circ}$C

electrical characteristics over recommended operating free-air temperature range (unless otherwise noted)

PARAMETER		TEST CONDITIONS[†]		SN54LS248			SN74LS248			UNIT
				MIN	TYP[‡]	MAX	MIN	TYP[‡]	MAX	
V_{IH}	High-level input voltage			2			2			V
V_{IL}	Low-level input voltage					0.7			0.8	V
V_{IK}	Input clamp voltage	V_{CC} = MIN,	$I_I = -18$ mA			-1.5			-1.5	V
V_{OH}	High-level output voltage	a thru g and $\overline{BI}/\overline{RBO}$	V_{CC} = MIN, V_{IH} = 2 V, $V_{IL} = V_{IL}$ max, I_{OH} = MAX	2.4	4.2		2.4	4.2		V
I_O	Output current	a thru g	V_{CC} = MIN, V_O = 0.85 V, Input conditions as for V_{OH}	-1.3	-2		-1.3	-2		mA
V_{OL}	Low-level output voltage	a thru g	V_{CC} = MIN, V_{IH} = 2 V, $V_{IL} = V_{IL}$ max	I_{OL} = 2 mA	0.25	0.4	0.25	0.4		V
				I_{OL} = 6 mA				0.35	0.5	
		$\overline{BI}/\overline{RBO}$	V_{CC} = MIN, V_{IH} = 2 V, $V_{IL} = V_{IL}$ max	I_{OL} = 1.6 mA	0.25	0.4	0.25	0.4		V
				I_{OL} = 3.2 mA				0.35	0.5	
I_I	Input current at maximum input voltage	Any input except $\overline{BI}/\overline{RBO}$	V_{CC} = MAX, V_I = 7 V			0.1			0.1	mA
I_{IH}	High-level input current	Any input except $\overline{BI}/\overline{RBO}$	V_{CC} = MAX, V_I = 2.7 V			20			20	μA
I_{IL}	Low-level input current	Any input except $\overline{BI}/\overline{RBO}$	V_{CC} = MAX, V_I = 0.4 V			-0.4			-0.4	mA
		$\overline{BI}/\overline{RBO}$				-1.2			-1.2	
I_{OS}	Short-circuit output current	$\overline{BI}/\overline{RBO}$	V_{CC} = MAX	-0.3		-2	-0.3		-2	mA
I_{CC}	Supply current		V_{CC} = MAX, See Note 2		25	38		25	38	mA

[†]For conditions shown as MIN or MAX, use the appropriate value specified under recommended operating conditions.
[‡]All typical values are at V_{CC} = 5 V, T_A 25°C.
NOTE 2: I_{CC} is measured with all outputs open and all inputs at 4.5 V.

switching characteristics, V_{CC} = 5 V, T_A = 25°C

PARAMETER		TEST CONDITIONS	MIN	TYP	MAX	UNIT
t_{PHL}	Propagation delay time, high-to-low-level output from A input	C_L = 15 pF, R_L = 4 kΩ, See Note 3			100	ns
t_{PLH}	Propagation delay time, low-to-high-level output from A input				100	
t_{PHL}	Propagation delay time, high-to-low-level output from $\overline{RBI}$ input	C_L = 15 pF, R_L = 6 kΩ, See Note 3			100	ns
t_{PLH}	Propagation delay time, low-to-high-level output from $\overline{RBI}$ input				100	

NOTE 3: See General Information Section for load circuits and voltage waveforms.

TEXAS
INSTRUMENTS

3

TTL DEVICES

- Three-State Versions of '151, 'LS151, 'S151
- Three-State Outputs Interface Directly with System Bus
- Perform Parallel-to-Serial Conversion
- Permit Multiplexing from N-lines to One Line
- Complementary Outputs Provide True and Inverted Data
- Fully Compatible with Most TTL Circuits

SN54251, SN54LS251, SN54S251 . . . J OR W PACKAGE
SN74251 . . . J OR N PACKAGE
SN74LS251, SN74S251 . . . D, J OR N PACKAGE

(TOP VIEW)

```
        ___
D3 [ 1  U 16 ] VCC
D2 [ 2    15 ] D4
D1 [ 3    14 ] D5
D0 [ 4    13 ] D6
 Y [ 5    12 ] D7
 W [ 6    11 ] A
 G [ 7    10 ] B
GND[ 8     9 ] C
```

TYPE	MAX NO. OF COMMON OUTPUTS	TYPICAL AVG PROP DELAY TIME (D TO Y)	TYPICAL POWER DISSIPATION
SN54251	49	17 ns	250 mW
SN74251	129	17 ns	250 mW
SN54LS251	49	17 ns	35 mW
SN74LS251	129	17 ns	35 mW
SN54S251	39	8 ns	275 mW
SN74S251	129	8 ns	275 mW

description

These monolithic data selectors/multiplexers contain full on-chip binary decoding to select one-of-eight data sources and feature a strobe-controlled three-state output. The strobe must be at a low logic level to enable these devices. The three-state outputs permit a number of outputs to be connected to a common bus. When the strobe input is high, both outputs are in a high-impedance state in which both the upper and lower totem-pole output of each totem-pole output are off, and the output neither drives nor loads the bus significantly. When the strobe is low, the outputs are activated and operate as standard TTL totem-pole outputs.

To minimize the possibility that two outputs will attempt to take a common bus to opposite logic levels, the output control circuitry is designed so that the 'average output disable time is shorter than the average output enable time. The SN54251 and SN74251 have output clamp diodes to attenuate reflections on the bus line.

SN54LS251, SN54S251 . . . FK PACKAGE
SN74LS251, SN74S251

(TOP VIEW)

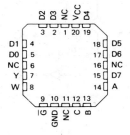

```
        D2 D3 NC VCC D4
         3  2  1 20 19
 D1 [ 4            18 ] D5
 D0 [ 5            17 ] D6
 NC [ 6            16 ] NC
  Y [ 7            15 ] D7
  W [ 8            14 ] A
         9 10 11 12 13
         G GND NC C B
```

NC - No internal connection

FUNCTION TABLE

INPUTS				OUTPUTS	
SELECT			ENABLE		
C	B	A	$\overline{G}$	Y	W
X	X	X	H	Z	Z
L	L	L	L	D0	$\overline{D0}$
L	L	H	L	D1	$\overline{D1}$
L	H	L	L	D2	$\overline{D2}$
L	H	H	L	D3	$\overline{D3}$
H	L	L	L	D4	$\overline{D4}$
H	L	H	L	D5	$\overline{D5}$
H	H	L	L	D6	$\overline{D6}$
H	H	H	L	D7	$\overline{D7}$

H = high logic level, L = low logic level
X = irrelevant, Z = high impedance (off)
D0, D1 . . . D7 = the level of the respective D input

3

TTL DEVICES

TEXAS INSTRUMENTS

logic diagram

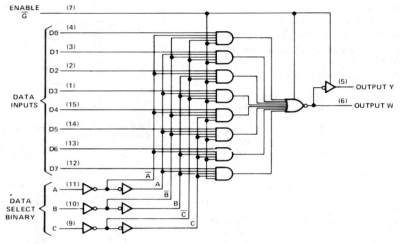

Pin numbers shown on logic notation are for D, J or N packages.

TEXAS
INSTRUMENTS

absolute maximum ratings over operating free-air temperature range (unless otherwise noted)

Supply voltage, V_{CC} (see Note 1)	7 V
Input voltage	5.5 V
Off-state output voltage	5.5 V
Operating free-air temperature range: SN54251	-55°C to 125°C
SN74251	0°C to 70°C
Storage temperature range	-65°C to 150°C

NOTE 1: Voltage values are with respect to network ground terminal.

recommended operating conditions

	SN54251			SN74251			UNIT
	MIN	NOM	MAX	MIN	NOM	MAX	
Supply voltage, V_{CC}	4.5	5	5.5	4.75	5	5.25	V
High-level output current, I_{OH}			-2			-5.2	mA
Low-level output current, I_{OL}			16			16	mA
Operating free-air temperature, T_A	-55		125	0		70	$^\circ$C

electrical characteristics over recommended operating free-air temperature range (unless otherwise noted)

	PARAMETER	TEST CONDITIONS[†]		MIN	TYP[‡]	MAX	UNIT
V_{IH}	High-level input voltage			2			V
V_{IL}	Low-level input voltage					0.8	V
V_{IK}	Input clamp voltage	V_{CC} = MIN,	I_I = -12 mA			-1.5	V
V_{OH}	High-level output voltage	V_{CC} = MIN, V_{IL} = 0.8 V,	V_{IH} = 2 V, I_{OH} = MAX	2.4	3.2		V
V_{OL}	Low-level output voltage	V_{CC} = MIN, V_{IL} = 0.8 V,	V_{IH} = 2 V, I_{OL} = 16 mA		0.2	0.4	V
I_{OZ}	Off-state (high-impedance-state) output current	V_{CC} = MAX, V_{IH} = 2 V	V_O = 2.4 V			40	μA
			V_O = 0.4 V			-40	
V_O	Output clamp voltage	V_{CC} = MAX, V_{IH} = 4.5 V	I_O = -12 mA			-1.5	V
			I_O = 12 mA			V_{CC}+1.5	
I_I	Input current at maximum input voltage	V_{CC} = MAX,	V_I = 5.5 V			1	mA
I_{IH}	High-level input current	V_{CC} = MAX,	V_I = 2.4 V			40	μA
I_{IL}	Low-level input current	V_{CC} = MAX,	V_I = 0.4 V			-1.6	mA
I_{OS}	Short-circuit output current[§]	V_{CC} = MAX		-18		-55	mA
I_{CC}	Supply current	V_{CC} = MAX, All inputs at 4.5 V, All outputs open			38	62	mA

[†]For conditions shown as MIN or MAX, use the appropriate value specified under recommended operating conditions for the applicable type.
[‡]All typical values are at V_{CC} = 5 V, T_A = 25°C.
[§]Not more than one output should be shorted at a time.

3

TTL DEVICES

switching characteristics, V_{CC} = 5 V, T_A = 25°C

PARAMETER¶	FROM (INPUT)	TO (OUTPUT)	TEST CONDITIONS	MIN	TYP	MAX	UNIT
t_{PLH}	A, B, or C	Y			29	45	ns
t_{PHL}	(4 levels)				28	45	
t_{PLH}	A, B, or C	W			20	33	ns
t_{PHL}	(3 levels)				21	33	
t_{PLH}	Any D	Y	C_L = 50 pF,		17	28	ns
t_{PHL}			R_L = 400 Ω,		18	28	
t_{PLH}	Any D	W	See Note 2		10	15	ns
t_{PHL}					9	15	
t_{PZH}	$\overline{G}$	Y			17	27	ns
t_{PZL}					26	40	
t_{PZH}	$\overline{G}$	W			17	27	ns
t_{PZL}					24	40	
t_{PHZ}	$\overline{G}$	Y	C_L = 5 pF,		5	8	ns
t_{PLZ}			R_L = 400 Ω,		15	23	
t_{PHZ}	$\overline{G}$	W	See Note 2		5	8	ns
t_{PLZ}					15	23	

t_{PLH} = Propagation delay time, low-to-high-level output
t_{PHL} = Propagation delay time, high-to-low-level output
t_{PZH} = Output enable time to high level
t_{PZL} = Output enable time to low level.
t_{PHZ} = Output disable time from high level
t_{PLZ} = Output disable time from low level
NOTE 2: See General Information Section for load circuits and voltage waveforms.

schematics of inputs and outputs

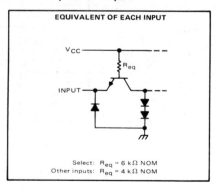

EQUIVALENT OF EACH INPUT

V_{CC}

R_{eq}

INPUT

Select: R_{eq} = 6 kΩ NOM
Other inputs: R_{eq} = 4 kΩ NOM

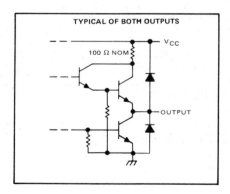

TYPICAL OF BOTH OUTPUTS

V_{CC}

100 Ω NOM

OUTPUT

TEXAS
INSTRUMENTS

absolute maximum ratings over operating free-air temperature range (unless otherwise noted)

Supply voltage, V_{CC} (see Note 1) . . . . 7 V
Input voltage . . . . 7 V
Off-state output voltage . . . . 5.5 V
Operating free-air temperature range: SN54LS251 . . . . 55°C to 125°C
$\qquad\qquad\qquad\qquad\qquad\qquad\quad$ SN74LS251 . . . . 0°C to 70°C
Storage temperature range . . . . -65°C to 150°C

NOTE 1: Voltage values are with respect to network ground terminal.

recommended operating conditions

		SN54LS251			SN74LS251			UNIT
		MIN	NOM	MAX	MIN	NOM	MAX	
V_{CC}	Supply voltage	4.5	5	5.5	4.75	5	5.25	V
V_{IH}	High-level input voltage	2			2			V
V_{IL}	Low-level input voltage			0.7			0.8	V
I_{OH}	High-level output current			-1			-2.6	mA
I_{OL}	Low-level output current			4			8	mA
T_A	Operating free-air temperature	-55		125	0		70	$^{\circ}$C

electrical characteristics over recommended operating free-air temperature range (unless otherwise noted)

PARAMETER		TEST CONDITIONS†		SN54LS251			SN74LS251			UNIT
				MIN	TYP‡	MAX	MIN	TYP‡	MAX	
V_{IK}		V_{CC} = MIN,	$I_I = -18$ mA			-1.5			-1.5	V
V_{OH}		V_{CC} = MIN, V_{IH} = 2 V, $\quad V_{IL}$ = MAX I_{OH} = MAX		2.4	3.4		2.4	3.1		V
V_{OL}		V_{CC} = MIN, V_{IH} = 2 V, V_{IL} = MAX	I_{OL} = 4 mA		0.25	0.4		0.25	0.4	V
			I_{OL} = 8 mA					0.35	0.5	
I_{OZ}		V_{CC} = MAX, V_{IH} = 2 V	V_O = 2.7 V			20			20	μA
			V_O = 0.4 V			-20			-20	
I_I		V_{CC} = MAX, V_I = 7 V				0.1			0.1	mA
I_{IH}		V_{CC} = MAX, V_I = 2.7 V				20			20	μA
I_{IL}	Enable $\overline{G}$	V_{CC} = MAX, V_I = 0.4				-0.2			-0.2	mA
	All other					-0.4			-0.4	
I_{OS}§		V_{CC} = MAX		-30		-130	-30		-130	mA
I_{CC}		V_{CC} = MAX, See Note 3	Condition A		6.1	10		6.1	10	mA
			Condition B		7.1	12		7.1	12	

† For conditions shown as MIN or MAX, use the appropriate value specified under recommended operating conditions for the applicable type.
‡ All typical values are at V_{CC} = 5 V, T_A = 25°C.
§ Not more than one output should be shorted at a time, and duration of the short-circuit should not exceed one second.
NOTE 3: I_{CC} is measured with the outputs open and all data and select inputs at 4.5 V under the following conditions:
$\qquad$ A. Enable grounded.
$\qquad$ B. Strobe at 4.5 V.

3

TTL DEVICES

TEXAS
INSTRUMENTS

switching characteristics, V_{CC} = 5 V, T_A = 25°C

PARAMETER¶	FROM (INPUT)	TO (OUTPUT)	TEST CONDITIONS	MIN	TYP	MAX	UNIT
t_{PLH}	A, B, or C	Y			29	45	ns
t_{PHL}	(4 levels)				28	45	
t_{PLH}	A, B, or C	W			20	33	ns
t_{PHL}	(3 levels)				21	33	
t_{PLH}	Any D	Y	C_L = 5 pF,		17	28	ns
t_{PHL}			R_L = 2 kΩ,		18	28	
t_{PLH}	Any D	W	See Note 2		10	15	ns
t_{PHL}					9	15	
t_{PZH}	$\overline{G}$	Y			30	45	ns
t_{PZL}					26	40	
t_{PZH}	$\overline{G}$	W			17	27	ns
t_{PZL}					24	40	
t_{PHZ}	$\overline{G}$	Y	C_L = 15 pF,		30	45	ns
t_{PLZ}			R_L = 2 kΩ,		15	25	
t_{PHZ}	$\overline{G}$	W	See Note 2		37	55	ns
t_{PLZ}					15	25	

¶t_{PLH} = Propagation delay time, low-to-high-level output
t_{PHL} = Propagation delay time, low-to-high-level output
t_{PZH} = Output enable time to high level
t_{PZL} = Output enable time to low level
t_{PHZ} = Output disable time from high level
t_{PLZ} = Output disable time from low level
NOTE 2:   See General Information Section for load circuits and voltage waveforms.

schematics of inputs and outputs

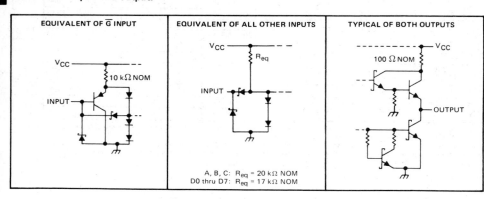

EQUIVALENT OF $\overline{G}$ INPUT	EQUIVALENT OF ALL OTHER INPUTS	TYPICAL OF BOTH OUTPUTS
V_{CC} — 10 kΩ NOM — INPUT	V_{CC} — R_{eq} — INPUT — A, B, C: R_{eq} = 20 kΩ NOM / D0 thru D7: R_{eq} = 17 kΩ NOM	100 Ω NOM — V_{CC} — OUTPUT

TEXAS
INSTRUMENTS

absolute maximum ratings over operating free-air temperature range (unless otherwise noted)

Supply voltage, V_{CC} (see Note 1) . . . . 7 V
Input voltage . . . . 5.5 V
Off-state output voltage . . . . 5.5 V
Operating free-air temperature range: SN54S251 . . . . -55°C to 125°C
　　　　　　　　　　　　　　　　　　　 SN74S251 . . . . 0°C to 70°C
Storage temperature range . . . . -65°C to 150°C

NOTE 1: Voltage values are with respect to network ground terminal.

recommended operating conditions

	SN54S251			SN74S251			UNIT
	MIN	NOM	MAX	MIN	NOM	MAX	
Supply voltage, V_{CC}	4.5	5	5.5	4.75	5	5.25	V
High-level output current, I_{OH}			-2			-6.5	mA
Low-level output current, I_{OL}			20			20	mA
Operating free-air temperature, T_A	-55		125	0		70	°C

electrical characteristics over recommended operating free-air temperature range (unless otherwise noted)

PARAMETER		TEST CONDITIONS[†]			MIN	TYP[‡]	MAX	UNIT
V_{IH}	High-level input voltage				2			V
V_{IL}	Low-level input voltage						0.8	V
V_{IK}	Input clamp voltage	V_{CC} = MIN,	$I_I = -18$ mA				-1.2	V
V_{OH}	High-level output voltage	V_{CC} = MIN,	V_{IH} = 2 V,	SN54S'	2.4	3.4		V
		V_{IL} = 0.8 V,	I_{OH} = MAX	SN74S'	2.4	3.2		
V_{OL}	Low-level output voltage	V_{CC} = MIN,	V_{IH} = 2 V,				0.5	V
		V_{IL} = 0.8 V,	I_{OL} = 20 mA					
I_{OZ}	Off-state (high-impedance-state) output current	V_{CC} = MAX,	V_O = 2.4 V				50	μA
		V_{IH} = 2 V	V_O = 0.5 V				50	
I_I	Input current at maximum input voltage	V_{CC} = MAX,	V_I = 5.5 V				1	mA
I_{IH}	High-level input current	V_{CC} = MAX,	V_I = 2.7 V				50	μA
I_{IL}	Low-level input current	V_{CC} = MAX,	V_I = 0.5 V				2	mA
I_{OS}	Short-circuit output current [§]	V_{CC} = MAX			40		100	mA
I_{CC}	Supply current	V_{CC} = MAX,	All inputs at 4.5 V,			55	85	mA
		All outputs open						

[†]For conditions shown as MIN or MAX, use the appropriate value specified under recommended operating conditions for the applicable type.
[‡]All typical values are at V_{CC} = 5 V, T_A = 25°C.
[§]Not more than one output should be shorted at a time, and duration of the short-circuit should not exceed one second.

3

TTL DEVICES

TEXAS
INSTRUMENTS

TYPES SN54S251, SN74S251
DATA SELECTORS/MULTIPLEXERS WITH 3-STATE OUTPUTS

switching characteristics, V_{CC} = 5 V, T_A = 25°C

PARAMETER¶	FROM (INPUT)	TO (OUTPUT)	TEST CONDITIONS	MIN	TYP	MAX	UNIT
t_{PLH}	A, B, or C	Y			12	18	ns
t_{PHL}	(4 levels)				13	19.5	
t_{PLH}	A, B, or C	W	C_L = 15 pF,		10	15	ns
t_{PHL}	(3 levels)		R_L = 280 Ω,		9	13.5	
t_{PLH}	Any D	Y	See Note 2		8	12	ns
t_{PHL}					8	12	
t_{PLH}	Any D	W			4.5	7	ns
t_{PHL}					4.5	7	
t_{PZH}	$\overline{G}$	Y	C_L = 50 pF,		13	19.5	ns
t_{PZL}			R_L = 280 Ω,		14	21	
t_{PZH}	$\overline{G}$	W	See Note 2		13	19.5	ns
t_{PZL}					14	21	
t_{PHZ}	$\overline{G}$	Y	C_L = 5 pF,		5.5	8.5	ns
t_{PLZ}			R_L = 280 Ω,		9	14	
t_{PHZ}	$\overline{G}$	W	See Note 2		5.5	8.5	ns
t_{PLZ}					9	14	

¶ t_{PLH} = Propagation delay time, low-to-high-level output
t_{PHL} = Propagation delay time, high-to-low-level output
t_{PZH} = Output enable time to high level
t_{PZL} = Output enable time to low level
t_{PHZ} = Output disable time from high level
t_{PLZ} = Output disable time from low level
NOTE 2: See General Information Section for load circuits and voltage waveforms.

schematics of inputs and outputs

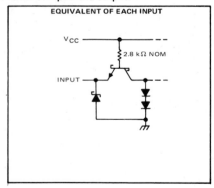

EQUIVALENT OF EACH INPUT

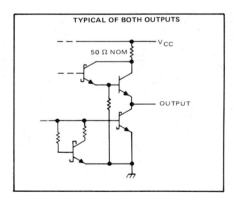

TYPICAL OF BOTH OUTPUTS

TEXAS INSTRUMENTS

3

TTL DEVICES

TYPES SN54LS253, SN54S253, SN74LS253, SN74S253
DUAL 4-LINE TO 1-LINE DATA SELECTORS/MULTIPLEXERS
WITH 3-STATE OUTPUTS

SEPTEMBER 1972 – REVISED DECEMBER 1983

- **Three-State Version of SN54/74LS153, SN54/74S153**
- **Schottky-Diode-Clamped Transistors**
- **Permits Multiplexing from N Lines to 1 Line**
- **Performs Parallel-to Serial Conversion**
- **Fully Compatible with Most TTL Circuits**
- **Low Power Dissipation**
  'LS253 . . . 35 mW Typical
  'S253 . . . 225 mW Typical

description

Each of these Schottky-clamped data selectors/multiplexers contains inverters and drivers to supply fully complementary, on-chip, binary decoding data selection to the AND-OR gates. Separate output control inputs are provided for each of the two four-line sections.

The three-state outputs can interface with and drive data lines of bus-organized systems. With all but one of the common outputs disabled (at a high-impedance state) the low-impedance of the single enabled output will drive the bus line to a high or low logic level.

SN54LS253, SN54S253 . . . J OR W PACKAGE
SN74LS253, SN74S253 . . . D, J OR N PACKAGE
(TOP VIEW)

1G	1	16	VCC
B	2	15	2G
1C3	3	14	A
1C2	4	13	2C3
1C1	5	12	2C2
1C0	6	11	2C1
1Y	7	10	2C0
GND	8	9	2Y

SN54LS253, SN54S253 . . . FK PACKAGE
SN74LS253, SN74S253
(TOP VIEW)

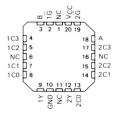

NC-No internal connection

FUNCTION TABLE

SELECT INPUTS		DATA INPUTS				OUTPUT CONTROL	OUTPUT
B	A	C0	C1	C2	C3	G̅	Y
X	X	X	X	X	X	H	Z
L	L	L	X	X	X	L	L
L	L	H	X	X	X	L	H
L	H	X	L	X	X	L	L
L	H	X	H	X	X	L	H
H	L	X	X	L	X	L	L
H	L	X	X	H	X	L	H
H	H	X	X	X	L	L	L
H	H	X	X	X	H	L	H

Address inputs A and B are common to both sections.

H = high level, L = low level, X = irrelevant, Z = high impedance (off)

absolute maximum ratings over operating free-air temperature range (unless otherwise noted)

Supply voltage, VCC (see Note 1) .... 7 V
Input voltage: 'LS253 .... 7 V
             'S253 .... 5.5 V
Off-state output voltage .... 5.5 V
Operating free-air temperature range: SN54LS253, SN54S253 .... −55°C to 125°C
                               SN74LS253, SN74S253 .... 0°C to 70°C
Storage temperature range .... −65°C to 150°C

NOTE 1: Voltage values are with respect to network ground terminal.

TEXAS
INSTRUMENTS

3-699

3

TTL DEVICES

logic diagram

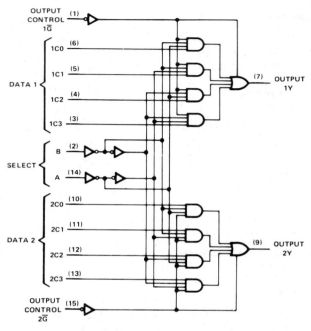

Pin numbers shown on logic notation are for D, J or N packages.

TEXAS
INSTRUMENTS

schematic (each selector/multiplexer, and the common select section)

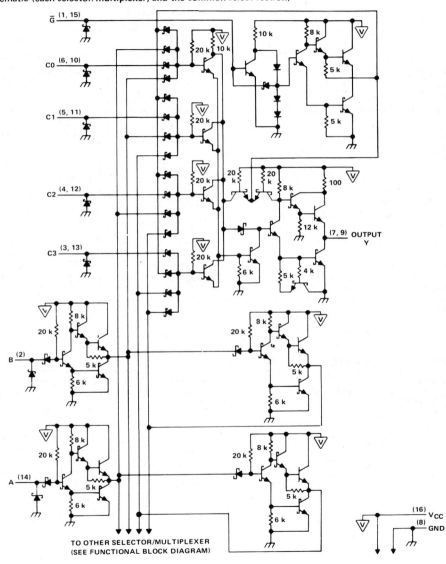

TO OTHER SELECTOR/MULTIPLEXER
(SEE FUNCTIONAL BLOCK DIAGRAM)

Pin numbers shown are for D, J or N packages.

TEXAS
INSTRUMENTS

TTL DEVICES

3

recommended operating conditions

		SN54LS253			SN74LS253			UNIT
		MIN	NOM	MAX	MIN	NOM	MAX	
V_{CC}	Supply voltage	4.5	5	5.5	4.75	5	5.25	V
V_{IH}	High-level input voltage	2			2			V
V_{IL}	Low-level input voltage			0.7			0.8	V
I_{OH}	High-level output current			-1			-2.6	mA
I_{OL}	Low-level output current			4			8	mA
T_A	Operating free-air temperature	-55		125	0		70	$^\circ$C

electrical characteristics over recommended operating free-air temperature range (unless otherwise noted)

PARAMETER	TEST CONDITIONS†				SN54LS253			SN74LS253			UNIT
					MIN	TYP‡	MAX	MIN	TYP‡	MAX	
V_{IK}	V_{CC} = MIN,	$I_I = -18$ mA					-1.5			-1.5	V
V_{OH}	V_{CC} = MIN,	V_{IH} = 2 V,	V_{IL} = MAX,	I_{OH} = MAX	2.4	3.4		2.4	3.1		V
V_{OL}	V_{CC} = MIN,	V_{IH} = 2 V,	V_{IL} = MAX	I_{OL} = 4 mA		0.25	0.4		0.25	0.4	V
				I_{OL} = 8 mA					0.25	0.5	
I_{OZ}	V_{CC} = MAX,	V_{IH} = 2 V		V_O = 2.7 V			20			20	μA
				V_O = 0.4 V			-20			-20	
I_I	V_{CC} = MAX,	V_I = 7 V					0.1			0.1	mA
I_{IH}	V_{CC} = MAX,	V_I = 2.7 V					20			20	μA
I_{IL}	V_{CC} = MAX,	V_I = 0.4 V		$\overline{G}$			-0.2			-0.2	mA
				All other			-0.4			-0.4	
I_{OS}§	V_{CC} = MAX				-30		-130	-30		-130	mA
I_{CC}	V_{CC} = MAX,	See Note 2		Condition A		7	12		7	12	mA
				Condition B		8.5	14		8.5	14	

† For conditions shown as MIN or MAX, use the appropriate value spcified under recommended operating conditions.
‡ All typical values are at V_{CC} = 5 V, T_A = 25°C.
§ Not more than one output should be shorted at a time, and duration for the short-circuit should exceed one second.
NOTE 2: I_{CC} is measured with the outputs open under the following conditions:
    A. All inputs grounded.
    B. Output control at 4.5 V, all inputs grounded.

switching characteristics, V_{CC} = 5 V, T_A = 25°C

PARAMETER	FROM (INPUT)	TO (OUTPUT)	TEST CONDITIONS		MIN	TYP	MAX	UNIT
t_{PLH}	Data	Y				17	25	ns
t_{PHL}						13	20	
t_{PLH}	Select	Y	C_L = 15 pF,	R_L = 2 kΩ,		30	45	ns
t_{PHL}			See Note 3			21	32	
t_{PZH}	Output	Y				15	28	ns
t_{PZL}	Control					15	23	
t_{PHZ}	Output	Y	C_L = 5 pF,	R_L = 2 kΩ,		27	41	ns
t_{PLZ}	Control		See Note 3			18	27	

NOTE 3: See General Information Section for load circuits and voltage waveforms.

3

TTL DEVICES

TEXAS
INSTRUMENTS

recommended operating conditions

		SN54S253			SN74S253			UNIT
		MIN	NOM	MAX	MIN	NOM	MAX	
V_{CC}	Supply voltage	4.5	5	5.5	4.75	5	5.25	V
V_{IH}	High-level input voltage	2			2			V
V_{IL}	Low-level input voltage			0.8			0.8	V
I_{OH}	High-level output current			−2			−6.5	mA
I_{OL}	Low-level output current			20			20	mA
T_A	Operating free-air temperature	−55		125	0		70	°C

electrical characteristics over recommended operating free-air temperature range (unless otherwise noted)

PARAMETER	TEST CONDITIONS†				MIN	TYP‡	MAX	UNIT
V_{IK}	V_{CC} = MIN,	I_I = −18 mA					−1.2	V
V_{OH}	V_{CC} = MIN,	V_{IH} = 2 V,	V_{IL} = 0.8 V,	I_{OH} = MAX	Series 54S	2.5	3.4		V
					Series 74S	2.7	3.4		
V_{OL}	V_{CC} = MIN,	V_{IH} = 2 V,	V_{IL} = 0.8 V,	I_{OL} = 20 mA			0.5	V
I_{OZ}	V_{CC} = MAX,	V_{IH} = 2 V		V_O = 2.4 V			50	μA
				V_O = 0.5 V			−50	
I_I	V_{CC} = MAX,	V_I = 5.5 V					1	mA
I_{IH}	V_{CC} = MAX,	V_I = 2.7 V					50	μA
I_{IL}	V_{CC} = MAX,	V_I = 0.5 V		$\overline{G}$ = 0.8 V,			−2	mA
				$\overline{G}$ = 2 V			−0.25	
I_{OS}§	V_{CC} = MAX				−40		−100	mA
I_{CC}	V_{CC} = MAX,	See Note 2		Condition A		45	70	mA
				Condition B		65	85	

† For conditions shown as MIN or MAX, use the appropriate value specified under recommended operating conditions.
‡ All typical values are at V_{CC} = 5 V, T_A = 25°C.
 § Not more than one output should be shorted at a time and duration of short-circuit should not exceed one second.
NOTE 2: I_{CC} is measured with the outputs open under the following conditions:
    A. All inputs grounded.
    B. Output control at 4.5 V, all inputs grounded.

switching characteristics, V_{CC} = 5 V, T_A = 25°C

PARAMETER	FROM (INPUT)	TO (OUTPUT)	TEST CONDITIONS		MIN	TYP	MAX	UNIT
t_{PLH}	Data	Y				6	9	ns
t_{PHL}						6	9	
t_{PLH}	Select	Y	R_L = 280 Ω,	C_L = 15 pF		11.5	18	ns
t_{PHL}			See Note 3			12	18	
t_{PZH}	Output Control	Y				11	16.5	ns
t_{PZL}						12	18	
t_{PHZ}	Output Control	Y	R_L = 280 Ω,	C_L = 5 pF		6.5	9.5	ns
t_{PLZ}			See Note 3			10	15	

NOTE 3: See General Information Section for load circuits and voltage waveforms.

TTL DEVICES 3

TEXAS
INSTRUMENTS

TYPES SN54LS257B, SN54LS258B, SN54S257, SN54S258, SN74LS257B, SN74LS258B, SN74S257, SN74S258
QUADRUPLE 2-LINE TO 1-LINE DATA SELECTORS/MULTIPLEXERS

OCTOBER 1976 – REVISED DECEMBER 1983

- **Three-State Outputs Interface Directly with System Bus**

- **'LS257B and 'LS258B Offer Three Times the Sink-Current Capability of the Original 'LS257 and 'LS258**

- **Same Pin Assignments as SN54LS157, SN74LS157, SN54S157, SN74S157, and SN54LS158, SN74LS158, SN54S158, SN74S158**

- **Provides Bus Interface from Multiple Sources in High-Performance Systems**

	AVERAGE PROPAGATION DELAY FROM DATA INPUT	TYPICAL POWER DISSIPATION[†]
'LS257B	9 ns	55 mW
'LS258B	9 ns	55 mW
'S257	4.8 ns	320 mW
'S258	4 ns	280 mW

[†]Off state (worst case)

description

These devices are designed to multiplex signals from four-bit data sources to four-output data lines in bus-organized systems. The 3-state outputs will not load the data lines when the output control pin ($\overline{G}$) is at a high-logic level.

Series 54LS and 54S are characterized for operation over the full military temperature range of $-55°C$ to $125°C$; Series 74LS and 74S are characterized for operation from $0°C$ to $70°C$.

SN54LS257B, SN54S257,
SN54LS258B, SN54S258 . . . J OR W PACKAGE
SN74LS257B, SN74S257,
SN74LS258B, SN74S258 . . . D, J OR N PACKAGE
(TOP VIEW)

```
         ___
 A/B [ 1  U 16 ] VCC
  1A [ 2    15 ] G
  1B [ 3    14 ] 4A
  1Y [ 4    13 ] 4B
  2A [ 5    12 ] 4Y
  2B [ 6    11 ] 3A
  2Y [ 7    10 ] 3B
 GND [ 8     9 ] 3Y
```

SN54LS257B, SN54S257, SN54LS258B,
SN54S258, SN74LS257B, SN74LS258B,
SN74LS258B, SN74S258 . . . FK PACKAGE
(TOP VIEW)

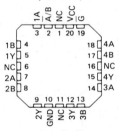

NC–No internal connection.

FUNCTION TABLE

INPUTS				OUTPUT Y	
OUTPUT CONTROL	SELECT	A	B	'LS257B 'S257	'LS258B 'S258
H	X	X	X	Z	Z
L	L	L	X	L	H
L	L	H	X	H	L
L	H	X	L	L	H
L	H	X	H	H	L

H = high level, L = low level, X = irrelevant,
Z = high impedance (off)

TEXAS INSTRUMENTS

3

TTL DEVICES

logic diagrams

'LS257B, 'S257

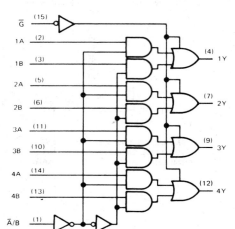

'LS258B, 'S258

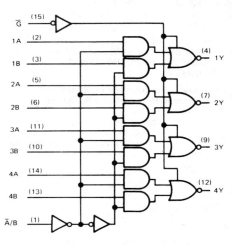

logic symbol

'LS257B

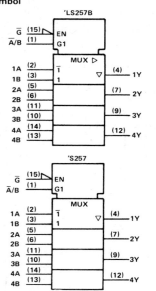

'LS258B

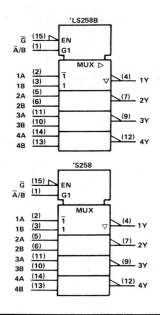

'S257

'S258

Pin numbers shown on logic notation are for D, J or N packages.

TEXAS
INSTRUMENTS

schematics of inputs and outputs

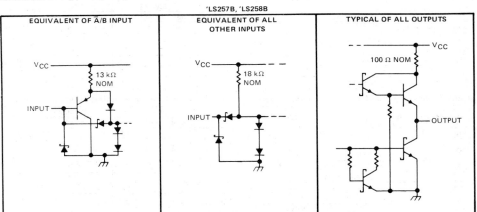

'LS257B, 'LS258B

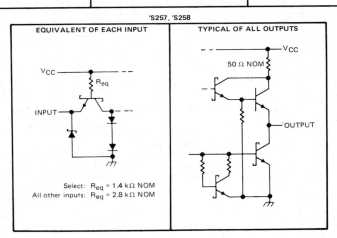

'S257, 'S258

absolute maximum ratings over operating free-air temperature range (unless otherwise noted)

Supply voltage, V_{CC} (see Note 1) .... 7 V
Input voltage: 'LS257B, 'LS258B Circuits .... 7 V
        'S257, 'S258 Circuits .... 5.5 V
Off-state output voltage .... 5.5 V
Operating free-air temperature range: SN54LS', SN54S' Circuits .... -55°C to 125°C
        SN74LS', SN74S' Circuits .... 0°C to 70°C
Storage temperature range .... -65°C to 150°C

NOTE 1: Voltage values are with respect to network ground terminal.

recommended operating conditions

		SN54LS' MIN	SN54LS' NOM	SN54LS' MAX	SN74LS' MIN	SN74LS' NOM	SN74LS' MAX	UNIT
V_{CC}	Supply voltage	4.5	5	5.5	4.75	5	5.25	V
V_{IH}	High-level input voltage	2			2			V
V_{IL}	Low-level input voltage			0.7			0.8	V
I_{OH}	High-level output current			-1			-2.6	mA
I_{OL}	Low-level output current			12			24	mA
T_A	Operating free-air temperature	-55		125	0		70	°C

electrical characteristics over recommended operating free-air temperature range (unless otherwise noted)

PARAMETER		TEST CONDITIONS†			SN54LS' MIN	SN54LS' TYP‡	SN54LS' MAX	SN74LS' MIN	SN74LS' TYP‡	SN74LS' MAX	UNIT
V_{IK}		$V_{CC} = MIN$,	$I_I = -18$ mA				-1.5			-1.5	V
V_{OH}		$V_{CC} = MIN$, $I_{OH} = MAX$	$V_{IH} = 2$ V,	$V_{IL} = MAX$,	2.4	3.4		2.4	3.1		V
V_{OL}		$V_{CC} = MIN$, $V_{IL} = MAX$,	$V_{IH} = 2$ V,	$I_{OL} = 12$ mA		0.25	0.4		0.25	0.4	V
				$I_{OL} = 24$ mA					0.35	0.5	
I_{OZH}		$V_{CC} = MAX$,	$V_{IH} = 2$ V,	$V_O = 2.7$ V			20			20	µA
I_{OZL}		$V_{CC} = MAX$,	$V_{IH} = 2$ V,	$V_O = 0.4$ V			-20			-20	µA
I_I		$V_{CC} = MAX$,	$V_I = 7$ V				0.1			0.1	mA
I_{IH}		$V_{CC} = MAX$,	$V_I = 2.7$ V				20			20	µA
I_{IL}		$V_{CC} = MAX$,	$V_I = 0.4$ V				-0.4			-0.4	mA
I_{OS} §		$V_{CC} = MAX$,			-30		-130	-30		-130	mA
I_{CC}	All outputs high	$V_{CC} = MAX$, See Note 2	'LS257B			8	12		8	12	mA
	All outputs low					12	18		12	18	
	All outputs off					13	19		13	19	
	All outputs high		'LS258B			6	9		6	9	
	All outputs low					10	15		10	15	
	All outputs off					11	16		11	16	

†For conditions shown as MIN or MAX, use the appropriate value specified under recommended operating conditions.
‡All typical values are at $V_{CC} = 5$ V, $T_A = 25°C$.
§Not more than one output should be shorted at a time and duration of the short-circuit should not exceed one second.
NOTE 2: I_{CC} is measured with all outputs open and all possible inputs grounded while achieving the stated output conditions.

switching characteristics, $V_{CC} = 5$ V, $T_A = 25°C$, $R_L = 667$ Ω

PARAMETER	FROM (INPUT)	TO (OUTPUT)	TEST CONDITIONS		'LS257B MIN	'LS257B TYP	'LS257B MAX	'LS258B MIN	'LS258B TYP	'LS258B MAX	UNIT
t_{PLH}	Data	Any				8	13		7	12	ns
t_{PHL}						10	15		11	17	
t_{PLH}	Select	Any	$C_L = 45$ pF,	See Note 3		16	21		14	21	ns
t_{PHL}						17	24		19	24	
t_{PZH}	Output Control	Any				15	30		15	30	ns
t_{PZL}						19	30		20	30	
t_{PHZ}	Output Control	Any	$C_L = 5$ pF,	See Note 3		18	30		18	30	ns
t_{PLZ}						16	25		16	25	

t_{PLH} = propagation delay time, low-to-high-level output
t_{PHL} = propagation delay time, high-to-low-level output
t_{PZH} = output enable time to high level
t_{PZL} = output enable time to low level
t_{PHZ} = output disable time from high level
t_{PLZ} = output disable time from low level
NOTE 3: See General Information Section for load circuits and voltage waveforms.

recommended operating conditions

	SN54S' MIN	SN54S' NOM	SN54S' MAX	SN74S' MIN	SN74S' NOM	SN74S' MAX	UNIT
Supply voltage, V_{CC}	4.5	5	5.5	4.75	5	5.25	V
High-level output current, I_{OH}			−2			−6.5	mA
Low-level output current, I_{OL}			20			20	mA
Operating free-air temperature, T_A	−55		125	0		70	°C

electrical characteristics over recommended operating free-air temperature range (unless otherwise noted)

PARAMETER		TEST CONDITIONS[†]		'S257 MIN	'S257 TYP[‡]	'S257 MAX	'S258 MIN	'S258 TYP[‡]	'S258 MAX	UNIT
V_{IH}	High-level input voltage			2			2			V
V_{IL}	Low-level input voltage					0.8			0.8	V
V_{IK}	Input clamp voltage	V_{CC} = MIN, I_I = −18 mA				−1.2			−1.2	V
V_{OH}	High-level output voltage	V_{CC} = MIN, V_{IH} = 2 V, V_{IL} = 0.8 V, I_{OH} = −1 mA	SN74S'	2.7			2.7			V
		V_{CC} = MIN, V_{IH} = 2 V,	SN54S'	2.4	3.4		2.4	3.4		
		V_{IL} = 0.8 V, I_{OH} = MAX	SN74S'	2.4	3.2		2.4	3.2		
V_{OL}	Low-level output voltage	V_{CC} = MIN, V_{IH} = 2 V, V_{IL} = 0.8 V, I_{OL} = 20 mA				0.5			0.5	V
I_{OZH}	Off-state output current, high-level voltage applied	V_{CC} = MAX, V_{IH} = 2 V, V_O = 2.4 V				50			50	µA
I_{OZL}	Off-state output current, low-level voltage applied	V_{CC} = MAX, V_{IH} = 2 V, V_O = 0.5 V				−50			−50	µA
I_I	Input current at maximum input voltage	V_{CC} = MAX, V_I = 5.5 V				1			1	mA
I_{IH}	High-level input current	S input	V_{CC} = MAX, V_I = 2.7 V			100			100	µA
		Any other				50			50	
I_{IL}	Low-level input current	S input	V_{CC} = MAX V_I = 0.5 V			−4			−4	mA
		Any other				−2			−2	
I_{OS}	Short-circuit output current[§]	V_{CC} = MAX		−40		−100	−40		−100	mA
I_{CC}	Supply current	All outputs high	V_{CC} = MAX, See Note 2		44	68		36	56	mA
		All outputs low			60	93		52	81	
		All outputs off			64	99		56	87	

[†] For conditions shown as MIN or MAX, use the appropriate value specified under recommended operating conditions.
[‡] All typical values are at V_{CC} = 5 V, T_A = 25°C.
[§] Not more than one output should be shorted at a time and duration of the short-circuit should not exceed one second.
NOTE 2: I_{CC} is measured with all outputs open and all possible inputs grounded while achieving the stated output conditions.

switching characteristics, V_{CC} = 5 V, T_A = 25°C, R_L = 280 Ω

PARAMETER[¶]	FROM (INPUT)	TO (OUTPUT)	TEST CONDITIONS	'S257 MIN	'S257 TYP	'S257 MAX	'S258 MIN	'S258 TYP	'S258 MAX	UNIT
t_{PLH}	Data	Any			5	7.5		4	6	ns
t_{PHL}					4.5	6.5		4	6	
t_{PLH}	Select	Any	C_L = 15 pF, See Note 3		8.5	15		8	12	ns
t_{PHL}					8.5	15		7.5	12	
t_{PZH}	Output Control	Any			13	19.5		13	19.5	ns
t_{PZL}					14	21		14	21	
t_{PHZ}	Output Control	Any	C_L = 5 pF, See Note 3		5.5	8.5		5.5	8.5	ns
t_{PLZ}					9	14		9	14	

[¶] f_{max} = Maximum clock frequency
t_{PLH} = propagation delay time, low-to-high-level output
t_{PHL} = propagation delay time, high-to-low-level output
t_{PZH} = output enable time to high level

t_{PZL} output enable time to low level
t_{PHZ} output disable time from high level
t_{PLZ} output disable time from low level
NOTE 3: See General Information Section for load circuits and voltage waveforms.

TEXAS INSTRUMENTS

3

TTL DEVICES

- **8-Bit Parallel-Out Storage Register Performs Serial-to-Parallel Conversion with Storage**
- **Asynchronous Parallel Clear**
- **Active High Decoder**
- **Enable/Disable Input Simplifies Expansion**
- **Expandable for N-Bit Applications**
- **Four Distinct Functional Modes**
- **Package Options Include Both Plastic and Ceramic Chip Carriers in Addition to Plastic and Ceramic DIPS**
- **Dependable Texas Instruments Quality and Reliability**

SN54259, SN54LS259B . . . J OR W PACKAGE
SN74259 . . . J OR N PACKAGE
SN74LS259B . . . D, J OR N PACKAGE
(TOP VIEW)

SN54LS259B . . . FK PACKAGE
SN74LS259B
(TOP VIEW)

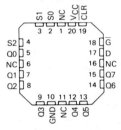

NC - No internal connection

description

These 8-bit addressable latches are designed for general purpose storage applications in digital systems. Specific uses include working registers, serial-holding registers, and active-high decoders or demultiplexers. They are multifunctional devices capable of storing single-line data in eight addressable latches, and being a 1-of-8 decoder or demultiplexer with active-high outputs.

Four distinct modes of operation are selectable by controlling the clear (CLR) and enable (G) inputs as enumerated in the function table. In the addressable-latch mode, data at the data-in terminal is written into the addressed latch. The addressed latch will follow the data input with all unaddressed latches remaining in their previous states. In the memory mode, all latches remain in their previous states and are unaffected by the data or address inputs. To eliminate the possiblity of entering erroneous data in the latches, enable G should be held high (inactive) while the address lines are changing. In the 1-of-8 decoding or demultiplexing mode, the addressed output will follow the level of the D input with all other outputs low. In the clear mode, all outputs are low and unaffected by the address and data inputs.

The SN54259 and SN54LS259B are characterized for operation over the full military temperature range of −55°C to 125°C. The SN74259 and SN74LS259B are characterized for operation from 0°C to 70°C.

logic symbol

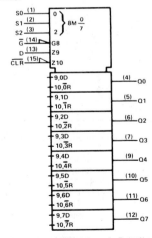

Pin numbers shown on logic notation are for D, J or N packages.

TTL DEVICES

3

TEXAS
INSTRUMENTS

TYPES SN54259, SN54LS259B, SN74259, SN74LS259B
8-BIT ADDRESSABLE LATCHES

FUNCTION TABLE

INPUTS		OUTPUT OF ADDRESSED LATCH	EACH OTHER OUTPUT	FUNCTION
$\overline{CLR}$	$\overline{G}$			
H	L	D	Q_{i0}	Addressable Latch
H	H	Q_{i0}	Q_{i0}	Memory
L	L	D	L	8-Line Demultiplexer
L	H	L	L	Clear

H   high level, L   low level
D   the level at the data input
Q_{i0} the level of Q_i ($i = 0, 1, \ldots 7$, as appropriate) before the indicated steady-state input conditions were established.

LATCH SELECTION TABLE

SELECT INPUTS			LATCH ADDRESSED
S2	S1	S0	
L	L	L	0
L	L	H	1
L	H	L	2
L	H	H	3
H	L	L	4
H	L	H	5
H	H	L	6
H	H	H	7

schematic of inputs and outputs

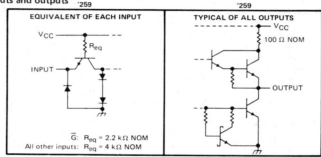

$\overline{G}$: R_{eq} = 2.2 kΩ NOM
All other inputs: R_{eq} = 4 kΩ NOM

absolute maximum ratings over operating free-air temperature range (unless otherwise noted)

Supply voltage (see Note 1) . . . . 7 V
Input voltage: SN54259, SN74259 . . . . 5.5 V
  SN54LS259B, SN74LS259B . . . . 7 V
Operating free-air temperature range: SN54259, SN54LS259B . . . . -55°C to 125°C
  SN74259, SN74LS259B . . . . 0°C to 70°C
Storage temperature range . . . . -65°C to 150°C

NOTE 1: Voltage values are with respect to network ground terminal.

recommended operating conditions

		SN54259 MIN	SN54259 NOM	SN54259 MAX	SN74259 MIN	SN74259 NOM	SN74259 MAX	UNIT
Supply voltage, V_{CC}		4.5	5	5.5	4.75	5	5.25	V
High-level output current, I_{OH}				−800			−800	µA
Low-level output current, I_{OL}				16			16	mA
Width of clear or enable pulse, t_W		15			15			ns
Setup time, t_{su}	Data	15↑			15↑			ns
	Address	5↑			5↑			
Hold time, t_h	Data	0↑			0↑			ns
	Address	20↑			20↑			
Operating free-air temperature, T_A		−55		125	0		70	°C

↑The arrow indicates that the rising edge of the enable pulse is used for reference.

electrical characteristics over recommended operating free-air temperature range (unless otherwise noted)

PARAMETER		TEST CONDITIONS[†]	SN54259 MIN	SN54259 TYP[‡]	SN54259 MAX	SN74259 MIN	SN74259 TYP[‡]	SN74259 MAX	UNIT
V_{IH} High-level input voltage			2			2			V
V_{IL} Low-level input voltage					0.8			0.8	V
V_{IK} Input clamp voltage		V_{CC} = MIN, I_I = 12 mA			−1.5			−1.5	V
V_{OH} High-level output voltage		V_{CC} = MIN, V_{IH} = 2 V, V_{IL} = 0.8 V, I_{OH} = −800 µA	2.4	3.4		2.4	3.4		V
V_{OL} Low-level output voltage		V_{CC} = MIN, V_{IH} = 2 V, V_{IL} = 0.8 V, I_{OL} = 16 mA		0.2	0.4		0.2	0.4	V
I_I Input current at maximum input voltage		V_{CC} = MAX, V_I = 5.5 V			1			1	mA
I_{IH} High-level input current	$\overline{G}$	V_{CC} = MAX, V_I = 2.4 V			80			80	µA
	Other inputs				40			40	
I_{IL} Low-level input current	$\overline{G}$	V_{CC} = MAX, V_I = 0.4 V			−3.2			−3.2	mA
	Other inputs				−1.6			−1.6	
I_{OS} Short-circuit output current[§]		V_{CC} = MAX	−18		−57	−18		−57	mA
I_{CC} Supply current		V_{CC} = MAX, See Note 2		60	90		60	90	mA

[†] For conditions shown as MIN or MAX, use the appropriate value specified under recommended operating conditions.
[‡] All typical values are at V_{CC} = 5 V, T_A = 25°C.
[§] Not more than one output should be shorted at a time.
NOTE 2: I_{CC} is measured with the inputs grounded and the outputs open.

switching characteristics, V_{CC} = 5 V, T_A = 25°C

PARAMETER	FROM (INPUT)	TO (OUTPUT)	TEST CONDITIONS	MIN	TYP	MAX	UNIT
t_{PHL}	$\overline{CLR}$	Any Q			16	25	ns
t_{PLH}	Data	Any Q	C_L = 15 pF, R_L = 400 Ω, See Note 3		14	24	ns
t_{PHL}					11	20	
t_{PLH}	Address	Any Q			15	28	ns
t_{PHL}					17	28	
t_{PLH}	$\overline{G}$	Any Q			12	20	ns
t_{PHL}					11	20	

t_{PLH} ≡ propagation delay time, low-to-high-level output
t_{PHL} ≡ propagation delay time, high-to-low-level output
NOTE 3: See General Information Section for load circuits and voltage waveforms.

TEXAS
INSTRUMENTS

recommended operating conditions

			SN54LS259B			SN74LS259B			UNIT
			MIN	NOM	MAX	MIN	NOM	MAX	
V_{CC}	Supply voltage		4.5	5	5.5	4.75	5	5.25	V
V_{IH}	High-level input voltage		2			2			V
V_{IL}	Low-level input voltage				0.7			0.8	V
I_{OH}	High-level output current				− 0.4			− 0.4	mA
I_{OL}	Low-level output current				4			8	mA
t_w	Pulse duration	$\overline{G}$ low	17			17			ns
		$\overline{CLR}$ low	10			10			
t_{su}	Set up time	Data before $\overline{G}\uparrow$	20			20			ns
		Address before $\overline{G}\uparrow$	17			17			
		Address before $\overline{G}\downarrow$	0			0			
t_h	Hold time	Data after $\overline{G}\uparrow$	0			0			ns
		Address after $\overline{G}\uparrow$	0			0			
T_A	Operating free-air temperature		− 55		125	0		70	°C

electrical characteristics over recommended operating free-air temperature range (unless otherwise noted)

PARAMETER	TEST CONDITIONS[†]			SN54LS259B			SN74LS259B			UNIT
				MIN	TYP	MAX	MIN	TYP	MAX	
V_{IK}	V_{CC} = MIN,	I_I = − 18 mA				− 1.5			− 1.5	V
V_{OH}	V_{CC} = MIN, V_{IH} = 2 V, V_{IL} = MAX, I_{OH} = − 0.4 mA			2.5	3.4		2.7	3.4		V
V_{OL}	V_{CC} = MIN, V_{IH} = 2 V, V_{IL} = MAX		I_{OL} = 4 mA		0.25	0.4		0.25	0.4	V
			I_{OL} = 8 mA					0.35	0.5	
I_I	V_{CC} = MAX,	V_I = 7 V				0.1			0.1	mA
I_{IH}	V_{CC} = MAX,	V_I = 2.7 V				20			20	μA
I_{IL}	V_{CC} = MAX,	V_I = 0.4 V				− 0.4			− 0.4	mA
I_{OS}[§]	V_{CC} = MAX			− 20		− 100	− 20		− 100	mA
I_{CC}	V_{CC} = MAX,	See Note 2			27	36		22	36	mA

[†]For conditions shown as MIN or MAX, use the appropriate value specified under recommended operating conditions
[‡]All typical values are at V_{CC} = 5 V, T_A = 25°C.
[§]Not more than one output should be shorted at a time, and duration short-circuit should not exceed one second.
NOTE 2: I_{CC} is measured with the inputs grounded and the outputs open.

switching characteristics, V_{CC} = 5 V, T_A = 25°C

PARAMETER	FROM (INPUT)	TO (OUTPUT)	TEST CONDITIONS	MIN	TYP	MAX	UNIT
t_{PHL}	$\overline{CLR}$	Any Q			12	18	ns
t_{PLH}	Data	Any Q			19	30	ns
t_{PHL}					13	20	
t_{PLH}	Address	Any Q	C_L = 15 pF, R_L = 2 kΩ, See Note 3		17	27	ns
t_{PHL}					14	20	
t_{PLH}	$\overline{G}$	Any Q			15	24	ns
t_{PHL}					15	24	

t_{PLH} = propagation delay time, low-to-high level output
t_{PHL} = propagation delay time, high-to-low level output
NOTE 3: See General Information Section for load circuits and voltage waveforms.

TEXAS
INSTRUMENTS

- **Package Options Include Both Plastic and Ceramic Chip Carriers in Addition to Plastic and Ceramic DIPs**

- **Dependable Texas Instruments Quality and Reliability**

description

These devices contain two independent 5-input positive -NOR gates. They perform the Boolean function $Y = \overline{A + B + C + D + E}$ in positive logic.

The SN54S260 is characterized for operation over the full military temperature range of $-55°C$ to $125°C$. The SN74S260 is characterized for operation from $0°C$ to $70°C$.

logic diagram (each gate)

SN54S260 . . . J OR W PACKAGE
SN74S260 . . . D, J OR N PACKAGE
(TOP VIEW)

```
1A  [1    14] VCC
1B  [2    13] 1E
1C  [3    12] 1D
2A  [4    11] 2E
1Y  [5    10] 2D
2Y  [6     9] 2C
GND [7     8] 2B
```

SN54S260 . . . FK PACKAGE
SN74S260
(TOP VIEW)

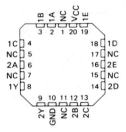

NC - No internal connection

TEXAS INSTRUMENTS

3

TTL DEVICES

schematic (each gate)

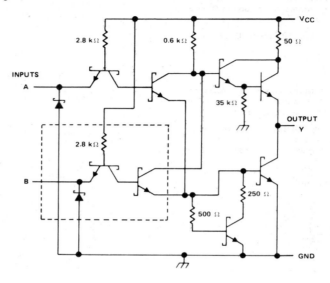

Resistor values shown are nominal.
The portion of the schematic within the dashed-line is repeated for each additional input.

absolute maximum ratings over operating free-air temperature range (unless otherwise noted)

Supply voltage, V_{CC} (see Note 1) .... 7 V
Input voltage .... 5.5 V
Operating free-air temperature range: SN54' .... -55°C to 125°C
                                       SN74' .... 0°C to 70°C
Storage temperature range .... -65°C to 150°C

NOTE 1: Voltage values are with respect to network ground terminal.

3

TTL DEVICES

recommended operating conditions

		SN54S260			SN74S260			UNIT
		MIN	TYP	MAX	MIN	TYP	MAX	
V_{CC}	Supply voltage	4.5	5	5.5	4.75	5	5.25	V
V_{IH}	High-level input voltage	2			2			V
V_{IL}	Low-level input voltage			0.8			0.8	V
I_{OH}	High-level output current			-1			-1	mA
I_{OL}	Low-level output current			20			20	mA
T_A	Operating free-air temperature	-55		125	0		70	$^\circ$C

electrical characteristics over recommended operating free-air temperature range (unless otherwise noted)

PARAMETER	TEST CONDITIONS †			SN54S260			SN74S260			UNIT
				MIN	TYP‡	MAX	MIN	TYP‡	MAX	
V_{IK}	V_{CC} = MIN,	$I_I = -18$ mA				-1.2			-1.2	V
V_{OH}	V_{CC} = MIN,	V_{IL} = 0.8 V,	$I_{OH} = -1$ mA	2.5	3.4		2.7	3.4		V
V_{OL}	V_{CC} = MIN,	V_{IH} = 2 V,	I_{OL} = 20 mA			0.5			0.5	V
I_I	V_{CC} = MAX,	V_I = 5.5 V				1			1	mA
I_{IH}	V_{CC} = MAX,	V_{IH} = 2.7 V				50			50	μA
I_{IL}	V_{CC} = MAX,	V_{IL} = 0.5 V				-2			-2	mA
I_{OS} §	V_{CC} = MAX			-40		-100	-40		-100	mA
I_{CCH}	V_{CC} = MAX,	V_I = 0 V			17	29		17	29	mA
I_{CCL}	V_{CC} = MAX,	See Note 2			26	45		26	45	mA

† For conditions shown as MIN or MAX, use the appropriate value specified under recommended operating conditions.
‡ All typical values are at V_{CC} = 5 V, T_A = 25°C.
§ Not more than one output should be shorted at a time, and the duration of the short-circuit should not exceed one second.
NOTE 2: One input at 4.5 V, all others at GND.

switching characteristics, V_{CC} = 5 V, T_A = 25°C (see note 3)

PARAMETER	FROM (INPUT)	TO (OUTPUT)	TEST CONDITIONS		MIN	TYP	MAX	UNIT
t_{PLH}	Any	Y	R_L = 280 Ω,	C_L = 15 pF		4	5.5	ns
t_{PHL}						4	6	ns

NOTE 3: See General Information Section for load circuits and voltage waveforms.

TEXAS INSTRUMENTS

MARCH 1974 – REVISED DECEMBER 1983

- Fast Multiplication . . . 5-Bit Product in 26 ns Typ
- Power Dissipation . . . 110 mW Typical
- Latch Outputs for Synchronous Operation
- Expandable for m-Bit-by-n-Bit Applications
- Fully Compatible with Most TTL and Other Saturated Low-Level Logic Families
- Diode-Clamped Inputs Simplify System Design

description

These low-power Schottky circuits are designed to be used in parallel multiplication applications. They perform binary multiplication in two's-complement form, two bits at a time.

The M inputs are for the multiplier bits and the B inputs are for the multiplicand. The Q outputs represent the partial product as a recoded base-4 number. This recoding effectively reduces the Wallace-tree hardware requirements by a factor of two.

The outputs represent partial products in one's-complement form generated as a result of multiplication. A simple rounding scheme using two additional gates is needed for each partial product to generate two's complement.

The leading (most-significant) bit of the product is inverted for ease in extending the sign to square (left justify) the partial-product bits.

The SN54LS261 is characterized for operation over the full military temperature range of -55°C to 125°C; the SN74LS261 for operation from 0°C to 70°C.

SN54LS261 . . . J OR W PACKAGE
SN74LS261 . . . D, J OR N PACKAGE
(TOP VIEW)

```
        B3 [ 1  U 16 ] VCC
        B4 [ 2    15 ] B2
         C [ 3    14 ] B1
        M2 [ 4    13 ] B0
        Q4 [ 5    12 ] M1
        Q3 [ 6    11 ] M0
        Q2 [ 7    10 ] Q0
       GND [ 8     9 ] Q1
```

SN54LS261 . . . FK PACKAGE
SN74LS261
(TOP VIEW)

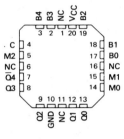

NC - No internal connection

FUNCTION TABLE

INPUTS				OUTPUTS				
LATCH CONTROL C	MULTIPLIER			$\overline{Q4}$	Q3	Q2	Q1	Q0
	M2	M1	M0					
L	X	X	X	$\overline{Q4}_0$	$Q3_0$	$Q2_0$	$Q1_0$	$Q0_0$
H	L	L	L	H	L	L	L	L
H	L	L	H	$\overline{B4}$	B4	B3	B2	B1
H	L	H	L	$\overline{B4}$	B4	B3	B2	B1
H	L	H	H	$\overline{B4}$	B3	B2	B1	B0
H	H	L	L	B4	$\overline{B3}$	$\overline{B2}$	$\overline{B1}$	$\overline{B0}$
H	H	L	H	B4	$\overline{B4}$	$\overline{B3}$	$\overline{B2}$	$\overline{B1}$
H	H	H	L	B4	$\overline{B4}$	$\overline{B3}$	$\overline{B2}$	$\overline{B1}$
H	H	H	H	H	L	L	L	L

H = high level, L = low level, X = irrelevant
$\overline{Q4}_0$ . . . $Q0_0$ = The logic level of the same output before the high-to-low transition of C.
B4 . . . B0 = The logic level of the indicated multiplicand (B) input.

3

TTL DEVICES

TEXAS
INSTRUMENTS

TYPES SN54LS261, SN74LS261
2-BIT BY 4-BIT PARALLEL BINARY MULTIPLEXERS

schematics of inputs and outputs

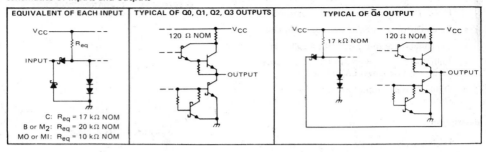

EQUIVALENT OF EACH INPUT	TYPICAL OF Q0, Q1, Q2, Q3 OUTPUTS	TYPICAL OF $\overline{Q}4$ OUTPUT

C: R_{eq} = 17 kΩ NOM
B or M_2: R_{eq} = 20 kΩ NOM
MO or MI: R_{eq} = 10 kΩ NOM

logic diagram

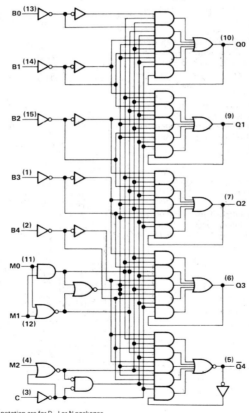

Pin numbers shown on logic notation are for D, J or N packages.

3

TTL DEVICES

absolute maximum ratings over operating free-air temperature range (unless otherwise noted)

Supply voltage, V_{CC} (see Note 1)	7 V
Input voltage	7 V
Operating free-air temperature range: SN54LS261	$-55°C$ to $125°C$
SN74LS261	$0°C$ to $70°C$
Storage temperature range	$-65°C$ to $150°C$

NOTE 1: Voltage values are with respect to network ground terminal.

recommended operating conditions

	SN54LS261			SN74LS261			UNIT
	MIN	NOM	MAX	MIN	NOM	MAX	
Supply voltage, V_{CC}	4.5	5	5.5	4.75	5	5.25	V
High-level output current, I_{OH}			-400			-400	μA
Low-level output current, I_{OL}			4			8	mA
Width of enable pulse, t_W	25			25			ns
Setup time, t_{su} Any M input	17↓			17↓			ns
Any B input	15↓			15↓			
Hold time, t_h Any M input	0↓			0↓			ns
Any B input	0↓			0↓			
Operating free-air temperature, T_A	-55		125	0		70	°C

↓The arrow indicates that the falling edge of the enable pulse is used for reference.

electrical characteristics over recommended operating free-air temperature range (unless otherwise noted)

PARAMETER		TEST CONDITIONS†		SN54LS261			SN74LS261			UNIT
				MIN	TYP‡	MAX	MIN	TYP‡	MAX	
V_{IH}	High-level input voltage			2			2			V
V_{IL}	Low-level input voltage					0.7			0.8	V
V_{IK}	Input clamp voltage	V_{CC} = MIN,	$I_I = -18$ mA			-1.5			-1.5	V
V_{OH}	High-level output voltage	V_{CC} = MIN, V_{IH} = 2 V, $V_{IL} = V_{IL}$ max, $I_{OH} = -400$ μA		2.5	3.4		2.7	3.4		V
V_{OL}	Low-level output voltage	V_{CC} = MIN, V_{IH} = 2 V, $V_{IL} = V_{IL}$ max	I_{OL} = 4 mA		0.25	0.4		0.25	0.4	V
			I_{OL} = 8 mA					0.35	0.5	
I_I	Input current at maximum input voltage	V_{CC} = MAX, V_I = 7 V	MO or MI			0.2			0.2	mA
			All others			0.1			0.1	
I_{IH}	High-level input current	V_{CC} = MAX, V_I = 2.7 V	MO or MI			40			40	μA
			All others			20			20	
I_{IL}	Low-level input current	V_{CC} = MAX, V_I = 0.4 V	MO or MI			-0.8			-0.8	mA
			All others			-0.4			-0.4	
I_{OS}	Short-circuit output current§	V_{CC} = MAX		-20		-100	-20		-100	mA
I_{CC}	Supply current	V_{CC} = MAX, All inputs at 0 V, Outputs open			20	38		20	40	mA

‡All typical values are at V_{CC} = 5 V, T_A = 25°C.
§Not more than one output should be shorted at a time and duration of the output short-circuit should not exceed one second.

switching characteristics, V_{CC} = 5 V, T_A = 25°C

PARAMETER¶	FROM (INPUT)	TO (OUTPUT)	TEST CONDITIONS	MIN	TYP	MAX	UNIT
t_{PLH}	C	Any Q			22	35	ns
t_{PHL}					20	30	ns
t_{PLH}	Any M input	Any Q	C_L = 15 pF, R_L = 2 kΩ, See Note 2		25	40	ns
t_{PHL}					22	35	ns
t_{PLH}	Any B input	Any Q			27	42	ns
t_{PHL}					24	37	ns

¶t_{PLH} = propagation delay time, low-to-high-level output; t_{PHL} = propagation delay time, high-to-low-level output.
NOTE 2: See General Information Section for load circuits and voltage waveforms.

TEXAS
INSTRUMENTS

3

TTL DEVICES

TYPICAL APPLICATION DATA

Multiplication of the numbers 26 (multiplicand) by 29 (multiplier) in decimal, binary, and 2-bit-at-a-time-binary is shown here:

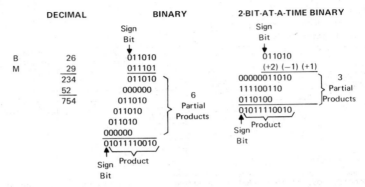

Two points should be noted in the two-bit-at-a-time-binary example above. First, in positioning the partial products beneath each other for final addition, each partial product is shifted two places to the left of the partial products above it instead of one place as is done in regular multiplication. Second, the msb of the partial product (the sign bit) is extended to the sign-bit column of the final answer.

A substantial reduction of multiplication time, cost, and power is obtained by implementing a parallel partial-product-generation scheme using a 2-bit-at-a-time algorithm, followed by a Wallace Tree summation.

Partial-product-generation rules of the algorithm are:

1. Examine two bits of multiplier M plus the next lower bit. For the first partial product (PP1) the next lower bit is zero.

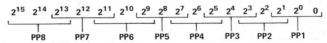

TEXAS
INSTRUMENTS

TYPICAL APPLICATION DATA

2. Generate partial product (PPi) as shown in the following table:

MULTIPLIER BITS FROM STEP 1			OPERATOR SYMBOL	TO OBTAIN PARTIAL PRODUCT
2^{2i-1}	2^{2i-2}	2^{2i-3}		
0	0	0	0	Replace multiplicand by zero
0	0	1	+1 B	Copy multiplicand
0	1	0	+1 B	Copy multiplicand
0	1	1	+2 B	Shift multiplicand left one bit
1	0	0	−2 B	Shift two's complement of multiplicand left one bit
1	0	1	−1 B	Replace multiplicand by two's complement
1	1	0	−1 B	Replace multiplicand by two's complement
1	1	1	0	Replace multiplicand by zero

3. Weight the partial products by indexing each two places left relative to the next-less-significant product.

4. Extend the most-significant bit of the partial product to the sign-bit place value of the final product.

EXAMPLE OF ALGORITHM

M = 29 = 011101	Operator Symbol	B = 26 = 011010
010	+1 B	00000011010
110	−1 B	111100110
011	+2 B	0110100

The summation of these partial products was shown in the 2-bit-at-a-time binary multiplication example above.

The 'LS261 generates partial products according to this algorithm with two exceptions:

1. The one's complement is generated for the cases requiring the two's complement. The two's complement can be obtained by adding one to the one's complement; this rounding can be done by using one NAND gate and one AND gate as shown in Figure B.

2. The most-significant bit is complemented to reduce the hardware required to extend the sign bit. This extension can be accomplished by adding a hard-wired logic 1 in bit position 2^{2i+15} of each partial product and also in bit position 2^{16} of the first partial product (PP1).

3

TTL DEVICES

TEXAS
INSTRUMENTS

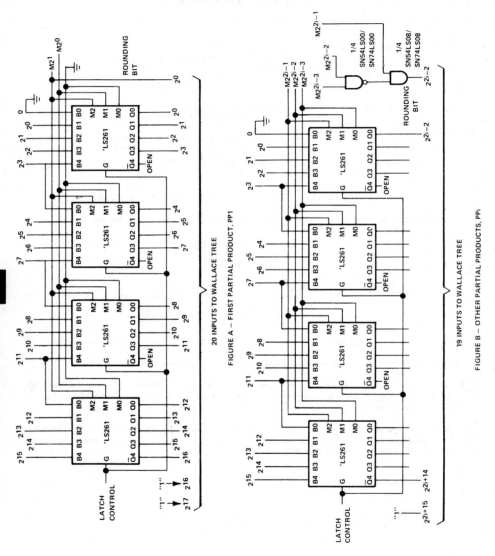

FIGURE A — FIRST PARTIAL PRODUCT, PP1

FIGURE B — OTHER PARTIAL PRODUCTS, PPi

3

TTL DEVICES

TEXAS
INSTRUMENTS

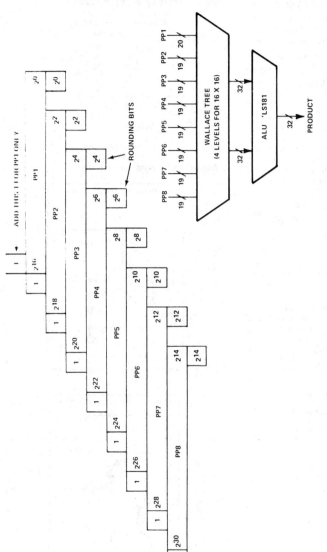

FIGURE C—MANIPULATION OF PARTIAL PRODUCTS FOR ENTRY INTO WALLACE TREE

In general, the 4 x 2 bit 'LS261 can be expanded for use in 4m x 2n bit multipliers. Partial-product generation uses m x n 'LS261s m x n ÷ 16 'LS00s, and m x n ÷ 16 'LS08s. The size of the Wallace tree and ALU requirements vary depending on the size of the problem. The count for the 16 x 16 bit multiplier is:

32	SN54LS261/SN74LS261
2	SN54LS00/SN74LS00
2	SN54LS08/SN74LS08
56	SN54LS183/SN74LS183
7	SN54LS181/SN74LS181
2	SN54S182/SN74S182

3

TTL DEVICES

FOR SYMMETRICAL GENERATION OF COMPLEMENTARY TTL SIGNALS

- Switching Time Skew of the Complementary Outputs Is Typically 0.5 ns . . . Guaranteed to be No More than 3 ns at Rated Loading

- Full Fan-Out to 20 High-Level and 10 Low-Level 54/74 Loads

- Active Pull-Down Provides Square Transfer Characteristic

SN54265 . . . J OR W PACKAGE
SN74265 . . . J OR N PACKAGE
(TOP VIEW)

1A	1	16	V$_{CC}$
1W	2	15	4A
1Y	3	14	4W
2A	4	13	4Y
2B	5	12	3B
2W	6	11	3A
2Y	7	10	3W
GND	8	9	3Y

NC - No internal connection

description

The SN54265 and SN74265 circuits feature complementary outputs from each logic element, which have virtually symmetrical switching time delays from the triggering input. They are designed specifically for use in applications such as:

- Symmetrical clock/$\overline{clock}$ generators
- Complementary input circuit for decoders and code converters
- Switch debouncing
- Differential line driver

Examples of these four functions are illustrated in the typical application data.

The SN54265 is characterized for operation over the full military temperature range of -55°C to 125°C; the SN74265 is characterized for operation from 0°C to 70°C.

schematics of inputs and outputs

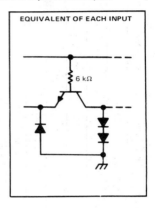

EQUIVALENT OF EACH INPUT

6 kΩ

logic diagrams

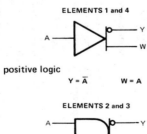

ELEMENTS 1 and 4

A ▷ Y
W

positive logic

$$Y = \overline{A} \qquad W = A$$

ELEMENTS 2 and 3

A, B

positive logic

$$Y = \overline{AB} \quad \text{or} \quad Y = \overline{A} + \overline{B}$$
$$W = AB \quad \text{or} \quad W = \overline{\overline{A} + \overline{B}}$$

TYPICAL OF ALL OUTPUTS

V$_{CC}$

100 Ω

OUTPUT

TEXAS INSTRUMENTS

3

TTL DEVICES

absolute maximum ratings over operating free-air temperature range (unless otherwise noted)

Supply voltage, V_{CC} (see Note 1) . . . . 7 V
Input voltage . . . . 5.5 V
Operating free-air temperature range: SN54265 . . . . $-55°$C to $125°$C
 SN74265 . . . . $0°$C to $70°$C
Storage temperature range . . . . $-65°$C to $150°$C

NOTE 1. Voltage values are with respect to network ground terminal.

recommended operating conditions

	SN54265			SN74265			UNIT
	MIN	NOM	MAX	MIN	NOM	MAX	
Supply voltage, V_{CC}	4.5	5	5.5	4.75	5	5.25	V
High-level output current, I_{OH}			-800			-800	μA
Low-level output current, I_{OL}			16			16	mA
Operating free-air temperature, T_A	-55		125	0		70	°C

electrical characteristics over recommended operating free-air temperature range (unless otherwise noted)

	PARAMETER	TEST CONDITIONS[†]	MIN	TYP[‡]	MAX	UNIT
V_{IH}	High-level input voltage		2			V
V_{IL}	Low-level input voltage				0.8	V
V_{IK}	Input clamp voltage	V_{CC} = MIN, I_I = -12 mA			-1.5	V
V_{OH}	High-level output voltage	V_{CC} = MIN, I_{OH} = -800 μA	2.4	3.4		V
V_{OL}	Low-level output voltage	V_{CC} = MIN, I_{OL} = 16 mA		0.2	0.4	V
I_I	Input current at maximum input voltage	V_{CC} = MAX, V_I = 5.5 V			1	mA
I_{IH}	High-level input current	V_{CC} = MAX, V_I = 2.4 V			40	μA
I_{IL}	Low-level input current	V_{CC} = MAX, V_I = 0.4 V			-1.6	mA
I_{OS}	Short-circuit output current[§]	V_{CC} = MAX, SN54265	-20		-57	mA
		SN74265	-18		-57	
I_{CC}	Supply current	V_{CC} = MAX, See Note 2		25	34	mA

[†] For conditions shown as MIN or MAX, use the appropriate value specified under recommended operating conditions.
[‡] All typical values are at V_{CC} = 5 V, T_A = 25°C.
[§] Not more than one output should be shorted at a time.
NOTE 2: I_{CC} is measured with all outputs open and all inputs grounded.

switching characteristics, V_{CC} = 5 V, T_A = 25°C

PARAMETER[¶]	FROM (INPUT)	TO (OUTPUT)	TEST CONDITIONS	MIN	TYP	MAX	UNIT
$t_{PLH(W)}$	A or B	W			11.6	18	ns
$t_{PHL(Y)}$	(as applicable)	Y	R_L = 400 Ω, C_L = 15 pF, See Note 3		11.3	18	
$t_{PHL(W)}$	A or B	W			9.8	18	ns
$t_{PLH(Y)}$	(as applicable)	Y			10.2	18	
$t_{PLH(W)} - t_{PHL(Y)}$	A or B	W with			+0.3	3	ns
$t_{PHL(W)} - t_{PLH(Y)}$	(as applicable)	respect to Y			-0.4	3	

t_{PLH} ≡ Propagation delay time, low-to-high-level output.
t_{PHL} ≡ Propagation delay time, high-to-low-level output.
$t_{PXX(W)} - t_{PXX(Y)}$ ≡ Difference in indicated propagation delay times at the W and Y outputs, respectively.
NOTE 3: See General Information Section for load circuits and voltage waveforms.

TEXAS
INSTRUMENTS

TYPICAL CHARACTERISTICS†

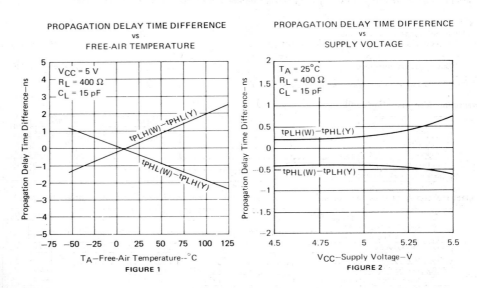

PROPAGATION DELAY TIME DIFFERENCE
vs
FREE-AIR TEMPERATURE

FIGURE 1

PROPAGATION DELAY TIME DIFFERENCE
vs
SUPPLY VOLTAGE

FIGURE 2

PROPAGATION DELAY TIME DIFFERENCE vs LOAD CAPACITANCE

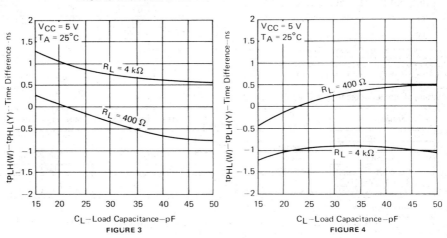

FIGURE 3

FIGURE 4

†Data for temperatures below 0°C and above 70°C and for supply voltages below 4.75 V and above 5.25 V are applicable for SN54265 only.

3

TTL DEVICES

TYPICAL APPLICATION DATA

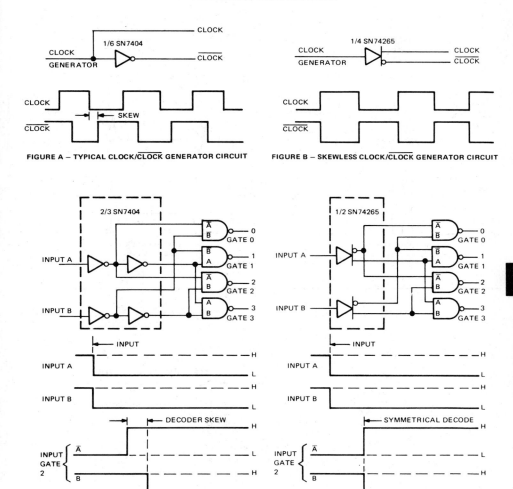

FIGURE A – TYPICAL CLOCK/CLOCK GENERATOR CIRCUIT

FIGURE B – SKEWLESS CLOCK/CLOCK GENERATOR CIRCUIT

FIGURE C – TYPICAL DECODER/CODE CONVERTER

FIGURE D – SYMMETRICAL DECODER/CODE CONVERTER

TTL DEVICES

TEXAS
INSTRUMENTS

TYPICAL APPLICATION DATA

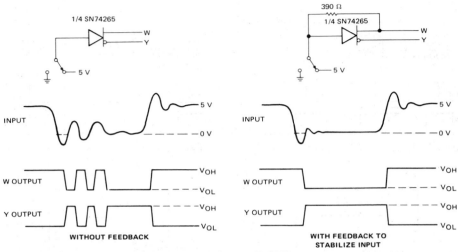

WITHOUT FEEDBACK

WITH FEEDBACK TO
STABILIZE INPUT

FIGURE E – SWITCH DEBOUNCER

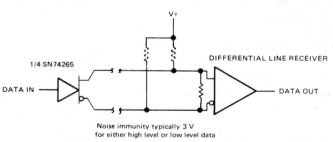

Noise immunity typically 3 V
for either high level or low level data

FIGURE F – DIFFERENTIAL LINE DRIVER

TEXAS
INSTRUMENTS

- Can Be Used as a 4-Bit Digital Comparator
- Input Clamping Diodes Simplify System Design
- Fully Compatible with Most TTL Circuits

FUNCTION TABLE

INPUTS		OUTPUT
A	B	Y
L	L	H
L	H	L
H	L	L
H	H	H

H = high level, L = low level

SN54LS266 . . . J OR W PACKAGE
SN74LS266 . . . D, J OR N PACKAGE
(TOP VIEW)

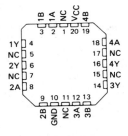

```
  1A [ 1    14 ] VCC
  1B [ 2    13 ] 4B
  1Y [ 3    12 ] 4A
  2Y [ 4    11 ] 4Y
  2A [ 5    10 ] 3Y
  2B [ 6     9 ] 3B
 GND [ 7     8 ] 3A
```

SN54LS266 . . . FK PACKAGE
SN74LS266
(TOP VIEW)

```
        1B 1A NC VCC 4B
         3  2  1  20 19
   1Y [ 4           18 ] 4A
   NC [ 5           17 ] NC
   2Y [ 6           16 ] 4Y
   NC [ 7           15 ] NC
   2A [ 8           14 ] 3Y
         9 10 11 12 13
        2B GND NC 3A 3B
```

NC - No internal connection

description

The 'LS266 is comprised of four independent 2-input exclusive-NOR gates with open-collector outputs. The open-collector outputs permit tying outputs together for multiple-bit comparisons.

logic symbol (each gate)

positive logic

$$Y = \overline{A \oplus B} = AB + \overline{AB}$$

schematic of inputs and outputs

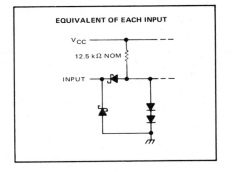

EQUIVALENT OF EACH INPUT

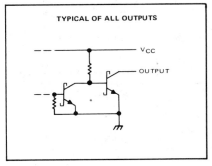

TYPICAL OF ALL OUTPUTS

3

TTL DEVICES

TEXAS
INSTRUMENTS

TYPES SN54LS266, SN74LS266
QUADRUPLE 2-INPUT EXCLUSIVE-NOR GATES
WITH OPEN-COLLECTOR OUTPUTS

absolute maximum ratings over operating free-air temperature range (unless otherwise noted)

Supply voltage, V_{CC} (see Note 1)	7 V
Input voltage	7 V
Operating free-air temperature range: SN54LS266	−55°C to 125°C
SN74LS266	0°C to 70°C
Storage temperature range	−65°C to 150°C

NOTE 1: Voltage values are with respect to network ground terminal.

recommended operating conditions

	SN54LS266 MIN	NOM	MAX	SN74LS266 MIN	NOM	MAX	UNIT
Supply voltage, V_{CC}	4.5	5	5.5	4.75	5	5.25	V
High-level output voltage, V_{OH}			5.5			5.5	V
Low-level output current, I_{OL}			4			8	mA
Operating free-air temperature, T_A	−55		125	0		70	C

electrical characteristics over recommended operating free-air temperature range (unless otherwise noted)

PARAMETER		TEST CONDITIONS[†]	SN54LS266 MIN	TYP	MAX	SN74LS266 MIN	TYP	MAX	UNIT
V_{IH}	High-level input voltage		2			2			V
V_{IL}	Low-level input voltage				0.7			0.8	V
V_{IK}	Input clamp voltage	V_{CC} = MIN, I_I = −18 mA			−1.5			−1.5	V
I_{OH}	High-level output current	V_{CC} = MIN, V_{IH} = 2 V, V_{IL} = V_{IL} max, V_{OH} = 5.5 V			100			100	µA
V_{OL}	Low-level output voltage	V_{CC} = MIN, V_{IH} = 2 V, I_{OL} = 4 mA	0.25	0.4		0.25	0.4		V
		V_{IL} = V_{IL} max, I_{OL} = 8 mA				0.35	0.5		
I_I	Input current at maximum input voltage	V_{CC} = MAX, V_I = 7 V			0.2			0.2	mA
I_{IH}	High-level input current	V_{CC} = MAX, V_I = 2.7 V			40			40	µA
I_{IL}	Low-level input current	V_{CC} = MAX, V_I = 0.4 V			−0.8			−0.8	mA
I_{CC}	Supply current	V_{CC} = MAX, See Note 2	8	13		8	13		mA

[†] For conditions shown as MIN or MAX, use the appropriate value specified under recommended operating conditions for the applicable type.
[‡] All typical values are at V_{CC} = 5 V, T_A = 25 C.
NOTE 2: I_{CC} is measured with one input of each gate at 4.5 V, the other inputs grounded, and the outputs open.

switching characteristics, V_{CC} = 5 V, T_A = 25 C

PARAMETER[¶]	FROM (INPUT)		TEST CONDITIONS	MIN	TYP	MAX	UNIT
t_{PLH}	A or B	Other input low	C_L = 15 pF, R_L = 2 kΩ, See Note 3		18	30	ns
t_{PHL}					18	30	
t_{PLH}	A or B	Other input high			18	30	ns
t_{PHL}					18	30	

[¶] t_{PLH} propagation delay time, low to high level output
t_{PHL} propagation delay time, high to low level output
NOTE 3: See General Information Section for load circuits and voltage waveforms.

3

TTL DEVICES

3-732

TEXAS
INSTRUMENTS

OCTOBER 1976 - REVISED DECEMBER 1983

- Contains Eight Flip-Flops with Single-Rail Outputs
- Buffered Clock and Direct Clear Inputs
- Individual Data Input to Each Flip-Flop
- Applications Include:
  Buffer/Storage Registers
  Shift Registers
  Pattern Generators

SN54273, SN54LS273 . . . J PACKAGE
SN74273 . . . J OR N PACKAGE
SN74LS273 . . . DW, J OR N PACKAGE
(TOP VIEW)

```
        ___  ___
CLR  [ 1  U  20 ]  VCC
 1Q  [ 2     19 ]  8Q
 1D  [ 3     18 ]  8D
 2D  [ 4     17 ]  7D
 2Q  [ 5     16 ]  7Q
 3Q  [ 6     15 ]  6Q
 3D  [ 7     14 ]  6D
 4D  [ 8     13 ]  5D
 4Q  [ 9     12 ]  5Q
GND  [ 10    11 ]  CLK
```

SN54LS273 . . . FK PACKAGE
SN74LS273
(TOP VIEW)

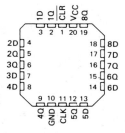

description

These monolithic, positive-edge-triggered flip-flops utilize TTL circuitry to implement D-type flip-flop logic with a direct clear input.

Information at the D inputs meeting the setup time requirements is transferred to the Q outputs on the positive-going edge of the clock pulse. Clock triggering occurs at a particular voltage level and is not directly related to the transition time of the positive-going pulse. When the clock input is at either the high or low level, the D input signal has no effect at the output.

These flip-flops are guaranteed to respond to clock frequencies ranging from 0 to 30 megahertz while maximum clock frequency is typically 40 megahertz. Typical power dissipation is 39 milliwatts per flip-flop for the '273 and 10 milliwatts for the 'LS273.

FUNCTION TABLE
(EACH FLIP-FLOP)

INPUTS			OUTPUT
CLEAR	CLOCK	D	Q
L	X	X	L
H	↑	H	H
H	↑	L	L
H	L	X	Q_0

TEXAS
INSTRUMENTS

3

TTL DEVICES

schematics of inputs and outputs

'273

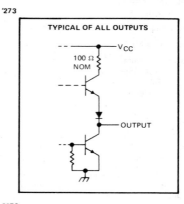

EQUIVALENT OF EACH INPUT

V_CC

R_eq

INPUT

Clear: R_{eq} = 3 kΩ NOM
Clock: R_{eq} = 6 kΩ NOM
All other inputs: R_{eq} = 8 kΩ NOM

TYPICAL OF ALL OUTPUTS

V_CC

100 Ω NOM

OUTPUT

'LS273

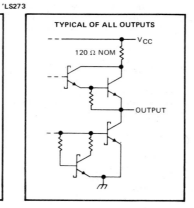

EQUIVALENT OF EACH INPUT

V_CC

20 kΩ NOM

INPUT

TYPICAL OF ALL OUTPUTS

V_CC

120 Ω NOM

OUTPUT

logic diagram

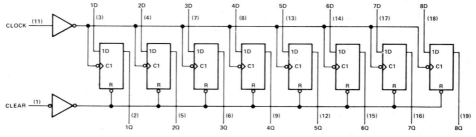

Pin numbers shown on logic notation are for DW, J or N packages.

Texas Instruments

3 TTL DEVICES

absolute maximum ratings over operating free-air temperature range (unless otherwise noted)

Supply voltage, V_{CC} (see Note 1) . . . . 7 V
Input voltage . . . . 5.5 V
Operating free-air temperature range: SN54273 . . . . $-55°C$ to $125°C$
SN74273 . . . . $0°C$ to $70°C$
Storage temperature range . . . . $-65°C$ to $150°C$

NOTE 1: Voltage values are with respect to network ground terminal.

recommended operating conditions

		SN54273			SN74273			UNIT
		MIN	NOM	MAX	MIN	NOM	MAX	
Supply voltage, V_{CC}		4.5	5	5.5	4.75	5	5.25	V
High-level output current, I_{OH}				-800			-800	μA
Low-level output current, I_{OL}				16			16	mA
Clock frequency, f_{clock}		0		30	0		30	MHz
Width of clock or clear pulse, t_w		16.5			16.5			ns
Set-up time, t_{su}	Data input	20†			20†			ns
	Clear inactive state	25†			25†			
Data hold time, t_h		5†			5†			ns
Operating free-air temperature, T_A		-55		125	0		70	$°C$

† The arrow indicates that the rising edge of the clock pulse is used for reference.

electrical characteristics over recommended operating free-air temperature range (unless otherwise noted)

PARAMETER		TEST CONDITIONS†	MIN	TYP‡	MAX	UNIT
V_{IH} High-level input voltage			2			V
V_{IL} Low-level input voltage					0.8	V
V_{IK} Input clamp voltage		V_{CC} = MIN, I_I = -12 mA			-1.5	V
V_{OH} High-level output voltage		V_{CC} = MIN, V_{IH} = 2 V, V_{IL} = 0.8 V, I_{OH} = -800 μA	2.4	3.4		V
V_{OL} Low-level output voltage		V_{CC} = MIN, V_{IH} = 2 V, V_{IL} = 0.8 V, I_{OL} = 16 mA			0.4	V
I_I Input current at maximum input voltage		V_{CC} = MAX, V_I = 5.5 V			1	mA
I_{IH} High-level input current	Clear	V_{CC} = MAX, V_I = 2.4 V			80	μA
	Clock or D				40	
I_{IL} Low-level input current	Clear	V_{CC} = MAX, V_I = 0.4 V			-3.2	mA
	Clock or D				-1.6	
I_{OS} Short-circuit output current§		V_{CC} = MAX	-18		-57	mA
I_{CC} Supply current		V_{CC} = MAX, See Note 2		62	94	mA

† For conditions shown as MIN or MAX, use the appropriate value specified under recommended operating conditions.
‡ All typical values are at V_{CC} = 5 V, T_A = 25°C.
§ Not more than one output should be shorted at a time.
NOTE 2: With all outputs open and 4.5 V applied to all data and clear inputs, I_{CC} is measured after a momentary ground, then 4.5 V, is applied to clock.

switching characteristics, V_{CC} = 5 V, T_A = 25°C

PARAMETER	TEST CONDITIONS	MIN	TYP	MAX	UNIT
f_{max} Maximum clock frequency	C_L = 15 pF, R_L = 400 Ω, See Note 3	30	40		MHz
t_{PHL} Propagation delay time, high-to-low-level output from clear			18	27	ns
t_{PLH} Propagation delay time, low-to-high-level output from clock			17	27	ns
t_{PHL} Propagation delay time, high-to-low-level output from clock			18	27	ns

NOTE 3: See General Information Section for load circuits and voltage waveforms.

TEXAS
INSTRUMENTS

3

TTL DEVICES

TYPES SN54LS273, SN74LS273
OCTAL D-TYPE FLIP-FLOP WITH CLEAR

absolute maximum ratings over operating free-air temperature range (unless otherwise noted)

Supply voltage, V_{CC} (see Note 1) . . . . 7 V
Input voltage . . . . 7 V
Operating free-air temperature range: SN54LS273 . . . . −55°C to 125°C
    SN74LS273 . . . . 0°C to 70°C
Storage temperature range . . . . −65°C to 150°C

NOTE 1: Voltage values are with respect to network ground terminal.

recommended operating conditions

		SN54LS273			SN74LS273			UNIT
		MIN	NOM	MAX	MIN	NOM	MAX	
Supply voltage, V_{CC}		4.5	5	5.5	4.75	5	5.25	V
High-level output current, I_{OH}				−400			−400	µA
Low-level output current, I_{OL}				4			8	mA
Clock frequency, f_{clock}		0		30	0		30	MHz
Width of clock or clear pulse, t_w		20			20			ns
Set-up time, t_{su}	Data input	20†			20†			ns
	Clear inactive state	25†			25†			
Data hold time, t_h		5†			5†			ns
Operating free-air temperature, T_A		−55		125	0		70	°C

†The arrow indicates that the rising edge of the clock pulse is used for reference.

electrical characteristics over recommended operating free-air temperature range (unless otherwise noted)

PARAMETER		TEST CONDITIONS†			SN54LS273			SN74LS273			UNIT
					MIN	TYP‡	MAX	MIN	TYP‡	MAX	
V_{IH}	High-level input voltage				2			2			V
V_{IL}	Low-level input voltage						0.7			0.8	V
V_{IK}	Input clamp voltage	V_{CC} = MIN,	I_I = −18 mA				−1.5			−1.5	V
V_{OH}	High-level output voltage	V_{CC} = MIN, V_{IH} = 2 V, V_{IL} = V_{IL}max, I_{OH} = −400 µA			2.5	3.4		2.7	3.4		V
V_{OL}	Low-level output voltage	V_{CC} = MIN, V_{IH} = 2 V, V_{IL} = V_{IL}max	I_{OL} = 4 mA			0.25	0.4		0.25	0.4	V
			I_{OL} = 8 mA						0.35	0.5	
I_I	Input current at maximum input voltage	V_{CC} = MAX,	V_I = 7 V				0.1			0.1	mA
I_{IH}	High-level input current	V_{CC} MAX,	V_I = 2.7 V				20			20	µA
I_{IL}	Low-level input current	V_{CC} = MAX,	V_I = −0.4 V				−0.4			−0.4	mA
I_{OS}	Short-circuit output current §	V_{CC} = MAX			−20		−100	−20		−100	mA
I_{CC}	Supply current	V_{CC} = MAX,	See Note 2			17	27		17	27	mA

†For conditions shown as MIN or MAX, use the appropriate value specified under recommended operating conditions.
‡All typical values are at V_{CC} = 5 V, T_A = 25 C.
§Not more than one output should be shorted at a time and duration of short circuit should not exceed one second.
NOTE 2: With all outputs open and 4.5 V applied to all data and clear inputs, I_{CC} is measured after a momentary ground, then 4.5 V is applied to clock.

switching characteristics, V_{CC} = 5 V, T_A = 25°C

PARAMETER		TEST CONDITIONS	MIN	TYP	MAX	UNIT
f_{max}	Maximum clock frequency	C_L = 15 pF, R_L = 2 kΩ, See Note 4	30	40		MHz
t_{PHL}	Propagation delay time, high-to-low-level output from clear			18	27	ns
t_{PLH}	Propagation delay time, low-to-high-level output from clock			17	27	ns
t_{PHL}	Propagation delay time, high-to-low-level output from clock			18	27	ns

NOTE 4: See General Information Section for load circuits and voltage waveforms.

features

- Four J-K̄ Flip-Flops in a Single Package . . . Can Reduce FF Package Count by 50%
- Separate Negative-Edge-Triggered Clocks with Hysteresis . . . Typically 200 mV
- Typical Clock Input Frequency . . . 50 MHz
- Fully Buffered Outputs

description

These quadruple TTL J-K̄ flip-flops incorporate a number of third-generation IC features that can simplify system design and reduce flip-flop package count by up to 50%. They feature hysteresis at each clock input, fully buffered outputs, and direct clear capability, and are presettable through a buffer that also features an input hysteresis loop. The negative-edge-triggering clocks are directly compatible with earlier Series 54/74 single and dual pulse-triggered flip-flops. These circuits can be used to emulate D- or T-type flip-flops by hard-wiring the inputs, or to implement asynchronous sequential functions.

The SN54276 is characterized for operation over the full military temperature range of −55°C to 125°C; the SN74726 is characterized for operation from 0°C to 70°C.

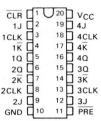

SN54276 . . . J PACKAGE
SN74276 . . . J OR N PACKAGE
(TOP VIEW)

C̄L̄R̄	1	20	V_CC
1J	2	19	4J
1CLK	3	18	4CLK
1K̄	4	17	4K̄
1Q	5	16	4Q
2Q	6	15	3Q
2K̄	7	14	3K̄
2CLK	8	13	3CLK
2J	9	12	3J
GND	10	11	P̄R̄Ē

FUNCTION TABLE (EACH FLIP-FLOP)

COMMON INPUTS		INPUTS			OUTPUT
P̄R̄Ē	C̄L̄R̄	CLK	J	K̄	Q
L	H	X	X	X	H
H	L	X	X	X	L
L	L	X	X	X	H†
H	H	↓	L	H	Q_0
H	H	↓	H	H	H
H	H	↓	L	L	L
H	H	↓	H	L	TOGGLE
H	H	H	X	X	Q_0

† This configuration is nonstable; that is, it may not persist when preset and clear return to their inactive (high) level.

logic symbol†

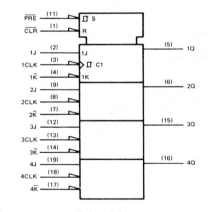

P̄R̄Ē (11) ⎍ S
C̄L̄R̄ (1) R
1J (2) 1J (5) 1Q
1CLK (3) ⎍ C1
1K̄ (4) 1K̄
2J (9)
2CLK (8)
2K̄ (7) (6) 2Q
3J (12)
3CLK (13)
3K̄ (14) (15) 3Q
4J (19)
4CLK (18)
4K̄ (17) (16) 4Q

† Pin numbers shown on logic symbol are for J and N packages only.

3

TTL DEVICES

TEXAS
INSTRUMENTS

schematics of inputs and outputs

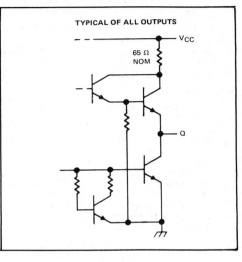

EQUIVALENT OF EACH INPUT

V_{CC}

R_{eq}

INPUT

$\overline{CLR}$, J, $\overline{K}$: R_{eq} = 4 kΩ NOM
CLK: R_{eq} = 10.2 kΩ NOM
$\overline{PRE}$: R_{eq} = 11.6 KΩ NOM

TYPICAL OF ALL OUTPUTS

V_{CC}

65 Ω NOM

Q

absolute maximum ratings over operating free-air temperature range (unless otherwise noted)

Supply voltage, V_{CC} (see Note 1) . . . . 7 V
Input voltage . . . . 5.5 V
Operating free-air temperature range: SN54276 . . . . −55°C to 125°C
SN74276 . . . . 0°C to 70°C
Storage temperature range . . . . −65°C to 150°C

NOTE 1: Voltage values are with respect to network ground terminal.

TEXAS INSTRUMENTS

3 TTL DEVICES

recommended operating conditions

		SN54276			SN74276			UNIT
		MIN	NOM	MAX	MIN	NOM	MAX	
Supply voltage, V_{CC}		4.5	5	5.5	4.75	5	5.25	V
High-level output current, I_{OH}				−800			−800	μA
Low-level output current, I_{OL}				16			16	mA
Clock frequency		0		35	0		35	MHz
Pulse width, t_w	Clock high	13.5			13.5			ns
	Clock low	15			15			
	Preset or clear low	12			12			
Setup time, t_{su}	J, K inputs	3↓			3↓			ns
	Clear and preset inactive state	10↓			10↓			
Input hold time, t_h		10↓			10↓			ns
Operating free-air temperature, T_A		−55		125	0		70	°C

↓ The arrow indicates that the falling edge of the clock pulse is used for reference.

electrical characteristics over recommended operating free-air temperature range (unless otherwise noted)

	PARAMETER	TEST CONDITIONS†	MIN	TYP‡	MAX	UNIT
V_{IH}	High-level input voltage		2			V
V_{IL}	Low-level input voltage				0.8	V
V_{IK}	Input clamp voltage	V_{CC} = MIN, I_I = −12 mA			−1.5	V
V_{OH}	High-level output voltage	V_{CC} = MIN, V_{IH} = 2 V, V_{IL} = 0.8 V, I_{OH} = −800 μA	2.4	3.4		V
V_{OL}	Low-level output voltage	V_{CC} = MIN, V_{IH} = 2 V, V_{IL} = 0.8 V, I_{OL} = 16 mA		0.2	0.4	V
I_I	Input current at maximum input voltage	V_{CC} = MAX, V_I = 5.5 V			1	mA
I_{IH}	High-level input current	V_{CC} = MAX, V_I = 2.4 V			40	μA
I_{IL}	Low-level input current	V_{CC} = MAX, V_I = 0.4 V			−1.6	mA
I_{OS}	Short-circuit output current§	V_{CC} = MAX	−30		−85	mA
I_{CC}	Supply current	V_{CC} = MAX		60	81	mA

†For conditions shown as MIN or MAX, use the appropriate value specified under recommended operating conditions.
‡All typical values are at V_{CC} = 5 V, T_A = 25°C.
§Not more than one output should be shorted at a time.

switching characteristics, V_{CC} = 5 V, T_A = 25°C

	PARAMETER	TEST CONDITIONS	MIN	TYP	MAX	UNIT
f_{max}	Maximum clock frequency		35	50		MHz
t_{PLH}	Propagation delay time, low-to-high-level output from preset	C_L = 15 pF, R_L = 400 Ω, See Note 2		15	25	ns
t_{PHL}	Propagation delay time, high-to-low-level output from clear			18	30	ns
t_{PLH}	Propagation delay time, low-to-high-level output from clock			17	30	ns
t_{PHL}	Propagation delay time, high-to-low-level output from clock			20	30	ns

NOTE 2: See General Information Section for load circuits and voltage waveforms.

TTL DEVICES

3

TEXAS
INSTRUMENTS

MAY 1972 – REVISED APRIL 1985

- Latched Data Inputs Serve as Buffer Register and Can also:
    Synchronize Data Acquisition
    "Debounce" Mechanical Switch Input

- Cascading Input P0 and Output P1 Provides "Busy" Signal Inhibiting All Lower-Order Bits

- Full TTL Compatibility

- Use for:
    Priority Interrupt
    Synchronous Priority Line Selection

SN54278 . . . J OR W PACKAGE
SN74278 . . . J OR N PACKAGE
(TOP VIEW)

STRB	1	14	V$_{CC}$
D3	2	13	D2
D4	3	12	D1
P0	4	11	NC
P1	5	10	Y1
Y4	6	9	Y2
GND	7	8	Y3

NC—No internal connection

description

The SN54278 and SN74278 each consist of four data latches, full priority output gating, and a cascading gate. The highest-order data applied at a D latch input is transferred to the appropriate Y output while the strobe input is high, and when the strobe goes low all data is latched. The cascading input P0 is fully overriding and on the highest-order package this input must be held at a low logic level. The P1 output is intended for connection to the P0 input of the next lower-order package and will provide a "busy" (high-level) signal to inhibit all subsequent lower-order packages.

After the overriding P0 input, the order of priority is D1, D2, D3, and D4, respectively, within the package.

FUNCTION TABLE

INPUTS							INTERNAL LATCH NODES				OUTPUTS				
P0	G	D1	D2	D3	D4		Q̄1	Q̄2	Q̄3	Q̄4	Y1	Y2	Y3	Y4	P1
L	H	H	X	X	X		L	X	X	X	H	L	L	L	H
L	H	L	H	X	X		H	L	X	X	L	H	L	L	H
L	H	L	L	H	X		H	H	L	X	L	L	H	L	H
L	H	L	L	L	H		H	H	H	L	L	L	L	H	H
L	H	L	L	L	L		H	H	H	H	L	L	L	L	L
L	L	X	X	X	X		Latched when G goes low				Same function of Q̄ nodes as on 1st 5 lines				
H	L	X	X	X	X						L	L	L	L	H
H	H						Internal Q̄ levels are same function of D inputs as on first 5 lines				L	L	L	L	H

H = high level, L = low level, X = irrelevant

logic diagram

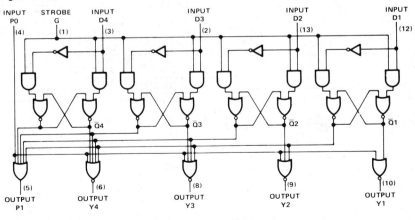

INPUT P0 (4)   STROBE G (1)   INPUT D4 (3)   INPUT D3 (2)   INPUT D2 (13)   INPUT D1 (12)

Q̄4   Q̄3   Q̄2   Q̄1

(5) OUTPUT P1   (6) OUTPUT Y4   (8) OUTPUT Y3   (9) OUTPUT Y2   (10) OUTPUT Y1

3   TTL DEVICES

TEXAS
INSTRUMENTS

3-741

absolute maximum ratings over operating free-air temperature range (unless otherwise noted)

Supply voltage, V_{CC} (see Note 1) . . . . 7 V
Input voltage . . . . 5.5 V
Interemitter voltage (see Note 2) . . . . 5.5 V
Operating free-air temperature range: SN54278 Circuits . . . . −55°C to 125°C
  SN74278 Circuits . . . . 0°C to 70°C
Storage temperature range . . . . −65°C to 150°C

NOTES: 1. Voltage values, except interemitter voltage, are with respect to network ground terminal.
2. This is the voltage between two emitters of a multiple-emitter transistor. For this circuit, this rating applies between the strobe input and any of the four data inputs.

recommended operating conditions

	SN54278			SN74278			UNIT
	MIN	NOM	MAX	MIN	NOM	MAX	
Supply voltage, V_{CC}	4.5	5	5.5	4.75	5	5.25	V
High-level output current, I_{OH}			−800			−800	µA
Low-level output current, I_{OL}			16			16	mA
Data setup time, t_{su} (see Figure 1)	20			20			ns
Data hold time, t_h (see Figure 1)	5			5			ns
Strobe pulse width, t_w (see Figure 1)	20			20			ns
Operating free-air temperature, T_A	−55		125	0		70	°C

electrical characteristics over recommended operating free-air temperature range (unless otherwise noted)

PARAMETER		TEST CONDITIONS†		MIN	TYP	MAX	UNIT
V_{IH}	High-level input voltage			2			V
V_{IL}	Low-level input voltage					0.8	V
V_{IK}	Input clamp voltage	V_{CC} = MIN, I_I = −12 mA				−1.5	V
V_{OH}	High-level output voltage	V_{CC} = MIN, V_{IH} = 2 V, V_{IL} = 0.8 V, I_{OH} = −800 µA		2.4	3.4		V
V_{OL}	Low-level output voltage	V_{CC} = MIN, V_{IH} = 2 V, V_{IL} = 0.8 V, I_{OL} = 16 mA			0.2	0.4	V
I_I	Input current at maximum input voltage	V_{CC} = MAX, V_I = 5.5 V				1	mA
I_{IH}	High-level input current	Any D input	V_{CC} = MAX, V_I = 2.4 V			80	µA
		P0 input				200	
		G input				320	
I_{IL}	Low-level input current	Any D input	V_{CC} = MAX, V_I = 0.4 V			−3.2	mA
		P0 input				−8	
		G input				−12.8	
I_{OS}	Short-circuit output current §	SN54278	V_{CC} = MAX	−18		−55	mA
		SN74278		−18		−57	
I_{CC}	Supply current	V_{CC} = MAX, See Note 3			55	80	mA

† For conditions shown as MIN or MAX, use the appropriate value specified under recommended operating conditions for the applicable type.
‡ All typical values are at V_{CC} = 5 V, T_A = 25°C.
§ Not more than one output should be shorted at a time.
NOTE 3: I_{CC} is measured with the P0 input grounded, all other inputs at 4.5 V, and outputs open.

TEXAS
INSTRUMENTS

switching characteristics, V_{CC} = 5 V, T_A = 25°C

PARAMETER[¶]	FROM (INPUT)	TO (OUTPUT)	WAVEFORMS	TEST CONDITIONS	MIN	TYP	MAX	UNIT
t_{PLH}	Data	Y	A and C (with strobe high)				30	ns
t_{PHL}							39	
t_{PLH}	Data	Y	A and D (with strobe high)				38	ns
t_{PHL}							31	
t_{PLH}	Data	P1	A and E (with strobe high)	C_L = 15 pF,			46	ns
t_{PHL}				R_L = 400 Ω,			39	
t_{PLH}	Strobe	Any Y	B and C or B and D	See Figure 1			30	ns
t_{PHL}							31	
t_{PLH}	Strobe	P1	B and E				38	ns
t_{PHL}							42	
t_{PLH}	P0	P1	F and G				23	ns
t_{PHL}							30	

[¶] t_{PLH} = propagation delay time, low-to-high-level output
t_{PHL} = propagation delay time, high-to-low-level output

schematics of inputs and outputs

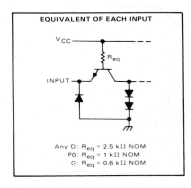

EQUIVALENT OF EACH INPUT

Any D: R_{eq} = 2.5 kΩ NOM
P0: R_{eq} = 1 kΩ NOM
G: R_{eq} = 0.6 kΩ NOM

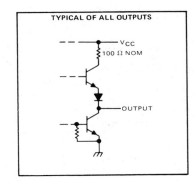

TYPICAL OF ALL OUTPUTS

3

TTL DEVICES

PARAMETER MEASUREMENT INFORMATION

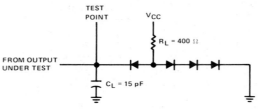

C$_L$ includes probe and jig capacitance.
All diodes are 1N3064.

LOAD CIRCUIT

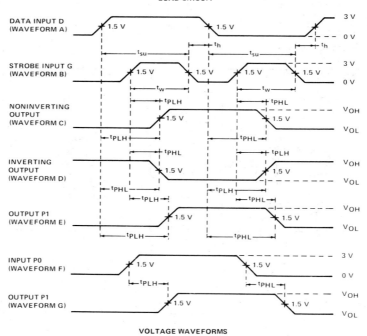

VOLTAGE WAVEFORMS

NOTE: Input pulses are supplied by a generator having the following
characteristics: t$_r$ ⩽ 7 ns, t$_f$ ⩽ 7 ns, PRR ⩽ MHz, Z$_{out}$ ≈ 50Ω.

FIGURE 1—SWITCHING TIMES

TEXAS
INSTRUMENTS

- **Package Options Include Both Plastic and Ceramic Chip Carriers in Addition to Plastic and Ceramic DIPs**

- **Dependable Texas Instruments Quality and Reliability**

description

The '279 offers 4 basic S-R flip-flop latches in one 16-pin, 300-mil package. Under conventional operation, the S-R inputs are normally held high. When the S input is pulsed low, the Q output will be set high. When R is pulsed low, the Q output will be reset low. Normally, the S-R inputs should not be taken low simultaneously. The Q output will be unpredictable in this condition.

FUNCTION TABLE
(each latch)

INPUTS		OUTPUT
S†	R	Q
H	H	Q_0
L	H	H
H	L	L
L	L	H*

H = high level L = low level

Q_0 = the level of Q before the indicated input conditions were established.

*This configuration is nonstable: that is, it may not persist when the S and R inputs return to their inactive (high) level.

† For latches with double S inputs:

H = both S inputs high

L = one or both S inputs low

SN54279, SN54LS279A . . . J OR W PACKAGE
SN74279 . . . J OR N PACKAGE
SN74LS279A . . . D, J OR N PACKAGE
(TOP VIEW)

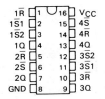

1R̄	1	16 V_CC
1S̄1	2	15 4S̄
1S̄2	3	14 4R̄
1Q	4	13 4Q
2R̄	5	12 3S̄2
2S̄	6	11 3S̄1
2Q	7	10 3R̄
GND	8	9 3Q

SN54LS279A . . . FK PACKAGE
SN74LS279A
(TOP VIEW)

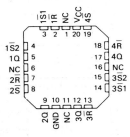

NC - No internal connection

logic diagram

(latches 1 and 3)

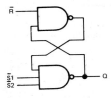

(latches 2 and 4)

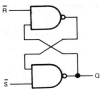

TEXAS INSTRUMENTS

TTL DEVICES

3

TYPES SN54279, SN54LS279A, SN74279, SN74LS279A
QUADRUPLE S̄-R̄ LATCHES

schematics of inputs and outputs

'279 CIRCUITS

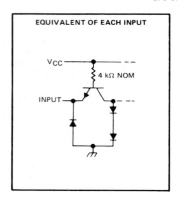

EQUIVALENT OF EACH INPUT

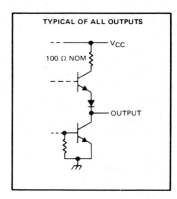

TYPICAL OF ALL OUTPUTS

'LS279A CIRCUITS

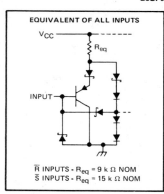

EQUIVALENT OF ALL INPUTS

R̄ INPUTS - R_{eq} = 9 k Ω NOM
S̄ INPUTS - R_{eq} = 15 k Ω NOM

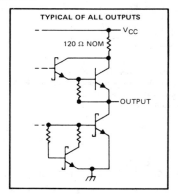

TYPICAL OF ALL OUTPUTS

absolute maximum ratings over operating free-air temperature range (unless otherwise noted)

Supply voltage, V_{CC} (see Note 1) . . . . 7 V
Input voltage: '279 . . . . 5.5 V
              ' LS279A . . . . 7 V
Operating free-air temperature range: SN54' TYPES . . . . − 55°C to 125°C
                               SN74' TYPES . . . . 0°C to 70°C
Storage temperature range . . . . − 65°C to 150°C

NOTE 1: Voltage values are with respect to network ground terminal.

TEXAS
INSTRUMENTS

recommended operating conditions

		SN54279			SN74279			UNIT
		MIN	NOM	MAX	MIN	NOM	MAX	
V_{CC}	Supply voltage	4.5	5	5.5	4.75	5	5.25	V
V_{IH}	High-level input voltage	2			2			V
V_{IL}	Low-level input voltage			0.8			0.8	V
I_{OH}	High-level output current			− 0.8			− 0.8	mA
I_{OL}	Low-level output current			16			16	mA
t_w	Pulse duration, low	20			20			ns
T_A	Operating free-air temperature	− 55		125	0		70	°C

electrical characteristics over recommended operating free-air temperature range (unless otherwise noted)

PARAMETER	TEST CONDITIONS[†]			SN54279			SN74279			UNIT
				MIN	TYP[‡]	MAX	MIN	TYP[‡]	MAX	
V_{IK}	V_{CC} = MIN,	I_I = − 12 mA				− 1.5			− 1.5	V
V_{OH}	V_{CC} = MIN,	V_{IL} = 0.8 V,	I_{OH} = − 0.8 mA	2.4	3.4		2.4	3.4		V
V_{OL}	V_{CC} = MIN,	V_{IH} = 2 V,	I_{OL} = 16 mA		0.2	0.4		0.2	0.4	V
I_I	V_{CC} = MAX,	V_I = 5.5 V				1			1	mA
I_{IH}	V_{CC} = MAX,	V_I = 2.4 V				40			40	µA
I_{IL}	V_{CC} = MAX,	V_I = 0.4 V				− 1.6			− 1.6	mA
I_{OS}[§]	V_{CC} = MAX			− 18		− 55	− 18		− 57	mA
I_{CC}	V_{CC} = MAX,	See Note 2			18	30		18	30	mA

† For conditions shown as MIN or MAX, use the appropriate value specified under recommended operating conditions.
‡ All typical values are at V_{CC} = 5 V, T_A = 25°C.
§ Not more than one output should be shorted at a time.
NOTE 2: I_{CC} is measured with all R inputs grounded, all S inputs at 4.5 V, and all outputs open.

switching characteristics, V_{CC} = 5 V, T_A = 25°C (see note 3)

PARAMETER	FROM (INPUT)	TO (OUTPUT)	TEST CONDITIONS		MIN	TYP	MAX	UNIT
t_{PLH}	$\overline{S}$	Q	R_L = 400 Ω,	C_L = 15 pF		12	22	ns
t_{PHL}						9	15	
t_{PHL}	$\overline{R}$	Q				15	27	ns

NOTE 3: See General Information Section for load circuits and voltage waveforms.

3

TTL DEVICES

recommended operating conditions

		SN54LS279A			SN74LS279A			UNIT
		MIN	NOM	MAX	MIN	NOM	MAX	
V_{CC}	Supply voltage	4.5	5	5.5	4.75	5	5.25	V
V_{IH}	High-level input voltage	2			2			V
V_{IL}	Low-level input voltage			0.7			0.8	V
I_{OH}	High-level output current			-0.4			-0.4	mA
I_{OL}	Low-level output current			4			8	mA
t_w	Pulse duration, low	20			20			ns
T_A	Operating free-air temperature	-55		125	0		70	$^{\circ}$C

electrical characteristics over recommended operating free-air temperature range (unless otherwise noted)

PARAMETER	TEST CONDITIONS†			SN54LS279A			SN74LS279A			UNIT
				MIN	TYP‡	MAX	MIN	TYP‡	MAX	
V_{IK}	V_{CC} = MIN,	$I_I = -18$ mA				-1.5			-1.5	V
V_{OH}	V_{CC} = MIN,	V_{IL} = MAX,	$I_{OH} = -0.4$ mA	2.5	3.4		2.7	3.4		V
V_{OL}	V_{CC} = MIN,	V_{IH} = 2 V,	I_{OL} = 4 mA		0.25	0.4		0.25	0.4	V
	V_{CC} = MIN,	V_{IH} = 2 V,	I_{OL} = 8 mA					0.25	0.5	
I_I	V_{CC} = MAX,	V_I = 7 V				0.1			0.1	mA
I_{IH}	V_{CC} = MAX,	V_I = 2.7 V				20			20	μA
I_{IL}	V_{CC} = MAX,	V_I = 0.4 V				-0.2			-0.2	mA
I_{OS}§	V_{CC} = MAX			-20		-100	-20		-100	mA
I_{CC}	V_{CC} = MAX,	See note 2			3.8	7		3.8	7	mA

† For conditions shown as MIN or MAX, use the appropriate value specified under recommended operating conditions.
‡ All typical values are at V_{CC} = 5 V, T_A = 25°C.
§ Not more than one output should be shorted at a time, and the duration of the short-circuit should be less than one second.
NOTE 2: I_{CC} is measured with all R inputs grounded, all S inputs at 4.5 V, and all outputs open.

switching characteristics, V_{CC} = 5 V, T_A = 25°C (see note 3)

PARAMETER	FROM (INPUT)	TO (OUTPUT)	TEST CONDITIONS		MIN	TYP	MAX	UNIT
t_{PLH}	$\overline{S}$	Q	R_L = 2 kΩ,	C_L = 15 pF		12	22	ns
t_{PHL}						13	21	
t_{PHL}	$\overline{R}$	Q				15	27	ns

NOTE 3: See General Information Section for load circuits and voltage waveforms.

TEXAS INSTRUMENTS

TYPES SN54LS280, SN54S280, SN74LS280, SN74S280
9-BIT ODD/EVEN PARITY GENERATORS/CHECKERS

DECEMBER 1972–REVISED DECEMBER 1983

- **Generates Either Odd or Even Parity for Nine Data Lines**
- **Cascadable for n-Bits**
- **Can Be Used to Upgrade Existing Systems using MSI Parity Circuits**
- **Typical Data-to-Output Delay of Only 14 ns for 'S280 and 33 ns for 'LS280**
- **Typical Power Dissipation:**
  'LS280 . . . 80 mW
  'S280 . . . 335 mW

SN54LS280, SN54S280 . . . J OR W PACKAGE
SN74LS280, SN74S280 . . . D, J OR N PACKAGE
(TOP VIEW)

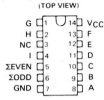

SN54LS280, SN54S280 . . . FK PACKAGE
SN74LS280, SN74S280
(TOP VIEW)

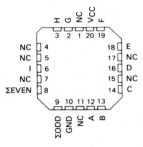

NC - No internal connection

FUNCTION TABLE

NUMBER OF INPUTS A THRU I THAT ARE HIGH	OUTPUTS	
	Σ EVEN	Σ ODD
0, 2, 4, 6, 8	H	L
1, 3, 5, 7, 9	L	H

H = high level, L = low level

description

These universal, monolithic, nine-bit parity generators/checkers utilize Schottky-clamped TTL high-performance circuitry and feature odd/even outputs to faciliate operation of either odd or even parity application. The word-length capability is easily expanded by cascading as shown under typical application data.

Series 54LS/74LS and Series 54S/74S parity generators/checkers offer the designer a trade-off between reduced power consumption and high performance. These devices can be used to upgrade the performance of most systems utilizing the '180 parity generator/checker. Although the 'LS280 and 'S280 are implemented without expander inputs, the corresponding function is provided by the availability of an input at pin 4 and the absence of any internal connection at pin 3. This permits the 'LS280 and 'S280 to be substituted for the '180 in existing designs to produce an identical function even if 'LS280's and 'S280's are mixed with existing '180's.

These devices are fully compatible with most other TTL circuits. All 'LS280 and 'S280 inputs are buffered to lower the drive requirements to one Series 54LS/74LS or Series 54S/74S standard load, respectively.

TEXAS INSTRUMENTS

3
TTL DEVICES

TYPES SN54S280, SN74S280
9-BIT ODD/EVEN PARITY GENERATORS/CHECKERS

schematics of inputs and outputs

'LS280

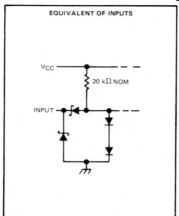

EQUIVALENT OF INPUTS

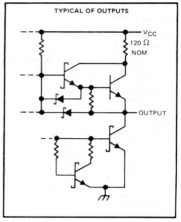

TYPICAL OF OUTPUTS

'S280

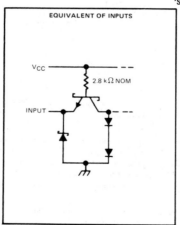

EQUIVALENT OF INPUTS

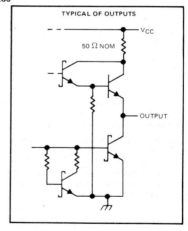

TYPICAL OF OUTPUTS

absolute maximum ratings over operating free-air temperature range (unless otherwise noted)

Supply voltage (see Note 1) . . . . 7 V
Input voltage: 'LS280 . . . . 7 V
           'S280 . . . . 5.5 V
Operating free-air temperature range: SN54' . . . . $-55°$C to $125°$C
                             SN74' . . . . $0°$C to $70°$C
Storage temperature range . . . . $-65°$C to $150°$C

NOTE 1: Voltage values are with respect to network ground terminal.

TEXAS
INSTRUMENTS

recommended operating conditions

		SN54LS280			SN74LS280			UNIT
		MIN	NOM	MAX	MIN	NOM	MAX	
V_{CC}	Supply voltage	4.5	5	5.5	4.75	5	5.25	V
V_{IH}	High-level input voltage	2			2			V
V_{IL}	Low-level input voltage			0.7			0.8	V
I_{OH}	High-level output current			−0.4			−0.4	mA
I_{OL}	Low-level output current			4			8	mA
T_A	Operating free-air temperature	−55		125	0		70	C

electrical characteristics over recommended operating free-air temperature range (unless otherwise noted)

PARAMETER	TEST CONDITIONS		SN54LS280			SN74LS280			UNIT
			MIN	TYP‡	MAX	MIN	TYP‡	MAX	
V_{IK}	V_{CC} = MIN,	I_I = −18 mA			−1.5			−1.5	V
V_{OH}	V_{CC} = MIN, V_{IH} = 2 V, V_{IL} = MAX, I_{OH} = −0.4 mA		2.5	3.4		2.7	3.4		V
V_{OL}	V_{CC} = MIN, V_{IH} = 2 V, V_{IL} = MAX	I_{OL} = 4 mA		0.25	0.4		0.25	0.4	V
		I_{OL} = 8 mA					0.35	0.5	
I_I	V_{CC} = MAX,	V_I = 7 V			0.1			0.1	mA
I_{IH}	V_{CC} = MAX,	V_I = 2.7 V			20			20	μA
I_{IL}	V_{CC} = MAX,	V_I = 0.4 V			−0.4			−0.4	mA
I_{OS}§	V_{CC} = MAX,		−20		−100	−20		−100	mA
I_{CC}	V_{CC} = MAX,	See Note 2		16	27		16	27	mA

† For conditions shown as MIN or MAX, use the appropriate value specified under recommended operating conditions.
‡ All typical values are at V_{CC} = 5 V, T_A = 25°C.
§ Not more than one output should be shorted at a time and duration of the short circuit should not exceed one second.
NOTE 2: I_{CC} is measured with all inputs grounded and all outputs open.

switching characteristics, V_{CC} = 5 V, T_A = 25°C

PARAMETER¶	FROM (INPUT)	TO (OUTPUT)	TEST CONDITIONS	MIN	TYP	MAX	UNIT
t_{PLH}	Data	Σ Even	C_L = 15 pF, R_L = 2 kΩ, Inputs not under test at 0 V, See Note 3		33	50	ns
t_{PHL}					29	45	
t_{PLH}	Data	Σ Odd			23	35	ns
t_{PHL}					31	50	

¶ t_{PLH} propagation delay time, low-to-high-level output; t_{PHL} propagation delay time, high-to-low-level output
NOTE 3: See General Information Section for load circuits and voltage waveforms.

3

TTL DEVICES

recommended operating conditions

	SN54S280			SN74S280			UNIT
	MIN	NOM	MAX	MIN	NOM	MAX	
Supply voltage, V_{CC}	4.5	5	5.5	4.75	5	5.25	V
High-level output current, I_{OH}			−1			−1	mA
Low-level output current, I_{OL}			20			20	mA
Operating free-air temperature, T_A	−55		125	0		70	C

electrical characteristics over recommended operating free-air temperature range (unless otherwise noted)

	PARAMETER	TEST CONDITIONS[†]		MIN	TYP	MAX	UNIT
V_{IH}	High-level input voltage			2			V
V_{IL}	Low-level input voltage					0.8	V
V_{IK}	Input clamp voltage	V_{CC} = MIN, I_I = −18 mA				−1.2	V
V_{OH}	High-level output voltage	V_{CC} = MIN, V_{IH} = 2 V,	SN54S'	2.5	3.4		V
		V_{IL} = 0.8 V, I_{OH} = −1 mA	SN74S'	2.7	3.4		
V_{OL}	Low-level output voltage	V_{CC} = MIN, V_{IH} = 2 V, V_{IL} = 0.8 V, I_{OL} = 20 mA				0.5	V
I_I	Input current at maximum input voltage	V_{CC} = MAX, V_I = 5.5 V				1	mA
I_{IH}	High-level input current	V_{CC} = MAX, V_I = 2.7 V				50	μA
I_{IL}	Low-level input current	V_{CC} = MAX, V_I = 0.5 V				−2	mA
I_{OS}	Short-circuit output current[§]	V_{CC} = MAX		−40		−100	mA
I_{CC}	Supply current	V_{CC} = MAX, See Note 2	SN54S280		67	99	mA
			SN74S280		67	105	
		V_{CC} = MAX, T_A = 125 C, See Note 2	SN54S280N			94	mA

[†] For conditions shown as MIN or MAX, use the appropriate value specified under recommended operating conditions.
[‡] All typical values are at V_{CC} = 5 V, T_A = 25 C.
[§] Not more than one output should be shorted at a time and duration of the short circuit should not exceed one second.
NOTE 2: I_{CC} is measured with all inputs grounded and all outputs open.

switching characteristics, V_{CC} = 5 V, T_A = 25°C

PARAMETER[¶]	FROM (INPUT)	TO (OUTPUT)	TEST CONDITIONS	MIN	TYP	MAX	UNIT
t_{PLH}	Data	Σ Even	C_L = 15 pF, R_L = 280 Ω, See Note 3		14	21	ns
t_{PHL}					11.5	18	
t_{PLH}	Data	Σ Odd			14	21	ns
t_{PHL}					11.5	18	

[¶] t_{PLH} = propagation delay time, low-to-high-level output; t_{PHL} = propagation delay time, high-to-low-level output
NOTE 3: See General Information Section for load circuits and voltage waveforms.

TEXAS
INSTRUMENTS

logic diagram

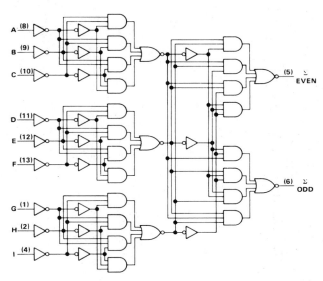

Pin numbers shown on logic notation are for D, J or N packages.

TYPICAL APPLICATION DATA

25-LINE PARITY/GENERATOR CHECKER

Three 'LS280's or 'S280's can be used to implement a 25-line parity generator/checker. This arrangement will provide parity in typically 75 or 25 nanoseconds respectively.

As an alternative, the outputs of two or three parity generators/checkers can be decoded with a 2-input ('S86 or 'LS86) or 3-input ('S135) exclusive-OR gate for 18- or 27-line parity applications.

81-LINE PARITY/GENERATOR CHECKER

Longer word lengths can be implemented by cascading 'LS280's or 'S280's. As shown here, parity can be generated for word lengths up to 81 bits in typically 75 or 25 nanoseconds respectively.

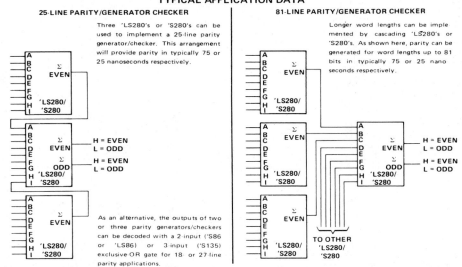

TEXAS INSTRUMENTS

3-753

TTL DEVICES

3

- Full-Carry Look-Ahead Across the Four Bits

- Systems Achieve Partial Look-Ahead Performance with the Economy of Ripple Carry

- Supply Voltage and Ground on Corner Pins to Simplify P-C Board Layout

TYPICAL ADD TIMES

TYPE	TWO 8-BIT WORDS	TWO 16-BIT WORDS	TYPICAL POWER DISSIPATION PER ADDER
'283	23ns	43ns	310 mW
'LS283	25ns	45ns	95 mW
'S283	15ns	30ns	510 mW

description

The '283 and 'LS283 adders are electrically and functionally identical to the '83A and 'LS283, respectively; only the arrangement of the terminals has been changed. The 'S283 high performance versions are also functionally identical.

These improved full adders perform the addition of two 4-bit binary words. The sum (Σ) outputs are provided for each bit and the resultant carry (C4) is obtained from the fourth bit. These adders feature full internal look-ahead across all four bits generating the carry term in ten nanoseconds, typically, for the '283 and 'LS283, and 7.5 nanoseconds for the 'S283. This capability provides the system designer with partial look-ahead performance at the economy and reduced package count of a ripple-carry implementation.

The adder logic, including the carry, is implemented in its true form. End around carry can be accomplished without the need for logic or level inversion.

Series 54, Series 54LS, and Series 54S circuits are characterized for operation over the full temperature range of $-55°C$ to $125°C$. Series 74, Series 74LS, and Series 74S circuits are characterized for $0°C$ to $70°C$ operation.

SN54283, SN54LS283 . . . J OR W PACKAGE
SN54S283 . . . J PACKAGE
SN74283 . . . J OR N PACKAGE
SN74LS283, SN74S283 . . . D, J OR N PACKAGE
(TOP VIEW)

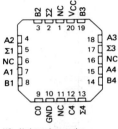

SN54LS283, SN54S283 . . . FK PACKAGE
SN74LS283, SN74S283
(TOP VIEW)

NC – No internal connection

FUNCTION TABLE

INPUT				OUTPUT					
				WHEN C0 = L			WHEN C0 = H		
						WHEN C2 = L			WHEN C2 = H
A1 / A3	B1 / B3	A2 / A4	B2 / B4	Σ1 / Σ3	Σ2 / Σ4	C2 / C4	Σ1 / Σ3	Σ2 / Σ4	C2 / C4
L	L	L	L	L	L	L	H	L	L
H	L	L	L	H	L	L	L	H	L
L	H	L	L	H	L	L	L	H	L
H	H	L	L	L	H	L	H	H	L
L	L	H	L	L	H	L	H	H	L
H	L	H	L	H	H	L	L	L	H
L	H	H	L	H	H	L	L	L	H
H	H	H	L	L	L	H	H	H	L
L	L	L	H	L	H	L	H	H	L
H	L	L	H	H	H	L	L	L	H
L	H	L	H	H	H	L	L	L	H
H	H	L	H	L	L	H	H	L	H
L	L	H	H	L	L	H	H	L	H
H	L	H	H	H	L	H	L	H	H
L	H	H	H	H	L	H	L	H	H
H	H	H	H	L	H	H	H	H	H

H = high level, L = low level

NOTE: Input conditions at A1, B1, A2, B2, and C0 are used to determine outputs $\Sigma1$ and $\Sigma2$ and the value of the internal carry C2. The values at C2, A3, B3, A4, and B4 are then used to determine outputs $\Sigma3$, $\Sigma4$, and C4.

3

TTL DEVICES

TEXAS
INSTRUMENTS

logic diagram

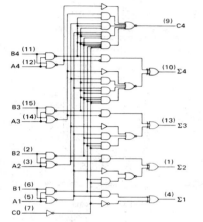

Pin numbers shown on logic notation are for D, J or N packages.

schematics of inputs and outputs

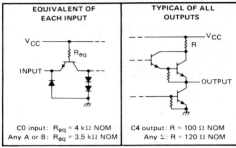

'283

| EQUIVALENT OF EACH INPUT | TYPICAL OF ALL OUTPUTS |

C0 input: R_{eq} = 4 kΩ NOM
Any A or B: R_{eq} = 3.5 kΩ NOM

C4 output: R = 100 Ω NOM
Any Σ: R = 120 Ω NOM

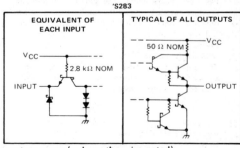

'LS283

EQUIVALENT OF EACH INPUT — TYPICAL OF ALL OUTPUTS

100 Ω NOM

C0 input: R_{eq} = 17 kΩ NOM
Any A or B: R_{eq} = 8.5 kΩ NOM

'S283

EQUIVALENT OF EACH INPUT — TYPICAL OF ALL OUTPUTS

2.8 kΩ NOM

50 Ω NOM

absolute maximum ratings over operating free-air temperature range (unless otherwise noted)

Supply voltage, V_{CC} (see Note 1)	7V
Input voltage: '283, 'S283	5.5V
'LS283	7V
Interemitter voltage (see Note 2)	5.5V
Operating free-air temperature range: SN54283, SN54LS283, SN54S283	-55°C to 125°C
SN74283, SN74LS283, SN74S283	0°C to 70°C
Storage temperature range	-65°C to 150°C

NOTES: 1. Voltage values, except interemitter voltage, are with respect to network ground terminal.

2. This is the voltage between two emitters of a multiple-emitter transistor. This rating applies for the '283 and 'S283 only between the following pairs: A1 and B1, A2 and B2, A3 and B3, A4 and B4.

TEXAS
INSTRUMENTS

recommended operating conditions

		SN54283 MIN	NOM	MAX	SN74283 MIN	NOM	MAX	UNIT
Supply Voltage, V_{CC}		4.5	5	5.5	4.75	5	5.25	V
High-level output current, I_{OH}	Any output except C4			−800			−800	μA
	Output C4			−400			−400	
Low-level output current, I_{OL}	Any output except C4			16			16	mA
	Output C4			8			8	
Operating free-air temperature, T_A		−55		125	0		70	°C

electrical characteristics over recommended operating free-air temperature range (unless otherwise noted)

PARAMETER		TEST CONDITIONS[†]	SN54283 MIN	TYP[‡]	MAX	SN74283 MIN	TYP[‡]	MAX	UNIT
V_{IH}	High-level input voltage		2			2			V
V_{IL}	Low-level input voltage				0.8			0.8	V
V_{IK}	Input clamp voltage	V_{CC} = MIN, I_I = −12 mA			−1.5			−1.5	V
V_{OH}	High-level output voltage	V_{CC} = MIN, V_{IH} = 2 V, V_{IL} = 0.8 V, I_{OH} = MAX	2.4	3.6		2.4	3.6		V
V_{OL}	Low-level output voltage	V_{CC} = MIN, V_{IH} = 2 V, V_{IL} = 0.8 V, I_{OL} = MAX		0.2	0.4		0.2	0.4	V
I_I	Input current at maximum input voltage	V_{CC} = MAX, V_I = 5.5 V			1			1	mA
I_{IH}	High-level input current	V_{CC} = MAX, V_I = 2.4 V			40			40	μA
I_{IL}	Low-level input current	V_{CC} = MAX, V_I = 0.4 V			−1.6			−1.6	mA
I_{OS}	Short-circuit output current[§] — Any output except C4	V_{CC} = MAX	−20		−55	−18		−55	mA
	Output C4		−20		−70	−18		−70	
I_{CC}	Supply current	V_{CC} = MAX, Outputs open — All B low, other inputs at 4.5 V		56			56		mA
		All inputs at 4.5 V		66	99		66	110	

[†]For conditions shown as MIN or MAX, use the appropriate value specified under recommended operating conditions.
[‡]All typical values are at V_{CC} = 5 V, T_A = 25°C.
[§]Only one output should be shorted at a time.

switching characteristics, V_{CC} = 5 V, T_A = 25°C

PARAMETER[¶]	FROM (INPUT)	TO (OUTPUT)	TEST CONDITIONS	MIN	TYP	MAX	UNIT
t_{PLH}	C0	Any Σ	C_L = 15 pF, R_L = 400 Ω, See Note 3		14	21	ns
t_{PHL}					12	21	
t_{PLH}	A_i or B_i	$Σ_i$			16	24	ns
t_{PHL}					16	24	
t_{PLH}	C0	C4	C_L = 15 pF, R_L = 780 Ω, See Note 3		9	14	ns
t_{PHL}					11	16	
t_{PLH}	A_i or B_i	C4			9	14	ns
t_{PHL}					11	16	

[¶]t_{PLH} Propagation delay time, low to high level output
t_{PHL} Propagation delay time, high to low level output
NOTE 3: See General Information Section for load circuits and voltage waveforms.

3

TTL DEVICES

TEXAS
INSTRUMENTS

recommended operating conditions

	SN54LS283			SN74LS283			UNIT
	MIN	NOM	MAX	MIN	NOM	MAX	
Supply voltage, V_{CC}	4.5	5	5.5	4.75	5	5.25	V
High-level output current, I_{OH}			−400			−400	μA
Low-level output current, I_{OL}			4			8	mA
Operating free-air temperature, T_A	−55		125	0		70	°C

electrical characteristics over recommended operating free-air temperature range (unless otherwise noted)

PARAMETER		TEST CONDITIONS[†]		SN54LS283			SN74LS283			UNIT
				MIN	TYP[‡]	MAX	MIN	TYP[‡]	MAX	
V_{IH} High-level input voltage				2			2			V
V_{IL} Low-level input voltage						0.7			0.8	V
V_{IK} Input clamp voltage		V_{CC} = MIN, I_I = −18 mA				−1.5			−1.5	V
V_{OH} High-level output voltage		V_{CC} = MIN, V_{IH} = 2 V, V_{IL} = V_{IL} max, I_{OH} = −400 μA		2.5	3.4		2.7	3.4		V
V_{OL} Low-level output voltage		V_{CC} = MIN, V_{IH} = 2 V, V_{IL} = V_{IL} max	I_{OL} = 4 mA		0.25	0.4		0.25	0.4	V
			I_{OL} = 8 mA					0.35	0.5	
I_I Input current at maximum input voltage	Any A or B	V_{CC} = MAX, V_I = 7 V				0.2			0.2	mA
	C0					0.1			0.1	
I_{IH} High-level input current	Any A or B	V_{CC} = MAX, V_I = 2.7 V				40			40	μA
	C0					20			20	
I_{IL} Low-level input current	Any A or B	V_{CC} = MAX, V_I = 0.4 V				−0.8			−0.8	mA
	C0					−0.4			−0.4	
I_{OS} Short-circuit output current[§]		V_{CC} = MAX		−20		−100	−20		−100	mA
I_{CC} Supply current		V_{CC} = MAX, Outputs open	All inputs grounded		22	39		22	39	mA
			All B low, other inputs at 4.5 V		19	34		19	34	
			All inputs at 4.5 V		19	34		19	34	

[†]For conditions shown as MIN or MAX, use the appropriate value specified under recommended operating conditions.
[‡]All typical values are at V_{CC} = 5 V, T_A = 25°C.
[§]Only one output should be shorted at a time and duration of the short-circuit should not exceed one second.

switching characteristics, V_{CC} = 5 V, T_A = 25°C

PARAMETER[¶]	FROM (INPUT)	TO (OUTPUT)	TEST CONDITIONS	MIN	TYP	MAX	UNIT
t_{PLH}	C0	Any Σ			16	24	ns
t_{PHL}					15	24	
t_{PLH}	A_i or B_i	Σ_i	C_L = 15 pF, R_L = 2 kΩ, See Note 3		15	24	ns
t_{PHL}					15	24	
t_{PLH}	C0	C4			11	17	ns
t_{PHL}					11	22	
t_{PLH}	A_i or B_i	C4			11	17	ns
t_{PHL}					12	17	

[¶]t_{PLH} = Propagation delay time, low-to-high-level output
t_{PHL} = Propagation delay time, high-to-low-level output
NOTE 3: See General Information Section for load circuits and voltage waveforms.

Texas
Instruments

recommended operating conditions

		SN54S283			SN74S283			UNIT
		MIN	NOM	MAX	MIN	NOM	MAX	
Supply voltage, V_{CC}		4.5	5	5.5	4.75	5	5.25	V
High-level output current, I_{OH}	Any output except C4			−1			−1	mA
	Output C4			−500			−500	μA
Low-level output current, I_{OL}	Any output except C4			20			20	mA
	Output C4			10			10	
Operating free-air temperature, T_A		−55		125	0		70	°C

electrical characteristics over recommended operating free-air temperature range (unless otherwise noted)

PARAMETER		TEST CONDITIONS[†]		MIN	TYP[‡]	MAX	UNIT
V_{IH}	High-level input voltage			2			V
V_{IL}	Low-level input voltage					0.8	V
V_{IK}	Input clamp voltage	V_{CC} = MIN,	I_I = −18 mA			−1.2	V
V_{OH}	High-level output voltage SN54S283	V_{CC} = MIN,	V_{IH} = 2 V,	2.5	3.4		V
	SN74S283	V_{IL} = 0.8 V,	I_{OH} = MAX	2.7	3.4		
V_{OL}	Low-level output voltage	V_{CC} = MIN, V_{IH} = 2 V, V_{IL} = 0.8 V, I_{OL} = MAX				0.5	V
I_I	Input current at maximum input voltage	V_{CC} = MAX,	V_I = 5.5 V			1	mA
I_{IH}	High-level input current	V_{CC} = MAX,	V_I = 2.7 V			50	μA
I_{IL}	Low-level input current	V_{CC} = MAX,	V_I = 0.5 V			−2	mA
I_{OS}	Short-circuit output current[§] Any output except C4	V_{CC} = MAX		−40		−100	mA
	Output C4			−20		−100	
I_{CC}	Supply current	V_{CC} = MAX, Outputs open	All B low, other inputs at 4.5 V		80		mA
			All inputs at 4.5 V		95	160	

[†]For conditions shown as MIN or MAX, use the appropriate value specified under recommended operating conditions for the applicable device type.

[‡]All typical values are at V_{CC} = 5 V, T_A = 25°C.

[§] Only one output should be shorted at a time, and duration of the short-circuit should not exceed one second.

switching characteristics, V_{CC} = 5 V, T_A = 25°C

PARAMETER[¶]	FROM (INPUT)	TO (OUTPUT)	TEST CONDITIONS	MIN	TYP	MAX	UNIT
t_{PLH}	C0	Any Σ	C_L = 15 pF, R_L = 280 Ω, See Note 3		11	18	ns
t_{PHL}					12	18	
t_{PLH}	A_i or B_i	Σ_i			12	18	ns
t_{PHL}					11.5	18	
t_{PLH}	C0	C4	C_L = 15 pF, R_L = 560 Ω, See Note 3		6	11	ns
t_{PHL}					7.5	11	
t_{PLH}	A_i or B_i	C4			7.5	12	ns
t_{PHL}					8.5	12	

[¶] t_{PLH} = Propagation delay time, low-to-high-level output

t_{PHL} = Propagation delay time, high-to-low-level output

NOTE 3: See General Information Section for load circuits and voltage waveforms.

3

TTL DEVICES

3

MAY 1972 – REVISED DECEMBER 1983

- **Fast Multiplication of Two Binary Numbers 8-Bit Product in 40 ns Typical**
- **Expandable for N-Bit-by-n-Bit Applications:**
  16-Bit Product in 70 ns Typical
  32-Bit Product in 103 ns Typical
- **Fully Compatible with Most TTL Circuits**
- **Diode-Clamped Inputs Simplify System Design**

SN54285 ... J OR W PACKAGE
SN74285 ... J OR N PACKAGE
(TOP VIEW)

```
        ___ ___
2C  [ 1  U  16 ]  VCC
2B  [ 2     15 ]  2D
2A  [ 3     14 ]  GA
1D  [ 4     13 ]  GB
1A  [ 5     12 ]  Y0
1B  [ 6     11 ]  Y1
1C  [ 7     10 ]  Y2
GND [ 8      9 ]  Y3
```

description

These high-speed TTL circuits are designed to be used in high-performance parallel multiplication applications. When connected as shown in Figure A, these circuits perform the positive-logic multiplication of two 4-bit binary words. The eight-bit binary product is generated with typically only 40 nanoseconds delay.

This basic four-by-four multiplier can be utilized as a fundamental building block for implementing larger multipliers. For example, the four-by-four building blocks can be connected as shown in Figure B to generate submultiple partial products. These results can then be summed in a Wallace tree, and, as illustrated, will produce a 16-bit product for the two eight-bit words typically in 70 nanoseconds. SN54LS183/SN74LS183 carry-save adders and SN54S181/SN74S181 arithmetic logic units with the SN54S182/SN74S182 look-ahead generator are used to achieve this high performance. The scheme is expandable for implementing N × M bit multipliers.

The SN54285 is characterized for operation over the full military temperature range of −55°C to 125°C; the SN74285 is characterized for operation from 0°C to 70°C.

logic symbol

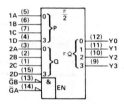

Pin numbers shown are for J and N packages.

3

TTL DEVICES

schematics

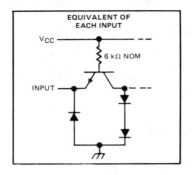

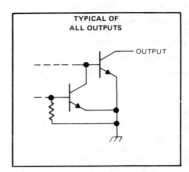

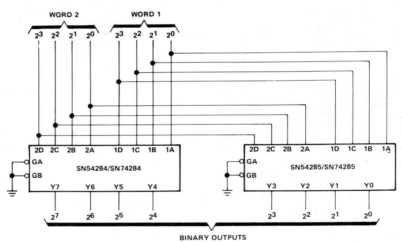

FIGURE A—4 X 4 MULTIPLIER

TEXAS
INSTRUMENTS

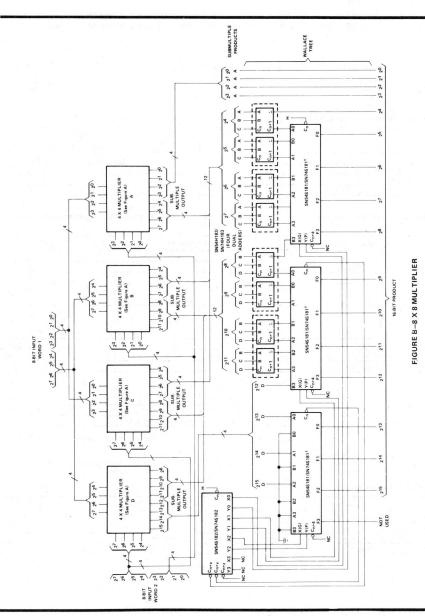

FIGURE 8—8 X 8 MULTIPLIER

†Other terminals of the three SN54S181/SN74S181 ALU's are connected as follows: S3 = H, S2 = L, S1 = L, S0 = H, M = L. Output A = B is not used for this application.

TTL DEVICES

3

absolute maximum ratings over operating free-air temperature range (unless otherwise noted)

Supply voltage, V_{CC} (see Note 1) . . . . 7 V
Input voltage . . . . 5.5 V
Operating free-air temperature range: SN54' Circuits . . . . $-55°C$ to $125°C$
                                      SN74' Circuits . . . . $0°C$ to $70°C$
Storage temperature range . . . . $-65°C$ to $150°C$

NOTE 1: Voltage values are with respect to network ground terminal.

recommended operating conditions

	SN54285			SN74285			UNIT
	MIN	NOM	MAX	MIN	NOM	MAX	
Supply voltage, V_{CC}	4.5	5	5.5	4.75	5	5.25	V
High-level output voltage, V_{OH}			5.5			5.5	V
Low-level output current, I_{OL}			16			16	mA
Operating free-air temperature, T_A	-55		125	0		70	°C

electrical characteristics over recommended operating free-air temperature range (unless otherwise noted)

	PARAMETER	TEST CONDITIONS†		MIN	TYP*	MAX	UNIT
V_{IH}	High-level input voltage			2			V
V_{IL}	Low-level input voltage					0.8	V
V_I	Input clamp voltage	V_{CC} = MIN,	I_I = -12 mA			-1.5	V
I_{OH}	High-level output current	V_{CC} = MIN, V_{IH} = 2 V, V_{IL} = 0.8 V,	V_{OH} = 5.5 V			40	μA
V_{OL}	Low-level output voltage	V_{CC} = MIN, V_{IH} = 2 V, V_{IL} = 0.8 V	I_{OL} = 12 mA			0.4	V
			I_{OL} = 16 mA			0.45	
I_I	Input current at maximum input voltage	V_{CC} = MAX,	V_I = 5.5 V			1	mA
I_{IH}	High-level input current	V_{CC} = MAX,	V_I = 2.4 V			40	μA
I_{IL}	Low-level input current	V_{CC} = MAX,	V_I = 0.4 V			-1	mA
I_{CC}	Supply current	V_{CC} = MAX, T_A = 125°C, See Note 2	SN54285 N package only			99	mA
		V_{CC} = MAX, See Note 2	SN54284, SN54285		92	110	
			SN74284, SN74285		92	130	

† For conditions shown as MIN or MAX, use the appropriate value specified under recommended operating conditions for the applicable device type.
* All typical values are at V_{CC} = 5 V, T_A = 25°C.
NOTE 2: With outputs open and both enable inputs grounded, I_{CC} is measured first by selecting an output product which contains three or more high-level bits, then by selecting an output product which contains four low-level bits.

switching characteristics, V_{CC} = 5 V, T_A = 25°C

PARAMETER	TEST CONDITIONS	MIN	TYP	MAX	UNIT
t_{PLH} Propagation delay time, low-to-high-level output from enable	C_L = 30pF to GND,		20	30	ns
t_{PHL} Propagation delay time, high-to-low-level output from enable	R_{L1} = 300 Ω to V_{CC},		20	30	
t_{PLH} Propagation delay time, low-to-high-level output from word inputs	R_{L2} = 600 Ω to GND,		40	60	ns
t_{PHL} Propagation delay time, high-to-low-level output from word inputs	See Note 3		40	60	

NOTE 3: See General Information Section for load circuits and voltage waveforms.

3

TTL DEVICES

TEXAS
INSTRUMENTS

'290, 'LS290 . . . DECADE COUNTERS
'293, 'LS293 . . . 4-BIT BINARY COUNTERS

- GND and V$_{CC}$ on Corner Pins
  (Pins 7 and 14 Respectively)

description

The SN54290/SN74290, SN54LS290/SN74LS290, SN54293/SN74293, and SN54LS293/SN74LS293 counters are electrically and functionally identical to the SN5490A/SN7490A, SN54LS90/SN74LS90, SN5493A/SN7493A, and SN54LS93/SN74LS93, respectively. Only the arrangement of the terminals has been changed for the '290, 'LS290, '293, and 'LS293.

Each of these monolithic counters contains four master-slave flip-flops and additional gating to provide a divide-by-two counter and a three-stage binary counter for which the count cycle length is divide-by-five for the '290 and 'LS290 and divide-by-eight for the '293 and 'LS293.

All of these counters have a gated zero reset and the '290 and 'LS290 also have gated set-to-nine inputs for use in BCD nine's complement applications.

To use the maximum count length (decade or four-bit binary) of these counters, the B input is connected to the Q$_A$ output. The input count pulses are applied to input A and the outputs are as described in the appropriate function table. A symmetrical divide-by-ten count can be obtained from the '290 and 'LS290 counters by connecting the Q$_D$ output to the A input and applying the input count to the B input which gives a divide-by-ten square wave at output Q$_A$.

SN54290, SN54LS290, SN54293,
SN54LS293 . . . J OR W PACKAGE
SN74290, SN74293 . . . J OR N PACKAGE
SN74LS290, SN74LS293 . . . D, J OR N PACKAGE
(TOP VIEW)

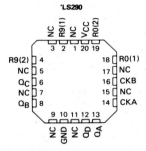

SN54LS290, SN54LS293 . . . FK PACKAGE
SN74LS290, SN74LS293
(TOP VIEW)

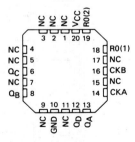

NC - No internal connection

TEXAS
INSTRUMENTS

3 TTL DEVICES

TYPES SN54290, SN54293, SN54LS290, SN54LS293,
SN74290, SN74293, SN74LS290, SN74LS293
DECADE AND 4–BIT BINARY COUNTERS

'290, 'LS290 BCD COUNT SEQUENCE (See Note A)

COUNT	QD	QC	QB	QA
0	L	L	L	L
1	L	L	L	H
2	L	L	H	L
3	L	L	H	H
4	L	H	L	L
5	L	H	L	H
6	L	H	H	L
7	L	H	H	H
8	H	L	L	L
9	H	L	L	H

'290, 'LS290 BI-QUINARY (5-2) (See Note B)

COUNT	QA	QD	QC	QB
0	L	L	L	L
1	L	L	L	H
2	L	L	H	L
3	L	L	H	H
4	L	H	L	L
5	H	L	L	L
6	H	L	L	H
7	H	L	H	L
8	H	L	H	H
9	H	H	L	L

'290, 'LS290 RESET/COUNT FUNCTION TABLE

R0(1)	R0(2)	R9(1)	R9(2)	QD	QC	QB	QA
H	H	L	X	L	L	L	L
H	H	X	L	L	L	L	L
X	X	H	H	H	L	L	H
X	L	X	L	COUNT			
L	X	L	X	COUNT			
L	X	X	L	COUNT			
X	L	L	X	COUNT			

'293, 'LS293 COUNT SEQUENCE (See Note C)

COUNT	QD	QC	QB	QA
0	L	L	L	L
1	L	L	L	H
2	L	L	H	L
3	L	L	H	H
4	L	H	L	L
5	L	H	L	H
6	L	H	H	L
7	L	H	H	H
8	H	L	L	L
9	H	L	L	H
10	H	L	H	L
11	H	L	H	H
12	H	H	L	L
13	H	H	L	H
14	H	H	H	L
15	H	H	H	H

'293, 'LS293 RESET/COUNT FUNCTION TABLE

R0(1)	R0(2)	QD	QC	QB	QA
H	H	L	L	L	L
L	X	COUNT			
X	L	COUNT			

NOTES: A. Output Q_A is connected to input B for BCD count.
   B. Output Q_D is connected to input A for bi-quinary count.
   C. Output Q_A is connected to input B.
   D. H = high level, L = low level, X = irrelevant

logic diagrams

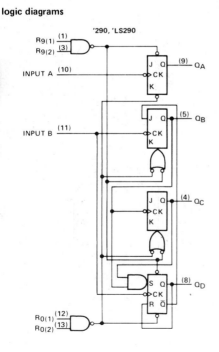

'290, 'LS290

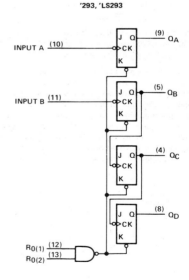

'293, 'LS293

Pin numbers shown on logic notation are for D, J or N packages.

The J and K inputs shown without connection are for reference only and are functionally at a high level.

3

TTL DEVICES

schematics of inputs and outputs

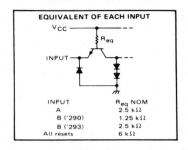

EQUIVALENT OF EACH INPUT

INPUT	R_{eq} NOM
A	2.5 kΩ
B ('290)	1.25 kΩ
B ('293)	2.5 kΩ
All resets	6 kΩ

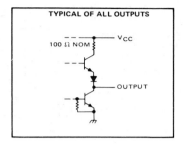

TYPICAL OF ALL OUTPUTS

100 Ω NOM

absolute maximum ratings over operating free-air temperature range (unless otherwise noted)

Supply voltage, V_{CC} (see Note 1)	7 V
Input voltage	5.5 V
Interemitter voltage (see Note 2)	5.5 V
Operating free-air temperature range: SN54' Circuits	-55°C to 125°C
SN74' Circuits	0°C to 70°C
Storage temperature range	-65°C to 150°C

NOTES: 1. Voltage values, except interemitter voltage, are with respect to network ground terminal.
2. This is the voltage between two emitters of a multiple-emitter transistor. For these circuits, this rating applies between the two R_0 inputs, and for the '290 circuit, it also applies between the two R9 inputs.

recommended operating conditions

		SN54'			SN74'			UNIT
		MIN	NOM	MAX	MIN	NOM	MAX	
Supply voltage, V_{CC}		4.5	5	5.5	4.75	5	5.25	V
High-level output current, I_{OH}				-800			-800	μA
Low-level output current, I_{OL}				16			16	mA
Count frequency, f_{count}	A input	0		32	0		32	MHz
	B input	0		16	0		16	
Pulse width, t_w	A input	15			15			
	B input	30			30			ns
	Reset inputs	15			15			
Reset inactive-state setup time, t_{su}		25			25			ns
Operating free-air temperature, T_A		-55		125	0		70	$^{\circ}$C

3

TTL DEVICES

TEXAS
INSTRUMENTS

electrical characteristics over recommended operating free-air temperature range (unless otherwise noted)

PARAMETER		TEST CONDITIONS†	'290 MIN	'290 TYP‡	'290 MAX	'293 MIN	'293 TYP‡	'293 MAX	UNIT
V_{IH} High-level input voltage			2			2			V
V_{IL} Low-level input voltage					0.8			0.8	V
V_{IK} Input clamp voltage		V_{CC} = MIN, I_I = −12 mA			−1.5			−1.5	V
V_{OH} High-level output voltage		V_{CC} = MIN, V_{IH} = 2 V, V_{IL} = 0.8 V, I_{OH} = −800 µA	2.4	3.4		2.4	3.4		V
V_{OL} Low-level output voltage		V_{CC} = MIN, V_{IH} = 2 V, V_{IL} = 0.8 V, I_{OL} = 16 mA¶		0.2	0.4		0.2	0.4	V
I_I Input current at maximum input voltage		V_{CC} = MAX, V_I = 5.5 V			1			1	mA
I_{IH} High-level input current	Any reset	V_{CC} = MAX, V_I = 2.4 V			40			40	µA
	A input				80			80	
	B input				120			80	
I_{IL} Low-level input current	Any reset	V_{CC} = MAX, V_I = 0.4 V			−1.6			−1.6	mA
	A input				−3.2			−3.2	
	B input				−4.8			−3.2	
I_{OS} Short-circuit output current§	SN54′	V_{CC} = MAX	−20		−57	−20		−57	mA
	SN74′		−18		−57	−18		−57	
I_{CC} Supply current		V_{CC} = MAX, See Note 3		29	42		26	39	mA

†For conditions shown as MIN or MAX, use the appropriate value specified under recommended operating conditions.
‡All typical values are at V_{CC} = 5 V, T_A = 25°C.
§Not more than one output should be shorted at a time.
¶Q_A outputs are tested at I_{OL} = 16 mA plus the limit value of I_{IL} for the B input. This permits driving the B input while maintaining full fan-out capability.
NOTE 3: I_{CC} is measured with all outputs open, both R_0 inputs grounded following momentary connection to 4.5 V, and all other inputs grounded.

switching characteristics, V_{CC} = 5 V, T_A = 25°C

PARAMETER	FROM (INPUT)	TO (OUTPUT)	TEST CONDITIONS	'290 MIN	'290 TYP	'290 MAX	'293 MIN	'293 TYP	'293 MAX	UNIT
f_{max}	A	Q_A		32	42		32	42		MHz
	B	Q_B		16			16			
t_{PLH}	A	Q_A			10	16		10	16	ns
t_{PHL}					12	18		12	18	
t_{PLH}	A	Q_D			32	48		46	70	ns
t_{PHL}					34	50		46	70	
t_{PLH}	B	Q_B	C_L = 15 pF, R_L = 400 Ω, See Note 4		10	16		10	16	ns
t_{PHL}					14	21		14	21	
t_{PLH}	B	Q_C			21	32		21	32	ns
t_{PHL}					23	35		23	35	
t_{PLH}	B	Q_D			21	32		34	51	ns
t_{PHL}					23	35		34	51	
t_{PHL}	Set-to-0	Any			26	40		26	40	ns
t_{PLH}	Set-to-9	Q_A, Q_D			20	30				ns
t_{PHL}		Q_B, Q_C			26	40				

f_{max} maximum count frequency
t_{PLH} propagation delay time, low-to-high-level output
t_{PHL} propagation delay time, high-to-low-level output
NOTE 4: See General Information Section for load circuits and voltage waveforms.

3
TTL DEVICES

TEXAS
INSTRUMENTS

schematics of inputs and outputs

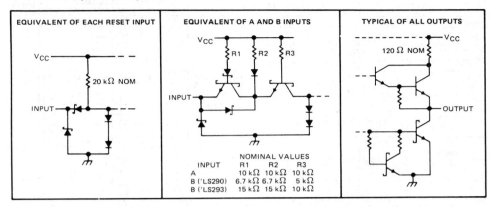

EQUIVALENT OF EACH RESET INPUT	EQUIVALENT OF A AND B INPUTS	TYPICAL OF ALL OUTPUTS

NOMINAL VALUES

INPUT	R1	R2	R3
A	10 kΩ	10 kΩ	10 kΩ
B ('LS290)	6.7 kΩ	6.7 kΩ	5 kΩ
B ('LS293)	15 kΩ	15 kΩ	10 kΩ

absolute maximum ratings over operating free-air temperature range (unless otherwise noted)

Supply voltage, V_{CC} (see Note 5)	7 V
Input voltage: R inputs	7 V
A and B inputs	5.5 V
Operating free-air temperature range: SN54LS290, SN54LS293	-55°C to 125°C
SN74LS290, SN74LS293	0°C to 70°C
Storage temperature range	-65°C to 150°C

NOTE 5: Voltage values are with respect to network ground terminal.

recommended operating conditions

		SN54LS'			SN74LS'			UNIT
		MIN	NOM	MAX	MIN	NOM	MAX	
Supply voltage, V_{CC}		4.5	5	5.5	4.75	5	5.25	V
High-level output current, I_{OH}				−400			−400	µA
Low-level output current, I_{OL}				4			8	mA
Count frequency, f_{count}	A input	0		32	0		32	MHz
	B input	0		16	0		16	
Pulse width, t_w	A input	15			15			ns
	B input	30			30			
	Reset inputs	30			30			
Reset inactive-state setup time, t_{su}		25			25			ns
Operating free-air temperature, T_A		−55		125	0		70	$^{\circ}$C

TTL DEVICES

3

TYPES SN54LS290, SN54LS293, SN74LS290, SN74LS293
DECADE AND 4-BIT BINARY COUNTERS

electrical characteristics over recommended operating free-air temperature range (unless otherwise noted)

PARAMETER		TEST CONDITIONS[†]		SN54LS' MIN	SN54LS' TYP[‡]	SN54LS' MAX	SN74LS' MIN	SN74LS' TYP[‡]	SN74LS' MAX	UNIT
V_{IH} High-level input voltage				2			2			V
V_{IL} Low-level input voltage						0.7			0.8	V
V_{IK} Input clamp voltage		V_{CC} = MIN,	I_I = -18 mA			-1.5			-1.5	V
V_{OH} High-level output voltage		V_{CC} = MIN, V_{IH} = 2 V, V_{IL} = V_{IL} max, I_{OH} = -400 µA		2.5	3.4		2.7	3.4		V
V_{OL} Low-level output voltage		V_{CC} = MIN, V_{IH} = 2 V, V_{IL} = V_{IL} max	I_{OL} = 4 mA[¶]		0.25	0.4		0.25	0.4	V
			I_{OL} = 8 mA[¶]					0.35	0.5	
I_I Input current at maximum input voltage	Any reset	V_{CC} = MAX, V_I = 7 V				0.1			0.1	mA
	A input	V_{CC} = MAX, V_I = 5.5 V				0.2			0.2	
	B of 'LS290					0.4			0.4	
	B of 'LS293					0.2			0.2	
I_{IH} High-level input current	Any reset	V_{CC} = MAX, V_I = 2.7 V				20			20	µA
	A input					40			40	
	B of 'LS290					80			80	
	B of 'LS293					40			40	
I_{IL} Low-level input current	Any reset	V_{CC} = MAX, V_I = 0.4 V				-0.4			-0.4	mA
	A input					-2.4			-2.4	
	B of 'LS290					-3.2			-3.2	
	B of 'LS293					-1.6			-1.6	
I_{OS} Short-circuit output current[§]		V_{CC} = MAX		-20		-100	-20		-100	mA
I_{CC} Supply current		V_{CC} = MAX, See Note 3	'LS290		9	15		9	15	mA
			'LS293		9	15		9	15	

[†]For conditions shown as MIN or MAX, use the appropriate value specified under recommended operating conditions.
[‡]All typical values are at V_{CC} = 5 V, T_A = 25°C.
[§]Not more than one output should be shorted at a time, and duration of the short-circuit should not exceed one second.
[¶]Q_A outputs are tested at specified I_{OL} plus the limit value of I_{IL} for the B input. This permits driving the B input while maintaining full fan-out capability.
NOTE 3: I_{CC} is measured with all outputs open, both R_0 inputs grounded following momentary connection to 4.5 V, and all other inputs grounded.

switching characteristics, V_{CC} = 5 V, T_A = 25°C

PARAMETER[◇]	FROM (INPUT)	TO (OUTPUT)	TEST CONDITIONS	'LS290 MIN	'LS290 TYP	'LS290 MAX	'LS293 MIN	'LS293 TYP	'LS293 MAX	UNIT
f_{max}	A	Q_A		32	42		32	42		MHz
	B	Q_B		16			16			
t_{PLH}	A	Q_A			10	16		10	16	ns
t_{PHL}					12	18		12	18	
t_{PLH}	A	Q_D			32	48		46	70	ns
t_{PHL}					34	50		46	70	
t_{PLH}	B	Q_B	C_L = oF, R_L = 2 kΩ, See Note 4		10	16		10	16	ns
t_{PHL}					14	21		14	21	
t_{PLH}	B	Q_C			21	32		21	32	ns
t_{PHL}					23	35		23	35	
t_{PLH}	B	Q_D			21	32		34	51	ns
t_{PHL}					23	35		34	51	
t_{PHL}	Set-to-0	Any			26	40		26	40	ns
t_{PLH}	Set-to-9	Q_A, Q_D			20	30				ns
t_{PHL}		Q_B, Q_C			26	40				

[◇]f_{max} = maximum count frequency
t_{PLH} = Propagation delay time, low-to-high-level output
t_{PHL} = Propagation delay time, high-to-low-level output
NOTE 4: See General Information Section for load circuits and voltage waveforms.

TEXAS INSTRUMENTS

TYPES SN54LS292, SN54LS294, SN74LS292, SN74LS294
PROGRAMMABLE FREQUENCY DIVIDERS/DIGITAL TIMERS

D2628, JANUARY 1981—REVISED DECEMBER 1983

- **Count Divider Chain**
- **Digitally Programmable from 2^2 to 2^n**
  (n = 31 for 'LS292, n = 15 for 'LS294)
- **Useable Frequency Range from DC to 30 MHz**
- **Easily Expandable**
- **Applications**
  - **Frequency Division**
  - **Digital Timing**

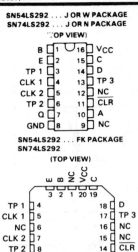

SN54LS292 . . . J OR W PACKAGE
SN74LS292 . . . J OR N PACKAGE
(TOP VIEW)

SN54LS292 . . . FK PACKAGE
SN74LS292
(TOP VIEW)

description

These programmable frequency dividers/digital timers contain 31 flip-flops plus 30 gates ('LS292) or 15 flip-flops plus 29 gates ('LS294) on a single chip. The count modulo is under digital control of the inputs provided.

Both types feature an active-low clear input to initialize the state of all flip-flops. To facilitate incoming inspection, test points are provided (TP1, TP2, and TP3 on the 'LS292 and TP on the 'LS294). These test points are not intended to drive system loads. Both types feature two clock inputs; either one may be used for clock gating. (See the function table below.)

A brief look at the digital timing capabilities of the 'LS292 will show that with a 1-MHz input frequency, programming for 2^{10} will give a period of 1.024 ms, and 2^{20} will give a period of 1.05 sec, 2^{26} will give a period of 1.12 min, and 2^{31} will give a period of 35.79 min.

These devices are easily cascadable giving limitless possibilities to timing delays that can be achieved.

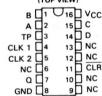

SN54LS294 . . . J OR W PACKAGE
SN74LS294 . . . J OR N PACKAGE
(TOP VIEW)

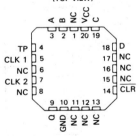

SN54LS294 . . . FK PACKAGE
SN74LS294
(TOP VIEW)

NC — No internal connection.

FUNCTION TABLE

CLEAR	CLK 1	CLK 2	Q OUTPUT MODE
L	X	X	Cleared to L
H	↑	L	Count
H	L	↑	Count
H	H	X	Inhibit
H	X	H	Inhibit

3

TTL DEVICES

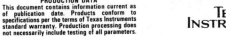

TEXAS
INSTRUMENTS

TYPES SN54LS292, SN54LS294, SN74LS292, SN74LS294
PROGRAMMABLE FREQUENCY DIVIDERS/DIGITAL TIMERS

schematics of inputs and outputs

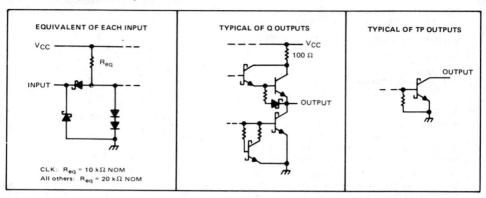

EQUIVALENT OF EACH INPUT

CLK: R_{eq} = 10 kΩ NOM
All others: R_{eq} = 20 kΩ NOM

TYPICAL OF Q OUTPUTS

TYPICAL OF TP OUTPUTS

operation

The functional block diagram shows that the count modulo is controlled by an X/Y decoder connected to the mode control inputs of several flip-flops. These flip flops with mode controls each have a "D" input connected to the parallel clock line and a "T" input driven by the preceding stage. The parallel clock frequency is always the input frequency divided by four.

The X/Y decoder output selected by the programming inputs goes low. While a mode control is low, the "D" input of that flip-flop is enabled, and the signal from the parallel clock line ($f_{in} \div 4$) is passed to the "T" input of the following stage. All the other mode controls are high enabling the "T" inputs and causing each flip-flop in turn to divide by two.

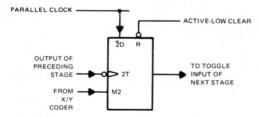

logic symbols

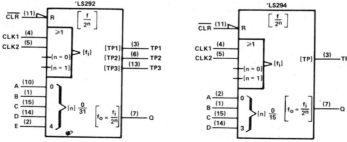

Pin numbers shown on logic notation are for J or N packages.

TEXAS
INSTRUMENTS

logic diagram (positive logic)

'LS292

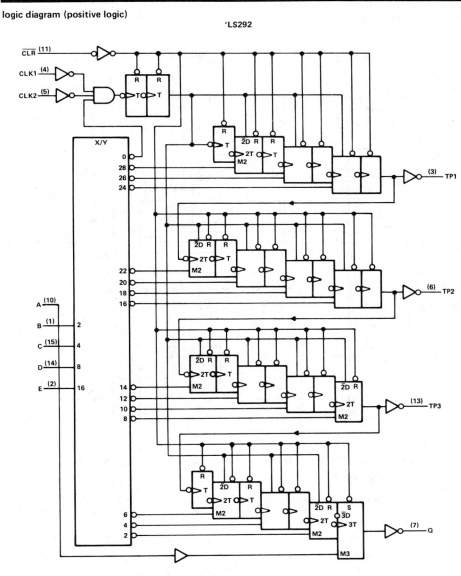

Pin numbers shown on logic notation are for J or N packages.

TTL DEVICES

3-773

logic diagram (positive logic)

'LS294

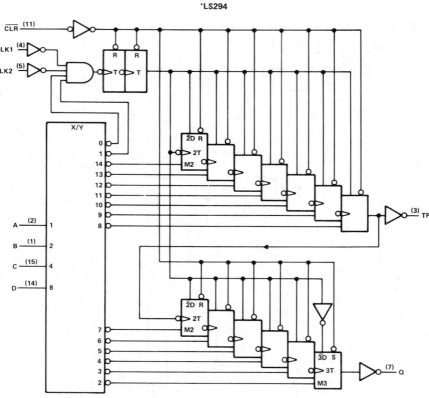

Pin numbers shown on logic notation are for J or N packages.

absolute maximum ratings over operating free-air temperature range (unless otherwise noted)

Supply voltage, V_{CC} (see Note 1)	7 V
Input voltage	7 V
Operating free-air temperature range: SN54LS292, SN54LS294	−55°C to 125°C
SN74LS292, SN74LS294	0°C to 70°C
Storage temperature range	−65°C to 150°C

NOTE 1: Voltage values are with respect to network ground terminal.

TEXAS
INSTRUMENTS

recommended operating conditions

		SN54LS'			SN74LS'			UNIT
		MIN	NOM	MAX	MIN	NOM	MAX	
V_{CC}	Supply voltage	4.5	5	5.5	4.75	5	5.25	V
V_{IH}	High-level input voltage	2			2			V
V_{IL}	Low-level input voltage			0.7			0.8	V
I_{OH}	High-level output current (Q only)			−1.2			−1.2	mA
I_{OL}	Low-level output current (Q only)			12			24	mA
f_{clock}	Clock frequency	0		30	0		30	MHz
t_w	Duration of clock input pulse	16			16			ns
t_w	Duration of clear pulse 'LS292	55			55			ns
	'LS294	35			35			
t_{su}	Clear inactive-state setup time	15			15			ns
T_A	Operating free-air temperature	−55		125	0		70	°C

electrical characteristics over recommended operating free-air temperature range (unless otherwise noted)

PARAMETER		TEST CONDITIONS†			SN54LS'			SN74LS'			UNIT
					MIN	TYP	MAX	MIN	TYP	MAX	
V_{IK}		V_{CC} = MIN,	I_I = −18 mA				−1.5			−1.5	V
V_{OH}	Q	V_{CC} = MIN, V_{IH} = 2 V, V_{IL} = MAX		I_{OH} = −1.2 mA,	2.4	3.4		2.4	3.4		V
V_{OL}	Q	V_{CC} = MIN, V_{IH} = 2 V, V_{IL} = MAX		I_{OL} = 12 mA		0.25	0.4		0.25	0.4	V
	Q			I_{OL} = 24 mA					0.35	0.5	
	TP♦			I_{OL} = 0.5 mA					0.25	0.4	
I_I		V_{CC} = MAX,	V_I = 7 V				0.1			0.1	mA
I_{IH}		V_{CC} = MAX,	V_I = 2.7 V				20			20	μA
I_{IL}	CLK1, CLK2	V_{CC} = MAX,	V_I = 0.4 V				−0.8			−0.8	mA
	All others						−0.4			−0.4	
I_{OS}§	Q	V_{CC} = MAX			−30		−130	−30		−130	mA
I_{CC}	'LS292	V_{CC} = MAX, All inputs grounded,				40	75		40	75	mA
	'LS294	All outputs open				30	50		30	50	

† For conditions shown as MIN or MAX, use the appropriate value specified under recommended operating conditions.
‡ All typical values are at V_{CC} = 5 V, T_A = 25°C.
§ The duration of the short-circuit should not exceed one second.
♦ The TP output or outputs are not intended to drive external loads but are solely provided for test points.

3

TTL DEVICES

TEXAS
INSTRUMENTS

switching characteristics, V_{CC} = 5 V, T_A = 25°C, R_L = 667 Ω, C_L = 45 pF, (see note 2)

PARAMETER	FROM (INPUT)	TO (OUTPUT)	TEST CONDITIONS	'LS292 MIN	'LS292 TYP	'LS292 MAX	'LS294 MIN	'LS294 TYP	'LS294 MAX	UNIT
f_{max}				30	50		30	50		MHz
t_{PLH}	CLK1 or 2	Q	Modulo set at 22, A thru E = LLLHL ('LS292) A thru D = LLHL ('LS294)		55	90		55	90	ns
t_{PHL}		Q			80	120		80	120	ns
t_{PHL}	$\overline{CLR}$	Q			85	130		35	65	ns

f_{MAX} = maximum clock frequency
t_{PLH} = Propagation delay time, low-to-high-level output
t_{PHL} = Propagation delay time, high-to-low-level output
NOTE 2: See General Information Section for load circuits and voltage waveforms.
To be used on TP outputs only.

'LS292 FUNCTION TABLE

E	D	C	B	A	Q BINARY	Q DECIMAL	TP1 BINARY	TP1 DECIMAL	TP2 BINARY	TP2 DECIMAL	TP3 BINARY	TP3 DECIMAL
L	L	L	L	L	Inhibit	Inhibit	Inhibit	Inhibit	Inhibit	Inhibit	Inhibit	Inhibit
L	L	L	L	H	Inhibit	Inhibit	Inhibit	Inhibit	Inhibit	Inhibit	Inhibit	Inhibit
L	L	L	H	L	2^2	4	2^9	512	2^{17}	131,072	2^{24}	16,777,216
L	L	L	H	H	2^3	8	2^9	512	2^{17}	131,072	2^{24}	16,777,216
L	L	H	L	L	2^4	16	2^9	512	2^{17}	131,072	2^{24}	16,777,216
L	L	H	L	H	2^5	32	2^9	512	2^{17}	131,072	2^{24}	16,777,216
L	L	H	H	L	2^6	64	2^9	512	2^{17}	131,072	2^{24}	16,777,216
L	L	H	H	H	2^7	128	2^9	512	2^{17}	131,072	2^{24}	16,777,216
L	H	L	L	L	2^8	256	2^9	512	2^{17}	131,072	2^2	4
L	H	L	L	H	2^9	512	2^9	512	2^{17}	131,072	2^2	4
L	H	L	H	L	2^{10}	1,024	2^9	512	2^{17}	131,072	2^4	16
L	H	L	H	H	2^{11}	2,048	2^9	512	2^{17}	131,072	2^4	16
L	H	H	L	L	2^{12}	4,096	2^9	512	2^{17}	131,072	2^6	64
L	H	H	L	H	2^{13}	8,192	2^9	512	2^{17}	131,072	2^6	64
L	H	H	H	L	2^{14}	16,384	2^9	512	Disabled Low		2^8	256
L	H	H	H	H	2^{15}	32,768	2^9	512	Disabled Low		2^8	256
H	L	L	L	L	2^{16}	65,536	2^9	512	2^3	8	2^{10}	1,024
H	L	L	L	H	2^{17}	131,072	2^9	512	2^3	8	2^{10}	1,024
H	L	L	H	L	2^{18}	262,144	2^9	512	2^5	32	2^{12}	4,096
H	L	L	H	H	2^{19}	524,288	2^9	512	2^5	32	2^{12}	4,096
H	L	H	L	L	2^{20}	1,048,576	2^9	512	2^7	128	2^{14}	16,384
H	L	H	L	H	2^{21}	2,097,152	2^9	512	2^7	128	2^{14}	16,384
H	L	H	H	L	2^{22}	4,194,304	Disabled Low		2^9	512	2^{16}	65,536
H	L	H	H	H	2^{23}	8,388,608	Disabled Low		2^9	512	2^{16}	65,536
H	H	L	L	L	2^{24}	16,777,216	2^3	8	2^{11}	2,048	2^{18}	262,144
H	H	L	L	H	2^{25}	33,554,432	2^3	8	2^{11}	2,048	2^{18}	262,144
H	H	L	H	L	2^{26}	67,108,864	2^5	32	2^{13}	8,192	2^{20}	1,048,576
H	H	L	H	H	2^{27}	134,217,728	2^5	32	2^{13}	8,192	2^{20}	1,048,576
H	H	H	L	L	2^{28}	268,435,456	2^7	128	2^{15}	32,768	2^{22}	4,194,304
H	H	H	L	H	2^{29}	536,870,912	2^7	128	2^{15}	32,768	2^{22}	4,194,304
H	H	H	H	L	2^{30}	1,073,741,824	2^9	512	2^{17}	131,072	2^{24}	16,777,216
H	H	H	H	H	2^{31}	2,147,483,648	2^9	512	2^{17}	131,072	2^{24}	16,777,216

3 — TTL DEVICES

Texas Instruments

'LS294 FUNCTION TABLE

PROGRAMMING INPUTS				FREQUENCY DIVISION			
				Q		TP	
D	C	B	A	BINARY	DECIMAL	BINARY	DECIMAL
L	L	L	L	Inhibit	Inhibit	Inhibit	Inhibit
L	L	L	H	Inhibit	Inhibit	Inhibit	Inhibit
L	L	H	L	2^2	4	2^9	512
L	L	H	H	2^3	8	2^9	512
L	H	L	L	2^4	16	2^9	512
L	H	L	H	2^5	32	2^9	512
L	H	H	L	2^6	64	2^9	512
L	H	H	H	2^7	128	Disabled Low	
H	L	L	L	2^8	256	2^2	4
H	L	L	H	2^9	512	2^3	8
H	L	H	L	2^{10}	1,024	2^4	16
H	L	H	H	2^{11}	2,048	2^5	32
H	H	L	L	2^{12}	4,096	2^6	64
H	H	L	H	2^{13}	8,192	2^7	128
H	H	H	L	2^{14}	16,384	2^8	256
H	H	H	H	2^{15}	32,768	2^9	512

switching loads

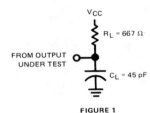

V_{CC}

$R_L = 667\ \Omega$

FROM OUTPUT UNDER TEST

$C_L = 45\ pF$

FIGURE 1

'LS292 and 'LS294 timing diagram

CLR

CLK1

Q_22

Q_23

CLK2

3

TTL DEVICES

- **'LS295B Offers Three Times the Sink-Current Capability of 'LS295A**

- **Schottky-Diode-Clamped Transistors**

- **Low Power Dissipation . . . 80 mW Typical (Enabled)**

- **Applications:**
  N-Bit Serial-To-Parallel Converter
  N-Bit Parallel-To-Serial Converter
  N-Bit Storage Register

SN54LS295B . . . J OR W PACKAGE
SN74LS295B . . . D, J OR N PACKAGE
(TOP VIEW)

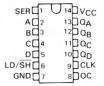

SN54LS295B . . . FK PACKAGE
SN74LS295B
(TOP VIEW)

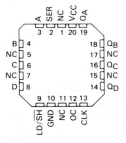

NC - No internal connection

description

These 4-bit registers feature parallel inputs, parallel outputs, and clock (CLK), serial (SER), mode (LD/SH), and outputs control (OC) inputs. The registers have three modes of operation:

Parallel (broadside) load
Shift right (the direction Q_A toward Q_D)
Shift left (the direction Q_D toward Q_A)

Parallel loading is accomplished by applying the four bits of data and taking the mode control input high. The data is loaded into the associated flip-flops and appears at the outputs after the high-to-low transition of the clock input. During parallel loading, the entry of serial data is inhibited.

Shift right is accomplished when the mode control is low; shift left is accomplished when the mode control is high by connecting the output of each flip-flop to the parallel input of the previous flip-flop (Q_D to input C, etc.) and serial data is entered at input D.

When the output control is high, the normal logic levels of the four outputs are available for driving the loads or bus lines. The outputs are disabled independently from the level of the clock by a low logic level at the output control input. The outputs then present a high impedance and neither load nor drive the bus line; however, sequential operation of the registers is not affected.

The SN54LS295B is characterized for operation over the full military temperature range of −55°C to 125°C; the SN74LS295B is characterized for operation from 0°C to 70°C.

3

TTL DEVICES

logic diagram

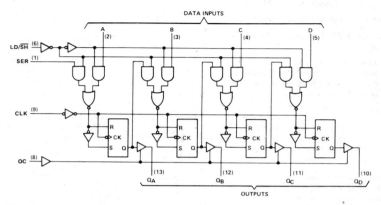

Pin numbers shown on logic notation are for D, J or N packages.

schematics of inputs and outputs

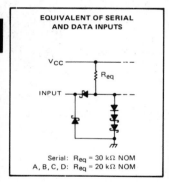

EQUIVALENT OF SERIAL
AND DATA INPUTS

Serial: R_{eq} = 30 kΩ NOM
A, B, C, D: R_{eq} = 20 kΩ NOM

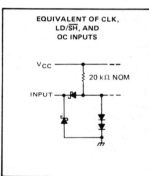

EQUIVALENT OF CLK,
LD/$\overline{SH}$, AND
OC INPUTS

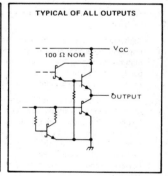

TYPICAL OF ALL OUTPUTS

TEXAS
INSTRUMENTS

FUNCTION TABLE

INPUTS							OUTPUTS			
LD/$\overline{\text{SH}}$	CLK	SER	PARALLEL				Q_A	Q_B	Q_C	Q_D
			A	B	C	D				
H	H	X	X	X	X	X	Q_{A0}	Q_{B0}	Q_{C0}	Q_{D0}
H	↓	X	a	b	c	d	a	b	c	d
H	↓	X	Q_B†	Q_C†	Q_D†	d	Q_{Bn}	Q_{Cn}	Q_{Dn}	d
L	H	X	X	X	X	X	Q_{A0}	Q_{B0}	Q_{C0}	Q_{D0}
L	↓	H	X	X	X	X	H	Q_{An}	Q_{Bn}	Q_{Cn}
L	↓	L	X	X	X	X	L	Q_{An}	Q_{Bn}	Q_{Cn}

When the output control is low, the outputs are disabled to the high-impedance state; however, sequential operation of the registers is not affected.

†Shifting left requires external connection of Q_B to A, Q_C to B, and Q_D to C. Serial data is entered at input D.

H = high level (steady state), L = low level (steady state), X = irrelevant (any input, including transitions)
↓ = transition from high to low level.
a, b, c, d = the level of steady-state input at inputs A, B, C, or D, respectively.
Q_{A0}, Q_{B0}, Q_{C0}, Q_{D0} = the level of Q_A, Q_B, Q_C, or Q_D, respectively, before the indicated steady-state input conditions were established.
Q_{An}, Q_{Bn}, Q_{Cn}, Q_{Dn} = the level of Q_A, Q_B, Q_C, or Q_D, respectively, before the most-recent ↓ transition of the clock.

absolute maximum ratings over operating free-air temperature range (unless otherwise noted)

Supply voltage, V_{CC} (see Note 1) . . . . 7 V
Input voltage . . . . 7 V
Operating free-air temperature range: SN54LS295B . . . . −55°C to 125°C
                              SN74LS295B . . . . 0°C to 70°C
Storage temperature range . . . . −65°C to 150°C

NOTE 1: Voltage values are with respect to network ground terminal.

recommended operating conditions

			SN54LS295B			SN74LS295B			UNIT
			MIN	NOM	MAX	MIN	NOM	MAX	
V_{CC}	Supply voltage		4.5	5	5.5	4.75	5	5.25	V
I_{OH}	High-level output current				−1			−2.6	mA
I_{OL}	Low-level output current				12			24	mA
f_{clock}	Clock frequency		0		30	0		30	MHz
$t_{w(clock)}$	Width of clock pulse		16			16			ns
t_{su}	Setup time, high-level or low-level data		20			20			ns
t_{su}	Setup time, LD/$\overline{\text{SH}}$ to CLK	high-level	25			25			ns
		low-level	30			30			
t_h	Hold time, high-level or low-level data		5			5			ns
t_h	Hold time, high-level or low-level LD/$\overline{\text{SH}}$ to CLK		0			0			ns
T_A	Operating free-air temperature		−55		125	0		70	°C

electrical characteristics over recommended operating free-air temperature range (unless otherwise noted)

PARAMETER		TEST CONDITIONS[†]		SN54LS295B MIN	SN54LS295B TYP[‡]	SN54LS295B MAX	SN74LS295B MIN	SN74LS295B TYP[‡]	SN74LS295B MAX	UNIT
V_{IH}	High-level input voltage			2			2			V
V_{IL}	Low-level input voltage					0.7			0.8	V
V_{IK}	Input clamp voltage	V_{CC} = MIN,	I_I = −18 mA			−1.5			−1.5	V
V_{OH}	High-level output voltage	V_{CC} = MIN, V_{IH} = 2 V, V_{IL} = V_{IL} max, I_{OH} = MAX		2.4	3.4		2.4	3.1		V
V_{OL}	Low-level output voltage	V_{CC} = MIN, V_{IH} = 2 V, V_{IL} = V_{IL} max	I_{OL} = 12 mA		0.25	0.4		0.25	0.4	V
			I_{OL} = 24 mA					0.35	0.5	
I_{OZH}	Off-state output current, high-level voltage applied	V_{CC} = MAX, V_{IL} = V_{IL} max, V_O = 2.7 V				20			20	µA
I_{OZL}	Off-state output current, low-level voltage applied	V_{CC} = MAX, V_{IH} = 2 V, V_O = 0.4 V				−20			−20	µA
I_I	Input current at maximum input voltage	V_{CC} = MAX, V_I = 7 V				0.1			0.1	mA
I_{IH}	High-level input current	V_{CC} = MAX, V_I = 2.7 V				20			20	µA
I_{IL}	Low-level input current	V_{CC} = MAX, V_I = 0.4 V				−0.4			−0.4	mA
I_{OS}	Short-circuit output current[§]	V_{CC} = MAX		−30		−130	−30		−130	mA
I_{CC}	Supply current	V_{CC} = MAX, See Note 2	Condition A		20	29		20	29	mA
			Condition B		22	33		22	33	

[†]For conditions shown as MIN or MAX, use the appropriate value specified under recommended operating conditions.

[‡]All typical values are at V_{CC} = 5 V, T_A = 25°C.

[§]Not more than one output should be shorted at a time, and duration of the short-circuit should not exceed one second.

NOTE 2: I_{CC} is measured with the outputs open, the serial input and mode control at 4.5 V, and the data inputs grounded under the following conditions:
    A. Output control at 4.5 V and a momentary 3 V, then ground, applied to clock input.
    B. Output control and clock input grounded.

switching characteristics, V_{CC} = 5 V, T_A = 25 C, R_L = 667 Ω

PARAMETER		TEST CONDITIONS	MIN	TYP	MAX	UNIT
f_{max}	Maximum clock frequency		30	45		MHz
t_{PLH}	Propagation delay time, low-to-high-level output	C_L = 45 pF, See Note 3		14	20	ns
t_{PHL}	Propagation delay time, high-to-low-level output			19	30	ns
t_{PZH}	Output enable time to high level			18	26	ns
t_{PZL}	Output enable time to low level			20	30	ns
t_{PHZ}	Output disable time from high level	C_L = 5 pF, See Note 3		13	20	ns
t_{PLZ}	Output disable time from low level			13	20	ns

NOTE 3: See General Information Section for load circuits and voltage waveforms.

TEXAS INSTRUMENTS

- **Digital Design Avoids Analog Compensation Errors**

- **Easily Cascadable for Higher Order Loops**

- **Useful Frequency from DC to:**
  50 MHz Typical (K Clock)
  35 MHz Typical (I/D Clock)

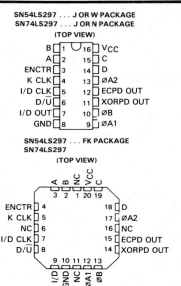

SN54LS297 . . . J OR W PACKAGE
SN74LS297 . . . J OR N PACKAGE
(TOP VIEW)

B	1	16 VCC
A	2	15 C
ENCTR	3	14 D
K CLK	4	13 ØA2
I/D CLK	5	12 ECPD OUT
D/U̅	6	11 XORPD OUT
I/D OUT	7	10 ØB
GND	8	9 ØA1

SN54LS297 . . . FK PACKAGE
SN74LS297
(TOP VIEW)

ENCTR	4	18 D
K CLK	5	17 ØA2
NC	6	16 NC
I/D CLK	7	15 ECPD OUT
D/U̅	8	14 XORPD OUT

NC-No internal connection

description

The SN54LS297 and SN74LS297 devices are designed to provide a simple, cost-effective solution to high-accuracy, digital, phase-locked-loop applications. These devices contain all the necessary circuits, with the exception of the divide-by-N counter, to build first order phase-locked loops as described in Figure 1.

Both exclusive-OR (XORPD) and edge-controlled (ECPD) phase detectors are provided for maximum flexibility.

Proper partitioning of the loop function, with many of the building blocks external to the package, makes it easy for the designer to incorporate ripple cancellation or to cascade to higher order phase-locked loops.

The length of the up/down K counter is digitally programmable according to the K counter function table. With A, B, C, and D all low, the K counter is disabled. With A high and B, C, and D low, the K counter is only three stages long, which widens the bandwidth or capture range and shortens the lock time of the loop. When A, B, C, and D are all programmed high, the K counter becomes seventeen stages long, which narrows the bandwidth or capture range and lengthens the lock time. Real-time control of loop bandwidth by manipulating the A through D inputs can maximize the overall performance of the digital phase-locked loop.

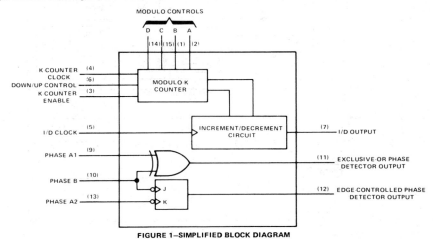

FIGURE 1—SIMPLIFIED BLOCK DIAGRAM

TEXAS INSTRUMENTS

3

TTL DEVICES

TYPES SN54LS297, SN74LS297
DIGITAL PHASE-LOCKED-LOOP FILTERS

description (continued)

The 'LS297 can perform the classic first-order phase-locked loop function without using analog components. The accuracy of the digital phase-locked loop (DPLL) is not affected by V_{CC} and temperature variations, but depends solely on accuracies of the K clock, I/D clock, and loop propagation delays. The I/D clock frequency and the divide-by-N modulos will determine the center frequency of the DPLL. The center frequency is defined by the relationship $f_C = $ I/D Clock/2N (Hz).

logic diagram

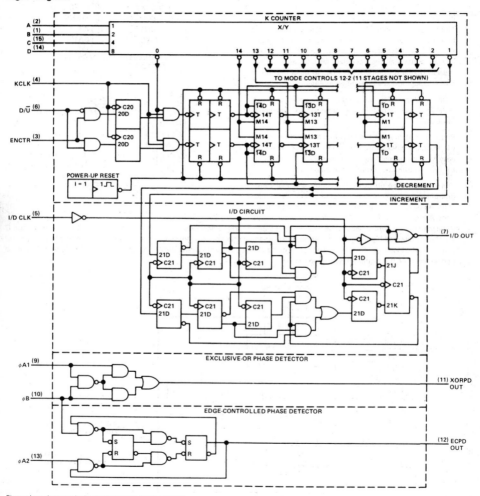

Pin numbers shown on logic notation are for J or N packages.

TEXAS
INSTRUMENTS

K COUNTER FUNCTION TABLE
(DIGITAL CONTROL)

D	C	B	A	MODULO (K)
L	L	L	L	Inhibited
L	L	L	H	2^3
L	L	H	L	2^4
L	L	H	H	2^5
L	H	L	L	2^6
L	H	L	H	2^7
L	H	H	L	2^8
L	H	H	H	2^9
H	L	L	L	2^{10}
H	L	L	H	2^{11}
H	L	H	L	2^{12}
H	L	H	H	2^{13}
H	H	L	L	2^{14}
H	H	L	H	2^{15}
H	H	H	L	2^{16}
H	H	H	H	2^{17}

FUNCTION TABLE
EXCLUSIVE-OR PHASE DETECTOR

$\phi A1$	ϕB	XORPD OUT
L	L	L
L	H	H
H	L	H
H	H	L

FUNCTION TABLE
EDGE-CONTROLLED PHASE DETECTOR

$\phi A2$	ϕB	ECPD OUT
H or L	↓	H
↓	H or L	L
H or L	↑	No change
↑	H or L	No change

H = steady-state high level
L = steady-state low level
↓ = transition from high to low
↑ = transition from low to high

schematics of inputs and outputs

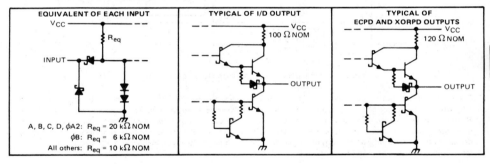

A, B, C, D, $\phi A2$: R_{eq} = 20 kΩ NOM
ϕB: R_{eq} = 6 kΩ NOM
All others: R_{eq} = 10 kΩ NOM

operation

The phase detector generates an error signal waveform that, at zero phase error, is a 50% duty cycle square wave. At the limits of linear operation, the phase detector output will be either high or low all of the time, depending on the direction of the phase error ($\phi_{in} - \phi_{out}$). Within these limits, the phase detector output varies linearly with the input phase error according to the gain k_d, which is expressed in terms of phase detector output per cycle of phase error. The phase detector output can be defined to vary between ±1 according to the relation:

$$\text{PD Output} = \frac{\% \text{ high} - \% \text{ low}}{100} \qquad (1)$$

The output of the phase detector will be $k_d \phi_e$, where the phase error $\phi_e = \phi_{in} - \phi_{out}$.

TEXAS
INSTRUMENTS

3-785

Exclusive-OR phase detectors (XORPD) and edge-controlled phase detectors (ECPD) are commonly used digital types. The ECPD is more complex than the XORPD logic function, but can be described generally as a circuit that changes states on one of the transitions of its inputs. k_d for an XORPD is 4 because its output remains high (PD output = 1) for a phase error of 1/4 cycle. Similarly, k_d for the ECPD is 2 since its output remains high for a phase error of 1/2 cycle. The type of phase detector will determine the zero-phase-error point, i.e., the phase separation of the phase detector inputs for ϕ_e defined to be zero. For the basic DPLL system of Figure 2, $\phi_e = 0$ when the phase detector output is a square wave. The XORPD inputs are 1/4 cycle out of phase for zero phase error. For the ECPD, $\phi_e = 0$ when the inputs are 1/2 cycle out of phase.

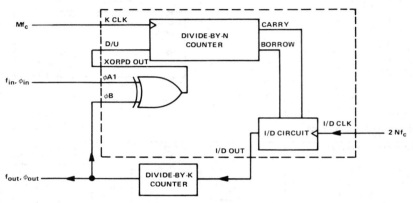

FIGURE 2—DPLL USING EXCLUSIVE-OR PHASE DETECTION

The phase detector output controls the up/down input to the K counter. The counter is clocked by input frequency Mf_c, which is a multiple M of the loop center frequency f_c. When the K counter recycles up, it generates a carry pulse. Recycling while counting down generates a borrow pulse. If the carry and borrow outputs are conceptually combined into one output that is positive for a carry and negative for a borrow, and if the K counter is considered as a frequency divider with the ratio Mf_c/K, the output of the K counter will equal the input frequency multiplied by the division ratio. Thus the output from the K counter is $(k_d \phi_e Mf_c)/K$.

The carry and borrow pulses go to the increment/decrement (I/D) circuit, which, in the absence of any carry or borrow pulse, has an output that is 1/2 the input clock I/D CLK. The input clock is just a multiple, 2N, of the loop center frequency. In response to a carry or borrow pulse, the I/D circuit will either add or delete a pulse at I/D OUT. Thus the output of the I/D circuit will be $Nf_c + (k_d \phi_e Mf_c)/2K$.

The output of the N counter (or the output of the phase-locked loop) is thus:

$$f_o = f_c + (k_d \phi_e Mf_c)/2KN$$

If this result is compared to the equation for a first-order analog phase-locked loop, the digital equivalent of the gain of the VCO is just $Mf_c/2KN$ or f_c/K for $M = 2N$.

Thus the simple first-order phase-locked loop with an adjustable K counter is the equivalent of an analog phase-locked loop with a programmable VCO gain.

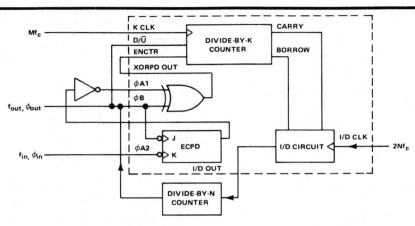

FIGURE 3—DPLL USING BOTH PHASE DETECTORS IN A RIPPLE-CANCELLATION SCHEME

absolute maximum rating over operating free-air temperature range (unless otherwise noted)

Supply voltage, V_{CC} (see Note 1) .... 7 V
Input voltage .... 7 V
Operating free-air temperature range: SN54LS297 .... $-55°$C to $125°$C
SN74LS297 .... $0°$C to $70°$C
Storage temperature range .... $-65°$C to $150°$C

NOTE 1: Voltage values are with respect to network ground terminal.

recommended operating conditions

			SN54LS297			SN74LS297			UNIT
			MIN	NOM	MAX	MIN	NOM	MAX	
V_{CC}	Supply voltage		4.5	5	5.5	4.75	5	5.25	V
I_{OH}	High-level output current	I/D OUT			-1.2			-1.2	mA
		EXOR, ECPD			-400			-400	μA
I_{OL}	Low-level output current	I/D OUT			12			24	mA
		XOR, ECPD			4			8	mA
f_{clock}	Clock frequency	K Clock	0		32	0		32	MHz
		I/D Clock	0		16	0		16	MHz
t_w	Width of clock input pulse	K Clock	16			16			ns
		I/D Clock	33			33			ns
t_{su}, to K	Setup time to K Clock ↑	U/$\overline{D}$, ENCTR	30			30			ns
t_h	Hold time from K Clock ↑	U/$\overline{D}$, ENCTR	0			0			ns
T_A	Operating free-air temperature		-55		125	0		70	$°$C

TEXAS
INSTRUMENTS

electrical characteristics over recommended operating free-air temperature range (unless otherwise noted)

PARAMETER		TEST CONDITIONS†			SN54LS297 MIN	SN54LS297 TYP‡	SN54LS297 MAX	SN74LS297 MIN	SN74LS297 TYP‡	SN74LS297 MAX	UNIT
V_{IH} High-level input voltage					2			2			V
V_{IL} Low-level input voltage							0.7			0.8	V
V_{IK} Input clamp voltage		V_{CC} = MIN,	$I_I = -18$ mA				−1.5			−1.5	V
V_{OH} High-level output voltage	I/D OUT	V_{CC} = MIN, V_{IH} = 2 V,		I_{OH} = MAX	2.4			2.4			V
	Others	$V_{IL} = V_{IL}$ max		I_{OH} = MAX	2.5			2.7			
V_{OL} Low-level output voltage	I/D OUT	V_{CC} = MIN, V_{IH} = 2 V, $V_{IL} = V_{IL}$ max		I_{OL} = 12 mA		0.25	0.4		0.25	0.4	V
				I_{OL} = 24 mA					0.35	0.5	
	Others			I_{OL} = 4 mA		0.25	0.4		0.25	0.4	
				I_{OL} = 8 mA					0.35	0.5	
I_I Input current at maximum input voltage		V_{CC} = MAX,	V_I = 7 V				0.1			0.1	mA
I_{IH} High-level input current	U/D̄, EN, φA1	V_{CC} = MAX,	V_I = 2.7 V				40			40	μA
	φB						60			60	
	All others						20			20	
I_{IL} Low-level input current	U/D̄, EN, φA1	V_{CC} = MAX, V_I = 0.4 V	V_I = 0.4 V				− 0.8			− 0.8	mA
	φB						−1.2			−1.2	
	All others						− 0.4			− 0.4	
I_{OS} Short-circuit output current §	I/D OUT	V_{CC} = MAX			−30		−130	−30		−130	mA
	Others				−20		−100	−20		−100	
I_{CC} Supply current		V_{CC} = MAX, All inputs grounded, All outputs open				75	120		75	120	mA

†For conditions shown as MIN or MAX, use the appropriate value specified under recommended operating conditions.
‡All typical values are of V_{CC} = 5 V, T_A = 25°C.
§ Not more than one output should be shorted at a time and the duration of the short-circuit should not exceed one second.

switching characteristics, V_{CC} = 5 V, T_A = 25°C

PARAMETER¶	FROM (INPUT)		TO (OUTPUT)	TEST CONDITIONS	MIN	TYP	MAX	UNIT
f_{max}	K CLK		I/D OUT	R_L = 667 Ω, C_L = 45 pF, See Note 2	32	50		MHz
	I/D CLK		I/D OUT		16	35		
t_{PLH}	I/D CLK ↑		I/D OUT			15	25	ns
t_{PHL}	I/D CLK ↑		I/D OUT			22	35	ns
t_{PLH}	φA1 or φB	Other input low	XOR OUT	R_L = 2 kΩ, C_L = 45 pF, See Note 2		10	15	ns
	φA1 or φB	Other input high	XOR OUT			17	25	
t_{PHL}	φA1 or φB	Other input low	XOR OUT			15	25	ns
	φA1 or φB	Other input high	XOR OUT			17	25	
t_{PLH}	φB ↓		ECPD OUT			20	30	ns
t_{PHL}	φA2↓		ECPD OUT			20	30	ns

¶ t_{PLH} = propagation delay time, low-to-high level output
t_{PHL} = propagation delay time, high-to-low level output
NOTE 2: See General Information Section for load circuits and voltage waveforms.

3

TTL DEVICES

Texas
INSTRUMENTS

MARCH 1974 – REVISED DECEMBER 1983

- Selects One of Two 4-Bit Data Sources and Stores Data Synchronously with System Clock

- Applications:

  Dual Source for Operands and Constants in Arithmetic Processor; Can Release Processor Register Files for Acquiring New Data

  Implement Separate Registers Capable of Parallel Exchange of Contents Yet Retain External Load Capability

  Universal Type Register for Implementing Various Shift Patterns; Even Has Compound Left-Right Capabilities

description

These monolithic quadruple two-input multiplexers with storage provide essentially the equivalent functional capabilities of two separate MSI functions (SN54157/SN74157 or SN54LS157/SN74LS157 and SN54175/SN74175 or SN54LS175/SN74LS175) in a single 16-pin package.

When the word-select input is low, word 1 (A1, B1, C1, D1) is applies to the flip-flops. A high input to word select will cause the selection of word 2 (A2, B2, C2, D2). The selected word is clocked to the output terminals on the negative-going edge of the clock pulse.

Typical power dissipation is 195 milliwatts for the '298 and 65 milliwatts for the 'LS298. SN54298 and SN54LS298 are characterized for operation over the full military temperature range of −55°C to 125°C; SN74298 and SN74LS298 are characterized for operation from 0°C to 70°C.

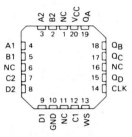

SN54298, SN54LS298 . . . J OR W PACKAGE
SN74298 . . . J OR N PACKAGE
SN74LS298 . . . D, J OR N PACKAGE
(TOP VIEW)

B2	1	16	VCC
A2	2	15	QA
A1	3	14	QB
B1	4	13	QC
C2	5	12	QD
D2	6	11	CLK
D1	7	10	WS
GND	8	9	C1

SN54LS298 . . . FK PACKAGE
SN74LS298
(TOP VIEW)

NC - No internal connection

FUNCTION TABLE

INPUTS		OUTPUTS			
WORD SELECT	CLOCK	QA	QB	QC	QD
L	↓	a1	b1	c1	d1
H	↓	a2	b2	c2	d2
X	H	QA0	QB0	QC0	QD0

H = high level (steady state)
L = low level (steady state)
X = irrelevant (any input, including transitions)
↓ = transition from high to low level
a1, a2, etc. = the level of steady state input at A1, A2, etc.
Q_{A0}, Q_{B0}, etc. = the level of Q_A, Q_B, etc. entered on the most recent ↓ transition of the clock input.

TEXAS
INSTRUMENTS

3

TTL DEVICES

TYPES SN54298, SN54LS298, SN74298, SN74LS298
QUADRUPLE 2-INPUT MULTIPLEXERS WITH STORAGE

logic diagram

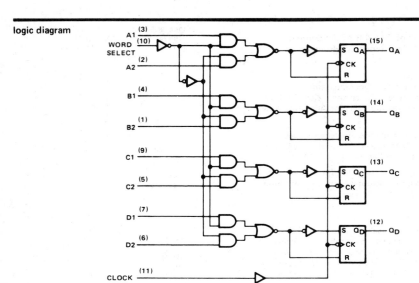

Pin numbers shown on logic notation are for D, J or N packages.

schematics of inputs and outputs

'298

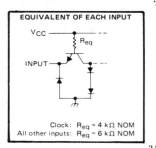

EQUIVALENT OF EACH INPUT

Clock: R_{eq} = 4 kΩ NOM
All other inputs: R_{eq} = 6 kΩ NOM

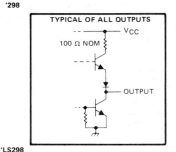

TYPICAL OF ALL OUTPUTS

100 Ω NOM

'LS298

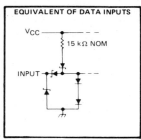

EQUIVALENT OF DATA INPUTS

15 kΩ NOM

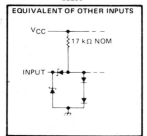

EQUIVALENT OF OTHER INPUTS

17 kΩ NOM

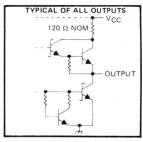

TYPICAL OF ALL OUTPUTS

120 Ω NOM

TEXAS
INSTRUMENTS

absolute maximum ratings over operating free-air temperature range (unless otherwise noted)

Supply voltage, V_{CC} (see Note 1) . . . . 7 V
Input voltage . . . . 5.5 V
Operating free-air temperature range: SN54298 . . . . -55°C to 125°C
SN74298 . . . . 0°C to 70°C
Storage temperature . . . . -65°C to 150°C

NOTE 1: Voltage values are with respect to network ground terminal.

recommended operating conditions

			SN54298		SN74298			UNIT
		MIN	NOM	MAX	MIN	NOM	MAX	
Supply voltage, V_{CC}		4.5	5	5.5	4.75	5	5.25	V
High-level output current, I_{OH}				-800			-800	μA
Low-level output current, I_{OL}				16			16	mA
Width of clock pulse, high or low level, t_w		20			20			ns
Setup time, t_{su}	Data	15			15			ns
	Word select	25			25			
Hold time, t_h	Data	5			5			ns
	Word select	0			0			
Operating free-air temperature, T_A		-55		125	0		70	$^\circ$C

electrical characteristics over recommended operating free-air temperature range (unless otherwise noted)

	PARAMETER	TEST CONDITIONS[†]	MIN	TYP[‡]	MAX	UNIT
V_{IH}	High-level input voltage		2			V
V_{IL}	Low-level input voltage				0.8	V
V_{IK}	Input clamp voltage	V_{CC} = MIN, $I_I = -12$ mA			-1.5	V
V_{OH}	High-level output voltage	V_{CC} = MIN, V_{IH} = 2 V, V_{IL} = 0.8 V, $I_{OH} = -800$ μA	2.4	3.2		V
V_{OL}	Low-level output voltage	V_{CC} = MIN, V_{IH} = 2 V, V_{IL} = 0.8 V, I_{OL} = 16 mA			0.4	V
I_I	Input current at maximum input voltage	V_{CC} = MAX, V_I = 5.5 V			1	mA
I_{IH}	High-level input current	V_{CC} = MAX, V_I = 2.4 V			40	μA
I_{IL}	Low-level input current	V_{CC} = MAX, V_I = 0.4 V			-1.6	mA
I_{OS}	Short-circuit output current[§]	V_{CC} = MAX SN54298	-20		-57	mA
		SN74298	-18		-57	
I_{CC}	Supply current	V_{CC} = MAX, See Note 2		39	65	mA

[†]For conditions shown as MIN or MAX, use the appropriate value specified under recommended operating conditions.
[‡]All typical values are at V_{CC} = 5 V, T_A = 25°C.
[§]Not more than one output should be shorted at a time.
NOTE 2: With all outputs open and all inputs except clock low, I_{CC} is measured after applying a momentary 4.5 V, followed by ground, to the clock input.

switching characteristics, V_{CC} = 5 V, T_A = 25°C

	PARAMETER	TEST CONDITIONS	MIN	TYP	MAX	UNIT
t_{PLH}	Propagation delay time, low-to-high-level output	C_L = 15 pF, R_L = 400 Ω, See Note 3		18	27	ns
t_{PHL}	Propagation delay time, high-to-low-level output			21	32	

NOTE 3: See General Information Section for load circuits and voltage waveforms.

3

TTL DEVICES

TYPES SN54LS298, SN74LS298
QUADRUPLE 2-INPUT MULTIPLEXERS WITH STORAGE

absolute maximum ratings over operating free-air temperature range (unless otherwise noted)

Supply voltage, V_{CC} (see Note 1) . . . . 7 V
Input voltage . . . . 7 V
Operating free-air temperature range: SN54LS298 . . . . $-55°$C to $125°$C
                        SN74LS298 . . . . $0°$C to $70°$C
Storage temperature range . . . . $-65°$C to $150°$C

NOTE 1: Voltage values are with respect to network ground terminal.

recommended operating conditions

		SN54LS298 MIN	NOM	MAX	SN74LS298 MIN	NOM	MAX	UNIT
Supply voltage, V_{CC}		4.5	5	5.5	4.75	5	5.25	V
High-level output current, I_{OH}				-400			-400	μA
Low-level output current, I_{OL}				4			8	mA
Width of clock pulse, high or low level, t_w		20			20			ns
Setup time, t_{su}	Data	15			15			ns
	Word select	25			25			
Hold time, t_h	Data	5			5			ns
	Word select	0			0			
Operating free-air temperature, T_A		-55		125	0		70	$°$C

electrical characteristics over recommended operating free-air temperature range (unless otherwise noted)

PARAMETER		TEST CONDITIONS[†]	SN54LS298 MIN	TYP[‡]	MAX	SN74LS298 MIN	TYP[‡]	MAX	UNIT
V_{IH}	High-level input voltage		2			2			V
V_{IL}	Low-level input voltage				0.7			0.8	V
V_{IK}	Input clamp voltage	V_{CC} = MIN, $I_I = -18$ mA			-1.5			-1.5	V
V_{OH}	High-level output voltage	V_{CC} = MIN, V_{IH} = 2 V, $V_{IL} = V_{IL}$ max, $I_{OH} = -400 \mu$A	2.5	3.4		2.7	3.4		V
V_{OL}	Low-level output voltage	V_{CC} = MIN, V_{IH} = 2 V, $V_{IL} = V_{IL}$ max I_{OL} = 4 mA		0.25	0.4		0.25	0.4	V
		I_{OL} = 8 mA					0.35	0.5	
I_I	Input current at maximum input voltage	V_{CC} = MAX, V_I = 7 V			0.1			0.1	mA
I_{IH}	High-level input current	V_{CC} = MAX, V_I = 2.7 V			20			20	μA
I_{IL}	Low-level input current	V_{CC} = MAX, V_I = 0.4 V			-0.4			-0.4	mA
I_{OS}	Short-circuit output current[§]	V_{CC} = MAX	-20		-100	-20		-100	mA
I_{CC}	Supply current	V_{CC} = MAX, See Note 2		13	21		13	21	mA

[†]For conditions shown as MIN or MAX, use the appropriate value specified under recommended operating conditions.
[‡]All typical values are at V_{CC} = 5 V, T_A = 25$°$C.
[§]Not more than one output should be shorted at a time, and duration of the short-circuit should not exceed one second.
NOTE 2: With all outputs open and all inputs except clock low, I_{CC} is measured after applying a momentary 4.5 V, followed by ground, to the clock input.

switching characteristics, V_{CC} = 5 V, T_A = 25$°$C

PARAMETER	TEST CONDITIONS	MIN	TYP	MAX	UNIT
t_{PLH} Propagation delay time, low-to-high-level output	C_L = 15 pF, R_L = 2 kΩ, See Note 3		18	27	ns
t_{PHL} Propagation delay time, high-to-low-level output			21	32	

NOTE 3: See General Information Section for load circuits and voltage waveforms.

3

TTL DEVICES

TEXAS INSTRUMENTS

TYPICAL APPLICATION DATA

This versatile multiplexer/register can be connected to operate as a shift register that can shift N-places in a single clock pulse.

The following figure illustrates a BCD shift register that will shift an entire 4-bit BCD digit in one clock pulse.

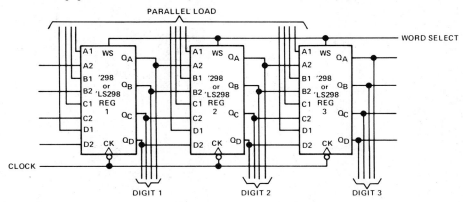

When the word-select input is high and the registers are clocked, the contents of register 1 is transferred (shifted) to register 2 and etc. In effect, the BCD digits are shifted one position. In addition, this application retains a parallel-load capability which means that new BCD data can be entered in the entire register with one clock pulse. This arrangement can be modified to perform the shifting of binary data for any number of bit locations.

Another function that can be implemented with the '298 or 'LS298 is a register that can be designed specifically for supporting multiplier or division operations. The example below is a one place/two-place shift register.

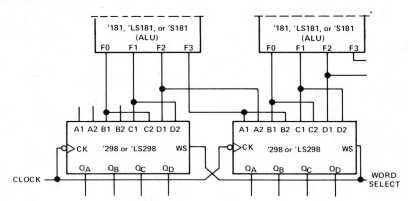

When word select is low and the register is clocked, the outputs of the arithmetic/logic units (ALU's) are shifted one place. When word select is high and the registers are clocked, the data is shifted two places.

3

TTL DEVICES

- **Multiplexed Inputs/Outputs Provide Improved Bit Density**

- **Four Modes of Operations:**
  - Hold (Store)
  - Shift Left
  - Shift Right
  - Load Data

- **Operates with Outputs Enabled or at High Z**

- **3-State Outputs Drive Bus Lines Directly**

- **Can Be Cascaded for N-Bit Word Lengths**

- **SN54LS323 and SN74LS323 Are Similar But Have Synchronous Clear**

- **Applications:**
  - Stacked or Push-Down Registers
  - Buffer Storage, and Accumulator Registers

TYPE	GUARANTEED SHIFT (CLOCK) FREQUENCY	TYPICAL POWER DISSIPATION
'LS299	25 MHz	175 mW
'S299	50 MHz	700 mW

SN54LS299, SN54S299 ... J OR W PACKAGE
SN74LS299, SN74S299 ... DW, J OR N PACKAGE
(TOP VIEW)

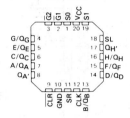

SN54LS299, SN54S299 ... FK PACKAGE
SN74LS299, SN74S299
(TOP VIEW)

description

These Schottky TTL eight-bit universal registers feature multiplexed inputs/outputs to achieve full eight-bit data handling in a single 20-pin package. Two function-select inputs and two output-control inputs can be used to choose the modes of operation listed in the function table.

Synchronous parallel loading is accomplished by taking both function-select lines, S0 and S1, high. This places the three-state outputs in a high-impedance state, which permits data that is applied on the input/output lines to be clocked into the register. Reading out of the register can be accomplished while the outputs are enabled in any mode. A direct overriding input is provided to clear the register whether the outputs are enabled or off.

FUNCTION TABLE

MODE	INPUTS						INPUTS/OUTPUTS								OUTPUTS	
	CLR	FUNCTION SELECT		OUTPUT CONTROL		CLK	SERIAL		A/Q_A	B/Q_B	C/Q_C	D/Q_D	E/Q_E	F/Q_F	G/Q_G	H/Q_H	Q_A'	Q_H'
		S1	S0	G1†	G2†		SL	SR										
Clear	L	X	L	L	L	X	X	X	L	L	L	L	L	L	L	L	L	L
	L	L	X	L	L	X	X	X	L	L	L	L	L	L	L	L	L	L
	L	H	H	X	X	X	X	X	X	X	X	X	X	X	X	X	L	L
Hold	H	L	L	L	L	X	X	X	Q_{A0}	Q_{B0}	Q_{C0}	Q_{D0}	Q_{E0}	Q_{F0}	Q_{G0}	Q_{H0}	Q_{A0}	Q_{H0}
	H	X	X	L	L	X	X	X	Q_{A0}	Q_{B0}	Q_{C0}	Q_{D0}	Q_{E0}	Q_{F0}	Q_{G0}	Q_{H0}	Q_{A0}	Q_{H0}
Shift Right	H	L	H	L	L	↑	X	H	H	Q_{An}	Q_{Bn}	Q_{Cn}	Q_{Dn}	Q_{En}	Q_{Fn}	Q_{Gn}	H	Q_{Gn}
	H	L	H	L	L	↑	X	L	L	Q_{An}	Q_{Bn}	Q_{Cn}	Q_{Dn}	Q_{En}	Q_{Fn}	Q_{Gn}	L	Q_{Gn}
Shift Left	H	H	L	L	L	↑	H	X	Q_{Bn}	Q_{Cn}	Q_{Dn}	Q_{En}	Q_{Fn}	Q_{Gn}	Q_{Hn}	L	Q_{Bn}	H
	H	H	L	L	L	↑	L	X	Q_{Bn}	Q_{Cn}	Q_{Dn}	Q_{En}	Q_{Fn}	Q_{Gn}	Q_{Hn}	L	Q_{Bn}	L
Load	H	H	H	X	X	↑	X	X	a	b	c	d	e	f	g	h	a	h

†When one or both output controls are high the eight input/output terminals are disabled to the high-impedance state; however, sequential operation or clearing of the register is not affected.

a . . . h = the level of the steady-state input at inputs A through H, respectively. These data are loaded into the flip-flops while the flip-flop outputs are isolated from the input/output terminals.

TEXAS INSTRUMENTS

TTL DEVICES

3

logic diagram

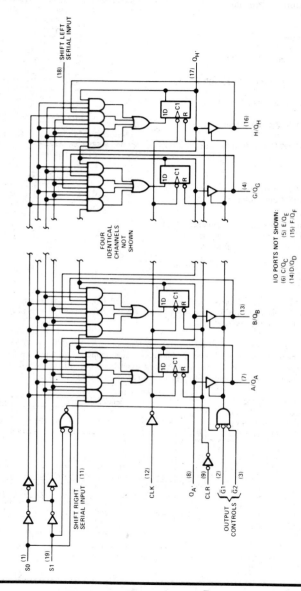

Pin numbers shown on logic notation are for DW, J or N packages.

3

TTL DEVICES

schematics of inputs and outputs

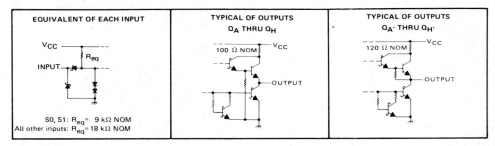

| EQUIVALENT OF EACH INPUT | TYPICAL OF OUTPUTS Q_A THRU Q_H | TYPICAL OF OUTPUTS $Q_{A'}$ THRU $Q_{H'}$ |

S0, S1: R_{eq} = 9 kΩ NOM
All other inputs: R_{eq} = 18 kΩ NOM

100 Ω NOM

120 Ω NOM

absolute maximum ratings over operating free-air temperature range (unless otherwise noted)

Supply voltage, V_{CC} (see Note 1) . . . . 7 V
Input voltage . . . . 7 V
Off-state output voltage . . . . 5.5 V
Operating free-air temperature range: SN54LS299 . . . . −55°C to 125°C
                             SN74LS299 . . . . 0°C to 70°C
Storage temperature . . . . −65°C to 150°C

NOTE 1: Voltage values are with respect to network ground terminal.

recommended operating conditions

		SN54LS299			SN74LS299			UNIT
		MIN	NOM	MAX	MIN	NOM	MAX	
Supply voltage, V_{CC}		4.5	5	5.5	4.75	5	5.25	V
High-level output current, I_{OH}	Q_A thru Q_H			−1			−2.6	mA
	$Q_{A'}$ or $Q_{H'}$			−0.4			−0.4	
Low-level output current, I_{OL}	Q_A thru Q_H			12			24	mA
	$Q_{A'}$ or $Q_{H'}$			4			8	
Clock frequency, f_{clock}		0		20	0		20	MHz
Width of clock pulse, $t_{w(clock)}$	Clock high	30			30			ns
	Clock low	10			10			
Width of clear pulse, $t_{w(clear)}$	Clear low	20			20			ns
Setup time, t_{su}	Select	35↑			35↑			ns
	High-level data◇	20↑			20↑			
	Low-level data◇	20↑			20↑			
	Clear inactive-state	20↑			20↑			
Hold time, t_h	Select	10↑			10↑			ns
	Data◇	0↑			0↑			
Operating free-air temperature, T_A		−55		125	0		70	C

◇Data includes the two serial inputs and the eight input/output data lines.

electrical characteristics over recommended operating free-air temperature range (unless otherwise noted)

PARAMETER		TEST CONDITIONS[†]		SN54LS299 MIN	TYP[‡]	MAX	SN74LS299 MIN	TYP[‡]	MAX	UNIT
V_{IH} High-level input voltage				2			2			V
V_{IL} Low-level input voltage						0.7			0.8	V
V_{IK} Input clamp voltage		V_{CC} = MIN,	$I_I = -18$ mA			−1.5			−1.5	V
V_{OH} High-level output voltage	Q_A thru Q_H	V_{CC} = MIN, V_{IH} = 2 V,	V_{IH} = 2 V,	2.4	3.2		2.4	3.1		V
	Q_A' or Q_H'	V_{IL} = V_{IL}max,	I_{OH} = MAX	2.5	3.4		2.7	3.4		
V_{OL} Low-level output voltage	Q_A thru Q_H	V_{CC} = MIN, V_{IH} = 2 V, V_{IL} = V_{IL}max	I_{OL} = 12 mA		0.25	0.4		0.25	0.4	V
			I_{OL} = 24 mA					0.35	0.5	
	Q_A' or Q_H'		I_{OL} = 4 mA		0.25	0.4		0.25	0.4	
			I_{OL} = 8 mA					0.35	0.5	
I_{OZH} Off-state output current, high-level voltage applied	Q_A thru Q_H	V_{CC} = MAX, V_O = 2.7 V	V_{IH} = 2 V,			40			40	μA
I_{OZL} Off-state output current, low-level voltage applied	Q_A thru Q_H	V_{CC} = MAX, V_O = 0.4 V	V_{IH} = 2 V,			−400			−400	μA
I_I Input current at maximum input voltage	S0, S1	V_{CC} = MAX	V_I = 7 V			200			200	μA
	A thru H		V_I = 5.5 V			100			100	
	Any other		V_I = 7 V			100			100	
I_{IH} High-level input current	A thru H, S0, S1	V_{CC} = MAX, V_I = 2.7 V				40			40	μA
	Any other					20			20	
I_{IL} Low-level input current	S0, S1	V_{CC} = MAX, V_I = 0.4 V				−0.8			−0.8	mA
	Any other					−0.4			−0.4	
I_{OS} Short-circuit output current[§]	Q_A thru Q_H	V_{CC} = MAX		−30	−130		−30	−130		mA
	Q_A' or Q_H'			−20	−100		−20	−100		
I_{CC} Supply current		V_{CC} = MAX			33	53		33	53	mA

[†]For conditions shown as MIN or MAX, use the appropriate value specified under recommended operating conditions.
[‡]All typical values are at V_{CC} = 5 V, T_A = 25°C.
[§]Not more than one output should be shorted at a time and duration of the short-circuit should not exceed one second.

switching characteristics, V_{CC} = 5 V, T_A = 25°C

PARAMETER[¶]	FROM (INPUT)	TO (OUTPUT)	TEST CONDITIONS	MIN	TYP	MAX	UNIT
f_{max}			See Note 2	20	35		MHz
t_{PLH}	CLK	Q_A' or Q_H'	R_L = 2 kΩ, C_L = 15 pF		22	33	ns
t_{PHL}					26	39	
t_{PHL}	$\overline{CLR}$	Q_A' or Q_H'			27	40	ns
t_{PLH}	CLK	Q_A thru Q_H	R_L = 665 Ω, C_L = 45 pF		17	25	ns
t_{PHL}					26	39	
t_{PHL}	$\overline{CLR}$	Q_A thru Q_H			26	40	ns
t_{PZH}	$\overline{G1}$, $\overline{G2}$	Q_A thru Q_H			13	21	ns
t_{PZL}					19	30	
t_{PHZ}	$\overline{G1}$, $\overline{G2}$	Q_A thru Q_H	R_L = 665 Ω, C_L = 5 pF		10	20	ns
t_{PLZ}					10	15	

[¶] f_{max} ≡ maximum clock frequency
t_{PLH} ≡ propagation delay time, low-to-high-level output
t_{PHL} ≡ propagation delay time, high-to-low-level output
t_{PZH} ≡ output enable time to high level
t_{PZL} ≡ output enable time to low level
t_{PHZ} ≡ output disable time from high level
t_{PLZ} ≡ output disable time from low level
NOTE 2: For testing f_{max}, all outputs are loaded simultaneously, each with C_L and R_L as specified for the propagation times. See General Information Section for load circuits and voltage waveforms.

TEXAS
INSTRUMENTS

schematics of inputs and outputs

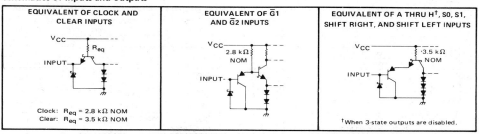

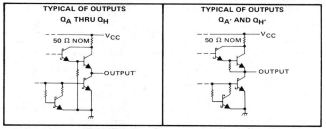

absolute maximum ratings over operating free-air temperature range (unless otherwise noted)

Supply voltage, V_{CC} (see Note 1) . . . . 7 V
Input voltage . . . . 5.5 V
Off-state output voltage . . . . 5.5 V
Operating free-air temperature range: SN54S299 (see Note 2) . . . . $-55^{\circ}C$ to $125^{\circ}C$
                              SN74S299 . . . . $0^{\circ}C$ to $70^{\circ}C$
Storage temperature . . . . $-65^{\circ}C$ to $150^{\circ}C$

NOTE 1: Voltage values are with respect to network ground terminal.

recommended operating conditions

		SN54S299			SN74S299			UNIT
		MIN	NOM	MAX	MIN	NOM	MAX	
Supply voltage, V_{CC}		4.5	5	5.5	4.75	5	5.25	V
High-level output current, I_{OH}	Q_A thru Q_H			-2			-6.5	mA
	$Q_{A'}$ or $Q_{H'}$			-0.5			-0.5	
Low-level output current, I_{OL}	Q_A thru Q_H			20			20	mA
	$Q_{A'}$ or $Q_{H'}$			6			6	
Clock frequency, f_{clock}		0		50	0		50	MHz
Width of clock pulse, $t_{w(clock)}$	Clock high	10			10			ns
	Clock low	10			10			
Width of clear pulse, $t_{w(clear)}$	Clear low	10			10			ns
Setup time, t_{su}	Select	15†			15†			ns
	High-level data$^{\diamond}$	7†			7†			
	Low-level data$^{\diamond}$	5†			5†			
	Clear inactive-state	10†			10†			
Hold time, t_h	Select	5†			5†			ns
	Data$^{\diamond}$	5†			5†			
Operating free-air temperature, T_A		-55		125	0		70	$^{\circ}C$

$^{\diamond}$Data includes the two serial inputs and the eight input/output data lines.

TEXAS
INSTRUMENTS

TTL DEVICES

3

electrical characteristics over recommended operating free-air temperature range (unless otherwise noted)

	PARAMETER		TEST CONDITIONS†	MIN	TYP‡	MAX	UNIT
V_{IH}	High-level input voltage			2			V
V_{IL}	Low-level input voltage					0.8	V
V_{IK}	Input clamp voltage		V_{CC} = MIN, I_I = −18 mA			−1.2	V
V_{OH}	High-level output voltage	Q_A thru Q_H	V_{CC} = MIN, V_{IH} = 2 V,	2.4	3.2		V
		$Q_{A'}$ or $Q_{H'}$	V_{IL} = 0.8 V, I_{OH} = MAX	2.7	3.4		
V_{OL}	Low-level output voltage		V_{CC} = MIN, V_{IH} = 2 V, V_{IL} = 0.8 V, I_{OL} = MAX			0.5	V
I_{OZH}	Off-state output current, high-level voltage applied	Q_A thru Q_H	V_{CC} = MAX, V_{IH} = 2 V, V_O = 2.4 V			100	µA
I_{OZL}	Off-state output current, low-level voltage applied	Q_A thru Q_H	V_{CC} = MAX, V_{IH} = 2 V, V_O = 0.5 V			−250	µA
I_I	Input current at maximum input voltage		V_{CC} = MAX, V_I = 5.5 V			1	mA
I_{IH}	High-level input current	A thru H, S0, S1	V_{CC} = MAX, V_I = 2.7 V			100	µA
		Any other				50	
I_{IL}	Low-level input current	CLK or $\overline{CLR}$	V_{CC} = MAX, V_I = 0.5 V			−2	mA
		S0, S1				−500	µA
		Any other				−250	µA
I_{OS}	Short-circuit output current§	Q_A thru Q_H	V_{CC} = MAX	−40		−100	mA
		$Q_{A'}$ or $Q_{H'}$		−20		−100	
I_{CC}	Supply current		V_{CC} = MAX		140	225	mA

† For conditions shown as MIN or MAX, use the appropriate value specified under recommended operating conditions.
‡ All typical values are at V_{CC} = 5 V, T_A = 25°C.
§ Not more than one output should be shorted at a time and duration of the short-circuit should not exceed one second.

switching characteristics, V_{CC} = 5 V, T_A = 25°C

PARAMETER¶	FROM (INPUT)	TO (OUTPUT)	TEST CONDITIONS	MIN	TYP	MAX	UNIT
f_{max}			See Note 2	50	70		MHz
t_{PLH}	CLK	$Q_{A'}$ or $Q_{H'}$	R_L = 1 kΩ, C_L = 15 pF		12	20	ns
t_{PHL}					13	20	
t_{PHL}	$\overline{CLR}$	$Q_{A'}$ or $Q_{H'}$			14	21	ns
t_{PLH}	CLK	Q_A thru Q_H			15	21	ns
t_{PHL}			R_L = 280 Ω, C_L = 45 pF		15	21	
t_{PHL}	$\overline{CLR}$	Q_A thru Q_H			16	24	ns
t_{PZH}	$\overline{G}1, \overline{G}2$	Q_A thru Q_H			10	18	ns
t_{PZL}					12	18	
t_{PHZ}	$\overline{G}1, \overline{G}2$	Q_A thru Q_H	R_L = 280 Ω, C_L = 5 pF		7	12	ns
t_{PLZ}					7	12	

¶ f_{max} = maximum clock frequency
t_{PLH} = Propagation delay time, low-to-high-level output
t_{PHL} = Propagation delay time, high-to-low-level output
t_{PZH} = output enable time to high level
t_{PZL} = output enable time to low level
t_{PHZ} = output disable time from high level
t_{PLZ} = output disable time from low level
NOTE 2: For testing f_{max}, all outputs are loaded simultaneously, each with C_L and R_L as specified for the propagation times.
See General Information Section for load circuits and voltage waveforms.

TEXAS
INSTRUMENTS

'LS320

- **Crystal-Controlled Oscillator Operation from 1 MHz to 20 MHz**
- **2-Phase Driver Outputs**

'LS321

- **Similar to 'LS320 But Includes f/2 and f/4 Count-Down Outputs**

description

The 'LS320 is a crystal-controlled oscillator/clock driver. It features complementary standard and high-current driver outputs. A synchronization flip-flop is included.

The driver outputs, F' and $\overline{F}'$ have very-low impedance and can be used to drive highly capacitive TTL-level lines. If the driver outputs are not used, then the V_{CC}' terminal can be left open.

The 'LS321 is identical to the 'LS320 except it additionally features two count-down outputs, F/2 and F/4.

These circuits were designed for series resonant crystal control of frequency, and a capacitive control is not recommended. The crystal is connected between the inputs XTAL1 and XTAL2. A parallel-resonant circuit has to be connected between the inputs TANK1 and TANK2 (see Typical Application Data).

Interaction of the driver outputs with the other outputs limits useful frequencies as shown in the frequency-limits table.

The SN54LS320 and SN54LS321 are characterized for operation over the full military temperature range of −55°C to 125°C. The SN74LS320 and SN74LS321 are characterized for operation from 0°C to 70°C.

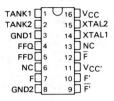

SN54LS320 . . . J PACKAGE
SN74LS320 . . . J OR N PACKAGE
(TOP VIEW)

TANK1	1	16	V_CC
TANK2	2	15	XTAL2
GND1	3	14	XTAL1
FFQ	4	13	NC
FFD	5	12	F̄
NC	6	11	V_CC'
F	7	10	F'
GND2	8	9	F̄'

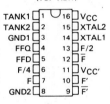

SN54LS321 . . . J PACKAGE
SN74LS321 . . . J OR N PACKAGE
(TOP VIEW)

TANK1	1	16	V_CC
TANK2	2	15	XTAL2
GND1	3	14	XTAL1
FFQ	4	13	F/2
FFD	5	12	F̄
F/4	6	11	V_CC'
F	7	10	F'
GND2	8	9	F̄'

NC – No internal connection

For chip carrier information, contact the factory.

FREQUENCY LIMITS

OUTPUTS IN USE	V_CC	V_CC'	f_max
Driver outputs only	5 V	5 V	20 MHz
Other outputs only	5 V	Open	20 MHz
Driver and any other outputs	5 V	5 V	10 MHz

logic symbols

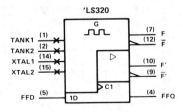

'LS320

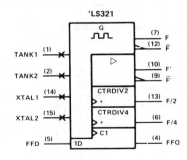

'LS321

TEXAS INSTRUMENTS

3

TTL DEVICES

TYPES SN54LS320, SN54LS321, SN74LS320, SN74LS321
CRYSTAL-CONTROLLED OSCILLATORS

logic diagram (positive logic)

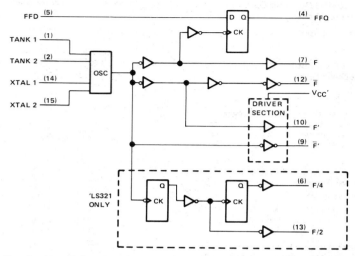

Pin numbers shown on logic notation are for J or N packages.

absolute maximum ratings over operating free-air temperature range (unless otherwise noted)

Supply voltage, V_{CC} (see Note 1) . . . . 7 V
Supply voltage, V_{CC}' . . . . 7 V
Input voltage to FFD terminal . . . . −0.5 V to 7 V
Operating free-air temperature range: SN54LS320, SN54LS321 . . . . −55°C to 125°C
              SN74LS320, SN74LS321 . . . . 0°C to 70°C
Storage temperature range . . . . −65°C to 150°C

NOTE 1: Voltage values are with respect to network ground terminals.

recommended operating conditions

		SN54LS320 SN54LS321			SN74LS320 SN74LS321			UNIT
		MIN	NOM	MAX	MIN	NOM	MAX	
Supply voltage, V_{CC}		4.5	5	5.5	4.75	5	5.25	V
Supply voltage, V_{CC}'		4.5	5	5.5	4.75	5	5.25	V
High-level output current, I_{OH}	F' or $\overline{F}'$			−12			−24	mA
	F, $\overline{F}$, F/2, F/4			−0.4			−0.4	
Low-level output current, I_{OL}	F' or $\overline{F}'$			12			24	mA
	F, $\overline{F}$, F/2, F/4			4			8	
Output frequency, f_{out}	F/2 ('LS321)	0.5		10	0.5		10	MHz
	F/4 ('LS321)	0.25		5	0.25		5	
	F or $\overline{F}$	1		20	1		20	
Operating free-air temperature, T_A		−55		125	0		70	°C

Input and output schematics are similar to those shown for SN74LS326.

TEXAS
INSTRUMENTS

electrical characteristics over recommended operating free-air temperature range (unless otherwise noted)

PARAMETER		TEST CONDITIONS†			SN54LS320 SN54LS321			SN74LS320 SN74LS321			UNIT
					MIN	TYP‡	MAX	MIN	TYP‡	MAX	
V_{IH}	High-level input voltage				2			2			V
V_{IL}	Low-level input voltage						0.7			0.8	V
V_{IK}	Input clamp voltage	V_{CC} = MIN,	V_{CC}' = MIN,	I_I = −18 mA			−1.5			−1.5	V
V_{OH}	High-level output voltage	F', $\overline{F}'$	V_{CC} = 4.5 V, V_{CC}' = 4.5 V, I_{OH} = −12 mA		2.5	3.3					V
			V_{CC} = 4.75 V, V_{CC}' = 4.75 V, I_{OH} = −24 mA					2.7	3.3		
		Others	V_{CC} = MIN, V_{IH} = 2 V, I_{OH} = −400 μA		2.5	3.4		2.7	3.4		
V_{OL}	Low-level output voltage	F', $\overline{F}'$	V_{CC} = MIN, V_{CC}' = MIN	I_{OL} = 12 mA		0.25	0.4		0.25	0.4	V
				I_{OL} = 24 mA					0.35	0.5	
		Others	V_{CC} = MIN, V_{IL} = V_{IL} max	I_{OL} = 4 mA		0.25	0.4		0.25	0.4	
				I_{OL} = 8 mA					0.35	0.5	
I_I	Input current at maximum input voltage	V_{CC} = MAX,	V_I = 7 V				0.1			0.1	mA
I_{IH}	High-level input current	V_{CC} = MAX,	V_I = 2.7 V				20			20	μA
I_{IL}	Low-level input current	V_{CC} = MAX,	V_I = 0.4 V				−0.4			−0.4	mA
I_{OS}	Short-circuit output current§	V_{CC} = MAX			−20		−100	−20		−100	mA
I_{CC}	Supply current from V_{CC}	V_{CC} = MAX,	FFD at GND	'LS320		42	70		42	70	mA
				'LS321		47	75		47	75	
I_{CC}'	Supply current from V_{CC}'	V_{CC} = MAX,	V_{CC}' = MAX,	FFD at GND		4	8		4	8	mA

†For conditions shown as MIN or MAX, use the appropriate value specified under recommended operating conditions.
‡All typical values are at V_{CC} = 5 V, V_{CC}' = 5 V, and T_A = 25°C.
§Not more than one output should be shorted at a time, and duration of the short-circuit should not exceed one second. Outputs F' and $\overline{F}'$ do not have short-circuit protection and these limits do not apply.

switching characteristics, V_{CC} = 5 V, V_{CC} = 5 V, T_A = 25°C

PARAMETER		OUTPUTS	TEST CONDITIONS		'LS320			'LS321			UNIT
					MIN	TYP	MAX	MIN	TYP	MAX	
f_{max}	Maximum operating frequency	F/2	C_L = 100 pF	R_L = 667 Ω				10	15		MHz
		F/4						5	7.5		
		All others		R_L = 2 kΩ	20	30		20	30		
t_r	Rise time, 1 V to 3 V	F', F'	C_L = 50 pF	R_L = 667 Ω		6	12		6	12	ns
			C_L = 100 pF			7	14		7	14	
			C_L = 200 pF			7	14		7	14	
		Others	C_L = 50 pF	R_L = 2 kΩ		11	22		11	22	
			C_L = 100 pF			25	40		25	40	
			C_L = 200 pF			45	70		45	70	
t_r	Fall time, 3 V to 1 V	F', F'	C_L = 50 pF	R_L = 667 Ω		5	10		5	10	ns
			C_L = 100 pF			5	10		5	10	
			C_L = 200 pF			6	12		6	12	
		Others	C_L = 50 pF	R_L = 2 kΩ		6	12		6	12	
			C_L = 100 pF			10	20		10	20	
			C_L = 200 pF			17	30		17	30	

¶ See General Information Section for load circuits and voltage waveforms.

TEXAS
INSTRUMENTS

3
TTL DEVICES

TYPICAL APPLICATION DATA

The SN54/74LS320 and 'LS321 are crystal-controlled oscillators. Figure 1 shows the device with all required external components.

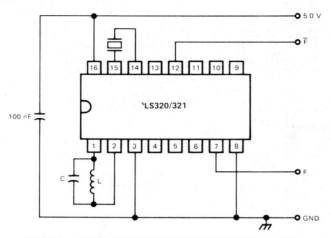

FIGURE 1.   CRYSTAL–CONTROLLED OSCILLATOR 'LS320/321

If a fundamental crystal is used the value of the inductor L has to be determined according to curve 1 in figure 2. The value of the capacitor C is calculated:

$$C = \frac{1}{4 \times \pi^2 \times f^2 \times L} \quad (1)$$

The XTAL1 and XTAL2 inputs have a input capacitance of 6 to 8 pF. These values have to be included into the calculation.

If a capacitor C1 for frequency adjustment is included in the circuit, the value of the inductor L has to be determined according to curve 2 in figure 2. In this case no capacitor in parallel to the inductor is needed.

If an overtone crystal is used, the value of the inductor L is calculated:

$$L = \frac{65}{f} \quad (2)$$

The value of the capacitor C has to be calculated according to formula 1.

TEXAS
INSTRUMENTS

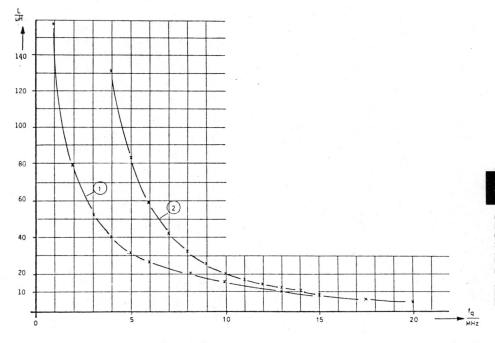

—FUNDAMENTAL CRYSTAL FREQUENCY—MHz

FIGURE 2

3

TTL DEVICES

TEXAS
INSTRUMENTS

- **Multiplexed Inputs/Outputs Provide Improved Bit Density**

- **3-State Outputs Drive Bus Lines Directly**

- **Sign Extend Function**

- **Direct Overriding Clear**

description

These low-power Schottky eight-bit shift registers feature multiplexed input/output data ports to achieve full eight-bit data handling in a single 20-pin package. Serial data may be entered into the shift-right register through either the D0 or the D1 input as selected by the data select input. A serial output (Q_H') is also provided to facilitate expansion. Synchronous parallel loading is accomplished by taking both the register enable and the $S/\overline{P}$ inputs low. This places the three-state input/output ports in the data input mode. Data are entered on the low-to-high transition of the clock. The data extend function repeats the sign in the Q_A flip-flop during shifting. A direct overriding clear input clears the internal registers when taken low whether the outputs are enabled or off. The output enable does not interfere with synchronous operation of the register.

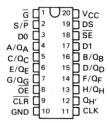

SN54LS322A . . . J PACKAGE
SN74LS322A . . . DW, J OR N PACKAGE
(TOP VIEW)

```
  G   [ 1  U 20 ]  VCC
 S/P  [ 2    19 ]  DS
  D0  [ 3    18 ]  SE
 A/QA [ 4    17 ]  D1
 C/QC [ 5    16 ]  B/QB
 E/QE [ 6    15 ]  D/QD
 G/QG [ 7    14 ]  F/QF
  OE  [ 8    13 ]  H/QH
 CLR  [ 9    12 ]  QH'
 GND  [ 10   11 ]  CLK
```

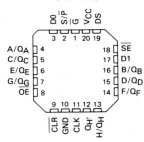

SN54LS322A . . . FK PACKAGE
SN74LS322A
(TOP VIEW)

FUNCTION TABLE

	INPUTS							INPUTS/OUTPUTS				OUTPUT
OPERATION	CLR	REGISTER ENABLE $\overline{G}$	$S/\overline{P}$	SIGN EXTEND $\overline{SE}$	DATA SELECT DS	OUTPUT ENABLE $\overline{OE}$	CLK	A/Q_A	B/Q_B	C/Q_C . . . H/Q_H		Q_H'
Clear	L	H	X	X	X	L	X	L	L	L	L	L
	L	X	H	X	X	L	X	L	L	L	L	L
Hold	H	H	X	X	X	L	X	Q_{A0}	Q_{B0}	Q_{C0}	Q_{H0}	Q_{H0}
Shift Right	H	L	H	H	L	L	↑	D0	Q_{An}	Q_{Bn}	Q_{Gn}	Q_{Gn}
	H	L	H	H	H	L	↑	D1	Q_{An}	Q_{Bn}	Q_{Gn}	Q_{Gn}
Sign Extend	H	L	H	L	X	L	↑	Q_{An}	Q_{An}	Q_{Bn}	Q_{Gn}	Q_{Gn}
Load	H	L	L	X	X	X	↑	a	b	c	h	h

When the output enable is high, the eight input/output terminals are disabled to the high-impedance state; however, sequential operation or clearing of the register is not affected. If both the register enable input and the $S/\overline{P}$ input are low while the clear input is low, the register is cleared while the eight input/output terminals are disabled to the high-impedance state.

H = high level (steady state)

L = low level (steady state)

X = irrelevant (any input, including transitions)

↑ = transition from low to high level

$Q_{A0} \ldots Q_{H0}$ = the level of Q_A through Q_H, respectively, before the indicated steady-state conditions were established

$Q_{An} \ldots Q_{Hn}$ = the level of Q_A through Q_H, respectively, before the most recent ↑ transition of the clock

D0, D1 = the level of steady-state inputs at inputs D0 and D1 respectively

a . . . h = the level of steady-state inputs at inputs A through H respectively

TEXAS INSTRUMENTS

TTL DEVICES

3

TYPES SN54LS332A, SN74LS322A
8-BIT SHIFT REGISTERS WITH SIGN EXTEND

logic diagram (positive logic)

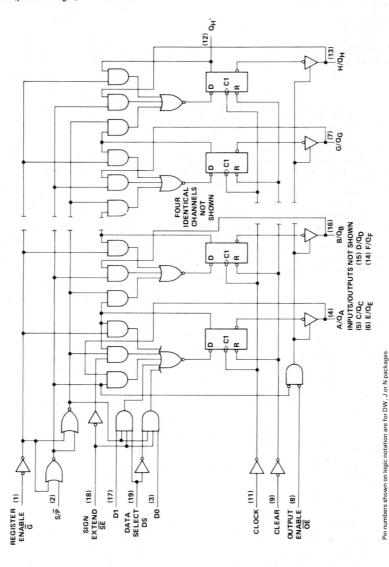

Pin numbers shown on logic notation are for DW, J or N packages.

Texas Instruments

logic symbol

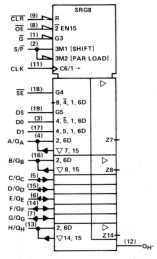

Pin numbers shown on logic notation are for DW, J or N packages.

schematics of inputs and outputs

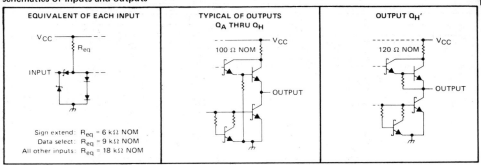

| EQUIVALENT OF EACH INPUT | TYPICAL OF OUTPUTS Q_A THRU Q_H | OUTPUT Q_H' |

TTL DEVICES

3

absolute maximum ratings over operating free-air temperature range (unless otherwise noted)

Supply voltage, V_{CC} (see Note 1) . . . . 7 V
Input voltage . . . . 7 V
Off-state output voltage . . . . 7 V
Operating free-air temperature range: SN54LS322A . . . . $-55°C$ to $125°C$
                            SN74LS322A . . . . $0°C$ to $70°C$
Storage temperature . . . . $-65°C$ to $150°C$

NOTE 1: Voltage values are with respect to network ground terminal.

recommended operating conditions

			SN54LS322A			SN74LS322A			UNIT
			MIN	NOM	MAX	MIN	NOM	MAX	
V_{CC}	Supply voltage		4.5	5	5.5	4.75	5	5.25	V
V_{IH}	High-level input voltage		2			2			V
V_{IL}	Low-level input voltage				0.7			0.8	V
I_{OH}	High-level output current	Q_A thru Q_H			−1			−2.6	mA
		Q_H'			−0.4			−0.4	
I_{OL}	Low-level output current	Q_A thru Q_H			12			24	mA
		Q_H'			4			8	
f_{clock}	Clock frequency		0		20	0		20	MHz
$t_{w(clock)}$	Width of clock pulse	Clock high	30			30			ns
		Clock low	10			10			
$t_{w(clear)}$		Clear low	20			20			ns
t_{su}	Setup time	Data select	10†			10†			ns
		High-level data◊	20†			20†			
		Low-level data◊	20†			20†			
		Clear inactive-state	20†			20†			
t_h	Hold time	Data select	10†			10†			ns
		Data◊	2.0†			2.0†			
T_A	Operating free-air temperature		−55		125	0		70	°C

◊ Data includes the two serial inputs and the eight input/output data lines.
† The arrow indicates that the rising edge of the clock pulse is used for reference.

3

TTL DEVICES

TEXAS
INSTRUMENTS

electrical characteristics over recommended operating free-air temperature range (unless otherwise noted)

PARAMETER		TEST CONDITIONS†			SN54LS322A			SN74LS322A			UNIT
					MIN	TYP‡	MAX	MIN	TYP‡	MAX	
V_{IK}		V_{CC} = MIN,	I_I = −18 mA				−1.5			−1.5	V
V_{OH}	Q_A thru Q_H	V_{CC} = MIN,	V_{IH} = 2 V,	V_{IL} = MAX,	2.4	3.2		2.4	3.1		V
	$Q_H{}'$	I_{OH} = MAX			2.5	3.4		2.7	3.4		
V_{OL}	Q_A thru Q_H	V_{CC} = MIN, V_{IH} = 2 V, V_{IL} = MAX		I_{OL} = 12 mA		0.25	0.4		0.25	0.4	V
				I_{OL} = 24 mA					0.35	0.5	
	$Q_H{}'$			I_{OL} = 4 mA		0.25	0.4		0.25	0.4	
				I_{OL} = 8 mA					0.35	0.5	
I_{OZH}	Q_A thru Q_H	V_{CC} = MAX,	V_{IH} = 2 V,	V_O = 2.7 V			40			40	µA
I_{OZL}	Q_A thru Q_H	V_{CC} = MAX,	V_{IH} = 2 V,	V_O = 0.4 V			−0.4			−0.4	mA
I_I	A thru H	V_{CC} = MAX		V_I = 5.5 V			0.1			0.1	mA
	Data select			V_I = 7 V			0.2			0.2	
	Sign extend			V_I = 7 V			0.3			0.3	
	Any other			V_I = 7 V			0.1			0.1	
I_{IH}	A thru H, DS	V_{CC} = MAX,	V_I = 2.7 V				40			40	µA
	Sign extend						60			60	
	Any other						20			20	
I_{IL}	Data select	V_{CC} = MAX,	V_I = 0.4 V				−0.8			−0.8	mA
	Sign extend						−1.2			−1.2	
	Any other						−0.4			−0.4	
I_{OS}§	Q_A thru Q_H	V_{CC} = MAX			−30		−130	−30		−130	mA
	$Q_H{}'$				−20		−100	−20		−100	
I_{CC}		V_{CC} = MAX				35	60		35	60	mA

† For conditions shown as MIN or MAX, use the appropriate value specified under recommended operating conditions.
‡ All typical values are at V_{CC} = 5 V, T_A = 25°C.
§ Not more than one output should be shorted at a time and duration of the short-circuit should not exceed one second.

switching characteristics, V_{CC} = 5 V, T_A = 25°C

PARAMETER¶	FROM (INPUT)	TO (OUTPUT)	TEST CONDITIONS		MIN	TYP	MAX	UNIT
f_{max}			See Note 2		20	35		MHz
t_{PLH}	CLK	$Q_H{}'$	R_L = 2 kΩ,	C_L = 15 pF,		22	33	ns
t_{PHL}			See Note 2			26	35	
t_{PHL}	$\overline{CLR}$	$Q_H{}'$				27	35	ns
t_{PLH}	CLK	Q_A thru Q_H				16	25	ns
t_{PHL}			R_L = 665 Ω,	C_L = 45 pF,		22	33	
t_{PHL}	$\overline{CLR}$	Q_A thru Q_H	See Note 2			22	35	ns
t_{PZH}	$\overline{OE}$	Q_A thru Q_H				15	35	ns
t_{PZL}						15	35	
t_{PHZ}	$\overline{OE}$	Q_A thru Q_H	R_L = 665 Ω,	C_L = 5 pF,		15	25	ns
t_{PLZ}			See Note 2			15	25	

¶ f_{max} ≡ maximum clock frequency
t_{PLH} ≡ propagation delay time, low-to-high-level output
t_{PHL} ≡ propagation delay time, high-to-low-level output
t_{PZH} ≡ output enable time to high level
t_{PZL} ≡ output enable time to low level
t_{PHZ} ≡ output disable time from high level
t_{PLZ} ≡ output disable time from low level
NOTE 2: For testing f_{max}, all outputs are loaded simultaneously, each with C_L and R_L as specified for the propagation times. See General Information Section for load circuits and voltage waveforms.

3

TTL DEVICES

TEXAS
INSTRUMENTS

3-811

- Multiplexed Inputs/Outputs Provide Improved Bit Density

- Four Modes of Operation:
  Hold (Store)   Shift Left
  Shift Right   Load Data

- Operates with Outputs Enabled or at High Z

- 3-State Outputs Drive Bus Lines Directly

- Can Be Cascaded for N-Bit Word Lengths

- Typical Power Dissipation . . . 175 mW

- Guaranteed Shift (Clock) Frequency . . . 25 MHz

- Applications:
  Stacked or Push-Down Registers,
  Buffer Storage, and
  Accumulator Registers

- SN54LS299 and SN74LS299 Are Similar But Have Direct Overriding Clear

SN54LS323 . . . J PACKAGE
SN74LS323 . . . DW, J OR N PACKAGE
(TOP VIEW)

SN54LS323 . . . FK PACKAGE
SN74LS323
(TOP VIEW)

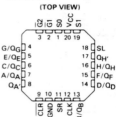

description

These Low-Power Schottky eight-bit universal registers feature multiplexed inputs/outputs to achieve full eight-bit data handling in a single 20-pin package. Two function-select inputs and two output-control inputs can be used to choose the modes of operation listed in the function table. Synchronous parallel loading is accomplished by taking both function-select lines, S0 and S1, high. This places the three-state outputs in a high-impedance state, which permits data that is applied on the input/output lines to be clocked into the register. Reading out of the register can be accomplished while the outputs are enabled in any mode. The clear function is synchronous, and a low level at the clear input clears the register on the next low-to-high transition of the clock.

FUNCTION TABLE

MODE	INPUTS									INPUTS/OUTPUTS								OUTPUTS	
	CLR	FUNCTION SELECT		OUTPUT CONTROL		CLK	SERIAL		A/QA	B/QB	C/QC	D/QD	E/QE	F/QF	G/QG	H/QH	QA'	QH'
		S1	S0	G1†	G2†		SL	SR										
Clear	L	X	L	L	L	↑	X	X	L	L	L	L	L	L	L	L	L	L
	L	L	X	L	L	↑	X	X	L	L	L	L	L	L	L	L	L	L
	L	H	H	X	X	↑	X	X	X	X	X	X	X	X	X	X	L	L
Hold	H	L	L	L	L	X	X	X	QA0	QB0	QC0	QD0	QE0	QF0	QG0	QH0	QA0	QH0
	H	X	X	L	L	L	X	X	QA0	QB0	QC0	QD0	QE0	QF0	QG0	QH0	QA0	QH0
Shift Right	H	L	H	L	L	↑	X	H	H	QAn	QBn	QCn	QDn	QEn	QFn	QGn	H	QGn
	H	L	H	L	L	↑	X	L	L	QAn	QBn	QCn	QDn	QEn	QFn	QGn	L	QGn
Shift Left	H	H	L	L	L	↑	H	X	QBn	QCn	QDn	QEn	QFn	QGn	QHn	H	QBn	H
	H	H	L	L	L	↑	L	X	QBn	QCn	QDn	QEn	QFn	QGn	QHn	L	QBn	L
Load	H	H	H	X	X	↑	X	X	a	b	c	d	e	f	g	h	a	h

†When one or both output controls are high the eight input/output terminals are disabled to the high-impedance state; however, sequential operation or clearing of the register is not affected.

a . . . h   the level of the steady-state input at inputs A through H, respectively. These data are loaded into the flip-flops while the flip-flop outputs are isolated from the input/output terminals.

TEXAS
INSTRUMENTS

3

TTL DEVICES

logic diagram

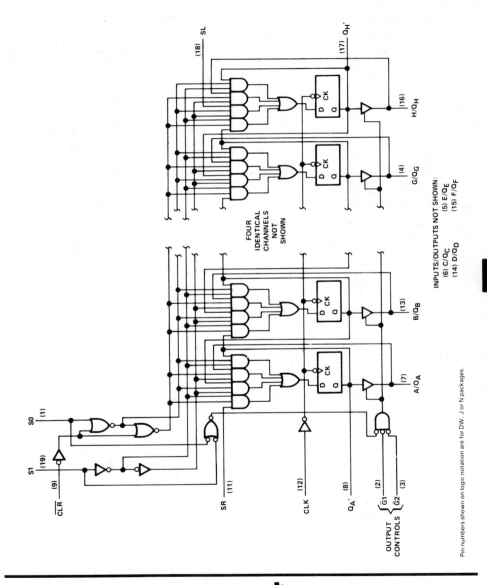

INPUTS/OUTPUTS NOT SHOWN:
(5) E/Q_E
(15) F/Q_F
(6) C/Q_C
(14) D/Q_D

Pin numbers shown on logic notation are for DW, J or N packages.

**TEXAS
INSTRUMENTS**

TYPES SN54LS323, SN74LS323
8-BIT UNIVERSAL SHIFT/STORAGE REGISTERS

schematics of inputs and outputs, absolute maximum ratings, recommended operating conditions, and electrical characteristics

Same as SN54LS299 and SN74LS299, except t_{su} (Clear inactive) does not apply.

switching characteristics, V_{CC} = 5 V, T_A = 25°C

PARAMETER ¶	FROM (INPUT)	TO (OUTPUT)	TEST CONDITIONS	MIN	TYP	MAX	UNIT
f_{max}			See Note 1	25	35		MHz
t_{PLH}	CLK	Q_A' or Q_H'	C_L = 15 pF, R_L = 2 kΩ		22	33	ns
t_{PHL}					26	39	
t_{PLH}	CLK	Q_A thru Q_H	C_L = 45 pF, R_L = 665 Ω		17	25	ns
t_{PHL}					25	39	
t_{PZH}	$\overline{G}1$, $\overline{G}2$	Q_A thru Q_H			14	21	ns
t_{PZL}					20	30	
t_{PHZ}	$\overline{G}1$, $\overline{G}2$	Q_A thru Q_H	C_L = 5 pF, R_L = 665 Ω		10	20	ns
t_{PLZ}					10	15	

¶ f_{max} ≡ maximum clock frequency
t_{PLH} ≡ propagation delay time, low-to-high-level output
t_{PHL} ≡ propagation delay time, high-to-low-level output
t_{PZH} ≡ output enable time to high level
t_{PZL} ≡ output enable time to low level
t_{PHZ} ≡ output disable time from high level
t_{PLZ} ≡ output disable time from low level
NOTE 1: For testing f_{max}, all outputs are loaded simultaneously, each with C_L and R_L as specified for the propagation times. See General Information Section for load circuits and voltage waveforms.

3

TTL DEVICES

- 3-State Outputs Drive Bus Lines Directly
- Encodes 8 Data Lines to 3-Line Binary (Octal)
- Applications Include:
  - N-Bit Encoding
  - Code Converters and Generators
- Typical Data Delay . . . 15 ns
- Typical Power Dissipation . . . 60 mW

description

These TTL encoders feature priority decoding of the inputs to ensure that only the highest-order data line is encoded. The 'LS348 circuits encode eight data lines to three-line (4-2-1) binary (octal). Cascading circuitry (enable input E1 and enable output EO) has been provided to allow octal expansion. Outputs A0, A1, and A2 are implemented in three-state logic for easy expansion up to 64 lines without the need for external circuitry. See Typical Application Data.

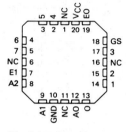

SN54LS348 . . . J OR W PACKAGE
SN74LS348 . . . D, J OR N PACKAGE
(TOP VIEW)

4	1	16	VCC
5	2	15	EO
6	3	14	GS
7	4	13	3
E1	5	12	2
A2	6	11	1
A1	7	10	0
GND	8	9	A0

SN54LS348 . . . FK PACKAGE
SN74LS348
(TOP VIEW)

6	4	18	GS
7	5	17	3
NC	6	16	NC
E1	7	15	2
A2	8	14	1

NC – No internal connection

FUNCTION TABLE

INPUTS										OUTPUTS				
EI	0	1	2	3	4	5	6	7		A2	A1	A0	GS	EO
H	X	X	X	X	X	X	X	X		Z	Z	Z	H	H
L	H	H	H	H	H	H	H	H		Z	Z	Z	H	L
L	X	X	X	X	X	X	X	L		L	L	L	L	H
L	X	X	X	X	X	X	L	H		L	L	H	L	H
L	X	X	X	X	X	L	H	H		L	H	L	L	H
L	X	X	X	X	L	H	H	H		L	H	H	L	H
L	X	X	X	L	H	H	H	H		H	L	L	L	H
L	X	X	L	H	H	H	H	H		H	L	H	L	H
L	X	L	H	H	H	H	H	H		H	H	L	L	H
L	L	H	H	H	H	H	H	H		H	H	H	L	H

H = high logic level, L = low logic level, X = irrelevant
Z = high-impedance state

TEXAS
INSTRUMENTS

3

TTL DEVICES

TYPES SN54LS348, SN74LS348 (TIM9908)
8-LINE TO 3-LINE PRIORITY ENCODERS WITH 3-STATE OUTPUTS

logic diagram

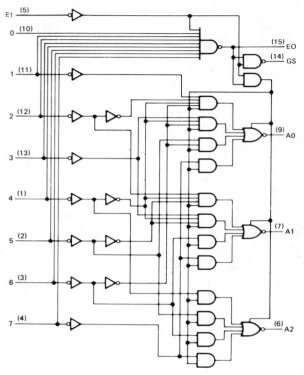

Pin numbers shown on logic notation are for D, J or N packages.

schematic of inputs and outputs

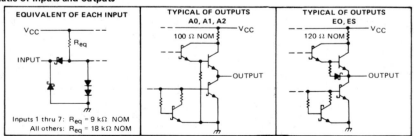

EQUIVALENT OF EACH INPUT	TYPICAL OF OUTPUTS A0, A1, A2	TYPICAL OF OUTPUTS EO, ES
V_{CC} — R_{eq} — INPUT —	100 Ω NOM — V_{CC} — OUTPUT	120 Ω NOM — V_{CC} — OUTPUT

Inputs 1 thru 7: R_{eq} = 9 kΩ NOM
All others: R_{eq} = 18 kΩ NOM

TEXAS
INSTRUMENTS

absolute maximum ratings over operating free-air temperature range (unless otherwise noted)

Supply voltage, V_{CC} (see Note 1) . . . . 7 V
Input voltage . . . . 7 V
Operating free-air temperature range: SN54LS348 . . . . $-55°C$ to $125°C$
                               SN74LS348 . . . . $0°C$ to $70°C$
Storage temperature range . . . . $-65°C$ to $150°C$

NOTE 1: Voltage values are with respect to network ground terminal.

recommended operating conditions

		SN54LS348			SN74LS348			UNIT
		MIN	NOM	MAX	MIN	NOM	MAX	
Supply voltage, V_{CC}		4.5	5	5.5	4.75	5	5.25	V
High-level output current, I_{OH}	A0, A1, A2			-1			-2.6	mA
	EO, GS			-400			-400	μA
Low-level output current, I_{OL}	A0, A1, A2			12			24	mA
	EO, GS			4			8	mA
Operating free-air temperature, T_A		-55		125	0		70	$°C$

electrical characteristics over recommended operating free-air temperature range (unless otherwise noted)

PARAMETER			TEST CONDITIONS[†]		SN54LS348			SN74LS348			UNIT
					MIN	TYP[‡]	MAX	MIN	TYP[‡]	MAX	
V_{IH}	High-level input voltage				2			2			V
V_{IL}	Low-level input voltage						0.7			0.8	V
V_{IK}	Input clamp voltage		V_{CC} = MIN,	$I_I = -18$ mA			-1.5			-1.5	V
V_{OH}	High-level output voltage	A0, A1, A2	V_{CC} = MIN, V_{IH} = 2 V,	$I_{OH} = -1$ mA	2.4	3.1					V
		EO, GS	$V_{IL} = V_{IL}$max	$I_{OH} = -2.6$ mA				2.4	3.1		
				$I_{OH} = -400 \mu$A	2.5	3.4		2.7	3.4		
V_{OL}	Low-level Output voltage	A0, A1, A2	V_{CC} = MIN, V_{IH} = 2 V, $V_{IL} = V_{IL}$max	$I_{OL} = 12$ mA		0.25	0.4		0.25	0.4	V
				$I_{OL} = 24$ mA					0.35	0.5	
		EO, GS		$I_{OL} = 4$ mA		0.25	0.4		0.25	0.4	
				$I_{OL} = 8$ mA					0.35	0.5	
I_{OZ}	Off-State (high-impedance state) output current	A0, A1, A2	V_{CC} = MAX, V_{IH} = 2 V	$V_O = 2.7$ V			20			20	μA
				$V_O = 0.4$ V			-20			-20	
I_I	Input current at maximum input voltage	Inputs 1 thru 7	V_{CC} = MAX, $V_I = 7$ V				0.2			0.2	mA
		All other inputs					0.1			0.1	
I_{IH}	High-level input current	Inputs 1 thru 7	V_{CC} = MAX, $V_I = 2.7$ V				40			40	μA
		All other inputs					20			20	
I_{IL}	Low-level input current	Inputs 1 thru 7	V_{CC} = MAX, $V_I = 0.4$ V				-0.8			-0.8	mA
		All other inputs					-0.4			-0.4	
I_{OS}	Short-circuit output current[§]	Outputs A0, A1, A2	V_{CC} = MAX		-30		-130	-30		-130	mA
		Outputs EO, GS			-20		-100	-20		-100	
I_{CC}	Supply current		V_{CC} = MAX, See Note 2	Condition 1		13	25		13	25	mA
				Condition 2		12	23		12	23	

[†] For conditions shown as MIN or MAX, use the appropriate value specified under recommended operating conditions.
[‡] All typical values are at V_{CC} = 5 V, $T_A = 25°C$.
[§] Not more than one output should be shorted at a time.

NOTE 2: I_{CC} (condition 1) is measured with inputs 7 and EI grounded, other inputs and outputs open. I_{CC} (condition 2) is measured with all inputs and outputs open.

3

TTL DEVICES

TEXAS INSTRUMENTS

switching characteristics, V_{CC} = 5 V, T_A = 25°C

PARAMETER¶	FROM (INPUT)	TO (OUTPUT)	WAVEFORM	TEST CONDITIONS	MIN	TYP	MAX	UNIT
t_{PLH}	1 thru 7	A0, A1, or A2	In-phase output	C_L = 45 pF, R_L = 667 Ω, See Note 3		11	17	ns
t_{PHL}	1 thru 7	A0, A1, or A2	In-phase output			20	30	
t_{PLH}	1 thru 7	A0, A1, or A2	Out-of-phase output			23	35	ns
t_{PHL}	1 thru 7	A0, A1, or A2	Out-of-phase output			23	35	
t_{PZH}	EI	A0, A1, or A2				25	39	ns
t_{PZL}	EI	A0, A1, or A2				24	41	
t_{PLH}	0 thru 7	EO	Out-of-phase output	C_L = 15 pF, R_L = 2 kΩ, See Note 3		11	18	ns
t_{PHL}	0 thru 7	EO	Out-of-phase output			26	40	
t_{PLH}	0 thru 7	GS	In-phase output			38	55	ns
t_{PHL}	0 thru 7	GS	In-phase output			9	21	
t_{PLH}	EI	GS	In-phase output			11	17	ns
t_{PHL}	EI	GS	In-phase output			14	36	
t_{PLH}	EI	EO	In-phase output			17	26	ns
t_{PHL}	EI	EO	In-phase output			25	40	
t_{PHZ}	EI	A0, A1, or A2		C_L = 5 pF, R_L = 667 Ω		18	27	ns
t_{PLZ}	EI	A0, A1, or A2				23	35	

¶ t_{PLH} = propagation delay time, low-to-high-level output
t_{PHL} = propagation delay time, high-to-low-level output
t_{PZH} = output enable time to high level
t_{PZL} = output enable time to low level
t_{PHZ} = output disable time from high level
t_{PLZ} = output disable time from low level
NOTE 3: See General Information Section for load circuits and voltage waveforms.

TYPICAL APPLICATION DATA

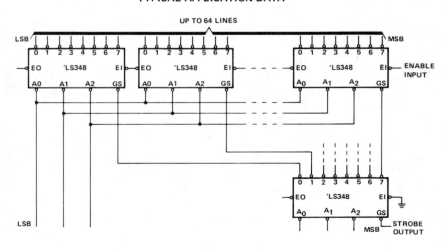

FIGURE 1—PRIORITY ENCODER WITH UP TO 64 INPUTS.

TEXAS
INSTRUMENTS

OCTOBER 1976 — REVISED DECEMBER 1983

- **Inverting Versions of SN54LS153, SN74LS153**
- **Schottky-Diode-Clamped Transistors**
- **Permits Multiplexing from N lines to 1 line**
- **Performs Parallel-to-Serial Conversion**
- **Typical Average Propagation Delay Times:**
  Data Input to Output . . . 15 ns
  Strobe Input to Output . . . 19 ns
  Select Input to Output . . . 22 ns
- **Fully Compatible with most TTL Circuits**
- **Low Power Dissipation . . . 31 mW Typical (Enabled)**

description

Each of these Schottky-clamped data selectors/-multiplexers contains inverters and drivers to supply fully complementary, on-chip, binary decoding data selection to the AND-OR-invert gates. Separate strobe inputs are provided for each of the two four-line sections.

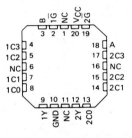

SN54LS352 . . . J OR W PACKAGE
SN74LS352 . . . D, J OR N PACKAGE
(TOP VIEW)

1Ḡ	1	16	V_{CC}
B	2	15	2G
1C3	3	14	A
1C2	4	13	2C3
1C1	5	12	2C2
1C0	6	11	2C1
1Y	7	10	2C0
GND	8	9	2Y

SN54LS352 . . . FK PACKAGE
SN74LS352
(TOP VIEW)

NC – No internal connection

FUNCTION TABLE

SELECT INPUTS		DATA INPUTS				STROBE	OUTPUT
B	A	C0	C1	C2	C3	Ḡ	Y
X	X	X	X	X	X	H	H
L	L	L	X	X	X	L	H
L	L	H	X	X	X	L	L
L	H	X	L	X	X	L	H
L	H	X	H	X	X	L	L
H	L	X	X	L	X	L	H
H	L	X	X	H	X	L	L
H	H	X	X	X	L	L	H
H	H	X	X	X	H	L	L

Select inputs A and B are common to both sections.
H = high level, L = low level, X = irrelevant

absolute maximum ratings over operating free-air temperature range (unless otherwise noted)

Supply voltage, V_{CC} (see Note 1)	7 V
Input voltage	7 V
Operating free-air temperature range: SN54LS352	−55°C to 125°C
SN74LS352	0°C to 70°C
Storage temperature range	−65°C to 150°C

NOTE 1: Voltage values are with respect to network ground terminal.

TEXAS INSTRUMENTS

3
TTL DEVICES

logic diagram

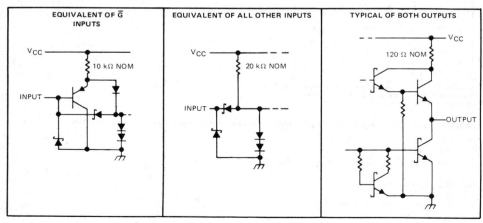

Pin numbers shown on logic notation are for D, J or N packages.

3

TTL DEVICES

schematics of inputs and outputs

EQUIVALENT OF G̅ INPUTS	EQUIVALENT OF ALL OTHER INPUTS	TYPICAL OF BOTH OUTPUTS
V_{CC} 10 kΩ NOM INPUT	V_{CC} 20 kΩ NOM INPUT	V_{CC} 120 Ω NOM OUTPUT

TEXAS
INSTRUMENTS

recommended operating conditions

		SN54LS352			SN74LS352			UNIT
		MIN	NOM	MAX	MIN	NOM	MAX	
V_{CC}	Supply voltage	4.5	5	5.5	4.75	5	5.25	V
V_{IH}	High-level input voltage	2			2			V
V_{IL}	Low-level input voltage			0.7			0.8	V
I_{OH}	High-level output current			− 0.4			− 0.4	mA
I_{OL}	Low-level output current			4			8	mA
T_A	Operating free-air temperature	− 55		125	0		70	°C

electrical characteristics over recommended operating free-air temperature range (unless otherwise noted)

PARAMETER		TEST CONDITIONS†		SN54LS352			SN74LS352			UNIT
				MIN	TYP	MAX	MIN	TYP	MAX	
V_{IK}		V_{CC} = MIN,	I_I = − 18 mA			− 1.5			− 1.5	V
V_{OH}		V_{CC} = MIN, V_{IH} = 2 V, V_{IL} = MAX, I_{OH} = − 0.4 mA		2.5	3.4		2.7	3.4		V
V_{OL}		V_{CC} = MIN, V_{IH} = 2 V, V_{IL} = MAX	I_{OL} = 4 mA		0.25	0.4		0.25	0.4	V
			I_{OL} = 8 mA					0.35	0.5	
I_I		V_{CC} = MAX,	V_I = 7 V			0.1			0.1	mA
I_{IH}		V_{CC} = MAX,	V_I = 2.7 V			20			20	µA
I_{IL}	$\overline{G}$	V_{CC} = MAX,	V_I = 0.4 V			− 0.2			− 0.2	mA
	All other					− 0.4			− 0.4	
I_{OS} §		V_{CC} = MAX		− 20		− 100	− 20		− 100	mA
I_{CCL}		V_{CC} = MAX,	See Note 2		6.2	10		6.2	10	mA

† For conditions shown as MIN or MAX, use the appropriate value specified under recommended operating.
  All typical values are at V_{CC} = 5 V, T_A = 25°C.
§ Not more than one output should be shorted at a time, and duration of the short-circuit should not exceed one second.
NOTE 2: I_{CCL} is measured with the outputs open and all inputs grounded.

switching characteristics, V_{CC} = 5 V, T_A = 25°C

PARAMETER¶	FROM (INPUT)	TO (OUTPUT)	TEST CONDITIONS		MIN	TYP	MAX	UNIT
t_{PLH}	Data	Y				13	20	ns
t_{PHL}	Data	Y				17	26	ns
t_{PLH}	A or B	Y	R_L = 2 kΩ,	C_L = 15 pF,		19	29	ns
t_{PHL}	A or B	Y	See Note 3			25	38	ns
t_{PLH}	$\overline{G}$	Y				16	24	ns
t_{PHL}	$\overline{G}$	Y				21	32	ns

¶ t_{PLH} = propagation delay time, low-to-high-level output
  t_{PHL} = propagation delay time, high-to-low-level output
NOTE 3: See General Information Section for load circuits and voltage waveforms.

3

TTL DEVICES

**TEXAS
INSTRUMENTS**

- **Inverting Versions of SN54LS253, SN74LS253**
- **Schottky-Diode-Clamped Transistors**
- **Permits Multiplexing from N lines to 1 line**
- **Performs Parallel-to-Serial Conversion**
- **Typical Average Propagation Delay Times:**
  Data Input to Output . . . 12 ns
  Control Input to Output . . . 16 ns
  Select Input to Output . . . 21 ns
- **Fully Compatible with most TTL Circuits**
- **Low Power Dissipation . . . 35 mW Typical (Enabled)**
- **Inverted Data**

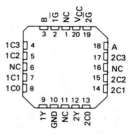

SN54LS353 . . . J OR W PACKAGE
SN74LS353 . . . D, J OR N PACKAGE
(TOP VIEW)

SN54LS353 . . . FK PACKAGE
SN74LS353
(TOP VIEW)

NC — No internal connection

description

Each of these Schottky-clamped data selectors/multiplexers contains inverters and drivers to supply fully complementary, on-chip, binary decoding data selection to the AND-OR-invert gates. Separate output control inputs are provided for each of the two four-line sections.

The three-state outputs can interface with and drive data lines of bus-organized systems. With all but one of the common outputs disabled (at a high-impedance state) the low-impedance of the single enabled output will drive the bus line to a high or low logic level.

logic

FUNCTION TABLE

SELECT INPUTS		DATA INPUTS				OUTPUT CONTROL	OUTPUT
B	A	C0	C1	C2	C3	G̅	Y
X	X	X	X	X	X	H	Z
L	L	L	X	X	X	L	H
L	L	H	X	X	X	L	L
L	H	X	L	X	X	L	H
L	H	X	H	X	X	L	L
H	L	X	X	L	X	L	H
H	L	X	X	H	X	L	L
H	H	X	X	X	L	L	H
H	H	X	X	X	H	L	L

Select inputs A and B are common to both sections.

H = high level, L = low level, X = irrelevant, Z = high impedance (off)

absolute maximum ratings over operating free-air temperature range (unless otherwise noted)

Supply voltage, V_{CC} (see Note 1)	7 V
Input voltage	7 V
Off-state output voltage	5.5 V
Operating free-air temperature range: SN54LS353	−55°C to 125°C
SN74LS353	0°C to 70°C
Storage temperature range	−65°C to 150°C

NOTE 1: Voltage values are with respect to network ground terminal.

TEXAS INSTRUMENTS

logic diagram

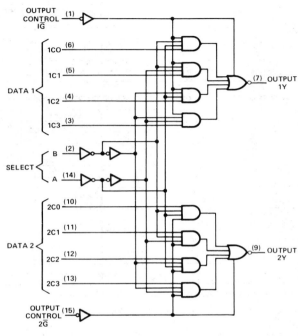

Pin numbers shown on logic notation are for D, J or N packages.

schematic of inputs and outputs

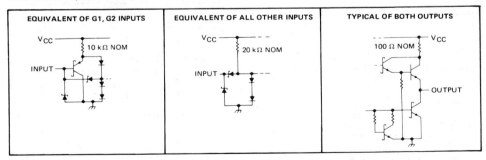

EQUIVALENT OF G1, G2 INPUTS	EQUIVALENT OF ALL OTHER INPUTS	TYPICAL OF BOTH OUTPUTS

TTL DEVICES

3

recommended operating conditions

		SN54LS353			SN74LS353			UNIT
		MIN	NOM	MAX	MIN	NOM	MAX	
V_{CC}	Supply voltage	4.5	5	5.5	4.75	5	5.25	V
V_{IH}	High-level input voltage	2			2			V
V_{IL}	Low-level input voltage			0.7			0.8	V
I_{OH}	High-level output current			−1			−2.6	mA
I_{OL}	Low-level output current			4			8	mA
T_A	Operating free-air temperature	−55		125	0		70	°C

electrical characteristics over recommended operating free-air temperature range (unless otherwise noted)

PARAMETER		TEST CONDITIONS †		SN54LS353			SN74LS353			UNIT
				MIN	TYP‡	MAX	MIN	TYP‡	MAX	
V_{IK}		V_{CC} = MIN,	I_I = −18 mA			−1.5			−1.5	V
V_{OH}		V_{CC} = MIN, V_{IH} = 2 V, V_{IL} = MAX, I_{OH} = MAX		2.4	3.4		2.4	3.1		V
V_{OL}		V_{CC} = MIN, V_{IH} = 2 V, V_{IL} = MAX	I_{OL} = 4 mA		0.25	0.4		0.25	0.4	V
			I_{OL} = 8 mA					0.35	0.5	
I_{OZ}		V_{CC} = MAX, V_{IH} = 2 V	V_O = 2.7 V			20			20	µA
			V_O = 0.4 V			−20			−20	
I_I		V_{CC} = MAX, V_I = 7 V				0.1			0.1	mA
I_{IH}		V_{CC} = MAX, V_I = 2.7 V				20			20	µA
I_{IL}	G1, G1	V_{CC} = MAX, V_I = 0.4 V				−0.2			−0.2	mA
	All other					−0.4			−0.4	
I_{OS} §		V_{CC} = MAX		−30		−130	−30		−130	mA
I_{CC}		V_{CC} = MAX, See Note 2	Condition A		7	12		7	12	mA
			Condition B		8.5	14		8.5	14	

† For conditions shown as MIN or MAX, use the appropriate value specified under recommended operating conditions.
‡ All typical values are at V_{CC} = 5 V, T_A = 25°C.
§ Not more than one output should be shorted at a time, and duration of the short-circuit should not exceed one second.
NOTE 2: I_{CC} is measured with the outputs open under the following conditions:
    A. All inputs grounded.
    B. Output control at 4.5 V, all inputs grounded.

switching characteristics, V_{CC} = 5 V, T_A = 25°C

PARAMETER¶	FROM (INPUT)	TO (OUTPUT)	TEST CONDITIONS		MIN	TYP	MAX	UNIT
t_{PLH}	Data	Y				11	25	ns
t_{PHL}						13	20	
t_{PLH}	Select	Y	C_L = 15 pF, R_L = 2 kΩ, See Note 3			20	45	ns
t_{PHL}						21	32	
t_{PZH}	Output Control	Y				11	23	ns
t_{PZL}						15	23	
t_{PHZ}	Output Control	Y	C_L = 5 pF, R_L = 2 kΩ, See Note 3			27	41	ns
t_{PLZ}						12	27	

¶ t_{PLH} ≡ Propagation delay time, low-to-high-level output
  t_{PHL} ≡ Propagation delay time, high-to-low-level output
  t_{PZH} ≡ Output enable time to high level
  t_{PZL} ≡ Output enable time to low level
  t_{PHZ} ≡ Output disable time from high level
  t_{PLZ} ≡ Output disable time from low level
NOTE 3: See General Information Section for load circuits and voltage waveforms.

TEXAS
INSTRUMENTS

TYPES SN54LS354, SN54LS355, SN54LS356,
SN74LS354, SN74LS355, SN74LS356
8-LINE TO 1-LINE DATA SELECTORS/MULTIPLEXERS/REGISTERS

D2544, JULY 1979 – REVISED APRIL 1985

- ● Transparent Latches on Data Select Inputs
- ● Choice of Data Registers:
    - Transparent ('LS354, 'LS355)
    - Edge-Triggered ('LS356)
- ● Choice of Outputs:
    - Three-State ('LS354, 'LS356)
    - Open-Collector ('LS355)
- ● Complementary Outputs
- ● Easily Expandable
- ● High-Density 20-Pin Package

description

These monolithic data selectors/multiplexers contain full on-chip binary decoding to select one of eight data sources. The data-select address is stored in transparent latches that are enabled by a low level on pin 11, $\overline{SC}$. On the 'LS354 and 'LS355 a similar enable for data is obtained by a low level on pin 9, $\overline{DC}$. The edge-triggered data register of the 'LS356 is clocked by a low-to-high transition on pin 9, CLK. Complementary outputs are available in either three-state versions ('LS354 and 'LS356) or open-collector version ('LS355).

The SN54LS354 through SN54LS356 are characterized for operation over the full military temperature range of –55° to 125°C; the SN74LS354 through SN74LS356 are characterized for operation from 0°C to 70°C.

SN54LS354, SN54LS355 ... J PACKAGE
SN74LS354, SN74LS355 ... DW, J OR N PACKAGE
(TOP VIEW)

D7	1	20	VCC
D6	2	19	Y
D5	3	18	W
D4	4	17	G3
D3	5	16	$\overline{G2}$
D2	6	15	$\overline{G1}$
D1	7	14	S0
D0	8	13	S1
$\overline{DC}$	9	12	S2
GND	10	11	$\overline{SC}$

SN54LS354, SN54LS355 ... FK PACKAGE
SN74LS354, SN74LS355
(TOP VIEW)

SN54LS356 ... J. PACKAGE
SN74LS356 ... DW, J OR N PACKAGE
(TOP VIEW)

D7	1	20	VCC
D6	2	19	Y
D5	3	18	W
D4	4	17	G3
D3	5	16	$\overline{G2}$
D2	6	15	$\overline{G1}$
D1	7	14	S0
D0	8	13	S1
CLK	9	12	$\overline{S2}$
GND	10	11	$\overline{SC}$

SN54LS356 ... FK PACKAGE
SN74LS356
(TOP VIEW)

3

TTL DEVICES

TYPES SN54LS354, SN54LS355, SN54LS356, SN74LS354, SN74LS355, SN74LS356
8-LINE TO 1-LINE DATA SELECTORS/MULTIPLEXERS/REGISTERS

FUNCTION TABLE

| INPUTS | | | | | | | | | OUTPUTS | |
| SELECT | | | DATA CONTROL ('LS354, 'LS355) | CLOCK ('LS356) | OUTPUT ENABLES | | | | | |
S2	S1	S0			$\overline{G1}$	$\overline{G2}$	G3		W	Y
X	X	X	X	X	H	X	X		Z	Z
X	X	X	X	X	X	H	X		Z	Z
X	X	X	X	X	X	X	L		Z	Z
L	L	L	L		L	L	H		$\overline{D0}$	$\overline{D0}$
L	L	L	H	H or L	L	L	H		$\overline{D0}_n$	$\overline{D0}_n$
L	L	H	L		L	L	H		$\overline{D1}$	D1
L	L	H	H	H or L	L	L	H		$\overline{D1}_n$	$D1_n$
L	H	L	L		L	L	H		$\overline{D2}$	D2
L	H	L	H	H or L	L	L	H		$\overline{D2}_n$	$D2_n$
L	H	H	H		L	L	H		$\overline{D3}$	D3
L	H	H	H	H or L	L	L	H		$\overline{D3}_n$	$D3_n$
H	L	L	L		L	L	H		$\overline{D4}$	D4
H	L	L	H	H or L	L	L	H		$\overline{D4}_n$	$D4_n$
H	L	H	L		L	L	H		$\overline{D5}$	D5
H	L	H	H	H or L	L	L	H		$\overline{D5}_n$	$D5_n$
H	H	L	L		L	L	H		$\overline{D6}$	D6
H	H	L	H	H or L	L	L	H		$\overline{D6}_n$	$D6_n$
H	H	H	L		L	L	H		$\overline{D7}$	D7
H	H	H	L	H or L	L	LL	H		$\overline{D7}_n$	$D7_n$

H = high level (steady state)
L = low level (steady state)
X = irrelevant (any input, including transitions)
Z = high-impedance state (off state)
↑ = transition from low to high level
D0 . . . D7 = the level of steady-state inputs at inputs D0 through D7, respectively, at the time of the low-to-high clock transition in the case of 'LS356
$D0_n$ . . . $D7_n$ = the level of steady state inputs at inputs D0 through D7, respectively, before the most recent low-to-high transition of data control or clock
This column shows the input address setup with $\overline{SC}$ low.

TYPICAL OF BOTH OUTPUTS ON 'LS355

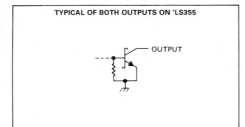

OUTPUT

schematics of inputs and outputs

EQUIVALENT OF EACH DATA OR SELECT INPUT

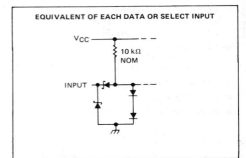

V_CC
10 kΩ NOM
INPUT

EQUIVALENT OF ALL OTHER INPUTS

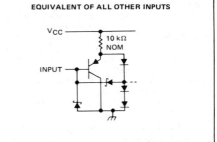

V_CC
10 kΩ NOM
INPUT

TYPICAL OF BOTH OUTPUTS ON 'LS354 AND 'LS356

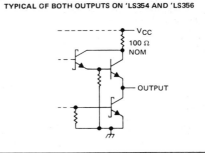

V_CC
100 Ω NOM
OUTPUT

absolute maximum ratings over operating free-air temperature range (unless otherwise noted)

Supply voltage (see Note 1). . . . . 7 V
Input voltage. . . . . 7 V
Operating free-air temperature range: SN54LS'. . . . . −55°C to 125°C
                                   SN74LS'. . . . . 0°C to 70°C
Storage temperature range . . . . −65°C to 150°C

NOTE 1: Voltage values are with respect to network ground terminal.

TEXAS INSTRUMENTS

3
TTL DEVICES

logic symbols

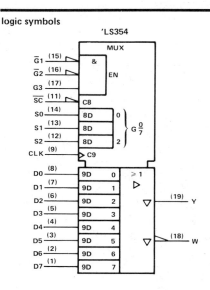

'LS354

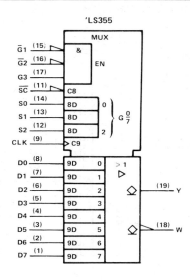

'LS355

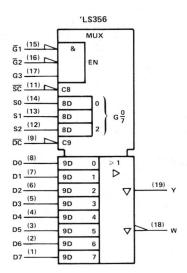

'LS356

Pin numbers shown on logic notation are for DW, J or N packages.

TTL DEVICES

3

TYPES SN54LS354, SN54LS355, SN74LS354, SN74LS355
8-LINE TO 1-LINE DATA SELECTORS/MULTIPLEXERS/REGISTERS

logic diagram (positive logic)

'LS354, 'LS355

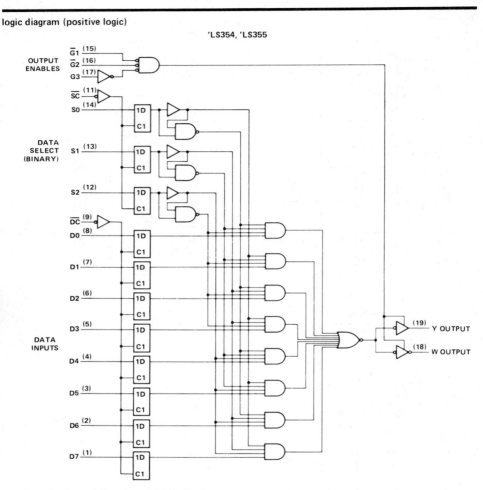

Pin numbers shown on logic notation are for DW, J or N packages.

TEXAS
INSTRUMENTS

logic diagram (positive logic)

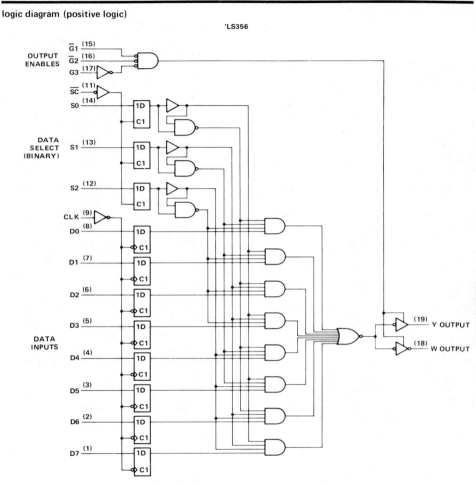

'LS356

Pin numbers shown on logic notation are for DW, J or N packages.

recommended operating conditions

			SN54LS354 SN54LS356			SN74LS354 SN74LS356			UNIT
			MIN	NOM	MAX	MIN	NOM	MAX	
V_{CC}	Supply voltage		4.5	5	5.5	4.75	5	5.25	V
V_{IH}	High-level input voltage		2			2			V
V_{IL}	Low-level input voltage				0.7			0.8	V
I_{OH}	High-level output current				−1			−2.6	mA
I_{OL}	Low-level output current				12			24	mA
t_{su}	Setup times, high-or-low-level data (with respect to ↑ at pin 9)	'LS354	15			15			ns
		'LS356	15			15			
t_h	Hold times, high-or-low-level data (with respect to ↑ at pin 9)	'LS354	15			15			ns
		'LS356	0			0			
T_A	Operating free-air temperature		−55		125	0		70	°C

electrical characteristics over recommended operating free-air temperature range (unless otherwise noted)

PARAMETER		TEST CONDITIONS[†]			SN54LS354 SN54LS356			SN74LS354 SN74LS356			UNIT
					MIN	TYP[‡]	MAX	MIN	TYP[‡]	MAX	
V_{IK}		V_{CC} = MIN,	I_I = −18 mA				−1.5			−1.5	V
V_{OH}		V_{CC} = MIN, V_{IH} = 2 V, I_{OH} = MAX,		V_{IL} = MAX	2.4			2.4			V
V_{OL}		V_{CC} = MIN, V_{IH} = 2 V, V_{IL} = MAX	I_{OL} = 12 mA			0.25	0.4		0.25	0.4	V
			I_{OL} = 24 mA						0.35	0.5	
I_{OZ}		V_{CC} = MAX	V_O = 2.7 V				20			20	μA
			V_O = 0.4 V				−20			−20	
I_I		V_{CC} = MAX,	V_I = 7 V				0.1			0.1	mA
I_{IH}		V_{CC} = MAX,	V_I = 2.7 V				20			20	μA
I_{IL}	$\overline{DC}$ or CLK, $\overline{G1}$, $\overline{G2}$, G3	V_{CC} = MAX,	V_I = 0.4 V				−0.2			−0.2	mA
	All others						−0.4			−0.4	
I_{OS}§		V_{CC} = MAX			−30		−130	−30		−130	mA
I_{CC}		V_{CC} = MAX,	See Note 2			29	46		29	46	mA

[†] For conditions shown as MIN or MAX, use the appropriate values specified under recommended operating conditions.
[‡] All typical values are at V_{CC} = 5 V, T_A = 25°C.
§ Not more than one output should be shorted at a time, and duration of the short-circuit should not exceed one second.
NOTE 2: I_{CC} is measured with the inputs grounded and the outputs open.

TEXAS
INSTRUMENTS

3
TTL DEVICES

switching characteristics, V_{CC} = 5 V, T_A = 25°C, R_L = 667 Ω

PARAMETER	FROM (INPUT)	TO (OUTPUT)	TEST CONDITIONS	'LS354 MIN	'LS354 TYP	'LS354 MAX	'LS356 MIN	'LS356 TYP	'LS356 MAX	UNIT
t_{PLH}	D0-D7	Y			24	36				ns
t_{PHL}	D0-D7	Y			23	35				ns
t_{PLH}	D0-D7	W			18	27				ns
t_{PHL}	D0-D7	W			29	44				ns
t_{PLH}	$\overline{DC}$ or CLK	Y			28	42		18	27	ns
t_{PHL}	$\overline{DC}$ or CLK	Y			26	39		33	50	ns
t_{PLH}	$\overline{DC}$ or CLK	W			22	33		24	36	ns
t_{PHL}	$\overline{DC}$ or CLK	W			33	50		18	27	ns
t_{PLH}	S0, S1 S2	Y	C_L = 45 pF, See Note 3		29	44		30	45	ns
t_{PHL}	S0, S1 S2	Y	C_L = 45 pF, See Note 3		24	45		28	48	ns
t_{PLH}	S0, S1 S2	W			28	42		36	54	ns
t_{PHL}	S0, S1 S2	W			34	51		30	45	ns
t_{PLH}	$\overline{SC}$	Y			34	51		36	54	ns
t_{PHL}	$\overline{SC}$	Y			31	47		40	60	ns
t_{PLH}	$\overline{SC}$	W			27	41		32	48	ns
t_{PHL}	$\overline{SC}$	W			40	60		36	54	ns
t_{PZH}	$\overline{G}1, \overline{G}2$	Y			14	27		14	25	ns
t_{PZL}	$\overline{G}1, \overline{G}2$	Y			18	27		17	25	ns
t_{PHZ}	$\overline{G}1, \overline{G}2$	Y	C_L = 5 pF, See Note 3		15	25		16	24	ns
t_{PLZ}	$\overline{G}1, \overline{G}2$	Y	C_L = 5 pF, See Note 3		15	25		16	24	ns
t_{PZH}	$\overline{G}1, \overline{G}2$	W	C_L = 45 pF, See Note 3		12	24		14	23	ns
t_{PZL}	$\overline{G}1, \overline{G}2$	W	C_L = 45 pF, See Note 3		16	24		16	23	ns
t_{PHZ}	$\overline{G}1, \overline{G}2$	W	C_L = 5 pF, See Note 3		15	25		16	23	ns
t_{PLZ}	$\overline{G}1, \overline{G}2$	W	C_L = 5 pF, See Note 3		15	25		16	23	ns
t_{PZH}	G3	Y	C_L = 45 pF, See Note 3		15	29		15	27	ns
t_{PZL}	G3	Y	C_L = 45 pF, See Note 3		19	29		18	27	ns
t_{PHZ}	G3	Y	C_L = 5 pF, See Note 3		15	25		16	25	ns
t_{PLZ}	G3	Y	C_L = 5 pF, See Note 3		15	25		16	25	ns
t_{PZH}	G3	W	C_L = 45 pF, See Note 3		13	25		14-	25	ns
t_{PZL}	G3	W	C_L = 45 pF, See Note 3		17	25		16	25	ns
t_{PHZ}	G3	W	C_L = 5 pF, See Note 3		15	25		16	25	ns
t_{PLZ}	G3	W	C_L = 5 pF, See Note 3		15	25		16	25	ns

NOTE 3: See General Information Section for load circuits and voltage waveforms.

TEXAS INSTRUMENTS

TTL DEVICES

3

recommended operating conditions

		SN54LS355			SN74LS355			UNIT
		MIN	NOM	MAX	MIN	NOM	MAX	
V_{CC}	Supply voltage	4.5	5	5.5	4.75	5	5.25	V
V_{IH}	High-level input voltage	2			2			V
V_{IL}	Low-level input voltage			0.7			0.8	V
V_{OH}	High-level output voltage			5.5			5.5	V
I_{OL}	Low-level output current			12			24	mA
t_{su}	Setup times, high-or-low-level data (with respect to ↑ at pin 9)	15			15			ns
t_h	Hold times, high-or-low-level data (with respect to ↑ at pin 9)	15			15			ns
T_A	Operating free-air temperature	−55		125	0		70	°C

electrical characteristics over recommended operating free-air temperature range (unless otherwise noted)

PARAMETER		TEST CONDITIONS†		SN54LS355			SN74LS355			UNIT
				MIN	TYP*	MAX	MIN	TYP*	MAX	
V_{IK}		V_{CC} = MIN,	I_I = −18 mA			−1.5			−1.5	V
I_{OH}		V_{CC} = MIN, V_{IH} = 2 V V_{IL} = MAX V_{OH} = 5.5 V				0.1			0.1	mA
V_{OL}		V_{CC} = MIN, V_{IH} = 2 V, V_{IL} = MAX	I_{OL} = 12 mA	0.25	0.4		0.25		0.4	V
			I_{OL} = 24 mA					0.35	0.5	
I_I		V_{CC} = MAX,	V_I = 7 V			0.1			0.1	mA
I_{IH}		V_{CC} = MAX,	V_I = 2.7 V			20			20	μA
I_{IL}	$\overline{DC}$ or CLK, $\overline{G1}$, $\overline{G2}$, $\overline{G3}$	V_{CC} = MAX,	V_I = 0.4 V			−0.2			−0.2	mA
	All others					−0.4			−0.4	
I_{CC}		V_{CC} = MAX,	See Note 2		29	46		29	46	mA

† For conditions shown as MIN or MAX, use the appropriate value specified under recommended operating conditions for the applicable type.
* All typical values are at V_{CC} = 5 V, T_A = 25°C.
NOTE 2: I_{CC} is measured with the inputs grounded and the outputs open.

3

TTL DEVICES

TEXAS
INSTRUMENTS

switching characteristics, V_{CC} = 5 V, T_A = 25°C, R_L = 667 Ω

PARAMETER	FROM (INPUT)	TO (OUTPUT)	TEST CONDITIONS	'LS355 MIN	'LS355 TYP	'LS355 MAX	UNIT
tPLH	D0 – D7	Y			34	41	ns
tPHL					26	39	
tPLH		W			30	45	ns
tPHL					33	50	
tPLH	$\overline{DC}$ or CLK	Y			38	57	ns
tPHL					31	47	
tPLH		W			33	50	ns
tPHL					39	59	
tPLH	S0, S1, S2	Y			39	59	ns
tPHL					36	49	
tPLH		W	CL = 45 pF, See Note 3		32	48	ns
tPHL					39	58	
tPLH	$\overline{SC}$	Y			45	68	ns
tPHL					42	63	
tPLH		W			44	66	ns
tPHL					45	68	
tPLH	$\overline{G1}$, $\overline{G2}$	Y			21	32	ns
tPHL					22	33	
tPLH		W			18	27	ns
tPHL					19	29	
tPLH	G3	Y			24	36	ns
tPHL					25	40	
tPLH		W			19	31	ns
tPHL					19	29	

NOTE 3: See General Information Section for load circuits and voltage waveforms.

- **3-State Outputs Drive Bus Lines or Buffer Memory Address Registers**

- **Choice of True or Inverting Outputs**

- **Package Options Include Both Plastic and Ceramic Chip Carriers in Addition to Plastic and Ceramic DIP's**

- **Dependable Texas Instruments Quality and Reliability**

**'365A, '367A, 'LS365A, 'LS367A True Outputs
'366A, '368A, 'LS366A, 'LS368A Inverting Outputs**

description

These Hex buffers and line drivers are designed specifically to improve both the performance and density of three-state memory address drivers, clock drivers, and bus oriented receivers and transmitters. The designer has a choice of selected combinations of inverting and noninverting outputs, symmetrical $\overline{G}$ (active-low control) inputs.

These devices feature high fan-out, improved fan-in, and can be used to drive terminated lines down to 133 ohms.

The SN54365A thru SN54368A and SN54LS365A thru SN54LS368A are characterized for operation over the full military temperature range of $-55°C$ to $125°C$. The SN74365A thru SN74368A and SN74LS365A thru SN74LS368A are characterized for operation from $0°C$ to $70°C$.

SN54365A, 366A, SN54LS365A, 366A . . . J PACKAGE
SN74365A, 366A . . . J OR N PACKAGE
SN74LS365A, SN74LS366A . . . D, J OR N PACKAGE
(TOP VIEW)

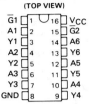

SN54LS365A, SN54LS366A . . . FK PACKAGE
SN74LS365A, SN74LS366A
(TOP VIEW)

SN54367A, 368A, SN54LS367A, 368A . . . J PACKAGE
SN74367A, 368A . . . J OR N PACKAGE
SN74LS367A, SN74LS368A . . . D, J OR N PACKAGE
(TOP VIEW)

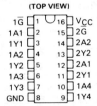

SN54LS367A, SN54LS368A . . . FK PACKAGE
SN74LS367A, SN74LS368A
(TOP VIEW)

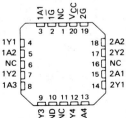

NC – No internal connection

TEXAS INSTRUMENTS

3-835

TTL DEVICES

3

schematics of inputs and outputs

'365A thru '368A

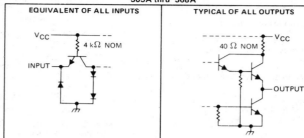

'LS365A thru 'LS368A

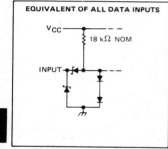
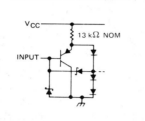
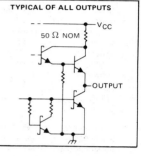

logic diagrams (positive logic)

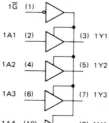
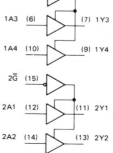

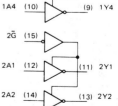

Pin numbers shown on logic notation are for D, J or N packages.

3

TTL DEVICES

TEXAS
INSTRUMENTS

logic symbols

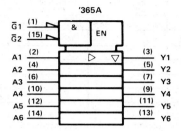

'365A

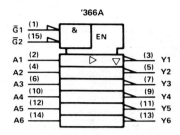

'366A

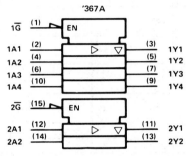

'367A

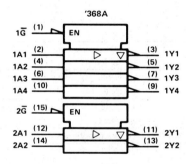

'368A

Pin numbers shown on logic notation are for D, J or N packages.

absolute maximum ratings over operating free-air temperature range (unless otherwise noted)

Supply voltage, V_CC (see Note 1) .... 7 V
Input voltage: '365A, '366A, '367A, '368A .... 5.5 V
              'LS365A, 'LS366A, 'LS367A, 'LS368A .... 7 V
Voltage applied to a disabled 3-state output .... 5.5 V
Operating free-air temperature: SN54' .... -55°C to 125°C
                  SN74' .... 0°C to 70°C
Storage temperature range .... -65°C to 150°C

NOTE 1: Voltage values are with respect to network ground terminal.

3

TTL DEVICES

recommended operating conditions

		SN54365A SN54367A			SN74365A SN74367A			UNIT
		MIN	NOM	MAX	MIN	NOM	MAX	
V_{CC}	Supply voltage	4.5	5	5.5	4.75	5	5.25	V
V_{IH}	High-level input voltage	2			2			V
V_{IL}	Low-level input voltage			0.8			0.8	V
I_{OH}	High-level output current			−2			−5.2	mA
I_{OL}	Low-level output current			32			32	mA
T_A	Operating free-air temperature	−55		125	0		70	°C

electrical characteristics over recommended operating free-air temperature range (unless otherwise noted)

PARAMETER		TEST CONDITIONS†			SN54365A SN54367A			SN74365A SN74367A			UNIT
					MIN	TYP‡	MAX	MIN	TYP‡	MAX	
V_{IK}		V_{CC} = MIN,	I_I = −12 mA				−1.5			−1.5	V
V_{OH}		V_{CC} = MIN, I_{OH} = MAX	V_{IH} = 2 V,	V_{IL} = 0.8 V,	2.4	3.3		2.4	3.1		V
V_{OL}		V_{CC} = MIN, I_{OL} = 32 mA	V_{IH} = 2 V,	V_{IL} = 0.8 V,			0.4			0.4	V
I_{OZ}		V_{CC} = MAX, V_O = 2.4 V	V_{IH} = 2 V,	V_{IL} = 0.8 V,			40			40	μA
		V_{CC} = MAX, V_O = 0.4 V	V_{IH} = 2 V	V_{IL} = 0.8 V,			−40			−40	
I_I		V_{CC} = MAX,	V_I = 5.5 V				1			1	mA
I_{IH}		V_{CC} = MAX,	V_I = 2.4 V				40			40	μA
I_{IL}	A Inputs	V_{CC} = MAX,	V_I = 0.5 V,	Either $\overline{G}$ input at 2 V			−40			−40	μA
		V_{CC} = MAX,	V_I = 0.4 V,	Both $\overline{G}$ inputs at 0.4 V			−1.6			−1.6	mA
	$\overline{G}$ Inputs	V_{CC} = MAX,	V_I = 0.4 V				−1.6			−1.6	
I_{OS}§		V_{CC} = MAX			−40		−130	−40		−130	mA
I_{CC}		V_{CC} = MAX,	Data inputs = 0 V,	Output controls = 4.5 V		65	85		65	85	mA

† For conditions shown as MIN or MAX, use the appropriate value specified under recommended operating conditions.
‡ All typical values are at V_{CC} = 5 V, T_A = 25°C.
§ Not more than one output should be shorted at a time.

switching characteristics, V_{CC} = 5 V, T_A = 25°C (see note 2)

PARAMETER	FROM (INPUT)	TO (OUTPUT)	TEST CONDITIONS		MIN	TYP	MAX	UNIT
t_{PLH}	Any	Y	R_L = 400 Ω,	C_L = 50 pF			16	ns
t_{PHL}							22	ns
t_{PZH}							35	ns
t_{PZL}							37	ns
t_{PHZ}			R_L = 400 Ω,	C_L = 5 pF			11	ns
t_{PLZ}							27	ns

NOTE 2: See General Information Section for load circuits and voltage waveforms.

TEXAS
INSTRUMENTS

recommended operating conditions

		SN54366A SN54368A			SN74366A SN74368A			UNIT
		MIN	NOM	MAX	MIN	NOM	MAX	
V_{CC}	Supply voltage	4.5	5	5.5	4.75	5	5.25	V
V_{IH}	High-level input voltage	2			2			V
V_{IL}	Low-level input voltage			0.8			0.8	V
I_{OH}	High-level output current			−2			−5.2	mA
I_{OL}	Low-level output current			32			32	mA
T_A	Operating free-air temperature	−55		125	0		70	°C

electrical characteristics over recommended operating free-air temperature range (unless otherwise noted)

PARAMETER		TEST CONDITIONS†			SN54366A SN54368A			SN74366A SN74368A			UNIT
					MIN	TYP‡	MAX	MIN	TYP‡	MAX	
V_{IK}		V_{CC} = MIN,	I_I = −12 mA				−1.5			−1.5	V
V_{OH}		V_{CC} = MIN,	V_{IH} = 2 V,	V_{IL} = 0.8 V,	2.4	3.3		2.4	3.1		V
		I_{OH} = MAX									
V_{OL}		V_{CC} = MIN,	V_{IH} = 2 V,	V_{IL} = 0.8 V,			0.4			0.4	V
		I_{OL} = 32 mA									
I_{OZ}		V_{CC} = MAX,	V_{IH} = 2 V,	V_{IL} = 0.8 V,			40			40	µA
		V_O = 2.4 V									
		V_{CC} = MAX,	V_{IH} = 2 V	V_{IL} = 0.8 V,			−40			−40	
		V_O = 0.4 V									
I_I		V_{CC} = MAX,	V_I = 5.5 V				1			1	mA
I_{IH}		V_{CC} = MAX,	V_I = 2.4 V				40			40	µA
I_{IL}	A Inputs	V_{CC} = MAX,	V_I = 0.5 V,	Either $\overline{G}$ input at 2 V			−40			−40	µA
		V_{CC} = MAX,	V_I = 0.4 V,	Both $\overline{G}$ inputs at 0.4 V			−1.6			−1.6	mA
	$\overline{G}$ Inputs	V_{CC} = MAX,	V_I = 0.4 V				−1.6			−1.6	
I_{OS}§		V_{CC} = MAX			−40		−130	−40		−130	mA
I_{CC}		V_{CC} = MAX,	Data inputs = 0 V,	Output controls = 4.5 V,		59	77		59	77	mA

† For conditions shown as MIN or MAX, use the appropriate value specified under recommended operating conditions.
‡ All typical values are at V_{CC} = 5 V, T_A = 25°C.
§ Not more than one output should be shorted at a time.

switching characteristics, V_{CC} = 5 V, T_A = 25°C (see note 2)

PARAMETER	FROM (INPUT)	TO (OUTPUT)	TEST CONDITIONS		MIN	TYP	MAX	UNIT
t_{PLH}	Any	Y	R_L = 400 Ω,	C_L = 50 pF			17	ns
t_{PHL}							16	ns
t_{PZH}							35	ns
t_{PZL}							37	ns
t_{PHZ}			R_L = 400 Ω,	C_L = 5 pF			11	ns
t_{PLZ}							27	ns

NOTE 2: See General Information Section for load circuits and voltage waveforms.

TEXAS
INSTRUMENTS

3-839

TTL DEVICES

3

recommended operating conditions

		SN54LS365A SN54LS367A			SN74LS365A SN74LS367A			UNIT
		MIN	NOM	MAX	MIN	NOM	MAX	
V_{CC}	Supply voltage	4.5	5	5.5	4.75	5	5.25	V
V_{IH}	High-level input voltage	2			2			V
V_{IL}	Low-level input voltage			0.7			0.8	V
I_{OH}	High-level output current			− 1			− 2.6	mA
I_{OL}	Low-level output current			12			24	mA
T_A	Operating free-air temperature	− 55		125	0		70	°C

electrical characteristics over recommended operating free-air temperature range (unless otherwise noted)

PARAMETER		TEST CONDITIONS†			SN54LS365A SN54LS367A			SN74LS365A SN74LS367A			UNIT
					MIN	TYP‡	MAX	MIN	TYP‡	MAX	
V_{IK}		V_{CC} = MIN,	I_I = − 18 mA				− 1.5			− 1.5	V
V_{OH}		V_{CC} = MIN, I_{OH} = MAX	V_{IH} = 2 V,	V_{IL} = MAX,	2.4	3.3		2.4	3.1		V
V_{OL}		V_{CC} = MIN, I_{OL} = 12 mA	V_{IH} = 2 V,	V_{IL} = MAX,		0.25	0.4		0.25	0.4	V
		V_{CC} = MIN, I_{OL} = 24 mA	V_{IH} = 2 V,	V_{IL} = 0.8 V,					0.35	0.5	
I_{OZ}		V_{CC} = MAX, V_O = 2.4 V	V_{IH} = 2 V,	V_{IL} = MAX,			20			20	μA
		V_{CC} = MAX, V_O = 0.4 V	V_{IH} = 2 V,	V_{IL} = MAX,			− 20			− 20	
I_I		V_{CC} = MAX,	V_I = 7 V				0.1			0.1	mA
I_{IH}		V_{CC} = MAX,	V_I = 2.7 V				20			20	μA
I_{IL}	A Inputs	V_{CC} = MAX,	V_I = 0.5 V,	Either $\overline{G}$ input at 2 V			− 20			− 20	μA
		V_{CC} = MAX,	V_I = 0.4 V,	Both $\overline{G}$ inputs at 0.4 V			− 0.4			− 0.4	mA
	$\overline{G}$ Inputs	V_{CC} = MAX,	V_I = 0.4 V				− 0.2			− 0.2	
I_{OS}§		V_{CC} = MAX			− 40		− 225	− 40		− 225	mA
I_{CC}		V_{CC} = MAX,	Data inputs = 0 V,	Output controls = 4.5 V,		14	24		14	24	mA

† For conditions shown as MIN or MAX, use the appropriate value specified under recommended operating conditions.
‡ All typical values are at V_{CC} = 5 V, T_A = 25°C.
§ Not more than one output should be shorted at a time, and the duration of the short circuit should not exceed one second.

3

TTL DEVICES

TEXAS
INSTRUMENTS

switching characteristics, V_{CC} = 5 V, T_A = 25°C (see note 2)

PARAMETER	FROM (INPUT)	TO (OUTPUT)	TEST CONDITIONS		MIN	TYP	MAX	UNIT
t_{PLH}	Any	Y	R_L = 667 Ω,	C_L = 45 pF		10	16	ns
t_{PHL}						9	22	ns
t_{PZH}						19	35	ns
t_{PZL}						24	40	ns
t_{PHZ}			R_L = 667 Ω,	C_L = 5 pF			30	ns
t_{PLZ}							35	ns

NOTE 2: See General Information Section for load circuits and voltage waveforms.

3

TTL DEVICES

TEXAS
INSTRUMENTS

TYPES SN54LS366A, SN54LS368A
SN74LS366A, SN74LS368A
HEX BUS DRIVERS WITH 3-STATE OUTPUTS

recommended operating conditions

		SN74LS366A SN74LS368A			SN54LS366A SN54LS368A			UNIT
		MIN	NOM	MAX	MIN	NOM	MAX	
V_{CC}	Supply voltage	4.5	5	5.5	4.75	5	5.25	V
V_{IH}	High-level input voltage	2			2			V
V_{IL}	Low-level input voltage			0.7			0.8	V
I_{OH}	High-level output current			−1			−2.6	mA
I_{OL}	Low-level output current			12			24	mA
T_A	Operating free-air temperature	−55		125	0		70	°C

electrical characteristics over recommended operating free-air temperature range (unless otherwise noted)

PARAMETER		TEST CONDITIONS†			SN54LS366A SN54LS368A			SN74LS366A SN74LS368A			UNIT
					MIN	TYP‡	MAX	MIN	TYP‡	MAX	
V_{IK}		V_{CC} = MIN,	I_I = −18 mA				−1.5			−1.5	V
V_{OH}		V_{CC} = MIN,	V_{IH} = 2 V,	V_{IL} = MAX,	2.4	3.3		2.4	3.1		V
		I_{OH} = MAX									
V_{OL}		V_{CC} = MIN,	V_{IH} = 2 V,	V_{IL} = MAX,		0.25	0.4		0.25	0.4	V
		I_{OL} = 12 mA									
		V_{CC} = MIN,	V_{IH} = 2 V,	V_{IL} = 0.8 V,					0.35	0.5	
		I_{OL} = 24 mA									
I_{OZ}		V_{CC} = MAX,	V_{IH} = 2 V,	V_{IL} = MAX,			20			20	μA
		V_O = 2.4 V									
		V_{CC} = MAX,	V_{IH} = 2 V,	V_{IL} = MAX,			−20			−20	
		V_O = 0.4 V									
I_I		V_{CC} = MAX,	V_I = 7 V				0.1			0.1	mA
I_{IH}		V_{CC} = MAX,	V_I = 2.7 V				20			20	μA
I_{IL}	A Inputs	V_{CC} = MAX,	V_I = 0.5 V,	Either $\overline{G}$ input at 2 V			−20			−20	μA
		V_{CC} = MAX,	V_I = 0.4 V,	Both $\overline{G}$ inputs at 0.4 V			−0.4			−0.4	mA
	$\overline{G}$ Inputs	V_{CC} = MAX,	V_I = 0.4 V				−0.2			−0.2	
I_{OS}§		V_{CC} = MAX			−40		−225	−40		−225	mA
I_{CC}		V_{CC} = MAX,	Data inputs = 0 V,	Output controls = 4.5 V,		12	21		12	21	mA

† For conditions shown as MIN or MAX, use the appropriate value specified under recommended operating conditions.
‡ All typical values are at V_{CC} = 5 V, T_A = 25°C.
§ Not more than one output should be shorted at a time, and the duration of the short circuit should not exceed one second.

TEXAS
INSTRUMENTS

3

TTL DEVICES

switching characteristics, V_{CC} = 5 V, T_A = 25°C (see note 2)

PARAMETER	FROM (INPUT)	TO (OUTPUT)	TEST CONDITIONS		MIN	TYP	MAX	UNIT
t_{PLH}						7	15	ns
t_{PHL}			R_L = 667 Ω,	C_L = 45 pF		12	18	ns
t_{PZH}	Any	Y				18	35	ns
t_{PZL}						28	45	ns
t_{PHZ}			R_L = 667 Ω,	C_L = 5 pF			32	ns
t_{PLZ}							35	ns

NOTE 2: See General Information Section for load circuits and voltage waveforms.

3

TTL DEVICES

TYPES SN54LS373, SN54LS374, SN54S373, SN54S374, SN74LS373, SN74LS374, SN74S373, SN74S374
OCTAL D-TYPE TRANSPARENT LATCHES AND EDGE-TRIGGERED FLIP-FLOPS

OCTOBER 1975 – REVISED APRIL 1985

- **Choice of 8 Latches or 8 D-Type Flip-Flops In a Single Package**
- **3-State Bus-Driving Outputs**
- **Full Parallel-Access for Loading**
- **Buffered Control Inputs**
- **Clock/Enable Input Has Hysteresis to Improve Noise Rejection ('S373 and 'S374)**
- **P-N-P Inputs Reduce D-C Loading on Data Lines ('S373 and 'S374)**

'LS373, 'S373 FUNCTION TABLE

OUTPUT ENABLE	ENABLE LATCH	D	OUTPUT
L	H	H	H
L	H	L	L
L	L	X	Q_0
H	X	X	Z

'LS374, 'S374 FUNCTION TABLE

OUTPUT ENABLE	CLOCK	D	OUTPUT
L	↑	H	H
L	↑	L	L
L	L	X	Q_0
H	X	X	Z

description

These 8-bit registers feature three-state outputs designed specifically for driving highly-capacitive or relatively low-impedance loads. The high-impedance third state and increased high-logic-level drive provide these registers with the capability of being connected directly to and driving the bus lines in a bus-organized system without need for interface or pull-up components. They are particularly attractive for implementing buffer registers, I/O ports, bidirectional bus drivers, and working registers.

The eight latches of the 'LS373 and 'S373 are transparent D-type latches meaning that while the enable (C) is high the Q outputs will follow the data (D) inputs. When the enable is taken low the output will be latched at the level of the data that was set up.

SN54LS373, SN54LS374, SN54S373, SN54S374 . . . J PACKAGE
SN74LS373, SN74LS374, SN74S373, SN74S374 . . . DW, J OR N PACKAGE

(TOP VIEW)

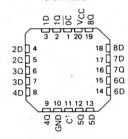

```
    0C  [ 1    U  20 ]  VCC
    1Q  [ 2       19 ]  8Q
    1D  [ 3       18 ]  8D
    2D  [ 4       17 ]  7D
    2Q  [ 5       16 ]  7Q
    3Q  [ 6       15 ]  6Q
    3D  [ 7       14 ]  6D
    4D  [ 8       13 ]  5D
    4Q  [ 9       12 ]  5Q
   GND  [ 10      11 ]  C†
```

SN54LS373, SN54LS374, SN54S373, SN54S374, SN74LS373, SN74LS374, SN74S373, SN74S374 . . . FK PACKAGE

(TOP VIEW)

```
         1D 1Q 0C VCC 8Q
          3  2  1  20 19
    2D [ 4              18 ] 8D
    2Q [ 5              17 ] 7D
    3Q [ 6              16 ] 7Q
    3D [ 7              15 ] 6Q
    4D [ 8              14 ] 6D
          9  10 11 12 13
         4Q GND C† 5Q 5D
```

†C for 'LS373 and 'S373; CLK for 'LS374 and 'S374.

3

TTL DEVICES

TEXAS INSTRUMENTS

TYPES SN54LS373, SN54LS374, SN54S373, SN54S374, SN74LS373, SN74LS374, SN74S373, SN74S374
OCTAL D-TYPE TRANSPARENT LATCHES AND EDGE-TRIGGERED FLIP-FLOPS

description (continued)

The eight flip-flops of the 'LS374 and 'S374 are edge-triggered D-type flip-flops. On the positive transition of the clock, the Q outputs will be set to the logic states that were setup at the D inputs.

Schmitt-trigger buffered inputs at the enable/clock lines of the 'S373 and 'S374 devices, simplify system design as ac and dc noise rejection is improved by typically 400 mV due to the input hysteresis. A buffered output control input can be used to place the eight outputs in either a normal logic state (high or low logic levels) or a high-impedance state. In the high-impedance state the outputs neither load nor drive the bus lines significantly.

The output control does not affect the internal operation of the latches or flip-flops. That is, the old data can be retained or new data can be entered even while the outputs are off.

logic diagrams

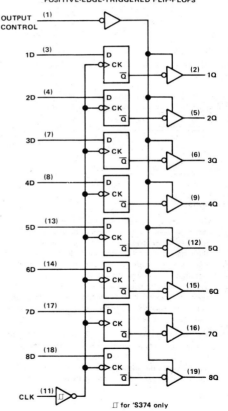

'LS373, 'S373
TRANSPARENT LATCHES

'LS374, 'S374
POSITIVE-EDGE-TRIGGERED FLIP-FLOPS

□ for 'S373 only

□ for 'S374 only

Pin numbers shown on logic notation are for DW, J or N packages.

TEXAS
INSTRUMENTS

schematic of inputs and outputs

'LS373

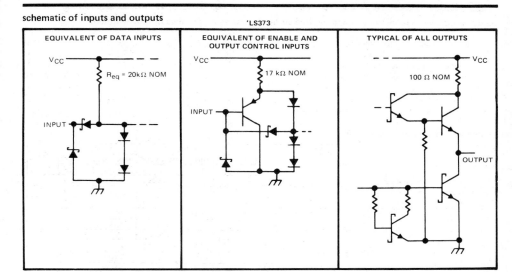

'LS374

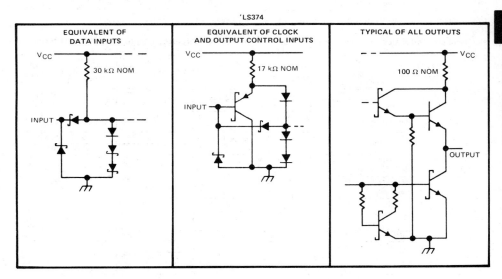

3

TTL DEVICES

absolute maximum ratings over operating free-air temperature range (unless otherwise noted)

Supply voltage, V_{CC} (see Note 1)	7 V
Input voltage	7 V
Off-state output voltage	5.5 V
Operating free-air temperature range: SN54LS'	-55°C to 125°C
SN74LS'	0°C to 70°C
Storage temperature range	-65°C to 150°C

NOTE 1: Voltage values are with respect to network ground terminal.

recommended operating conditions

			SN54LS'			SN74LS'			UNIT
			MIN	NOM	MAX	MIN	NOM	MAX	
V_{CC}	Supply voltage		4.5	5	5.5	4.75	5	5.25	V
V_{OH}	High-level output voltage				5.5			5.5	V
I_{OH}	High-level output current				-1			-2.6	mA
I_{OL}	Low-level output current				12			24	mA
t_w	Pulse duration	CLK high	15			15			ns
		CLK low	15			15			
t_{su}	Data setup time	'LS373	5↓			5↓			ns
		'LS374	20↑			20↑			
t_h	Data hold time	'LS373	20↓			20↓			ns
		'LS374 †	0↑			0↑			
T_A	Operating free-air temperature		-55		125	0		70	$^\circ$C

† The t_h specification applies only for data frequency below 10 MHz. Designs above 10 MHz should use a minimum of 5 ns.

electrical characteristics over recommended operating free-air temperature range (unless otherwise noted)

PARAMETER		TEST CONDITIONS†		SN54LS'			SN74LS'			UNIT
				MIN	TYP‡	MAX	MIN	TYP‡	MAX	
V_{IH}	High-level input voltage			2			2			V
V_{IL}	Low-level input voltage					0.7			0.8	V
V_{IK}	Input clamp voltage	V_{CC} = MIN, I_I = -18 mA				-1.5			-1.5	V
V_{OH}	High-level output voltage	V_{CC} = MIN, V_{IH} = 2 V, V_{IL} = V_{IL}max, I_{OH} = MAX		2.4	3.4		2.4	3.1		V
V_{OL}	Low-level output voltage	V_{CC} = MIN, V_{IH} = 2 V, V_{IL} = V_{IL}max	I_{OL} = 12 mA		0.25	0.4		0.25	0.4	V
			I_{OL} = 24 mA					0.35	0.5	
I_{OZH}	Off-state output current, high-level voltage applied	V_{CC} = MAX, V_{IH} = 2 V, V_O = 2.7 V				20			20	μA
I_{OZL}	Off-state output current, low-level voltage applied	V_{CC} = MAX, V_{IH} = 2 V, V_O = 0.4 V				-20			-20	μA
I_I	Input current at maximum input voltage	V_{CC} = MAX, V_I = 7 V				0.1			0.1	mA
I_{IH}	High-level input current	V_{CC} = MAX, V_I = 2.7 V				20			20	μA
I_{IL}	Low-level input current	V_{CC} = MAX, V_I = 0.4 V				-0.4			-0.4	mA
I_{OS}	Short-circuit output current §	V_{CC} = MAX		-30		-130	-30		-130	mA
I_{CC}	Supply current	V_{CC} = MAX, Output control at 4.5 V	'LS373		24	40		24	40	mA
			'LS374		27	40		27	40	

† For conditions shown as MIN or MAX, use the appropriate value specified under recommended operating conditions.
‡ All typical values are at V_{CC} = 5 V, T_A = 25°C.
§ Not more than one output should be shorted at a time and duration of the short circuit should not exceed one second.

Texas Instruments

3

TTL DEVICES

switching characteristics, V_{CC} = 5 V, T_A = 25°C

PARAMETER	FROM (INPUT)	TO (OUTPUT)	TEST CONDITIONS		'LS373 MIN	'LS373 TYP	'LS373 MAX	'LS374 MIN	'LS374 TYP	'LS374 MAX	UNIT
f_{max}								35	50		MHz
t_{PLH}	Data	Any Q	C_L = 45 pF, R_L = 667 Ω See Notes 2 and 3			12	18				ns
t_{PHL}						12	18				
t_{PLH}	Clock or enable	Any Q				20	30		15	28	ns
t_{PHL}						18	30		19	28	
t_{PZH}	Output Control	Any Q				15	28		20	26	ns
t_{PZL}						25	36		21	28	
t_{PHZ}	Output Control	Any Q	C_L = 5 pF, R_L = 667 Ω See Note 3	SN54		28	32		28	32	ns
				SN74		15	25		15	28	
t_{PLZ}	Output Control	Any Q				12	20		12	20	ns

NOTES: 2. Maximum clock frequency is tested with all outputs loaded.
3. See General Information Section for load circuits and voltage waveforms.

f_{max} ≡ maximum clock frequency
t_{PLH} ≡ propagation delay time, low-to-high-level output
t_{PHL} ≡ propagation delay time, high-to-low-level output
t_{PZH} ≡ output enable time to high level
t_{PZL} ≡ output enable time to low level
t_{PHZ} ≡ output disable time from high level
t_{PLZ} ≡ output disable time from low level

3

TTL DEVICES

TEXAS
INSTRUMENTS

TYPES SN54S373, SN54S374, SN74S373, SN74S374
OCTAL D-TYPE TRANSPARENT LATCHES AND
EDGE-TRIGGERED FLIP-FLOPS

schematic of inputs and outputs

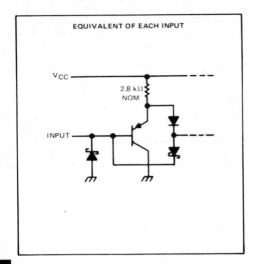

EQUIVALENT OF EACH INPUT

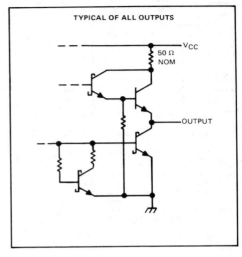

TYPICAL OF ALL OUTPUTS

absolute maximum ratings over operating free-air temperature range (unless otherwise noted)

Supply voltage, V_{CC} (see Note 1) . . . . 7 V
Input voltage . . . . 5.5 V
Off-state output voltage . . . . 5.5 V
Operating free-air temperature range: SN54S' . . . . $-55°C$ to $125°C$
SN74S' . . . . $0°C$ to $70°C$
Storage temperature range . . . . $-65°C$ to $150°C$

NOTE 1: Voltage values are with respect to network ground terminal.

recommended operating conditions

		SN54S'			SN74S'			UNIT
		MIN	NOM	MAX	MIN	NOM	MAX	
Supply voltage, V_{CC}		4.5	5	5.5	4.75	5	5.25	V
High-level output voltage, V_{OH}				5.5			5.5	V
High-level output current, I_{OH}				−2			−6.5	mA
Width of clock/enable pulse, t_w	High	6			6			ns
	Low	7.3			7.3			
Data setup time, t_{su}	'S373	0↓			0↓			ns
	'S374	5↑			5↑			
Data hold time, t_h	'S373	10↓			10↓			ns
	'S374	2↑			2↑ ·			
Operating free-air temperature, T_A		−55		125	0		70	°C

TEXAS
INSTRUMENTS

electrical characteristics over recommended operating free-air temperature range (unless otherwise noted)

PARAMETER		TEST CONDITIONS[†]				MIN	TYP[‡]	MAX	UNIT
V_{IH}						2			V
V_{IL}								0.8	V
V_{IK}		V_{CC} = MIN,	I_I = −18 mA					−1.2	V
V_{OH}	SN54S'	V_{CC} = MIN,	V_{IH} = 2 V,	V_{IL} = 0.8 V,	I_{OH} = MAX	2.4	3.4		V
	SN74S'					2.4	3.1		
V_{OL}		V_{CC} = MIN,	V_{IH} = 2 V,	V_{IL} = 0.8 V,	I_{OL} = 20 mA			0.5	V
I_{OZH}		V_{CC} = MAX,	V_{IH} = 2 V,	V_O = 2.4 V				50	μA
I_{OZL}		V_{CC} = MAX,	V_{IH} = 2 V,	V_O = 0.5 V				−50	μA
I_I		V_{CC} = MAX,	V_I = 5.5 V					1	mA
I_{IH}		V_{CC} = MAX,	V_I = 2.7 V					50	μA
I_{IL}		V_{CC} = MAX,	V_I = 0.5 V					−250	μA
I_{OS} §		V_{CC} = MAX				−40		−100	mA
I_{CC}		V_{CC} = MAX	'S373	outputs high				160	mA
				outputs low				160	
				outputs disabled				190	
			'S374	outputs high				110	
				outputs low				140	
				outputs disabled				160	

† For conditions shown as MIN or MAX, use the appropriate value specified under recommended operating conditions.
‡ All typical values are at V_{CC} = 5 V, T_A = 25°C.
§ Not more than one output should be shorted at a time and duration of the short-circuit should not exceed one second.

switching characteristics, V_{CC} = 5 V, T_A = 25°C

PARAMETER	FROM (INPUT)	TO (OUTPUT)	TEST CONDITIONS	'S373 MIN	'S373 TYP	'S373 MAX	'S374 MIN	'S374 TYP	'S374 MAX	UNIT
f_{max}							75	100		MHz
t_{PLH}	Data	Any Q	C_L = 15 pF, R_L = 280 Ω, See Notes 2 and 4		7	12				ns
t_{PHL}					7	12				
t_{PLH}	Clock or enable	Any Q			7	14		8	15	ns
t_{PHL}					12	18		11	17	
t_{PZH}	Output Control	Any Q			8	15		8	15	ns
t_{PZL}					11	18		11	18	
t_{PHZ}	Output Control	Any Q	C_L = 5 pF, R_L = 280 Ω, See Note 3		6	9		5	9	ns
t_{PLZ}					8	12		7	12	

NOTES: 2. Maximum clock frequency is tested with all outputs loaded.
        4. See General Information Section for load circuits and voltage waveforms.

f_{max} ≡ maximum clock frequency
t_{PLH} ≡ propagation delay time, low-to-high-level output
t_{PHL} ≡ propagation delay time, high-to-low-level output
t_{PZH} ≡ output enable time to high level
t_{PZL} ≡ output enable time to low level
t_{PHZ} ≡ output disable time from high level
t_{PLZ} ≡ output disable time from low level

3

TTL DEVICES

TEXAS
INSTRUMENTS

TYPES SN54LS373, SN54LS374, SN54S373, SN54S374, SN74LS373, SN74LS374, SN74S373, SN74S374
OCTAL D-TYPE TRANSPARENT LATCHES AND EDGE-TRIGGERED FLIP-FLOPS

TYPICAL APPLICATION DATA

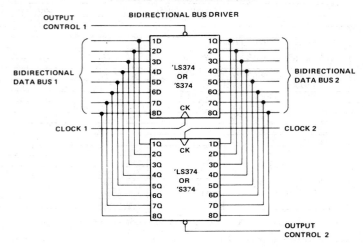

CLOCK CIRCUIT FOR BUS EXCHANGE

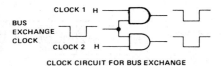

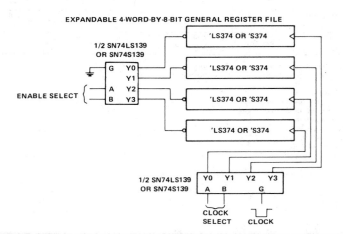

TEXAS
INSTRUMENTS

- **Supply Voltage and Ground on Corner Pins To Simplify P-C Board Layout**

logic

FUNCTION TABLE
(EACH LATCH)

INPUTS		OUTPUTS	
D	G	Q	$\overline{Q}$
L	H	L	H
H	H	H	L
X	L	Q_0	$\overline{Q_0}$

H = high level, L = low level, X = irrelevant
Q_0 = the level of Q before the high-to-low transition of C.

logic diagram (each latch)

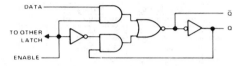

description

The SN54LS375 and SN74LS375 bistable latches are electrically and functionally identical to the SN54LS75 and SN74LS75, respectively. Only the arrangement of the terminals has been changed in the SN54LS375 and SN74LS375.

These latches are ideally suited for use as temporary storage for binary information between processing units and input/output or indicator units. Information present at a data (D) input is transferred to the Q output when the enable (C) is high and the Q output will follow the data input as long as the enable remains high. When the enable goes low, the information (that was present at the data input at the time the transition occurred) is retained at the Q output until the enable goes high.

These circuits are completely compatible with all popular TTL or DTL families. All inputs are diode-clamped to minimize transmission-line effects and simplify system design. The SN54LS375 is characterized for operation over the full military temperature range of −55°C to 125°C; SN74LS375 is characterized for operation from 0°C to 70°C.

SN54LS375 . . . J OR W PACKAGE
SN74LS375 . . . D, J OR N PACKAGE
(TOP VIEW)

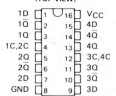

SN54LS375 . . . FK PACKAGE
SN74LS375
(TOP VIEW)

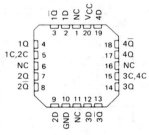

NC - No internal connection

schematics of inputs and outputs

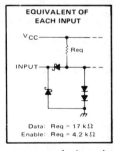

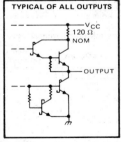

absolute maximum ratings over operating free-air temperature range (unless otherwise noted)

Supply voltage, V_{CC} (see Note 1) . . . . 7 V
Input voltage . . . . 7 V
Operating free-air temperature range: SN54LS375 . . . . −55°C to 125°C
                         SN74LS375 . . . . 0°C to 70°C
Storage temperature range . . . . −65°C to 150°C

NOTE 1: Voltage values are with respect to network ground terminal.

TEXAS INSTRUMENTS

TTL DEVICES

3

TYPES SN54LS375, SN74LS375
4-BIT BISTABLE LATCHES

recommended operating conditions

		SN54LS375			SN74LS375			UNIT
		MIN	NOM	MAX	MIN	NOM	MAX	
V_{CC}	Supply voltage	4.5	5	5.5	4.75	5	5.25	V
V_{IH}	High-level input voltage	2			2			V
V_{IL}	Low-level input voltage			0.7			0.8	V
I_{OH}	High-level output current			−0.4			−0.4	mA
I_{OL}	Low-level output current			4			8	mA
t_w	Width of enabling pulse	20			20			ns
t_{setup}	Setup time	20			20			ns
t_{hold}	Hold time	0			0			ns
T_A	Operating free-air temperature	−55		125	0		70	°C

electrical characteristics over recommended operating free-air temperature range (unless otherwise noted)

PARAMETER	TEST CONDITIONS †			SN54LS375			SN74LS375			UNIT
			MIN	TYP‡	MAX	MIN	TYP‡	MAX		
V_{IK}	V_{CC} = MIN,	I_I = −18 mA			−1.5			−1.5		V
V_{OH}	V_{CC} = MIN, V_{IH} = 2 V, V_{IL} = MAX I_{OH} = −0.4 mA		2.5	3.5		2.7	3.5			V
V_{OL}	V_{CC} = MIN, V_{IH} = 2 V, V_{IL} = MAX	I_{OL} = 4 mA		0.25	0.4		0.25			V
		I_{OL} = 8 mA					0.35	0.5		
I_I	V_{CC} = MAX, V_I = 7 V	D input			0.1			0.1		mA
		C input			0.4			0.4		
I_{IH}	V_{CC} = MAX, V_I = 2.7 V	D input			20			20		μA
		C input			80			80		
I_{IL}	V_{CC} = MAX, V_I = 0.4 V	D input			−0.4			−0.4		mA
		C input			−1.6			−1.6		
I_{OS} §	V_{CC} = MAX		−20		−100	−20		−100		mA
I_{CC}	V_{CC} = MAX, See Note 2			6.3	12		6.3	12		mA

† For conditions shown as MIN or MAX, use the appropriate value specified under recommended operating conditions.
‡ All typical values are at V_{CC} = 5 V, T_A = 25°C.
§ Not more than one output should be shorted at a time.
 NOTE 2: I_{CC} is tested with all inputs grounded and all outputs open.

switching characteristics, V_{CC} = 5 V, T_A = 25°C (see note 3)

PARAMETER◇	FROM (INPUT)	TO (OUTPUT)	TEST CONDITIONS	MIN	TYP	MAX	UNIT
t_{PLH}	D	Q			15	27	ns
t_{PHL}					9	17	
t_{PLH}	D	$\overline{Q}$	R_L = 2 kΩ, C_L = 15 pF		12	20	ns
t_{PHL}					7	15	
t_{PLH}	D	Q			15	27	ns
t_{PHL}					14	25	
t_{PLH}	C	$\overline{Q}$			16	30	ns
t_{PHL}					7	15	

◇ t_{PLH} = propagation delay time, low-to-high-level output
 t_{PHL} = propagation delay time, high-to-low-level output
NOTE 3: See General Information Section for load circuits and voltage waveforms.

TEXAS
INSTRUMENTS

3

TTL DEVICES

- Four J-K̄ Flip-Flops in a Single Package . . . Can Reduce FF Package Count by 50%

- Common Positive-Edge-Triggered Clocks with Hysteresis . . . Typically 200 mV

- Fully Buffered Outputs

- Typical Clock Input Frequency . . . 45 MHz

SN54376 . . . J OR W PACKAGE
SN74376 . . . J OR N PACKAGE
(TOP VIEW)

description

These quadruple TTL J-K̄ flip-flops incorporate a number of third-generation IC features that can simplify system design and reduce flip-flop package count by as much as 50%. They feature hysteresis at the clock input, fully buffered outputs, and direct clear capability. The positive-edge-triggered SN54376 and SN74376 are directly compatible with most Series 54/74 MSI registers.

The SN54376 is characterized for operation over the full military temperature range of −55°C to 125°C; the SN74376 is characterized for operation from 0°C to 70°C.

logic symbol†

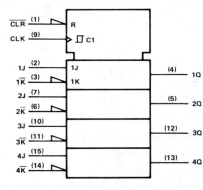

Pin numbers shown on logic notation are for J or N packages.

FUNCTION TABLE (EACH FLIP-FLOP)

COMMON INPUTS		INPUTS		OUTPUT
CLEAR	CLOCK	J	K̄	Q
L	X	X	X	L
H	↑	L	H	Q_0
H	↑	H	H	H
H	↑	L	L	L
H	↑	H	L	TOGGLE
H	L	X	X	Q_0

schematics of inputs and outputs

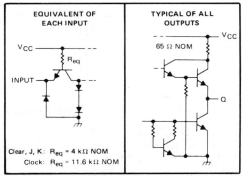

Resistor values shown are nominal.

TTL DEVICES

3

absolute maximum ratings over operating free-air temperature range (unless otherwise noted)

Supply voltage, V_{CC} (see Note 1) . . . . 7 V
Input voltage . . . . 5.5 V
Operating free-air temperature range: SN54376 . . . . $- 5.5^{\circ}$C to 125°C
SN74376 . . . . $.0^{\circ}$C to 70°C
Storage temperature range . . . . $- 65^{\circ}$C to 150°C

NOTE: Voltage values are with respect to network ground terminal.

recommended operating conditions

		SN54376			SN74376			UNIT
		MIN	NOM	MAX	MIN	NOM	MAX	
Supply voltage, V_{CC}		4.5	5	5.5	4.75	5	5.25	V
High-level output current, I_{OH}				−800			−800	µA
Low-level output current, I_{OL}				16			16	mA
Clock frequency		0		30	0		30	MHz
Pulse width, t_w	Clock high	22			22			ns
	Clock low	12			12			
	Preset or clear low	12			12			
Setup time, t_{su}	J, K inputs	0↑			0↑			ns
	Clear inactive state	10↑			10↑			
Input hold time, t_h		20↑			20↑			ns
Operating free-air temperature, T_A		55		125	0		70	°C

↑↓The arrow indicates the edge of the clock pulse used for reference: ↑ for the rising edge, ↓ for the falling edge.

electrical characteristics over recommended operating free-air temperature range (unless otherwise noted)

	PARAMETER	TEST CONDITIONS†	MIN	TYP‡	MAX	UNIT
V_{IH}	High-level input voltage		2			V
V_{IL}	Low-level input voltage				0.8	V
V_{IK}	Input clamp voltage	V_{CC} = MIN, I_I = −12 mA			−1.5	V
V_{OH}	High-level output voltage	V_{CC} = MIN, V_{IH} = 2 V, V_{IL} = 0.8 V, I_{OH} = −800 µA	2.4	3.4		V
V_{OL}	Low-level output voltage	V_{CC} = MIN, V_{IH} = 2 V, V_{IL} = 0.8 V, I_{OL} = 16 mA		0.2	0.4	V
I_I	Input current at maximum input voltage	V_{CC} = MAX, V_I = 5.5 V			1	mA
I_{IH}	High-level input current	V_{CC} = MAX, V_I = 2.4 V			40	µA
I_{IL}	Low-level input current	V_{CC} = MAX, V_I = 0.4 V			−1.6	mA
I_{OS}	Short-circuit output current§	V_{CC} = MAX	−30		−85	mA
I_{CC}	Supply current	V_{CC} = MAX		52	74	mA

†For conditions shown as MIN or MAX, use the appropriate value specified under recommended operating conditions.
‡All typical values are at V_{CC} = 5 V, T_A = 25°C.
§Not more than one output should be shorted at a time.

switching characteristics, V_{CC} = 5 V, T_A = 25°C

	PARAMETER	TEST CONDITIONS	MIN	TYP	MAX	UNIT
f_{max}	Maximum clock frequency	C_L = 15 pF, R_L = 400 Ω, See Note 2	30	45		MHz
t_{PHL}	Propagation delay time, high-to-low-level output from clear			17	30	ns
t_{PLH}	Propagation delay time, low-to-high-level output from clock			22	35	ns
t_{PHL}	Propagation delay time, high-to-low-level output from clock			24	35	ns

NOTE 2: See General Information Section for load circuits and voltage waveforms.

TEXAS
INSTRUMENTS

3

TTL DEVICES

- 'LS377 and 'LS378 Contain Eight and Six Flip-Flops, Respectively, with Single-Rail Outputs

- 'LS379 Contains Four Flip-Flops with Double-Rail Outputs

- Individual Data Input to Each Flip-Flop

- Applications Include:
  Buffer/Storage Registers
  Shift Registers
  Pattern Generators

description

These monolithic, positive-edge-triggered flip-flops utilize TTL circuitry to implement D-type flip-flop logic with an enable input. The 'LS377, 'LS378, and 'LS379 devices are similar to 'LS273, 'LS174, and 'LS175, respectively, but feature a common enable instead of a common clear.

Information at the D inputs meeting the setup time requirements is transferred to the Q outputs on the positive-going edge of the clock pulse if the enable input $\overline{G}$ is low. Clock triggering occurs at a particular voltage level and is not directly related to the transition time of the positive-going pulse. When the clock input is at either the high or low level, the D input signal has no effect at the output. The circuits are designed to prevent false clocking by transitions at the $\overline{G}$ input.

These flip-flops are guaranteed to respond to clock frequencies ranging from 0 to 30 MHz while maximum clock frequency is typically 40 megahertz. Typical power dissipation is 10 milliwatts per flip-flop.

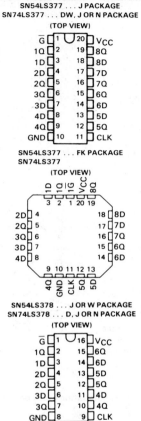

SN54LS377 . . . J PACKAGE
SN74LS377 . . . DW, J OR N PACKAGE
(TOP VIEW)

SN54LS377 . . . FK PACKAGE
SN74LS377
(TOP VIEW)

SN54LS378 . . . J OR W PACKAGE
SN74LS378 . . . D, J OR N PACKAGE
(TOP VIEW)

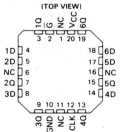

SN54LS378 . . . FK PACKAGE
SN74LS378
(TOP VIEW)

NC — No internal connection

FUNCTION TABLE
(EACH FLIP-FLOP)

INPUTS			OUTPUTS	
$\overline{G}$	CLOCK	DATA	Q	$\overline{Q}$
H	X	X	Q_0	$\overline{Q}_0$
L	↑	H	H	L
L	↑	L	L	H
X	L	X	Q_0	$\overline{Q}_0$

3

TTL DEVICES

TEXAS
INSTRUMENTS

TYPES SN54LS377, SN54LS378, SN54LS379
SN74LS377, SN74LS378, SN74LS379
OCTAL, HEX, AND QUAD D-TYPE FLIP-FLOPS WITH ENABLE

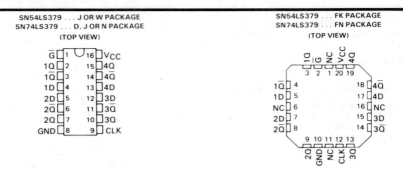

SN54LS379 . . . J OR W PACKAGE
SN74LS379 . . . D, J OR N PACKAGE
(TOP VIEW)

SN54LS379 . . . FK PACKAGE
SN74LS379 . . . FN PACKAGE
(TOP VIEW)

NC — No internal connection

logic diagram

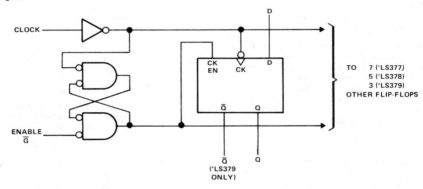

absolute maximum rating over operating free-air temperature range (unless otherwise noted)

Supply voltage, V_{CC} (see Note 1) . . . . 7 V
Input voltage . . . . 7 V
Operating free-air temperature range: SN54LS' . . . . −55°C to 125°C
SN74LS' . . . . 0°C to 70°C
Storage temperature range . . . . −65°C to 150°C

NOTE 1: Voltage values are with respect to network ground terminal.

**TEXAS
INSTRUMENTS**

schematics of inputs and outputs

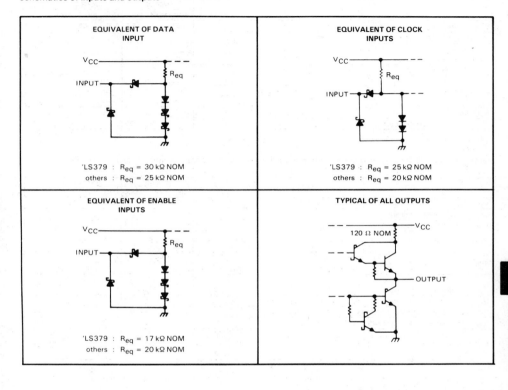

EQUIVALENT OF DATA
INPUT

'LS379 : R_{eq} = 30 kΩ NOM
others : R_{eq} = 25 kΩ NOM

EQUIVALENT OF CLOCK
INPUTS

'LS379 : R_{eq} = 25 kΩ NOM
others : R_{eq} = 20 kΩ NOM

EQUIVALENT OF ENABLE
INPUTS

'LS379 : R_{eq} = 17 kΩ NOM
others : R_{eq} = 20 kΩ NOM

TYPICAL OF ALL OUTPUTS

120 Ω NOM

3

TTL DEVICES

recommended operating conditions

		SN54LS' MIN	SN54LS' NOM	SN54LS' MAX	SN74LS' MIN	SN74LS' NOM	SN74LS' MAX	UNIT
Supply voltage, V_{CC}		4.5	5	5.5	4.75	5	5.25	V
High-level output current, I_{OH}				−400			−400	μA
Low-level output current, I_{OL}				4			8	mA
Clock frequency, f_{clock}		0		30	0		30	MHz
Width of clock pulse, t_w		20			20			ns
Setup time, t_{su}	Data input	20†			20†			ns
	Enable active-state	25†			25†			
	Enable inactive-state	10†			10†			
Hold time, t_h	Data and enable	5†			5†			ns
Operating free-air temperature, T_A		−55		125	0		70	°C

† The arrow indicates that the rising edge of the clock pulse is used for reference.

electrical characteristics over recommended operating free-air temperature range (unless otherwise noted)

PARAMETER		TEST CONDITIONS[1]		SN54LS' MIN	SN54LS' TYP‡	SN54LS' MAX	SN74LS' MIN	SN74LS' TYP‡	SN74LS' MAX	UNIT
V_{IH}	High-level input voltage			2			2			V
V_{IL}	Low-level input voltage					0.7			0.8	V
V_{IK}	Input clamp voltage	V_{CC} = MIN,	I_I = −18 mA			−1.5			−1.5	V
V_{OH}	High-level output voltage	V_{CC} = MIN, V_{IL} = V_{IL} max,	V_{IH} = 2 V, I_{OH} = −400 μA	2.5	3.5		2.7	3.5		V
V_{OL}	Low-level output voltage	V_{CC} = MIN, V_{IH} = 2 V, V_{IL} = V_{IL} max	I_{OL} = 4 mA		0.25	0.4		0.25	0.4	V
			I_{OL} = 8 mA					0.35	0.5	
I_I	Input current at maximum input voltage	V_{CC} = MAX,	V_I = 7 V			0.1			0.1	mA
I_{IH}	High-level input current	V_{CC} = MAX,	V_I = 2.7 V			20			20	μA
I_{IL}	Low-level input current	V_{CC} = MAX,	V_I = 0.4 V			−0.4			−0.4	mA
I_{OS}	Short-circuit output current§	V_{CC} = MAX		−20		−100	−20		−100	mA
I_{CC}	Supply current	V_{CC} = MAX,	See Note 2 'LS377		17	28		17	28	mA
			'LS378		13	22		13	22	mA
			'LS379		9	15		9	15	mA

† For conditions shown as MIN or MAX, use the appropriate value specified under recommended operating conditions.
‡ All typical values are at V_{CC} = 5 V, T_A = 25°C.
§ Note more than one input should be shorted at a time, and duration of the short-circuit should not exceed one second.
NOTE 2: With all outputs open and ground applied to all data and enable inputs, I_{CC} is measured after a momentary ground, then 4.5 V, is applied to clock.

switching characteristics, V_{CC} = 5 V, T_A = 25°C

PARAMETER		TEST CONDITIONS	MIN	TYP	MAX	UNIT
f_{max}	Maximum clock frequency	C_L = 15 pF,	30	40		MHz
t_{PLH}	Propagation delay time, low-to-high-level output from clock	R_L = 2 kΩ		17	27	ns
t_{PHL}	Propagation delay time, high-to-low-level output from clock	See Note 3		18	27	ns

NOTE 3: See General Information Section for load circuits and voltage waveforms.

3

TTL DEVICES

TEXAS
INSTRUMENTS

TYPES SN54LS381A, SN54LS382A, SN54S381, SN74LS381A, SN74LS382A, SN74S381
ARITHMETIC LOGIC UNITS/FUNCTION GENERATORS

D2430, JANUARY 1981 – REVISED DECEMBER 1983

PIN DESIGNATIONS

DESIGNATION	PIN NOS.	FUNCTION
A3, A2, A1, A0	17, 19, 1, 3	WORD A INPUTS
B3, B2, B1, B0	16, 18, 2, 4	WORD B INPUTS
S2, S1, S0	7, 6, 5	FUNCTION-SELECT INPUTS
C_n	15	CARRY INPUT FOR ADDITION, INVERTED CARRY INPUT FOR SUBTRACTION
F3, F2, F1, F0	12, 11, 9, 8	FUNCTION OUTPUTS
$\overline{P}$ ('LS381A 'S381 ONLY)	14	ACTIVE-LOW CARRY PROPAGATE OUTPUT
$\overline{G}$ ('LS381A 'S381 ONLY)	13	ACTIVE-LOW CARRY GENERATE OUTPUT
C_{n+4} ('LS382 ONLY)	14	RIPPLE-CARRY OUTPUT
OVR ('LS382 ONLY)	13	OVERFLOW OUTPUT
V_{CC}	20	SUPPLY VOLTAGE
GND	10	GROUND

- Fully Parallel 4-Bit ALU's in 20-Pin Package for 0.300-Inch Row Spacing
- Ideally Suited for High-Density Economical Processors
- 'LS381A and 'S381 Feature $\overline{G}$ and $\overline{P}$ Outputs for Look-Ahead Carry Cascading
- 'LS382A Features Ripple Carry ($C_n + 4$) and Overflow (OVR) Outputs
- Arithmetic and Logic Operations Selected Specifically to Simplify System Implementation:
  A Minus B
  B Minus A
  A Plus B
  and Five Other Functions

SN54LS381A, SN54S381
. . . J PACKAGE
SN74LS381A, SN74S381
. . . DW, J OR N PACKAGE
(TOP VIEW)

SN54LS381A, SN54S381
SN74LS381A, SN74S381
. . . FK PACKAGE
(TOP VIEW)

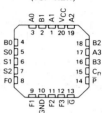

SN54LS382A . . . J PACKAGE
SN74LS382A
DW, J OR N PACKAGE
(TOP VIEW)

SN54LS382A . . . FK PACKAGE
SN74LS382A
(TOP VIEW)

FUNCTION TABLE

SELECTION			ARITHMETIC/LOGIC
S2	S1	S0	OPERATION
L	L	L	CLEAR
L	L	H	B MINUS A
L	H	L	A MINUS B
L	H	H	A PLUS B
H	L	L	A $\oplus$ B
H	L	H	A + B
H	H	L	AB
H	H	H	PRESET

H = high level, L = low level

description

The 'LS381A, 'S381 and 'LS382A are low-power Schottky and Schottky TTL arithmetic logic units (ALUs)/function generators that perform eight binary arithmetic/logic operations on two 4-bit words as shown in the function table. The exclusive-OR, AND, or OR function of the two Boolean variables is provided without the use of external circuitry. Also, the outputs can be cleared (low) or preset (high) as desired. The 'LS381A and 'S381 provide two cascade outputs ($\overline{P}$ and $\overline{G}$) for expansion utilizing SN54S182/SN74S182 look-ahead carry generators. The 'LS382A provides a $C_n + 4$ output to ripple the carry to the C_n input of the next stage. The 'LS382A detects and indicates two's complement overflow condition via the OVR output. The overflow output is logically equivalent to $C_{n+3} \oplus C_{n+4}$. When the 'LS382A is cascaded to handle word lengths longer than four bits in length, only the most significant overflow (OVR) output is used.

The SN54' Family is characterized for operation over the full military temperature range of $-55°C$ to $125°C$. The SN74' family is characterized for operation from $0°C$ to $70°C$.

TEXAS
INSTRUMENTS

3

TTL DEVICES

TYPES SN54LS381A, SN54LS382A, SN54S381, SN74LS381A, SN74LS382A, SN74S381
ARITHMETIC LOGIC UNITS/FUNCTION GENERATORS

function table

Certain differences exist in the $\overline{G}$, $\overline{P}$ ('LS381A, 'S381) and OVR, C_{n+4} ('LS382A) function table compared with similar parts from other vendors. No differences exist in the arithmetic modes (B minus A, A minus B, and A plus B), where these outputs perform valuable cascade functions.

There are slight differences in the other modes (CLEAR, A + B, A $\oplus$ B, AB, and PRESET), where these outputs are strictly "don't care".

This function table is a condensed version and assumes for A_n that A0, A1, A2, and A3 inputs all agree and for B_n that B0, B1, B2, and B3 inputs all agree. This table is intended to point out the response of these $\overline{G}$, $\overline{P}$ ('LS381A, 'S381) and OVR, C_{n+4} ('LS382A) outputs in all modes of operation to facilitate incoming inspection.

FUNCTION TABLE

ARITHMETIC/LOGIC OPERATION	INPUTS						OUTPUTS				$\overline{G}$	$\overline{P}$
	S2	S1	S0	C_n	A_n	B_n	F3	F2	F1	F0		
CLEAR	L	L	L	X	X	X	L	L	L	L	L	L
B MINUS A	L	L	H	L	L	L	H	H	H	H	H	L
				L	L	H	H	H	H	L	L	L
				L	H	L	L	L	L	L	H	H
				L	H	H	H	H	H	H	H	L
				H	L	L	L	L	L	L	H	L
				H	L	H	H	H	H	H	L	L
				H	H	L	L	L	L	H	H	H
				H	H	H	L	L	L	L	H	L
A MINUS B	L	H	L	L	L	L	H	H	H	H	H	L
				L	L	H	L	L	L	L	H	H
				L	H	L	H	H	H	L	L	L
				L	H	H	H	H	H	H	H	L
				H	L	L	L	L	L	L	H	L
				H	L	H	L	L	L	H	H	H
				H	H	L	H	H	H	H	L	L
				H	H	H	L	L	L	L	H	L
A PLUS B	L	H	H	L	L	L	L	L	L	L	H	H
				L	L	H	H	H	H	H	H	L
				L	H	L	H	H	H	H	H	L
				L	H	H	H	H	H	L	L	L
				H	L	L	L	L	L	L	H	H
				H	L	H	L	L	L	L	H	L
				H	H	L	L	L	L	L	H	L
				H	H	H	H	H	H	H	L	L
A $\oplus$ B	H	L	L	X	L	L	L	L	L	L	H	H
				X	L	H	H	H	H	H	H	H
				X	H	L	H	H	H	H	H	L
				X	H	H	L	L	L	L	L	L
A + B	H	L	H	X	L	L	L	L	L	L	H	H
				X	L	H	H	H	H	H	H	H
				X	H	L	H	H	H	H	H	H
				X	H	H	H	H	H	H	H	L
AB	H	H	L	X	L	L	L	L	L	L	L	L
				X	L	H	L	L	L	L	H	H
				X	H	L	L	L	L	L	L	L
				X	H	H	H	H	H	H	H	L
PRESET	H	H	H	X	L	L	H	H	H	H	H	H
				X	L	H	H	H	H	H	H	H
				X	H	L	H	H	H	H	H	H
				X	H	H	H	H	H	H	H	L

TEXAS INSTRUMENTS

logic diagram (positive logic)   'LS381A, 'LS382A

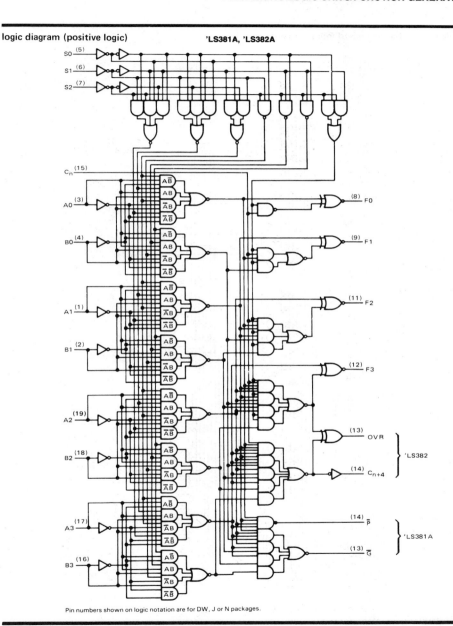

Pin numbers shown on logic notation are for DW, J or N packages.

TEXAS INSTRUMENTS

TTL DEVICES

3

logic diagram and schematics of inputs and outputs

'S381

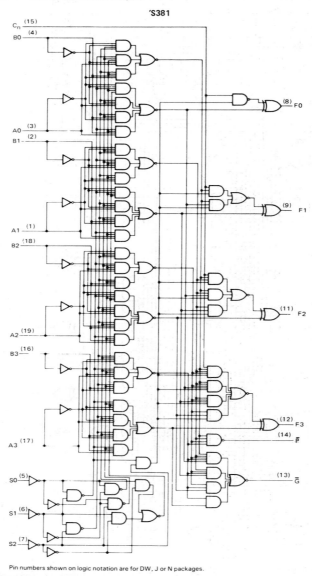

Pin numbers shown on logic notation are for DW, J or N packages.

TEXAS
INSTRUMENTS

TYPES SN54LS381A, SN54LS382A, SN54S381, SN74LS381A, SN74LS382A, SN74S381
ARITHMETIC LOGIC UNITS/FUNCTION GENERATORS

logic symbols

'LS381A, 'S381

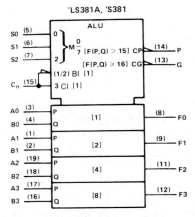

'LS382A

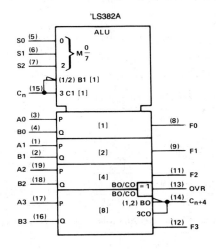

Pin numbers shown on logic notation are for DW, J or N packages.

schematics of inputs and outputs

'LS381, 'LS382A

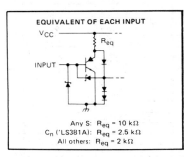

EQUIVALENT OF EACH INPUT

Any S: R_{eq} = 10 kΩ
C_n ('LS381A): R_{eq} = 2.5 kΩ
All others: R_{eq} = 2 kΩ

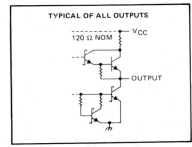

TYPICAL OF ALL OUTPUTS

120 Ω NOM

'S381

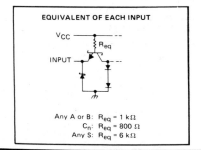

EQUIVALENT OF EACH INPUT

Any A or B: R_{eq} = 1 kΩ
C_n: R_{eq} = 800 Ω
Any S: R_{eq} = 6 kΩ

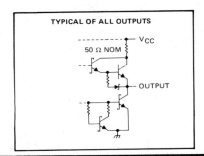

TYPICAL OF ALL OUTPUTS

50 Ω NOM

TEXAS
INSTRUMENTS

3

TTL DEVICES

3-865

absolute maximum ratings over operating free-air temperature range (unless otherwise noted)

Supply voltage, V_{CC} (see Note 1) . . . . 7 V
Input voltage . . . . 7 V
Operating free-air temperature range: SN54LS381A, SN54LS382A . . . . -55°C to 125°C
SN74LS381A, SN74LS382A . . . . 0°C to 70°C
Storage temperature range . . . . -65°C to 150°C

NOTE 1: Voltage values are with respect to the network ground terminal.

recommended operating conditions

		SN54LS'			SN74LS'			UNIT
		MIN	NOM	MAX	MIN	NOM	MAX	
V_{CC}	Supply voltage	4.5	5	5.5	4.75	5	5.25	V
V_{IH}	High-level input voltage	2			2			V
V_{IL}	Low-level input voltage			0.7			0.8	V
I_{OH}	High-level output current			-0.4			-0.4	mA
I_{OL}	Low-level output current	$\overline{G}$ output of 'LS381A		16			16	mA
		All other outputs		4			8	
T_A	Operating free-air temperature	-55		125	0		70	$^{\circ}$C

electrical characteristics over recommended operating free-air temperature range (unless otherwise noted)

PARAMETER		TEST CONDITIONS[†]			SN54LS'			SN74LS'			UNIT
					MIN	TYP[‡]	MAX	MIN	TYP[‡]	MAX	
V_{IK}		V_{CC} = MIN,	$I_I = -18$ mA				-1.5			-1.5	V
V_{OH}		V_{CC} = MIN, V_{IH} = 2 V, $I_{OH} = -0.4$ mA		V_{IL} = MAX,	2.5	3.4		2.7	3.4		V
V_{OL}	$\overline{G}$ ('LS381A)	V_{CC} = MIN, V_{IH} = 2 V, V_{IL} = MAX		I_{OL} = 16 mA		0.47	0.7		0.47	0.7	V
	Other outputs			I_{OL} = 4 mA		0.25	0.4		0.25	0.4	
				I_{OL} = 8 mA					0.35	0.5	
I_I		V_{CC} = MAX,	V_I = 7 V				0.1			0.1	mA
I_{IH}	Any S	V_{CC} = MAX,	V_I = 2.7 V				20			20	μA
	Any A or B						100			100	
	C_n ('LS381A)						80			80	
	C_n ('LS382)						100			100	
I_{IL}	Any S	V_{CC} = MAX,	V_I = 0.4 V				-0.2			-0.2	mA
	Any A or B						-1			-1	
	C_n ('LS381A)						-0.8			-0.8	
	C_n ('LS382)						-0.8			-0.8	
I_{OS}[§]		V_{CC} = MAX			-20		-100	-20		-100	mA
I_{CC}		V_{CC} = MAX, All inputs grounded, outputs open				35	65		35	65	mA

† For conditions shown as MIN or MAX, use the appropriate value specified under recommended operating conditions.
‡ All typical values are at V_{CC} = 5 V, $T_A = 25^{\circ}$C.
§ Not more than one output should be shorted at a time, and duration of the short circuit should not exceed one second.

TEXAS INSTRUMENTS

switching characteristics, V_{CC} = 5 V, T_A = 25°C (see note 3)

PARAMETER	FROM (INPUT)	TO (OUTPUT)	TEST CONDITIONS	'LS381A MIN	'LS381A TYP	'LS381A MAX	'LS382A MIN	'LS382A TYP	'LS382A MAX	UNIT
t_{PLH}	C_n	Any F			18	27		18	27	ns
t_{PHL}					14	21		14	21	
t_{PLH}	Any A or B	$\overline{G}$			20	30				ns
t_{PHL}					21	33				
t_{PLH}	Any A or B	$\overline{P}$			21	33				ns
t_{PHL}					23	33				
t_{PLH}	A_i or B_i	F_i			20	30		20	30	ns
t_{PHL}					15	23		15	23	
t_{PLH}	S0, S1, S2	F_i			35	53		35	53	ns
t_{PHL}					34	51		34	51	
t_{PLH}	S0, S1, S2	$\overline{G}$ or $\overline{P}$	R_L = 2 kΩ, C_L = 15 pF		31	47				ns
t_{PHL}					32	48				
t_{PLH}	Any A or B	C_{n+4}						28	42	ns
t_{PHL}								26	39	
t_{PLH}	Any A or B	OVR						23	35	ns
t_{PHL}								27	41	
t_{PLH}	S0, S1, S2	C_{n+4} or OVR						38	57	ns
t_{PHL}								36	54	
t_{PLH}	C_n	OVR						10	15	ns
t_{PHL}								13	23	
t_{PLH}	C_n	C_{n+4}						13	21	ns
t_{PHL}								11	20	

NOTE 3:   See General Information Section for load circuits and voltage waveforms.

3

TTL DEVICES

TEXAS
INSTRUMENTS

absolute maximum ratings over operating free-air temperature range (unless otherwise noted)

Supply voltage, V_{CC} (see Note 1) . . . . 7 V
Input voltage . . . . 5.5 V
Interemitter voltage (see Note 2) . . . . 5.5 V
Operating free-air temperature range: SN54S381 . . . . -55°C to 125°C
SN74S381 . . . . 0°C to 70°C
Storage free-air temperature range . . . . -65°C to 150°C

NOTES: 1. Voltage values, except interemitter voltage, are with respect to network ground terminal.
2. This is the voltage between two emitters of a multiple-emitter transistor. For this circuit, this rating applies to each A input in conjunction with its respective B input; for example A0 with B0, etc.

recommended operating conditions

	SN54S381			SN74S381			UNIT
	MIN	NOM	MAX	MIN	NOM	MAX	
Supply voltage, V_{CC}	4.5	5	5.5	4.75	5	5.25	V
High-level output current, I_{OH}			-1			-1	mA
Low-level output current, I_{OL}			20			20	mA
Operating free-air temperature, T_A	-55		125	0		70	$^{\circ}$C

electrical characteristics over recommended operating free-air temperature range (unless otherwise noted)

	PARAMETER		TEST CONDITIONS[†]	MIN	TYP[‡]	MAX	UNIT
V_{IH}	High-level input voltage			2			V
V_{IL}	Low-level input voltage					0.8	V
V_{IK}	Input clamp voltage		V_{CC} = MIN, I_I = -18 mA			-1.2	V
V_{OH}	High-level output voltage	SN54S381	V_{CC} = MIN, V_{IH} = 2 V,	2.4	3.4		V
		SN74S381	V_{IL} = 0.8 V, I_{OH} = -1 mA	2.7	3.4		
V_{OL}	Low-level output voltage		V_{CC} = MIN, V_{IH} = 2 V, V_{IL} = 0.8 V, I_{OL} = 20 mA			0.5	V
I_I	Input current at maximum input voltage		V_{CC} = MAX, V_I = 5.5 V			1	mA
I_{IH}	High-level input current	Any S input	V_{CC} = MAX, V_I = 2.7 V			50	μA
		C_n				250	
		All others				200	
I_{IL}	Low-level input current	Any S input	V_{CC} = MAX, V_I = 0.5 V			-2	mA
		C_n				-8	
		All others				-6	
I_{OS}	Short-circuit output current[§]		V_{CC} = MAX	-40		-100	mA
I_{CC}	Supply current		V_{CC} = MAX		105	160	mA

[†] For conditions shown as MIN or MAX, use the appropriate value specified under recommended operating conditions.
[‡] All typical values are at V_{CC} = 5 V, T_A = 25°C.
[§] Not more than one output should be shorted at a time.

switching characteristics, V_{CC} = 5 V, T_A = 25°C

PARAMETER[¶]	FROM (INPUT)	TO (OUTPUT)	TEST CONDITIONS	MIN	TYP	MAX	UNIT
t_{PLH}	C_n	Any F			10	17	ns
t_{PHL}					10	17	
t_{PLH}	Any A or B	$\overline{G}$			12	20	ns
t_{PHL}					12	20	
t_{PLH}	Any A or B	$\overline{P}$	C_L = 15 pF, R_L = 280 Ω,		11	18	ns
t_{PHL}			See Note 3		11	18	
t_{PLH}	A_i or B_i	F_i			18	27	ns
t_{PHL}					16	25	
t_{PLH}	Any S	Any			18	30	ns
t_{PHL}					18	30	

[¶] t_{PLH} propagation delay time, low-to-high-level output
t_{PHL} propagation delay time, high-to-low-level output
NOTE 3: See General Information Section for load circuits and voltage waveforms.

TEXAS
INSTRUMENTS

3
TTL DEVICES

D2419, JANUARY 1981 — REVISED DECEMBER 1983

- Two's-Complement Multiplication
- Magnitude Only Multiplication
- Cascadable for Any Number of Bits
- 8-Bit Parallel Multiplicand Data Input
- Serial Multiplier Data Input
- Serial Data Output for Multiplication Product
- 40 MHz Typical Maximum Clock Frequency

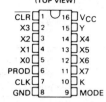

SN54LS384 . . . J PACKAGE
SN74LS384 . . . J OR N PACKAGE
(TOP VIEW)

description

The 'LS384 is an 8-bit by 1-bit sequential logic element that performs digital multiplication of two numbers represented in two's-complement form to produce a two's-complement product without external correction by using Booth's algorithm internally. The device accepts an 8-bit multiplicand (X input) and stores this data in eight internal latches. These X latches are controlled via the clear input. When the clear input is low, all internal flip-flops are cleared and the X latches are opened to accept new multiplicand data. When the clear input is high, the latches are closed and are insensitive to X input changes.

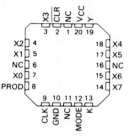

SN54LS384 . . . FK PACKAGE
SN74LS384
(TOP VIEW)

NC — No internal connection

The multiplier word data is passed by the Y input in a serial bit stream, least significant bit first. The product is clocked out the PROD output, least significant bit first.

The multiplication of an m-bit multiplicand by an n-bit multiplier results in an (m + n)-bit product. The 'LS384 must be clocked for m + n clock cycles to produce this two's complement product. The n-bit multiplier (Y-input) sign bit data must be extended for the remaining m bits to complete the multiplication cycle.

The device also contains a K input so that devices can be cascaded for longer length X words. The PROD output of one device is connected to the K input of the succeeding device when cascading. The mode input is used to indicate which device contains the most significant bit. The mode input is wired high or low depending on the position of the 8-bit slice in the total X word length. The device with the most significant bit is wired low and all lower order bit packages are wired high.

The SN54LS384 will be characterized for operation over the full military temperature range from —55°C to 125°C. The SN74LS384 will be characterized for operation from 0°C to 70°C.

TTL DEVICES **3**

TEXAS
INSTRUMENTS

TYPES SN54LS384, SN74LS384
8-BIT BY 1-BIT TWO'S-COMPLEMENT MULTIPLIERS

FUNCTION TABLE

CLR	CLK	X$_i$	Y	INTERNAL Y$_{-1}$	OUTPUT PROD	FUNCTION
L	X	Data	X	L	L	Load new multiplicand and clear internal sum and carry registers
H	↑	X	L	L	Output	Shift sum register
H	↑	X	L	H	per	Add multiplicand to sum register and shift
H	↑	X	H	L	Booth's	Subtract multiplicand from sum register and shift
H	↑	X	H	H	algorithm	Shift sum register

H = high-level, L = low-level, X = irrelevant, ↑ = low-to-high-level transition

schematics of inputs and outputs

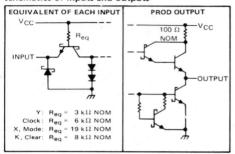

Y: R$_{eq}$ = 3 kΩ NOM
Clock: R$_{eq}$ = 6 kΩ NOM
X, Mode: R$_{eq}$ = 19 kΩ NOM
K, Clear: R$_{eq}$ = 8 kΩ NOM

logic symbol

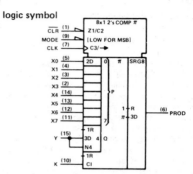

Pin numbers shown on logic notation are for J or N packages.

logic diagram (positive logic)

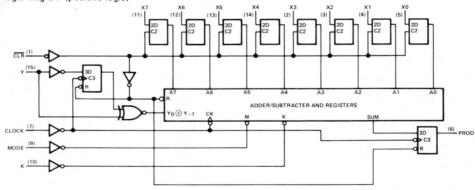

absolute maximum ratings over operating free-air temperature range (unless otherwise noted)

Supply voltage, V$_{CC}$ (see Note 1)	7 V
Input voltage (see Note 2)	5.5 V
Operating free-air temperature range: SN54LS384	−55°C to 125°C
SN74LS384	0°C to 70°C
Storage temperature range	−65°C to 150°C

NOTES: 1. Voltage values are with respect to network ground terminal.
2. Input voltages must be zero or positive with respect to network ground terminal.

TEXAS INSTRUMENTS

recommended operating conditions

		SN54LS384 MIN	NOM	MAX	SN74LS384 MIN	NOM	MAX	UNIT
Supply voltage, V_{CC}		4.5	5	5.5	4.75	5	5.25	V
High-level output current, I_{OH}				−400			−400	µA
Low-level output current, I_{OL}				4			8	mA
Clock frequency, f_{clock}		0		25	0		25	MHz
Setup time, t_{su}	Y before Clock ↑	45			38			ns
	K before Clock ↑	30			24			
	X before Clear ↑	23			19			
Clear inactive-state set up time before Clock ↑		30			20			
Hold time, t_h	Y after Clock ↑	0			0			ns
	K after Clock ↑	0			0			
	X after Clear ↑	2			2			
Pulse width, t_w	Clock high	20			20			ns
	Clock low	20			20			
	Clear low	38			33			
Operating free-air temperature, T_A		−55		125	0		70	°C

electrical characteristics over recommended operating free-air temperature range (unless otherwise noted)

PARAMETER		TEST CONDITIONS[†]		SN54LS384 MIN	TYP[‡]	MAX	SN74LS384 MIN	TYP[‡]	MAX	UNIT
V_{IH}	High-level input voltage			2			2			V
V_{IL}	Low-level input voltage					0.7			0.8	V
V_{IK}	Input clamp voltage	V_{CC} = MIN, I_I = −18 mA				−1.5			−1.5	V
V_{OH}	High-level output voltage	V_{CC} = MIN, V_{IH} = 2 V, V_{IL} = V_{IL} max, V_{OH} = −400 µA		2.5	3.4		2.7	3.4		V
V_{OL}	Low-level output voltage	V_{CC} = MIN, V_{IH} = 2 V, V_{IL} = V_{IL} max	I_{OL} = 4 mA		0.25	0.4		0.25	0.4	V
			I_{OL} = 8 mA					0.35	0.5	
I_I	Input current at maximum input voltage	V_{CC} = MAX, V_I = 5.5 V				1			1	mA
I_{IH}	High-level input current	X, Mode	V_{CC} = MAX, V_I = 2.7 V			20			20	µA
		K, Clear				30			30	
		Clock				40			40	
		Y				80			80	
I_{IL}	Low-level input current	X, Mode	V_{CC} = MAX, V_I = 0.4 V			−0.48			−0.48	mA
		K, Clear				−1.2			−1.2	
		Clock				−1.6			−1.6	
		Y				−3.2			−3.2	
I_{OS}	Short-circuit output current[§]	V_{CC} = MAX		−20		−100	−20		−100	mA
I_{CC}	Supply current	V_{CC} = MAX, See Note 3			91	132		91	132	mA

[†] For conditions shown at MIN or MAX, use the appropriate value specified under recommended operating conditions.
[‡] All typical values are at V_{CC} = 5 V, T_A = 25°C.
[§] Not more than one output should be shorted at a time, and duration of the short-circuit should not exceed one second.
NOTE 3: I_{CC} is measured with the clear input grounded and all other inputs and outputs open.

switching characteristics, V_{CC} = 5 V, T_A = 25°C

PARAMETER		TEST CONDITIONS	MIN	TYP	MAX	UNIT
f_{max}	Maximum clock frequency	C_L = 15 pF, R_L = 2 kΩ, See Note 4	25	40		MHz
t_{PLH}	Propagation delay time, low-to-high-level output from clock			15	23	ns
t_{PHL}	Propagation delay time, high-to-low-level output from clock			15	23	ns
t_{PHL}	Propagation delay time, high-to-low-level output from clear			17	25	ns

NOTE 4: See General Information Section for load circuits and voltage waveforms.

TEXAS
INSTRUMENTS

3

TTL DEVICES

TYPES SN54LS384, SN74LS384
8-BIT BY 1-BIT TWO'S-COMPLEMENT MULTIPLIERS

TYPICAL APPLICATION DATA

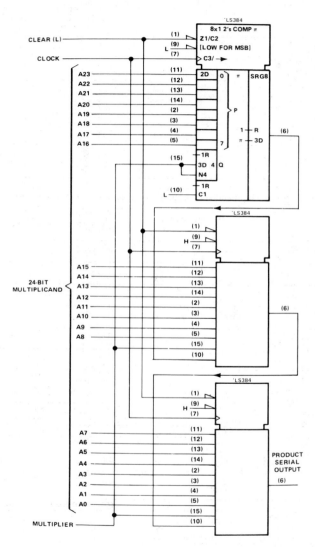

FIGURE 1—BASIC 24-BIT SERIAL/PARALLEL CONNECTION

TYPICAL APPLICATION DATA

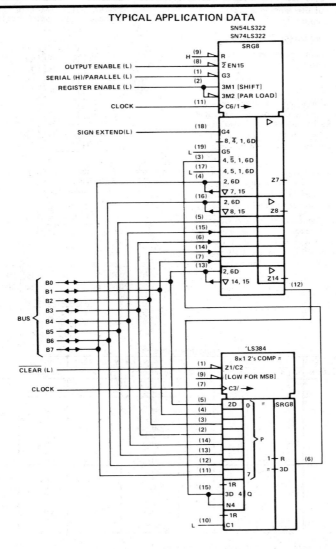

FIGURE 2—8-BIT BY 8-BIT MULTIPLIER, BUS ORGANIZED,
WITH 8-BIT TRUNCATED PRODUCT

TEXAS
INSTRUMENTS

3

TTL DEVICES

- Four Synchronous Elements in a Single 20-Pin Package
- Buffered Clock and Direct Clear Inputs
- Independent Two's-Complement Addition/Subtraction

description

The 'LS385 is a general purpose adder/subtractor and is particularly useful as a companion part to the SN54LS384/SN74LS384 serial/parallel two's-complement multiplier. The 'LS385 contains four independent adder/subtractor elements with common clock and clear.

Each of the four independent sum (Σ) outputs reflects its respective A and B input as controlled by the $S/\overline{A}$ control. When $S/\overline{A}$ is high the Σ function is A minus B. When $S/\overline{A}$ is low the Σ function is A plus B.

When low, the clear input asynchronously resets the sum flip-flop low and the carry flip-flop either high in the subtract mode or low in the add mode. The clock is positive-edge triggered and controls the sum and carry flip-flops according to the function table.

SN54LS385 . . . J PACKAGE
SN74LS385 . . . DW, J OR N PACKAGE
(TOP VIEW)

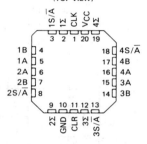

SN54LS385 . . . FK PACKAGE
SN74LS385
(TOP VIEW)

FUNCTION TABLE

SELECTED FUNCTION	INPUTS					DATA IN CARRY FLIP-FLOP		Σ OUTPUT
	CLR	$S/\overline{A}$	A	B	CLK	BEFORE ↑	AFTER ↑	AFTER ↑
Clear	L	L	X	X	X	L	L	L
	L	H	X	X	X	H	H	L
Add	H	L	L	L	↑	L	L	L
	H	L	L	L	↑	H	L	H
	H	L	L	H	↑	L	L	H
	H	L	L	H	↑	H	H	L
	H	L	H	L	↑	L	L	H
	H	L	H	L	↑	H	H	L
	H	L	H	H	↑	L	H	L
	H	L	H	H	↑	H	H	H
Subtract	H	H	L	L	↑	L	L	H
	H	H	L	L	↑	H	H	L
	H	H	L	H	↑	L	L	L
	H	H	L	H	↑	H	L	H
	H	H	H	L	↑	L	H	H
	H	H	H	L	↑	H	H	H
	H	H	H	H	↑	L	L	H
	H	H	H	H	↑	H	H	L

H = high level, L = low level, X = irrelevant,
↑ = transition from low to high level at the clock input

TEXAS
INSTRUMENTS

3
TTL DEVICES

schematics of inputs and outputs

logic symbol

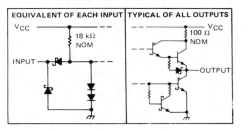

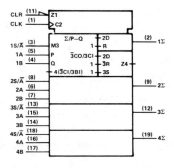

logic diagram (each adder/subtractor, positive logic)

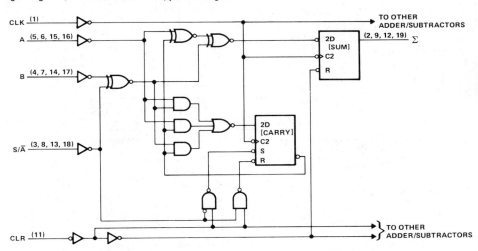

Pin numbers shown on logic notation are for DW, J or N packages.

3

TTL DEVICES

recommended operating conditions

	SN54LS385 MIN	NOM	MAX	SN74LS385 MIN	NOM	MAX	UNIT
Supply voltage, V_{CC} (see Note 1)	4.5	5	5.5	4.75	5	5.25	V
High-level output current, I_{OH}			−400			−400	μA
Low-level output current, I_{OL}			4			8	mA
Clock frequency, f_{clock}	0		30	0		30	MHz
Width of clock pulse, t_w	16			16			ns
Setup time, t_{su}	10			10			ns
Hold time, t_h	3			3			ns
Operating free-air temperature, T_A	−55		125	0		70	°C

NOTE 1: Voltage values are with respect to network ground terminal.

electrical characteristics over recommended operating free-air temperature range (unless otherwise noted)

PARAMETER		TEST CONDITIONS[†]		SN54LS385 MIN	TYP[‡]	MAX	SN74LS385 MIN	TYP[‡]	MAX	UNIT
V_{IH}	High-level input voltage			2			2			V
V_{IL}	Low-level input voltage					0.7			0.8	V
V_{IK}	Input clamp voltage	V_{CC} = MIN,	I_I = −18 mA			−1.5			−1.5	V
V_{OH}	High-level output voltage	V_{CC} = MIN, V_{IH} = 2 V, $V_{IL} = V_{IL}$max, I_{OH} = −400 μA		2.5	3.5		2.7	3.5		V
V_{OL}	Low-level output voltage	V_{CC} = MIN, V_{IH} = 2 V, $V_{IL} = V_{IL}$max	I_{OL} = 4 mA		0.25	0.4		0.25	0.4	V
			I_{OL} = 8 mA					0.35	0.5	
I_I	Input current at maximum input voltage	V_{CC} = MAX,	V_I = 7 V			0.1			0.1	mA
I_{IH}	High-level input current	V_{CC} = MAX,	V_I = 2.7 V			20			20	μA
I_{IL}	Low-level input current	V_{CC} = MAX,	V_I = 0.4 V			−0.4			−0.4	mA
I_{OS}	Short-circuit output current[§]	V_{CC} = MAX		−20		−100	−20		−100	mA
I_{CC}	Supply current	V_{CC} = MAX,	See Note 2		48	75		48	75	mA

[†] For conditions shown as MIN or MAX, use the appropriate value specified under recommended operating conditions.
[‡] All typical values are at V_{CC} = 5 V, T_A = 25°C.
[§] Not more than one output should be shorted at a time.
NOTE 2: I_{CC} is measured with all inputs grounded and all outputs open.

switching characteristics, V_{CC} = 5 V, T_A = 25°C

PARAMETER	FROM (INPUT)	TO (OUTPUT)	TEST CONDITIONS	MIN	TYP	MAX	UNIT
f_{max}			C_L = 15 pF, R_L = 2 kΩ, See Note 3	30	40		MHz
t_{PLH}	Clock	Σ			14	22	ns
t_{PHL}					18	27	
t_{PHL}	Clear	Σ			18	30	ns

f_{max} = maximum clock frequency
t_{PLH} = propagation delay time, low-to-high-level output
t_{PHL} = propagation delay time, high-to-low-level output
NOTE 3: See General Information Section for load circuits and voltage waveforms.

3

TTL DEVICES

TEXAS
INSTRUMENTS

MARCH 1974 – REVISED DECEMBER 1983

- Electrically Identical to
  SN54LS86A/SN74LS86A

- Mechanically Identical to
  SN54L86/SN74L86

- Total Average Propagation Delay
  Times . . . 10 ns

- Typical Total Power
  Dissipation . . . 30.5 mW

SN54LS386A . . . J OR W PACKAGE
SN74LS386A . . . D, J OR N PACKAGE
(TOP VIEW)

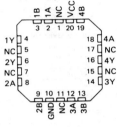

1A	1	14	V_{CC}
1B	2	13	4B
1Y	3	12	4A
2Y	4	11	4Y
2A	5	10	3Y
2B	6	9	3B
GND	7	8	3A

FUNCTION TABLE
(EACH GATE)

INPUTS		OUTPUT
A	B	
L	L	L
L	H	H
H	L	H
H	H	L

H = high level
L = low level

SN54LS386A . . . FK PACKAGE
SN74LS386A
(TOP VIEW)

1Y, NC, 2Y, NC, 2A
4A, NC, 4Y, NC, 3Y
1B, 1A, NC, V_{CC}, 4B
2B, GND, NC, 3A, 3B

NC – No internal connection

logic diagram (each gate)

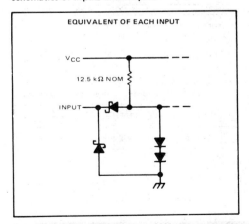

A
B
Y

positive logic

$$Y = A \oplus B = \overline{A}B + A\overline{B}$$

schematics of inputs and outputs

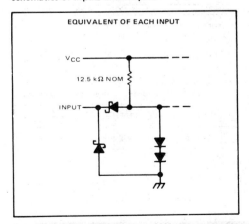

EQUIVALENT OF EACH INPUT

V_{CC}

12.5 kΩ NOM

INPUT

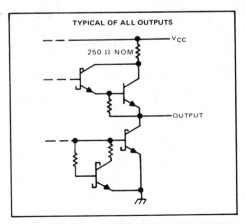

TYPICAL OF ALL OUTPUTS

V_{CC}

250 Ω NOM

OUTPUT

3

TTL DEVICES

TEXAS
INSTRUMENTS

absolute maximum ratings over operating free-air temperature range (unless otherwise noted)

Supply voltage, V_{CC} (see Note 1) . . . . 7 V
Input voltage . . . . 7 V
Operating free-air temperature range: SN54LS386A . . . . $-55°$C to $125°$C
SN74LS386A . . . . $0°$C to $70°$C
Storage temperature range . . . . $-65°$C to $150°$C

NOTE 1: Voltage values are with respect to network ground terminal.

recommended operating conditions

	SN54LS386A			SN74LS386A			UNIT
	MIN	NOM	MAX	MIN	NOM	MAX	
Supply voltage, V_{CC}	4.5	5	5.5	4.75	5	5.25	V
High-level output current, I_{OH}			-400			-400	μA
Low-level output current, I_{OL}			4			8	mA
Operating free-air temperature, T_A	-55		125	0		70	$°$C

electrical characteristics over recommended operating free-air temperature range (unless otherwise noted)

PARAMETER		TEST CONDITIONS[†]		SN54LS386A			SN74LS386A			UNIT
				MIN	TYP[‡]	MAX	MIN	TYP[‡]	MAX	
V_{IH}	High-level input voltage			2			2			V
V_{IL}	Low-level input voltage					0.7			0.8	V
V_{IK}	Input clamp voltage	V_{CC} = MIN,	$I_I = -18$ mA			-1.5			-1.5	V
V_{OH}	High-level output voltage	V_{CC} = MIN, V_{IH} = 2 V, $V_{IL} = V_{IL}$ max, $I_{OH} = -400\,\mu$A		2.5	3.4		2.7	3.4		V
V_{OL} Low-level output voltage		V_{CC} = MIN V_{IH} = 2 V, $V_{IL} = V_{IL}$ max	I_{OL} = 4 mA		0.25	0.4		0.25	0.4	V
			I_{OL} = 8 mA					0.35	0.5	
I_I	Input current at maximum input voltage	V_{CC} = MAX,	V_I = 7 V			0.2			0.2	mA
I_{IH}	High-level input current	V_{CC} = MAX,	V_I = 2.7 V			40			40	μA
I_{IL}	Low-level input current	V_{CC} = MAX,	V_I = 0.4 V			-0.8			-0.8	mA
I_{OS}	Short-circuit output current [§]	V_{CC} = MAX		-20		-100	-20		-100	mA
I_{CC}	Supply current	V_{CC} = MAX,	See Note 2		6.1	10		6.1	10	mA

[†] For conditions shown as MIN or MAX, use the appropriate value specified under recommended operating conditions.
[‡] All typical values are at V_{CC} = 5 V, $T_A = 25°$C.
[§] Not more than one output should be shorted at a time.
NOTE 2: I_{CC} is measured with the inputs grounded and the outputs open.

switching characteristics, V_{CC} = 5 V, $T_A = 25°$C

PARAMETER[¶]	FROM (INPUT)	TEST CONDITIONS		MIN	TYP	MAX	UNIT
t_{PLH}	A or B	Other input low	C_L = 15 pF, R_L = 2 kΩ, See Note 3		12	23	ns
t_{PHL}					10	17	
t_{PLH}	A or B	Other input high			20	30	ns
t_{PHL}					13	22	

[¶] t_{PLH} = propagation delay time, low-to-high-level output
t_{PHL} = propagation delay time, high-to-low-level output
NOTE 3: See General Information Section for load circuits and voltage waveforms.

TEXAS
INSTRUMENTS

3

TTL DEVICES

- Dual Versions of the Popular '90A, 'LS90 and '93A, 'LS93

- '390, 'LS390 . . . Individual Clocks for A and B Flip-Flops Provide Dual ÷ 2 and ÷ 5 Counters

- '393, 'LS393 . . . Dual 4-Bit Binary Counter with Individual Clocks

- All Have Direct Clear for Each 4-Bit Counter

- Dual 4-Bit Versions Can Significantly Improve System Densities by Reducing Counter Package Count by 50%

- Typical Maximum Count Frequency . . . 35 MHz

- Buffered Outputs Reduce Possibility of Collector Commutation

description

Each of these monolithic circuits contains eight master-slave flip-flops and additional gating to implement two individual four-bit counters in a single package. The '390 and 'LS390 incorporate dual divide-by-two and divide-by-five counters, which can be used to implement cycle lengths equal to any whole and/or cumulative multiples of 2 and/or 5 up to divide-by-100. When connected as a bi-quinary counter, the separate divide-by-two circuit can be used to provide symmetry (a square wave) at the final output stage. The '393 and 'LS393 each comprise two independent four-bit binary counters each having a clear and a clock input. N-bit binary counters can be implemented with each package providing the capability of divide-by-256. The '390, 'LS390, '393, and 'LS393 have parallel outputs from each counter stage so that any submultiple of the input count frequency is available for system-timing signals.

Series 54 and Series 54LS circuits are characterized for operation over the full military temperature range of -55°C to 125°C; Series 74 and Series 74LS circuits are characterized for operation from 0°C to 70°C.

SN54390, SN54LS390 . . . J OR W PACKAGE
SN74390 . . . J OR N PACKAGE
SN74LS390 . . . D, J OR N PACKAGE
(TOP VIEW)

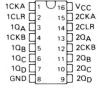

SN54LS390 . . . FK PACKAGE
SN74LS390
(TOP VIEW)

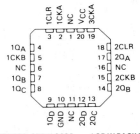

SN54393, SN54LS393 . . . J OR W PACKAGE
SN74393 . . . J OR N PACKAGE
SN74LS393 . . . D, J OR N PACKAGE
(TOP VIEW)

SN54LS393 . . . FK PACKAGE
SN74LS393
(TOP VIEW)

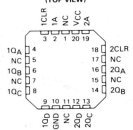

NC - No internal connection

3

TTL DEVICES

TEXAS
INSTRUMENTS

TYPES SN54390, SN54LS390, SN54393, SN54LS393, SN74390, SN74LS390, SN74393, SN74LS393
DUAL 4-BIT DECADE AND BINARY COUNTERS

FUNCTION TABLES

'390, 'LS390
BCD COUNT SEQUENCE
(EACH COUNTER)
(See Note A)

COUNT	OUTPUT			
	Q_D	Q_C	Q_B	Q_A
0	L	L	L	L
1	L	L	L	H
2	L	L	H	L
3	L	L	H	H
4	L	H	L	L
5	L	H	L	H
6	L	H	H	L
7	L	H	H	H
8	H	L	L	L
9	H	L	L	H

'390, 'LS390
BI-QUINARY (5-2)
(EACH COUNTER)
(See Note B)

COUNT	OUTPUT			
	Q_A	Q_D	Q_C	Q_B
0	L	L	L	L
1	L	L	L	H
2	L	L	H	L
3	L	L	H	H
4	L	H	L	L
5	H	L	L	L
6	H	L	L	H
7	H	L	H	L
8	H	L	H	H
9	H	H	L	L

'393, 'LS393
COUNT SEQUENCE
(EACH COUNTER)

COUNT	OUTPUT			
	Q_D	Q_C	Q_B	Q_A
0	L	L	L	L
1	L	L	L	H
2	L	L	H	L
3	L	L	H	H
4	L	H	L	L
5	L	H	L	H
6	L	H	H	L
7	L	H	H	H
8	H	L	L	L
9	H	L	L	H
10	H	L	H	L
11	H	L	H	H
12	H	H	L	L
13	H	H	L	H
14	H	H	H	L
15	H	H	H	H

NOTES: A. Output Q_A is connected to input B for BCD count.
B. Output Q_D is connected to input A for bi-quinary count.
C. H = high level, L = low level.

logic diagrams

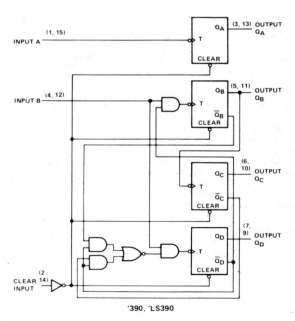

'390, 'LS390

Pin numbers shown on logic notation are for D, J or N packages.

TEXAS
INSTRUMENTS

logic diagrams (continued)

'393, 'LS393

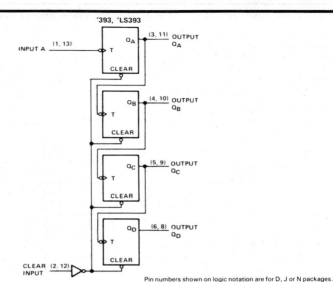

Pin numbers shown on logic notation are for D, J or N packages.

schematics of inputs and outputs

'390, '393

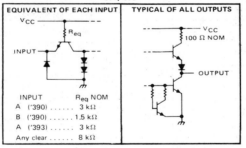

'LS390, 'LS393

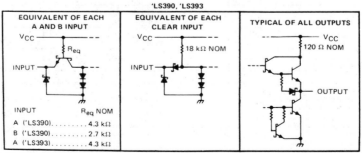

absolute maximum ratings over operating free-air temperature range (unless otherwise noted)

Supply voltage, V_{CC} (see Note 1) . . . . 7 V
Input voltage . . . . 5.5 V
Operating free-air temperature range: SN54390, SN54393 . . . . $-55°C$ to $125°C$
                                     SN74390, SN74393 . . . . $0°C$ to $70°C$
Storage temperature range . . . . $-65°C$ to $150°C$

NOTE 1: Voltage values are with respect to network ground terminal.

recommended operating conditions

		SN54390 SN54393			SN74390 SN74393			UNIT
		MIN	NOM	MAX	MIN	NOM	MAX	
Supply voltage, V_{CC}		4.5	5	5.5	4.75	5	5.25	V
High-level output current, I_{OH}				−800			−800	µA
Low-level output current, I_{OL}				16			16	mA
Count frequency, f_{count}	A input	0		25	0		25	MHz
	B input	0		20	0		20	
Pulse width, t_w	A input high or low	20			20			ns
	B input high or low	25			25			
	Clear high	20			20			
Clear inactive-state setup time, t_{su}		25↓			25↓			ns
Operating free-air temperature, T_A		−55		125	0		70	°C

↓ The arrow indicates that the falling edge of the clock pulse is used for reference.

electrical characteristics over recommended operating free-air temperature range (unless otherwise noted)

PARAMETER		TEST CONDITIONS[†]		'390			'393			UNIT
				MIN	TYP[‡]	MAX	MIN	TYP[‡]	MAX	
V_{IH}	High-level input voltage			2			2			V
V_{IL}	Low-level input voltage					0.8			0.8	V
V_{IK}	Input clamp voltage	V_{CC} = MIN, I_I = −12 mA				−1.5			−1.5	V
V_{OH}	High-level output voltage	V_{CC} = MIN, V_{IH} = 2 V, V_{IL} = 0.8 V, I_{OH} = −800 µA		2.4	3.4		2.4	3.4		V
V_{OL}	Low-level output voltage	V_{CC} = MIN, V_{IH} = 2 V, V_{IL} = 0.8 V, I_{OL} = 16 mA¶			0.2	0.4		0.2	0.4	V
I_I	Input current at maximum input voltage	V_{CC} = MAX, V_I = 5.5 V				1			1	mA
I_{IH}	High-level input current	Clear	V_{CC} = MAX, V_I = 2.4 V			40			40	µA
		Input A				80			80	
		Input B				120				
I_{IL}	Low-level input current	Clear	V_{CC} = MAX, V_I = 0.4 V			−1			−1	mA
		Input A				−3.2			−3.2	
		Input B				−4.8				
I_{OS}	Short-circuit output current[§]	V_{CC} = MAX	SN54'	−20		−57	−20		−57	mA
			SN74'	−18		−57	−18		−57	
I_{CC}	Supply current	V_{CC} = MAX, See Note 2			42	69		38	64	mA

[†]For conditions shown as MIN or MAX, use the appropriate value specified under recommended operating conditions.

[‡]All typical values are at V_{CC} = 5 V, T_A = 25°C.

¶ The Q_A outputs of the '390 are tested at I_{OL} = 16 mA plus the limit value for I_{IL} for the B input. This permits driving the B input while maintaining full fan-out capability.

[§]Not more than one output should be shorted at a time.

NOTE 2: I_{CC} is measured with all outputs open, both clear inputs grounded following momentary connection to 4.5 V, and all other inputs grounded.

TEXAS
INSTRUMENTS

3
TTL DEVICES

switching characteristics, V_{CC} = 5 V, T_A = 25°C

PARAMETER[*]	FROM (INPUT)	TO (OUTPUT)	TEST CONDITIONS	'390			'393			UNIT
				MIN	TYP	MAX	MIN	TYP	MAX	
f_{max}	A	Q_A		25	35		25	35		MHz
	B	Q_B		20	30					
t_{PLH}	A	Q_A			12	20		12	20	ns
t_{PHL}					13	20		13	20	
t_{PLH}	A	Q_C of '390	C_L = 15 pF,		37	60		40	60	ns
t_{PHL}		Q_D of '393	R_L = 400 Ω,		39	60		40	60	
t_{PLH}	B	Q_B	See Note 3		13	21				ns
t_{PHL}			and		14	21				
t_{PLH}	B	Q_C	Figure 1		24	39				ns
t_{PHL}					26	39				
t_{PLH}	B	Q_D			13	21				ns
t_{PHL}					14	21				
t_{PHL}	Clear	Any			24	39		24	39	ns

[*] $f_{max} \equiv$ maximum count frequency
$t_{PLH} \equiv$ propagation delay time, low-to-high-level output
$t_{PHL} \equiv$ propagation delay time, high-to-low-level output
NOTE 3: See General Information Section for load circuits and voltage waveforms.

TEXAS
INSTRUMENTS

TTL DEVICES

3

PARAMETER MEASUREMENT INFORMATION

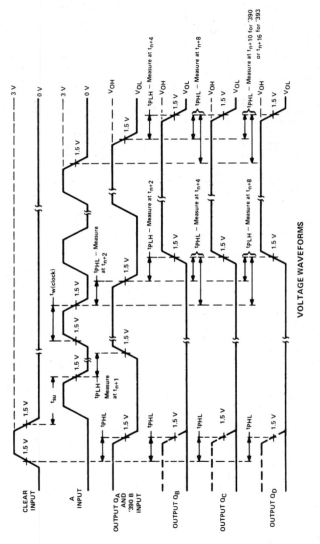

VOLTAGE WAVEFORMS

FIGURE 1

NOTE A: Input pulses are supplied by a generator having the following characteristics $t_r \leqslant 5$ ns, $t_f \leqslant 5$ ns, PRR = 1 MHz, duty cycle = 50%, $Z_{out} \approx 50$ ohms.

TEXAS
INSTRUMENTS

3

TTL DEVICES

absolute maximum ratings over operating free-air temperature range (unless otherwise noted)

Supply voltage, V_{CC} (see Note 1) . . . . 7 V
Clear input voltage . . . . 7 V
Any A or B clock input voltage . . . . 5.5 V
Operating free-air temperature range: SN54LS390, SN54LS393 . . . . −55°C to 125°C
SN74LS390, SN74LS393 . . . . 0°C to 70°C
Storage temperature range . . . . −65°C to 150°C

NOTE 1: Voltage values are with respect to network ground terminal.

recommended operating conditions

		SN54LS390 SN54LS393			SN74LS390 SN74LS393			UNIT
		MIN	NOM	MAX	MIN	NOM	MAX	
Supply voltage, V_{CC}		4.5	5	5.5	4.75	5	5.25	V
High-level output current, I_{OH}				−400			−400	μA
Low-level output current, I_{OL}				4			8	mA
Count frequency, f_{count}	A input	0		25	0		25	MHz
	B input	0		12.5	0		12.5	
Pulse width, t_w	A input high or low	20			20			ns
	B input high or low	40			40			
	Clear high	20			20			
Clear inactive-state setup time, t_{su}		25↓			25↓			ns
Operating free-air temperature, T_A		−55		125	0		70	°C

↓ The arrow indicates that the falling edge of the clock pulse is used for reference.

electrical characteristics over recommended operating free-air temperature range (unless otherwise noted)

PARAMETER			TEST CONDITIONS[†]		SN54LS'			SN74LS'			UNIT
					MIN	TYP[‡]	MAX	MIN	TYP[‡]	MAX	
V_{IH}	High-level input voltage				2			2			V
V_{IL}	Low-level input voltage						0.7			0.8	V
V_{IK}	Input clamp voltage		V_{CC} = MIN,	I_I = −18 mA			−1.5			−1.5	V
V_{OH}	High-level output voltage		V_{CC} = MIN, V_{IH} = 2 V, $V_{IL} = V_{IL}$max, V_{OH} = −400 μA		2.5	3.4		2.7	3.4		V
V_{OL}	Low-level output voltage		V_{CC} = MIN, V_{IH} = 2 V, V_{IL} = 0.8 V,	I_{OL} = 4 mA[¶]		0.25	0.4		0.25	0.4	V
				I_{OL} = 8 mA[¶]					0.35	0.5	
I_I	Input current at maximum input voltage	Clear	V_{CC} = MAX	V_I = 7 V			0.1			0.1	mA
		Input A		V_I = 5.5 V			0.2			0.2	
		Input B					0.4			0.4	
I_{IH}	High-level input current	Clear	V_{CC} = MAX, V_I = 2.7 V				0.02			0.02	mA
		Input A					0.1			0.1	
		Input B					0.2			0.2	
I_{IL}	Low-level input current	Clear	V_{CC} = MAX, V_I = 0.4 V				−0.4			−0.4	mA
		Input A					−1.6			−1.6	
		Input B					−2.4			−2.4	
I_{OS}	Short-circuit output current[§]		V_{CC} = MAX		−20		−100	−20		−100	mA
I_{CC}	Supply current		V_{CC} = MAX, See Note 2	'LS390		15	26		15	26	mA
				'LS393		15	26		15	26	

[†] For conditions shown as MIN or MAX, use the appropriate value specified under recommended operating conditions.

[‡] All typical values are at V_{CC} = 5 V, T_A = 25°C.

[¶] The Q_A outputs of the 'LS390 are tested at I_{OL} = MAX plus the limit value for I_{IL} for the clock B input. This permits driving the clock B input while maintaining full fan-out capability.

[§] Not more than one output should be shorted at a time, and duration of the short-circuit should not exceed one second.

NOTE 2: I_{CC} is measured with all outputs open, both clear inputs grounded following momentary connection to 4.5 V, and all other inputs grounded.

TEXAS
INSTRUMENTS

3

TTL DEVICES

switching characteristics, V_{CC} = 5 V, T_A = 25°C

PARAMETER¶	FROM (INPUT)	TO (OUTPUT)	TEST CONDITIONS	'LS390			'LS393			UNIT
				MIN	TYP	MAX	MIN	TYP	MAX	
f_{max}	A	Q_A		25	35		25	35		MHz
	B	Q_B		12.5	20					
t_{PLH}	A	Q_A			12	20		12	20	ns
t_{PHL}					13	20		13	20	
t_{PLH}	A	Q_C of 'LS390	C_L = 15 pF,		37	60		40	60	ns
t_{PHL}		Q_D of 'LS393	R_L = 2 kΩ,		39	60		40	60	
t_{PLH}	B	Q_B	See Note 4 and Figure 2		13	21				ns
t_{PHL}					14	21				
t_{PLH}	B	Q_C			24	39				ns
t_{PHL}					26	39				
t_{PLH}	B	Q_D			13	21				ns
t_{PHL}					14	21				
t_{PHL}	Clear	Any			24	39		24	39	ns

¶ f_{max} ⎯ maximum count frequency
t_{PLH} ⎯ propagation delay time, low-to-high-level output
t_{PHL} ⎯ propagation delay time, high-to-low-level output
NOTE 4: See General Information Section for load circuits and voltage waveforms.

TEXAS
INSTRUMENTS

PARAMETER MEASUREMENT INFORMATION

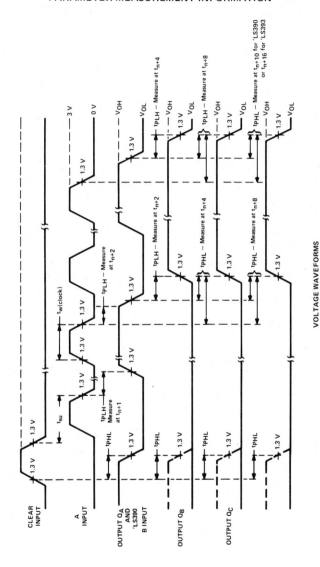

VOLTAGE WAVEFORMS

FIGURE 2

NOTE A: Input pulses are supplied by a generator having the following characteristics $t_r \leqslant 15$ ns, $t_f \leqslant 6$ ns, PRR = 1 MHz, duty cycle = 50 %, $Z_{out} \approx 50$ ohms.

3

TTL DEVICES

OCTOBER 1976–REVISED DECEMBER 1983

- **Three-State, 4 Bit, Cascadable, Parallel-In, Parallel-Out Registers**

- **'LS395A Offers Three Times the Sink-Current Capability of 'LS395**

- **Low Power Dissipation . . . 75 mW Typical (Enabled)**

- **Applications:**
  N-Bit Serial-To-Parallel Converter
  N-Bit Parallel-To-Serial Converter
  N-Bit Storage Register

SN54LS395A . . . J OR W PACKAGE
SN74LS395A . . . D, J OR N PACKAGE
(TOP VIEW)

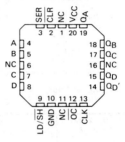

SN54LS395A . . . FK PACKAGE
SN74LS395A
(TOP VIEW)

NC - No internal connection

description

These 4-bit registers feature parallel inputs, parallel outputs, and clock (CLK), serial (SER), load shift (LD/$\overline{SH}$), output control ($\overline{OC}$) and direct overriding clear ($\overline{CLR}$) inputs.

Shifting is accomplished when the load/shift control is low. Parallel loading is accomplished by applying the four bits of data and taking the load/shift control input high. The data is loaded into the associated flip-flops and appears at the outputs after the high-to-low transition of the clock input. During parallel loading, the entry of serial data is inhibited.

When the output control is low, the normal logic levels of the four outputs are available for driving the loads or bus lines. The outputs are disabled independently from the level of the clock by a high logic level at the output control input. The outputs then present a high impedance and neither load nor drive the bus line; however, sequential operation of the registers is not affected. During the high-impedance mode, the output at Q_D' is still available for cascading.

3

TTL DEVICES

TEXAS
INSTRUMENTS

logic diagram

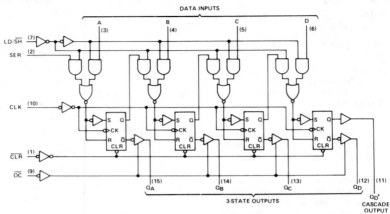

Pin numbers shown on logic notation are for D, J or N packages.

schematics of inputs and outputs

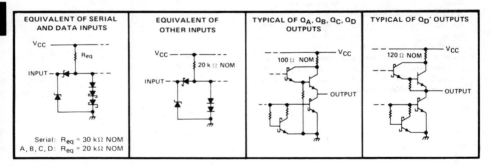

EQUIVALENT OF SERIAL AND DATA INPUTS	EQUIVALENT OF OTHER INPUTS	TYPICAL OF Q_A, Q_B, Q_C, Q_D OUTPUTS	TYPICAL OF Q_D' OUTPUTS

Serial: R_{eq} = 30 kΩ NOM
A, B, C, D: R_{eq} = 20 kΩ NOM

FUNCTION TABLE

INPUTS								3-STATE OUTPUTS				CASCADE
$\overline{CLR}$	LD/$\overline{SH}$	CLK	SER	PARALLEL				Q_A	Q_B	Q_C	Q_D	OUTPUT $Q_D{}'$
				A	B	C	D					
L	X	X	X	X	X	X	X	L	L	L	L	L
H	H	H	X	X	X	X	X	Q_{A0}	Q_{B0}	Q_{C0}	Q_{D0}	Q_{D0}
H	H	↓	X	a	b	c	d	a	b	c	d	d
H	L	H	X	X	X	X	X	Q_{A0}	Q_{B0}	Q_{C0}	Q_{D0}	Q_{D0}
H	L	↓	H	X	X	X	X	H	Q_{An}	Q_{Bn}	Q_{Cn}	Q_{Cn}
H	L	↓	L	X	X	X	X	L	Q_{An}	Q_{Bn}	Q_{Cn}	Q_{Cn}

When the output control is high, the 3-state outputs are disabled to the high-impedance state; however, sequential operation of the registers and the output at $Q_D{}'$ are not affected.

absolute maximum ratings over operating free-air temperature range (unless otherwise noted)

Supply voltage, V_{CC} (see Note 1) . . . . 7 V
Input voltage . . . . 7 V
Operating free-air temperature range: SN54LS395A . . . . −55°C to 125°C
SN74LS395A . . . . 0°C to 70°C
Storage temperature range . . . . −65°C to 150°C

NOTE 1: Voltage values are with respect to network ground terminal.

recommended operating conditions

		SN54LS395A			SN74LS395A			UNIT
		MIN	NOM	MAX	MIN	NOM	MAX	
Supply voltage, V_{CC}		4.5	5	5.5	4.75	5	5.25	V
High-level output current, I_{OH}	Q_A, Q_B, Q_C, Q_D			−1			−2.6	mA
	$Q_D{}'$			−400			−400	μA
Low-level output current, I_{OL}	Q_A, Q_B, Q_C, Q_D			12			24	mA
	$Q_D{}'$			4			8	mA
Clock frequency, f_{clock}		0		30	0		30	MHz
Width of clock pulse, $t_{w(clock)}$		16			16			ns
Setup time, high-level or low-level data, t_{su}	LD/$\overline{SH}$	40			40			ns
	All other inputs	20			20			
Hold time, high-level or low-level data, t_h		10			10			ns
Operating free-air temperature, T_A		−55		125	0		70	°C

3

TTL DEVICES

TEXAS
INSTRUMENTS

electrical characteristics over recommended operating free-air temperature range (unless otherwise noted)

PARAMETER		TEST CONDITIONS[†]		SN54LS395A			SN74LS395A			UNIT
				MIN	TYP[‡]	MAX	MIN	TYP[‡]	MAX	
V_{IH}	High-level input voltage			2			2			V
V_{IL}	Low-level input voltage					0.7			0.8	V
V_{IK}	Input clamp voltage	V_{CC} = MIN,	I_I = −18 mA			−1.5			−1.5	V
V_{OH}	High-level output voltage	V_{CC} = MIN, V_{IH} = 2 V, V_{IL} = V_{IL} max, I_{OH} = MAX	Q_A, Q_B, Q_C, Q_D	2.4	3.4		2.4	3.1		V
			Q_D'	2.5	3.4		2.7	3.4		V
V_{OL}	Low-level output voltage	V_{CC} = MIN, V_{IL} = V_{IL} max, V_{IH} = 2 V	Q_A, Q_B, Q_C, Q_D I_{OL} = 12 mA		0.25	0.4		0.25	0.4	V
			I_{OL} = 24 mA					0.35	0.5	
			Q_D I_{OL} = 4 mA		0.25	0.4		0.25	0.4	V
			I_{OL} = 8 mA					0.35	0.5	
I_{OZH}	Off-state output current, high-level voltage applied	V_{CC} = MAX, V_{IH} = 2 V, V_O = 2.7 V	Q_A, Q_B, Q_C, Q_D			20			20	μA
I_{OZL}	Off-state output current, low-level voltage applied	V_{CC} = MAX, V_{IH} = 2 V, V_O = 0.4 V	Q_A, Q_B, Q_C, Q_D			−20			−20	μA
I_I	Input current at maximum input voltage	V_{CC} = MAX,	V_I = 7 V			0.1			0.1	mA
I_{IH}	High-level input current	V_{CC} = MAX,	V_I = 2.7 V			20			20	μA
I_{IL}	Low-level input current	V_{CC} = MAX,	V_I = 0.4 V			−0.4			−0.4	mA
I_{OS}	Short-circuit output current[§]	V_{CC} = MAX	Q_A, Q_B, Q_C, Q_D	−30		−130	−30		−130	mA
			Q_D'	−20		−100	−20		−100	mA
I_{CC}	Supply current	V_{CC} = MAX,	See Note 2 Condition A		22	34		22	34	mA
			Condition B		21	31		21	31	

[†]For conditions shown as MIN or MAX, use the appropriate value specified under recommended operating conditions.

[‡]All typical values are at V_{CC} - 5 V, T_A - 25°C.

[§]Not more than one output should be shorted at a time, and duration of the short-circuit should not exceed one second.

NOTE 2: I_{CC} is measured with the outputs open, the serial input and mode control at 4.5 V, and the data inputs grounded under the following conditions:
    A. Output control at 4.5 V and a momentary 3 V, then ground, applied to clock input.
    B. Output control and clock input grounded.

switching characteristics, V_{CC} = 5 V, T_A = 25°C

PARAMETER		TEST CONDITIONS	MIN	TYP	MAX	UNIT
f_{max}	Maximum clock frequency	See Note 3, Q_A, Q_B, Q_C, Q_D outputs: R_L = 667 Ω, C_L = 45 pF Q_D' output: R_L = 2 kΩ, C_L = 15 pF C_L = 5 pF, See Note 3	30	45		MHz
t_{PHL}	Propagation delay time, high-to-low-level output from clear			22	35	ns
t_{PLH}	Propagation delay time, low-to-high-level output			15	30	ns
t_{PHL}	Propagation delay time, high-to-low-level output			20	30	ns
t_{PZH}	Output enable time to high level			15	25	ns
t_{PZL}	Output enable time to low level			17	25	ns
t_{PHZ}	Output disable time from high level			11	17	ns
t_{PLZ}	Output disable time from low level			12	20	ns

NOTE 3: See General Information Section for load circuits and voltage waveforms.

TEXAS
INSTRUMENTS

3

TTL DEVICES

- Parallel Access
- Typical Propagation Delay Time . . . 20 ns
- Typical Power Dissipation . . . 120 mW
- Applications:
  N-Bit Storage Files
  Hex/BCD Serial-To-Parallel Converters

description

These octal registers are organized as two 4-bit bytes of storage. Upon application of a positive-going clock signal, the information stored in byte 1 is transferred into byte 2 as a new 4-bit byte is loaded into the byte 1 location via the four data lines. The full 8-bit word is available at the outputs after two clock cycles. Both the clock and the strobe lines are fully buffered.

SN54LS396 . . . J OR W PACKAGE
SN74LS396 . . . D, J OR N PACKAGE
(TOP VIEW)

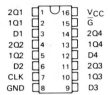

SN54LS396 . . . FK PACKAGE
SN74LS396
(TOP VIEW)

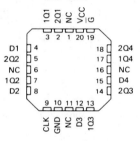

NC - No internal connection

logic symbol

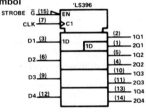

'LS396

Pin numbers shown on logic notation are for D, J or N packages.

FUNCTION TABLE

INPUTS						OUTPUTS							
STROBE	CLOCK	DATA				BYTE 1				BYTE 2			
$\overline{G}$		D1	D2	D3	D4	1Q1	1Q2	1Q3	1Q4	2Q1	2Q2	2Q3	2Q4
H	X	X	X	X	X	L	L	L	L	L	L	L	L
L	↑	a	b	c	d	a	b	c	d	$1Q1_n$	$1Q2_n$	$1Q3_n$	$1Q4_n$

H = high level (steady state), L = low level (steady state), X = irrelevant (any input, including transitions)
↑ = transition from low to high level
$1Q1_n$, $1Q2_n$, $1Q3_n$, $1Q4_n$ = the level of 1Q1, 1Q2, 1Q3, and 1Q4, respectively, before the most recent ↑ transition of the clock.

TEXAS INSTRUMENTS

3

TTL DEVICES

TYPES SN54LS396, SN74LS396
OCTAL STORAGE REGISTERS

logic diagram

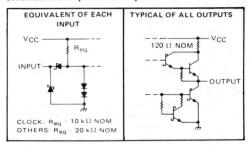

schematics of inputs and outputs

EQUIVALENT OF EACH INPUT	TYPICAL OF ALL OUTPUTS

CLOCK: $R_{eq} \approx 10\ k\Omega$ NOM
OTHERS: $R_{eq} \approx 20\ k\Omega$ NOM

Pin numbers shown on logic notation are for D, J or N packages.

absolute maximum ratings over operating free-air temperature range (unless otherwise noted)

Supply voltage, V_{CC} (see Note 1) . . . . 7 V
Input voltage . . . . 7 V
Operating free-air temperature range: SN54LS396 . . . . $-55°C$ to $125°C$
                               SN74LS396 . . . . $0°C$ to $70°C$
Storage temperature range . . . . $-65°C$ to $150°C$

NOTE 1: Voltage values are with respect to network ground terminal.

recommended operating conditions

	SN54LS396			SN74LS396			UNIT
	MIN	NOM	MAX	MIN	NOM	MAX	
Supply voltage, V_{CC}	4.5	5	5.5	4.75	5	5.25	V
High-level output current, I_{OH}			−400			−400	µA
Low-level output current, I_{OL}			4			8	mA
Clock frequency, f_{clock}	0		30	0		30	MHz
Width of clock pulse, t_W	20			20			ns
Setup time, t_{su}	20			20			ns
Hold time, t_h	5			5			ns
Operating free-air temperature, T_A	−55		125	0		70	°C

electrical characteristics over recommended operating free-air temperature range (unless otherwise noted)

PARAMETER		TEST CONDITIONS[†]	SN54LS396 MIN	SN54LS396 TYP[‡]	SN54LS396 MAX	SN74LS396 MIN	SN74LS396 TYP[‡]	SN74LS396 MAX	UNIT
V_{IH} High-level input voltage			2			2			V
V_{IL} Low-level input voltage					0.7			0.8	V
V_{IK} Input clamp voltage		V_{CC} = MIN, I_I = −18 mA			−1.5			−1.5	V
V_{OH} High-level output voltage		V_{CC} = MIN, V_{IH} = 2 V, V_{IL} = MAX, I_{OH} = −400 µA	2.5	3.4		2.7	3.4		V
V_{OL} Low-level output voltage		V_{CC} = MIN, V_{IH} = 2 V, V_{IL} = MAX, I_{OL} = 4 mA		0.25	0.4		0.25	0.4	V
		I_{OL} = 8 mA					0.35	0.5	
I_I Input current at maximum input voltage	Clock input	V_{CC} = MAX, V_I = 7 V			0.2			0.2	mA
	Other inputs				0.1			0.1	
I_{IH} High-level input current	Clock input	V_{CC} = MAX, V_I = 2.7 V			40			40	µA
	Other inputs				20			20	
I_{IL} Low-level input current	Clock input	V_{CC} = MAX, V_I = 0.4 V			−0.8			−0.8	mA
	Other inputs				−0.4			−0.4	
I_{OS} Short-circuit output current[§]		V_{CC} = MAX	−20		−100	−20		−100	mA
I_{CC} Supply current		V_{CC} = MAX, See Note 2		24	40		24	40	mA

[†]For conditions shown as MIN or MAX, use the appropriate value specified under recommended operating conditions.

[‡]All typical values are at V_{CC} = 5 V, T_A = 25°C.

[§]Not more than one output should be shorted at a time and duration of the short-circuit should not exceed one second.

NOTE 2: I_{CC} is measured with 4.5 V applied to all inputs and all outputs open.

switching characteristics, V_{CC} = 5 V, T_A = 25°C

PARAMETER		TEST CONDITIONS	MIN	TYP	MAX	UNIT
t_{PLH}	Propagation delay time, low-to-high-level output from clock	C_L = 15 pF, R_L = 2 kΩ, See Note 3		20	30	ns
t_{PHL}	Propagation delay time, high-to-low-level output from clock			20	30	
t_{PLH}	Propagation delay time, low-to-high-level output from strobe			20	30	ns
t_{PHL}	Propagation delay time, high-to-low-level output from strobe			20	30	

NOTE 3: See General Information Section for load circuits and voltage waveforms.

3

TTL DEVICES

TEXAS
INSTRUMENTS

3

TTL DEVICES

- Single-Rail Outputs on 'LS399
- Selects One of Two 4-Bit Data Sources and Stores Data Synchronously with System Clock
- Applications:

  Dual Source for Operands and Constants in Arithmetic Processor; Can Release Processor Register Files for Acquiring New Data

  Implement Separate Registers Capable of Parallel Exchange of Contents Yet Retain External Load Capability

  Universal Type Register for Implementing Various Shift Patterns; Even Has Compound Left-Right Capabilities

SN54LS399 ... J OR W PACKAGE
SN74LS399 ... D, J OR N PACKAGE
(TOP VIEW)

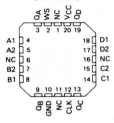

SN54LS399 ... FK PACKAGE
SN74LS399
(TOP VIEW)

NC – No internal connection

description

These monolithic quadruple two-input multiplexers with storage provide essentially the equivalent functional capabilities of two separate MSI functions (SN54LS157/SN74LS157 and SN54LS175/SN74LS175) in a single 16-pin or 20-pin package.

When the word-select input is low, word 1 (A1, B1, C1, D1) is applied to the flip-flops. A high input to word select will cause the selection of word 2 (A2, B2, C2, D2). The selected word is clocked to the output terminals on the positive-going edge of the clock pulse.

Typical power dissipation is 37 milliwatts. SN54LS399 is characterized for operation over the full military range of –55°C to 125°C. SN74LS399 is characterized for operation from 0°C to 70°C.

FUNCTIONAL TABLE

INPUTS		OUTPUTS			
WORD SELECT	CLOCK	Q_A	Q_B	Q_C	Q_D
L	↑	a1	b1	c1	d1
H	↑	a2	b2	c2	d2
X	L	Q_{A0}	Q_{B0}	Q_{C0}	Q_{D0}

3

TTL DEVICES

logic diagram

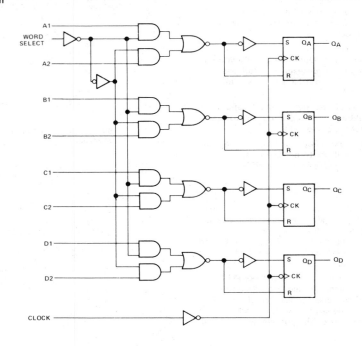

schematics of inputs and outputs

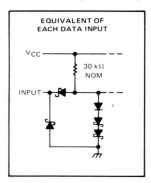

EQUIVALENT OF
EACH DATA INPUT

V_CC

30 kΩ
NOM

INPUT

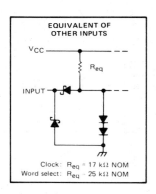

EQUIVALENT OF
OTHER INPUTS

V_CC

R_{eq}

INPUT

Clock: R_{eq} = 17 kΩ NOM
Word select: R_{eq} = 25 kΩ NOM

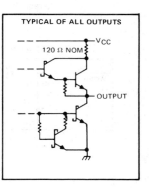

TYPICAL OF ALL OUTPUTS

V_CC

120 Ω NOM

OUTPUT

3

TTL DEVICES

TEXAS
INSTRUMENTS

absolute maximum ratings over operating free-air temperature range (unless otherwise noted)

Supply voltage, V_{CC} (see Note 1) . . . . 7 V
Input voltage . . . . 7 V
Operating free-air temperature range: SN54LS' . . . . -55°C to 125°C
SN74LS' . . . . 0°C to 70°C
Storage temperature range . . . . -65°C to 150°C

NOTE 1: Voltage values are with respect to network ground terminal.

recommended operating conditions

		SN54LS'			SN74LS'			UNIT
		MIN	NOM	MAX	MIN	NOM	MAX	
Supply voltage, V_{CC}		4.5	5	5.5	4.75	5	5.25	V
High-level output current, I_{OH}				−400			−400	μA
Low-level output current, I_{OL}				4			8	mA
Width of clock pulse, high or low level, t_W		20			20			ns
Setup time, t_{su}	Data	25			25			ns
	Word select	45			45			
Hold time, t_h	Data	0			0			ns
	Word select	0			0			
Operating free-air temperature, T_A		−55		125	0		70	$^{\circ}$C

electrical characteristics over recommended operating free-air temperature range (unless otherwise noted)

PARAMETER		TEST CONDITIONS[†]		SN54LS'			SN74LS'			UNIT
				MIN	TYP[‡]	MAX	MIN	TYP[‡]	MAX	
V_{IH}	High-level input voltage			2			2			V
V_{IL}	Low-level input voltage					0.7			0.8	V
V_{IK}	Input clamp voltage	V_{CC} = MIN,	I_I = −18 mA			−1.5			−1.5	V
V_{OH}	High-level output voltage	V_{CC} = MIN, V_{IH} = 2 V, V_{IL} = V_{IL}max I_{OH} = −400 μA		2.5	3.4		2.7	3.4		V
V_{OL}	Low-level output voltage	V_{CC} = MIN, V_{IH} = 2 V, V_{IL} = V_{IL}max	I_{OL} = 4 mA	0.25	0.4		0.25	0.4		V
			I_{OL} = 8 mA					0.35	0.5	
I_I	Input current at maximum input voltage	V_{CC} = MAX,	V_I = 7 V			0.1			0.1	mA
I_{IH}	High-level input current	V_{CC} = MAX,	V_I = 2.7 V			20			20	μA
I_{IL}	Low-level input current	V_{CC} = MAX,	V_I = 0.4 V			−0.4			−0.4	mA
I_{OS}	Short-circuit output current[§]	V_{CC} = MAX		−20		−100	−20		−100	mA
I_{CC}	Supply current	V_{CC} = MAX,	See Note 2		7.3	13		7.3	13	mA

[†] For conditions shown as MIN or MAX, use the appropriate value specified under recommended operating conditions.
[‡] All typical values are at V_{CC} = 5 V, T_A = 25°C.
[§] Not more than one output should be shorted at a time, duration of the short-circuit should not exceed one second.
NOTE 2: With all outputs open and all inputs except clock low, I_{CC} is measured after applying a momentary 4.5 V, followed by ground, to the clock input.

switching characteristics, V_{CC} = 5 V, T_A = 25°C

PARAMETER		TEST CONDITIONS	MIN	TYP	MAX	UNIT
t_{PLH}	Propagation delay time, low-to-high-level output	C_L = 15 pF, R_L = 2 kΩ, See Note 3		18	27	ns
t_{PHL}	Propagation delay time, high-to-low-level output			21	32	

NOTE 3: See General Information Section for load circuits and voltage waveforms.

3

TTL DEVICES

TEXAS INSTRUMENTS

TYPES SN54LS422, SN54LS423, SN74LS422, SN74LS423
RETRIGGERABLE MONOSTABLE MULTIVIBRATORS

D2536, JANUARY 1980

- Will Not Trigger from Clear
- D-C Triggered from Active-High or Active-Low Gated Logic Inputs
- Retriggerable for Very Long Output Pulses, Up to 100% Duty Cycle
- Overriding Clear Teminates Output Pulse
- 'LS422 Has Internal Timing Resistor

description

The 'LS422 and 'LS423 are identical to 'LS122 and 'LS123 except they cannot be triggered via clear.

These d-c triggered multivibrators feature output-pulse-width control by three methods. The basic pulse time is programmed by selection of external resistance and capacitance values (see typical application data). The 'LS422 contains an internal timing resistor that allows the circuits to be used with only an external capacitor, if so desired. Once triggered, the basic pulse width may be extended by retriggering the gated low-level-active (A) or high-level-active (B) inputs, or be reduced by use of the overriding clear. Figure 1 illustrates pulse control by retriggering and early clear.

The 'LS422 and 'LS423 have enough Schmitt hysteresis to ensure jitter-free triggering from the B input with transition rates as slow as 0.1 millivolt per nanosecond. The 'LS422 R_{int} is nominally 10 k ohms.

The SN54LS422 and SN54LS423 are characterized for operation over the full military temperature range of $-55°C$ to $125°C$. The SN74LS422 and SN74LS423 are characterized for operation from $0°C$ to $70°C$.

SN54LS423 . . . J OR W PACKAGE
SN74LS423 . . . D, J OR N PACKAGE
(TOP VIEW) (SEE NOTES 1 THRU 4)

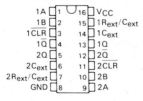

SN54LS422 . . . J OR W PACKAGE
SN74LS422 . . . D, J OR N PACKAGE
(TOP VIEW) (SEE NOTES 1 THRU 4)

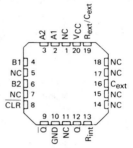

SN54LS422 . . . FK PACKAGE
SN74LS422
(TOP VIEW) (SEE NOTES 1 THRU 4)

SN54LS423 . . . FK PACKAGE
SN74LS423
(TOP VIEW) (SEE NOTES 1 THRU 4)

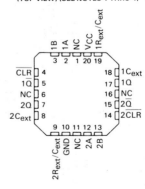

NOTES 1. An external timing capacitor may be connected between C_{ext} and R_{ext}/C_{ext} (positive).

2. To use the internal timing resistor of 'LS422, connect R_{int} to V_{CC}.

3. For improved pulse width accuracy and repeatability, connect an external resistor between R_{ext}/C_{ext} and V_{CC} with R_{int} open circuited.

4. To obtain variable pulse widths, connect an external variable resistance between R_{int} or R_{ext}/C_{ext} and V_{CC}.

TEXAS INSTRUMENTS

description (continued)

'LS422
FUNCTION TABLE

INPUTS				OUTPUTS	
CLEAR	A1	A2	B1	B2	Q	Q̄
L	X	X	X	X	L	H
X	H	H	X	X	L↑	H↑
X	X	X	L	X	L↑	H↑
X	X	X	X	L	L↑	H↑
H	L	X	↑	H	⊓	⊔
H	L	X	H	↑	⊓	⊔
H	X	L	↑	H	⊓	⊔
H	X	L	H	↑	⊓	⊔
H	H	↓	H	H	⊓	⊔
H	↓	↓	H	H	⊓	⊔
H	↓	H	H	H	⊓	⊔

'LS423
FUNCTION TABLE

INPUTS			OUTPUTS	
CLEAR	A	B	Q	Q̄
L	X	X	L	H
X	H	X	L↑	H↑
X	X	L	L↑	H↑
H	L	↑	⊓	⊔
H	↓	H	⊓	⊔

† These lines of the functional tables assume that the indicated steady-state conditions at the A and B inputs have been set up long enough to complete any pulse started before the set up.

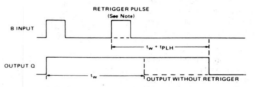

OUTPUT PULSE CONTROL USING RETRIGGER PULSE

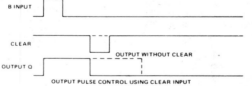

OUTPUT PULSE CONTROL USING CLEAR INPUT

NOTE: Retrigger pulses starting before 0.22 C_{ext} (in picofrads) nanoseconds after the initial trigger pulse will be ignored and the output pulse will remain unchanged.

FIGURE 1—TYPICAL INPUT/OUTPUT PULSES

TEXAS
INSTRUMENTS

3

TTL DEVICES

logic symbols

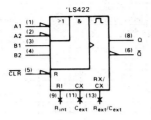

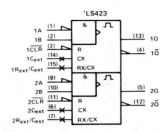

logic diagrams

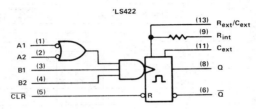

R_{int} is nominally 10 k ohms

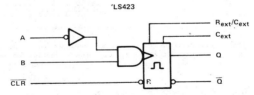

Pin numbers shown on logic notation are for D, J or N packages.

schematics of inputs and outputs

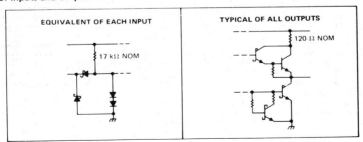

recommended operating conditions

	SN54LS' MIN	SN54LS' NOM	SN54LS' MAX	SN74LS' MIN	SN74LS' NOM	SN74LS' MAX	UNIT
Supply voltage, V_{CC}	4.5	5	5.5	4.75	5	5.25	V
High-level output current, I_{OH}			−400			−400	μA
Low-level output current, I_{OL}			4			8	mA
Pulse width, t_w	40			40			ns
External timing resistance, R_{ext}	5		180	5		260	kΩ
External capacitance, C_{ext}	No restriction			No restriction			
Wiring capacitance at R_{ext}/C_{ext} terminal			50			50	pF
Operating free-air temperature, T_A	−55		125	0		70	°C

electrical characteristics over recommended operating free-air temperature range (unless otherwise noted)

PARAMETER	TEST CONDITIONS[†]		SN54LS' MIN	SN54LS' TYP[‡]	SN54LS' MAX	SN74LS' MIN	SN74LS' TYP[‡]	SN74LS' MAX	UNIT
V_{IH} High-level input voltage			2			2			V
V_{IL} Low-level input voltage					0.7			0.8	V
V_{IK} Input clamp voltage	V_{CC} = MIN,	I_I = −18 mA			−1.5			−1.5	V
V_{OH} High-level output voltage	V_{CC} = MIN, $V_{IL} = V_{IL}$max	V_{IH} = 2 V, I_{OH} = −400 μA	2.5	3.5		2.7	3.5		V
V_{OL} Low-level output voltage	V_{CC} = MIN, V_{IH} = 2 V, $V_{IL} = V_{IL}$max	I_{OL} = 4 mA		0.25	0.4		0.25	0.4	V
		I_{OL} = 8 mA					0.35	0.5	
I_I Input current at maximum input voltage	V_{CC} = MAX,	V_I = 7 V			0.1			0.1	mA
I_{IH} High-level input current	V_{CC} = MAX,	V_I = 2.7 V			20			20	μA
I_{IL} Low-level input current	V_{CC} = MAX,	V_I = 0.4 V			−0.4			−0.4	mA
I_{OS} Short-circuit output current[♦]	V_{CC} = MAX		−20		−100	−20		−100	mA
I_{CC} Supply current (quiescent or triggered)	V_{CC} = MAX, See Note 6	'LS422		6	11		6	11	mA
		'LS423		12	20		12	20	

[†] For conditions shown as MIN or MAX, use the appropriate value specified under recommended operating conditions.
[‡] All typical values are at V_{CC} = 5 V, T_A = 25°C.
[♦] Not more than one output should be shorted at a time and duration of the short-circuit should not exceed one second.
NOTES: 5. To measure V_{OH} at Q, V_{OL} at $\overline{Q}$, or I_{OS} at Q, ground R_{ext}/C_{ext}, apply 2 V to B and clear, and pulse A from 2 V to 0 V.
6. With all outputs open and 4.5 V applied to all data and clear inputs, I_{CC} is measured after a momentary ground, then 4.5 V, is applied to clock.

switching characteristics, V_{CC} = 5 V, T_A = 25°C, see note 7

PARAMETER[¶]	FROM (INPUT)	TO (OUTPUT)	TEST CONDITIONS	MIN	TYP	MAX	UNIT
t_{PLH}	A	Q			23	33	ns
	B				23	44	
t_{PHL}	A	$\overline{Q}$	C_{ext} = 0, R_{ext} = 5 kΩ,		32	45	ns
	B		C_L = 15 pF, R_L = 2 kΩ		34	56	
t_{PHL}	Clear	Q			20	27	ns
t_{PLH}		$\overline{Q}$			28	45	
t_{wQ} (min)	A or B	Q			116	200	ns
t_{wQ}	A or B	Q	C_{ext} = 1000 pF, R_{ext} = 10 kΩ, C_L = 15 pF, R_L = 2 kΩ	4	4.5	5	μs

[¶] t_{PLH} = propagation delay time, low-to-high-level output
t_{PHL} = propagation delay time, high-to-low-level output
t_{wQ} = width of pulse at output Q
NOTE 7: See General Information Section for load circuits and voltage waveforms.

TEXAS
INSTRUMENTS

TYPICAL APPLICATION DATA FOR 'LS422, 'LS423[†]

The basic output pulse width is essentially determined by the values of external capacitance and timing resistance. For pulse widths when $C_{ext} \leq 1000$ pF, use Figure 3, or may be defined as:

$$t_W \approx K \cdot R_T \cdot C_{ext}$$

When $C_{ext} \geq 1$ μF, the output pulse width is defined as:

$$t_W \approx 0.33 \cdot R_T \cdot C_{ext}$$

Where

    K is multiplier factor, see Figure 4
    R_T is in K ohms (internal or external timing resistance)
    C_{ext} is in pF
    t_W is in nanoseconds

For maximum noise immunity, system ground should be applied to the C_{ext} node, even though the C_{ext} node is already tied to the ground lead internally. Due to the timing scheme used by the 'LS422 and 'LS423, a switching diode is not required to prevent reverse biasing when using electrolytic capacitors.

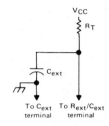

TIMING COMPONENT CONNECTIONS

FIGURE 2

'LS422, 'LS423
TYPICAL OUTPUT PULSE WIDTH
vs
EXTERNAL TIMING CAPACITANCE

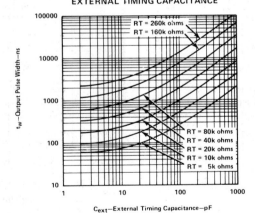

[†] This value of resistance exceeds the maximum recommended for use over the full temperature range of the SN54LS circuits.

FIGURE 3

TYPICAL APPLICATION DATA FOR 'LS422, 'LS423 †

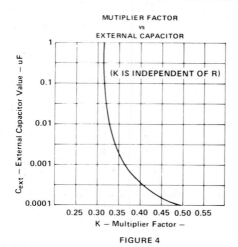

MUTIPLIER FACTOR
vs
EXTERNAL CAPACITOR

(K IS INDEPENDENT OF R)

C_{ext} — External Capacitor Value — uF

K — Multiplier Factor —

FIGURE 4

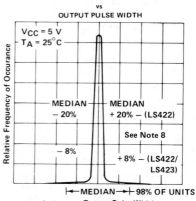

DISTRIBUTION OF UNIT
vs
OUTPUT PULSE WIDTH

V_{CC} = 5 V
T_A = 25°C

Relative Frequency of Occurance

MEDIAN — 20%   MEDIAN + 20% — (LS422)

See Note 8

— 8%   + 8% — (LS422/LS423)

|←—MEDIAN—→|←98% OF UNITS

$t_{w(out)}$ — Output Pulse Width

FIGURE 5

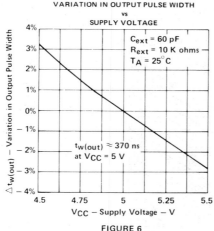

VARIATION IN OUTPUT PULSE WIDTH
vs
SUPPLY VOLTAGE

C_{ext} = 60 pF
R_{ext} = 10 K ohms
T_A = 25°C

$\Delta t_{w(out)}$ — Variation in Output Pulse Width

$t_{w(out)}$ ≈ 370 ns
at V_{CC} = 5 V

V_{CC} — Supply Voltage — V

FIGURE 6

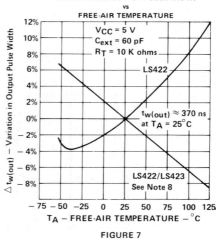

VARIATION IN OUTPUT PULSE WIDTH
vs
FREE-AIR TEMPERATURE

V_{CC} = 5 V
C_{ext} = 60 pF
R_T = 10 K ohms

LS422

$t_{w(out)}$ ≈ 370 ns
at T_A = 25°C

LS422/LS423
See Note 8

$\Delta t_{w(out)}$ — Variation in Output Pulse Width

T_A — FREE-AIR TEMPERATURE — °C

FIGURE 7

NOTE 8: For the LS422, the internal timing resistor, R_{int} was used. For the LS422/423, an external timing resistor was used for R_T.
† Data for temperatures below 0°C and above 70°C and for supply voltages below 4.75 V and above 5.25 V are applicable for SN54LS422 and SN54LS423 only.

TEXAS
INSTRUMENTS

- **3-Way Asynchronous Communication**
- **On-Chip Bus Selection Decoding**
- **Input Hysteresis Improves Noise Margin**
- **Choice of Open-Collector or 3-State Outputs**

description

These bus transceivers are designed for asynchronous three-way communication between four-line data buses. They give the designer a choice of selecting inverting, noninverting, or a combination of inverting and noninverting data paths with either 3-state or open-collector outputs.

The S0 and S1 inputs select the bus from which data are to be transferred. The $\overline{G}$ inputs enable the bus or buses to which data are to be transferred. The port for any bus selected for input and any other bus not enabled for output will be at high impedance including those of the open-collector devices.

The SN54LS440 through SN54LS444 are characterized for operation over the full military temperature range of $-55°C$ to $125°C$. The SN74LS440 through SN74LS444 are characterized for operation from $0°C$ to $70°C$.

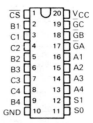

SN54LS' ... J PACKAGE
SN74LS' ... DW, J OR N PACKAGE
(TOP VIEW)

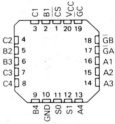

SN54LS' ... FK PACKAGE
SN74LS'
(TOP VIEW)

DEVICE	OUTPUT	LOGIC
'LS440	Open-Collector	True
'LS441	Open-Collector	Inverting
'LS442	3-State	True
'LS443	3-State	Inverting
'LS444	3-State	True/Inverting

3

TTL DEVICES

FUNCTION TABLE

INPUTS						TRANSFERS BETWEEN BUSES		
$\overline{CS}$	S1	S0	$\overline{GA}$	$\overline{GB}$	$\overline{GC}$	'LS440 'LS442	'LS441 'LS443	'LS444
H	X	X	X	X	X	None	None	None
X	H	H	X	X	X	None	None	None
X	X	X	H	H	H	None	None	None
X	L	L	X	H	H	None	None	None
X	L	H	H	X	H	None	None	None
X	H	L	H	H	X	None	None	None
L	L	L	X	L	L	A·B, A·C	$\overline{A}$·B, $\overline{A}$·C	$\overline{A}$·B, $\overline{A}$·C
L	L	H	L	X	L	B·C, B·A	$\overline{B}$·C, $\overline{B}$·A	$\overline{B}$·C, $\overline{B}$·A
L	H	L	L	L	X	C·A, C·B	C·A, C·B	$\overline{C}$·A, $\overline{C}$·B
L	L	L	X	L	H	A·B	$\overline{A}$·B	$\overline{A}$·B
L	L	H	H	X	L	B·C	$\overline{B}$·C	B·C
L	H	L	L	H	X	C·A	$\overline{C}$·A	$\overline{C}$·A
L	L	L	X	H	L	A·B	$\overline{A}$·C	$\overline{A}$·C
L	L	H	L	X	H	B·A	$\overline{B}$·A	$\overline{B}$·A
L	H	L	H	L	X	C·B	$\overline{C}$·B	C·B

TEXAS INSTRUMENTS

TYPES SN54LS440 THRU SN54LS444, SN74LS440 THRU SN74LS444
QUADRUPLE TRIDIRECTIONAL BUS TRANSCEIVERS

logic symbols

'LS440

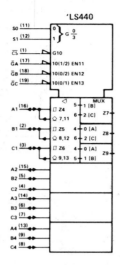

'LS441

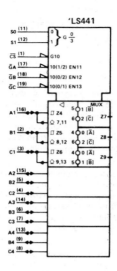

'LS442

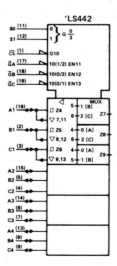

'LS444

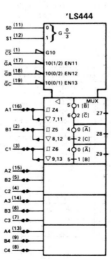

Pin numbers shown on logic notation are for DW, J or N packages.

TEXAS
INSTRUMENTS

logic diagram (composite showing one of four transceivers from each type, positive logic)

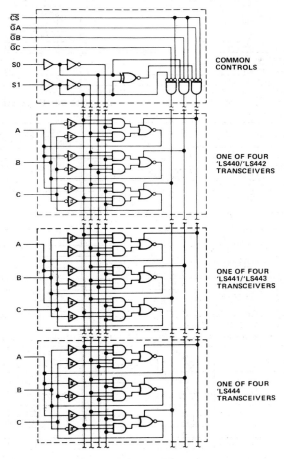

COMMON CONTROLS

ONE OF FOUR 'LS440/'LS442 TRANSCEIVERS

ONE OF FOUR 'LS441/'LS443 TRANSCEIVERS

ONE OF FOUR 'LS444 TRANSCEIVERS

3

TTL DEVICES

absolute maximum ratings over operating free-air temperature range (unless otherwise noted)

Supply voltage, V_{CC} (see Note 1)	7 V
Input voltage	7 V
Off-state output voltage	5.5 V
Operating free-air temperature range: SN54LS'	$-55°C$ to $125°C$
SN74LS'	$0°C$ to $70°C$
Storage temperature range	$-65°C$ to $150°C$

NOTE 1: Voltage values are with respect to network ground terminal.

TEXAS
INSTRUMENTS

recommended operating conditions

		SN54LS440 SN54LS441			SN74LS440 SN74LS441			UNIT
		MIN	NOM	MAX	MIN	NOM	MAX	
Supply voltage, V_{CC} (see Note 1)		4.5	5	5.5	4.75	5	5.25	V
High-level output voltage, V_{OH}				5.5			5.5	V
Low-level output current, I_{OL}				12			24	mA
Operating free-air temperature, T_A		−55		125	0		70	°C

NOTE 1: Voltage values are with respect to the network ground terminal.

electrical characteristics over recommended operating free-air temperature range (unless otherwise noted)

PARAMETER		TEST CONDITIONS†		SN54LS′			SN74LS′			UNIT
				MIN	TYP*	MAX	MIN	TYP*	MAX	
V_{IH} High-level input voltage				2			2			V
V_{IL} Low-level input voltage						0.5			0.6	V
V_{IK} Input clamp voltage		$V_{CC} = MIN$,	$I_I = -18\,mA$			−1.5			−1.5	V
Hysteresis ($V_{T+} - V_{T-}$)	A,B,C input	$V_{CC} = MIN$		0.1	0.4		0.2	0.4		V
I_{OH} High-level output current		$V_{CC} = MIN$, $V_{OH} = 5.5\,V$,	$V_{IH} = 2\,V$, $V_{IL} = V_{ILmax}$			100			100	μA
V_{OL} Low-level output voltage		$V_{CC} = MIN$, $V_{IH} = 2\,V$, $V_{IL} = V_{ILmax}$	$I_{OL} = 12\,mA$		0.25	0.4		0.25	04	V
			$I_{OL} = 24\,mA$					0.35	0.5	V
I_I Input current at	A,B,C input	$V_{CC} = MAX$	$V_I = 5.5\,V$			0.1			0.1	mA
maximum input voltage	All others		$V_I = 7\,V$			0.1			0.1	
I_{IH} High-level input current		$V_{CC} = MAX$, $V_I = 2.7\,V$				20			20	μA
I_{IL} Low-level input current		$V_{CC} = MAX$, $V_I = 0.4\,V$				−0.4			−0.4	mA
I_{CC} Supply current	Outputs low	$V_{CC} = MAX$, Outputs open			62	90		62	90	mA
	Outputs disabled				64	95		64	95	

† For conditions shown as MIN or MAX, use the appropriate value specified under recommended operating conditions.
* All typical values are at $V_{CC} = 5\,V$, $T_A = 25°C$.

switching characteristics at $V_{CC} = 5\,V$, $R_L = 667\,\Omega$, $C_L = 45\,pF$, $T_A = 25°C$, see note 2

PARAMETER		FROM (INPUT)	TO (OUTPUT)	'LS440			'LS441			UNIT
				MIN	TYP	MAX	MIN	TYP	MAX	
tPLH	Propagation delay time, low-to-high level output	A	B		24	35		21	30	ns
		A	C		24	35		21	30	
		B	A		24	35		21	30	
		B	C		24	35		21	30	
		C	A		24	35		21	30	
		C	B		24	35		21	30	
tPHL	Propagation delay time, high-to-low level output	A	B		20	30		9	15	ns
		A	C		20	30		9	15	
		B	A		20	30		9	15	
		B	C		20	30		9	15	
		C	A		20	30		9	15	
		C	B		20	30		9	15	
tPLH	Propagation delay time, low-to-high level output	any $\overline{G}$	A, B, C		29	45		23	35	ns
		S0, S1	A, B, C		33	50		27	40	
		$\overline{CS}$	A, B, C		31	45		26	40	
tPHL	Propagation delay time, high-to-low level output	any $\overline{G}$	A, B, C		27	40		20	30	ns
		S0, S1	A, B, C		32	50		26	40	
		$\overline{CS}$	A, B, C		28	45		21	30	

NOTE 2: See General Information Section for load circuits and voltage waveforms.

recommended operating conditions

	SN54LS442 SN54LS444			SN74LS442 SN74LS444			UNIT
	MIN	NOM	MAX	MIN	NOM	MAX	
Supply voltage, V_{CC} (see Note 1)	4.5	5	5.5	4.75	5	5.25	V
High-level output current, I_{OH}			−12			−15	V
Low-level output current, I_{OL}			12			24	mA
Operating free-air temperature, T_A	−55		125	0		70	°C

NOTE 1: Voltage values are with respect to the network ground terminal.

electrical characteristics over recommended operating free-air temperature range (unless otherwise noted)

PARAMETER		TEST CONDITIONS[†]		SN54LS'			SN74LS'			UNIT
				MIN	TYP[*]	MAX	MIN	TYP[*]	MAX	
V_{IH} High-level input voltage				2			2			V
V_{IL} Low-level input voltage						0.5			0.6	V
V_{IK} Input clamp voltage		V_{CC} = MIN, I_I = −18 mA				−1.5			−1.5	V
Hysteresis ($V_{T+} - V_{T-}$)	A,B,C input	V_{CC} = MIN		0.1	0.4		0.2	0.4		V
V_{OH} High-level output voltage		V_{CC} = MIN, V_{IH} = 2 V, V_{IL} = V_{ILmax}	I_{OL} = −3 mA	2.4	3.4		2.4	3.4		V
			I_{OH} = MAX	2			2			
V_{OL} Low-level output voltage		V_{CC} = MIN, V_{IH} = 2 V, V_{IL} = V_{ILmax}	I_{OL} = 12 mA		0.25	0.4		0.25	0.4	V
			I_{OL} = 24 mA					0.35	0.5	
I_{OZH} off-state output current, high-level voltage applied		V_{CC} = MAX, $\overline{CS}$ at 2 V	V_O = 2.7 V			20			20	μA
I_{OZL} Off-state output current, low-level voltage applied			V_O = 0.4 V			−400			−400	
I_I Input current at maximum input voltage	A, B, C	V_{CC} = MAX	V_I = 5.5 V			0.1			0.1	mA
	Others		V_I = 7 V			0.1			0.1	
I_{IH} High-level input current		V_{CC} = MAX, V_I = 2.7 V				20			20	μA
I_{IL} Low-level input current [§]		V_{CC} = MAX, V_I = 0.4 V				−0.4			−0.4	mA
I_{OS} Short circuit output current		V_{CC} = MAX		−40		−225	−40		−225	mA
I_{CC} Supply current	Output low	V_{CC} = MAX, Outputs open			62	90		62	90	mA
	Outputs at Hi-Z				64	95		64	95	

† For conditions shown as MIN or MAX, use the appropriate value specified under recommended operating conditions.
* All typical values are at V_{CC} = 5 V, T_A = 25°C.
§ Not more than one output should be shorted at a time, and duration of the short circuit should not exceed one second.

3

TTL DEVICES

TEXAS
INSTRUMENTS

switching characteristics, $V_{CC} = 5\,V$, $T_A = 25\,°C$, see note 2

PARAMETER		FROM (INPUT)	TO (OUTPUT)	TEST CONDITIONS	'LS442 MIN	'LS442 TYP	'LS442 MAX	'LS444 MIN	'LS444 TYP	'LS444 MAX	UNIT
tPLH	Propagation delay time, low-to-high level output	A	B			10	14		9	14	ns
		A	C			10	14		9	14	
		B	A			10	14		9	14	
		B	C			10	14		10	14	
		C	A			10	14		9	14	
		C	B			10	14		10	14	
tPHL	Propagation delay time, high-to-low level output	A	B	$C_L = 45\,pF$, $R_L = 667\,\Omega$,		13	20		7	13	ns
		A	C			13	20		7	13	
		B	A			13	20		7	13	
		B	C			13	20		13	20	
		C	A			13	20		7	13	
		C	B			13	20		13	20	
tPZL	Output enable time to low level	Any $\overline{G}$	A, B, C			22	33		22	33	ns
		S0 or S1	A, B, C			28	42		28	42	
		$\overline{CS}$	A, B, C			23	36		23	36	
tPZH	Output enable time to high level	$\overline{G}$, S, $\overline{CS}$	A, B, C			21	32		24	32	ns
tPLZ	Output disable time from low level	$\overline{G}$, S, $\overline{CS}$	A, B, C	$C_L = 5\,pF$, $R_L = 667\,\Omega$		14	25		14	25	ns
tPHZ	Output disable time from high level	$\overline{G}$, S, $\overline{CS}$	A, B, C			14	25		14	25	ns

NOTE 2: See General Information Section for load circuits and voltage waveforms.

schematics of inputs and outputs

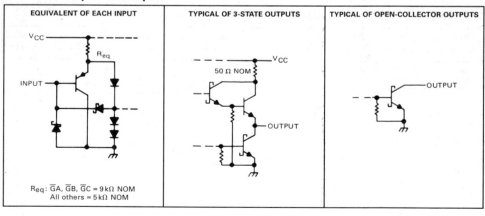

EQUIVALENT OF EACH INPUT

V_{CC}
R_{eq}
INPUT

R_{eq}: $\overline{GA}$, $\overline{GB}$, $\overline{GC} = 9\,k\Omega$ NOM
All others = $5\,k\Omega$ NOM

TYPICAL OF 3-STATE OUTPUTS

V_{CC}
$50\,\Omega$ NOM
OUTPUT

TYPICAL OF OPEN-COLLECTOR OUTPUTS

OUTPUT

3

TTL DEVICES

TEXAS
INSTRUMENTS

D2427, NOVEMBER 1977–REVISED DECEMBER 1983

FOR USE AS LAMP, RELAY, OR MOS DRIVERS

- Low-Voltage Version of SN54LS145/SN74LS145

- Full Decoding of Input Logic

- SN74LS445 Has 80-mA Sink-Current Capability

- All Outputs Are Off for Invalid BCD Input Conditions

- Low Power Dissipation . . . 35 mW Typical

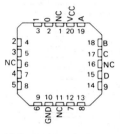

SN54LS445 . . . J PACKAGE
SN74LS445 . . . D, J OR N PACKAGE
(TOP VIEW)

SN54LS445 . . . FK PACKAGE
SN74LS445
(TOP VIEW)

NC - No internal connection

logic

FUNCTION TABLE

NO.	INPUTS				OUTPUTS									
	D	C	B	A	0	1	2	3	4	5	6	7	8	9
0	L	L	L	L	L	H	H	H	H	H	H	H	H	H
1	L	L	L	H	H	L	H	H	H	H	H	H	H	H
2	L	L	H	L	H	H	L	H	H	H	H	H	H	H
3	L	L	H	H	H	H	H	L	H	H	H	H	H	H
4	L	H	L	L	H	H	H	H	L	H	H	H	H	H
5	L	H	L	H	H	H	H	H	H	L	H	H	H	H
6	L	H	H	L	H	H	H	H	H	H	L	H	H	H
7	L	H	H	H	H	H	H	H	H	H	H	L	H	H
8	H	L	L	L	H	H	H	H	H	H	H	H	L	H
9	H	L	L	H	H	H	H	H	H	H	H	H	H	L
INVALID	H	L	H	L	H	H	H	H	H	H	H	H	H	H
	H	L	H	H	H	H	H	H	H	H	H	H	H	H
	H	H	L	L	H	H	H	H	H	H	H	H	H	H
	H	H	L	H	H	H	H	H	H	H	H	H	H	H
	H	H	H	L	H	H	H	H	H	H	H	H	H	H
	H	H	H	H	H	H	H	H	H	H	H	H	H	H

H = high level (off), L = low level (on)

description

These monolithic BCD-to-decimal decoder/drivers consist of eight inverters and ten four-input NAND gates. The inverters are connected in pairs to make BCD input data available for decoding by the NAND gates. Full decoding of valid BCD input logic ensures that all outputs remain off for all invalid binary input conditions. These decoders feature high-performance, n-p-n output transistors designed for use as indicator/relay drivers or as open-collector logic-circuit drivers. Each of the output transistors will sink up to 80 milliamperes of current. Each input is one Series 54LS/74LS standard load. Inputs and outputs are entirely compatible for use with TTL logic circuits, and the outputs are compatible for interfacing with most MOS integrated circuits. Power dissipation is typically 35 milliwatts.

logic diagram

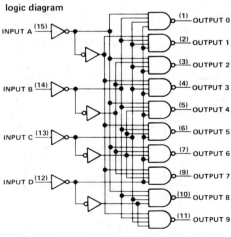

Pin numbers shown on logic notation are for D, J or N packages.

TEXAS INSTRUMENTS

TTL DEVICES

3

TYPES SN54LS445, SN74LS445
BCD-TO-DECIMAL DECODERS/DRIVERS

absolute maximum ratings over operating free-air temperature range (unless otherwise noted)

Supply voltage, V_{CC} (see Note 1) . . . . 7 V
Input voltage . . . . 7 V
Operating free-air temperature range: SN54LS445 . . . . $-55°C$ to $125°C$
                           SN74LS445 . . . . $0°C$ to $70°C$
Storage temperature range . . . . $-65°C$ to $150°C$

NOTE 1: Voltage values are with respect to network ground terminal.

recommended operating conditions

	SN54LS445			SN74LS445			UNIT
	MIN	NOM	MAX	MIN	NOM	MAX	
Supply voltage, V_{CC}	4.5	5	5.5	4.75	5	5.25	V
Off-state output voltage, $V_{O(off)}$			7			7	V
Operating free-air temperature, T_A	-55		125	0		70	°C

electrical characteristics over recommended operating free-air temperature range (unless otherwise noted)

PARAMETER		TEST CONDITIONS[†]		SN54LS445			SN74LS445			UNIT
				MIN	TYP[‡]	MAX	MIN	TYP[‡]	MAX	
V_{IH}	High-level input voltage			2			2			V
V_{IL}	Low-level input voltage					0.7			0.8	V
V_{IK}	Input clamp voltage	V_{CC} = MIN,	$I_I = -18$ mA			-1.5			-1.5	V
$I_{O(off)}$	Off-state output current	V_{CC} = MIN, $V_{IL} = V_{IL}$ max,	V_{IH} = 2 V, V_{OH} = 7 V			250			250	µA
$V_{O(on)}$	On-state output voltage	V_{CC} = MIN, V_{IH} = 2 V, $V_{IL} = V_{IL}$ max	I_{OL} = 12 mA	0.25		0.4	0.25		0.4	V
			I_{OL} = 24 mA				0.35		0.5	
			I_{OL} = 80 mA				2.3		3	
I_I	Input current at maximum input voltage	V_{CC} = MAX,	V_I = 7 V			0.1			0.1	mA
I_{IH}	High-level input current	V_{CC} = MAX,	V_I = 2.7 V			20			20	µA
I_{IL}	Low-level input current	V_{CC} = MAX,	V_I = 0.4 V			-0.4			-0.4	mA
I_{CC}	Supply current	V_{CC} = MAX,	See Note 2	7		13	7		13	mA

[†] For conditions shown as MIN or MAX, use the appropriate value specified under recommended operating conditions.
[‡] All typical values are at V_{CC} = 5 V, T_A = 25°C.
NOTE 2: I_{CC} is measured with all inputs grounded and outputs open.

switching characteristics, V_{CC} = 5 V, T_A = 25°C

PARAMETER		TEST CONDITIONS	MIN	MAX	UNIT
t_{PLH}	Propagation delay time, low-to-high-level output	C_L = 45 pF, R_L = 665 Ω, See Note 3		50	ns
t_{PHL}	Propagation delay time, high-to-low-level output			50	ns

NOTE 3: See General Information Section for load circuits and voltage waveforms.

logic symbol

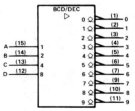

Pin numbers shown on logic notation are for D, J or N packages.

schematic of inputs and outputs

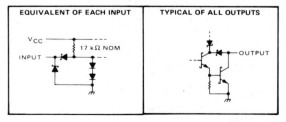

TEXAS
INSTRUMENTS

- 3-State Outputs Drive Bus Lines Directly
- P-N-P Inputs Reduce DC Loading on Bus Line
- Hysteresis at Bus Inputs Improves Noise Margins
- Flow-Thru Data Pinout (B Bus Opposite A Bus)
- Choice of True ('LS449) and Inverting ('LS446)

SN54LS446, SN54LS449 . . . J PACKAGE
SN74LS446, SN74LS449 . . . D, J OR N PACKAGE
(TOP VIEW)

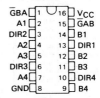

GBA	1	16	VCC
A1	2	15	GAB
DIR2	3	14	B1
A2	4	13	DIR1
A3	5	12	B2
DIR3	6	11	B3
A4	7	10	DIR4
GND	8	9	B4

SN54LS446, SN54LS449 . . . FK PACKAGE
SN74LS446, SN74LS449
(TOP VIEW)

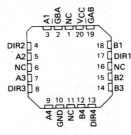

NC - No internal connection

description

These quadruple bus transceivers are designed for data transmission from individual lines of the A bus to individual lines of the B bus or the reverse, depending on the logic levels at the direction-control pins DIR1 through DIR4. These direction controls (one for each channel) allow maximum flexibility in timing. The enable inputs $\overline{GBA}$ and $\overline{GAB}$ can be used to disable the A or B outputs respectively, or to disable both buses for effective isolation.

The SN54LS446 and SN54LS449 are characterized for operation over the full military temperature range of -55°C to 125°C. The SN74LS446 and SN74LS449 are characterized for operation from 0°C to 70°C.

FUNCTION TABLE

ENABLE		DIRECTION	OPERATION	OPERATION
$\overline{GBA}$	$\overline{GAB}$	DIR	'LS446	'LS449
H	H	X	Isolation	Isolation
X	L	H	$\overline{A}$ data to B Bus	A data to B Bus
L	X	L	$\overline{B}$ data to A Bus	B data to A Bus
X	H	H	Isolation	Isolation
H	X	L	Isolation	Isolation

H = high level, L = low level, X = irrelevant

absolute maximum ratings over operating free-air temperature range (unless otherwise noted)

Supply voltage, V_{CC} (see Note 1)	7 V
Input voltage	7 V
Off-state output voltage	5.5 V
Operating free-air temperature range: SN54LS'	-55°C to 125°C
SN74LS'	0°C to 70°C
Storage temperature range	-65°C to 150°C

NOTE 1: Voltage values are with respect to the network ground terminal.

TEXAS
INSTRUMENTS

TTL DEVICES

3

logic symbols   logic diagrams (positive logic)

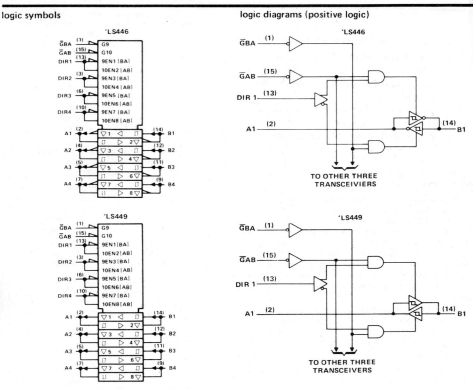

Pin numbers shown on logic notation are for D, J or N packages.

schematics of inputs and outputs

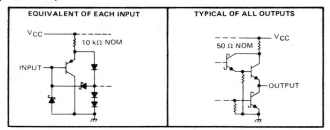

EQUIVALENT OF EACH INPUT	TYPICAL OF ALL OUTPUTS

TEXAS
INSTRUMENTS

recommended operating conditions

PARAMETER	SN54LS446 SN54LS449 MIN	NOM	MAX	SN74LS446 SN74LS449 MIN	NOM	MAX	UNIT
Supply voltage, V_{CC} (see Note 1)	4.5	5	5.5	4.75	5	5.25	V
High-level output current, I_{OH}			−12			−15	mA
Low-level output current, I_{OL}			12			24	mA
Operating free-air temperature, T_A	−55		125	0		70	°C

NOTE 1: Voltage values are with respect to network ground terminal.

electrical characteristics over recommended operating free-air temperature range (unless otherwise noted)

PARAMETER		TEST CONDITIONS†		SN54LS446 SN54LS449 MIN	TYP‡	MAX	SN74LS446 SN74LS449 MIN	TYP‡	MAX	UNIT
V_{IH}	High-level input voltage			2			2			V
V_{IL}	Low-level input voltage					0.6			0.7	V
V_{IK}	Input clamp voltage	V_{CC} = MIN,	I_I = −18 mA			−1.5			−1.5	V
	Hysteresis ($V_{T+} - V_{T-}$), A or B input	V_{CC} = MIN		0.1	0.4		0.2	0.4		V
V_{OH}	High-level output voltage	V_{CC} = MIN, V_{IH} = 2 V,	I_{OH} = −3 mA	2.4	3.4		2.4	3.4		V
		V_{IL} = V_{IL} max	I_{OH} = MAX	2			2			
V_{OL}	Low-level output voltage	V_{CC} = MIN, V_{IH} = 2 V,	I_{OL} = 12 mA		0.25	0.4		0.25	0.4	V
		V_{IL} = V_{IL} max	I_{OL} = 24 mA					0.35	0.5	
I_{OZH}	Off-state output current, high-level voltage applied	V_{CC} = MAX, V_O = 2.7 V	$\overline{G}$ at 2 V,			20			20	μA
I_{OZL}	Off-state output current, low-level voltage applied	V_{CC} = MAX, V_O = 0.4 V	$\overline{G}$ at 2 V,			−0.4			−0.4	mA
I_I	Input current at maximum input voltage	A or B	V_{CC} = MAX,	V_I = 5.5 V			0.1			0.1	mA
		$\overline{G}AB$ or $\overline{G}BA$		V_I = 7 V			0.1			0.1	
I_{IH}	High-level input current	V_{CC} = MAX,	V_I = 2.7 V			20			20	μA
I_{IL}	Low-level input current	V_{CC} = MAX,	V_I = 0.4 V			−0.4			−0.4	mA
I_{OS}	Short-circuit output current¶	V_{CC} = MAX		−40		−225	−40		−225	mA
I_{CC}	Total supply current	'LS446	V_{CC} = MAX, Outputs open	Outputs high		35	56		35	56	mA
				Outputs low		39	63		39	63	
				Outputs at Hi-Z		42	68		42	68	
		'LS449		Outputs high		42	68		42	68	
				Outputs low		47	75		47	75	
				Outputs at Hi-Z		50	80		50	80	

†For conditions shown as MIN or MAX, use the appropriate value specified under recommended operating conditions.

‡All typical values are at V_{CC} = 5 V, T_A = 25°C.

¶Not more than one output should be shorted at a time, and duration of the short-circuit should not exceed one second.

3

TTL DEVICES

TEXAS
INSTRUMENTS

switching characteristics at V_{CC} = 5 V, T_A = 25°C

PARAMETER		FROM (INPUT)	TO (OUTPUT)	TEST CONDITIONS	'LS446			'LS449			UNIT
					MIN	TYP	MAX	MIN	TYP	MAX	
t_{PLH}	Propagation delay time, low-to-high-level output	A	B			8	13		10	15	ns
		B	A	C_L = 45 pF,		8	13		10	15	
t_{PHL}	Propagation delay time, high-to-low-level output	A	B			7	12		11	17	ns
		B	A	R_L = 667 Ω,		7	12		11	17	
t_{PZL}	Output enable time to low level	$\overline{G}BA$	A			24	40		21	35	ns
		$\overline{G}AB$	B	See Note 2		24	40		21	35	
t_{PZH}	Output enable time to high level	$\overline{G}BA$	A			15	25		18	30	ns
		$\overline{G}AB$	B			15	25		18	30	
t_{PLZ}	Output disable time from low level	$\overline{G}BA$	A	C_L = 5 pF,		14	25		14	25	ns
		$\overline{G}AB$	B	R_L = 667 Ω,		14	25		14	25	
t_{PHZ}	Output disable time from high level	$\overline{G}BA$	A	See Note 2		10	15		10	15	ns
		$\overline{G}AB$	B			10	15		10	15	

NOTE 2: See General Information Section for load circuits and voltage waveforms.

3

TTL DEVICES

TEXAS
INSTRUMENTS

TYPES SN54LS465 THRU SN54LS468, SN74LS465 THRU SN74LS468
OCTAL BUFFERS WITH 3-STATE OUTPUTS

D2631, JANUARY 1981 – REVISED DECEMBER 1983

- Mechanically and Functionally Interchangeable With DM71/81LS95 thru DM71/81LS98
- P-N-P Inputs Reduce Bus Loading
- 3-State Outputs Rated at I_{OL} of 12 mA and 24 mA for 54LS and 74LS, Respectively

DEVICE	DATA PATH
'LS465	True
'LS466	Inverting
'LS467	True
'LS468	Inverting

description

These octal buffers utilize the latest low-power Schottky technology. The 'LS465 and 'LS466 have a two-input active-low AND enable gate controlling all eight data buffers. The 'LS467 and 'LS468 have two separate active-low enable inputs each controlling four data buffers. In either case, a high level on any $\overline{G}$ places the affected outputs at high impedance.

schematics of inputs and outputs

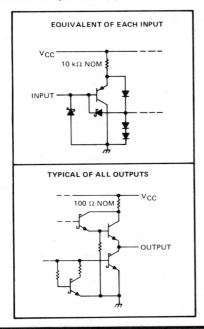

EQUIVALENT OF EACH INPUT

V_{CC}
10 kΩ NOM
INPUT

TYPICAL OF ALL OUTPUTS

V_{CC}
100 Ω NOM
OUTPUT

SN54LS465 AND SN54LS466 . . . J PACKAGE
SN74LS465 AND SN74LS466 . . . DW, J OR N PACKAGE
(TOP VIEW)

$\overline{G}1$	1	20	V_{CC}
A1	2	19	$\overline{G}2$
Y1	3	18	A8
A2	4	17	Y8
Y2	5	16	A7
A3	6	15	Y7
Y3	7	14	A6
A4	8	13	Y6
Y4	9	12	A5
GND	10	11	Y5

SN54LS465 AND SN54LS466 . . . FK PACKAGE
SN74LS465 AND SN74LS466
(TOP VIEW)

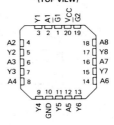

A2	4	18	A8
Y2	5	17	Y8
A3	6	16	A7
Y3	7	15	Y7
A4	8	14	A6

SN54LS467 AND SN54LS468 . . . J PACKAGE
SN74LS467 AND SN74LS468 . . . DW, J OR N PACKAGE
(TOP VIEW)

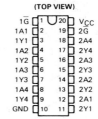

$1\overline{G}$	1	20	V_{CC}
1A1	2	19	$2\overline{G}$
1Y1	3	18	2A4
1A2	4	17	2Y4
1Y2	5	16	2A3
1A3	6	15	2Y3
1Y3	7	14	2A2
1A4	8	13	2Y2
1Y4	9	12	2A1
GND	10	11	2Y1

SN54LS467 AND SN54LS468 . . . FK PACKAGE
SN74LS467 AND SN74LS468
(TOP VIEW)

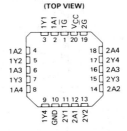

1A2	4	18	2A4
1Y2	5	17	2Y4
1A3	6	16	2A3
1Y3	7	15	2Y3
1A4	8	14	2A2

3

TTL DEVICES

TEXAS INSTRUMENTS

logic diagrams (positive logic)

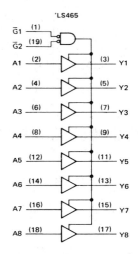

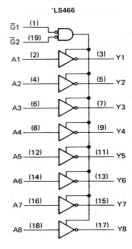

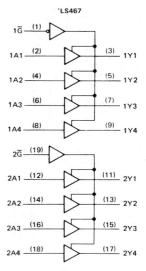

Pin numbers shown on logic notation are for DW, J or N packages.

TEXAS INSTRUMENTS

logic symbols

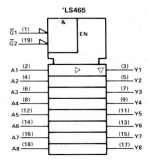

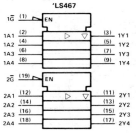

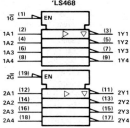

Pin numbers shown on logic notation are for DW, J or N packages.

absolute maximum ratings over operating free-air temperature range (unless otherwise noted)

Supply voltage, V_{CC} (see Note 1)	7 V
Input voltage	7 V
Off-state output voltage	5.5 V
Operating free-air temperature range: SN54LS465 thru SN54LS468	-55°C to 125°C
SN74LS465 thru SN74LS468	0°C to 70°C
Storage temperature range	-65°C to 150°C

NOTE 1: Voltage values are with respect to the network ground terminal.

recommended operating conditions

	SN54LS'			SN74LS'			UNIT
	MIN	NOM	MAX	MIN	NOM	MAX	
Supply voltage, V_{CC}	4.5	5	5.5	4.75	5	5.25	V
High-level output current, I_{OH}			-1			-2.6	mA
Low-level output current, I_{OL}			12			24	mA
Operating free-air temperature, T_A	-55		125	0		70	$^\circ$C

3

TTL DEVICES

electrical characteristics over recommended operating free-air temperature range (unless otherwise noted)

	PARAMETER		TEST CONDITIONS†		SN54LS' MIN	SN54LS' TYP‡	SN54LS' MAX	SN74LS' MIN	SN74LS' TYP‡	SN74LS' MAX	UNIT
V_{IH}	High-level input voltage				2			2			V
V_{IL}	Low-level input voltage						0.7			0.8	V
V_{IK}	Input clamp voltage		V_{CC} = MIN, I_I = −18 mA				−1.5			−1.5	V
V_{OH}	High-level output voltage		V_{CC} = MIN, V_{IH} = 2 V, V_{IL} = V_{IL} max	I_{OH} = −1 mA	2.4	3.3					V
				I_{OH} = −2.6 mA				2.4	3.1		
V_{OL}	Low-level output voltage		V_{CC} = MIN, V_{IH} = 2 V, V_{IL} = V_{IL} max	I_{OL} = 12 mA		0.25	0.4		0.25	0.4	V
				I_{OL} = 24 mA					0.35	0.5	
I_{OZH}	Off-state output current, high-level voltage applied		V_{CC} = MAX, V_{IH} = 2 V, V_{IL} = V_{IL} max, V_O = 2.7 V				20			20	µA
I_{OZL}	Off-state output current, low-level voltage applied		V_{CC} = MAX, V_{IH} = 2 V, V_{IL} = V_{IL} max, V_O = 0.4 V				−20			−20	µA
I_I	Input current at maximum input voltage		V_{CC} = MAX, V_I = 7 V				0.1			0.1	mA
I_{IH}	High-level input current		V_{CC} = MAX, V_I = 2.7 V				20			20	µA
I_{IL}	Low-level input current		V_{CC} = MAX, V_I = 0.4 V				−0.2			−0.2	mA
I_{OS}	Short-circuit output current§		V_{CC} = MAX, V_O = 0 V		−30		−130	−30		−130	mA
I_{CC}	Supply current	'LS465, 'LS467	V_{CC} = MAX	Outputs low		19	32		19	32	mA
				Outputs high		13	22		13	22	
				Output Hi-Z		22	37		22	37	
		'LS466, 'LS468		Outputs low		14	23		14	23	
				Outputs high		6	10		6	10	
				Outputs Hi-Z		17	28		17	28	

† For conditions shown as MIN or MAX, use the appropriate value specified under recommended operating conditions.
‡ All typical values are at V_{CC} = 5 V, T_A = 25°C.
§ Not more than one output should be shorted at a time, and duration of the short-circuit should not exceed one second.

switching characteristics, V_{CC} = 5 V, T_A = 25°C, see note 2

PARAMETER	FROM (INPUT)	TO (OUTPUT)	TEST CONDITIONS	'LS465, 'LS467 MIN	'LS465, 'LS467 TYP	'LS465, 'LS467 MAX	'LS466, 'LS468 MIN	'LS466, 'LS468 TYP	'LS466, 'LS468 MAX	UNIT
t_{PLH}	Ai	Yi	R_L = 667 Ω, C_L = 45 pF		9	15		7	12	ns
t_{PHL}	Ai	Yi			12	18		9	15	ns
t_{PZH}	$\overline{G}$ ↓	Y			25	40		25	40	ns
t_{PZL}	$\overline{G}$ ↓	Y			29	45		29	45	ns
t_{PHZ}	$\overline{G}$ ↑	Y	R_L = 667 Ω, C_L = 5 pF		25	40		25	40	ns
t_{PLZ}	$\overline{G}$ ↑	Y			30	45		30	45	ns

NOTE 2: See General Information Section for load circuits and voltage waveforms.

3

TTL DEVICES

TEXAS
INSTRUMENTS

- ● Dual Version of Popular SN5490A, SN54LS90, SN7490A, and SN74LS90 Counters
- ● Individual Clock, Direct Clear, and Set-to-9 Inputs for Each Decade Counter
- ● Dual Counters Can Significantly Improve System Densities as Package Count Can Be Reduced by 50%
- ● Maximum Count Frequency ... 35 MHz Typical
- ● Buffered Outputs Reduce Possibility of Collector Commutation

description

Each of these monolithic circuits contains eight master-slave flip-flops and additional gating to implement two individual 4-bit decade counters in a single package. Each decade counter has individual clock, clear, and set-to-9 inputs. BCD count sequences of any length up to divide-by-100 may be implemented with a single 'LS490. Buffering on each output is provided to ensure that susceptibility to collector commutation is reduced significantly. All inputs are diode-clamped to reduce the effects of line ringing. The counters have parallel outputs from each counter stage so that submultiples of the input count frequency are available for system timing signals.

The SN54LS490 is characterized for operation over the full military temperature range of −55°C to 125°C; the SN74LS490 is characterized for use in industrial systems operating from 0°C to 70°C.

SN74LS490 ... D, J OR N PACKAGE
(TOP VIEW)

1CLK	1	16	V_CC
1CLR	2	15	2CLK
1Q_A	3	14	2CLR
1SET9	4	13	2Q_A
1Q_B	5	12	2SET9
1Q_C	6	11	2Q_B
1Q_D	7	10	2Q_C
GND	8	9	2Q_D

SN54LS490 ... FK PACKAGE
SN74LS490
(TOP VIEW)

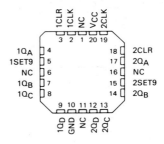

NC – No internal connection

logic symbol

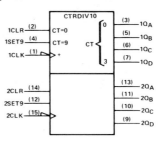

Pin numbers shown on logic notation are for D, J or N packages.

NC – No internal connection

BCD COUNT SEQUENCE
(EACH COUNTER)

COUNT	OUTPUT			
	Q_D	Q_C	Q_B	Q_A
0	L	L	L	L
1	L	L	L	H
2	L	L	H	L
3	L	L	H	H
4	L	H	L	L
5	L	H	L	H
6	L	H	H	L
7	L	H	H	H
8	H	L	L	L
9	H	L	L	H

CLEAR/SET-TO-9
FUNCTION TABLE
(EACH COUNTER)

INPUTS		OUTPUTS			
CLEAR	SET-TO-9	Q_A	Q_B	Q_C	Q_D
H	L	L	L	L	L
L	H	H	L	L	H
L	L	COUNT			

H = high level, L = low level

TTL DEVICES

3

TYPES SN54LS490, SN74LS490
DUAL 4-BIT DECADE COUNTERS

schematics of inputs and outputs

'LS490

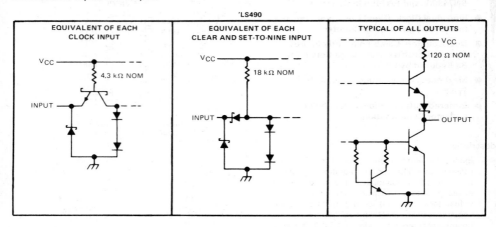

| EQUIVALENT OF EACH CLOCK INPUT | EQUIVALENT OF EACH CLEAR AND SET-TO-NINE INPUT | TYPICAL OF ALL OUTPUTS |

3

TTL DEVICES

TEXAS
INSTRUMENTS

logic diagram (each counter)

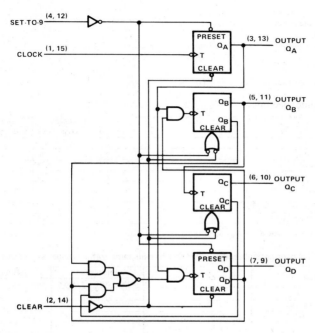

Pin numbers shown on logic notation are for D, J or N packages.

3

TTL DEVICES

TYPES SN54LS490, SN74LS490
DUAL 4-BIT DECADE COUNTERS

absolute maximum ratings over operating free-air temperature range (unless otherwise noted)

Supply voltage, V_{CC} (see Note 1) . . . . 7 V
Clear and set-to-9 input voltage . . . . 7 V
Clock input voltage . . . . 5.5 V
Operating free-air temperature range: SN54LS490 . . . . -55°C to 125°C
                               SN74LS490 . . . . 0°C to 70°C
Storage temperature range . . . . -65°C to 150°C

NOTE 1: Voltage values are with respect to network ground terminal.

recommended operating conditions

		SN54LS490			SN74LS490			UNIT
		MIN	NOM	MAX	MIN	NOM	MAX	
Supply voltage, V_{CC}		4.5	5	5.5	4.75	5	5.25	V
High-level output current, I_{OH}				-400			-400	μA
Low-level output current, I_{OL}				4			8	mA
Count frequency, f_{count}		0		25	0		25	MHz
Pulse width, t_W (any input)		20			20			ns
Clear or set-to-9 inactive-state setup time, t_{su}		25↓			25↓			ns
Operating free-air temperature, T_A		-55		125	0		70	°C

↓The arrow indicates that the falling edge of the clock pulse is used for reference.

electrical characteristics over recommended operating free-air temperature range (unless otherwise noted)

PARAMETER		TEST CONDITIONS[†]		SN54LS490			SN74LS490			UNIT
				MIN	TYP[‡]	MAX	MIN	TYP[‡]	MAX	
V_{IH}	High-level input voltage			2			2			V
V_{IL}	Low-level input voltage					0.7			0.8	V
V_{IK}	Input clamp voltage	$V_{CC} = $ MIN,	$I_I = -18$ mA			-1.5			-1.5	V
V_{OH}	High-level output voltage	$V_{CC} = $ MIN, $V_{IL} = V_{IL}$max	$V_{IH} = 2$ V,	2.5	3.4		2.7	3.4		V
V_{OL}	Low-level output voltage	$V_{CC} = $ MIN, $V_{IH} = 2$ V, $V_{IL} = V_{IL}$max	$I_{OL} = 4$ mA		0.25	0.4		0.25	0.4	V
			$I_{OL} = 8$ mA					0.35	0.5	
I_I	Input current at maximum input voltage	Clear, set-to-9	$V_{CC} = $ MAX, $V_I = 7$ V			0.1			0.1	mA
		Clock	$V_I = 5.5$ V			0.2			0.2	
I_{IH}	High-level input current	Clear, set-to-9	$V_{CC} = $ MAX, $V_I = 2.7$ V			20			20	μA
		Clock				100			100	
I_{IL}	Low-level input current	Clear, set-to-9	$V_{CC} = $ MAX, $V_I = 0.4$ V			-0.4			-0.4	mA
		Clock				-1.6			-1.6	
I_{OS}	Short-circuit output current[§]	$V_{CC} = $ MAX		-20		-100	-20		-100	mA
I_{CC}	Supply current	$V_{CC} = $ MAX,	See Note 2		15	26		15	26	mA

[†]For conditions shown as MIN or MAX, use the appropriate value specified under recommended operating conditions.
[‡]All typical values are at V_{CC} 5 V, T_A 25 C.
[§]Not more than one output should be shorted at a time, and duration of the short-circuit should not exceed one second.
NOTE 2: I_{CC} is measured with all outputs open, both clear inputs grounded following momentary connection to 4.5 V, and all other inputs grounded.

TEXAS
INSTRUMENTS

switching characteristics, V_{CC} = 5 V, T_A = 25°C

PARAMETER[¶]	FROM (INPUT)	TO (OUTPUT)	TEST CONDITIONS	MIN	TYP	MAX	UNIT
f_{max}	Clock	Q_A		25	35		MHz
t_{PLH}	Clock	Q_A			12	20	ns
t_{PHL}					13	20	
t_{PLH}	Clock	Q_B, Q_D	C_L = 15 pF, R_L = 2 kΩ		24	39	ns
t_{PHL}			See Figure 2 and Note 3		26	39	
t_{PLH}	Clock	Q_C			32	54	ns
t_{PHL}					36	54	
t_{PHL}	Clear	Any			24	39	ns
t_{PLH}	Set-to-9	Q_A, Q_D			24	39	ns
t_{PHL}		Q_B, Q_C			20	36	

¶ f_{max} = maximum count frequency
  t_{PLH} = Propagation delay time, low-to-high-level output
  t_{PHL} = Propagation delay time, high-to-low-level output
NOTE 3: See General Information Section for load circuits and voltage waveforms.

3

TTL DEVICES

TEXAS
INSTRUMENTS

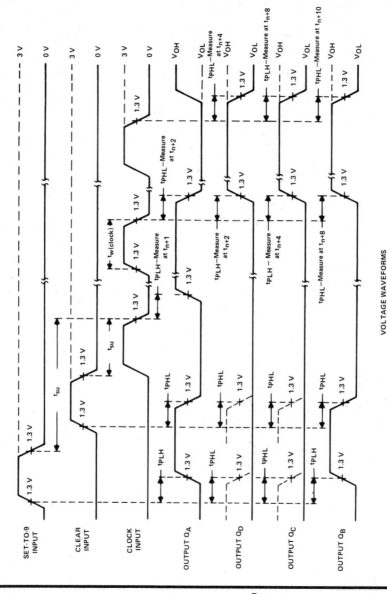

VOLTAGE WAVEFORMS

FIGURE 2

NOTES: A. Input pulses are supplied by a generator having the following characteristics: $t_r \leqslant 15$ ns, $t_f \leqslant 6$ ns, PRR = 1 MHz, duty cycle = 50%, $Z_{out} \approx 50$ ohms.

TEXAS
INSTRUMENTS

- 3-State Outputs Drive Bus Lines or Buffer Memory Address Registers
- P-N-P Inputs Reduce D-C Loading
- Hysteresis at Inputs Improves Noise Margins
- Data Flow-thru Pinout (All Inputs on Opposite Side from Outputs)

description

These octal buffers and line drivers are designed to have the performance of the popular SN54LS240/SN74LS240 series and, at the same time, offer a pinout having the inputs and outputs on opposite sides of the package. This arrangement greatly enhances printed circuit board layout.

The three-state control gate is a 2-input NOR such that if either $\overline{G1}$ or $\overline{G2}$ are high, all eight outputs are in the high-impedance state.

The 'LS540 offers inverting data and the 'LS541 offers true data at the outputs.

The SN54LS540 and SN54LS541 are characterized for operation over the full military temperature range of $-55°C$ to $125°C$. The SN74LS540 and SN74LS541 are characterized for operation from $0°C$ to $70°C$.

SN54LS540, SN54LS541 . . . J PACKAGE
SN74LS540, SN74LS541 . . . DW, J OR N PACKAGE
(TOP VIEW)

```
        ___  ___
 G1 [ 1     20 ] VCC
 A1 [ 2     19 ] G2
 A2 [ 3     18 ] Y1
 A3 [ 4     17 ] Y2
 A4 [ 5     16 ] Y3
 A5 [ 6     15 ] Y4
 A6 [ 7     14 ] Y5
 A7 [ 8     13 ] Y6
 A8 [ 9     12 ] Y7
GND [ 10    11 ] Y8
```

SN54LS540, SN54LS541 . . . FK PACKAGE
SN74LS540, SN74LS541
(TOP VIEW)

```
        A2  A1  G1  VCC  G2
         3   2   1   20  19
  A3 [ 4              18 ] Y1
  A4 [ 5              17 ] Y2
  A5 [ 6              16 ] Y3
  A6 [ 7              15 ] Y4
  A7 [ 8              14 ] Y5
         9  10  11  12  13
        A8  GND Y8  Y7  Y6
```

TYPE	RATED I_{OL} (SINK CURRENT)	RATED I_{OH} (SOURCE CURRENT)	TYPICAL POWER DISSIPATION (ENABLED)	
			'LS540	'LS541
SN54LS'	12 mA	-12 mA	92.5 mW	120 mW
SN74LS'	24 mA	-15 mA	92.5 mW	120 mW

schematics of inputs and outputs

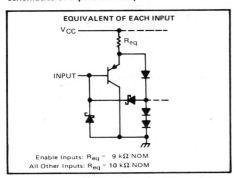

EQUIVALENT OF EACH INPUT

Enable Inputs: R_{eq} = 9 kΩ NOM
All Other Inputs: R_{eq} = 10 kΩ NOM

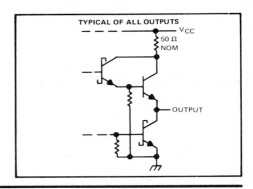

TYPICAL OF ALL OUTPUTS

50 Ω NOM

3

TTL DEVICES

TEXAS INSTRUMENTS

TYPES SN54LS540, SN54LS541, SN74LS540, SN74LS541
OCTAL BUFFERS AND LINE DRIVERS WITH 3-STATE OUTPUTS

logic symbols

'LS540

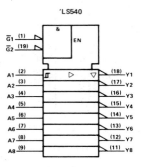

'LS541

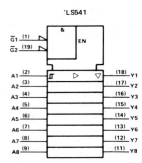

logic diagram (positive logic)

'LS540

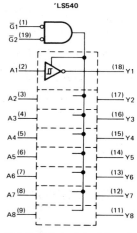

'LS541

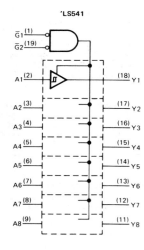

Pin numbers shown on logic notation are for DW, J or N packages.

absolute maximum ratings over operating free-air temperature range (unless otherwise noted)

Supply voltage, V_{CC} (see Note 1) . . . . 7 V

Input voltage . . . . 7 V

Operating free-air temperature range: SN54LS540, SN54LS541 . . . . -55°C to 125°C

SN74LS540, SN74LS541 . . . . 0°C to 70°C

Storage temperature range . . . . -65°C to 150°C

NOTE 1: Voltage values are with respect to the network ground terminal.

TEXAS
INSTRUMENTS

recommended operating conditions

PARAMETER	SN54LS' MIN	SN54LS' NOM	SN54LS' MAX	SN74LS' MIN	SN74LS' NOM	SN74LS' MAX	UNIT
Supply voltage, V_{CC} (see Note 1)	4.5	5	5.5	4.75	5	5.25	V
High-level output current, I_{OH}			−12			−15	mA
Low-level output current, I_{OL}			12			24	mA
Operating free-air temperature, T_A	−55		125	0		70	°C

NOTE 1: Voltage values are with respect to network ground terminal.

electrical characteristics over recommended operating free-air temperature range (unless otherwise noted)

PARAMETER		TEST CONDITIONS†		SN54LS' MIN	SN54LS' TYP‡	SN54LS' MAX	SN74LS' MIN	SN74LS' TYP‡	SN74LS' MAX	UNIT
V_{IH}	High-level input voltage			2			2			V
V_{IL}	Low-level input voltage					0.5			0.6	V
V_{IK}	Input clamp voltage	V_{CC} = MIN,	I_I = −18 mA			−1.5			−1.5	V
	Hysteresis ($V_{T+} - V_{T-}$)	V_{CC} = MIN		0.2	0.4		0.2	0.4		V
V_{OH}	High-level output voltage	V_{CC} = MIN, V_{IL} = V_{IL} max,	V_{IH} = 2 V, I_{OH} = −3 mA	2.4	3.4		2.4	3.4		V
		V_{CC} = MIN, V_{IL} = 0.5 V,	V_{IH} = 2 V, I_{OH} = MAX	2			2			
V_{OL}	Low-level output voltage	V_{CC} = MIN, V_{IH} = 2 V,	I_{OL} = 12 mA		0.25	0.4		0.25	0.4	V
		V_{IL} = V_{IL}max	I_{OL} = 24 mA					0.35	0.5	
I_{OZH}	Off-state output current, high-level voltage applied	V_{CC} = MAX, V_{IH} = 2 V,	V_O = 2.7 V			20			20	µA
I_{OZL}	Off-state output current, low-level voltage applied	V_{IL} = V_{IL}max	V_O = 0.4 V			−20			−20	
I_I	Input current at maximum input voltage	V_{CC} = MAX,	V_I = 7 V			0.1			0.1	mA
I_{IH}	High-level input current, any input	V_{CC} = MAX,	V_I = 2.7 V			20			20	µA
I_{IL}	Low-level input current	V_{CC} = MAX,	V_I = 0.4 V			−0.2			−0.2	mA
I_{OS}	Short-circuit output current♦	V_{CC} = MAX		−40		−225	−40		−225	mA
I_{CC}	Supply current	Outputs high 'LS540	V_{CC} = MAX, Outputs open		13	25		13	25	mA
		Outputs high 'LS541			18	32		18	32	
		Outputs low 'LS540			24	45		24	45	
		Outputs low 'LS541			30	52		30	52	
		All outputs disabled 'LS540			30	52		30	52	
		All outputs disabled 'LS541			32	55		32	55	

†For conditions shown as MIN or MAX, use the appropriate value specified under recommended operating conditions.

‡All typical values are at V_{CC} = 5 V, T_A = 25 C.

♦Not more than one output should be shorted at a time, and duration of the short-circuit should not exceed one second.

switching characteristics, V_{CC} = 5 V, T_A = 25°C

PARAMETER		TEST CONDITIONS	'LS540 MIN	'LS540 TYP	'LS540 MAX	'LS541 MIN	'LS541 TYP	'LS541 MAX	UNIT
t_{PLH}	Propagation delay time, low-to-high-level output	C_L = 45 pF, R_L = 667 Ω, See Note 2		9	15		9	15	ns
t_{PHL}	Propagation delay time, high-to-low-level output			9	15		10	18	ns
t_{PZL}	Output enable time to low level			25	38		25	38	ns
t_{PZH}	Output enable time to high level			15	25		20	32	ns
t_{PLZ}	Output disable time from low level	C_L = 5 pF, R_L = 667 Ω, See Note 2		10	18		10	18	ns
t_{PHZ}	Output disable time from high level			15	25		18	29	ns

NOTE 2: See General Information Section for load circuits and voltage waveforms.

TEXAS
INSTRUMENTS

3 TTL DEVICES

TYPES SN54LS590, SN54LS591, SN74LS590, SN74LS591
8-BIT BINARY COUNTERS WITH OUTPUT REGISTERS

D2632, JANUARY 1981 — REVISED JUNE 1983

- **8-Bit Counter with Register**
- **Parallel Register Outputs**
- **Choice of 3-State ('LS590) or Open-Collector ('LS591) Register Outputs**
- **Guaranteed Counter Frequency: DC to 20 MHz**

description

These devices each contain an 8-bit binary counter that feeds an 8-bit storage register. The storage register has parallel outputs. Separate clocks are provided for both the binary counter and storage register. The binary counter features a direct clear input $\overline{\text{CCLR}}$ and a count enable input $\overline{\text{CCKEN}}$. For cascading, a ripple carry output $\overline{\text{RCO}}$ is provided. Expansion is easily accomplished for two stages by connecting $\overline{\text{RCO}}$ of the first stage to $\overline{\text{CCKEN}}$ of the second stage. Cascading for larger count chains can be accomplished by connecting $\overline{\text{RCO}}$ of each stage to CCK of the following stage.

Both the counter and register clocks are positive-edge triggered. If the user wishes to connect both clocks together, the counter state will always be one count ahead of the register. Internal circuitry prevents clocking from the clock enable.

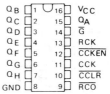

SN54LS590, SN54LS591 . . . J OR W PACKAGE
SN74LS590, SN74LS591 . . . J OR N PACKAGE
(TOP VIEW)

Q_B	1	16	V_{CC}
Q_C	2	15	Q_A
Q_D	3	14	$\overline{G}$
Q_E	4	13	RCK
Q_F	5	12	$\overline{\text{CCKEN}}$
Q_G	6	11	CCK
Q_H	7	10	$\overline{\text{CCLR}}$
GND	8	9	$\overline{\text{RCO}}$

SN54LS590, SN54LS591 . . . FK PACKAGE
SN74LS590, SN74LS591
(TOP VIEW)

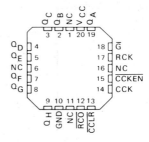

NC - No internal connection

schematics of inputs and outputs

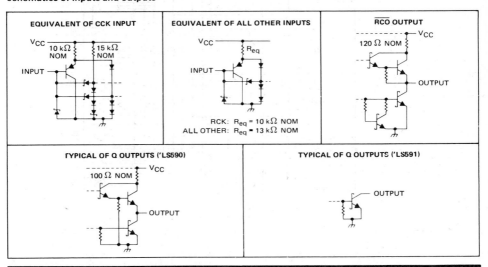

EQUIVALENT OF CCK INPUT	EQUIVALENT OF ALL OTHER INPUTS	$\overline{\text{RCO}}$ OUTPUT

RCK: R_{eq} = 10 kΩ NOM
ALL OTHER: R_{eq} = 13 kΩ NOM

TYPICAL OF Q OUTPUTS ('LS590)	TYPICAL OF Q OUTPUTS ('LS591)

TEXAS
INSTRUMENTS

3-933

3

TTL DEVICES

TYPES SN54LS590, SN54LS591, SN74LS590, SN74LS591
8-BIT BINARY COUNTERS WITH OUTPUT REGISTERS

logic diagram (positive logic)

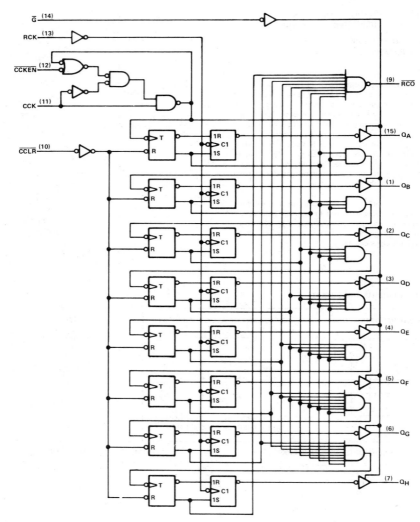

Pin numbers shown on logic notation are for J or N packages.

TEXAS
INSTRUMENTS

logic symbols

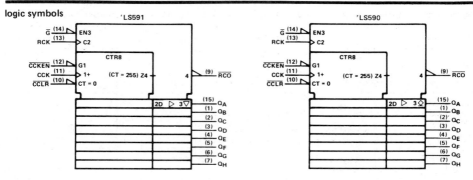

Pin numbers shown on logic notation are for J or N packages.

absolute maximum ratings over operating free-air temperature range (unless otherwise noted)

Supply voltage, V_{CC} (see Note 1) . . . . 7 V
Input voltage . . . . 7 V
Off-state output voltage . . . . 5.5 V
Operating free-air temperature range: SN54LS590, SN54LS591 . . . . -55°C to 125°C
SN74LS590, SN74LS591 . . . . 0°C to 70°C
Storage temperature range . . . . -65°C to 150°C

NOTE 1: Voltage values are with respect to the network ground terminal.

recommended operating conditions

			SN54LS'			SN74LS'			UNIT
			MIN	NOM	MAX	MIN	NOM	MAX	
V_{CC}	Supply voltage		4.5	5	5.5	4.75	5	5.25	V
V_{IH}	High-level input voltage		2			2			V
V_{IL}	Low-level input voltage				0.7			0.8	V
V_{OH}	High-level output voltage	Q, 'LS591 only			5.5			5.5	V
I_{OH}	High-level output current	$\overline{RCO}$			-1			-1	mA
		Q, 'LS590 only			-1			-2.6	
I_{OL}	Low-level output current	$\overline{RCO}$			8			16	mA
		Q			12			24	
f_{CCK}	Counter clock frequency		0		20	0		20	MHz
f_{RCK}	Register clock frequency		0		25	0		25	MHz
$t_{w(CCK)}$	Duration of counter clock pulse		25			25			ns
$t_{w(\overline{CCLR})}$	Duration of counter clear pulse		20			20			ns
$t_{w(RCK)}$	Duration of register clock pulse		20			20			ns
t_{su}	Setup time	CCKEN low before CCK↑	20			20			ns
		$\overline{CCLR}$ inactive before CCK↑	20			20			
		CCK before RCK↑ (see Note 2)	40			40			
t_h	Hold time	CCKEN low after CCK↑	0			0			ns
T_A	Operating free-air temperature		-55		125	0		70	C

NOTE 2: This setup time ensures the register will see stable data from the counter outputs. The clocks may be tied together in which case the register state will be one clock pulse behind the counter.

TEXAS
INSTRUMENTS

3

TTL DEVICES

TYPES SN54LS590, SN54LS591, SN74LS590, SN74LS591
8-BIT BINARY COUNTERS WITH OUTPUT REGISTERS

electrical characteristics over recommended operating free-air temperature range (unless otherwise noted)

PARAMETER		TEST CONDITIONS†		SN54LS' MIN	TYP‡	MAX	SN74LS' MIN	TYP‡	MAX	UNIT
V_{IK}		V_{CC} = MIN, I_I = -18 mA				-1.5			-1.5	V
V_{OH}	'LS590 Q	V_{CC} = MIN, V_{IH} = 2V, V_{IL} = MAX	I_{OH} = -1 mA	2.4	3.2					V
			I_{OH} = -2.6 mA				2.4	3.1		
	$\overline{RCO}$		I_{OH} = -1 mA	2.4	3.2		2.4	3.2		
I_{OH}	'LS591 Q	V_{CC} = MIN, V_{IH} = 2 V, V_{IL} = MAX	V_{OH} = 5.5 V,		0.1			0.1		mA
V_{OL}	Q	V_{CC} = MIN, V_{IH} = 2 V, V_{IL} = MAX	I_{OL} = 12 mA		0.25	0.4		0.25	0.4	V
			I_{OL} = 24 mA					0.35	0.5	
	$\overline{RCO}$		I_{OL} = 8 mA		0.25	0.4		0.25	0.4	
			I_{OL} = 16 mA					0.35	0.5	
I_{OZH}	'LS590 Q	V_{CC} = MAX, V_{IH} = 2 V, V_{IL} = MAX, V_O = 2.7 V				20			20	µA
I_{OZL}	'LS590 Q	V_{CC} = MAX, V_{IH} = 2 V, V_{IL} = MAX, V_O = 0.4 V				-20			-20	µA
I_I		V_{CC} = MAX, V_I = 7 V				0.1			0.1	mA
I_{IH}		V_{CC} = MAX, V_I = 2.7 V				20			20	µA
I_{IL}	CCK	V_{CC} = MAX, V_I = 0.4 V				-0.8			-0.8	mA
	All others					-0.2			-0.2	
I_{OS}§	'LS590 Q	V_{CC} = MAX, V_O = 0 V		-30		-130	-30		-130	mA
	$\overline{RCO}$			-20		-100	-20		-100	
I_{CC}	'LS590 I_{CCH}	V_{CC} = MAX, All possible inputs grounded, All outputs open			33	55		33	55	mA
	I_{CCL}				44	65		44	65	
	I_{CCZ}				46	65		46	65	
	'LS591 I_{CCH}				35	55		35	55	
	I_{CCL}				42	65		42	65	

† For conditions shown as MIN or MAX, use the appropriate value specified under recommended operating conditions.
‡ All typical values are at V_{CC} = 5 V, T_A = 25°C
§ Not more than one output should be shorted at a time and the duration of the short-circuit should not exceed one second.

switching characteristics, V_{CC} = 5 V, T_A = 25°C (see note 3)

PARAMETER	FROM (INPUT)	TO (OUTPUT)	TEST CONDITIONS	'LS590 MIN	TYP	MAX	'LS591 MIN	TYP	MAX	UNIT
f_{max}	CCK	$\overline{RCO}$	R_L = 1 kΩ, C_L = 30 pF	20	35		20	35		MHz
t_{PLH}	CCK↑	$\overline{RCO}$			14	22		16	24	ns
t_{PHL}	CCK↑	$\overline{RCO}$			20	30		25	38	ns
t_{PLH}	$\overline{CCLR}$↓	$\overline{RCO}$			30	45		32	48	ns
t_{PLH}	RCK↑	Q	R_L = 667 Ω, C_L = 45 pF		12	18		25	38	ns
t_{PHL}	RCK↑	Q			22	33		28	42	ns
t_{PZH}	$\overline{G}$↓	Q			25	38				ns
t_{PZL}	$\overline{G}$↓	Q			30	45				ns
t_{PHZ}	$\overline{G}$↑	Q	R_L = 667 Ω, C_L = 5 pF		20	30				ns
t_{PLZ}	$\overline{G}$↑	Q			25	38				ns
t_{PLH}	$\overline{G}$↑	Q	R_L = 667 Ω, C_L = 45 pF					34	50	ns
t_{PHL}	$\overline{G}$↓	Q						32	48	ns

NOTE 3: See General Information Section for load circuits and voltage waveforms.

3
TTL DEVICES

TEXAS
INSTRUMENTS

TYPES SN54LS592, SN54LS593, SN74LS592, SN74LS593
8-BIT BINARY COUNTERS WITH INPUT REGISTERS

02633, JANUARY 1981 — REVISED DECEMBER 1983

- **Parallel Register Inputs ('LS592)**

- **Parallel 3–State I/O: Register Inputs/ Counter Outputs ('LS593)**

- **Counter has Direct Overriding Load and Clear**

- **Guaranteed Counter Frequency: DC to 20 MHz**

description

The 'LS592 comes in a 16-pin package and consists of a parallel input, 8-bit storage register feeding an 8-bit binary counter. Both the register and the counter have individual positive-edge-triggered clocks. In addition, the counter has direct load and clear functions. A low-going $\overline{RCO}$ pulse will be obtained when the counter reaches the hex word FF. Expansion is easily accomplished for two stages by connecting $\overline{RCO}$ of the first stage to $\overline{CCKEN}$ of the second stage. Cascading for larger count chains can be accomplished by connecting $\overline{RCO}$ of each stage to CCK of the following stage.

The 'LS593 comes in a 20-pin package and has all the features of the 'LS592 plus 3-state I/O, which provides parallel counter outputs. The tables below show the operation of the enable (CCKEN, $\overline{CCKEN}$) inputs. A register clock enable ($\overline{RCKEN}$) is also provided.

OUTPUT ENABLE CONTROL ('593 ONLY)

G	$\overline{G}$	A/Q_A thru H/Q_H
L	L	input mode
L	H	input mode
H	L	output mode
H	H	input mode

COUNTER CLOCK ENABLE CONTROL

CCKEN	$\overline{CCKEN}$	EFFECT ON CCK
L	L	Enable
L	H	Disable
H	L	Enable
H	H	Enable

SN54LS592 . . . J OR W PACKAGE
SN74LS592 . . . J OR N PACKAGE
(TOP VIEW)

B	1	16	V_{CC}
C	2	15	A
D	3	14	$\overline{CLOAD}$
E	4	13	RCK
F	5	12	$\overline{CCKEN}$
G	6	11	CCK
H	7	10	$\overline{CCLR}$
GND	8	9	$\overline{RCO}$

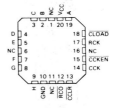

SN54LS592 . . . FK PACKAGE
SN74LS592
(TOP VIEW)

D 4 — 18 $\overline{CLOAD}$
E 5 — 17 RCK
NC 6 — 16 NC
F 7 — 15 $\overline{CCKEN}$
G 8 — 14 CCK

NC — No internal connection

SN54LS593 . . . J PACKAGE
SN74LS593 . . . DW, J OR N PACKAGE
(TOP VIEW)

A/Q_A	1	20	V_{CC}
B/Q_B	2	19	G
C/Q_C	3	18	$\overline{G}$
D/Q_D	4	17	$\overline{RCKEN}$
E/Q_E	5	16	RCK
F/Q_F	6	15	CCKEN
G/Q_G	7	14	$\overline{CCKEN}$
H/Q_H	8	13	CCK
$\overline{CLOAD}$	9	12	$\overline{CCLR}$
GND	10	11	$\overline{RCO}$

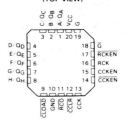

SN54LS593 . . . FK PACKAGE
SN74LS593
(TOP VIEW)

D/Q_D 4 — 18 $\overline{G}$
E/Q_E 5 — 17 $\overline{RCKEN}$
F/Q_F 6 — 16 RCK
G/Q_G 7 — 15 CCKEN
H/Q_H 8 — 14 $\overline{CCKEN}$

3

TTL DEVICES

TEXAS INSTRUMENTS

TYPES SN54LS592, SN54LS593, SN74LS592, SN74LS593
8-BIT BINARY COUNTERS WITH INPUT REGISTERS

schematics of inputs and outputs

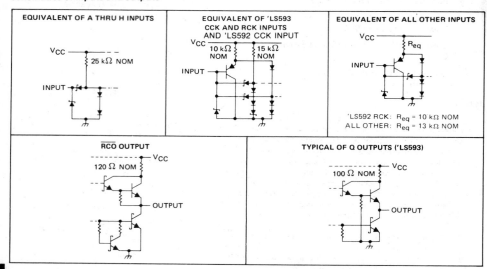

logic symbols

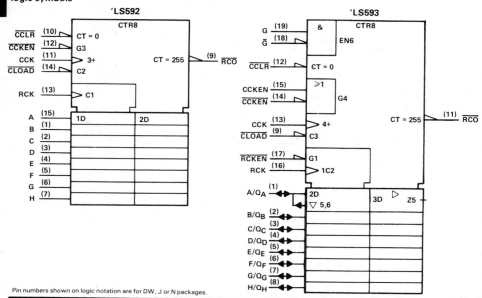

Pin numbers shown on logic notation are for DW, J or N packages.

TEXAS INSTRUMENTS

logic diagram (positive logic)

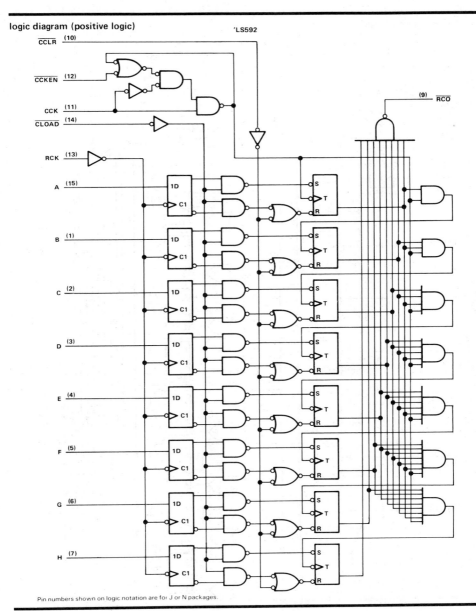

Pin numbers shown on logic notation are for J or N packages.

TTL DEVICES

logic diagram (positive logic)

'LS593

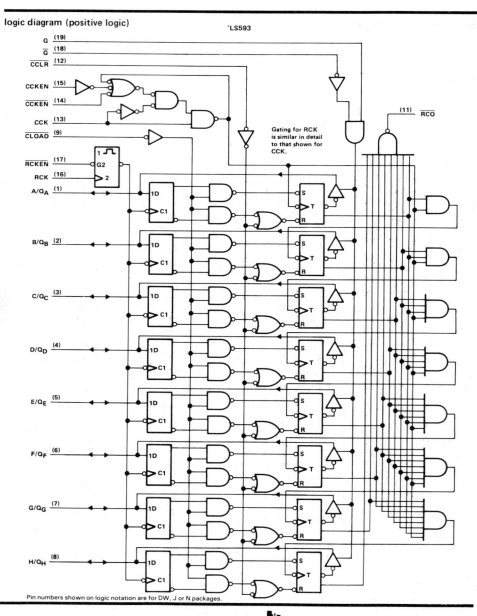

Pin numbers shown on logic notation are for DW, J or N packages.

TTL DEVICES

typical operating sequences

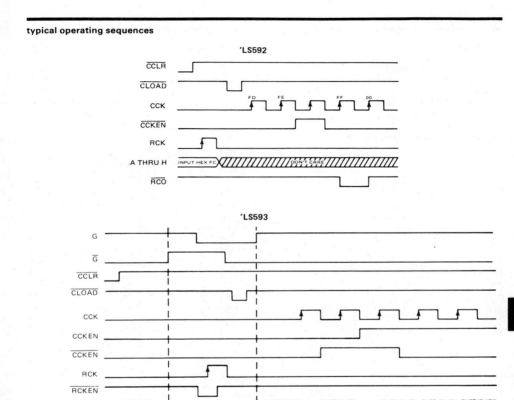

TEXAS
INSTRUMENTS

absolute maximum ratings over operating free-air temperature range (unless otherwise noted)

Supply voltage, V_{CC} (see Note 1) . . . . 7 V
Input voltage (excluding I/O ports) . . . . 7 V
Off-state output voltage (including I/O ports) . . . . 5.5 V
Operating free-air temperature range: SN54LS592, SN54LS593 . . . . -55°C to 125°C
SN74LS592, SN74LS593 . . . . 0°C to 70°C
Storage temperature range . . . . -65°C to 150°C

NOTE 1: Voltage values are with respect to the network ground terminal.

recommended operating conditions

			SN54LS'			SN74LS'			UNIT
			MIN	NOM	MAX	MIN	NOM	MAX	
V_{CC}	Supply voltage		4.5	5	5.5	4.75	5	5.25	V
V_{IH}	High-level input voltage		2			2			V
V_{IL}	Low-level input voltage				0.7			0.8	V
I_{OH}	High-level output current	$\overline{RCO}$			-1			-1	mA
		Q 'LS593 only			-1			-2.6	
I_{OL}	Low-level output current	$\overline{RCO}$			8			16	mA
		Q 'LS593 only			12			24	
f_{CCK}	Counter clock frequency		0		20	0		20	MHz
$t_{w (CCK)}$	Duration of counter clock pulse		25			25			ns
$t_{w (\overline{CCLR})}$	Duration of counter clear pulse		20			20			ns
$t_{w (RCK)}$	Duration of register clock pulse		20			20			ns
$t_{w (\overline{CLOAD})}$	Duration of counter load pulse		40			40			ns
t_{su}	Register enable setup time	$\overline{RCKEN}$ low to RCK ↑, 'LS593	20			20			ns
t_{su}	Counter enable setup time before CCK ↑	$\overline{CCKEN}$ low, 'LS592	30			30			ns
		$\overline{CCKEN}$ low or CCKEN high, 'LS593	30			30			
t_{su}	Setup time	$\overline{CCLR}$ inactive before CCK ↑	20			20			ns
		$\overline{CLOAD}$ inactive before CCK ↑	20			20			
		RCK ↑ before $\overline{CLOAD}$ ↑ (see Note 2)	30			30			
		Data A thru H before RCK ↑	20			20			
t_h	Hold time	Data A thru H after RCK ↑	0			0			ns
		All others	0			0			
T_A	Operating free-air temperature		-55		125	0		70	$^{\circ}$C

NOTE 2: This time insures the data saved by RCK ↑ will also be loaded into the counter.

TEXAS
INSTRUMENTS

3

TTL DEVICES

electrical characteristics over recommended operating free-air temperature range (unless otherwise noted)

PARAMETER		TEST CONDITIONS[†]		SN54LS' MIN	TYP‡	MAX	SN74LS' MIN	TYP‡	MAX	UNIT
V_{IK}		V_{CC} = MIN, I_I = −18 mA				−1.5			−1.5	V
V_{OH}	'LS593 Q	V_{CC} = MIN, V_{IH} = 2 V, V_{IL} = MAX	I_{OH} = −1 mA	2.4	3.2					V
			I_{OH} = −2.6 mA				2.4	3.1		
	$\overline{RCO}$		I_{OH} = −1 mA	2.4	3.2		2.4	3.2		
V_{OL}	'LS593 Q	V_{CC} = MIN, V_{IH} = 2 V, V_{IL} = MAX	I_{OL} = 12 mA		0.25	0.4		0.25	0.4	V
			I_{OL} = 24 mA					0.35	0.5	
	$\overline{RCO}$		I_{OL} = 8 mA		0.25	0.4		0.25	0.4	
			I_{OL} = 16 mA					0.35	0.5	
I_{OZH}	'LS593 Q	V_{CC} = MAX, V_{IH} = 2 V, V_{IL} = MAX, V_O = 2.7 V				20			20	µA
I_{OZL}	'LS593 Q	V_{CC} = MAX, V_{IH} = 2 V, V_{IL} = MAX, V_O = 0.4 V				−0.4			−0.4	mA
I_I	'LS593 Q	V_{CC} = MAX	V_I = 5.5 V			0.1			0.1	mA
	Others		V_I = 7 V			0.1			0.1	
I_{IH}		V_{CC} = MAX, V_I = 2.7 V				20			20	µA
I_{IL}	'LS593/593 CCK, RCK	V_{CC} = MAX, V_I = 0.4 V				−0.8			−0.8	mA
	A Thru H					−0.4			−0.4	
	Others					−0.2			−0.2	
I_{OS}§	'LS593 Q	V_{CC} = MAX, V_O = 0 V		−30		−130	−30		−130	mA
	$\overline{RCO}$			−20		−100	−20		−100	
I_{CC}	'LS592 I_{CCH}	V_{CC} = MAX, All possible inputs grounded, All outputs open			40	60		40	60	mA
	I_{CCL}				40	60		40	60	
	'LS593 I_{CCH}				47	70		47	70	
	I_{CCL}				53	80		53	80	
	I_{CCZ}				57	85		57	85	

† For conditions shown as MIN or MAX, use the appropriate value specified under recommended operating conditions.
‡ All typical values are at V_{CC} = 5 V, T_A = 25°C.
§ Not more than one output should be shorted at a time and the duration of the short-circuit should not exceed one second.

3

TTL DEVICES

TEXAS
INSTRUMENTS

TYPES SN54LS592, SN54LS593, SN74LS592, SN74LS593
8-BIT BINARY COUNTERS WITH INPUT REGISTERS

switching characteristics, V_{CC} = 5 V, T_A = 25°C, (see note 3)

PARAMETER	FROM (INPUT)	TO (OUTPUT)	TEST CONDITIONS	'LS592 MIN	'LS592 TYP	'LS592 MAX	'LS593 MIN	'LS593 TYP	'LS593 MAX	UNIT
f_{max}	CCK	$\overline{RCO}$	R_L = 1 kΩ, C_L = 30 pF	20	35		20	35		MHz
t_{PLH}	CCK ↑	Q						14	21	ns
t_{PHL}	CCK ↑	Q						26	39	ns
t_{PLH}	$\overline{CLOAD}$ ↓	Q						34	51	ns
t_{PHL}	$\overline{CLOAD}$ ↓	Q						28	42	ns
t_{PHL}	$\overline{CCLR}$ ↓	Q	R_L = 667 Ω, C_L = 45 pF					25	38	ns
t_{PZH}	G ↑	Q						31	47	ns
t_{PZL}	G ↑	Q						27	40	ns
t_{PZH}	$\overline{G}$ ↓	Q						29	45	ns
t_{PZL}	$\overline{G}$ ↓	Q						31	47	ns
t_{PHZ}	G ↓	Q						33	50	ns
t_{PLZ}	G ↓	Q	R_L = 667 Ω, C_L = 5 pF					35	52	ns
t_{PHZ}	$\overline{G}$ ↑	Q						26	39	ns
t_{PLZ}	$\overline{G}$ ↑	Q						28	42	ns
t_{PLH}	CCK ↑	$\overline{RCO}$			15	23		14	21	ns
t_{PHL}	CCK ↑	$\overline{RCO}$	R_L = 1 kΩ, C_L = 30 pF		20	30		20	30	ns
t_{PLH}	$\overline{CLOAD}$ ↓	$\overline{RCO}$			31	47		31	47	ns
t_{PHL}	$\overline{CLOAD}$ ↓	$\overline{RCO}$			27	41		27	41	ns
t_{PLH}	$\overline{CCLR}$ ↓	$\overline{RCO}$			30	45		30	45	ns
t_{PLH}	RCK ↑	$\overline{RCO}$	R_L = 1 kΩ, C_L = 30 pF $\overline{CLOAD}$ = L		35	53		42	63	ns
t_{PHL}	RCK ↑	$\overline{RCO}$			30	45		33	50	ns

NOTE 3: See General Information Section for load circuits and voltage waveforms.

TTL DEVICES

TEXAS
INSTRUMENTS

- **8-Bit Serial-In, Parallel-Out Shift Registers with Storage**

- **Choice of Output Configurations:**
  'LS594 ... Buffered
  'LS599 ... Open-Collector

- **Guaranteed Shift Frequency:**
  DC to 20 MHz

- **Independent Direct-Overriding Clears on Shift and Storage Registers**

- **Independent Clocks for Both Shift and Storage Registers**

description

These devices each contain an 8-bit D-type storage register. The storage register has buffered ('LS594) or open-collector ('LS599) outputs. Separate clocks and direct-overriding clears are provided on both the shift and storage registers. A shift output (Q_H') is provided for cascading purposes.

Both the shift register and the storage register clocks are positive-edge triggered. If the user wishes to connect both clocks together, the shift register will always be one clock pulse ahead of the storage register.

SN54LS594, SN54LS599 ... J OR W PACKAGE
SN74LS594, SN74LS599 ... J OR N PACKAGE

(TOP VIEW)

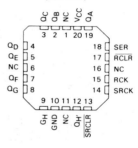

Q_B	1	16	V_{CC}
Q_C	2	15	Q_A
Q_D	3	14	SER
Q_E	4	13	$\overline{RCLR}$
Q_F	5	12	RCK
Q_G	6	11	SRCK
Q_H	7	10	$\overline{SRCLR}$
GND	8	9	$Q_{H'}$

SN54LS594, SN54LS599 ... FK PACKAGE
SN74LS594, SN74LS599

(TOP VIEW)

NC — No internal connection

schematics of inputs and outputs

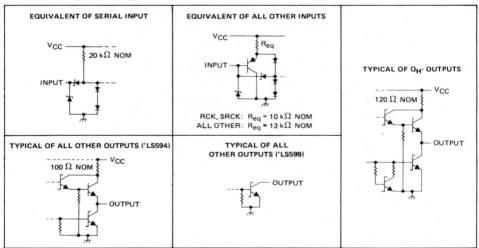

EQUIVALENT OF SERIAL INPUT	EQUIVALENT OF ALL OTHER INPUTS	
V_{CC} — 20 kΩ NOM, INPUT	V_{CC}, R_{eq}, INPUT. RCK, SRCK: R_{eq} = 10 kΩ NOM, ALL OTHER: R_{eq} = 13 kΩ NOM	TYPICAL OF $Q_{H'}$ OUTPUTS, 120 Ω NOM, V_{CC}, OUTPUT
TYPICAL OF ALL OTHER OUTPUTS ('LS594), 100 Ω NOM, V_{CC}, OUTPUT	TYPICAL OF ALL OTHER OUTPUTS ('LS599), OUTPUT	

TEXAS INSTRUMENTS

3

TTL DEVICES

TYPES SN54LS594, SN54LS599, SN74LS594, SN74LS599
8-BIT SHIFT REGISTERS WITH OUTPUT LATCHES

logic diagram (positive logic)

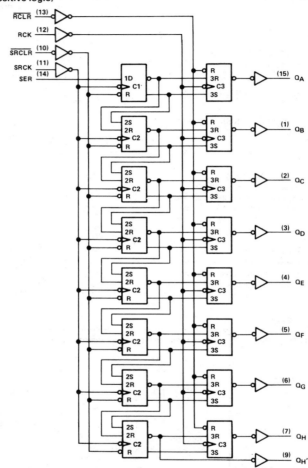

Pin numbers shown on logic notation are for J or N packages.

TEXAS
INSTRUMENTS

logic symbols

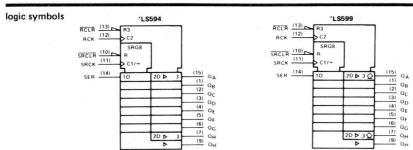

Pin numbers shown on logic notation are for J or N packages.

absolute maximum ratings over operating free-air temperature range (unless otherwise noted)

Supply voltage, V_{CC} (see Note 1). . . . . 7 V
Input voltage . . . . 7 V
Off-state output voltage . . . . 5.5 V
Operating free-air temperature range: SN54LS594, SN54LS599 . . . . $-55°C$ to $125°C$
                                         SN74LS594, SN74LS599 . . . . $0°C$ to $70°C$
Storage temperature range . . . . $-65°C$ to $150°C$

NOTE 1: Voltage values are with respect to the network ground terminal.

recommended operating conditions

			SN54LS'			SN74LS'			UNIT
			MIN	NOM	MAX	MIN	NOM	MAX	
V_{CC}	Supply voltage		4.5	5	5.5	4.75	5	5.25	V
V_{IH}	High-level input voltage		2			2			V
V_{IL}	Low-level input voltage				0.7			0.8	V
V_{OH}	High-level output voltage	Q_A thru Q_H, 'LS599 only			5.5			5.5	V
I_{OH}	High-level output current	Q_H'			-1			-1	mA
		Q_A thru Q_H, 'LS594 only			-1			-2.6	
I_{OL}	Low-level output current	Q_H'			8			16	mA
		Q			12			24	
f_{SRCK}	Shift clock frequency		0		20	0		20	MHz
f_{RCK}	Register clock frequency		0		25	0		25	MHz
$t_{w(SRCK)}$	Duration of shift clock pulse		25			25			ns
$t_{w(RCK)}$	Duration of register clock pulse		20			20			ns
$t_{w(SRCLR)}$	Duration of shift clear pulse, low level		20			20			ns
$t_{w(RCLR)}$	Duration of register clear pulse, low level		35			35			ns
t_{su}	Setup time	$\overline{SRCLR}$ inactive before SRCK↑	20			20			ns
		SER before SRCK↑	20			20			
		SRCK↑ before RCK↑ (see Note 2)	40			40			
		$\overline{SRCLR}$ low before RCK↑	40			40			
		$\overline{RCLR}$ high before RCK↑	20			20			
t_h	Hold time	SER after SRCK↑	0			0			ns
T_A	Operating free-air temperature		-55		125	0		70	C

NOTE 2: This setup time ensures the register will see stable data from the shift-register outputs. The clocks may be connected together, in which case the storage register state will be one clock pulse behind the shift register.

3

TTL DEVICES

TYPES SN54LS594, SN54LS599, SN74LS594, SN74LS599
8-BIT, SHIFT REGISTERS WITH OUTPUT LATCHES

electrical characteristics over recommended operating free-air temperature range (unless otherwise noted)

PARAMETER		TEST CONDITIONS †		SN54LS' MIN	SN54LS' TYP‡	SN54LS' MAX	SN74LS' MIN	SN74LS' TYP‡	SN74LS' MAX	UNIT
V_{IK}		V_{CC} = MIN,	I_I = −18 mA			−1.5			−1.5	V
V_{OH}	'LS594 Q	V_{CC} = MIN, V_{IH} = 2 V, V_{IL} = MAX	I_{OH} = −1 mA	2.4	3.2					V
			I_{OH} = −2.6 mA				2.4	3.1		
	Q_H'		I_{OH} = −1 mA	2.4	3.2		2.4	3.2		
I_{OH}	'LS599 Q	V_{CC} = MIN, V_{IH} = 2 V, V_{IL} = MAX, V_{OH} = 5.5 V				0.1			0.1	mA
V_{OL}	Q	V_{CC} = MIN, V_{IH} = 2 V, V_{IL} = MAX	I_{OL} = 12 mA		0.25	0.4	0.25	0.4		V
			I_{OL} = 24 mA				0.35	0.5		
	Q_H'		I_{OL} = 8 mA		0.25	0.4	0.25	0.4		
			I_{OL} = 16 mA				0.35	0.5		
I_I		V_{CC} = MAX,	V_I = 7 V			0.1			0.1	mA
I_{IH}		V_{CC} = MAX,	V_I = 2.7 V			20			20	µA
I_{IL}	SER	V_{CC} = MAX, V_I = 0.4 V				−0.4			−0.4	mA
	All others					−0.2			−0.2	
I_{OS} §	'LS594 Q	V_{CC} = MAX, V_O = 0		−30		−130	−30		−130	mA
	Q_H'			−20		−100	−20		−100	
I_{CCH}	'LS594	V_{CC} = MAX, All possible inputs grounded, All outputs open			34	50		34	50	mA
	'LS599				30	45		30	45	
I_{CCL}	'LS594				42	65		42	65	mA
	'LS599				38	55		38	55	

† For conditions shown as MIN or MAX, use the appropriate value specified under recommended operating conditions.
‡ All typical values are at V_{CC} = 5 V, T_A = 25°C.
§ Not more than one output should be shorted at a time, and duration of the short-circuit should not exceed one second.

switching characteristics, V_{CC} = 5 V, T_A = 25°C, (see note 3)

PARAMETER	FROM (INPUT)	TO (OUTPUT)	TEST CONDITIONS		'LS594 MIN	'LS594 TYP	'LS594 MAX	'LS599 MIN	'LS599 TYP	'LS599 MAX	UNIT
t_{PLH}	SRCK↑	Q_H'	R_L = 1 kΩ,	C_L = 30 pF		12	18		12	18	ns
t_{PHL}						15	23		17	25	ns
t_{PLH}	RCK↑	Q_A thru Q_H	R_L = 667 Ω,	C_L = 45 pF		12	18		28	42	ns
t_{PHL}						20	30		24	35	ns
t_{PHL}	SRCLR↓	Q_H'	R_L = 1 kΩ,	C_L = 30 pF		22	33		24	35	ns
t_{PHL}	RCLR↓	Q_A thru Q_H	R_L = 667 Ω,	C_L = 45 pF		38	57		40	60	ns

NOTE 3: See General Information Section for load circuits and voltage waveforms.

3

TTL DEVICES

Texas Instruments

02634, JANUARY 1981 – REVISED DECEMBER 1983

- **8-Bit Serial-In, Parallel-Out Shift Registers with Storage**

- **Choice of 3-State ('LS595) or Open-Collector ('LS596) Parallel Outputs**

- **Shift Register Has Direct Clear**

- **Guaranteed Shift Frequency: DC to 20 MHz**

description

These devices each contain an 8-bit serial-in, parallel-out shift register that feeds an 8-bit D-type storage register. The storage register has parallel 3-state ('LS595) or open-collector ('LS596) outputs. Separate clocks are provided for both the shift register and the storage register. The shift register has a direct-overriding clear, serial input, and serial output pins for cascading.

Both the shift register and storage register clocks are positive-edge triggered. If the user wishes to connect both clocks together, the shift register state will always be one clock pulse ahead of the storage register.

SN54LS595, SN54LS596 . . . J OR W PACKAGE
SN74LS595, SN74LS596 . . . J OR N PACKAGE
(TOP VIEW)

SN54LS595, SN54LS596 . . . FK PACKAGE
SN74LS595, SN74LS596
(TOP VIEW)

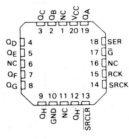

NC - No internal connection

schematics of inputs and outputs

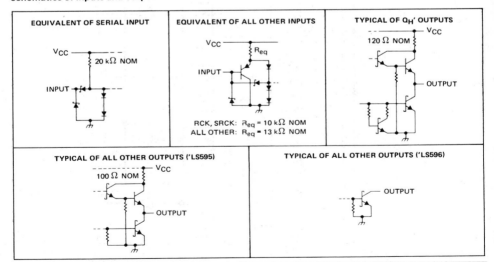

TEXAS
INSTRUMENTS

3

TTL DEVICES

TYPES SN54LS595, SN54LS596, SN74LS595, SN74LS596
8-BIT SHIFT REGISTERS WITH OUTPUT LATCHES

logic diagram (positive logic)

Pin numbers shown on logic notation are for J or N packages.

TEXAS
INSTRUMENTS

logic symbols

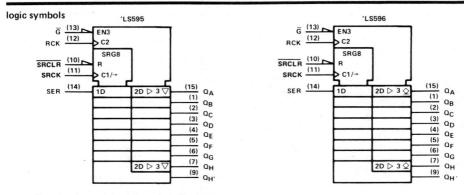

Pin numbers shown on logic notation are for J or N packages.

absolute maximum ratings over operating free-air temperature range (unless otherwise noted)

Supply voltage, V_{CC} (see Note 1) .... 7 V
Input voltage .... 7 V
Off-state output voltage .... 5.5 V
Operating free-air temperature range: SN54LS595, SN54LS596 .... −55°C to 125°C
SN74LS595, SN74LS596 .... 0°C to 70°C
Storage temperature range .... −65°C to 150°C

NOTE 1: Voltage values are with respect to the network ground terminal.

recommended operating conditions

			SN54LS'			SN74LS'			UNIT
			MIN	NOM	MAX	MIN	NOM	MAX	
V_{CC}	Supply voltage		4.5	5	5.5	4.75	5	5.25	V
V_{IH}	High-level input voltage		2			2			V
V_{IL}	Low-level input voltage				0.7			0.8	V
V_{OH}	High-level output voltage	Q_A thru Q_H, 'LS596 only			5.5			5.5	V
I_{OH}	High-level output current	Q_H'			−1			−1	mA
		Q_A thru Q_H, 'LS595 only			−1			−2.6	
I_{OL}	Low-level output current	Q_H'			8			16	mA
		Q			12			24	
f_{SRCK}	Shift clock frequency		0		20	0		20	MHz
$t_{w(SRCK)}$	Duration of shift clock pulse		25			25			ns
$t_{w(RCK)}$	Duration of register clock pulse		20			20			ns
$t_{w(\overline{SRCLR})}$	Duration of shift clear pulse, low level		20			20			ns
t_{su}	Setup time	$\overline{SRCLR}$ inactive before SRCK ↑	20			20			ns
		SER before SRCK ↑	20			20			
		SRCK ↑ before RCK ↑ (see Note 2)	40			40			
		$\overline{SRCLR}$ low before RCK ↑	40			40			
t_h	Hold time	SER after SRCK ↑	0			0			ns
T_A	Operating free-air temperature		−55		125	0		70	C

NOTE 2: This setup time ensures the register will see stable data from the shift-register outputs. The clocks may be connected together, in which case the storage register state will be one clock pulse behind the shift register.

TEXAS
INSTRUMENTS

3-951

3

TTL DEVICES

electrical characteristics over recommended operating free-air temperature range (unless otherwise noted)

PARAMETER		TEST CONDITIONS †		SN54LS' MIN	SN54LS' TYP‡	SN54LS' MAX	SN74LS' MIN	SN74LS' TYP‡	SN74LS' MAX	UNIT
V_{IK}		V_{CC} = MIN, I_I = −18 mA				−1.5			−1.5	V
V_{OH}	'LS595 Q	V_{CC} = MIN, V_{IH} = 2 V, V_{IL} = MAX	I_{OH} = −1 mA	2.4	3.2					V
			I_{OH} = −2.6 mA				2.4	3.1		
	Q_{H}'		I_{OH} = −1 mA	2.4	3.2		2.4	3.2		
I_{OH}	'LS596 Q	V_{CC} = MIN, V_{IH} = 2 V, V_{IL} = MAX, V_{OH} = 5.5 V				0.1			0.1	mA
V_{OL}	Q	V_{CC} = MIN, V_{IH} = 2 V, V_{IL} = MAX	I_{OL} = 12 mA		0.25	0.4		0.25	0.4	V
			I_{OL} = 24 mA					0.35	0.5	
	Q_{H}'		I_{OL} = 8 mA		0.25	0.4		0.25	0.4	
			I_{OL} = 16 mA					0.35	0.5	
I_{OZH}	'LS595 Q	V_{CC} = MAX, V_{IH} = 2 V, V_{IL} = MAX, V_{OH} = 2.7 V				20			20	μA
I_{OZL}	'LS595 Q	V_{CC} = MAX, V_{IH} = 2 V, V_{IL} = MAX, V_{OH} = 0.4 V				−20			−20	μA
I_I		V_{CC} = MAX, V_I = 7 V				0.1			0.1	mA
I_{IH}		V_{CC} = MAX, V_I = 2.7 V				20			20	μA
I_{IL}	SER	V_{CC} = MAX, V_I = 0.4 V				−0.4			−0.4	mA
	All others					−0.2			−0.2	
I_{OS} §	'LS595 Q	V_{CC} = MAX, V_O = 0 V		−30		−130	−30		−130	mA
	Q_{H}'			−20		−100	−20		−100	
I_{CCH}	'LS595	V_{CC} = MAX,			33	50		33	50	mA
	'LS596				30	45		30	45	
I_{CCL}	'LS595	All possible inputs grounded,			42	65		42	65	mA
	'LS596	All outputs open			36	55		36	55	
I_{CCZ}	'LS595				44	65		44	65	mA

† For conditions shown as MIN or MAX, use the appropriate value specified under recommended operating conditions.
‡ All typical values are at V_{CC} = 5 V, T_A = 25°C.
§ Not more than one output should be shorted at a time, and duration of the short-circuit should not exceed one second.

3

TTL DEVICES

TEXAS
INSTRUMENTS

switching characteristics, V_{CC} = 5 V, T_A = 25°C (see note 3)

PARAMETER	FROM (INPUT)	TO (OUTPUT)	TEST CONDITIONS		'LS595 MIN	'LS595 TYP	'LS595 MAX	'LS596 MIN	'LS596 TYP	'LS596 MAX	UNIT
t_{PLH}	SRCK ↑	Q_H'	R_L = 1kΩ,	C_L = 30 pF		12	18		14	21	ns
t_{PHL}						17	25		20	30	ns
t_{PLH}	RCK ↑	Q_A thru Q_H				12	18		28	42	ns
t_{PHL}			R_L = 667 Ω,	C_L = 45 pF		24	35		24	35	ns
t_{PZH}	$\overline{G}$ ↓	Q_A thru Q_H				20	30				ns
t_{PZL}						25	38				ns
t_{PHZ}	$\overline{G}$ ↑	Q_A thru Q_H	R_L = 667 Ω,	C_L = 5 pF		20	30				ns
t_{PLZ}						25	38				ns
t_{PLH}	$\overline{G}$ ↑	Q_A thru Q_H	R_L = 667 Ω,	C_L = 45 pF					40	60	ns
t_{PHL}	$\overline{G}$ ↓	Q_A thru Q_H							25	38	ns
t_{PHL}	$\overline{SRCLR}$ ↑	Q_H'	R_L = 1 kΩ,	C_L = 30 pF		24	35		24	35	ns

NOTE 3: See General Information Section for load circuits and voltage waveforms.

3

TTL DEVICES

3

TTL DEVICES

02635, JANUARY 1981—REVISED DECEMBER 1983

- **8-Bit Parallel Storage Register Inputs ('LS597)**

- **Parallel 3-State I/O, Storage Register Inputs, Shift Register Outputs ('LS598)**

- **Shift Register has Direct Overriding Load and Clear**

- **Guaranteed Shift Frequency ... DC to 20 MHz**

description

The 'LS597 comes in a 16-pin package and consists of an 8-bit storage latch feeding a parallel-in, serial-out 8-bit shift register. Both the storage register and shift register have positive-edge triggered clocks. The shift register also has direct load (from storage) and clear inputs.

The 'LS598 comes in a 20-pin package and has all the features of the 'LS597 plus 3-state I/O ports that provide parallel shift register outputs and also has multiplexed serial data inputs.

SN54LS597 ... J PACKAGE
SN74LS597 ... J OR N PACKAGE
(TOP VIEW)

SN54LS597 ... FK PACKAGE
SN74LS597
(TOP VIEW)

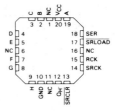

SN54LS598 ... J PACKAGE
SN74LS598 ... DW, J OR N PACKAGE
(TOP VIEW)

SN54LS598 ... FK PACKAGE
SN74LS598
(TOP VIEW)

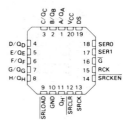

NC - No internal connection

3

TTL DEVICES

TEXAS
INSTRUMENTS

schematics of inputs and outputs

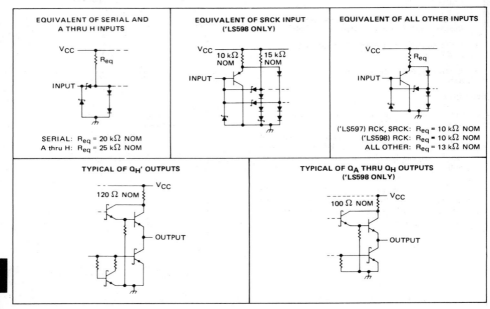

EQUIVALENT OF SERIAL AND A THRU H INPUTS	EQUIVALENT OF SRCK INPUT ('LS598 ONLY)	EQUIVALENT OF ALL OTHER INPUTS

SERIAL: R_{eq} = 20 kΩ NOM
A thru H: R_{eq} = 25 kΩ NOM

('LS597) RCK, SRCK: R_{eq} = 10 kΩ NOM
('LS598) RCK: R_{eq} = 10 kΩ NOM
ALL OTHER: R_{eq} = 13 kΩ NOM

TYPICAL OF Q_H' OUTPUTS

120 Ω NOM

TYPICAL OF Q_A THRU Q_H OUTPUTS ('LS598 ONLY)

100 Ω NOM

logic symbols

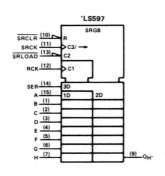

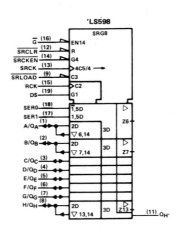

Pin numbers shown on logic notation are for DW, J or N packages.

3
TTL DEVICES

logic diagram (positive logic)

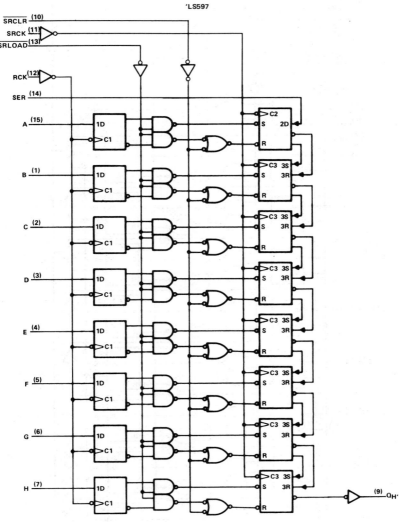

Pin numbers shown on logic notation are for J or N packages.

TEXAS
INSTRUMENTS

3

TTL DEVICES

TYPES SN54LS598, SN74LS598
8-BIT SHIFT REGISTERS WITH INPUT LATCHES

logic diagram (positive logic)

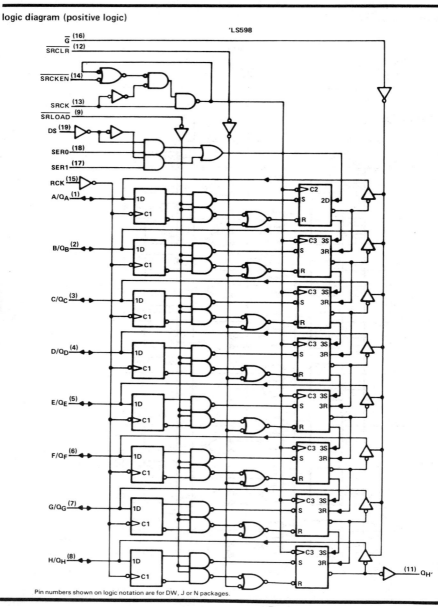

Pin numbers shown on logic notation are for DW, J or N packages.

TEXAS
INSTRUMENTS

absolute maximum ratings over operating free-air temperature range (unless otherwise noted)

Supply voltage, V_{CC} (see Note 1) . . . . 7 V
Input voltage (excluding I/O ports) . . . . 7 V
Off-state output voltage (including I/O ports) . . . . 5.5 V
Operating free-air temperature range: SN54LS597, SN54LS598 . . . . − 55°C to 125°C
SN74LS597, SN74LS598 . . . . 0°C to 70°C
Storage temperature range . . . . − 65°C to 150°C

NOTE 1: Voltage values are with respect to the network ground terminal.

recommended operating conditions

				SN54LS'			SN74LS'			UNIT
				MIN	NOM	MAX	MIN	NOM	MAX	
V_{CC}	Supply voltage			4.5	5	5.5	4.75	5	5.25	V
V_{IH}	High-level input voltage			2			2			V
V_{IL}	Low-level input voltage					0.7			0.8	V
I_{OH}	High-level output current	$Q_H{'}$				− 1			− 1	mA
		Q_A thru Q_H, 'LS598 only				− 1			− 2.6	
I_{OL}	Low-level output current	$Q_H{'}$				8			16	mA
		Q_A thru Q_H, 'LS598 only				12			24	
f_{SCK}	Shift clock frequency			0		20	0		20	MHz
t_w	Pulse duration	SRCK	high	15			15			ns
			low	35			35			
		RCK		20			20			
		SRCLR		20			20			
		SRLOAD		40			40			
t_{su}	Setup time	Data before RCK ↑		20			20			ns
		DS before SRCK ↑ ('LS598 only)		30			30			
		SRCKEN low before SRCK ↑ ('LS598 only)		20			20			
		SRCLR inactive before SRCK ↑		25			25			
		SRLOAD inactive before SRCK ↑		30			30			
		RCK ↑ before SRLOAD ↑ (see Note 2)		40			40			
		SER before SRCK ↑		20			20			
t_h	Hold time			0			0			ns
T_A	Operating free-air temperature			− 55		125	0		70	°C

NOTE 2: The RCK ↑ before SRLOAD ↑ setup time ensures the data saved by RCK ↑ will also be loaded into the shift register.

TTL DEVICES

3

electrical characteristics over recommended operating free-air temperature range (unless otherwise noted)

PARAMETER			TEST CONDITIONS[†]		SN54LS' MIN	SN54LS' TYP[‡]	SN54LS' MAX	SN74LS' MIN	SN74LS' TYP[‡]	SN74LS' MAX	UNIT
V_{IK}			V_{CC} = MIN,	I_I = $-$18 mA			$-$1.5			$-$1.5	V
V_{OH}	'LS598 Q		V_{CC} = MIN, V_{IH} = 2 V, V_{IL} = MAX	I_{OH} = $-$1 mA	2.4	3.2					V
				I_{OH} = $-$2.6 mA				2.4	3.1		
	Q_H'			I_{OH} = $-$1 mA	2.4	3.2		2.4	3.2		
V_{OL}	'LS598 Q		V_{CC} = MIN, V_{IH} = 2 V, V_{IL} = MAX	I_{OL} = 12 mA		0.25	0.4		0.25	0.4	V
				I_{OL} = 24 mA					0.35	0.5	
	Q_H'			I_{OL} = 8 mA		0.25	0.4		0.25	0.4	
				I_{OL} = 16 mA					0.35	0.5	
I_{OZH}	'LS598 Q		V_{CC} = MAX, V_{IH} = 2 V, V_{IL} = MAX, V_O = 2.7 V				20			20	μA
I_{OZL}	'LS598 Q		V_{CC} = MAX, V_{IH} = 2 V, V_{IL} = MAX, V_O = 0.4 V				$-$0.4			$-$0.4	mA
I_I	'LS598 Q		V_{CC} = MAX	V_I = 5.5 V			0.1			0.1	mA
	Others			V_I = 7 V			0.1			0.1	
I_{IH}			V_{CC} = MAX, V_I = 2.7 V				20			20	μA
I_{IL}	'LS598 SRCK		V_{CC} = MAX, V_I = 0.4 V				$-$0.8			$-$0.8	mA
	SER, A Thru H						$-$0.4			$-$0.4	
	Others						$-$0.2			$-$0.2	
I_{OS}[§]	'LS598 Q		V_{CC} = MAX, V_O = 0 V		$-$30		$-$130	$-$30		$-$130	mA
	Q_H'				$-$20		$-$100	$-$20		$-$100	
I_{CC}	'LS597	I_{CCH}	V_{CC} = MAX, All possible inputs grounded, All outputs open			35	53		35	53	mA
		I_{CCL}				35	53		35	53	
	'LS598	I_{CCH}				45	68		45	68	
		I_{CCL}				54	80		54	80	
		I_{CCZ}				56	85		56	85	

† For conditions shown as MIN or MAX, use the appropriate value specified under recommended operating conditions.
‡ All typical values are at V_{CC} = 5 V, T_A = 25°C
§Not more than one output should be shorted at a time and the duration of the short-circuit should not exceed one second.

3

TTL DEVICES

TEXAS
INSTRUMENTS

switching characteristics, V_{CC} = 5 V, T_A = 25°C, (see note 3)

PARAMETER	FROM (INPUT)	TO (OUTPUT)	TEST CONDITIONS		'LS597 MIN	'LS597 TYP	'LS597 MAX	'LS598 MIN	'LS598 TYP	'LS598 MAX	UNIT
f_{max}	SRCK				20	35		20	35		MHz
t_{PLH}	SRCK ↑	Q_H'				15	23		11	17	ns
t_{PHL}	SRCK ↑	Q_H'	R_L = 1 kΩ,	C_L = 30 pF		20	30		15	23	ns
t_{PLH}	$\overline{SRLOAD}$ ↓	Q_H'				38	57		28	42	ns
t_{PHL}	$\overline{SRLOAD}$ ↓	Q_H'				29	44		20	30	ns
t_{PHL}	$\overline{SRCLR}$ ↓	Q_H'				24	36		18	27	ns
t_{PLH}	RCK ↑	Q_H'	R_L = 1 kΩ,	C_L = 30 pF		41	60		32	48	ns
t_{PHL}	RCK ↑	Q_H'	SRLOAD = L			32	48		24	36	ns
t_{PLH}	SRCK ↑	Q							12	18	ns
t_{PHL}	SRCK ↑	Q							19	28	ns
t_{PLH}	$\overline{SRLOAD}$ ↓	Q							32	48	ns
t_{PHL}	$\overline{SRLOAD}$ ↓	Q	R_L = 667 Ω,	C_L = 45 pF					27	40	ns
t_{PHL}	$\overline{SRCLR}$ ↓	Q							25	38	ns
t_{PZH}	G ↓	Q							26	31	ns
t_{PZL}	G ↓	Q							29	43	ns
t_{PHZ}	G ↑	Q	R_L = 667 Ω,	C_L = 5 pF					25	38	ns
t_{PLZ}	G ↑	Q							20	30	ns

NOTE 3: See General Information Section for load circuits and voltage waveforms.

TEXAS INSTRUMENTS

TTL DEVICES

3

TYPES SN54LS597, SN54LS598, SN74LS597, SN74LS598
8-BIT SHIFT REGISTERS WITH INPUT LATCHES

typical operating sequences

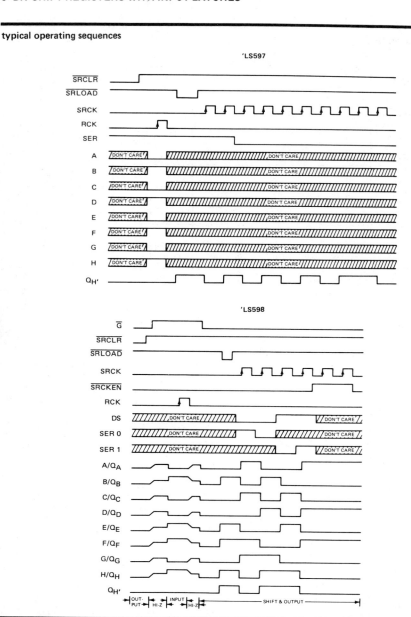

TEXAS
INSTRUMENTS

D2547, JANUARY 1981 – REVISED JUNE 1983

- **Controls Refresh Cycle of 4K, 16K, and 64K Dynamic RAMs**
- **Creates Static RAM Appearance**
- **Choice of Transparent, Cycle Steal, or Burst Refresh Modes**
- **3-State Outputs Drive Bus Lines Directly**
- **Critical Times Are User RC-Programmable to Optimize System Performance**

SN54LS' ... J PACKAGE
SN74LS' ... DW, J OR N PACKAGE
(TOP VIEW)

$\overline{BUSY}$	1	20	V_CC
A0	2	19	RC BURST
A1	3	18	SEE TABLE
A2	4	17	SEE TABLE
A3	5	16	$\overline{HOLD}$
A4	6	15	$\overline{RAS}$
A5	7	14	REF REQ2
A6	8	13	REF REQ1
SEE TABLE	9	12	RC $\overline{RAS}$ LO
GND	10	11	RC $\overline{RAS}$ HI

FOR CHIP CARRIER INFORMATION
CONTACT THE FACTORY

SELECTION TABLE

DEVICE	REFRESH MODES	MEMORY SIZE	PIN ASSIGNMENTS		
			PIN 9	PIN 17	PIN 18
'LS600A	Transparent, Burst	4K or 16K	4K/$\overline{16K}$	LATCHED RCO	RESET LATCHED RCO
'LS601A	Transparent, Burst	64K	A7	LATCHED RCO	RESET LATCHED RCO
'LS603A	Cycle Steal, Burst	64K	A7	$\overline{READY}$	RC CYCLE STEAL

description

The 'LS600A, 'LS601A, and 'LS603A memory refresh controllers contain one 8-bit synchronous counter, nine 3-state buffer drivers, four RC-controlled multivibrators, and other control circuitry on a single monolithic chip. These devices are designed to provide RAS-only refresh on 4K, 16K, and 64K dynamic RAMs. The 'LS600A and 'LS601A provide transparent refresh while the 'LS603A provide cycle-steal refresh. In addition, a burst-mode timer is provided to warn the CPU that the maximum allowable refresh time is about to be violated.

operating modes

In the transparent refresh mode ('LS600A or 'LS601A), row-refresh cycles only during inactive CPU-memory times. In most cases the entire memory refresh sequence can be completed "transparently" without interrupting CPU operations. During idle CPU-memory periods, the REF REQ pins should be taken high so as many rows as possible can be refreshed. A low from $\overline{BUSY}$ will signal the CPU to wait until the end of that current row refresh before reinstating operations. If all row addresses have been refreshed before the burst-mode timer expires, the burst-mode timer will reset.

If the maximum allowable refresh time of the dynamic RAM is about to be exceeded, the burst mode timer will expire causing the $\overline{HOLD}$ pin to go low. This signals the CPU that a burst-mode refresh in manadatory and the burst-mode refresh will be accomplished when the CPU takes the REF REQ pins high. To ensure that all rows are refreshed, the address counter is reset to zero whenever the burst-mode timer expires. After the last row has been refreshed, the $\overline{HOLD}$ pin will return high, and the burst-mode timer will reset. The CPU can then return to normal transparent operation.

A LATCHED RCO output pin is also provided on the 'LS600A and 'LS601A to detect when the last row has been refreshed. Upon seeing a RCO from the address counter, the LATCHED RCO output will be set high. This latch is reset by providing a high-going pulse on the RESET LATCHED RCO input.

In the cycle-steal refresh mode ('LS603A), refreshing is accomplished by dividing the safe refresh time into equal segments and refreshing one row in each segment. The segment time is programmed via the RC CYCLE STEAL input and will produce a low level on the $\overline{READY}$ output at the end of each segment period. This indicates to the CPU to suspend operations for one memory cycle for a row refresh. In effects it "steals" one memory cycle from the CPU. After the CPU recognizes the cycle-steal signal from the $\overline{READY}$ output, it must take both REF REQ pins high. These devices will then refresh one row and return control back to the CPU by taking $\overline{READY}$ high. The burst-mode timer is also provided to prevent exceeding the maximum allowable refresh time, and operates in the same manner as in the 'LS600A and 'LS601A. In applications where the burst-mode timer is not required, it can be disabled by connecting the RC Burst input to ground.

TTL DEVICES

3

3-963

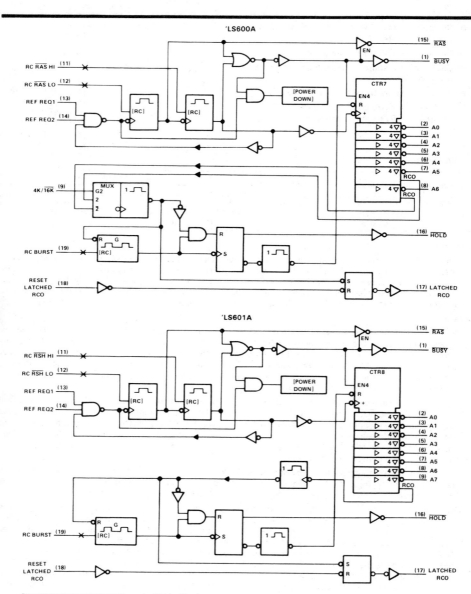

Pin numbers shown on logic notation are for DW, J or N packages.

TEXAS
INSTRUMENTS

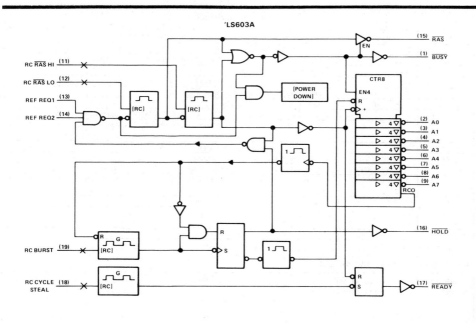

Pin numbers shown on logic notation are for DW, J or N packages.

TYPES SN74LS600A, SN74LS601A, SN74LS603A
MEMORY REFRESH CONTROLLERS

PIN FUNCTION TABLE

PIN	PIN NAME	FUNCTIONAL DESCRIPTION
1	$\overline{\text{BUSY}}$	Active output indicates to the CPU that a refresh cycle is in progress.
16	$\overline{\text{HOLD}}$	Active output should be a priority interrupt to the CPU for emergency burst refresh
15	$\overline{\text{RAS}}$	3-state output row address strobe.
11	RC $\overline{\text{RAS}}$ HI	Timing node for high-level portion of $\overline{\text{RAS}}$. See Note 1.
12	RC $\overline{\text{RAS}}$ LO	Timing node for low-level portion of $\overline{\text{RAS}}$. See Note 1.
2–8	A0 thru A6	3-state output row address lines.
9	A7	MSB row address line for 'LS601A and 'LS603A (64K-bit memory controllers).
9	4K/$\overline{16\text{K}}$	A high input level disables the A5 row address line for 'LS600A. (The high-level input makes the count chain 5 bits long while the low-level makes the count chain 6 bits long.)
17	$\overline{\text{READY}}$	Interrupt to CPU for cycle steal refresh ('LS603A).
17	LATCHED RCO	Normally high-level, will latch low upon RCO of counter ('LS600A or 'LS601A).
18	RC CYCLE STEAL	Timing node that controls the $\overline{\text{READY}}$ output ('LS603A). See Note 1.
18	RESET LATCHED RCO	Normally high-level, when pulsed low the LATCHED RCO output will be reset ('LS600A and 'LS601A).
19	RC BURST	Timing node for burst refresh. See Note 1.
13	REF REQ 1,	High level on both pins starts and continues row refresh. Low on either pin inhibits refresh.
14	REF REQ 2	
20, 10	V_CC, GND	5-V power supply and network ground pins.

NOTE 1: All timing nodes require a resistor to V_CC and a capacitor to GND.

schematics of inputs and outputs

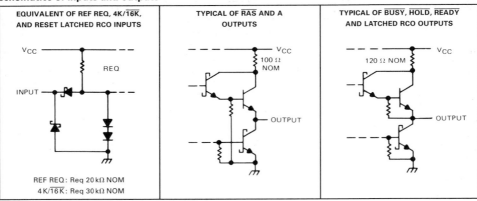

EQUIVALENT OF REF REQ, 4K/$\overline{16\text{K}}$, AND RESET LATCHED RCO INPUTS

REF REQ: Req 20 kΩ NOM
4K/$\overline{16\text{K}}$: Req 30 kΩ NOM

TYPICAL OF $\overline{\text{RAS}}$ AND A OUTPUTS

TYPICAL OF $\overline{\text{BUSY}}$, $\overline{\text{HOLD}}$, $\overline{\text{READY}}$ AND LATCHED RCO OUTPUTS

absolute maximum ratings over operating free-air temperature range (unless otherwise noted)

Supply voltage, V_CC (see Note 2) . . . . 7 V
Input voltage . . . . 7 V
Off-state output voltage . . . . 5.5 V
Operating free-air temperature range . . . . 0°C to 70°C
Storage temperature range . . . . −65°C to 150°C

NOTE 2: Voltage values are with respect to network ground terminal.

TEXAS
INSTRUMENTS

recommended operating conditions

		MIN	NOM	MAX	UNIT
Supply voltage, V_{CC}		4.75	5	5.25	V
High-level output current, I_{OH}	A, $\overline{RAS}$			−2.6	mA
	All others			−400	μA
Low-level output current, I_{OL}	A, $\overline{RAS}$			24	mA
	All others			8	
Duration or $\overline{RAS}$ output pulse[†]	High, t_{SHSL}	75			ns
	Low, t_{SLSH}	75			
Duration of RESET LATCHED RCO pulse, t_{RHRL}		35			ns
Duration of REF REQ pulse during CYCLE STEAL operation, t_{QHQL}		20			ns
External timing resistor, R_{ext}	RC $\overline{RAS}$ LO, RC $\overline{RAS}$ HI	1		6	kΩ
	RC BURST, RC CYCLE STEAL	1		1000	
Operating free-air temperature, T_A		0		70	°C

[†]Maximum operating frequency for the address counter corresponds to its minimum period, which is the sum of $t_{w(RAS-H)}$ min and $t_{w(RAS-L)}$ min.

electrical characteristics over recommended operating free-air temperature range (unless otherwise noted)

PARAMETER			TEST CONDITIONS		MIN	TYP[‡]	MAX	UNIT
V_{IH}	High-level input voltage				2			V
V_{IL}	Low-level input voltage						0.8	V
V_{IK}	Input clamp voltage		V_{CC} = 4.75 V, I_I = −1.8 mA				−1.5	V
V_{OH}	High-level output voltage	A, $\overline{RAS}$	V_{CC} = 4.75 V, V_{IH} = 2 V, V_{IL} = 0.8 V	I_{OH} = −2.6 mA	2.4	2.9		V
		All Others		I_{OH} = −400 μA	2.7	3.1		
V_{OL}	Low-level output voltage	A, $\overline{RAS}$	V_{CC} = 4.75 V, V_{IH} = 2 V, V_{IL} = 0.8 V	I_{OL} = 12 mA		0.25	0.4	V
				I_{OL} = 24 mA		0.35	0.5	
		All Others		I_{OL} = 4 mA		0.25	0.4	
				I_{OL} = 8 mA		0.35	0.5	
I_{OZH}	Off-state output current, high-level voltage applied	A, $\overline{RAS}$	V_{CC} = 5.25 V REF REQ at V_{IL} = 0.8 V	V_O = 2.7 V			20	μA
I_{OZL}	Off-state output current, low-level voltage applied			V_O = 0.4 V			−20	μA
I_I	Input current at maximum input voltage		V_{CC} = 5.25 V, V_I = 7 V				0.1	mA
I_{IH}	High-level input current		V_{CC} = 5.25 V, V_I = 2.7 V				20	μA
I_{IL}	Low-level input current		V_{CC} = 5.25 V, V_I = 0.4 V				−0.4	mA
I_{OS}	Short-circuit output current[§]	A, $\overline{RAS}$	V_{CC} = 5.25 V		−30		−130	mA
		All others			−20		−100	
I_{CC}	Supply current		V_{CC} = 5.25 V, RC $\overline{RAS}$ LO and REF REQ at 0 V			50	85	mA

[‡]All typical values are at V_{CC} = 5 V, T_A = 25°C.

[§]Not more than one output should be shorted at a time, and duration of the short-circuit should not exceed one second.

3

TTL DEVICES

TEXAS INSTRUMENTS

3-967

switching characteristics, V_{CC} = 5 V, T_A = 25°C, see note 3

PARAMETER	FROM (INPUT)	TO (OUTPUT)	TEST CONDITIONS	MIN	TYP	MAX	UNIT
t_{QHBL}	REF REQ↑	$\overline{BUSY}$	C_L = 15 pF, R_L = 2 kΩ		30	45	ns
t_{SLBH} [†]	$\overline{RAS}$↓	$\overline{BUSY}$			245	300	ns
t_{QHSV}	REF REQ↑	$\overline{RAS}$	C_L = 320 pF, R_L = 667Ω		47	70	ns
t_{SHSZ} [†]	$\overline{RAS}$↑	$\overline{RAS}$	C_L = 5 pF, R_L = 667Ω		245	300	ns
t_{QHAV}	REF REQ↑	ADDRESS	C_L = 160 pF, R_L = 667Ω		38	65	ns
t_{SHAZ} [†]	$\overline{RAS}$↑	ADDRESS	C_L = 5 pF, R_L = 667Ω		245	300	ns
t_{RHCL}	RESET LATCHED RCO↑	LATCHED RCO	C_L = 15 pF, R_L = 2 kΩ		37	55	ns
t_{SHYH}	$\overline{RAS}$↑	$\overline{READY}$			64	85	ns
t_{SLSH} [‡]	$\overline{RAS}$↓	$\overline{RAS}$	C_L = 320 pF, R_L = 667Ω		210		ns
t_{SHSL} [†]	$\overline{RAS}$↑	$\overline{RAS}$			245		ns
t_{DHDL} [§]	$\overline{HOLD}$↑	$\overline{HOLD}$	C_L = 15 pF, R_L = 2 kΩ		3.56		ms
t_{YLYL} [‖]	$\overline{READY}$↓	$\overline{READY}$			27		µs

[†] Depends on RC network at pin 11 (4 kΩ, 200 pF used for testing).

[‡] Depends on RC network at pin 12 (4 kΩ, 200 pF used for testing).

[§] Depends on RC network at pin 19 (680 kΩ, 0.022 µF used for testing).

[‖] Depends on RC network at pin 18 (10 kΩ, 0.01 µF used for testing).

NOTE 3: See General Information Section for load circuits and voltage waveforms.

explanation of letter symbols

This data sheet uses a new type of letter symbol to describe time intervals. The format is:

$$t_{AB\text{-}CD}$$

where: subscripts A and C indicate the names of the signals for which changes of state or level or establishment of state or level constitute signal events assumed to occur first and last, respectively, that is, at the beginning and end of the time interval.

Subscripts B and D indicate the direction of the transitions and/or the final states or levels of the signals represented by A and C, respectively. One or two of the following is used:

- H = high or transition to high
- L = low or transition to low
- V = a valid steady-state level
- X = unknown, changing, or "don't care" level
- Z = high-impedance (off) state.

The hyphen between the B and C subscripts is omitted when no confusion is likely to occur. For these letter symbols on this data sheet, the signal names are further abbreviated as follows:

SIGNAL NAME	A or C SUBSCRIPT
$\overline{BUSY}$	B
$\overline{HOLD}$	D
$\overline{RAS}$	S
A0 — A7	A
$\overline{READY}$	Y
LATCHED RCO	C
RESET LATCHED RCO	R
REF REQ	Q

TEXAS
INSTRUMENTS

TIMING DIAGRAMS

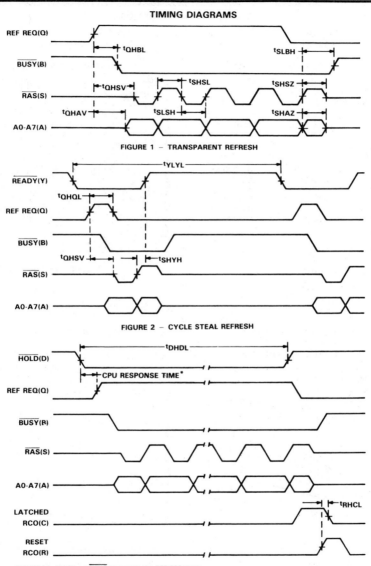

FIGURE 1 — TRANSPARENT REFRESH

FIGURE 2 — CYCLE STEAL REFRESH

* During testing, an 'LS04 is used to invert $\overline{\text{HOLD}}$ to provide the REF REQ input.

FIGURE 3 — BURST MODE REFRESH

TTL DEVICES | **3**

TYPICAL CHARACTERISTICS

PULSE DURATION, $\overline{RAS}$ LOW
vs
EXTERNAL TIMING RESISTOR

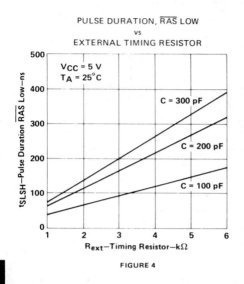

FIGURE 4

CYCLE STEAL REFRESH CYCLE TIME
vs
EXTERNAL TIMING RESISTOR

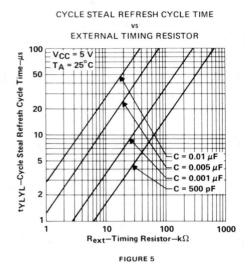

FIGURE 5

PULSE DURATION, RAS HIGH
vs
EXTERNAL TIMING RESISTOR

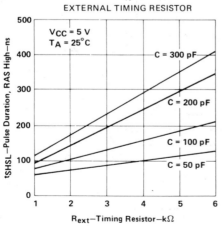

FIGURE 6

PULSE DURATION, BURST REFRESH
vs
EXTERNAL TIMING RESISTOR

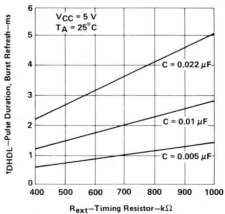

FIGURE 7

(TIM99604, TIM99606, TIM99607)

- **Choice of Outputs:**
  Three-State ('LS604, 'LS606)
  Open-Collector ('LS607)

- **16 D-Type Registers, One for each Data Input**

- **Multiplexer Selects Stored Data from Either A Bus or B Bus**

- **Application Oriented:**
  Maximum Speed ('LS604)
  Glitch-Free Operation ('LS606, 'LS607)

SN54LS604, SN54LS606, SN54LS607 ... JD PACKAGE
SN74LS604, SN74LS606, SN74LS607 ... JD OR N PACKAGE
(TOP VIEW)

```
        ____  ____
CLK [ 1  U  28 ] VCC
A/B [ 2     27 ] A5
 A1 [ 3     26 ] B5
 B1 [ 4     25 ] A6
 A2 [ 5     24 ] B6
 B2 [ 6     23 ] A7
 A3 [ 7     22 ] B7
 B3 [ 8     21 ] A8
 A4 [ 9     20 ] B8
 B4 [ 10    19 ] Y8
 Y4 [ 11    18 ] Y7
 Y3 [ 12    17 ] Y6
 Y2 [ 13    16 ] Y5
GND [ 14    15 ] Y1
```

description

The 'LS604, 'LS606, and 'LS607 multiplexed latches are ideal for storing data from two input buses, A and B, and providing the output bus with stored data from either the A or B register.

The clock loads data on the positive-going (low-level to high-level) transition. The clock pin also controls the active and high-impedance states of the outputs. When the clock pin is low, the outputs are in the high-impedance or off state. When the clock pin is high, the outputs are enabled.

The 'LS604 is optimized for high-speed operation. The 'LS606 and 'LS607 are especially designed to eliminate decoding voltage spikes.

Theses functions are ideal for interface from a 16-bit microprocessor to a 64K RAM board. The row and column addresses can be loaded as one word from the microprocessor and then multiplexed sequentially to the RAM during the time that RAS and CAS are active.

SN54LS604, SN54LS606, SN54LS607 ... FK PACKAGE
SN74LS604, SN74LS606, SN74LS607 ... FK PACKAGE
(TOP VIEW)

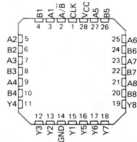

The SN54LS604, SN54LS606, and SN54LS607 are characterized for operation over the full military temperature range of –55°C to 125°C; the SN74LS604, SN74LS606, and SN74LS607 are characterized for operation from 0°C to 70°C.

3
TTL DEVICES

FUNCTION TABLE

INPUTS				OUTPUTS
A1 – A8	B1 – B8	SELECT A/B̄	CLOCK	Y1 – Y8
A data	B data	L	↑	B data
A data	B data	H	↑	A data
X	X	X	L	Z or Off
X	X	L	H	B register stored data
X	X	H	H	A register stored data

H = high level (steady state) L = low level (steady state)
X = irrelevant Z = high-impedance state
Off = H if pull-up resistor is connected to open-collector output
↑ = transition from low to high level

TYPES SN54LS604, SN54LS606, SN54LS607, SN74LS604, SN74LS606, SN74LS607
OCTAL 2-INPUT MULTIPLEXED LATCHES

schematics of inputs and outputs

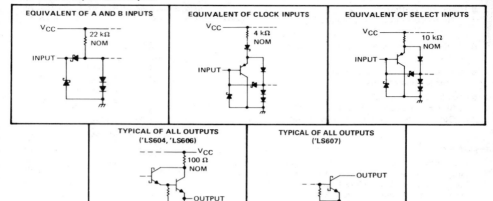

EQUIVALENT OF A AND B INPUTS

EQUIVALENT OF CLOCK INPUTS

EQUIVALENT OF SELECT INPUTS

TYPICAL OF ALL OUTPUTS ('LS604, 'LS606)

TYPICAL OF ALL OUTPUTS ('LS607)

logic symbols

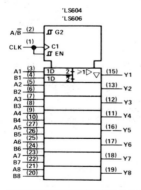

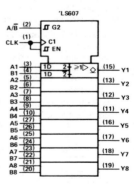

Pin numbers shown on logic notation are for JD or N packages.

TEXAS
INSTRUMENTS

TYPES SN54LS604, SN54LS606, SN54LS607, SN74LS604, SN74LS606, SN74LS607
OCTAL 2-INPUT MULTIPLEXED LATCHES

logic diagram (positive logic)

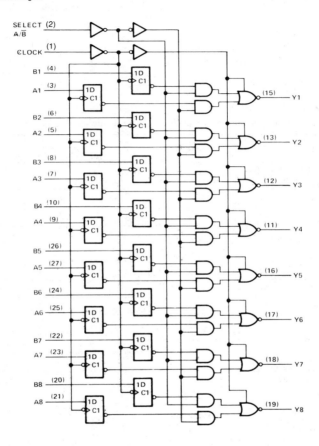

recommended operating conditions

		SN54LS604 SN54LS606			SN74LS604 SN74LS606			UNIT
		MIN	NOM	MAX	MIN	NOM	MAX	
Supply voltage, V_{CC} (see Note 1)		4.5	5	5.5	4.75	5	5.25	V
High-level output current, I_{OH}				−1			−2.6	mA
Low-level output current, I_{OL}				12			24	mA
Width of clock pulse, t_W		20			20			ns
Setup time, t_{su}		20↑			20↑			ns
Hold time, t_h		0↑			0↑			ns
Operating free-air temperature, T_A		−55		125	0		70	°C

NOTE 1: Voltage values are with respect to network ground terminal.

electrical characteristics over recommended operating free-air temperature range (unless otherwise noted)

PARAMETER		TEST CONDITIONS†			SN54LS604 SN54LS606			SN74LS604 SN74LS606			UNIT
					MIN	TYP‡	MAX	MIN	TYP‡	MAX	
V_{IH}	High-level input voltage				2			2			V
V_{IL}	Low-level input voltage						0.7			0.8	V
V_{IK}	Input clamp voltage	V_{CC} = MIN,	I_I = −18 mA				−1.5			−1.5	V
V_{OH}	High-level output voltage	V_{CC} = MIN, $V_{IL} = V_{IL}$ max,	V_{IH} = 2 V, I_{OH} = MAX		2.4	3.1		2.4	3.1		V
V_{OL}	Low-level output voltage	V_{CC} = MIN, V_{IH} = 2 V, $V_{IL} = V_{IL}$ max,	I_{OL} = 12 mA			0.25	0.4		0.25	0.4	V
			I_{OL} = 24 mA						0.35	0.5	
I_{OZH}	Off-state output current, high-level voltage applied	V_{CC} = MAX, V_{IH} = 2 V, $V_{IL} = V_{IL}$ max, V_O = 2.7 V					20			20	µA
I_{OZL}	Off-state output current, low-level voltage applied	V_{CC} = MAX, V_{IH} = 2 V, $V_{IL} = V_{IL}$ max, V_O = 0.4					−20			−20	µA
I_I	Input current at maximum input voltage	V_{CC} = MAX, V_I = 7 V	A, B				0.1			0.1	mA
			CLK, SELECT				0.1			0.1	
I_{IH}	High-level input current	V_{CC} = MAX, V_I = 2.7 V	A, B				20			20	µA
			CLK, SELECT				20			20	
I_{IL}	Low-level input current	V_{CC} = MAX, V_I = 0.4 V	A, B				−0.4			−0.4	mA
			CLK, SELECT				−0.2			−0.2	
I_{OS}	Short-circuit output current§	V_{CC} = MAX			−30		−130	−30		−130	mA
I_{CC}	Supply current	V_{CC} = MAX,	See Note 2			55	70		55	70	mA

†For conditions shown as MIN or MAX, use the appropriate value specified under recommended operating conditions.
‡All typical values are at V_{CC} = 5 V, T_A = 25°C.
§Note more than one output should be shorted at a time, and duration of the short-circuit should not exceed one second.
NOTE 2: I_{CC} is tested with all inputs grounded and all outputs open.

switching characteristics, V_{CC} = 5 V, T_A = 25°C

PARAMETER	FROM (INPUT)	TEST CONDITIONS	'LS604			'LS606			UNIT
			MIN	TYP	MAX	MIN	TYP	MAX	
t_{PLH}	Select A/B̄ (Data: A = H, B = L)			15	25		36	50	ns
t_{PHL}				23	35		16	30	
t_{PLH}	Select A/B̄ (Data: A = L, B = H)	C_L = 45 pF, R_L = 667 Ω, See Note 3		31	45		22	35	ns
t_{PHL}				19	30		22	35	
t_{PZH}	Clock			19	30		27	40	ns
t_{PZL}				28	40		35	50	
t_{PHZ}	Clock	C_L = 5 pF, R_L = 667 Ω, See Note 3		20	30		20	30	ns
t_{PLZ}				15	25		15	25	

t_{PLH} = propagation delay time, low-to-high-level output
t_{PHL} = propagation delay time, high-to-low-level output
t_{PZH} = output enable time to high level
t_{PZL} = output enable time to low level
t_{PHZ} = output disable time from high level
t_{PLZ} = output disable time from low level
NOTE 3: See General Information Section for load circuits and voltage waveforms.

TEXAS
INSTRUMENTS

recommended operating conditions

	SN54LS607			SN74LS607			UNIT
	MIN	NOM	MAX	MIN	NOM	MAX	
Supply voltage, V_{CC} (see Note 1)	4.5	5	5.5	4.75	5	5.25	V
High-level output voltage, V_{OH}			5.5			5.5	V
Low-level output current, I_{OL}			12			24	mA
Width of clock pulse, t_w	20			20			ns
Setup time, t_{su}	20↑			20↑			ns
Hold time t_h	0↑			0↑			ns
Operating free-air temperature, T_A	−55		125	0		−70	°C

NOTE 1: Voltage values are with respect to network ground terminal.

electrical characteristics over recommended operating free-air temperature range (unless otherwise noted)

PARAMETER		TEST CONDITIONS†		SN54LS607			SN74LS607			UNIT
				MIN	TYP*	MAX	MIN	TYP*	MAX	
V_{IH}	High-level input voltage			2			2			V
V_{IL}	Low-level input voltage					0.7			0.8	V
V_{IK}	Input clamp voltage	$V_{CC} = MIN,$ $I_I = −18\,mA$				−1.5			−1.5	V
I_{OH}	High-level output current	$V_{CC} = MIN,$ $V_{IH} = 2\,V,$ $V_{IL} = V_{ILmax},$ $V_{OH} = 5.5\,V$				250			250	μA
V_{OL}	Low-level output voltage	$V_{CC} = MIN,$ $V_{IH} = 2\,V,$ $V_{IL} = V_{ILmax}$	$I_{OL} = 12\,mA$	0.25		0.4	0.25		0.4	V
			$I_{OL} = 24\,mA$				0.35		0.5	
I_I	Input current at maximum input voltage	$V_{CC} = MAX,$ $V_I = 7\,V$	A, B			0.1			0.1	mA
			CLK, SELECT			0.1			0.1	
I_{IH}	High-level input current	$V_{CC} = MAX,$ $V_I = 2.7\,V$	A, B			20			20	μA
			CLK, SELECT			20			20	
I_{IL}	Low-level input current	$V_{CC} = MAX,$ $V_I = 0.4\,V$	A, B			−0.4			−0.4	mA
			CLK, SELECT			−0.2			−0.2	
I_{CC}	Supply current	$V_{CC} = MAX,$ See Note 2			40	60		40	60	mA

† For conditions shown as MIN or MAX, use the appropriate value specified under recommended operating conditions.
* All typical values are at $V_{CC} = 5\,V$, $T_A = 25°C$.
NOTE 2: I_{CC} is tested with all inputs grounded and all outputs open.

switching characteristics, $V_{CC} = 5\,V$, $T_A = 25°C$

PARAMETER	FROM (INPUT)	TEST CONDITIONS	'LS607			UNIT
			MIN	TYP	MAX	
t_{PLH}	Select A/$\overline{B}$			51	70	ns
t_{PHL}	(Data: A = H, B = L)			21	30	
t_{PLH}	Select A/$\overline{B}$	$C_L = 45\,pF,$ $R_L = 667\,\Omega,$ See Note 3		28	40	ns
t_{PHL}	(Data: A = L, B = H)			28	40	
t_{PLH}	Clock			30	45	ns
t_{PHL}				32	45	

t_{PLH} = propagation delay time, low-to-high-level output
t_{PHL} = propagation delay time, high-to-low-level output
NOTE 3: See General Information Section for load circuits and voltage waveforms.

3

TTL DEVICES

TEXAS
INSTRUMENTS

TYPES SN54LS610 THRU SN54LS613, SN74LS610 THRU SN74LS613
MEMORY MAPPERS

D2549, JANUARY 1981 − REVISED DECEMBER 1983

(TIM99610 THRU TIM99613)

- **Expands 4 Address Lines to 12 Address Lines**
- **Designed for Paged Memory Mapping**
- **Output Latches Provided on 'LS610 and 'LS611**
- **Choice of 3-State or Open-Collector Map Outputs**
- **Compatible with TMS 9900 and Other Microprocessors**

DEVICE	OUTPUTS LATCHED	MAP OUTPUT TYPE
'LS610	Yes	3-State
'LS611	Yes	Open-Collector
'LS612	No	3-State
'LS613	No	Open-Collector

SN54LS' . . . JD PACKAGE
SN74LS' . . . JD OR N PACKAGE
(TOP VIEW)

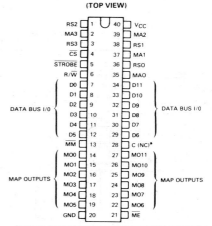

RS2	1	40	V_CC
MA3	2	39	MA2
RS3	3	38	RS1
CS̄	4	37	MA1
STROBE	5	36	RS0
R/W̄	6	35	MA0
D0	7	34	D11
D1	8	33	D10
D2	9	32	D9
D3	10	31	D8
D4	11	30	D7
D5	12	29	D6
MM̄	13	28	C (NC)*
MO0	14	27	MO11
MO1	15	26	MO10
MO2	16	25	MO9
MO3	17	24	MO8
MO4	18	23	MO7
MO5	19	22	MO6
GND	20	21	MĒ

DATA BUS I/O (pins 7–12, 29–34)
MAP OUTPUTS (pins 14–19, 22–27)

*Note: Pin 28 has no internal connection on 'LS612 and 'LS613
For chip carrier information, contact the factory.

description

These memory-mapper integrated circuits contain a 4-line to 16-line decoder, a 16-word by 12-bit RAM, 16 channels of 2-line to 1-line multiplexers, and other miscellaneous circuitry on a monolithic chip. The 'LS610 and 'LS611 also contain 12 latches with an enable control.

The memory mappers are designed to expand a microprocessor's memory address capability by eight bits. Four bits of the memory address bus (see the figure below) can be used to select one of 16 map registers that contain 12 bits each. These 12 bits are presented to the system memory address bus through the map output buffers along with the unused memory address bits from the CPU. However, addressable memory space without reloading the map registers is the same as would be available with the memory mapper left out. The addressable memory space is increased only by periodically reloading the map registers from the data bus.

This configuration lends itself to memory utilization of 16 pages of $2^{(n-4)}$ registers each without reloading (n   number of address bits available from CPU.)

These devices have four modes of operation (read, write, map, and pass). Data may be read from or loaded into the map register selected by the register select inputs (RS0 thru RS3) under control of R/W̄ whenever chip select (CS̄) is low. The data I/O takes place on the data bus D0 thru D7. The map operation will output the contents of the map register selected by the map address inputs (MA0 thru MA3) when CS̄ is high and MM̄ (map mode control) is low. The 'LS612 and 'LS613 output stages are transparent in this mode, while the 'LS610 and 'LS611 outputs may be transparent or latched. When CS̄ and MM̄ are both high (pass mode), the address bits on MA0 thru MA3 appear at MO8-MO11, respectively, (assuming appropriate latch control) with low levels in the other bit positions on the map outputs.

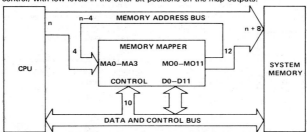

TEXAS
INSTRUMENTS

3

TTL DEVICES

TYPES SN54LS610 THRU SN54LS613, SN74LS610 THRU SN74LS613
MEMORY MAPPERS

functional block diagram (positive logic)

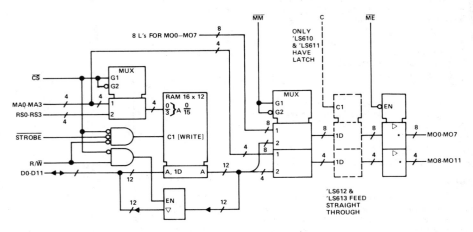

* 'LS610 and 'LS612 have 3-state (▽) map outputs.
'LS611 and 'LS613 have open-collector (Ω) map outputs.

PIN FUNCTION TABLE

PIN	PIN NAME	FUNCTIONAL DESCRIPTION
7–12, 29–34	D0 thru D11	I/O connections to data and control bus used for reading from and writing to the map register selected by RS0–RS3 when $\overline{CS}$ is low. Mode controlled by R/$\overline{W}$.
36, 38, 1, 3	RS0 thru RS3	Register select inputs for I/O operations.
6	R/$\overline{W}$	Read or write control used in I/O operations to select the condition of the data bus. When high, the data bus outputs are active for reading the map register. When low, the data bus is used to write into the register.
5	$\overline{STROBE}$	Strobe input used to enter data into the selected map register during I/O operations.
4	$\overline{CS}$	Chip select input. A low input level selects the memory mapper (assuming more than one used) for an I/O operation.
35, 37, 39, 2	MA0 thru MA3	Map address inputs to select one of 16 map registers when in map mode ($\overline{MM}$ low and $\overline{CS}$ high).
14–19, 22–27	MO0 thru MO11	Map outputs. Present the map register contents to the system memory address bus in the map mode. In the pass mode, these outputs provide the map address data on MO8–MO11 and low levels on MO0–MO7.
13	$\overline{MM}$	Map mode input. When low, 12 bits of data are transferred from the selected map register to the map outputs. When high (pass mode), the 4 bits present on the map address inputs MA0-MA3 are passed to the map outputs MO8-MO11, respectively, while MO0-MO7 are set low.
21	$\overline{ME}$	Map enable for the map outputs. A low level allows the outputs to be active while a high input level puts the outputs at high impedance.
28	C	Latch enable input for the 'LS610 and 'LS611 (no internal connection for 'LS612 and 'LS613). A high level will transparently pass data to the map outputs. A low level will latch the outputs.
40, 20	V_{CC}, GND	5-V power supply and network ground (substrate) pins.

3

TTL DEVICES

TEXAS
INSTRUMENTS

schematics of inputs and outputs

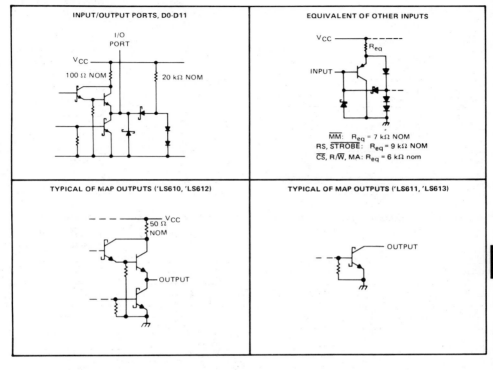

INPUT/OUTPUT PORTS, D0-D11	EQUIVALENT OF OTHER INPUTS
TYPICAL OF MAP OUTPUTS ('LS610, 'LS612)	TYPICAL OF MAP OUTPUTS ('LS611, 'LS613)

$\overline{MM}$: R_{eq} = 7 kΩ NOM
RS, $\overline{STROBE}$: R_{eq} = 9 kΩ NOM
$\overline{CS}$, R/$\overline{W}$, MA: R_{eq} = 6 kΩ nom

absolute maximum ratings over operating free-air temperature range (unless otherwise noted)

Supply voltage, V_{CC} (see Note 1) . . . . 7 V
Input voltage: Data Bus I/O . . . . 5.5 V
　　　　　　　All other inputs . . . . 7 V
Operating free-air temperature range: SN54LS610 through SN54LS613 . . . . −55°C to 125°C
　　　　　　　　　　　　　　　　　　 SN74LS610 through SN54LS613 . . . . 0°C to 70°C
Storage temperature range . . . . −65°C to 150°C

NOTE 1: Voltage values are with respect to network ground terminal.

TEXAS INSTRUMENTS

recommended operating conditions

				SN54LS610 SN54LS612			SN74LS610 SN74LS612			UNIT
				MIN	NOM	MAX	MIN	NOM	MAX	
V_{CC}	Supply voltage			4.5	5	5.5	4.75	5	5.25	V
I_{OH}	High-level output current	MO				−12			−15	mA
		D				−1			−2.6	
I_{OL}	Low-level output current	MO				12			24	mA
		D				4			8	
t_{AVCL}	C setup time (AV before C low) 'LS610 only		See Figure 2	30			30			ns
t_{SLSH}	Width of strobe input pulse			75			75			ns
t_{CSLSL}	$\overline{CS}$ setup ($\overline{CS}$ low to strobe low)			20			20			ns
t_{WLSL}	R/$\overline{W}$ setup time (R/$\overline{W}$ low to stobe low)			20			20			ns
t_{RVSL}	RS setup time (RS valid to strobe low)		See Figure 1	20			20			ns
t_{DVSH}	Data setup time (D0-D11 valid to strobe high)			75			75			ns
t_{SHCSH}	$\overline{CS}$ hold time (Strobe high to $\overline{CS}$ high)			20			20			ns
t_{SHWH}	R/$\overline{W}$ hold time (Strobe high to R/$\overline{W}$ high)			20			20			ns
t_{SHRX}	RS hold time (Strobe high to RS invalid)			20			20			ns
t_{SHDX}	Data hold time (Strobe high to D0-D11 invalid)			20			20			ns
T_A	Operating free-air temperature			−55		125	0		70	°C

electrical characteristics over recommended operating free-air temperature range (unless otherwise noted)

PARAMETER			TEST CONDITIONS[†]		SN54LS610 SN54LS612			SN74LS610 SN74LS612			UNIT
					MIN	TYP[‡]	MAX	MIN	TYP[‡]	MAX	
V_{IH}	High-level input voltage				2			2			V
V_{IL}	Low-level input voltage						0.7			0.8	V
V_{IK}	Input clamp voltage		V_{CC} = MIN, I_I = −18 mA				−1.5			−1.5	V
V_{OH}	High-level output voltage	MO	V_{CC} = MIN, V_{IH} = 2 V, V_{IL} = V_{IL} max	I_{OH} = −3 mA	2.4			2.4			V
				I_{OH} = MAX	2			2			
		D		I_{OH} = MAX	2.4			2.4			
V_{OL}	Low-level output voltage	MO	V_{CC} = MIN, V_{IH} = 2 V, V_{IL} = V_{IL} max	I_{OL} = 12 mA		0.25	0.4		0.25	0.4	V
				I_{OL} = 24 mA					0.35	0.5	
		D		I_{OL} = 4 mA		0.25	0.4		0.25	0.4	
				I_{OL} = 8 mA					0.35	0.5	
I_{OZH}	Off-state output current, high-level voltage applied		V_{CC} = MAX, V_{IH} = 2 V, V_{IL} = V_{IL} max, V_O = 2.7 V				20			20	μA
I_{OZL}	Off-state output current, low-level voltage applied	MO	V_{CC} = MAX, V_{IH} = 2 V, V_{IL} = V_{IL} max, V_O = 0.4 V				−20			−20	μA
		D					−400			−400	
I_I	Input current at maximum input voltage	D	V_{CC} = MAX	V_I = 5.5 V			100			100	μA
		All others		V_I = 7 V			100			100	
I_{IH}	High-level input current		V_{CC} = MAX, V_I = 2.7 V				20			20	μA
I_{IL}	Low-level input current		V_{CC} = MAX, V_I = 0.4 V				−0.4			−0.4	mA
I_{OS}	Short-circuit output current[§]	MO	V_{CC} = MAX		−40		−225	−40		−225	mA
		D			−30		−130	−30		−130	
I_{CC}	Supply current		V_{CC} = MAX	Outputs high		112	180		112	180	mA
				Outputs low		112	180		112	180	
				Outputs at high impedance		150	230		180	230	

† For conditions shown as MIN or MAX, use the appropriate value specified under recommended operating conditions.
‡ All typical values are at V_{CC} = 5 V, T_A = 25°C.
§ Not more than one output should be shorted at a time, and duration of the short-circuit should not exceed one second.

3
TTL DEVICES

TEXAS
INSTRUMENTS

switching characteristics, V_{CC} = 5 V, T_A = 25°C, C_L = 45 pF to GND

PARAMETER		FROM (INPUT)	TO (OUTPUT)	TEST CONDITIONS	'LS610			'LS612			UNIT
					MIN	TYP	MAX	MIN	TYP	MAX	
t_{CSLDV}	Access (enable) time	$\overline{CS}\downarrow$	D 0-11	R_L = 2 kΩ, See Figure 1, See Notes 3 and 4		28	50		26	50	ns
t_{WHDV}	Access (enable) time	R/$\overline{W}\uparrow$	D 0-11			20	35		20	35	ns
t_{RVDV}	Access time	RS	D 0-11			49	75		39	75	ns
t_{WLDZ}	Disable time	R/$\overline{W}\downarrow$	D 0-11			32	50		30	50	ns
t_{CSHDZ}	Disable time	$\overline{CS}\uparrow$	D 0-11			42	65		38	65	ns
t_{ELQV}	Access (enable) time	$\overline{ME}\downarrow$	MO 0-11	R_L = 667 Ω, See Figure 2, See Notes 3 and 4		19	30		17	30	ns
t_{CSHQV}	Access time	$\overline{CS}\uparrow$	MO 0-11			56	85		48	85	ns
t_{MLQV}	Access time	$\overline{MM}\downarrow$	MO 0-11			25	40		22	40	ns
t_{CHQV}	Access time	C↑	MO 0-11			24	40				ns
t_{AVQV1}	Access time ($\overline{MM}$ low)	MA	MO 0-11			46	70		39	70	ns
t_{MHQV}	Access time	$\overline{MM}\uparrow$	MO 0-11			24	40		22	40	ns
t_{AVQV2}	Propagation time ($\overline{MM}$ high)	MA	MO 8-11			19	30		13	30	ns
t_{EHQZ}	Disable time	$\overline{ME}\uparrow$	MO 0-11			14	25		14	25	ns

NOTE: 3. Access times are tested as t_{PLH} and t_{PHL} or t_{PZH} or t_{PZL}. Disable times are tested as t_{PHZ} and t_{PLZ}.
4. See General Information Section for load circuits and voltage waveforms.

explanation of letter symbols

This data sheet uses a new type of letter symbol to describe time intervals. The format is:

$$t_{AB-CD}$$

where: subscripts A and C indicate the names of the signals for which changes of state or level or establishment of state or level constitute signal events assumed to occur first and last, respectively, that is, at the beginning and end of the time interval.

Subscripts B and D indicate the direction of the transitions and/or the final states or levels of the signals represented by A and C, respectively. One or two of the following is used:

H = high or transition to high
L = low or transition to low
V = a valid steady-state level
X = unknown, changing, or "don't care" level
Z = high-impedance (off) state.

The hyphen between the B and C subscripts is omitted when no confusion is likely to occur. For these letter symbols on this data sheet, the signal names are further abbreviated as follows:

SIGNAL NAME	A AND C SUBSCRIPT
C	C
$\overline{CS}$	CS
D0–11	D
MA0—MA3	A
MO0—MO11	Q
$\overline{ME}$	E
$\overline{MM}$	M
R/$\overline{W}$	W
RS0—RS3	R
$\overline{STROBE}$	S

TEXAS
INSTRUMENTS

3

TTL DEVICES

recommended operating conditions

				SN54LS611 SN54LS613			SN74LS611 SN74LS613			UNIT
				MIN	NOM	MAX	MIN	NOM	MAX	
V_{CC}	Supply voltage			4.5	5	5.5	4.75	5	5.25	V
V_{OH}	High-level output voltage	MO				5.5			5.5	V
I_{OH}	High-level output current	D				−1			−2.6	mA
I_{OL}	Low-level output current	MO				12			24	mA
		D				4			8	
t_{AVCL}	C setup time (AV before C low) 'LS611 only	See Figure 2		30			30			ns
t_{SLSH}	Width of strobe input pulse			75			75			ns
t_{CSLSL}	$\overline{CS}$ setup time ($\overline{CS}$ low to strobe low)			20			20			ns
t_{WLSL}	R/$\overline{W}$ setup time (R/$\overline{W}$ low to strobe low)			20			20			ns
t_{RVSL}	RS setup time (RS valid to strobe low)	See Figure 1		20			20			ns
t_{DVSH}	Data setup time (D0-D11 valid to strobe high)			75			75			ns
t_{SHCSH}	$\overline{CS}$ hold time (Strobe high to $\overline{CS}$ high)			20			20			ns
t_{SHWH}	R/$\overline{W}$ hold time (Strobe high to R/$\overline{W}$ high)			20			20			ns
t_{SHRX}	RS hold time (Strobe high to RS invalid)			20			20			ns
t_{SHDX}	Data hold time (Strobe high to D0-D11 invalid)			20			20			ns
T_A	Operating free-air temperature			−55		125	0		70	°C

NOTE 2: Voltage values are with respect to network ground terminal.

electrical characteristics over recommended operating free-air temperature range (unless otherwise noted)

PARAMETER			TEST CONDITIONS[†]		SN54LS611 SN54LS613			SN74LS611 SN74LS613			UNIT
					MIN	TYP[‡]	MAX	MIN	TYP[‡]	MAX	
V_{IH}	High-level input voltage				2			2			V
V_{IL}	Low-level input voltage						0.7			0.8	V
V_{IK}	Input clamp voltage		V_{CC} = MIN, I_I = −18 mA				−1.5			−1.5	V
V_{OH}	High-level output voltage	D	V_{CC} = MIN, V_{IH} = 2 V, V_{IL} = V_{IL} max, I_{OH} = MAX		2.4			2.4			V
I_{OH}	High-level output current	MO	V_{CC} = MIN, V_{IH} = 2 V, V_{OH} = 5.5 V				100			100	μA
V_{OL}	Low-level output voltage	MO	V_{CC} = MIN, V_{IH} = 2 V, V_{IL} = V_{IL} max	I_{OL} = 12 mA		0.25	0.4		0.25	0.4	V
				I_{OL} = 24 mA					0.35	0.5	
		D		I_{OL} = 4 mA		0.25	0.4		0.25	0.4	
				I_{OL} = 8 mA					0.35	0.5	
I_{OZH}	Off-state output current, high-level voltage applied	D	V_{CC} = MAX, V_{IH} = 2 V, V_{IL} = V_{IL} max, V_O = 2.7 V				20			20	μA
I_{OZL}	Off-state output current, low-level voltage applied	D	V_{CC} = MAX, V_{IH} = 2 V, V_O = 0.4 V				−400			−400	
I_I	Input current at maximum input voltage	D	V_{CC} = MAX	V_I = 5.5 V			100			100	μA
		All others		V_I = 7 V			100			100	
I_{IH}	High-level input current		V_{CC} = MAX, V_I = 2.7 V				20			20	μA
I_{IL}	Low-level input current		V_{CC} = MAX, V_I = 0.4 V				−0.4			−0.4	mA
I_{OS}	Short-circuit output current[§]	D	V_{CC} = MAX		−30		−130	−30		−130	mA
I_{CC}	Supply current		V_{CC} = MAX	Outputs high		100	170		100	170	mA
				Outputs low		100	170		100	170	
				Outputs at high impedance		110	200		110	200	

[†]For conditions shown as MIN or MAX, use the appropriate value specified under recommended operating conditions.

[‡]All typical values are at V_{CC} = 5 V, T_A = 25°C.

[§]Not more than one output should be shorted at a time, and duration of the short-circuit should not exceed one second.

TEXAS
INSTRUMENTS

switching characteristics, V_{CC} = 5 V, T_A = 25°C, C_L = 45 pF to GND

PARAMETER		FROM (INPUT)	TO (OUTPUT)	TEST CONDITIONS	'LS611			'LS613			UNIT
					MIN	TYP	MAX	MIN	TYP	MAX	
t_{CSLDV}	Access (enable) time	$\overline{CS}\downarrow$	D 0-11	R_L = 2 kΩ, See Figure 1, See Notes 3 and 4		31	50		28	50	ns
t_{WHDV}	Access (enable) time	R/$\overline{W}\uparrow$	D 0-11			23	35		21	35	ns
t_{RVDV}	Access time	RS	D 0-11			51	75		47	75	ns
t_{WLDZ}	Disable time	R/$\overline{W}\downarrow$	D 0-11			32	50		31	50	ns
t_{CSHDZ}	Disable time	$\overline{CS}\uparrow$	D 0-11			41	65		40	65	ns
t_{ELQV}	Access (enable) time	$\overline{ME}\downarrow$	MO 0-11	R_L = 667 Ω, See Figure 2, See Notes 3 and 4		21	30		19	30	ns
t_{CSHQV}	Access time	$\overline{CS}\uparrow$	MO 0-11			57	90		53	90	ns
t_{MLQV}	Access time	MM↓	MO 0-11			25	40		25	40	ns
t_{CHQV}	Access time	C↑	MO 0-11			30	45				ns
t_{AVQV1}	Access time ($\overline{MM}$ low)	MA	MO 0-11			47	70		44	70	ns
t_{MHQV}	Access time	MM↑	MO 0-11			31	50		31	50	ns
t_{AVQV2}	Propagation time ($\overline{MM}$ high)	MA	MO 8-11			21	30		20	30	ns
t_{EHQZ}	Disable time	$\overline{ME}\uparrow$	MO 0-11			15	25		15	25	ns

NOTE: 3. Access times are tested as t_{PLH} and t_{PHL} or t_{PZH} or t_{PZL}. Disable times are tested as t_{PHZ} and t_{PLZ}.
4. See General Information Section for load circuits and voltage waveforms.

3

TTL DEVICES

TEXAS
INSTRUMENTS

TYPES SN54LS610 THRU SN54LS613, SN74LS610 THRU SN74LS613
MEMORY MAPPERS

TIMING DIAGRAMS

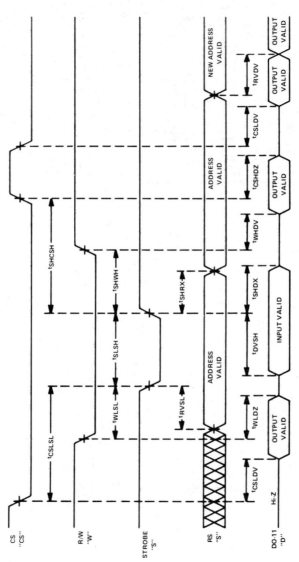

FIGURE 1—WRITE AND READ MODES

TEXAS
INSTRUMENTS

TIMING DIAGRAMS

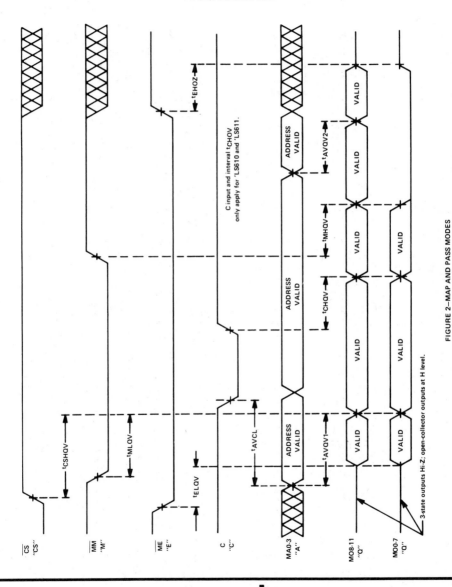

FIGURE 2–MAP AND PASS MODES

3

TTL DEVICES

3

TTL DEVICES

- Bidirectional Bus Transceivers in High-Density 20-Pin Packages
- Local Bus-Latch Capability
- Hysteresis at Bus Inputs Improves Noise Margins
- Choice of True or Inverting Logic
- Choice of 3-State or Open-Collector Outputs

DEVICE	OUTPUT	LOGIC
'LS620	3-State	Inverting
'LS621	Open-Collector	True
'LS623	3-State	True

SN54LS620, SN54LS621,
SN54LS623 ... J PACKAGE
SN74LS620, SN74LS621,
SN74LS623 ... DW, J OR N PACKAGE
(TOP VIEW)

```
        GAB [ 1  U 20 ] VCC
         A1 [ 2    19 ] GBA
         A2 [ 3    18 ] B1
         A3 [ 4    17 ] B2
         A4 [ 5    16 ] B3
         A5 [ 6    15 ] B4
         A6 [ 7    14 ] B5
         A7 [ 8    13 ] B6
         A8 [ 9    12 ] B7
        GND [ 10   11 ] B8
```

SN54LS620, SN54LS621,
SN54LS623, SN74LS620, SN74LS621,
SN74LS623 ... FK PACKAGE
(TOP VIEW)

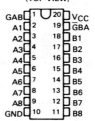

description

These octal bus transceivers are designed for asynchronous two-way communication between data buses. The control function implementation allows for maximum flexibility in timing.

These devices allow data transmission from the A bus to the B bus or from the B bus to the A bus depending upon the logic levels at the enable inputs ($\overline{GBA}$ und GAB).

The enable inputs can be used to disable the device so that the buses are effectively isolated.

The dual-enable configuration gives the 'LS620, 'LS621, and 'LS623 the capability to store data by simultaneous enabling of $\overline{GBA}$ and GAB. Each output reinforces its input in this transceiver configuration. Thus, when both control inputs are enabled and all other data sources to the two sets of bus lines are at high impedance, both sets of bus lines (16 in all) will remain at their last states. The 8-bit codes appearing on the two sets of buses will be identical for the 'LS621 and 'LS623 devices or complementary for the 'LS620.

FUNCTION TABLE

ENABLE	INPUTS	OPERATION	
$\overline{GBA}$	GAB	'LS620	'LS621, 'LS623
L	L	$\overline{B}$ data do A bus	B data to A bus
H	H	$\overline{A}$ data to B bus	A data to B bus
H	L	Isolation	Isolation
L	H	$\overline{B}$ data to A bus, $\overline{A}$ data to B bus	B data to A bus, A data to B bus

H = high level, L = low level

absolute maximum ratings over operation free-air temperature range (unless otherwise noted)

Supply voltage, VCC (see Note 1) .... 7 V
Input voltage .... 7 V
Off-state output voltage .... 5.5 V
Operating free-air temperature range: SN54LS' .... −55°C to 125°C
SN74LS' .... 0°C to 70°C
Storage temperature range .... −65°C to 150°C

NOTE 1: Voltage values are with respect to network ground terminal.

TTL DEVICES

3

logic symbols

'LS620

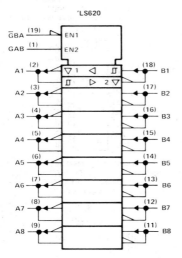

'LS621

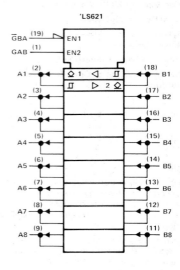

'LS623

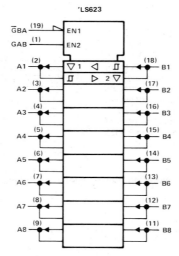

Pin numbers shown on logic notation are for DW, J or N packages.

TEXAS
INSTRUMENTS

3

TTL DEVICES

logic diagrams (positive logic)

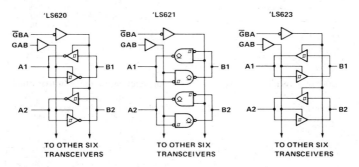

schematics of inputs and outputs

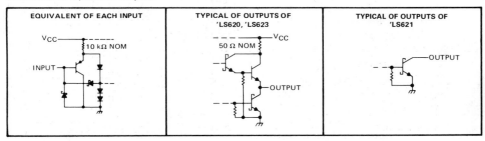

TEXAS
INSTRUMENTS

3

TTL DEVICES

recommended operating conditions

PARAMETER	SN54LS620 SN54LS623 MIN	NOM	MAX	SN74LS620 SN74LS623 MIN	NOM	MAX	UNIT
Supply voltage, V_{CC} (see Note 1)	4.5	5	5.5	4.75	5	5.25	V
High-level output current, I_{OH}			−12			−15	mA
Low-level output current, I_{OL}			12			24	mA
Operating free-air temperature, T_A	−55		125	0		70	°C

NOTE 1: Voltage values are with respect to network ground terminal.

electrical characteristics over recommended operating free-air temperature range (unless otherwise noted)

PARAMETER		TEST CONDITIONS†		SN54LS620 SN54LS623 MIN	TYP‡	MAX	SN74LS620 SN74LS623 MIN	TYP‡	MAX	UNIT
V_{IH}	High-level input voltage			2			2			V
V_{IL}	Low-level input voltage					0.5			0.6	V
V_{IK}	Input clamp voltage	V_{CC} = MIN,	I_I = −18 mA			−1.5			−1.5	V
	Hysteresis ($V_{T+} - V_{T-}$) A or B input	V_{CC} = MIN		0.1	0.4		0.2	0.4		V
V_{OH}	High-level output voltage	V_{CC} = MIN, V_{IH} = 2 V, V_{IL} = V_{IL} max	I_{OH} = −3 mA	2.4	3.4		2.4	3.4		V
			I_{OH} = MAX	2			2			
V_{OL}	Low-level output voltage	V_{CC} = MIN, V_{IH} = 2 V, V_{IL} = V_{IL} max	I_{OL} = 12 mA		0.25	0.4		0.25	0.4	V
			I_{OL} = 24 mA					0.35	0.5	
I_{OZH}	Off-state output current, high-level voltage applied	V_{CC} = MAX, $\overline{G}$ at 2 V, V_O = 2.7 V				20			20	µA
I_{OZL}	Off-state output current, low-level voltage applied	V_{CC} = MAX, $\overline{G}$ at 2 V, V_O = 0.4 V				−400			−400	µA
I_I	Input current at maximum input voltage	A or B	V_{CC} = MAX,	V_I = 5.5 V			0.1			0.1	mA
		$\overline{GBA}$ or GAB		V_I = 7 V			0.1			0.1	
I_{IH}	High-level input current	V_{CC} = MAX,	V_I = 2.7 V			20			20	µA
I_{IL}	Low-level input current	V_{CC} = MAX,	V_I = 0.4 V			−0.4			−0.4	mA
I_{OS}	Short-circuit output current §	V_{CC} = MAX		−40		−225	−40		−225	mA
I_{CC}	Total supply current	Outputs high	V_{CC} = MAX,	Outputs open		48	70		48	70	mA
		Outputs low				62	90		62	90	
		Outputs at Hi-Z				64	95		64	95	

†For conditions shown as MIN or MAX use the appropriate value specified under recommended operating conditions.
‡All typical values are at V_{CC} = 5 V, T_A = 25°C.
§Not more than one output should be shorted at a time, and duration of the short-circuit should not exceed one second.

switching characteristics at V_{CC} = 5 V, T_A = 25°C

PARAMETER		FROM (INPUT)	TO (OUTPUT)	TEST CONDITIONS	'LS620 MIN	TYP	MAX	'LS623 MIN	TYP	MAX	UNIT
t_{PLH}	Propagation delay time, low-to-high-level output	A	B	C_L = 45 pF, R_L = 667 Ω, See Note 2		6	10		8	15	ns
		B	A			6	10		8	15	
t_{PHL}	Propagation delay time, high-to-low-level output	A	B			8	15		11	15	ns
		B	A			8	15		11	15	
t_{PZL}	Output enable time to low level	$\overline{GBA}$	A			31	40		31	40	ns
		GAB	B			31	40		31	40	
t_{PZH}	Output enable time to high level	$\overline{GBA}$	A			23	40		26	40	ns
		GAB	B			23	40		26	40	
t_{PLZ}	Output disable time from low level	$\overline{GBA}$	A	C_L = 5 pF, R_L = 667 Ω, See Note 2		15	25		15	25	ns
		GAB	B			15	25		15	25	
t_{PHZ}	Output disable time from high level	$\overline{GBA}$	A			15	25		15	25	ns
		GAB	B			15	25		15	25	

t_{PLH} — Propagation delay time, low-to-high-level output
t_{PHL} — Propagation delay time, high-to-low-level output
t_{PZH} — Output enable time to high level
NOTE 2: See General Information Section for load circuits and voltage waveforms

t_{PZL} — Output enable time to low level
t_{PHZ} — Output disable time from high level
t_{PLZ} — Output disable time from low level

TEXAS
INSTRUMENTS

recommended operating conditions

PARAMETER	SN54LS621 MIN	SN54LS621 NOM	SN54LS621 MAX	SN74LS621 MIN	SN74LS621 NOM	SN74LS621 MAX	UNIT
Supply voltage, V_{CC} (see Note 1)	4.5	5	5.5	4.75	5	5.25	V
High-level output voltage, V_{OH}			5.5			5.5	V
Low-level output current, I_{OL}			12			24	mA
Operating free-air temperature, T_A	−55		125	0		70	°C

NOTE 1: Voltage values are with respect to network ground terminal.

electrical characteristics over recommended operating free-air temperature range (unless otherwise noted)

PARAMETER	TEST CONDITIONS†	SN54LS621 MIN	SN54LS621 TYP*	SN54LS621 MAX	SN74LS621 MIN	SN74LS621 TYP*	SN74LS621 MAX	UNIT
V_{IH} High-level input voltage		2			2			V
V_{IL} Low-level input voltage				0.5			0.6	V
V_{IK} Input clamp voltage	V_{CC} = MIN, I_I = −18 mA			−1.5			−1.5	V
Hysteresis ($V_{T+} - V_{T-}$) A or B input	V_{CC} = MIN	0.1	0.4		0.2	0.4		V
I_{OH} High-level output current	V_{CC} = MIN, V_{IH} = 2 V, V_{IL} = V_{ILmax}, V_{OH} = 5.5 V			100			100	μA
V_{OL} Low-level output voltage	V_{CC} = MIN, V_{IH} = 2 V, V_{IL} = V_{ILmax} — I_{OL} = 12 mA	0.25		0.4	0.25		0.4	V
	I_{OL} = 24 mA				0.35		0.5	
I_I Input current at maximum input voltage	A or B V_I = 5.5 V, V_{CC}=MAX GBA or GAB V_I = 7.0 V			0.1			0.1	mA
I_{IH} High-level input current	V_{CC} = MAX, V_I = 2.7 V			20			20	μA
I_{IL} Low-level input current	V_{CC} = MAX, V_I = 0.4 V			−0.4			−0.4	mA
I_{CC} Total supply current — Outputs high	V_{CC} = MAX, Outputs open		48	70		48	70	mA
— Outputs low			62	90		62	90	

† For conditions shown as MIN or MAX use the appropriate value specified under recommended operating conditions.
* All typical values are at V_{CC} = 5 V, T_A = 25°C.

switching characteristics at V_{CC} = 5 V, T_A = 25°C

PARAMETER	FROM (INPUT)	TO (OUTPUT)	TEST CONDITIONS	'LS621 MIN	'LS621 TYP	'LS621 MAX	'LS622 MIN	'LS622 TYP	'LS622 MAX	UNIT
t_{PLH} Propagation delay time, low-to-high-level output	A	B	C_L = 45 pF, R_L = 667 Ω, See Note 2		17	25		19	25	ns
	B	A			17	25		19	25	
t_{PHL} Propagation delay time, high-to-low-level output	A	B			16	25		14	25	ns
	B	A			16	25		14	25	
t_{PLH} Output disable time from low level	$\overline{G}BA$	A			23	40		26	40	ns
	GAB	B			25	40		28	40	
t_{PHL} Output enable time from high level	$\overline{G}BA$	A			34	50		43	60	ns
	GAB	B			37	50		39	60	

t_{PLH} = Propagation delay time, low-to-high-level input
t_{PHL} = Propagation delay time, high-to-low-level input
NOTE 2: See General Information Section for load circuits and voltage waveforms.

3

TTL DEVICES

TEXAS
INSTRUMENTS

- Separate Supply Voltage Pins for Isolation of Frequency Control Inputs and Oscillators from Output Circuitry

- Highly Stable Operation over Specified Temperature and/or Supply Voltage Ranges

DEVICE TYPE	SIMILAR TO	NUMBER VCO's	COMP'L Z OUT	ENABLE	RANGE INPUT	R_{ext}
'LS624	'LS324	single	yes	yes	yes	no
'LS625	'LS325	dual	yes	no	no	no
'LS626	'LS326	dual	yes	yes	no	no
'LS627	'LS327	dual	no	no	no	no
'LS628	'LS324	single	yes	yes	yes	yes
'LS629	'LS124	dual	no	yes	yes	no

description

These voltage-controlled oscillators (VCO's) are improved versions of the original VCO family: SN54LS124, SN54LS324 thru SN54LS327, SN74LS124, and SN74LS324 thru SN74LS327. These new devices feature improved voltage-to-frequency linearity, range, and compensation. With the exception of the 'LS624 and 'LS628, all of these devices feature two independent VCO's in a single monolithic chip. The 'LS624, 'LS625, 'LS626 and 'LS628 have complementary Z outputs. The output frequency for each VCO is established by a single external capacitor in combination with voltage-sensitive inputs used for frequency control and frequency range. Each device has a voltage-sensitive input for frequency control; however, the 'LS624, 'LS628, and 'LS629 devices also have one for frequency range. (See Figures 1 thru 6).

The 'LS628 offers more precise temperature compensation than its 'LS624 counterpart. The 'LS624 features a 600 ohm internal timing resistor. The 'LS628 requires a timing resistor to be connected externally across Rext pins. Temperature compensation will be improved due to the temperature coefficient of the external resistor.

Figure 3 and Figure 6 contain the necessary information to choose the proper capacitor value to obtain the desired operating frequency.

A single 5-volt supply can be used: however, one set of supply voltage and ground pins (V_{CC} and GND) is provided for the enable, synchronization-gating, and output sections, and a separate set (OSC V_{CC} and OSC GND) is provided for the oscillator and associated frequency-control circuits so that effective isolation can be accomplished in the system. For operation of frequencies greater than 10 MHz, it is recommended that two independent supplies be used. Disabling either VCO of the 'LS625 and 'LS625 and 'LS627 can be achieved by removing the appropriate OSC V_{CC}. An enable input is provided on the 'LS624, 'LS626, 'LS628, and 'LS629. When the enable input is low, the output is enabled: when the enable input is high, the internal oscillator is disabled, Y is high, and Z is low. Caution! Crosstalk may occur in the dual devices ('LS625, 'LS626, 'LS627 and 'LS629) when both VCO's are operated simultaneously.

The pulse-synchronization-gating section ensures that the first output pulse is neither clipped nor extended. The duty cycle of the square-wave output is fixed at approximately 50 percent.

The SN54LS624 thru SN54LS629 are characterized for operation over the full military temperature range of $-55°C$ to $125°C$. The SN74LS624 thru SN74LS629 are characterized for operation from $0°C$ to $70°C$.

3

TTL DEVICES

TEXAS
INSTRUMENTS

TYPES SN54LS624 THRU SN54LS629, SN74LS624 THRU SN74LS629 VOLTAGE-CONTROLLED OSCILLATORS

SN54LS624 . . . J OR W PACKAGE
SN74LS624 . . . D, J OR W PACKAGE
(TOP VIEW)

OSC GND	1	14 OSC V$_{CC}$
RNG	2	13 FREQ CONT
CX1	3	12 NC
CX2	4	11 NC
EN	5	10 NC
Y	6	9 V$_{CC}$
GND	7	8 Z

SN54LS625 . . . J OR W PACKAGE
SN74LS625 . . . D, J OR N PACKAGE
(TOP VIEW)

GND	1	16 V$_{CC}$
1Z	2	15 2Z
1Y	3	14 2Y
1CX1	4	13 2CX1
1CX2	5	12 2CX2
1FC	6	11 2FC
1OSC V$_{CC}$	7	10 2OSC V$_{CC}$
1OSC GND	8	9 2OSC GND

SN54LS626 . . . J OR W PACKAGE
SN74LS626 . . . D, J OR N PACKAGE
(TOP VIEW)

GND	1	16 V$_{CC}$
1Z	2	15 2Z
1Y	3	14 2Y
1EN	4	13 2EN
1CX1	5	12 2CX1
1CX2	6	11 2CX2
OSC V$_{CC}$	7	10 2FC
OSC GND	8	9 1FC

NC   No internal connection

SN54LS624 . . . FK PACKAGE
SN74LS624
(TOP VIEW)

Top pins (3 2 1 20 19): RNG, OSC GND, NC, OSC V$_{CC}$, FREQ CONT

CX1	4	18 NC
NC	5	17 NC
CX2	6	16 NC
NC	7	15 NC
EN	8	14 NC

Bottom pins (9 10 11 12 13): Y, GND, NC, Z, V$_{CC}$

SN54LS625 . . . FK PACKAGE
SN74LS625
(TOP VIEW)

Top pins (3 2 1 20 19): 1Z, GND, NC, V$_{CC}$, 2Z

1Y	4	18 2Y
1CX1	5	17 2CX1
NC	6	16 NC
1CX2	7	15 2CX2
1FC	8	14 2FC

Bottom pins (9 10 11 12 13): 1OSC V$_{CC}$, 1OSC GND, NC, 2OSC GND, 2OSC V$_{CC}$

SN54LS626 . . . FK PACKAGE
SN74LS626
(TOP VIEW)

Top pins (3 2 1 20 19): 1Z, GND, NC, V$_{CC}$, 2Z

1Y	4	18 2Y
1EN	5	17 2EN
NC	6	16 NC
1CX1	7	15 2CX1
1CX2	8	14 2CX2

Bottom pins (9 10 11 12 13): OSC V$_{CC}$, OSC GND, NC, 1FC, 2FC

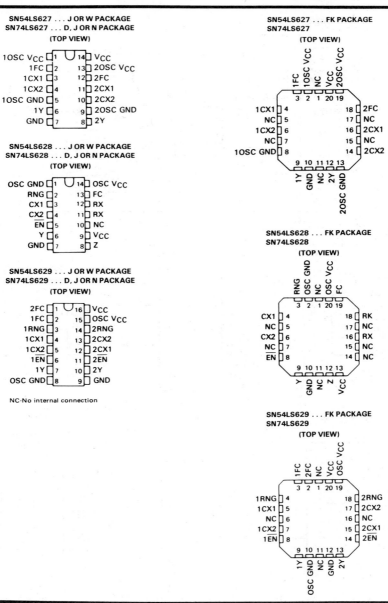

SN54LS627 ... J OR W PACKAGE
SN74LS627 ... D, J OR N PACKAGE
(TOP VIEW)

1OSC V_{CC}	1	14	V_{CC}
1FC	2	13	2OSC V_{CC}
1CX1	3	12	2FC
1CX2	4	11	2CX1
1OSC GND	5	10	2CX2
1Y	6	9	2OSC GND
GND	7	8	2Y

SN54LS628 ... J OR W PACKAGE
SN74LS628 ... D, J OR N PACKAGE
(TOP VIEW)

OSC GND	1	14	OSC V_{CC}
RNG	2	13	FC
CX1	3	12	RX
CX2	4	11	RX
$\overline{EN}$	5	10	NC
Y	6	9	V_{CC}
GND	7	8	Z

SN54LS629 ... J OR W PACKAGE
SN74LS629 ... D, J OR N PACKAGE
(TOP VIEW)

2FC	1	16	V_{CC}
1FC	2	15	OSC V_{CC}
1RNG	3	14	2RNG
1CX1	4	13	2CX2
1CX2	5	12	2CX1
1EN	6	11	2EN
1Y	7	10	2Y
OSC GND	8	9	GND

NC-No internal connection

SN54LS627 ... FK PACKAGE
SN74LS627
(TOP VIEW)

SN54LS628 ... FK PACKAGE
SN74LS628
(TOP VIEW)

SN54LS629 ... FK PACKAGE
SN74LS629
(TOP VIEW)

3

TTL DEVICES

TYPES SN54LS624 THRU SN54LS629, SN74LS624 THRU SN74LS629 VOLTAGE-CONTROLLED OSCILLATORS

logic diagram (positive logic)

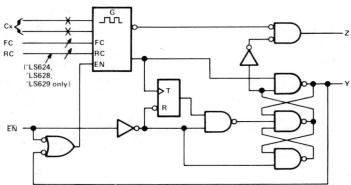

logic symbols

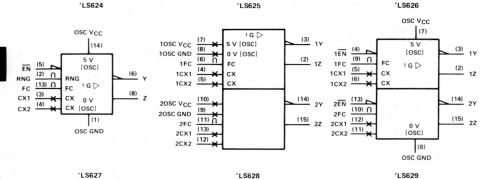

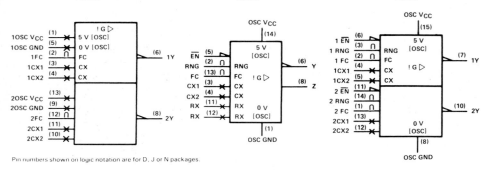

Pin numbers shown on logic notation are for D, J or N packages.

TEXAS
INSTRUMENTS

schematics of inputs and outputs

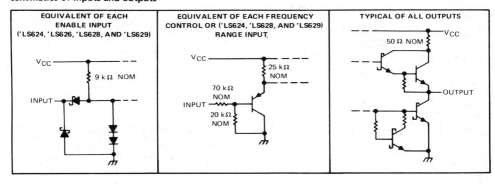

| EQUIVALENT OF EACH ENABLE INPUT ('LS624, 'LS626, 'LS628, AND 'LS629) | EQUIVALENT OF EACH FREQUENCY CONTROL OR ('LS624, 'LS628, AND 'LS629) RANGE INPUT | TYPICAL OF ALL OUTPUTS |

absolute maximum ratings over operating free-air temperature range (unless otherwise noted)

Supply voltage, V_{CC} (see Notes 1 and 2) . . . . 7 V

Input voltage: Enable input† . . . . 7 V

Frequency control or range input‡ . . . . V_{CC}

Operating free-air temperature range: SN54LS' Circuits . . . . −55°C to 125°C

SN74LS' Circuits . . . . 0°C to 70°C

Storage temperature range . . . . −65°C to 150°C

† The enable input is provided only on the 'LS624, 'LS626, 'LS628, and 'LS629.

‡ The range input is provided only on 'LS624, 'LS628, and 'LS629.

NOTE: 1. Voltage values are with respect to the appropriate ground terminal.
2. Throughout the data sheet, the symbol V_{CC} is used for the voltage applied to both the V_{CC} and OSC V_{CC} terminals, unless otherwise noted.

3

TTL DEVICES

**TEXAS
INSTRUMENTS**

recommended operating conditions

		SN54LS'			SN74LS'			UNIT
		MIN	NOM	MAX	MIN	NOM	MAX	
Supply voltage, V_{CC}		4.5	5	5.5	4.75	5	5.25	V
Input voltage at frequency control or range input, $V_{I(freq)}$ or $V_{I(rng)}$ ▲		0		5	0		5	V
High-level output current, I_{OH}				−1.2			−1.2	mA
Low-level output current, I_{OL}				12			24	mA
Output frequency, f_O		1			1			Hz
				20			20	MHz
Operating free-air temperature, T_A		−55		125	0		70	°C

electrical characteristics over recommended operating free-air temperature range (unless otherwise noted)

PARAMETER			TEST CONDITIONS†		SN54LS'			SN74LS'			UNIT
					MIN	TYP‡	MAX	MIN	TYP‡	MAX	
V_{IH}	High-level input voltage at enable♦				2			2			V
V_{IL}	Low-level input voltage at enable♦						0.7			0.8	V
V_{IK}	Input clamp voltage at enable♦		V_{CC} = MIN,	I_I = −18 mA			−1.5			−1.5	V
V_{OH}	High-level output voltage		V_{CC} = MIN, I_{OH} = −1.2 mA,	$\overline{EN}$ at V_{IL} max, See Note 3	2.5	3.4		2.7	3.4		V
V_{OL}	Low-level output voltage		V_{CC} = MIN, $\overline{EN}$ at V_{IL} max, See Note 3	I_{OL} = 12 mA		0.25	0.4		0.25	0.4	V
				I_{OL} = 24 mA					0.35	0.5	
I_I	Input current	Freq control or range ▲	V_{CC} = MAX	V_I = 5 V		50	250		50	250	μA
				V_I = 1 V		10	50		10	50	
I_I	Input current at maximum input voltage	Enable♦	V_{CC} = MAX,	V_I = 7 V			0.2			0.2	mA
I_{IH}	High-level input current	Enable♦	V_{CC} = MAX,	V_I = 2.7 V			40			40	μA
I_{IL}	Low-level input current	Enable♦	V_{CC} = MAX,	V_I = 0.4 V			−0.8			−0.8	mA
I_{OS}	Short-circuit output current §		V_{CC} = MAX		−40		−225	−40		−225	mA
I_{CC}	Supply current, total into V_{CC} and OSC V_{CC} pins		V_{CC} = MAX, Enable♦ = 4.5 V See Note 4	'LS624		20	35		20	35	mA
				'LS625		35	55		35	55	
				'LS626		35	55		35	55	
				'LS627		35	55		35	55	
				'LS628		20	35		20	35	
				'LS629		35	55		35	55	

† For conditions shown as MIN or MAX, use the appropriate value specified under recommended operating conditions.

‡ All typical values are at V_{CC} = 5 V, T_A = 25°C.

§ Not more than one output should be shorted at a time and duration of the short-circuit should not exceed one second.

▲ The range input is provided only on the 'LS624, 'LS628, and 'LS629.

♦ The enable input is provided only on the 'LS624, 'LS626, 'LS628, and 'LS629.

NOTES: 3. V_{OH} for Y outputs and V_{OL} for Z outputs are measured while enable inputs are at V_{IL} MAX, with individual 1-kΩ resistors connected from CX1 to V_{CC} and from CX2 to ground. The resistor connections are reversed for testing V_{OH} for Z outputs and V_{OL} for Y inputs.

4. For 'LS624, 'LS626, 'LS628, and 'LS629, I_{CC} is measured with the outputs disabled and open. For 'LS625 and 'LS627, I_{CC} is measured with one OSC V_{CC} = MAX, and with the other OSC V_{CC} and outputs open.

TEXAS
INSTRUMENTS

switching characteristics, V_{CC} = 5 V (unless otherwise noted), R_L = 667 Ω, C_L = 45 pF, T_A = 25 °C

PARAMETER		TEST CONDITIONS	'LS624, 'LS628, 'LS629			'LS625, 'LS626, 'LS627			UNIT
			MIN	TYP	MAX	MIN	TYP	MAX	
f_O	Output frequency	C_{ext} = 50 pF	$V_{I(freq)}$ = 5 V, $V_{I(rng)}$ = 0 V	15	20	25				MHz
			$V_{I(freq)}$ = 1 V, $V_{I(rng)}$ = 5 V	1.1	1.6	2.1				
			$V_{I(freq)}$ = 5 V				7	9.5	12	
			$V_{I(freq)}$ = 0 V				0.9	1.2	1.5	

TYPICAL CHARACTERISTICS

'LS624, 'LS628, 'LS629

OUTPUT FREQUENCY
vs
FREQUENCY-CONTROL INPUT VOLTAGE†

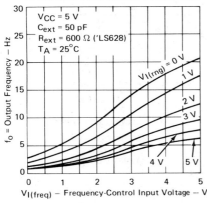

FIGURE 1

'LS624, 'LS628, 'LS629

OUTPUT FREQUENCY
vs
FREQUENCY-CONTROL INPUT VOLTAGE†

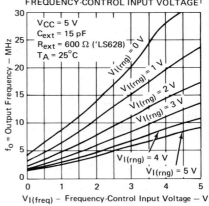

FIGURE 2

†Due to the effects of stray capacitance the output frequency may be unstable when the frequency control voltage is less than 1 volt.

TTL DEVICES

3

TYPES SN54LS624 THRU SN54LS629, SN74LS624 THRU SN74LS629 VOLTAGE-CONTROLLED OSCILLATORS

TYPICAL CHARACTERISTICS

'LS624, 'LS628, 'LS629

OUTPUT FREQUENCY
vs
EXTERNAL CAPACITANCE

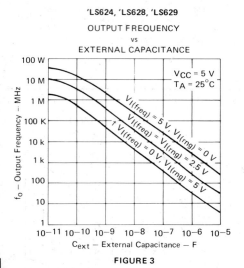

FIGURE 3

'LS625, 'LS626, 'LS627

OUTPUT FREQUENCY
vs
FREQUENCY-CONTROL INPUT VOLTAGE †

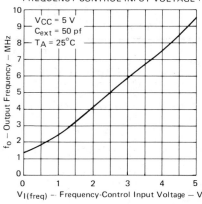

FIGURE 4

'LS625, 'LS626, 'LS627

OUTPUT FREQUENCY
vs
FREQUENCY-CONTROL INPUT VOLTAGE

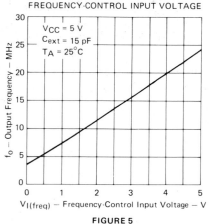

FIGURE 5

'LS625, 'LS626, 'LS627

OUTPUT FREQUENCY
vs
EXTERNAL CAPACITANCE

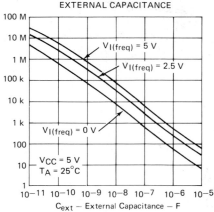

FIGURE 6

† Due to the effects of stray capacitance the output frequency may be unstable when the frequency control voltage is less than 1 volt.

TYPICAL CHARACTERISTICS

ENABLE TIME
vs
FREQUENCY

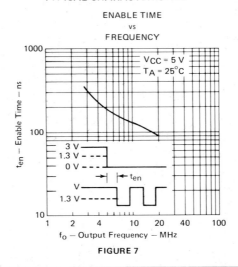

FIGURE 7

TYPICAL APPLICATIONS DATA

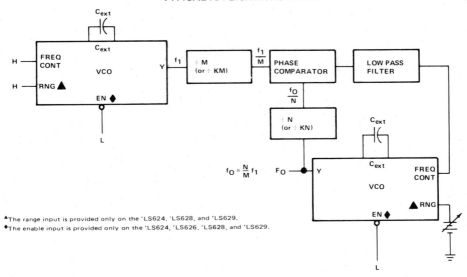

▲The range input is provided only on the 'LS624, 'LS628, and 'LS629.

◆The enable input is provided only on the 'LS624, 'LS626, 'LS628, and 'LS629.

3

TTL DEVICES

FIGURE A—PHASE-LOCKED LOOP

TYPES SN54LS630, SN54LS631, SN74LS630, SN74LS631
16-BIT PARALLEL ERROR DETECTION
AND CORRECTION CIRCUITS

D2550, MARCH 1980 – REVISED APRIL 1985

(TIM99630, TIM99631)

- **Detects and Corrects Single-Bit Errors**
- **Detects and Flags Dual-Bit Errors**
- **Fast Processing Times:**
  Write Cycle: **Generates Check Word in 45 ns Typical**
  Read Cycle: **Flags Errors in 27 ns Typical**
- **Power Dissipation 600 mW Typical**
- **Choice of Output Configurations:**
  'LS630 . . . 3-State
  'LS631 . . . Open-Collector

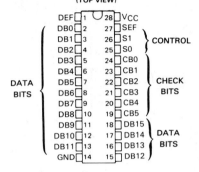

SN54LS630, SN54LS631 . . . JD PACKAGE
SN74LS630, SN74LS631 . . . JD OR N PACKAGE
(TOP VIEW)

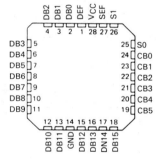

SN54LS630, SN54LS631 . . . FK PACKAGE
SN74LS630, SN74LS631
(TOP VIEW)

description

The 'LS630 and 'LS631 devices are 16-bit parallel error detection and correction circuits (EDACs) in 28-pin, 600-mil packages. They use a modified Hamming code to generate a 6-bit check word from a 16-bit data word. This check word is stored along with the data word during the memory write cycle. During the memory read cycle, the 22-bit words from memory are processed by the EDACs to determine if errors have occurred in memory.

Single-bit errors in the 16-bit data word are flagged and corrected.

Single-bit errors in the 6-bit check word are flagged, and the CPU sends the EDAC through the correction cycle even though the 16-bit word is not in error. The correction cycle will simply pass along the original 16-bit word in this case and produce error syndrome bits to pinpoint the error-generating location.

Dual-bit errors are flagged but not corrected. These dual errors may occur in any two bits of the 22-bit word from memory (two errors in the 16-bit data word, two errors in the 6-bit check word, or one error in each word).

The gross-error condition of all lows or all highs from memory will be detected. Otherwise, errors in three or more bits of the 22-bit word are beyond the capabilities of these devices to detect.

CONTROL FUNCTION TABLE

Memory Cycle	Control S1	Control S0	EDAC Function	Data I/O	Check Word I/O	Error Flags SEF	Error Flags DEF
WRITE	L	L	Generate Check Word	Input Data	Output Check Word	L	L
READ	L	H	Read Data & Check Word	Input Data	Input Check Word	L	L
READ	H	H	Latch & Flag Errors	Latch Data	Latch Check Word	Enabled	
READ	H	L	Correct Data Word & Generate Syndrome Bits	Output Corrected Data	Output Syndrome Bits	Enabled	

TEXAS
INSTRUMENTS

3

TTL DEVICES

functional block diagram

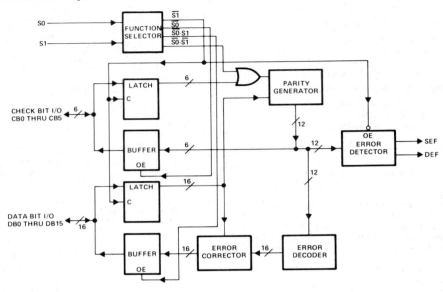

ERROR FUNCTION TABLE

Total Number of Errors		Error Flags		Data Correction
16-Bit Data	6-Bit Checkword	SEF	DEF	
0	0	L	L	Not Applicable
1	0	H	L	Correction
0	1	H	L	Correction
1	1	H	H	Interrupt
2	0	H	H	Interrupt
0	2	H	H	Interrupt

In order to be able to determine whether the data from the memory is acceptable to use as presented to the bus, the EDAC must be strobed to enable the error flags and the flags will have to be tested for the zero condition.

The first case in the error function table represents the normal, no-error condition. The CPU sees lows on both flags. The next two cases of single-bit errors require data correction. Although the EDAC can discern the single check bit error and ignore it, the error flags are identical to the single error in the 16-bit data word. The CPU will ask for data correction in both cases. An interrupt condition to the CPU results in each of the last three cases, where dual errors occur.

error detection and correction details

During a memory write cycle, six check bits (CB0-CB5) are generated by eight-input parity generators using the data bits as defined below. During a memory read cycle, the 6-bit check word is retrieved along with the actual data.

CHECKWORD	16-BIT DATA WORD															
BIT	0	1	2	3	4	5	6	7	8	9	10	11	12	13	14	15
CB0	x	x		x	x				x	x	x		x			
CB1	x		x	x		x	x		x			x			x	
CB2		x	x		x	x		x		x			x			x
CB3	x	x	x				x	x			x	x	x			
CB4				x	x	x	x	x						x	x	x
CB5									x	x	x	x	x	x	x	x

The six check bits are parity bits derived from the matrix of data bits as indicated by "x" for each bit.

Error detection is accomplished as the 6-bit check word and the 16-bit data word from memory are applied to internal parity generators/checkers. If the parity of all six groupings of data and check bits are correct, it is assumed that no error has occurred and both error flags will be low. (It should be noted that the sense of two of the check bits, bits CB0 and CB1, is inverted to ensure that the gross-error condition of all lows and all highs is detected.)

If the parity of one or more of the check groups is incorrect, an error has occurred and the proper error flag or flags will be set high. Any single error in the 16-bit data word will change the sense of exactly three bits of the 6-bit check word. Any single error in the 6-bit check word changes the sense of only that one bit. In either case, the single error flag will be set high while the dual error flag will remain low.

Any two-bit error will change the sense of an even number of check bits. The two-bit error is not correctable since the parity tree can only identify single-bit errors. Both error flags are set high when any two-bit error is detected.

Three or more simultaneous bit errors can fool the EDAC into believing that no error, a correctable error, or an uncorrectable error has occurred and produce erroneous results in all three cases.

Error correction is accomplished by identifying the bad bit and inverting it. Identification of the erroneous bit is achieved by comparing the 16-bit data word and 6-bit check word from memory with the new check word with one (check word error) or three (data word error) inverted bits.

As the corrected word is made available on the data word I/O port, the check word I/O port presents a 6-bit syndrome error code. This syndrome code can be used to identify the bad memory chip.

ERROR SYNDROME TABLE

ERROR LOCATION	SYNDROME ERROR CODE					
	CB0	CB1	CB2	CB3	CB4	CB5
DB0	L	L	H	L	H	H
DB1	L	H	L	L	H	H
DB2	H	L	L	L	H	H
DB3	L	L	H	H	L	H
DB4	L	H	L	H	L	H
DB5	H	L	L	H	L	H
DB6	H	L	H	L	L	H
DB7	H	H	L	L	L	H
DB8	L	L	H	H	H	L
DB9	L	H	L	H	H	L
DB10	L	H	H	L	H	L
DB11	H	L	H	L	H	L
DB12	H	H	L	L	H	L
DB13	L	H	H	H	L	L
DB14	H	L	H	H	L	L
DB15	H	H	L	H	L	L
CB0	L	H	H	H	H	H
CB1	H	L	H	H	H	H
CB2	H	H	L	H	H	H
CB3	H	H	H	L	H	H
CB4	H	H	H	H	L	H
CB5	H	H	H	H	H	L
NO ERROR	H	H	H	H	H	H

TEXAS
INSTRUMENTS

3

TTL DEVICES

TYPES SN54LS630, SN54LS631, SN74LS630, SN74LS631
16-BIT PARALLEL ERROR DETECTION AND CORRECTION CIRCUITS

schematics of inputs and outputs

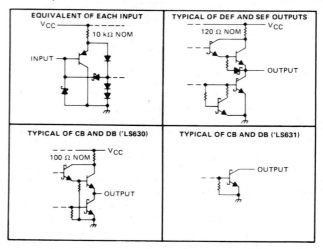

absolute maximum ratings over operating free-air temperature range (unless otherwise noted)

Supply voltage, V_{CC} (see Note 1)	7 V
Input voltage: S0 and S1	7 V
CB and DB	5.5 V
Off-state output voltage	5.5 V
Operating free-air temperature range: SN54LS630, SN54LS631	$-55°C$ to $125°C$
SN74LS630, SN74LS631	$0°C$ to $70°C$
Storage temperature range	$-65°C$ to $150°C$

NOTE 1: Voltage values are with respect to network ground terminal.

recommended operating conditions

			SN54LS630 SN54LS631			SN74LS630 SN74LS631			UNIT
			MIN	NOM	MAX	MIN	NOM	MAX	
V_{CC}	Supply voltage		4.5	5	5.5	4.75	5	5.25	V
I_{OH}	High-level output current	CB or DB, 'LS630 only			-1			-1	mA
		DEF or SEF			-0.4			-0.4	
V_{OH}	High-level output voltage	CB or DB, 'LS631 only			5.5			5.5	V
I_{OL}	Low-level output current	CB or DB			12			24	mA
		DEF or SEF			4			8	
t_{su}	Setup time	CB or DB before S1↑ †	15			15			ns
		CB or DB before S1↑ ‡	45			45			
t_h	Hold time	CB or DB after S1↑	15			15			ns
T_A	Operating free-air temperature		-55		125	0		70	°C

† This time guarantees the input data and checkword will be latched for generating a checkword and read data only.
‡ This time guarantees the input data and checkword will be latched plus that no glitch will occur on SEF or DEF flags.
↑ The upward-pointing arrow indicates a transition from low to high.

electrical characteristics over recommended operating free-air temperature range (unless otherwise noted)

PARAMETERS		TEST CONDITIONS †		SN54LS630 MIN	TYP‡	MAX	SN74LS630 MIN	TYP‡	MAX	UNIT
V_{IH} High-level input voltage				2			2			V
V_{IL} Low-level input voltage						0.7			0.8	V
V_{IK} Input clamp voltage		V_{CC} = MIN,	I_I = −18 mA			−1.5			−1.5	V
V_{OH} High-level output voltage	CB or DB	V_{CC} = MIN, V_{IH} = 2 V, $V_{IL} = V_{IL}$ min	I_{OH} = MAX	2.4	3.3		2.4	3.2		V
	DEF or SEF		I_{OH} = −400 µA	2.5	3.4		2.7	3.4		
V_{OL} Low-level output voltage	CB or DB	V_{CC} = MIN, V_{IH} = 2 V, $V_{IL} = V_{IL}$ max	I_{OL} = 12 mA		0.25	0.4		0.25	0.4	V
			I_{OL} = 24 mA					0.35	0.5	
	DEF or SEF		I_{OL} = 4 mA		0.25	0.4		0.25	0.4	
			I_{OL} = 8 mA					0.35	0.5	
I_{OZH} Off-state output current, high-level voltage applied	CB or DB	V_{CC} = MAX, S0 and S1 at 2 V	V_O = 2.7 V,			20			20	µA
I_{OZL} Off-state output current, low-level voltage applied	CB or DB	V_{CC} = MAX, S0 and S1 at 2 V	V_O = 0.4 V,			−200			−200	µA
I_I Input current at maximum input voltage	CB or DB	V_{CC} = MAX, V_{IH} = 4.5 V	V_I = 5.5 V			0.1			0.1	mA
	S0 or S1		V_I = 7 V			0.1			0.1	
I_{IH} High-level input current		V_{CC} = MAX,	V_I = 2.7 V			20			20	µA
I_{IL} Low-level input current		V_{CC} = MAX,	V_I = 0.4 V			−0.2			−0.2	mA
I_{OS}§ Short-circuit output current	CB or DB	V_{CC} = MAX		−30		−130	−30		−130	mA
	DEF or SEF			−20		−100	−20		−100	
I_{CC} Supply current		V_{CC} = MAX, S0 and S1 at 4.5 V, All CB and DB pins grounded, DEF and SEF open			143	230		143	230	mA

electrical characteristics over recommended operating free-air temperature range (unless otherwise noted)

PARAMETER		TEST CONDITIONS †		SN54LS631 MIN	TYP‡	MAX	SN74LS631 MIN	TYP‡	MAX	UNIT
V_{IH} High-level input voltage				2			2			V
V_{IL} Low-level input voltage						0.7			0.8	V
V_{IK} Input clamp voltage		V_{CC} = MIN,	I_I = −18 mA			−1.5			−1.5	V
V_{OH} High-level output voltage	DEF or SEF	V_{CC} = MIN, V_{IH} = 2 V,	I_{OH} = −400 µA, $V_{IL} = V_{IL}$ max	2.5	3.4		2.7	3.4		V
I_{OH} High-level output current	CB or DB	V_{CC} = MIN, V_{IH} = 2 V,	V_{OH} = 5.5 V, $V_{IL} = V_{IL}$ max			100			100	µA
V_{OL} Low-level output voltage	CB or DB	V_{CC} = MIN, V_{IH} = 2 V, $V_{IL} = V_{IL}$ max	I_{OL} = 12 mA		0.25	0.4		0.25	0.4	V
			I_{OL} = 24 mA					0.35	0.5	
	DEF or SEF		I_{OL} = 4 mA		0.25	0.4		0.25	0.4	
			I_{OL} = 8 mA					0.35	0.5	
I_I Input current at maximum input voltage	CB or DB	V_{CC} = MAX, V_{IH} = 4.5 V	V_I = 5.5 V			0.1			0.1	mA
	S0 or S1		V_I = 7 V			0.1			0.1	
I_{IH} High-level input current		V_{CC} = MAX	V_I = 2.7 V			20			20	µA
I_{IL} Low-level input current		V_{CC} = MAX,	V_I = 0.4 V			−0.2			−0.2	mA
I_{OS}§ Short-circuit output current	DEF or SEF	V_{CC} = MAX		−20		−100	−20		−100	mA
I_{CC} Supply current		V_{CC} = MAX, S0 and S1 at 4.5 V, All CB and DB grounded, SEF and DEF open			113	180		113	180	mA

†For conditions shown as MIN or MAX, use the appropriate value specified under recommended operating conditions.
‡All typical values are at V_{CC} = 5 V, T_A = 25°C.
§Not more than one output should be shorted at a time, and duration of the short circuit should not exceed one second.

TEXAS
INSTRUMENTS

3-1007

3

TTL DEVICES

switching characteristics, V_{CC} = 5 V, T_A = 25°C, C_L = 45 pF

PARAMETER		FROM (INPUT)	TO (OUTPUT)	TEST CONDITIONS	'LS630 MIN	'LS630 TYP	'LS630 MAX	UNIT
t_{PLH}	Propagation delay time, low-to-high-level output ◇	DB	CB	S0 at 0 V, S1 at 0 V, R_L = 667 Ω, See Figure 1		31	65	ns
t_{PHL}	Propagation delay time, high-to-low-level output ◇	DB	CB			45	65	ns
t_{PLH}	Propagation delay time, low-to-high-level output *	S1↑	DEF	S0 at 3 V, R_L = 2 kΩ, See Figure 1		27	40	ns
			SEF			20	30	
t_{PZH}	Output enable time to high level #	S0↓	CB, DB	S1 at 3 V, R_L = 667 Ω, See Figure 2		24	40	ns
t_{PZL}	Output enable time to low level #	S0↓	CB, DB	S1 at 3 V, R_L = 667 Ω, See Figure 1		30	45	ns
t_{PHZ}	Output disable time from high level ▲	S0↑	CB, DB	S1 at 3 V, R_L = 667 Ω, See Figure 2		43	65	ns
t_{PLZ}	Output disable time from low level ▲	S0↑	CB, DB	S1 at 3 V, R_L = 667 Ω, See Figure 1		31	65	ns

switching characteristics, V_{CC} = 5 V, T_A = 25°C, C_L = 45 pF, see Figure 1

PARAMETER		FROM (INPUT)	TO (OUTPUT)	TEST CONDITIONS	'LS631 MIN	'LS631 TYP	'LS631 MAX	UNIT
t_{PLH}	Propagation delay time, low-to-high level output ◇	DB	CB	S0 at 0 V, S1 at 0V, R_L = 667 Ω		38	55	ns
t_{PHL}	Propagation delay time, high-to-low-level output ◇	DB	CB			45	65	ns
t_{PLH}	Propagation delay time, low-to-high-level output *	S1↑	DEF	S0 at 3 V, R_L = 2 kΩ		27	40	ns
			SEF			20	30	ns
t_{PHL}	Propagation delay time, high-to-low-level output #	S0↓	CB, DB	S1 at 3 V, R_L = 667 kΩ		28	45	ns
t_{PLH}	Propagation delay time, low-to-high-level output ▲	S0↑	CB, DB	S1 at 3 V, R_L = 667 kΩ		33	50	ns

◇These parameters describe the time intervals taken to generate the check word during the memory write cycle.

*These parameters describe the time intervals taken to flag errors during the memory read cycle.

#These parameters describe the time intervals taken to correct and output the data word and to generate and output the syndrome error code during the memory read cycle.

▲These parameters describe the time intervals taken to disable the CB and DB buses in preparation for a new data word during the memory read cycle.

PARAMETER MEASUREMENT INFORMATION

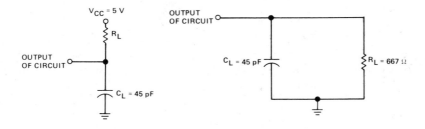

FIGURE 1—OUTPUT LOAD CIRCUIT   FIGURE 2—OUTPUT LOAD CIRCUIT

TTL DEVICES

3

typical operating sequences

READ, FLAG, AND CORRECT MODE SWITCHING WAVEFORMS

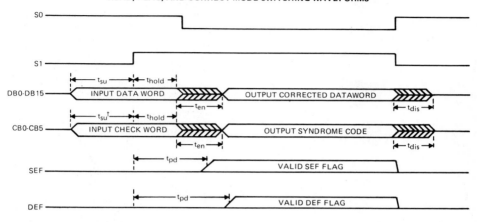

† NOTE: There are two conditions specified for t_{su} of Data or Checkword before S1†   See recommended operating conditions for details.

TEXAS
INSTRUMENTS

3

TTL DEVICES

TYPES SN54LS636, SN54LS637, SN74LS636, SN74LS637
8-BIT PARALLEL ERROR DETECTION AND CORRECTION CIRCUITS

D2728, APRIL 1983, REVISED DECEMBER 1983

- **Detects and Corrects Single-Bit Errors**

- **Detects and Flags Dual-Bit Errors**

- **Fast Processing Times:**
  Write Cycle: **Generates Check Word in 45 ns Typical**
  Read Cycle: **Flags Errors in 27 ns Typical**

- **Power Dissipation 500 mW Typical**

- **Choice of Output Configurations:**
  'LS636 . . . 3-State
  'LS637 . . . Open Collector

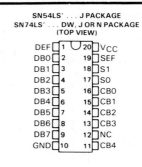

SN54LS' . . . J PACKAGE
SN74LS' . . . DW, J OR N PACKAGE
(TOP VIEW)

DEF	1	20 VCC
DB0	2	19 SEF
DB1	3	18 S1
DB2	4	17 S0
DB3	5	16 CB0
DB4	6	15 CB1
DB5	7	14 CB2
DB6	8	13 CB3
DB7	9	12 NC
GND	10	11 CB4

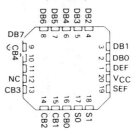

SN54LS' . . . FK PACKAGE
SN74LS'

(TOP VIEW)

NC No internal connection.

description

The 'LS636 and 'LS637 devices are 8-bit parallel error detection and correction circuits (EDACs) in 20-pin, 300-mil packages. They use a modified Hamming code to generate a 5-bit check word from an 8-bit data word. This check word is stored along with the data word during the memory write cycle. During the memory read cycle, the 13-bit words from memory are processed by the EDACs to determine if errors have occurred in memory.

Single-bit errors in the 8-bit data word are flagged and corrected.

Single-bit errors in the 5-bit check word are flagged, and the CPU sends the EDAC through the correction cycle even though the 8-bit word is not in error. The correction cycle will simply pass along the original 8-bit word in this case and produce error syndrome bits to pinpoint the error-generating location.

Dual-bit errors are flagged but not corrected. These dual errors may occur in any two bits of the 13-bit word from memory (two errors in the 8-bit data word, two errors in the 5-bit check word, or one error in each word).

The gross-error condition of all highs from memory will be detected. Otherwise, errors in three or more bits of the 13-bit word are beyond the capabilities of these devices to detect.

CONTROL FUNCTION TABLE

MEMORY CYCLE	CONTROL		EDAC FUNCTION	DATA I/O	CHECK WORD I/O	ERROR FLAGS	
	S1	S0				SEF	DEF
WRITE	L	L	Generate Check Word	Input Data	Output Check Word	L	L
READ	L	H	Read Data & Check Word	Input Data	Input Check Word	L	L
READ	H	H	Latch & Flag Errors	Latch Data	Latch Check Word	Enabled	
READ	H	L	Correct Data Word & Generate Syndrome Bits	Output Corrected Data	Output Syndrome Bits	Enabled	

TEXAS
INSTRUMENTS

3

TTL DEVICES

functional block diagram

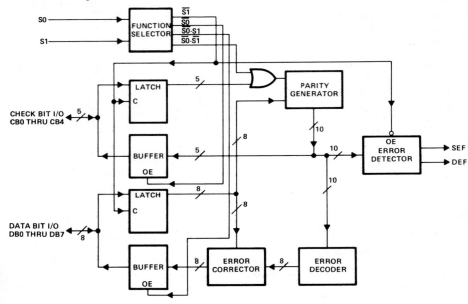

ERROR-FUNCTION TABLE

TOTAL NUMBER OF ERRORS		ERROR FLAGS		DATA
8-BIT DATA	5-BIT CHECKWORD	SEF	DEF	CORRECTION
0	0	L	L	Not Applicable
1	0	H	L	Correction
0	1	H	L	Correction
1	1	H	H	Interrupt
2	0	H	H	Interrupt
0	2	H	H	Interrupt

In order to be able to determine whether the data from the memory is acceptable to use as presented to the bus, the EDAC must be strobed to enable the error flags and the flags will have to be tested for the zero condition.

The first case in the error function table represents the normal, no-error condition. The CPU sees lows on both flags. The next two cases of single-bit errors require data correction. Although the EDAC can discern the single check bit error and ignore it, the error flags are identical to the single error in the 8-bit data word. The CPU will ask for data correction in both cases. An interrupt condition to the CPU results in each of the last three cases, where dual errors occur.

error detection and correction details

During a memory write cycle, five check bits (CB0-CB4) are generated by eight-input parity generators using the data bits as defined below. During a memory read cycle, the 5-bit check word is retrieved along with the 8-bit data word.

CHECKWORD	8-BIT DATA WORD							
BIT	0	1	2	3	4	5	6	7
CB0	X	X		X	X			
CB1	X		X	X		X	X	
CB2		X	X		X	X		X
CB3	X	X	X				X	X
CB4				X	X	X	X	X

The five check bits are parity bits derived from the matrix of data bits as indicated by "X" for each bit.

Error detection is accomplished as the 5-bit check word and the 8-bit data word from memory are applied to internal parity generators/checkers. If the parity of all five groupings of data and check bits are correct, it is assumed that no error has occurred and both error flags will be low.

If the parity of one or more of the check groups is incorrect, an error has occurred and the proper error flag or flags will be set high. Any single error in the 8-bit data word will change the sense of exactly three bits of the 5-bit check word. Any single error in the 5-bit check word changes the sense of only that one bit. In either case, the single error flag will be set high while the dual error flag will remain low.

Any two-bit error will change the sense of an even number of check bits. The two-bit error is not correctable since the parity tree can only identify single-bit errors. Both error flags are set high when any two-bit error is detected.

Three or more simultaneous bit errors can fool the EDAC into believing that no error, a correctable error, or an uncorrectable error has occurred and produce erroneous results in all three cases.

Error correction is accomplished by identifying the bad bit and inverting it. Identification of the erroneous bit is achieved by comparing the 8-bit data word and 5-bit check word from memory with the new check word with one (check word error) or three (data word error) inverted bits.

As the corrected word is made available on the data word I/O port, the check word I/O port presents a 5-bit syndrome error code. This syndrome code can be used to identify the bad memory chip.

ERROR SYNDROME TABLE

ERROR LOCATION	SYNDROME ERROR CODE				
	CB0	CB1	CB2	CB3	CB4
DB0	L	L	H	L	H
DB1	L	H	L	L	H
DB2	H	L	L	L	H
DB3	L	L	H	H	L
DB4	L	H	L	H	L
DB5	H	L	L	H	L
DB6	H	L	H	L	L
DB7	H	H	L	L	L
CB0	L	H	H	H	H
CB1	H	L	H	H	H
CB2	H	H	L	H	H
CB3	H	H	H	L	H
CB4	H	H	H	H	L
NO ERROR	H	H	H	H	H

3

TTL DEVICES

TEXAS
INSTRUMENTS

schematics of inputs and outputs

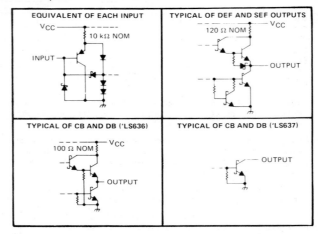

absolute maximum ratings over operating free-air temperature range (unless otherwise noted)

Supply voltage, V_{CC} (see Note 1) . . . . 7 V

Input voltage: S0 and S1 . . . . 7 V

CB and DB . . . . 5.5 V

Off-state output voltage . . . . 5.5 V

Operating free-air temperature range: SN54LS636, SN54LS637 . . . . $-55°C$ to $125°C$

SN74LS636, SN74LS637 . . . . $0°C$ to $70°C$

Storage temperature range . . . . $-65°C$ to $150°C$

NOTE 1: Voltage values are with respect to network ground terminal.

recommended operating conditions

			SN54LS636 SN54LS637			SN74LS636 SN74LS637			UNIT
			MIN	NOM	MAX	MIN	NOM	MAX	
V_{CC}	Supply voltage		4.5	5	5.5	4.75	5	5.25	V
I_{OH}	High-level output current	CB or DB, 'LS636 only			-1			-1	mA
		DEF or SEF			-0.4			-0.4	
V_{OH}	High-level output voltage	CB or DB, 'LS637 only			5.5			5.5	V
I_{OL}	Low-level output current	CB or DB			12			24	mA
		DEF or SEF			4			8	
t_{su}	Setup time	CB or DB before S1↑†	15			15			ns
		CB or DB before S1↑‡	45			45			
t_h	Hold time	CB or DB after S1↑	15			15			ns
T_A	Operating free-air temperature		-55		125	0		70	C

† This time guarantees the input data and checkword will be latched.
‡ This time guarantees the input data and checkword will be latched plus that no glitch will occur on SEF or DEF flags.
↑ The upward-pointing arrow indicates a transition from low to high.

TEXAS
INSTRUMENTS

electrical characteristics over recommended operating free-air temperature range (unless otherwise noted)

PARAMETERS		TEST CONDITIONS†		SN54LS636 MIN	TYP‡	MAX	SN74LS636 MIN	TYP‡	MAX	UNIT
V_{IH}	High-level input voltage			2			2			V
V_{IL}	Low-level input voltage					0.7			0.8	V
V_{IK}	Input clamp voltage	V_{CC} = MIN,	I_I = −18 mA			−1.5			−1.5	V
V_{OH}	High-level output voltage	CB or DB	V_{CC} = MIN, V_{IH} = 2 V, V_{IL} = V_{IL} min — I_{OH} = MAX	2.4	3.3		2.4	3.2		V
		DEF or SEF	I_{OH} = −400 µA	2.5	3.4		2.7	3.4		
V_{OL}	Low-level output voltage	CB or DB	V_{CC} = MIN, V_{IH} = 2 V, V_{IL} = V_{IL} max — I_{OL} = 12 mA		0.25	0.4		0.25	0.4	V
			I_{OL} = 24 mA					0.35	0.5	
		DEF or SEF	I_{OL} = 4 mA		0.25	0.4		0.25	0.4	
			I_{OL} = 8 mA					0.35	0.5	
I_{OZH}	Off-state output current, high-level voltage applied	CB or DB	V_{CC} = MAX, V_O = 2.7 V, S0 and S1 at 2 V			20			20	µA
I_{OZL}	Off-state output current, low-level voltage applied	CB or DB	V_{CC} = MAX, V_O = 0.4 V, S0 and S1 at 2 V			−0.2			−0.2	mA
I_I	Input current at maximum input voltage	CB or DB	V_{CC} = MAX, V_I = 5.5 V			0.1			0.1	mA
		S0 or S1	V_{IH} = 4.5 V, V_I = 7 V			0.1			0.1	
I_{IH}	High-level input current		V_{CC} = MAX, V_I = 2.7 V			20			20	µA
I_{IL}	Low-level input current		V_{CC} = MAX, V_I = 0.4 V			−0.2			−0.2	mA
I_{OS}§	Short-circuit output current	CB or DB	V_{CC} = MAX	−30		−130	−30		−130	mA
		DEF or SEF		−20		−100	−20		−100	
I_{CC}	Supply current		V_{CC} = MAX, S0 and S1 at 4.5 V, All CB and DB pins grounded, DEF and SEF open		100	160		100	160	mA

PARAMETER		TEST CONDITIONS†		SN54LS637 MIN	TYP‡	MAX	SN74LS637 MIN	TYP‡	MAX	UNIT
V_{IH}	High-level input voltage			2			2			V
V_{IL}	Low-level input voltage					0.7			0.8	V
V_{IK}	Input clamp voltage		V_{CC} = MIN, I_I = −18 mA			−1.5			−1.5	V
V_{OH}	High-level output voltage	DEF or SEF	V_{CC} = MIN, V_{IH} = 2 V, I_{OH} = −400 µA, V_{IL} = V_{IL} max	2.5	3.4		2.7	3.4		V
I_{OH}	High-level output current	CB or DB	V_{CC} = MIN, V_{IH} = 2 V, V_{OH} = 5.5 V, V_{IL} = V_{IL} max			0.1			0.1	mA
V_{OL}	Low-level output voltage	CB or DB	V_{CC} = MIN, V_{IH} = 2 V, V_{IL} = V_{IL} max — I_{OL} = 12 mA		0.25	0.4		0.25	0.4	V
			I_{OL} = 24 mA					0.35	0.5	
		DEF or SEF	I_{OL} = 4 mA		0.25	0.4		0.25	0.4	
			I_{OL} = 8 mA					0.35	0.5	
I_I	Input current at maximum input voltage	CB or DB	V_{CC} = MAX, V_I = 5.5 V			0.1			0.1	mA
		S0 or S1	V_{IH} = 4.5 V, V_I = 7 V			0.1			0.1	
I_{IH}	High-level input current		V_{CC} = MAX, V_I = 2.7 V			20			20	µA
I_{IL}	Low-level input current		V_{CC} = MAX, V_I = 0.4 V			−0.2			−0.2	mA
I_{OS}§	Short-circuit output current	DEF or SEF	V_{CC} = MAX	−20		−100	−20		−100	mA
I_{CC}	Supply current		V_{CC} = MAX, S0 and S1 at 4.5 V, All CB and DB grounded, SEF and DEF open		90	144		90	144	mA

†For conditions shown as MIN or MAX, use the appropriate value specified under recommended operating conditions.
‡All typical values are at V_{CC} = 5 V, T_A = 25°C.
§Not more than one output should be shorted at a time, and duration of the short circuit should not exceed one second.

TEXAS
INSTRUMENTS

3

TTL DEVICES

'LS636 switching characteristics, V_{CC} = 5 V, T_A = 25°C, C_L = 45 pF

PARAMETER		FROM (INPUT)	TO (OUTPUT)	TEST CONDITIONS	'LS636 MIN	'LS636 TYP	'LS636 MAX	UNIT
t_{PLH}	Propagation delay time, low-to-high-level output$^\diamond$	DB	CB	S0 at 0 V, S1 at 0 V, R_L = 667 Ω, See Figure 1		31	45	ns
t_{PHL}	Propagation delay time, high-to-low-level output$^\diamond$					45	65	ns
t_{PLH}	Propagation delay time, low-to-high-level output*	S1↑	DEF	S0 at 3 V, R_L = 2 kΩ, See Figure 1		27	40	ns
			SEF			20	30	
t_{PZH}	Output enable time to high level$^\#$	S0↓	CB, DB	S1 at 3 V, R_L = 667 Ω, See Figure 2		24	40	ns
t_{PZL}	Output enable time to low level$^\#$	S0↓	CB, DB	S1 at 3 V, R_L = 667 Ω, See Figure 1		30	45	ns
t_{PHZ}	Output disable time from high level$^\blacktriangle$	S0↑	CB, DB	S1 at 3 V, R_L = 667 Ω, See Figure 2		43	65	ns
t_{PLZ}	Output disable time from low level$^\blacktriangle$	S0↑	CB, DB	S1 at 3 V, R_L = 667 Ω, See Figure 1		31	45	ns

'LS637 switching characteristics, V_{CC} = 5 V, T_A = 25°C, C_L = 45 pF, see Figure 1

PARAMETER		FROM (INPUT)	TO (OUTPUT)	TEST CONDITIONS	'LS637 MIN	'LS637 TYP	'LS637 MAX	UNIT
t_{PLH}	Propagation delay time, low-to-high level output$^\diamond$	DB	CB	S0 at 0 V, S1 at 0V, R_L = 667 Ω		38	55	ns
t_{PHL}	Propagation delay time, high-to-low-level output$^\diamond$					45	65	ns
t_{PLH}	Propagation delay time, low-to-high-level output*	S1↑	DEF	S0 at 3 V, R_L = 2 kΩ		27	40	ns
			SEF			20	30	ns
t_{PHL}	Propagation delay time, high-to-low-level output$^\#$	S0↓	CB, DB	S1 at 3 V, R_L = 667 kΩ		28	45	ns
t_{PLH}	Propagation delay time, low-to-high-level output$^\blacktriangle$	S0↑	CB, DB	S1 at 3 V, R_L = 667 kΩ		33	50	ns

$^\diamond$These parameters describe the time intervals taken to generate the check word during the memory write cycle.

*These parameters describe the time intervals taken to flag errors during the memory read cycle.

$^\#$These parameters describe the time intervals taken to correct and output the data word and to generate and output the syndrome error code during the memory read cycle.

$^\blacktriangle$These parameters describe the time intervals taken to disable the CB and DB buses in preparation for a new data word during the memory read cycle.

PARAMETER MEASUREMENT INFORMATION

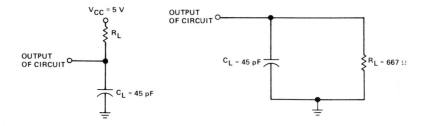

FIGURE 1—OUTPUT LOAD CIRCUIT   FIGURE 2—OUTPUT LOAD CIRCUIT

TEXAS
INSTRUMENTS

typical operating sequences

READ, FLAG, AND CORRECT MODE SWITCHING WAVEFORMS

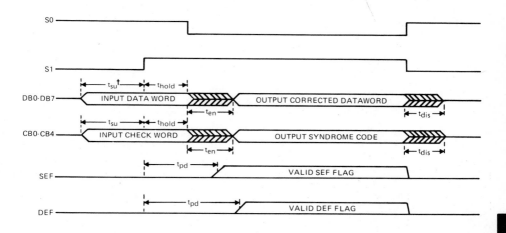

† NOTE: There are two conditions specified for t_{su} of Data or Checkword before S1↑. See recommended operating conditions for detail.

3

TTL DEVICES

3

TTL DEVICES

TYPES SN54LS638, SN54LS639, SN74LS638, SN74LS639
OCTAL BUS TRANSCEIVERS

D2636, JANUARY 1981 — REVISED DECEMBER 1983

- Bidirectional Bus Transceivers in High-Density 20-Pin Packages
- Hysteresis at Bus Inputs Improves Noise Margins
- Choice of True or Inverting Logic
- A Bus Outputs are Open-Collector, B Bus Outputs are 3-State

description

These octal bus transceivers are designed for asynchronous two-way communication between open-collector and 3-state buses. The devices transmit data from the A bus (open-collector) to the B bus (3-state) or from the B bus to the A bus depending upon the level at the direction control (DIR) input. The enable input ($\overline{G}$) can be used to disable the device so the buses are isolated.

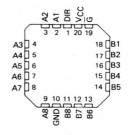

SN54LS638, SN54LS639 . . . J PACKAGE
SN74LS638, SN74LS639 . . . DW, J OR N PACKAGE
(TOP VIEW)

DIR	1	20	V_{CC}
A1	2	19	$\overline{G}$
A2	3	18	B1
A3	4	17	B2
A4	5	16	B3
A5	6	15	B4
A6	7	14	B5
A7	8	13	B6
A8	9	12	B7
GND	10	11	B8

SN54LS638, SN54LS639 . . . FK PACKAGE
SN74LS638, SN74LS639
(TOP VIEW)

FUNCTION TABLE

CONTROL INPUTS		OPERATION	
$\overline{G}$	DIR	'LS638	'LS639
L	L	$\overline{B}$ data to A bus	B data to A bus
L	H	$\overline{A}$ data to B bus	A data to B bus
H	X	Isolation	Isolation

H = high level, L = low level, X = irrelevant

DEVICE	A OUTPUT	B OUTPUT	LOGIC
'LS638	Open-Collector	3-State	Inverting
'LS639	Open-Collector	3-State	True

schematics of inputs and outputs

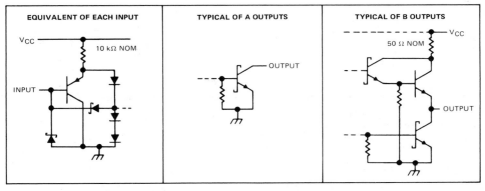

EQUIVALENT OF EACH INPUT	TYPICAL OF A OUTPUTS	TYPICAL OF B OUTPUTS

TEXAS
INSTRUMENTS

TTL DEVICES

3

3-1019

TYPES SN54LS638, SN54LS639, SN74LS638, SN74LS639
OCTAL BUS TRANSCEIVERS

logic symbols

'LS638

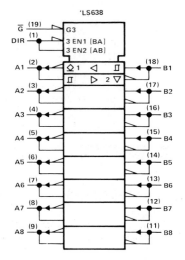

'LS639

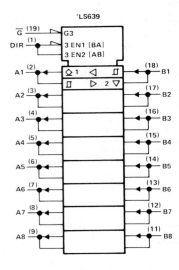

Pin numbers shown on logic notation are for DW, J or N packages.

logic diagrams (positive logic)

'LS638

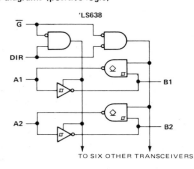

TO SIX OTHER TRANSCEIVERS

'LS639

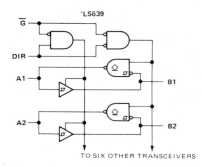

TO SIX OTHER TRANSCEIVERS

absolute maximum ratings over operating free-air temperature range (unless otherwise noted)

Supply voltage, V_{CC} (see Note 1) . . . . 7 V
Input voltage (DIR or $\overline{G}$) . . . . 7 V
Off-state output voltage (A or B) . . . . 5.5 V
Operating free-air temperature range: SN54LS638, SN54LS639 . . . . −55°C to 125°C
                                        SN74LS638, SN74LS639 . . . . 0°C to 70°C
Storage temperature range . . . . −65°C to 150°C

NOTE 1: Voltage values are with respect to the network ground terminal.

Texas
Instruments

recommended operating conditions

	SN54LS' MIN	SN54LS' NOM	SN54LS' MAX	SN74LS' MIN	SN74LS' NOM	SN74LS' MAX	UNIT
Supply voltage, V_{CC}	4.5	5	5.5	4.75	5	5.25	V
High-level output voltage, V_{OH} (A bus)			5.5			5.5	V
High-level output current, I_{OH} (B bus)			−12			−15	mA
Low-level output current, I_{OL} (A or B bus)			12			24	mA
Operating free-air temperature, T_A	−55		125	0		70	°C

electrical characteristics over recommended operating free-air temperature range (unless otherwise noted)

	PARAMETER		TEST CONDITIONS[†]		SN54LS' MIN	SN54LS' TYP[‡]	SN54LS' MAX	SN74LS' MIN	SN74LS' TYP[‡]	SN74LS' MAX	UNIT
V_{IH}	High-level input voltage				2			2			V
V_{IL}	Low-level input voltage						0.5			0.6	V
V_{IK}	Input clamp voltage		V_{CC} = MIN, I_I = −18 mA				−1.5			−1.5	V
	Hysteresis ($V_{T+}-V_{T-}$)		V_{CC} = MIN		0.1	0.4		0.2	0.4		V
I_{OH}	High-level output current	A	V_{CC} = MIN, V_{IH} = 2 V, V_{IL} = MAX, V_{OH} = 5.5 V				0.1			0.1	mA
V_{OH}	High-level output voltage	B	V_{CC} = MIN, V_{IH} = 2 V, V_{IL} = MAX	I_{OH} = −3 mA	2.4			2.4			V
				I_{OH} = MAX	2			2			
V_{OL}	Low-level output voltage	A or B	V_{CC} = MIN, V_{IH} = 2 V, V_{IL} = MAX	I_{OL} = 12 mA		0.25	0.4		0.25	0.4	V
				I_{OL} = 24 mA					0.35	0.5	
I_{OZH}	Off-state output current, high-level voltage applied	B	V_{CC} = MAX, $\overline{G}$ at 2 V, V_O = 2.7 V				20			20	µA
I_{OZL}	Off-state output current low-level voltage applied	A or B	V_{CC} = MAX, $\overline{G}$ at 2 V, V_O = 0.4 V				−0.4			−0.4	mA
I_I	Input current at maximum input voltage	A or B	V_{CC} = MAX	V_I = 5.5 V			0.1			0.1	mA
		DIR or $\overline{G}$		V_I = 7 V			0.1			0.1	
I_{IH}	High-level input current		V_{CC} = MAX, V_I = 2.7 V				20			20	µA
I_{IL}	Low-level input current		V_{CC} = MAX, V_I = 0.4 V				−0.4			−0.4	mA
I_{OS}	Short-circuit output current [§]	B	V_{CC} = MAX		−40		−225	−40		−225	mA
I_{CCH}	Supply current, outputs high		V_{CC} = MAX, Outputs open			48	70		48	70	mA
I_{CCL}	Supply current, outputs low		V_{CC} = MAX, Outputs open			62	90		62	90	mA
I_{CCZ}	Supply current, outputs off		V_{CC} = MAX, Outputs open			64	95		64	95	mA

[†] For conditions shown as MIN or MAX, use the appropriate value specified under recommended operating conditions.

[‡] All typical values are at V_{CC} = 5 V, T_A = 25°C.

[§] Not more than one output should be shorted at a time, and duration of the short circuit should not exceed one second.

switching characteristics, V_{CC} = 5 V, T_A = 25°C, see note 2

PARAMETER	FROM (INPUT)	TO (OUTPUT)	TEST CONDITIONS	'LS638 MIN	'LS638 TYP	'LS638 MAX	'LS639 MIN	'LS639 TYP	'LS639 MAX	UNIT
t_{PLH}	A	B			6	10		8	15	ns
	B	A			17	25		19	25	
t_{PHL}	A	B			8	15		11	15	ns
	B	A	C_L = 45 pF, R_L = 667 Ω		14	25		16	25	
t_{PLH}	$\overline{G}$	A			26	40		23	40	ns
t_{PHL}	$\overline{G}$	A			43	60		34	50	ns
t_{PZH}	$\overline{G}$	B			23	40		26	40	ns
t_{PZL}	$\overline{G}$	B			31	40		31	40	ns
t_{PHZ}	$\overline{G}$	B	C_L = 5 pF, R_L = 667 Ω		15	25		15	25	ns
t_{PLZ}	$\overline{G}$	B			15	25		15	25	ns

NOTE 2: See General Information Section for load circuits and voltage waveforms.

3

TTL DEVICES

TEXAS
INSTRUMENTS

TYPICAL CHARACTERISTICS

SN54LS'
INVERTING OUTPUT VOLTAGE
vs
INPUT VOLTAGE

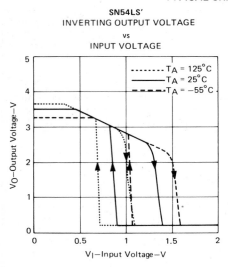

FIGURE 1

SN74LS'
INVERTING OUTPUT VOLTAGE
vs
INPUT VOLTAGE

FIGURE 2

SN54LS'
NONINVERTING OUTPUT VOLTAGE
vs
INPUT VOLTAGE

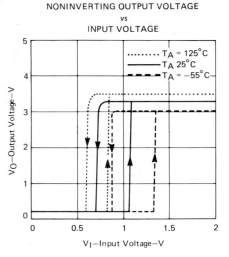

FIGURE 3

SN74LS'
NONINVERTING OUTPUT VOLTAGE
vs
INPUT VOLTAGE

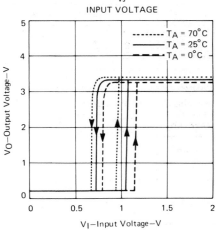

FIGURE 4

TEXAS
INSTRUMENTS

- **SN74LS64X-1 Versions Rated at I_{OL} of 48 mA**
- **Bi-directional Bus Transceivers in High-Density 20-Pin Packages**
- **Hysteresis at Bus Input Improves Noise Margins**
- **Choice of True or Inverting Logic**
- **Choice of 3-State or Open-Collector Outputs**

DEVICE	OUTPUT	LOGIC
'LS640A	3-State	Inverting
'LS641	Open-Collector	True
'LS642	Open-Collector	Inverting
'LS644	Open-Collector	True and inverting
'LS645	3-State	True

description

These octal bus transceivers are designed for asynchronous two-way communication between data buses. The devices transmit data from the A bus to the B bus or from the B bus to the A bus depending upon the level at the direction control (DIR) input. The enable input ($\overline{G}$) can be used to disable the device so the buses are effectively isolated.

The −1 versions of the SN74LS640A thru SN74LS642, SN74LS644, and SN74LS645 are identical to the standard versions except that the recommended maximum I_{OL} is increased to 48 milliamperes. There are no −1 versions of the SN54LS640A thru SN54LS642, SN54LS644, and SN54LS645.

The SN54LS640A thru SN54LS642, SN54LS644, and SN54LS645 are characterized for operation over the full military temperature range of −55°C to 125°C. The SN74LS640A thru SN74LS642, SN74LS644, and SN74LS645 are characterized for operation from 0°C to 70°C.

SN54LS' ... J PACKAGE
SN74LS' ... DW, J OR N PACKAGE
(TOP VIEW)

DIR	1	20	V_{CC}
A1	2	19	$\overline{G}$
A2	3	18	B1
A3	4	17	B2
A4	5	16	B3
A5	6	15	B4
A6	7	14	B5
A7	8	13	B6
A8	9	12	B7
GND	10	11	B8

SN54LS' ... FK PACKAGE
SN74LS'
(TOP VIEW)

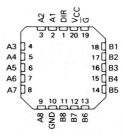

FUNCTION TABLE

CONTROL INPUTS		OPERATION		
$\overline{G}$	DIR	'LS640A 'LS642	'LS641 'LS645	'LS644
L	L	$\overline{B}$ data to A bus	B data to A bus	B data to A bus
L	H	$\overline{A}$ data to B bus	A data to B bus	$\overline{A}$ data to B bus
H	X	Isolation	Isolation	Isolation

H = high level, L = low level, X = irrelevant

TEXAS
INSTRUMENTS

3-1023

3

TTL DEVICES

logic symbols

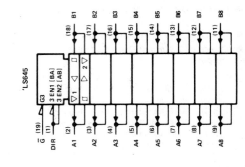

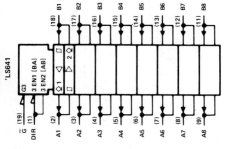

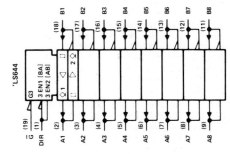

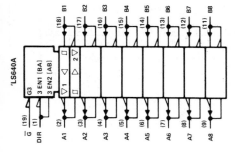

Pin numbers shown on logic notation are for DW, J or N packages.

3

TTL DEVICES

TEXAS
INSTRUMENTS

logic diagrams

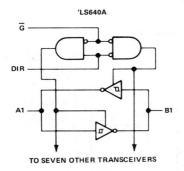

'LS640A

TO SEVEN OTHER TRANSCEIVERS

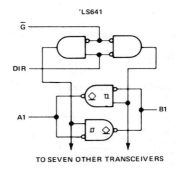

'LS641

TO SEVEN OTHER TRANSCEIVERS

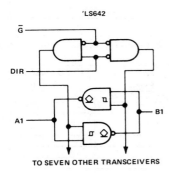

'LS642

TO SEVEN OTHER TRANSCEIVERS

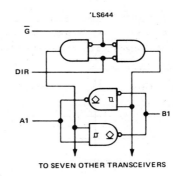

'LS644

TO SEVEN OTHER TRANSCEIVERS

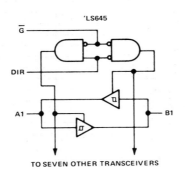

'LS645

TO SEVEN OTHER TRANSCEIVERS

TTL DEVICES

3

TEXAS
INSTRUMENTS

absolute maximum ratings over operating free-air temperature range (unless otherwise noted)

Supply voltage, V_{CC} (see Note 1) .... 7 V
Input voltage: All inputs .... 7 V
            I/O ports .... 5.5 V
Operating free-air temperature range: SN54LS640, SN54LS645 .... −55°C to 125°C
                             SN74LS640, SN74LS645 .... 0°C to 70°C
Storage temperature range .... −65°C to 150°C

NOTE 1: Voltage values are with respect to network ground terminal.

recommended operating conditions

	PARAMETER	SN54LS640A SN54LS645			SN74LS640A SN74LS645			UNIT
		MIN	NOM	MAX	MIN	NOM	MAX	
V_{CC}	Supply voltage	4.5	5	5.5	4.75	5	5.25	V
V_{IH}	High-level input voltage	2			2			V
V_{IL}	Low-level input voltage			0.5			0.6	V
I_{OH}	High-level output current			−12			−15	mA
I_{OL}	Low-level output current			12			24 / 48*	mA
T_A	Operating free-air temperature	−55		125	0		70	°C

* The 48 mA limit applies for the SN74LS640A-1 and SN74LS645-1 only.

electrical characteristics over recommended operating free-air temperature range (unless otherwise noted)

PARAMETER		TEST CONDITIONS†		SN54LS640A SN54LS645			SN74LS640A SN74LS645			UNIT
				MIN	TYP*	MAX	MIN	TYP*	MAX	
V_{IK}		V_{CC} = MIN, I_I = −18 mA				−1.5			−1.5	V
Hysteresis $(V_{T+} - V_{T-})$		V_{CC} = MIN	A or B input	0.1	0.4		0.2	0.4		V
V_{OH}		V_{CC} = MIN, V_{IH} = 2 V, V_{IL} = MAX	I_{OH} = −3 mA	2.4	3.4		2.4	3.4		
			I_{OH} = MAX	2			2			
V_{OL}		V_{CC} = MIN, V_{IH} = 2 V, V_{IL} = MAX	I_{OL} = 12 mA		0.25	0.4		0.25	0.4	V
			I_{OL} = 24 mA					0.35	0.5	
			I_{OL} = 48 mA£					0.4	0.5	
I_{OZH}		V_{CC} = MAX, $\overline{G}$ at 2 V,	V_O = 2.7 V			20			20	μA
I_{OZL}		V_{CC} = MAX, $\overline{G}$ at 2 V,	V_O = 0.4 V			−0.4			−0.4	mA
I_I	A or B	V_{CC} = MAX	V_I = 5.5 V			0.1			0.1	mA
	DIR or $\overline{G}$		V_I = 7 V			0.1			0.1	
I_{IH}		V_{CC} = MAX, V_{IH} = 2.7 V				20			20	μA
I_{IL}		V_{CC} = MAX, V_{IL} = 0.4 V				−0.4			−0.4	mA
I_{OS}§		V_{CC} = MAX		−40		−225	−40		−225	mA
I_{CC}	Outputs high	V_{CC} = MAX, Outputs open			48	70		48	70	mA
	Outputs low				62	90		62	90	
	Outputs at Hi-Z				64	95		64	95	

† For conditions shown as MIN or MAX, use the appropriate value specified under recommended operating conditions.
* All typical values are at V_{CC} = 5 V, T_A = 25°C.
§ Not more than one output should be shorted at a time, and duration of the short-circuit should not exceed one second.
£ The 48 mA condition applies for the SN74LS640A-1 and SN74LS645-1 only.

TEXAS
INSTRUMENTS

3

TTL DEVICES

switching characteristics at $V_{CC} = 5$ V, $T_A = 25°C$

PARAMETER		FROM (INPUT)	TO (OUTPUT)	TEST CONDITIONS	'LS640A, 'LS640A-1			'LS645, 'LS645-1			UNIT
					MIN	TYP	MAX	MIN	TYP	MAX	
t_{PLH}	Propagation delay time, low-to-high-level output	A	B	$C_L = 45pF$, $R_L = 667\Omega$, See Note 2		6	10		8	15	ns
		B	A			6	10		8	15	
t_{PHL}	Propagation delay time, high-to-low-level output	A	B			8	15		11	15	ns
		B	A			8	15		11	15	
t_{PZL}	Output enable time to low level	$\overline{G}$	B			31	40		31	40	ns
		$\overline{G}$	A			31	40		31	40	
t_{PZH}	Output enable time to high level	$\overline{G}$	B			23	40		26	40	ns
		$\overline{G}$	A			23	40		26	40	
t_{PLZ}	Output disable time from low level	$\overline{G}$	B	$C_L = 5pF$, $R_L = 667\Omega$, See Note 2		15	25		15	25	ns
		$\overline{G}$	A			15	25		15	25	
t_{PHZ}	Output disable time from high level	$\overline{G}$	A			15	25		15	25	ns
		$\overline{G}$	B			15	25		15	25	

NOTE 2: See General Information Section for load circuits and voltage waveforms.

schematics of inputs and outputs

EQUIVALENT OF EACH INPUT

TYPICAL OUTPUTS

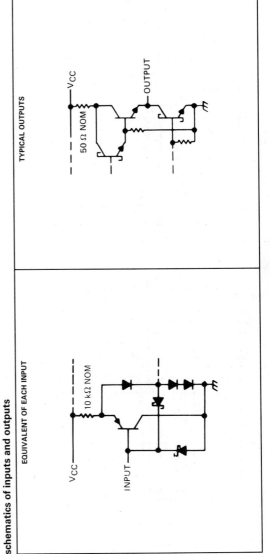

TTL DEVICES

3

TYPICAL CHARACTERISTICS

SN54LS'
INVERTING OUTPUT VOLTAGE
vs
INPUT VOLTAGE

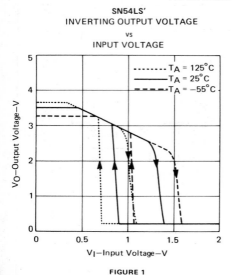

FIGURE 1

SN74LS'
INVERTING OUTPUT VOLTAGE
vs
INPUT VOLTAGE

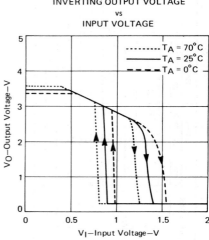

FIGURE 2

SN54LS'
NONINVERTING OUTPUT VOLTAGE
vs
INPUT VOLTAGE

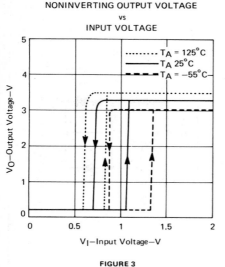

FIGURE 3

SN74LS'
NONINVERTING OUTPUT VOLTAGE
vs
INPUT VOLTAGE

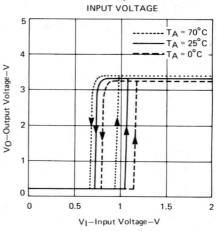

FIGURE 4

3

TTL DEVICES

TEXAS
INSTRUMENTS

absolute maximum ratings over operating free-air temperature range (unless otherwise noted)

Supply voltage, V_{CC} (see Note 1) .... 7 V
Input voltage: All inputs and I/O ports .... 7 V
Operating free-air temperature range: SN54LS641, SN54LS642, SN54LS644 .... $-55°$C to $125°$C
SN74LS641, SN74LS642, SN74LS644 .... $0°$C to $70°$C
Storage temperature range .... $-65°$C to $150°$C

NOTE 1: Voltage values are with respect to network ground terminal.

recommended operating conditions

PARAMETER		SN54LS641 SN54LS642 SN54LS644			SN74LS641 SN74LS642 SN74LS644			UNIT
		MIN	NOM	MAX	MIN	NOM	MAX	
V_{CC}	Supply voltage	4.5	5	5.5	4.75	5	5.25	V
V_{IH}	High-level input voltage	2			2			V
V_{IL}	Low-level input voltage			0.5			0.6	V
V_{OH}	High-level output voltage			5.5			5.5	V
I_{OL}	Low-level output current			12			24	mA
							48 §	
T_A	Operating free-air temperature	-55		125	0		70	$°$C

§ The 48 mA limit applies for the SN74LS641-1, SN74LS642-1, and SN74LS644-1 only.

electrical characteristics over recommended operating free-air temperature range (unless otherwise noted)

PARAMETER		TEST CONDITIONS†		SN54LS641 SN54LS642 SN54LS644			SN74LS641 SN74LS642 SN74LS644			UNIT
				MIN	TYP‡	MAX	MIN	TYP‡	MAX	
V_{IK}		V_{CC} = MIN,	$I_I = -18$ mA			-1.5			-1.5	V
Hysteresis $(V_{T+} - V_{T-})$		V_{CC} = MIN,	A or B input	0.1	0.4		0.2	0.4		V
I_{OH}		V_{CC} = MIN, V_{IL} = MAX,	V_{IH} = 2 V, V_{OH} = 5.5 V		0.1			0.1		mA
V_{OL}		V_{CC} = MIN, V_{IH} = 2 V, V_{IL} = MAX	I_{OL} = 12 mA		0.25	0.4		0.25	0.4	V
			I_{OL} = 24 mA					0.35	0.5	
			I_{OL} = 48 mA §					0.4	0.5	
I_I	A or B	V_{CC} = MAX	V_I = 5.5 V			0.1			0.1	mA
	DIR or $\overline{G}$		V_I = 7 V			0.1			0.1	
I_{IH}		V_{CC} = MAX,	V_I = 2.7 V			20			20	μA
I_{IL}		V_{CC} = MAX,	V_I = 0.4 V			-0.4			-0.4	mA
I_{CC}	Outputs high	V_{CC} = MAX,	Outputs open		48	70		48	70	mA
	Outputs low				62	90		62	90	
	Outputs at Hi-Z				64	95		64	95	

† For conditions shown as MIN or MAX, use the appropriate value specified under recommended operating conditions.
‡ All typical values are at V_{CC} = 5 V, T_A = 25°C.
§ The 48 mA condition applies for the SN74LS641-1, SN74LS642-1, and SN74LS644-1 only.

3

TTL DEVICES

TEXAS
INSTRUMENTS

switching characteristics at V_{CC} = 5 V, T_A = 25°C

PARAMETER	FROM (INPUT)	TO (OUTPUT)	TEST CONDITIONS	'LS641, 'LS641–1			'LS642, 'LS642–1			'LS644, 'LS644–1			UNIT
				MIN	TYP	MAX	MIN	TYP	MAX	MIN	TYP	MAX	
t_{PLH} Propagation delay time, low-to-high-level output	A	B	C_L = 45 pF, R_L = 667 Ω, See Note 2		17	25		19	25		17	25	ns
	B	A			17	25		19	25		19	25	
t_{PHL} Propagation delay time, high-to-low-level output	A	B			16	25		14	25		14	25	ns
	B	A			16	25		14	25		16	25	
t_{PLH} Output disable time from low level	Ḡ, DIR	A			23	40		26	40		26	40	ns
	Ḡ, DIR	B			25	40		28	40		25	40	
t_{PHL} Output enable time from high level	Ḡ, DIR	A			34	50		43	60		43	60	ns
	Ḡ, DIR	B			37	50		39	60		37	50	

NOTE 2: See General Information Section for load circuits and voltage waveforms.

schematics of inputs and outputs

EQUIVALENT OF EACH INPUT

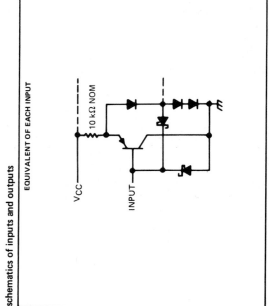

TYPICAL OF OUTPUTS

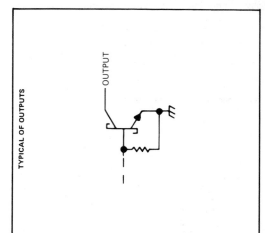

TEXAS INSTRUMENTS

3 TTL DEVICES

- Independent Registers for A and B Buses
- Multiplexed Real-Time and Stored Data
- Choice of True or Inverting Data Paths
- Choice of 3-State or Open-Collector Outputs
- Included Among the Package Options Are Compact 24-pin 300-mil Wide DIPs and Both 28-pin Plastic and Ceramic Chip Carriers
- Dependable Texas Instruments Quality and Reliability

DEVICE	OUTPUT	LOGIC
'LS646	3-State	True
'LS647	Open-Collector	True
'LS648	3-State	Inverting
'LS649	Open-Collector	Inverting

description

These devices consist of bus transceiver circuits with 3-state or open-collector outputs, D-type flip-flops, and control circuitry arranged for multiplexed transmission of data directly from the input bus or from the internal registers. Data on the A or B bus will be clocked into the registers on the low-to-high transition of the appropriate clock pin (CAB or CBA). The following examples demonstrate the four fundamental bus-management functions that can be performed with the octal bus transceivers and registers.

SN54LS'... JT PACKAGE
SN74LS'... DW, JT OR NT PACKAGE
(TOP VIEW)

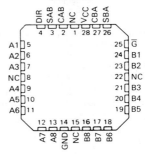

SN54LS'... FK PACKAGE
SN74LS'
(TOP VIEW)

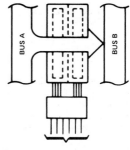

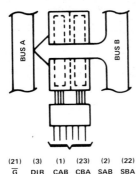

(21)	(3)	(1)	(23)	(2)	(22)
$\overline{G}$	DIR	CAB	CBA	SAB	SBA
L	L	X	H or L	X	L

REAL-TIME TRANSFER
BUS B TO BUS A

(21)	(3)	(1)	(23)	(2)	(22)
$\overline{G}$	DIR	CAB	CBA	SAB	SBA
L	H	H or L	X	L	X

REAL-TIME TRANSFER
BUS A TO BUS B

TEXAS
INSTRUMENTS

TTL DEVICES

3

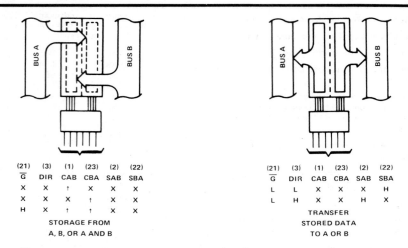

(21) Ḡ	(3) DIR	(1) CAB	(23) CBA	(2) SAB	(22) SBA
X	X	↑	X	X	X
X	X	X	↑	X	X
H	X	↑	↑	X	X

**STORAGE FROM
A, B, OR A AND B**

(21) Ḡ	(3) DIR	(1) CAB	(23) CBA	(2) SAB	(22) SBA
L	L	X	X	X	H
L	H	X	X	H	X

**TRANSFER
STORED DATA
TO A OR B**

Enable (Ḡ) and direction (DIR) pins are provided to control the transceiver functions. In the transceiver mode, data present at the high-impedance port may be stored in either register or in both. The select controls (SAB and SBA) can multiplex stored and real-time (transparent mode) data. The direction control determines which bus will receive data when enable Ḡ is active (low). In the isolation mode (control Ḡ high), A data may be stored in one register and/or B data may be stored in the other register.

When an output function is disabled, the input function is still enabled and may be used to store and transmit data. Only one of the two buses, A or B, may be driven at a time.

The SN54' family is characterized for operation over the full military temperature range of −55°C to 125°C. The SN74' family is characterized for operation from 0° to 70°C.

FUNCTION TABLE

INPUTS						DATA I/O†		OPERATION OR FUNCTION	
Ḡ	DIR	CAB	CBA	SAB	SBA	A1 THRU A8	B1 THRU B8	LS646, LS647	LS648, LS649
X	X	↑	X	X	X	Input	Not specified	Store A, B unspecified	Store A, B unspecified
X	X	X	↑	X	X	Not specified	Input	Store B, A unspecified	Store B, A unspecified
H	X	↑	↑	X	X	Input	Input	Store A and B Data	Store A and B Data
H	X	H or L	H or L	X	X			Isolation, hold storage	Isolation, hold storage
L	L	X	H or L	X	L	Output	Input	Real-Time B Data to A Bus	Real-Time B̄ Data to A Bus
L	L	X	X	X	H	Output	Input	Stored B Data to A Bus	Stored B̄ Data to A Bus
L	H	H or L	X	L	X	Input	Output	Real-Time A Data to B Bus	Real-Time Ā Data to B Bus
L	H	X	X	H	X	Input	Output	Stored A Data to B Bus	Stored Ā Data to B Bus

† The data output functions may be enabled or disabled by various signals at the Ḡ and DIR inputs. Data input functions are always enabled, i.e., data at the bus pins will be stored on every low-to-high transition on the clock inputs.

**TEXAS
INSTRUMENTS**

3

TTL DEVICES

logic diagrams (positive logic)

'LS646, 'LS647

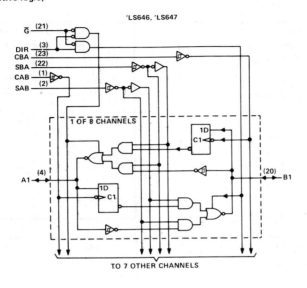

'LS648, 'LS649

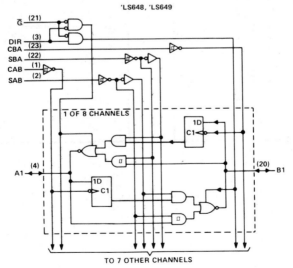

Pin numbers shown on logic notation are for DW or NT packages.

TEXAS
INSTRUMENTS

3

TTL DEVICES

TYPES SN54LS646 THRU SN54LS649,
SN74LS646 THRU SN74LS649
OCTAL BUS TRANSCEIVERS AND REGISTERS

schematics of inputs and outputs

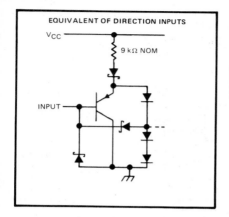

EQUIVALENT OF DIRECTION INPUTS

V_{CC}

9 kΩ NOM

INPUT

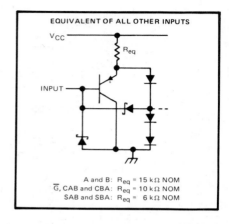

EQUIVALENT OF ALL OTHER INPUTS

V_{CC}

R_{eq}

INPUT

A and B: R_{eq} = 15 kΩ NOM
$\overline{G}$, CAB and CBA: R_{eq} = 10 kΩ NOM
SAB and SBA: R_{eq} = 6 kΩ NOM

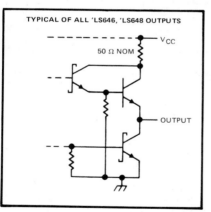

TYPICAL OF ALL 'LS646, 'LS648 OUTPUTS

V_{CC}

50 Ω NOM

OUTPUT

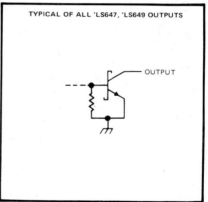

TYPICAL OF ALL 'LS647, 'LS649 OUTPUTS

OUTPUT

3

TTL DEVICES

TEXAS
INSTRUMENTS

logic symbols

'LS646

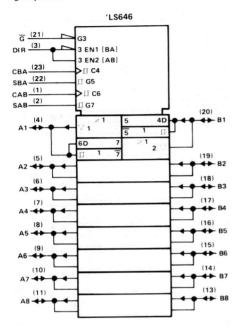

'LS647

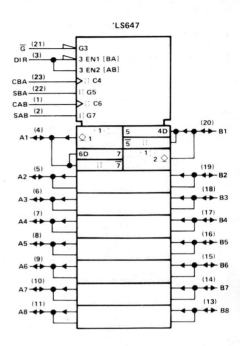

Pin numbers shown on logic notation are for DW or NT packages.

TEXAS
INSTRUMENTS

TYPES SN54LS648, SN54LS649, SN74LS648, SN74LS649
OCTAL BUS TRANSCEIVERS AND REGISTERS

logic symbols (continued)

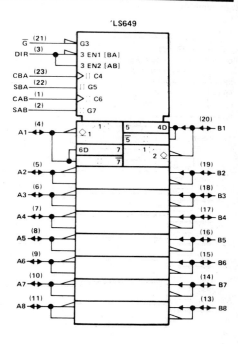

Pin numbers shown on logic notation are for DW or NT packages.

TEXAS
INSTRUMENTS

absolute maximum ratings over operating free-air temperature range (unless otherwise noted)

Supply voltage, V_{CC} .... 7 V
Input voltage: Control inputs .... 7 V
I/O ports .... 5.5 V
Operating free-air temperature range: SN54LS646, SN54LS648 .... -55°C to 125°C
SN74LS646, SN74LS648 .... 0°C to 70°C
Storage temperature range .... -65°C to 150°C

recommended operating conditions

			SN54LS646/648			SN74LS646/648			UNIT
			MIN	NOM	MAX	MIN	NOM	MAX	
V_{CC}	Supply voltage		4.5	5	5.5	4.75	5	5.25	V
V_{IH}	High-level input voltage		2			2			V
V_{IL}	Low-level input voltage				0.5			0.6	V
I_{OH}	High-level output current				-12			-15	mA
I_{OL}	Low-level output current				12			24	mA
t_w	Pulse duration	CBA or CAB high	15			15			ns
		CBA or CAB low	30			30			
		Data high or low	30			30			
t_{su}	Setup time before CAB↑ or CBA↑	A or B	15			15			ns
t_h	Hold time after CAB↑ or CBA↑	A or B	0			0			ns
T_A	Operating free-air temperature		-55		125	0		70	°C

electrical characteristics over recommended operating free-air temperature range (unless otherwise noted)

PARAMETER		TEST CONDITIONS†		SN54LS646/648			SN74LS646/648			UNIT
				MIN	TYP‡	MAX	MIN	TYP‡	MAX	
V_{IK}		V_{CC} = MIN, $I_I = -18$ mA				-1.5			-1.5	V
Hysteresis $(V_{T+} - V_{T-})$	A or B input	V_{CC} = MIN		0.1	0.4		0.2	0.4		V
V_{OH}		V_{CC} = MIN, V_{IH} = 2 V, V_{IL} = MAX	$I_{OH} = -3$ mA	2.4	3.4		2.4	3.4		V
			$I_{OH} = -12$ mA	2						
			$I_{OH} = -15$ mA				2			
V_{OL}		V_{CC} = MIN, V_{IH} = 2 V, V_{IL} = MAX	$I_{OL} = 12$ mA		0.25	0.4		0.25	0.4	V
			$I_{OL} = 24$ mA					0.35	0.5	
I_I	Control inputs	V_{CC} = MAX, V_I = 7 V				0.1			0.1	mA
	A or B ports	V_{CC} = MAX, V_I = 5.5 V				0.1			0.1	
I_{IH}	Control inputs	V_{CC} = MAX, V_I = 2.7 V				20			20	µA
	A or B ports ▲					20			20	
I_{IL}	Control inputs	V_{CC} = MAX, V_I = 0.4 V				-0.4			-0.4	mA
	A or B ports ▲					-0.4			-0.4	
I_{OS} ¶		V_{CC} = MAX, V_O = 0 V		-40		-225	-40		-225	mA
I_{CC}	LS646	V_{CC} = MAX	Outputs high		91	145		91	145	mA
			Outputs low		103	165		103	165	
			Outputs disabled		103	165		103	165	
	LS648		Outputs high		91	145		91	145	
			Outputs low		103	165		103	165	
			Outputs disabled		120	180		120	180	

† For conditions shown as MIN or MAX, use the appropriate value specified under recommended operating conditions.
‡ All typical values are at V_{CC} = 5 V, $T_A = 25^\circ$C.
¶ Not more than one output should be shorted at a time, and duration of the short circuit should not exceed one second.
▲ For I/O ports, the parameters I_{IH} and I_{IL} include the off-state output current.

3

TTL DEVICES

TEXAS
INSTRUMENTS

3-1037

switching characteristics, V_{CC} = 5 V, T_A = 25°C

PARAMETER	FROM (INPUT)	TO (OUTPUT)	TEST CONDITIONS	'LS646 MIN	'LS646 TYP	'LS646 MAX	'LS648 MIN	'LS648 TYP	'LS648 MAX	UNIT
t_{PLH}	CAB or CBA	A or B			15	25		15	25	ns
t_{PHL}	CAB or CBA	A or B			23	35		24	40	ns
t_{PLH}	A or B	B or A			12	18		12	18	ns
t_{PHL}	A or B	B or A			13	20		15	25	ns
t_{PLH}	SAB or SBA† with Bus input high	A or B	R_L = 667 Ω, C_L = 45 pF, See Note 2		26	40		37	55	ns
t_{PHL}	SAB or SBA† with Bus input high	A or B			21	35		24	40	ns
t_{PLH}	SAB or SBA† with Bus input low	A or B			33	50		26	40	ns
t_{PHL}	SAB or SBA† with Bus input low	A or B			14	25		23	40	ns
t_{PZH}	$\overline{G}$	A or B			33	55		30	50	ns
t_{PZL}	$\overline{G}$	A or B			42	65		37	55	ns
t_{PZH}	DIR	A or B			28	45		23	40	ns
t_{PZL}	DIR	A or B			39	60		30	45	ns
t_{PHZ}	$\overline{G}$	A or B	R_L = 667 Ω, C_L = 5 pF, See Note 2		23	35		28	45	ns
t_{PLZ}	$\overline{G}$	A or B			22	35		22	35	ns
t_{PHZ}	DIR	A or B			20	30		24	35	ns
t_{PLZ}	DIR	A or B			19	30		19	30	ns

t_{PLH} = propagation delay time, low-to-high-level output
t_{PHL} = propagation delay time, high-to-low-level output
t_{PZH} = output enable time to high level
t_{PZL} = output enable time to low level
t_{PHZ} = output disable time from high level
t_{PLZ} = output disable time from low level
† These parameters are measured with the internal output state of the storage register opposite to that of the bus input.
NOTE 2: See General Information Section for load circuits and voltage waveforms.

TEXAS
INSTRUMENTS

absolute maximum ratings over operating free-air temperature range (unless otherwise noted)

Supply voltage, V_{CC} (see Note 1) .... 7 V
Input voltage (control inputs) .... 7 V
Off-state output voltage (A and B ports) .... 5.5 V
Operating free-air temperature range: SN54LS647, SN54LS649 .... -55°C to 125°C
SN74LS647, SN74LS649 .... -0°C to 70°C
Storage temperature range .... -65°C to 150°C

recommended operating conditions

			SN54LS647 SN54LS649			SN74LS647 SN74LS649			UNIT
			MIN	NOM	MAX	MIN	NOM	MAX	
V_{CC}	Supply voltage		4.5	5	5.5	4.75	5	5.25	V
V_{IH}	High-level input voltage		2			2			V
V_{IL}	Low-level input voltage				0.5			0.6	V
V_{OH}	High-level output voltage				5.5			5.5	V
I_{OL}	Low-level output voltage				12			24	mA
t_w	Pulse duration	CBA or CAB high	15			15			ns
		CBA or CAB low	30			30			
		Data high or low	30			30			
t_{su}	Setup time before CAB↑ or CBA↑	A or B	15			15			ns
t_h	Hold time after CAB↑ or CBA↑	A or B	0			0			ns
T_A	Operating free-air temperature		-55		125	0		70	$^{\circ}$C

electrical characteristics over recommended operating free-air temperature range (unless otherwise noted)

PARAMETER		TEST CONDITIONS[†]		SN54LS647 SN54LS649			SN74LS647 SN74LS649			UNIT
				MIN	TYP[‡]	MAX	MIN	TYP[‡]	MAX	
V_{IK}		V_{CC} = MIN, I_I = -18 mA				-1.5			-1.5	V
Hysteresis $(V_{T+} - V_{T-})$	A or B input	V_{CC} = MIN		0.1	0.4		0.2	0.4		V
I_{OH}		V_{CC} = MIN, V_{IH} = 2 V, V_{OH} = 5.5 V	V_{IL} = MAX,			0.1			0.1	mA
V_{OL}		V_{CC} = MIN, V_{IH} = 2 V, V_{IL} = MAX	I_{OL} = 12 mA		0.25	0.4		0.25	0.4	V
			I_{OL} = 24 mA					0.35	0.5	
I_I	A or B	V_{CC} = MAX	V_I = 5.5 V			0.1			0.1	mA
	All others		V_I = 7 V			0.1			0.1	
I_{IH}		V_{CC} = MAX, V_I = 2.7 V				20			20	μA
I_{IL}		V_{CC} = MAX, V_I = 0.4 V				-0.4			-0.4	mA
I_{CC}	'LS647	V_{CC} = MAX, Outputs open	Outputs high		79	130		79	130	mA
			Outputs low		94	150		94	150	
	'LS649	V_{CC} = MAX, Outputs open	Outputs high		79	130		79	130	
			Outputs low		94	150		94	150	

† For conditions shown as MIN or MAX, use the appropriate value specified under recommended operating conditions.
‡ All typical values are at V_{CC} = 5 V, T_A = 25°C.

3

TTL DEVICES

TEXAS
INSTRUMENTS

TYPES SN54LS647, SN54LS649, SN74LS647, SN74LS649
OCTAL BUS TRANSCEIVERS AND REGISTERS WITH OPEN-COLLECTOR OUTPUTS

switching characteristics, V_{CC} = 5 V, T_A = 25°C

PARAMETER	FROM (INPUT)	TO (OUTPUT)	TEST CONDITIONS	'LS647 MIN	'LS647 TYP	'LS647 MAX	'LS649 MIN	'LS649 TYP	'LS649 MAX	UNIT
t_{PLH}	CAB or CBA	A or B			22	35		17	30	ns
t_{PHL}					28	45		28	45	ns
t_{PLH}	A or B	B or A			17	26		15	25	ns
t_{PHL}					18	27		20	30	ns
t_{PLH}	SAB or SBA† with Bus input high	A or B	R_L = 667 Ω, C_L = 45 pF, See Note 2		33	50		37	55	ns
t_{PHL}					29	45		28	45	ns
t_{PLH}	SAB or SBA† with Bus input low				39	60		30	45	ns
t_{PHL}					19	30		26	40	ns
t_{PLH}	G	A or B			25	40		21	40	ns
t_{PHL}					33	50		34	50	ns
t_{PLH}	DIR				23	35		19	30	ns
t_{PHL}					25	40		27	45	ns

t_{PLH} = propagation delay time, low-to-high-level output
t_{PHL} = propagation delay time, high-to-low-level output
† These parameters are measured with the internal outputs state of the storage register opposite to that of the bus input.
NOTE 2: See General Information Section for load circuits and voltage waveforms.

TEXAS
INSTRUMENTS

- **Bus Transceivers/Registers**
- **Independent Registers and Enables for A and B Buses**
- **Multiplexed Real-Time and Stored Data**
- **Choice of True and Inverting Data Paths**
- **Choice of 3-State or Open-Collector Outputs to A Bus**
- **Dependable Texas Instruments Quality and Reliability**

DEVICE	A OUTPUT	B OUTPUT	LOGIC
LS651	3-State	3-State	Inverting
LS652	3-State	3-State	True
LS653	Open-collector	3-State	Inverting

description

These devices consist of bus transceiver circuits, D-type flip-flops, and control circuitry arranged for multiplexed transmission of the data directly from the data bus or from the internal storage registers. Enable GAB and GBA are provided to control the transceiver functions. SAB and SBA control pins are provided to select whether real-time or stored data is transferred. A low input level selects real-time data, and a high selects stored data. The following examples demonstrate the four fundamental bus-management functions that can be performed with the 'LS651, 'LS652, and 'LS653.

SN54LS' . . . JT PACKAGE
SN74LS' . . . DW, JT OR NT PACKAGE
(TOP VIEW)

CAB	1	24	VCC
SAB	2	23	CBA
GAB	3	22	SA
A1	4	21	GBA
A2	5	20	B1
A3	6	19	B2
A4	7	18	B3
A5	8	17	B4
A6	9	16	B5
A7	10	15	B6
A8	11	14	B7
GND	12	13	B8

SN54LS' . . . FK PACKAGE
SN74LS'
(TOP VIEW)

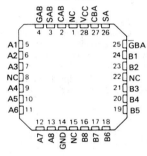

NC — No internal connection

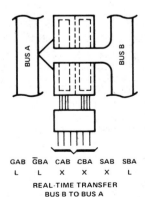

GAB	GBA	CAB	CBA	SAB	SBA
L	L	X	X	X	L

REAL-TIME TRANSFER
BUS B TO BUS A

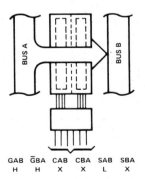

GAB	GBA	CAB	CBA	SAB	SBA
H	H	X	X	L	X

REAL-TIME TRANSFER
BUS A TO BUS B

TEXAS
INSTRUMENTS

TTL DEVICES

3

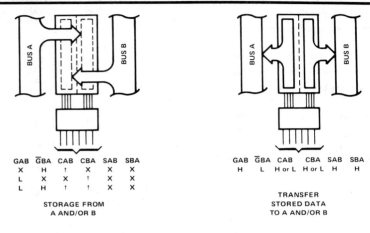

GAB	GBA	CAB	CBA	SAB	SBA
X	H	↑	X	X	X
L	X	X	↑	X	X
L	H	↑	↑	X	X

STORAGE FROM
A AND/OR B

GAB	GBA	CAB	CBA	SAB	SBA
H	L	H or L	H or L	H	H

TRANSFER
STORED DATA
TO A AND/OR B

Data on the A or B data bus, or both, can be stored in the internal D flip-flop by low-to-high transitions at the appropriate clock pins (CAB or CBA) regardless of the select or enable control pins. When SAB and SBA are in the real-time transfer mode, it is also possible to store data without using the internal D-type flip-flops by simultaneously enabling GAB and GBA. In this configuration each output reinforces its input. Thus, when all other data sources to the two sets of bus lines are at high impedance, each set of bus lines will remain at its last state.

The SN54LS651 through SN54LS653 are characterized for operation over the full military temperature range of −55°C to 125°C. The SN74LS651 through SN74LS653 are characterized for operation from 0°C to 70°C.

FUNCTION TABLE

INPUTS						DATA I/O*		OPERATION OR FUNCTION	
GAB	GBA	CAB	CBA	SAB	SBA	A1 THRU A8	B1 THRU B8	'LS651, 'LS653	'LS652, 'LS654
L	H	H or L	H or L	X	X	Input	Input	Isolation	Isolation
L	H	↑	↑	X	X			Store A and B Data	Store A and B Data
X	H	↑	H or L	X	X	Input	Not specified	Store A, Hold B	Store A, Hold B
H	H	↑	↑	X	X	Input	Output	Store A in both registers	Store A in both registers
L	X	H or L	↑	X	X	Not specified	Input	Hold A, Store B	Hold A, Store B
L	L	↑	↑	X	X	Output	Input	Store B in both registers	Store B in both registers
L	L	X	X	X	L	Output	Input	Real-Time B̄ Data to A Bus	Real-Time B Data to A Bus
L	L	X	H or L	X	H			Stored B̄ Data to A Bus	Stored B Data to A Bus
H	H	X	X	L	X	Input	Output	Real-Time Ā Data to B Bus	Real-Time A Data to B Bus
H	H	H or L	X	H	X			Stored Ā Data to B Bus	Stored A Data to B Bus
H	L	H or L	H or L	H	H	Output	Output	Stored B̄ Data to B Bus and Stored Ā Data to A Bus	Stored A Data to B Bus and Stored B Data to A Bus

* The data output functions may be enabled or disabled by various signals at the GAB and GBA inputs. Data input functions are always enabled, i.e., data at the bus pins will be stored on every low-to-high transition on the clock inputs.

TEXAS
INSTRUMENTS

logic diagrams (positive logic)

'LS651, 'LS653

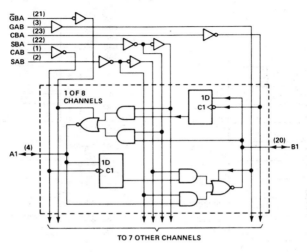

TO 7 OTHER CHANNELS

'LS652

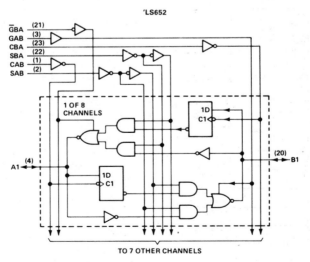

TO 7 OTHER CHANNELS

Pin numbers shown on logic notation are for DW, JT or NT packages.

3

TTL DEVICES

TYPES SN54LS651 THRU SN54LS653
SN74LS651 THRU SN74LS653
OCTAL BUS TRANSCEIVERS AND REGISTERS

logic symbols

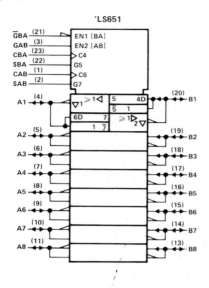

'LS651

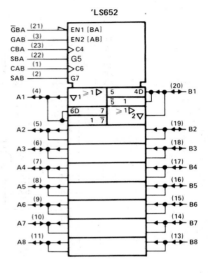

'LS652

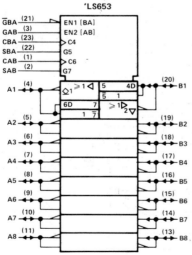

'LS653

Pin numbers shown on logic notation are for DW, JT or NT packages.

3

TTL DEVICES

absolute maximum ratings over operating free-air temperature range (unless otherwise noted)

Supply voltage, V_{CC} .... 7 V
Input voltage: Control inputs .... 7 V
               I/O ports .... 5.5 V
Operating free-air temperature range: SN54LS651, SN54LS652 .... -55°C to 125°C
                            SN74LS651, SN74LS652 .... 0°C to 70°C
Storage temperature range .... -65°C to 150°C

recommended operating conditions

			SN54LS651 SN54LS652			SN74LS651 SN74LS652			UNIT
			MIN	NOM	MAX	MIN	NOM	MAX	
V_{CC}	Supply voltage		4.5	5	5.5	4.75	5	5.25	V
V_{IH}	High-level input voltage		2			2			V
V_{IL}	Low-level input voltage				0.7			0.8	V
I_{OH}	High-level output current				-12			-15	mA
I_{OL}	Low-level output current				12			24	mA
t_w	Pulse duration	CBA or CAB high	15			15			ns
		CBA or CAB low	30			30			
		Data high or low	30			30			
t_{su}	Setup time before CAB↑ or CBA↑	A or B	15			15			ns
t_h	Hold time after CAB↑ or CBA↑	A or B	0			0			ns
T_A	Operating free-air temperature		-55		125	0		70	$^\circ$C

electrical characteristics over recommended operating free-air temperature range (unless otherwise noted)

PARAMETER		TEST CONDITIONS†		SN54LS651 SN54LS652			SN74LS651 SN74LS652			UNIT
				MIN	TYP‡	MAX	MIN	TYP‡	MAX	
V_{IK}		V_{CC} = MIN,	$I_I = -18$ mA			-1.5			-1.5	V
V_{OH}		V_{CC} = MIN, V_{IH} = 2 V, V_{IL} = MAX,	$I_{OH} = -3$ mA	2.4	3.4		2.4	3.4		V
			$I_{OH} = -12$ mA	2						
			$I_{OH} = -15$ mA				2			
V_{OL}		V_{CC} = MIN, V_{IH} = 2 V, V_{IL} = MAX,	$I_{OL} = 12$ mA		0.25	0.4		0.25	0.4	V
			$I_{OL} = 24$ mA					0.35	0.5	
I_I	Control inputs	V_{CC} = MAX,	V_I = 7 V			0.1			0.1	mA
	A or B ports	V_{CC} = MAX,	V_I = 5.5 V			0.1			0.1	
I_{IH}	Control inputs	V_{CC} = MAX,	V_I = 2.7 V			20			20	µA
	A or B ports ▲					20			20	
I_{IL}	Control inputs	V_{CC} = MAX,	V_I = 0.4 V			-0.4			-0.4	mA
	A or B ports ▲					-0.4			-0.4	
I_{OS} ¶		V_{CC} = MAX,	V_O = 0 V	-40		-225	-40		-225	mA
I_{CC}	LS651	V_{CC} = MAX	Outputs high		95	145		95	145	mA
			Outputs low		103	165		103	165	
			Outputs disabled		103	165		103	165	
	LS652		Outputs high		95	145		95	145	
			Outputs low		103	165		103	165	
			Outputs disabled		120	180		120	180	

† For conditions shown as MIN or MAX, use the appropriate value specified under recommended operating conditions.
‡ All typical values are at V_{CC} = 5 V, T_A = 25°C.
¶ Not more than one output should be shorted at a time, and duration of the short-circuit should not exceed one second.
▲ For I/O ports, the parameters I_{IH} and I_{IL} include the off-state output current.

3

TTL DEVICES

switching characteristics, V_{CC} = 5 V, T_A = 25°C

PARAMETER	FROM (INPUT)	TO (OUTPUT)	TEST CONDITIONS	'LS651 MIN	'LS651 TYP	'LS651 MAX	'LS652 MIN	'LS652 TYP	'LS652 MAX	UNIT
t_{PLH}	Clock	Bus			14	24		15	25	ns
t_{PHL}					23	35		24	36	ns
t_{PLH}	Bus	Bus			9	18		12	18	ns
t_{PHL}					20	30		13	20	ns
t_{PLH}	Select, with bus input high†	Bus	R_L = 667 Ω, C_L = 45 pF, See Note 2		31	47		23	35	ns
t_{PHL}					22	33		21	32	ns
t_{PLH}	Select, with bus input low†				23	35		33	50	ns
t_{PHL}					19	30		15	23	ns
t_{PZH}	$\overline{G}BA$	A Bus			29	44		30	45	ns
t_{PZL}					40	60		36	54	ns
t_{PZH}	GAB	B Bus			19	29		20	30	ns
t_{PZL}					26	40		25	38	ns
t_{PHZ}	$\overline{G}BA$	A Bus	R_L = 667 Ω, C_L = 5 pF, See Note 2		25	38		25	38	ns
t_{PLZ}					19	30		19	30	ns
t_{PHZ}	GAB	B Bus			25	38		25	38	ns
t_{PLZ}					19	30		19	30	ns

t_{PLH} = propagation delay time, low-to-high-level output.
t_{PHL} = propagation delay time, high-to-low-level output
t_{PZH} = output enable time to high level
t_{PZL} = output enable time to low level
t_{PHZ} = output disable time from high level
t_{PLZ} = output disable time from low level
† These parameters are measured with the internal output state of the storage register opposite to that of the bus input.
NOTE 2: See General Information Section for load circuits and voltage waveforms.

schematics of inputs and outputs

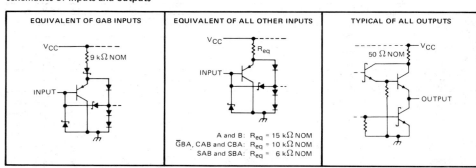

EQUIVALENT OF GAB INPUTS	EQUIVALENT OF ALL OTHER INPUTS	TYPICAL OF ALL OUTPUTS

A and B: R_{eq} = 15 kΩ NOM
$\overline{G}BA$, CAB and CBA: R_{eq} = 10 kΩ NOM
SAB and SBA: R_{eq} = 6 kΩ NOM

TEXAS
INSTRUMENTS

3

TTL DEVICES

absolute maximum ratings over operating free-air temperature range (unless otherwise noted)

Supply voltage, V_{CC} .... 7 V
Input voltage: All inputs and A I/O ports .... 7 V
    B I/O ports .... 5.5 V
Operating free-air temperature range: SN54LS653 .... $-55°C$ to $125°C$
    SN74LS653 .... $0°C$ to $70°C$
Storage temperature range .... $-65°C$ to $150°C$

recommended operating conditions

			SN54LS653			SN74LS653			UNIT
			MIN	NOM	MAX	MIN	NOM	MAX	
V_{CC}	Supply voltage		4.5	5	5.5	4.75	5	5.25	V
V_{IH}	High-level input voltage		2			2			V
V_{IL}	Low-level input voltage				0.7			0.8	V
V_{OH}	High-level output voltage	A ports			5.5			5.5	V
I_{OH}	High-level output current	B ports			-12			-15	mA
I_{OL}	Low-level output current				12			24	mA
t_w	Pulse duration	CBA or CAB high	15			15			ns
		CBA or CAB low	30			30			
		Data high or low	30			30			
t_{su}	Setup time before CAB↑ or CBA↑	A or B	15			15			ns
t_h	Hold time after CAB↑ or CBA↑	A or B	0			0			ns
T_A	Operating free-air temperature		-55		125	0		70	°C

electrical characteristics over recommended operating free-air temperature range (unless otherwise noted)

PARAMETER		TEST CONDITIONS†		SN54LS653			SN74LS653			UNIT
				MIN	TYP*	MAX	MIN	TYP*	MAX	
V_{IK}		$V_{CC} = MIN$, $I_I = -18\,mA$				-1.5			-1.5	V
V_{OH}	B ports	$V_{CC} = MIN$, $V_{IH} = 2\,V$, $V_{IL} = MAX$	$I_{OH} = -3\,mA$	2.4	3.4		2.4	3.4		V
			$I_{OH} = -12\,mA$	2						
			$I_{OH} = -15\,mA$				2			
I_{OH}	A ports	$V_{CC} = MIN$, $V_{OH} = 5.5\,V$				0.1			0.1	mA
V_{OL}		$V_{CC} = MIN$, $V_{IH} = 2\,V$, $V_{IL} = MAX$	$I_{OL} = 12\,mA$		0.25	0.4		0.25	0.4	V
			$I_{OL} = 24\,mA$					0.35	0.5	
I_I	Control inputs	$V_{CC} = MAX, V_I = 7\,V$				0.1			0.1	mA
	A or B ports	$V_{CC} = MAX, V_I = 5.5\,V$				0.1			0.1	
I_{IH}	Control inputs	$V_{CC} = MAX, V_I = 2.7\,V$				20			20	μA
	A or B ports ▲					20			20	
I_{IL}	Control inputs	$V_{CC} = MAX, V_I = 0.4\,V$				-0.4			-0.4	mA
	A or B ports ▲					-0.4			-0.4	
I_{OS}£	B ports	$V_{CC} = MAX, V_O = 0\,V$		-40		-225	-40		-225	mA
I_{CC}	LS653	$V_{CC} = MAX$	Outputs high		95	145		95	145	mA
			Outputs low		103	165		103	165	
			Outputs disabled		103	165		103	165	
	LS654		Outputs high		95	145		95	145	
			Outputs low		105	170		105	170	
			Outputs disabled		120	180		120	180	

† For conditions shown as MIN or MAX, use the appropriate value specified under recommended operating conditions.
* All typical values are at $V_{CC} = 5\,V$, $T_A = 25°C$.
£ Not more than one output should be shorted at a time, and duration of the short-circuit should not exceed one second.
▲ For I/O ports, the parameters I_{IH} and I_{IL} include the off-state output current.

3

TTL DEVICES

TEXAS
INSTRUMENTS

switching characteristics, $V_{CC} = 5\,V$, $T_A = 25°C$

PARAMETER	FROM (INPUT)	TO (OUTPUT)	TEST CONDITIONS	'LS653 MIN	'LS653 TYP	'LS653 MAX	UNIT
tPLH	CBA	A Bus			25	38	ns
tPHL					26	39	
tPLH	CAB	B Bus			15	23	ns
tPHL					24	36	
tPLH	A Bus	B Bus			10	18	ns
tPHL					20	30	
tPLH	B Bus	A Bus	$R_L = 667\,\Omega$, $C_L = 45\,pF$, See Note 2		21	32	ns
tPHL					16	24	
tPLH	SBA† (with B high)	A Bus			38	57	ns
tPHL					26	39	
tPLH	SBA† (with B low)	A Bus			34	51	ns
tPHL					23	35	
tPLH	SAB† (with A high)	B Bus			32	48	ns
tPHL					22	33	
tPLH	SAB† (with A low)	B Bus			24	36	ns
tPHL					20	30	
tPLH	$\overline{G}BA$	A Bus			23	35	ns
tPHL					37	55	
tPZH	GAB	B Bus	$R_L = 667\,V$, $C_L = 5\,pF$, See Note 2		19	29	ns
tPZL					25	38	
tPHZ	GAB	B Bus			26	39	ns
tPLZ					19	29	

† These parameters are measured with the internal output state of the storage register opposite to that of the bus input.
NOTE 2: See General Information Section for load circuits and voltage waveforms.

schematics of inputs and outputs

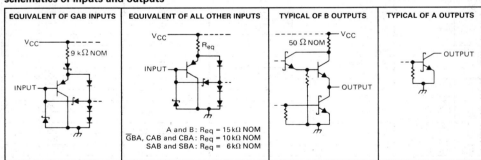

EQUIVALENT OF GAB INPUTS	EQUIVALENT OF ALL OTHER INPUTS	TYPICAL OF B OUTPUTS	TYPICAL OF A OUTPUTS

A and B: $R_{eq} = 15\,k\Omega$ NOM
$\overline{G}BA$, CAB and CBA: $R_{eq} = 10\,k\Omega$ NOM
SAB and SBA: $R_{eq} = 6\,k\Omega$ NOM

TEXAS INSTRUMENTS

'LS668 . . . SYNCHRONOUS UP/DOWN DECADE COUNTERS
'LS669 . . . SYNCHRONOUS UP/DOWN BINARY COUNTERS

Programmable Look-Ahead Up/Down Binary/Decade Counters

- **Fully Synchronous Operation for Counting and Programming**
- **Internal Look-Ahead for Fast Counting**
- **Carry Output for n-Bit Cascading**
- **Fully Independent Clock Circuit**
- **Buffered Outputs**

TYPE	TYPICAL MAXIMUM CLOCK FREQUENCY		TYPICAL POWER DISSIPATION
	COUNTING UP	COUNTING DOWN	
'LS668, 'LS669	32 MHz	32 MHz	100 mW

SN54LS668, SN54LS669 . . . J PACKAGE
SN74LS668, SN74LS669 . . . D, J OR N PACKAGE
(TOP VIEW)

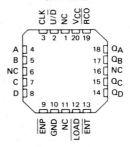

SN54LS668, SN54LS669 . . . FK PACKAGE
SN74LS668, SN74LS669
(TOP VIEW)

NC – No internal connection

description

These synchronous presettable counters feature an internal carry look-ahead for cascading in high-speed counting applications. The 'LS668 are decade counters and the 'LS669 are 4-bit binary counters. Synchronous operation is provided by having all flip-flops clocked simultaneously so that the outputs change coincident with each other when so instructed by the count-enable inputs and internal gating. This mode of operation helps eliminate the output counting spikes that are normally associated with asynchronous (ripple-clock) counters. A buffered clock input triggers the four master-slave flip-flops on the rising (positive-going) edge of the clock waveform.

These counters are fully programmable; that is, the outputs may each be preset to either level. The load input circuitry allows loading with the carry-enable output of cascaded counters. As loading is synchronous, setting up a low level at the load input disables the counter and causes the outputs to agree with the data inputs after the next clock pulse.

The carry look-ahead circuitry provides for cascading counters for n-bit synchronous applications without additional gating. Instrumental in accomplishing this function are two count-enable inputs ($\overline{P}$ and $\overline{T}$) must be low to count. The direction of the count is determined by the level of the up/down input. When the input is high, the counter counts up; when low, it counts down. Input $\overline{T}$ is fed forward to enable the carry output. The carry output thus enabled will produce a low-level output pulse when the count is maximum counting up or zero counting down. This low-level overflow carry pulse can be used to enable successive cascaded stages. Transitions at the enable $\overline{P}$ or $\overline{T}$ inputs are allowed regardless of the level of the clock input. All inputs are diode-clamped to minimize transmission-line effects, thereby simplifying system design.

These counters feature a fully independent clock circuit. Changes at control inputs (enable $\overline{P}$, enable $\overline{T}$, load, up/down) that will modify the operating mode have no effect until clocking occurs. The function of the counter (whether enabled, disabled, loading, or counting) will be dictated solely by the conditions meeting the stable setup and hold times.

The 'LS668 and 'LS669 are completely new designs. Compared to the original 'LS168 and 'LS169, they feature 0-nanosecond minimum hold time, reduced input currents I_{IH} and I_{IL}, and all buffered outputs.

TEXAS
INSTRUMENTS

3-1049

3

TTL DEVICES

logic diagram

SN54LS668, SN74LS668, DECADE COUNTERS

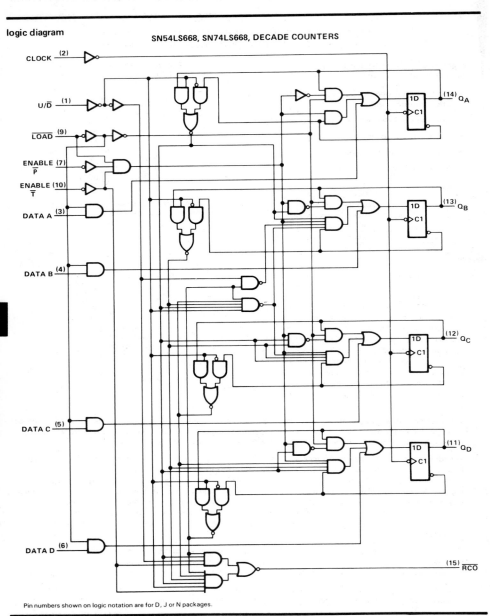

Pin numbers shown on logic notation are for D, J or N packages.

Texas
Instruments

logic diagram (continued)

SN54LS669, SN74LS669, BINARY COUNTERS

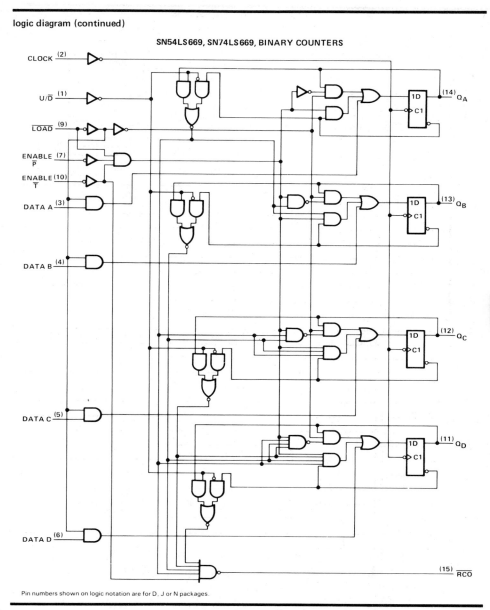

Pin numbers shown on logic notation are for D, J or N packages.

TEXAS
INSTRUMENTS

TTL DEVICES

3

TYPES SN54LS668, SN74LS668
SYNCHRONOUS 4-BIT UP/DOWN COUNTERS

'LS668 DECADE COUNTERS

typical load, count, and inhibit sequences

Illustrated below is the following sequence:

1. Load (preset) to BCD seven
2. Count up to eight, nine (maximum), zero, one, and two
3. Inhibit
4. Count down to one, zero (minimum), nine, eight, and seven

logic symbol

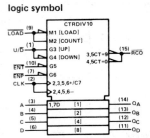

Pin numbers shown on logic notation are for D, J or N packages.

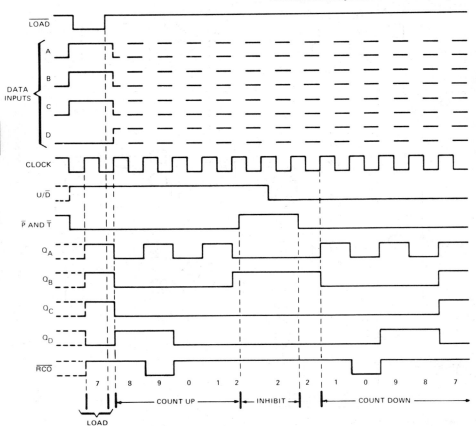

TEXAS INSTRUMENTS

'LS669 BINARY COUNTERS

typical load, count, and inhibit sequences

Illustrated below is the following sequence:

1. Load (preset) to binary thirteen
2. Count up to fourteen, fifteen (maximum), zero, one, and two
3. Inhibit
4. Count down to one, zero (minimum), fifteen, fourteen, and thirteen

logic symbol

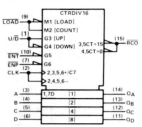

Pin numbers shown on logic notation are for D, J or N packages.

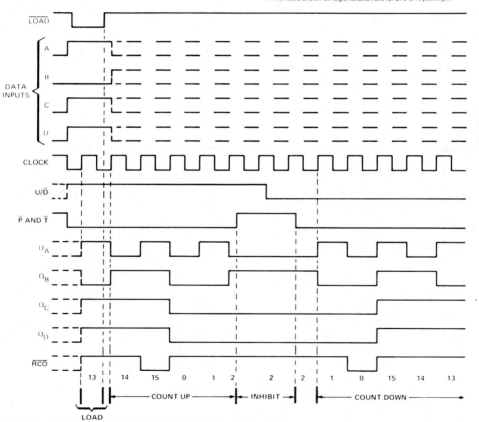

TYPES SN54LS668, SN54LS669, SN74LS668, SN74LS669
SYNCHRONOUS 4-BIT UP/DOWN COUNTERS

schematics of inputs and outputs

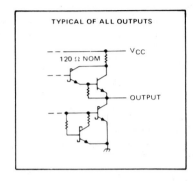

EQUIVALENT OF EACH INPUT

V_{CC}

R_{eq}

INPUT

Load: R_{eq} = 10 kΩ NOM
Data: R_{eq} = 25 kΩ NOM
Clock, Enable $\overline{P}$, $\overline{T}$, U/D: R_{eq} = 20 kΩ NOM

TYPICAL OF ALL OUTPUTS

120 Ω NOM

V_{CC}

OUTPUT

absolute maximum ratings over operating free-air temperature range (unless otherwise noted)

Supply voltage, V_{CC} (see Note 1) . . . . 7 V
Input voltage . . . . 7 V
Operating free-air temperature range: SN54LS668, SN54LS669 . . . . −55°C to 125°C
                                        SN74LS668, SN74LS669 . . . . 0°C to 70°C
Storage temperature range . . . . −65°C to 150°C

NOTE 1: Voltage values are with respect to network ground terminal.

recommended operating conditions

		SN54LS668 SN54LS669			SN74LS668 SN74LS669			UNIT
		MIN	NOM	MAX	MIN	NOM	MAX	
Supply voltage, V_{CC}		4.5	5	5.5	4.75	5	5.25	V
High-level output current, I_{OH}				-400			400	µA
Low-level output current, I_{OL}				4			8	mA
Clock frequency, f_{clock}		0		25	0		25	MHz
Width of clock pulse, $t_{w(clock)}$ (high or low) (see Figure 1)		20			20			ns
Setup time, t_{su} (see Figure 1)	Data inputs A, B, C, D	25			25			ns
	$\overline{ENP}$ or $\overline{ENT}$	40			40			
	$\overline{LOAD}$	30			30			
	U/$\overline{D}$	45			45			
Hold time at any input with respect to clock, t_h (see Figure 1)		0			0			ns
Operating free-air temperature, T_A		-55		125	0		70	°C

Texas
INSTRUMENTS

electrical characteristics over recommended operating free-air temperature range (unless otherwise noted)

PARAMETER		TEST CONDITIONS[†]		SN54LS668 SN54LS669			SN74LS668 SN74LS669			UNIT
				MIN	TYP[‡]	MAX	MIN	TYP[‡]	MAX	
V_{IH} High-level input voltage				2			2			V
V_{IL} Low-level input voltage						0.7			0.8	V
V_{IK} Input clamp voltage		V_{CC} = MIN,	I_I = −18 mA			−1.5			−1.5	V
V_{OH} High-level output voltage		V_{CC} = MIN, V_{IH} = 2 V, $V_{IL} = V_{IL}$ max, I_{OH} = −400 μA		2.5	3.4		2.7	3.4		V
V_{OL} Low-level output voltage		V_{CC} = MIN, V_{IH} = 2 V, $V_{IL} = V_{IL}$ max	I_{OL} = 4 mA		0.25	0.4		0.25	0.4	V
			I_{OL} = 8 mA					0.35	0.5	
I_I Input current at maximum input voltage	A, B, C, D, $\overline{P}$, U/$\overline{D}$	V_{CC} = MAX, V_I = 7 V				0.1			0.1	mA
	Clock, $\overline{T}$					0.1			0.1	
	$\overline{LOAD}$					0.2			0.2	
I_{IH} High-level input current	A, B, C, D, $\overline{P}$, U/$\overline{D}$	V_{CC} = MAX, V_I = 2.7 V				20			20	μA
	Clock, $\overline{T}$					20			20	
	$\overline{LOAD}$					40			40	
I_{IL} Low-level input current	A, B, C, D, $\overline{P}$, U/$\overline{D}$	V_{CC} = MAX, V_I = 0.4 V				−0.4			−0.4	mA
	Clock, $\overline{T}$					−0.4			−0.4	
	$\overline{LOAD}$					−0.8			−0.8	
I_{OS} Short-circuit output current[§]		V_{CC} = MAX		−20		−100	−20		−100	mA
I_{CC} Supply current		V_{CC} = MAX,	See Note 2		20	34		20	34	mA

[†] For conditions shown as MIN or MAX, use the appropriate value specified under recommended operating conditions.
[‡] All typical values are at V_{CC} = 5 V, T_A = 25 C.
[§] Not more than one output should be shorted at a time, and duration of the short-circuit should not exceed one second.
NOTE 2: I_{CC} is measured after applying a momentary 4.5 V, then ground, to the clock input with all other inputs grounded and the outputs open.

switching characteristics, V_{CC} = 5 V, T_A = 25 C

PARAMETER[¶]	FROM (INPUT)	TO (OUTPUT)	TEST CONDITIONS	MIN	TYP	MAX	UNIT
f_{max}				25	32		MHz
t_{PLH}	CLK	$\overline{RCO}$			26	40	ns
t_{PHL}			C_L = 15 pF, R_L = 2 kΩ, See Figures 2 and 3		40	60	
t_{PLH}	CLK	Any Q			18	27	ns
t_{PHL}					18	27	
t_{PLH}	$\overline{ENT}$	$\overline{RCO}$			11	17	ns
t_{PHL}					29	45	
t_{PLH}	U/$\overline{D}$	$\overline{RCO}$			22	35	ns
t_{PHL}					26	40	

[¶] f_{max} Maximum clock frequency
t_{PLH} propagation delay time, low to high level output.
t_{PHL} propagation delay time, high to low level output.
Propagation delay time from up/down to ripple carry must be measured with the counter at either a minimum or a maximum count. As the logic level of the up/down input is changed, the ripple carry output will follow. If the count is minimum (0), the ripple carry output transition will be in phase. If the count is maximum (9 for 'LS668 or 15 for 'LS669), the ripple carry output will be out of phase.

3

TTL DEVICES

TEXAS INSTRUMENTS

TYPES SN54LS668, SN54LS669, SN74LS668, SN74LS669
SYNCHRONOUS 4-BIT UP/DOWN COUNTERS

PARAMETER MEASUREMENT INFORMATION

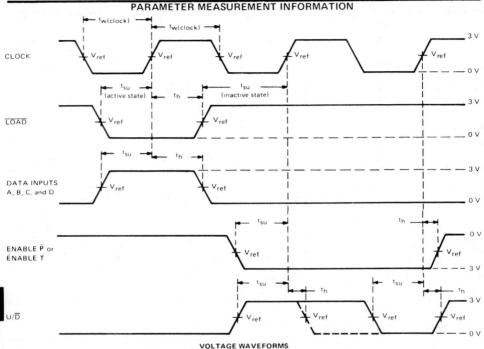

VOLTAGE WAVEFORMS

NOTES A. The input pulses are supplied by a generator having the following characteristics: PRR ≈ 1 MHz, duty cycle ≈ 50%, $Z_{out} \approx 50\ \Omega$, $t_r \approx 15$ ns, $t_f \approx 6$ ns.
      B. $V_{ref} = 1.3$ V.

FIGURE 1—PULSE WIDTHS, SETUP TIMES, HOLD TIMES

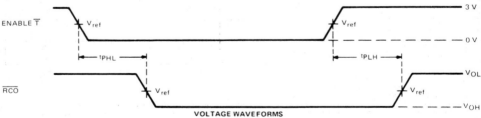

VOLTAGE WAVEFORMS

NOTES A. The input pulse is supplied by a generator having the following characteristics: PRR ≈ 1 MHz, duty cycle ≈ 50%, $Z_{out} \approx 50\ \Omega$, $t_r \approx 15$ ns, $t_f \approx 6$ ns.
      B. t_{PLH} and t_{PHL} from enable $\overline{T}$ input to ripple carry output assume that the counter is at the maximum count (Q_A and Q_D high for 'LS668, all Q outputs high for 'LS669).
      C. $V_{ref} = 1.3$ V.
      D. Propagation delay time from up/down to ripple carry must be measured with the counter at either a minimum or a maximum count. As the logic level of the up/down input is changed, the ripple carry output will follow. If the count is minimum (0) the ripple carry output transition will be in phase. If the count is maximum (9 for 'LS668, or 15 for 'LS669) the ripple carry output will be out of phase.

FIGURE 2—PROPAGATION DELAY TIMES TO CARRY OUTPUT

Texas
Instruments

PARAMETER MEASUREMENT INFORMATION

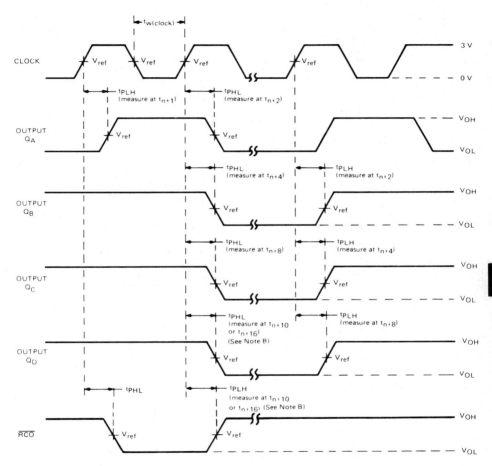

UP-COUNT VOLTAGE WAVEFORMS

NOTES: A. The input pulses are supplied by a generator having the following characteristics: PRR ≈ 1 MHz, duty cycle ≤ 50%, $Z_{out} \approx 50\ \Omega$, $t_r \leq 15$ ns, $t_f \leq 6$ ns. Vary PRR to measure f_{max}.

B. Outputs Q_D and carry are tested at t_{n+10} for the 'LS668, and at t_{n+16} for the 'LS669, where t_n is the bit-time when all outputs are low.

C. $V_{ref} = 1.3$ V.

FIGURE 3–PROPAGATION DELAY TIMES FROM CLOCK

TEXAS
INSTRUMENTS

3-1057

BULLETIN NO. DL-S 7612122, MARCH 1974-REVISED DECEMBER 1983

- **Separate Read/Write Addressing Permits Simultaneous Reading and Writing**

- **Fast Access Times . . . Typically 20 ns**

- **Organized as 4 Words of 4 Bits**

- **Expandable to 512 Words of n-Bits**

- **For Use as:**
  Scratch-Pad Memory
  Buffer Storage between Processors
  Bit Storage in Fast Multiplication Designs

- **3-State Outputs**

- **SN54LS170 and SN74LS170 Are Similar But Have Open-Collector Outputs**

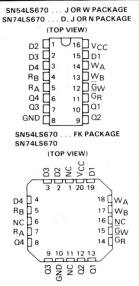

SN54LS670 . . . J OR W PACKAGE
SN74LS670 . . . D, J OR N PACKAGE
(TOP VIEW)

SN54LS670 . . . FK PACKAGE
SN74LS670
(TOP VIEW)

NC — No internal connection.

description

The SN54LS670 and SN74LS670 MSI 16-bit TTL register files incorporate the equivalent of 98 gates. The register file is organized as 4 words of 4 bits each and separate on-chip decoding is provided for addressing the four word locations to either write-in or retrieve data. This permits simultaneous writing into one location and reading from another word location.

Four data inputs are available which are used to supply the 4-bit word to be stored. Location of the word is determined by the write-address inputs A and B in conjunction with a write-enable signal. Data applied at the inputs should be in its true form. That is, if a high-level signal is desired from the output, a high-level is applied at the data input for that particular bit location. The latch inputs are arranged so that new data will be accepted only if both internal address gate inputs are high. When this condition exists, data at the D input is transferred to the latch output. When the write-enable input, $\overline{G_W}$, is high, the data inputs are inhibited and their levels can cause no change in the information stored in the internal latches. When the read-enable input, $\overline{G_R}$, is high, the data outputs are inhibited and go into the high-impedance state.

The individual address lines permit direct acquisition of data stored in any four of the latches. Four individual decoding gates are used to complete the address for reading a word. When the read address is made in conjunction with the read-enable signal, the word appears at the four outputs.

This arrangement — data-entry addressing separate from data-read addressing and individual sense line — eliminates recovery times, permits simultaneous reading and writing, and is limited in speed only by the write time (27 nanoseconds typical) and the read time (24 nanoseconds typical). The register file has a nondestructive readout in that data is not lost when addressed.

All inputs except read enable and write enable are buffered to lower the drive requirements to one Series 54LS/74LS standard load, and input-clamping diodes minimize switching transients to simplify system design. High-speed, double-ended AND-OR-INVERT gates are employed for the read-address function and have high-sink-current, three-state outputs. Up to 128 of these outputs may be bus connected for increasing the capacity up to 512 words. Any number of these registers may be paralleled to provide n-bit word length.

The SN54LS670 is characterized for operation over the full military temperature range of 55 C to 125 C; the SN74LS670 is characterized for operation from 0 C to 70 C.

TTL DEVICES

3

TEXAS INSTRUMENTS

3-1059

logic

WRITE FUNCTION TABLE (SEE NOTES A, B, AND C)

WRITE INPUTS			WORD			
W_B	W_A	$\overline{G}_W$	0	1	2	3
L	L	L	Q = D	Q_0	Q_0	Q_0
L	H	L	Q_0	Q = D	Q_0	Q_0
H	L	L	Q_0	Q_0	Q = D	Q_0
H	H	L	Q_0	Q_0	Q_0	Q = D
X	X	H	Q_0	Q_0	Q_0	Q_0

READ FUNCTION TABLE (SEE NOTES A AND D)

READ INPUTS			OUTPUTS			
R_B	R_A	$\overline{G}_R$	Q1	Q2	Q3	Q4
L	L	L	W0B1	W0B2	W0B3	W0B4
L	H	L	W1B1	W1B2	W1B3	W1B4
H	L	L	W2B1	W2B2	W2B3	W2B4
H	H	L	W3B1	W3B2	W3B3	W3B4
X	X	H	Z	Z	Z	Z

NOTES: A. H = high level, L = low level, X = irrelevant, Z = high impedance (off)
B. (Q - D) = The four selected internal flip flop outputs will assume the states applied to the four external data inputs.
C. Q_0 = the level of Q before the indicated input conditions were established.
D. W0B1 = The first bit of word 0, etc.

schematics of inputs and outputs

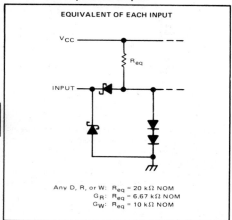

EQUIVALENT OF EACH INPUT

V_{CC}

R_{eq}

INPUT

Any D, R, or W: R_{eq} = 20 kΩ NOM
G_R: R_{eq} = 6.67 kΩ NOM
G_W: R_{eq} = 10 kΩ NOM

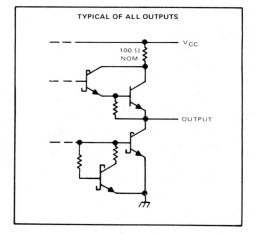

TYPICAL OF ALL OUTPUTS

100 Ω NOM

V_{CC}

OUTPUT

TEXAS
INSTRUMENTS

logic diagram

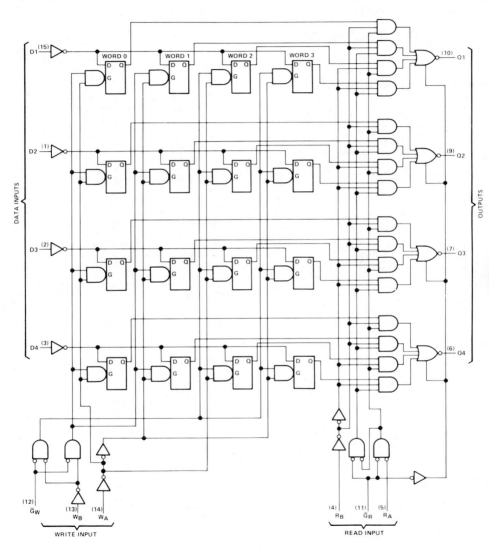

Pin numbers shown on logic notation are for D, J or N packages.

TTL DEVICES

3-1061

absolute maximum ratings over operating free-air temperature range (unless otherwise noted)

Supply voltage, V_{CC} (see Note 1)	7 V
Input voltage	7 V
Off-state output voltage	5.5 V
Operating free-air temperature range: SN54LS670	−55°C to 125°C
SN74LS670	0°C to 70°C
Storage temperature range	−65°C to 150°C

recommended operating conditions

		SN54LS670			SN74LS670			UNIT
		MIN	NOM	MAX	MIN	NOM	MAX	
Supply voltage, V_{CC}		4.5	5	5.5	4.75	5	5.25	V
High-level output current, I_{OH}				−1			−2.6	mA
Low-level output current, I_{OL}				4			8	mA
Width of write-enable or read-enable pulse, t_w		25			25			ns
Setup times, high- or low-level data (see Figure 2)	Data input with respect to write enable, $t_{su(D)}$	10			10			ns
	Write select with respect to write enable, $t_{su(W)}$	15			15			ns
Hold times, high- or low-level data (see Note 2 and Figure 2)	Data input with respect to write enable, $t_{h(D)}$	15			15			ns
	Write select with respect to write enable, $t_{h(W)}$	5			5			ns
Latch time for new data, t_{latch} (see Note 3)		25			25			ns
Operating free-air temperature range, T_A		−55		125	0		70	C

NOTES: 1. Voltage values are with respect to network ground terminal.
2. Write-select setup time will protect the data written into the previous address. If protection of data in the previous address is not required, $t_{su(W)}$ can be ignored as any address selection sustained for the final 30 ns of the write-enable pulse and during $t_{h(W)}$ will result in data being written into that location. Depending on the duration of the input conditions, one or a number of previous addresses may have been written into.
3. Latch time is the time allowed for the internal output of the latch to assume the state of new data. See Figure 2. This is important only when attempting to read from a location immediately after that location has received new data.

3

TTL DEVICES

TEXAS
INSTRUMENTS

electrical characteristics over recommended operating free-air temperature range (unless otherwise noted)

PARAMETER		TEST CONDITIONS[†]			SN54LS670 MIN	SN54LS670 TYP[‡]	SN54LS670 MAX	SN74LS670 MIN	SN74LS670 TYP[‡]	SN74LS670 MAX	UNIT
V_{IH}	High-level input voltage				2			2			V
V_{IL}	Low-level input voltage						0.7			0.8	V
V_{IK}	Input clamp voltage	V_{CC} = MIN,	I_I = −18 mA				−1.5			−1.5	V
V_{OH}	High-level output voltage	V_{CC} = MIN, $V_{IL} = V_{IL}$ max	V_{IH} = 2 V,	I_{OH} = −1 mA	2.4	3.4					V
				I_{OH} = −2.6 mA				2.4	3.1		
V_{OL}	Low-level output voltage	V_{CC} = MIN, $V_{IL} = V_{IL}$ max	V_{IH} = 2 V,	I_{OL} = 4 mA		0.25	0.4		0.25	0.4	V
				I_{OL} = 8 mA					0.35	0.5	
I_{OZH}	Off-state output current, high-level voltage applied	V_{CC} = MAX,	V_{IH} = 2 V,	V_O = 2.7 V			20			20	μA
I_{OZL}	Off-state output current, low-level voltage applied	V_{CC} = MAX,	V_{IH} = 2 V,	V_O = 0.4 V			−20			−20	μA
I_I	Input current at maximum input voltage	V_{CC} = MAX, V_I = 7 V	Any D, R, or W				0.1			0.1	mA
			$\overline{G}_W$				0.2			0.2	
			$\overline{G}_R$				0.3			0.3	
I_{IH}	High-level input current	V_{CC} = MAX, V_I = 2.7 V	Any D, R, or W				20			20	μA
			$\overline{G}_W$				40			40	
			$\overline{G}_R$				60			60	
I_{IL}	Low-level input current	V_{CC} = MAX, V_I = 0.4 V	Any D, R, or W				−0.4			−0.4	mA
			$\overline{G}_W$				−0.8			−0.8	
			$\overline{G}_R$				−1.2			−1.2	
I_{OS}	Short-circuit output current[§]	V_{CC} = MAX			−30		−130	−30		−130	mA
I_{CC}	Supply current	V_{CC} = MAX,	See Note 4			30	50		30	50	mA

[†]For conditions shown as MIN or MAX, use the appropriate value specified under recommended operating conditions.
[‡]All typical values are at V_{CC} = 5 V, T_A = 25°C.
[§]Not more than one output should be shorted at a time, and duration of the short-circuit should not exceed one second.
NOTE 4: Maximum I_{CC} is guaranteed for the following worst-case conditions: 4.5 V is applied to all data inputs and both enable inputs, all address inputs are grounded and all outputs are open.

switching characteristics, V_{CC} = 5 V, T_A = 25°C

PARAMETER[¶]	FROM (INPUT)	TO (OUTPUT)	TEST CONDITIONS	MIN	TYP	MAX	UNIT
t_{PLH}	Read select	Any Q	C_L = 15 pF, R_L = 2 kΩ, See Figures 1 and 2		23	40	ns
t_{PHL}					25	45	
t_{PLH}	Write enable	Any Q	C_L = 15 pF, R_L = 2 kΩ, See Figures 1 and 3		26	45	ns
t_{PHL}					28	50	
t_{PLH}	Data	Any Q			25	45	ns
t_{PHL}					23	40	
t_{PZH}	Read enable	Any Q	C_L = 15 pF, R_L = 2 kΩ, See Figures 1 and 4		15	35	ns
t_{PZL}					22	40	
t_{PHZ}			C_L = 5 pF, R_L = 2 kΩ, See Figures 1 and 4		30	50	ns
t_{PLZ}					16	35	

[¶] t_{PLH} = propagation delay time, low-to-high-level output
t_{PHL} = propagation delay time, high-to-low-level output
t_{PZH} = output enable time to high level
t_{PZL} = output enable time to low level
t_{PHZ} = output disable time from high level
t_{PLZ} = output disable time from low level

3

TTL DEVICES

TEXAS INSTRUMENTS

3-1063

PARAMETER MEASUREMENT INFORMATION

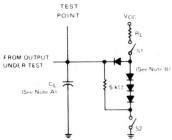

NOTES: A. C_L includes probe and jig capacitance.
B. All diodes are 1N3064 or equivalent.

LOAD CIRCUIT

FIGURE 1

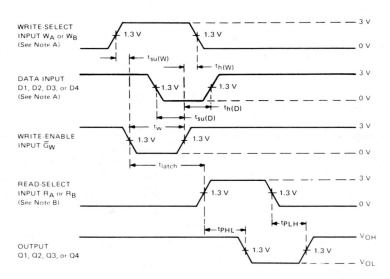

VOLTAGE WAVEFORMS (S1 AND S2 ARE CLOSED)

NOTES: A. High-level input pulses at the select and data inputs are illustrated, however, times associated with low-level pulses are measured from the same reference points.
B. When measuring delay times from a read-select input, the read-enable input is low.
C. Input waveforms are supplied by generators having the following characteristics: PRR ≤ 2 MHz, Z_{out} ≈ 50 Ω, duty cycle ≈ 50%, t_r ≤ 15 ns, t_f ≤ 6 ns.

FIGURE 2

PARAMETER MEASUREMENT INFORMATION

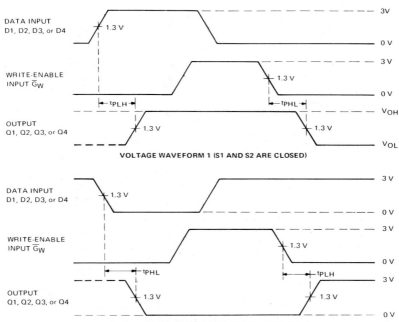

VOLTAGE WAVEFORM 1 (S1 AND S2 ARE CLOSED)

VOLTAGE WAVEFORM 2 (S1 AND S2 ARE CLOSED)

NOTES: A. Each select address is tested. Prior to the start of each of the above tests both write and read address inputs are stabilized with $W_A = R_A$ and $W_B = R_B$. During the test G_R is low.
B. Input waveforms are supplied by generators having the following characteristics: PRR $\leqslant$ 1 MHz, $Z_{out} \approx$ 50 Ω, duty cycle $\leqslant$ 50%, $t_r < 15$ ns, $t_r < 6$ ns.

FIGURE 3

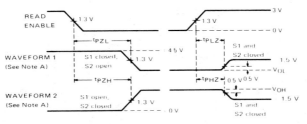

VOLTAGE WAVEFORMS
ENABLE AND DISABLE TIMES, THREE-STATE OUTPUTS

NOTES: A. Waveforms 1 is for an output with internal conditions such that the output is low except when disabled by the read enable input. Waveform 2 is for an output with internal conditions such that the output is high except when disabled by the read enable input.
B. When measuring delay times from the read enable input, both read select inputs have been established at steady states.
C. Input waveforms are supplied by generators having the following characteristics: PRR $\leqslant$ 1 MHz, $Z_{out} \approx$ 50 Ω, duty cycle $<$ 50%, $t_r < 15$ ns, $t_r < 6$ ns.

FIGURE 4

3

TTL DEVICES

3

TTL DEVICES

TYPES SN54LS671, SN54LS672, SN74LS671, SN74LS672
4-BIT UNIVERSAL SHIFT REGISTERS/LATCHES
WITH 3-STATE OUTPUTS

D2638, JANUARY 1981

- **4-Bit Universal Shift Registers/Latches**

- **Multiplexed Outputs for Shift Register or Latched Data**

- **Choice of Direct SR Clear ('LS671) or Synchronous SR Clear ('LS672)**

- **3-State Outputs Drive Bus Lines Directly**

- **Expandable to Any Word Length**

description

The 'LS671 and 'LS672 each contain a 4-bit universal shift register (similar to the 'LS194A) and a 4-bit storage register (similar to the 'LS175) multiplexed to a 3-state output stage (similar to the 'LS258). The user has the option of selecting the shift or storage register via the register/shift select input $R/\overline{S}$. The 'LS671 has a direct-overriding shift register clear while the 'LS672 features a synchronous shift register clear. The shift register has four distinct modes of operation, namely:

Inhibit clock (do nothing)
Shift right (in the direction Q_A toward Q_D)
Shift left (in the direction Q_D toward Q_A)
Parallel (broadside) load

A cascade output for the shift register is provided so that full shift register functionality is provided even while the outputs are in the high-impedance mode. The cascade output presents Q_A data in the shift-left mode, Q_D data in the shift-right mode.

Both the shift register clock and the latch clock are triggered on the positive transition. The output control $(\overline{G})$ activates Q_A thru Q_D when low, it places Q_A thru Q_D into the high-impedance state when high.

SN54LS671, SN54LS672 . . . J PACKAGE
SN74LS671, SN74LS672 . . . DW, J OR N PACKAGE
(TOP VIEW)

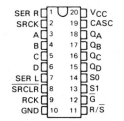

SN54LS671, SN54LS672 . . . FK PACKAGE
SN74LS671, SN74LS672
(TOP VIEW)

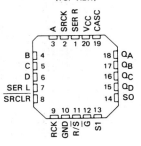

3

TTL DEVICES

TEXAS
INSTRUMENTS

3-1067

logic diagram (positive logic)

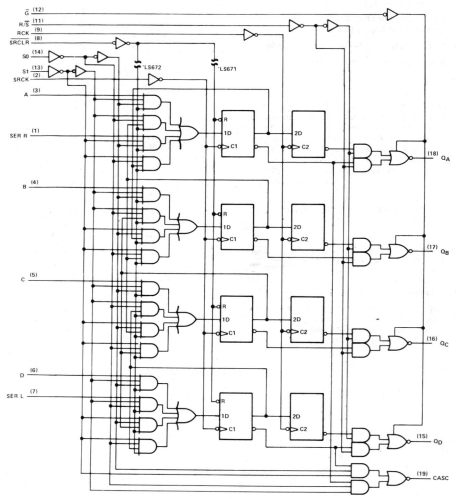

Pin numbers shown on logic notation are for DW, J or N packages.

TEXAS
INSTRUMENTS

logic symbols

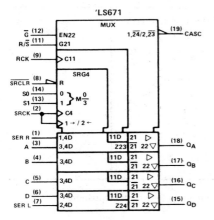

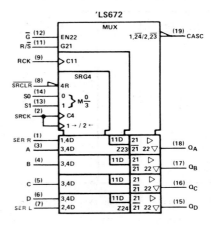

Pin numbers shown on logic notation are for DW, J or N packages.

FUNCTION TABLE

$\overline{G}$	R/$\overline{S}$	$\overline{SRCLR}$	SR MODE S1	SR MODE S0	SRCK 'LS671	SRCK 'LS672	SERIAL INPUTS SL	SERIAL INPUTS SR	A	B	C	D	Q_A	Q_B	Q_C	Q_D	CASC*
L	L	L	X	X	X	↑	X	X	X	X	X	X	L	L	L	L	(*)
L	L	H	X	X	L	L	X	X	X	X	X	X	Q_{A0}	Q_{B0}	Q_{C0}	Q_{D0}	(*)
L	L	H	L	L	X	X	X	X	X	X	X	X	Q_{A0}	Q_{B0}	Q_{C0}	Q_{D0}	H
L	L	H	L	H	↑	↑	X	H	X	X	X	X	H	Q_{An}	Q_{Bn}	Q_{Cn}	Q_{Cn}
L	L	H	L	H	↑	↑	X	L	X	X	X	X	L	Q_{An}	Q_{Bn}	Q_{Cn}	Q_{Cn}
L	L	H	H	L	↑	↑	H	X	X	X	X	X	Q_{Bn}	Q_{Cn}	Q_{Dn}	H	Q_{Bn}
L	L	H	H	L	↑	↑	L	X	X	X	X	X	Q_{Bn}	Q_{Cn}	Q_{Dn}	L	Q_{Bn}
L	L	H	H	H	↑	↑	X	X	a	b	c	d	a	b	c	d	H
H	X	X	X	L	↑	↑	X	X	X	X	X	X	Z	Z	Z	Z	Q_{Cn}
H	X	X	H	L	↑	↑	X	X	X	X	X	X	Z	Z	Z	Z	Q_{Bn}
L	H	X	X	X	X	X	X	X	X	X	X	X	Internal register contents				(*)

When the output control $\overline{G}$ is high, the 3-state outputs are disabled to the high-impedance state; however, sequential operation of the shift register and the output at CASC are not affected.

H = high level (steady state)
L = low level (steady state)
X = irrelevant (any input, including transitions)
↑ = transition from low to high level
a, b, c, d = the level of steady-state input at A, B, C, or D, respectively
Q_{A0}, Q_{B0}, Q_{C0}, Q_{D0} = the level of Q_A, Q_B, Q_C, or Q_D, respectively, before the indicated steady-state input conditions were established
Q_{An}, Q_{Bn}, Q_{Cn} = the level of Q_A, Q_B, or Q_C, respectively, before the most-recent transition of the clock
Z = high-impedance state
*The cascade output displays the D bit of the shift register in mode 1 (S1, S0 = L, H), the A bit in mode 2 (S1, S0 = HL), and is inactive (H) in modes 0 and 3 (S1, S0 = LL and HH).

TEXAS
INSTRUMENTS

3

TTL DEVICES

schematics of inputs and outputs

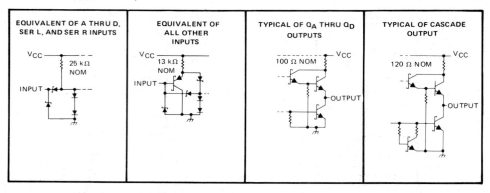

| EQUIVALENT OF A THRU D, SER L, AND SER R INPUTS | EQUIVALENT OF ALL OTHER INPUTS | TYPICAL OF Q_A THRU Q_D OUTPUTS | TYPICAL OF CASCADE OUTPUT |

absolute maximum ratings over operating free-air temperature range (unless otherwise noted)

Supply voltage V_{CC} (see Note 1) .... 7 V
Input voltage .... 7 V
Off-state output voltage .... 5.5 V
Operating free-air temperature range: SN54LS671, SN54LS672 .... $-55°C$ to $125°C$
                             SN74LS671, SN74LS672 .... $0°C$ to $70°C$
Storage temperature range .... $-65°C$ to $150°C$

NOTE 1: Voltage values are with respect to the network ground terminal.

recommended operating conditions

			SN54LS'			SN74LS'			UNIT
			MIN	NOM	MAX	MIN	NOM	MAX	
V_{CC}	Supply voltage		4.5	5	5.5	4.75	5	5.25	V
I_{OH}	High-level output current	Cascade out			-0.4			-0.4	mA
		Q_A, Q_B, Q_C, Q_D			-1			-2.6	
I_{OL}	Low-level output current	Cascade out			4			8	mA
		Q_A, Q_B, Q_C, Q_D			12			24	
t_W	Width of SRCK, RCK, or $\overline{SRCLR}$ ('LS671 only) input pulse		30			30			ns
t_{su}	Inactive state setup time	$\overline{SRCLR}$ before SRCK ↑ ('LS671 only)	30			30			ns
t_{su}	Setup time	S0 or S1 to SRCK ↑	45			45			ns
		$\overline{SRCLR}$ ↓ ('LS672 only) to SRCK ↑	25			25			
		A, B, C, D to SRCK ↑	30			30			
		SRCK ↑ to RCK ↑	30			30			
		SER to SRCK ↑	35			35			
t_h	Hold time	Any input from SRCK ↑	0			0			ns
T_A	Operating free-air temperature		-55		125	0		70	°C

Texas
INSTRUMENTS

electrical characteristics over recommended operating free-air temperature range (unless otherwise noted)

PARAMETER		TEST CONDITIONS†		SN54LS' MIN	TYP‡	MAX	SN74LS' MIN	TYP‡	MAX	UNIT
V_{IH}	High-level input voltage			2			2			V
V_{IL}	Low-level input voltage					0.7			0.8	V
V_{IK}	Input clamp voltage	V_{CC} = MIN, I_I = −18 mA				−1.5			−1.5	V
V_{OH}	High-level output voltage	$Q_A - Q_D$	V_{CC} = MIN, I_{OH} = −1 mA	2.4	3.1					V
		$Q_A - Q_D$	V_{IH} = 2 V, I_{OH} = −2.6 mA				2.4	3.1		
		CASC	$V_{IL} = V_{IL}$ max, I_{OH} = −400 µA	2.5	3.2		2.7	3.2		
V_{OL}	Low-level output voltage	$Q_A - Q_D$	V_{CC} = MIN, I_{OL} = 12 mA		0.25	0.4		0.25	0.4	V
		$Q_A - Q_D$	V_{IH} = 2 V, I_{OL} = 24 mA					0.35	0.5	
		CASC	I_{OL} = 4 mA		0.25	0.4		0.25	0.4	
		CASC	I_{OL} = 8 mA					0.35	0.5	
I_{OZH}	Off-state output current, high-level voltage applied	$Q_A - Q_D$	V_{CC} = MAX, V_{IH} = 2 V, V_O = 2.7 V, $V_{IL} = V_{IL}$ max			20			20	µA
I_{OZL}	Off-state output current, low-level voltage applied	$Q_A - Q_D$	V_{CC} = MAX, V_{IH} = 2 V, V_O = 0.4 V, $V_{IL} = V_{IL}$ max			−20			−20	µA
I_I	Input current at maximum input voltage		V_{CC} = MAX, V_I = 7 V			0.1			0.1	mA
I_{IH}	High-level input current		V_{CC} = MAX, V_I = 2.7 V			20			20	µA
I_{IL}	Low-level input current	A, B, C, D	V_{CC} = MAX, V_I = 0.4 V			−0.4			−0.4	mA
		All others				−0.2			−0.2	
I_{OS}	Short-circuit output current§	$Q_A - Q_D$	V_{CC} = MAX, V_O = 0 V	−30		−130	−30		−130	mA
		CASC		−20		−100	−20		−100	
I_{CC}	Supply current	All outputs low	V_{CC} = MAX, See Note 2		35	70		35	70	mA
		All outputs high	All outputs, See Note 3		30	65		30	65	
		Q_A thru Q_D, at Hi-Z	open, See Note 4		37	70		37	70	

†For conditions shown as MIN or MAX, use the appropriate value specified under recommended operating conditions.

‡All typical values are at V_{CC} = 5 V, T_A = 25°C.

§Not more than one output should be shorted at a time and duration of the short-circuit should not exceed one second.

NOTES: 2. I_{CCL} is tested after two 0-V to 4.5 V to 0-V pulses have been applied to SRCK and RCK while S0 is at 4.5 V and all other inputs are grounded.
3. I_{CCH} is tested after two 4.5-V to 0-V to 4.5-V pulses have been applied to SRCK and RCK while all other inputs are at 4.5 V.
4. I_{CCZ} is tested after two 0-V to 4.5-V to 0-V pulses have been applied to SRCK and RCK while S0 and $\overline{G}$ are at 4.5 V and all other inputs are grounded.

TEXAS
INSTRUMENTS

3-1071

3

TTL DEVICES

TYPES SN54LS671, SN54LS672, SN74LS671, SN74LS672
4-BIT UNIVERSAL SHIFT REGISTERS/LATCHES WITH 3-STATE OUTPUTS

switching characteristics, V_{CC} = 5 V, T_A = 25°C, see note 5

PARAMETER	FROM (INPUT)	TO (OUTPUT)	TEST CONDITIONS		'LS671			'LS672			UNIT
			MODE	LOAD	MIN	TYP	MAX	MIN	TYP	MAX	
t_{PLH}	SRCK ↑		SHIFT LEFT OR RIGHT	R_L = 2 kΩ, C_L = 15 pF		31	45		31	45	ns
t_{PHL}						14	25		14	25	
t_{PLH}	S0, S1	CASCADE				11	20		12	20	ns
t_{PHL}						11	20		12	20	
t_{PHL}	SRCK ↑		SR CLEAR						19	30	ns
t_{PHL}	$\overline{SRCLR}$ ↓					19	30				ns
t_{PLH}	SRCK ↑		SHIFT LEFT OR RIGHT			10	20		10	20	ns
t_{PHL}						16	25		16	25	
t_{PLH}			SR LOAD			10	20		10	20	ns
t_{PHL}						15	25		15	25	
t_{PHL}			SR CLEAR						17	30	ns
t_{PHL}	$\overline{SRCLR}$ ↓	$Q_A - Q_D$				21	30				ns
t_{PLH}	RCK ↑		LATCH	R_L = 667 Ω, C_L = 45 pF		10	20		10	20	ns
t_{PHL}						15	25		15	25	
t_{PLH}	R/$\overline{S}$ ↑		MUX			12	25		13	25	ns
t_{PHL}						15	25		15	25	
t_{PLH}	R/$\overline{S}$ ↓					17	25		17	25	ns
t_{PHL}						16	25		16	25	
t_{PZH}	$\overline{G}$ ↓		3-STATE ENABLE			16	25		16	25	ns
t_{PZL}						19	30		19	30	
t_{PHZ}	$\overline{G}$ ↑		3-STATE DISABLE	R_L = 667 Ω, C_L = 5 pF		16	25		16	25	ns
t_{PLZ}						16	25		16	25	

NOTE 5: See General Information Section for load circuits and voltage waveforms.

t_{PLH} ≡ Propagation delay time, low-to-high-level output
t_{PHL} ≡ Propagation delay time, high-to-low-level output
t_{PZH} ≡ Output enable time to high level
t_{PZL} ≡ Output enable time to low level
t_{PHZ} ≡ Output disable time from high level
t_{PLZ} ≡ Output disable time from low level

TYPICAL APPLICATION DATA

The 'LS671 or 'LS672 can easily be expanded utilizing the cascade output and the SER L and SER R inputs. A typical expansion is shown below.

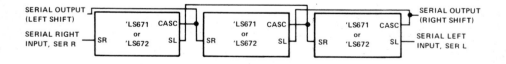

FIGURE 1 – 'LS671, 'LS672 EXPANDED TO 12 BITS, (3 PACKAGES)

Any desired word length may be obtained using the scheme shown. Corresponding control pins of all the packages are tied in common, i.e., all S0 pins are connected together, all S1 pins are connected together, etc.

TEXAS
INSTRUMENTS

D2421, REVISED APRIL 1985

'LS673

- 16-Bit Serial-In, Serial-Out Shift
  Register with 16-Bit Parallel-Out
  Storage Register

- Performs Serial-to-Parallel Conversion

'LS674

- 16-Bit Parallel-In, Serial-Out
  Shift Register

- Performs Parallel-to-Serial Conversion

description

SN54LS673, SN74LS673

The 'LS673 is a 16-bit shift register and a 16-bit storage register in a single 24-pin package. A three-state input/output (SER/Q15) port to the shift register allows serial entry and/or reading of data. The storage register is connected in a parallel data loop with the shift register and may be asynchronously cleared by taking the store-clear input low. The storage register may be parallel loaded with shift-register data to provide shift-register status via the parallel outputs. The shift register can be parallel loaded with the storage-register data upon command.

A high logic level at the chip-level ($\overline{CS}$) input disables both the shift-register clock and the storage register clock and places SER/Q15 in the high-impedance state. The store-clear function is not disabled by the chip select.

Caution must be exercised to prevent false clocking of either the shift register or the storage register via the chip-select input. The shift clock should be low during the low-to-high transition of chip select and the store clock should be low during the high-to-low transition of chip select.

SN54LS674, SN74LS674

The 'LS674 is a 16-bit parallel-in, serial-out shift register. A three-state input/output (SER/Q15) port provides access for entering a serial data or reading the shift-register word in a recirculating loop.

The device has four basic modes of operation:

1) Hold (do nothing)
2) Write (serially via input/output)
3) Read (serially)
4) Load (parallel via data inputs)

Low-to-high-level changes at the chip select input should be made only when the clock input is low to prevent false clocking.

SN54LS673 . . . J OR W PACKAGE
SN74LS673 . . . DW, J OR N PACKAGE
(TOP VIEW)

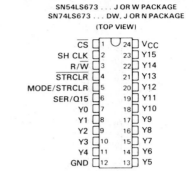

SN54LS673 . . . FK PACKAGE
SN74LS673
(TOP VIEW)

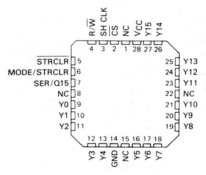

NC—No internal connection

TEXAS INSTRUMENTS

3

TTL DEVICES

SN54LS674 ... J OR W PACKAGE
SN74LS674 ... DW, J OR N PACKAGE
(TOP VIEW)

```
        ___
        CS  [ 1    U   24 ]  VCC
       CLK  [ 2        23 ]  P15
       R/W̄  [ 3        22 ]  P14
        NC  [ 4        21 ]  P13
      MODE  [ 5        20 ]  P12
   SER/Q15  [ 6        19 ]  P11
        P0  [ 7        18 ]  P10
        P1  [ 8        17 ]  P9
        P2  [ 9        16 ]  P8
        P3  [ 10       15 ]  P7
        P4  [ 11       14 ]  P6
       GND  [ 12       13 ]  P5
```

SN54LS674 ... FK PACKAGE
SN74LS674 ... FN PACKAGE
(TOP VIEW)

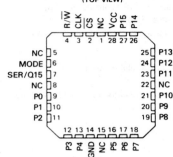

'LS673
FUNCTION TABLE

INPUTS					SER/ Q15	SHIFT REGISTER FUNCTIONS				STORAGE REGISTER FUNCTIONS	
C̄S̄	R/W̄	SH CLK	STRCLR	MODE/ STRCLK		SHIFT	READ FROM SERIAL OUTPUT	WRITE INTO SERIAL INPUT	PARALLEL LOAD	CLEAR	LOAD
H	X	X	X	X	Z	NO	NO	NO	NO		NO
X	X	X	L	X						YES	
L	L	↓	X	X	Z	YES	NO	YES	NO		
L	H	X	X	X	Q15		YES	NO			NO
L	H	↓	X	L	Q14n	YES	YES	NO	NO		NO
L	H	↓	L	H	L	NO	YES		YES	YES	NO
L	H	↓	H	H	Y15n	NO	YES		YES	NO	NO
L	L	X	H	↑	Z		NO		NO	NO	YES

'LS674 FUNCTION TABLE

INPUTS				SER/ Q15	OPERATION
CS	R/W̄	MODE	CLK		
H	X	X	X	Z	Do nothing
L	L	X	↓	Z	Shift and write (serial load)
L	H	L	↓	Q14n	Shift and read
L	H	H	↓	P15	Parallel load

H = high level (steady state)
L = low level (steady state)
↑ = transition from low to high level
↓ = transition from high to low level
X = irrelevant (any input including transitions)
Z = high impedance, input mode
Q14n = content of 14th bit of the shift register before the most recent ↓ transition of the clock.
Q15 = present content of 15th bit of the shift register
Y15n = content of the 15th bit of the storage register before the most recent ↓ transition of the clock.
P15 = level of input P15

TEXAS
INSTRUMENTS

logic symbols

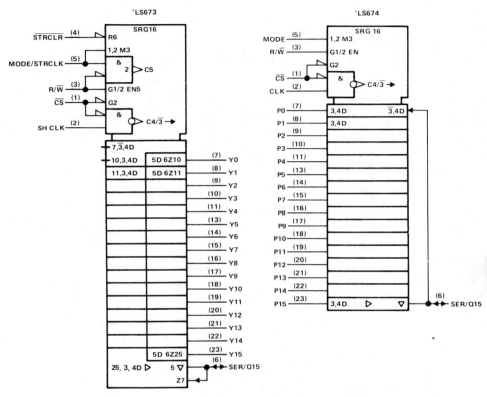

Pin numbers shown on logic notation are for DW, J or N packages.

3

TTL DEVICES

TYPES SN54LS673, SN54LS674, SN74LS673, SN74LS674
16-BIT SHIFT REGISTERS

functional block diagrams

SN54LS673, SN74LS673

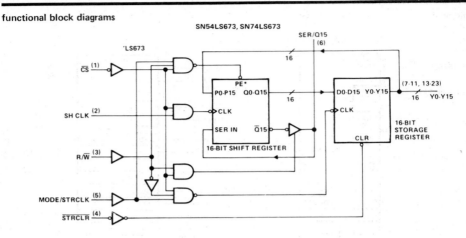

SN54LS674, SN74LS674

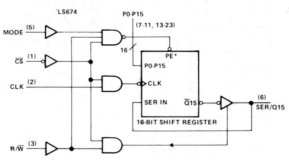

*When PE is active, data is synchronously parallel loaded into the shift registers from the 16 P inputs and no shifting takes place.
Pin numbers shown on logic notation are for DW, J or N packages.

TEXAS
INSTRUMENTS

schematics of inputs and outputs

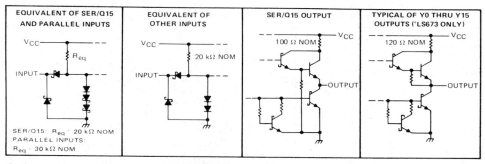

| EQUIVALENT OF SER/Q15 AND PARALLEL INPUTS | EQUIVALENT OF OTHER INPUTS | SER/Q15 OUTPUT | TYPICAL OF Y0 THRU Y15 OUTPUTS ('LS673 ONLY) |

SER/Q15: R_{eq} = 20 kΩ NOM
PARALLEL INPUTS:
R_{eq} = 30 kΩ NOM

absolute maximum ratings over operating free-air temperature range (unless otherwise noted)

Supply voltage, V_{CC} (see Note 1) . . . . 7 V
Input voltage: SER/Q15 . . . . 5.5 V
      All others . . . . 7 V
Off-state output voltage . . . . 5.5 V
Operating free-air temperature range: SN54LS673, SN54LS674 . . . . −55°C to 125°C
              SN74LS673, SN74LS674 . . . . 0°C to 70°C
Storage temperature range . . . . −65°C to 150°C

NOTE 1 Voltage values are with respect to network ground terminal.

recommended operating conditions

			SN54LS'			SN74LS'			UNIT
			MIN	NOM	MAX	MIN	NOM	MAX	
V_{CC}	Supply voltage		4.5	5	5.5	4.75	5	5.25	V
I_{OH}	High-level output current	SER/Q15			−1			−2.6	mA
		Y0 thru Y15			−0.4			−0.4	
I_{OL}	Low-level output current	SER/Q15			12			24	mA
		Y0 thru Y15			4			8	
f_{clock}	Clock frequency		0		20	0		20	MHz
$t_{w(clock)}$	Width of clock input pulse		20			20			ns
$t_{w(clear)}$	Width of clear input pulse		20			20			ns
t_{su}	Setup time	SER/Q15	20			20			ns
		P0 thru P15	20			20			
		Mode	35			35			
		R/W̄, C̄S̄	35			35			
		SH CLK ↓ to Mode/STR CLK ↑ See Note 2	25			25			
t_h	Hold time	SER/Q15	0			0			ns
		P0 thru P15 'LS673	0			0			
		'LS674	5.0			5.0			
		Mode	0			0			
T_A	Operating free-air temperature		−55		125	0		70	°C

NOTE 2: This setup time ensures the storage register will see stable data from the shift register.

3

TTL DEVICES

electrical characteristics over recommended operating free-air temperature range (unless otherwise noted)

PARAMETER		TEST CONDITIONS†			SN54LS' MIN	SN54LS' TYP‡	SN54LS' MAX	SN74LS' MIN	SN74LS' TYP‡	SN74LS' MAX	UNIT
V_{IH}	High-level input voltage				2			2			V
V_{IL}	Low-level input voltage						0.7			0.8	V
V_{IK}	Input clamp voltage	V_{CC} = MIN,	I_I = −18 mA				−1.5			−1.5	V
V_{OH}	High-level output voltage	SER/Q15	V_{CC} = MIN, V_{IH} = 2 V,		2.4	3.2		2.4	3.1		V
		Y0 thru Y15¶	$V_{IL} = V_{IL}$max, I_{OH} = MAX		2.5	3.4		2.7	3.4		
V_{OL}	Low-level output voltage	SER/Q15	V_{CC} = MIN, V_{IH} = 2 V, $V_{IL} = V_{IL}$max	I_{OL} = 12 mA		0.25	0.4		0.25	0.4	V
				I_{OL} = 24 mA					0.35	0.5	
		Y0 thru Y15¶		I_{OL} = 4 mA		0.25	0.4		0.25	0.4	
				I_{OL} = 8 mA					0.35	0.5	
I_{OZH}	Off-state output current, high-level voltage applied	SER/Q15	V_{CC} = MAX, V_{IH} = 2 V, $V_{IL} = V_{IL}$max, V_O = 2.7 V				40			40	µA
I_{OZL}	Off-state output current, low-level voltage applied	SER/Q15	V_{CC} = MAX, V_{IH} = 2 V, $V_{IL} = V_{IL}$max, V_O = 0.4 V				−0.4			−0.4	mA
I_I	Input current at maximum input voltage	SER/Q15	V_{CC} = MAX	V_I = 5.5 V			0.1			0.1	mA
		Others		V_I = 7 V			0.1			0.1	
I_{IH}	High-level input current	SER/Q15	V_{CC} = MAX, V_I = 2.7 V				40			40	µA
		Others					20			20	
I_{IL}	Low-level input current		V_{CC} = MAX, V_I = 0.4 V				−0.4			−0.4	mA
I_{OS}	Short-circuit output current§	SER/Q15	V_{CC} = MAX		−30		−130	−30		−130	mA
		Y0 thru Y15¶			−20		−100	−20		−100	
I_{CC}	Supply current	'LS673	V_{CC} = MAX			50	80		52	80	mA
		'LS674				25	40		25	40	

†For conditions shown as MIN or MAX use the appropriate value specified under recommended operating conditions.
‡All typical values are at V_{CC} = 5 V, T_A = 25°C.
§Not more than one output should be shorted at a time, and duration of the short circuit should not exceed one second.
¶'LS673 only.

switching characteristics, V_{CC} = 5 V, T_A = 25°C, see note 2

PARAMETER	'LS673 FROM	'LS673 TO	'LS674 FROM	'LS674 TO	TEST CONDITIONS	MIN	TYP	MAX	UNIT
f_{max}	SH CLK	SER/Q15	CLK	SER/Q15	R_L = 667 Ω, C_L = 45 pF	20	28		MHz
t_{PHL}	STRCLR	Y0 thru Y15					25	40	
t_{PLH}	MODE/ STRCLK	Y0 thru Y15			R_L = 2 kΩ, C_L = 15 pF		28	45	ns
t_{PHL}							30	45	
t_{PLH}	SH CLK	SER/Q15	CLK	SER/Q15	R_L = 667 Ω, C_L = 45 pF		21	33	ns
t_{PHL}							26	40	
t_{PZH}	$\overline{CS}$, R/$\overline{W}$	SER/Q15	$\overline{CS}$, R/$\overline{W}$	SER/Q15	R_L = 667 Ω, C_L = 45 pF		30	45	ns
t_{PZL}							30	45	
t_{PHZ}	$\overline{CS}$, R/$\overline{W}$	SER/Q15	$\overline{CS}$, R/$\overline{W}$	SER/Q15	R_L = 667 Ω, C_L = 5 pF		25	40	ns
t_{PLZ}							25	40	

NOTE 2: See General Information Section for load circuits and voltage waveforms.
f_{max} = maximum clock frequency
t_{PLH} = Propagation delay time, low-to-high-level output
t_{PHL} = Propagation delay time, high-to-low-level output
t_{PZH} = Output enable time to high level
t_{PZL} = Output enable time to low level
t_{PHZ} = Output disable time from low level
t_{PLZ} = Output disable time from high level

TEXAS
INSTRUMENTS

D2422, JANUARY 1981 REVISED APRIL 1985

- **Full 4-Bit Binary Accumulator in a Single 20-Pin Package**

- **Contains Two Synchronous Registers:**
  Word A
  Word B Shift/Accumulator

- **16 Arithmetic Operations Including B Minus A and A Minus B**

- **16 Logic-Mode Operations**

- **Expandable to Handle N-Bit Words with Full Carry Look-Ahead**

- **Bus Driving I/O Ports**

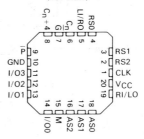

SN54LS681 . . . J PACKAGE
SN74LS681 . . . DW, J OR N PACKAGE
(TOP VIEW)

CLK 1	20 V_{CC}
RS2 2	19 RI/LO
RS1 3	18 AS0
RS0 4	17 AS1
LI/RO 5	16 AS2
C_n 6	15 M
$\overline{G}$ 7	14 I/O0
C_{n+4} 8	13 I/O1
$\overline{P}$ 9	12 I/O2
GND 10	11 I/O3

SN54LS681 . . . FK PACKAGE
SN74LS681
(TOP VIEW)

description

These low-power Schottky IC's integrate a high-speed arithmetic logic unit (ALU) complete with word A and word B registers on a single chip. The ALU performs 16 arithmetic and 16 logic functions (see Tables 1 and 2). Full carry look-ahead is provided for fast carry of four-bit words. The carry input (C_n) and propagate and generate outputs ($\overline{P}$ and $\overline{G}$) are provided for direct use with SN54S182/SN74S182 carry look-ahead generators for optimum performance with longer words.

The A and B registers are controlled by three inputs (RS0, RS1, and RS2). These pins define eight distinct register modes (see Table 3). The A register is a simple storage register while the B register is a combination storage/shift/accumulator register. The contents of the A and B registers provide the A and B words for the ALU.

Four I/O ports (I/O 0 thru I/O 3) are provided for parallel loading of word A and/or word B into their respective registers. These same ports also serve as bus driving outputs for the ALU/accumulator results (F_j). Two additional I/O ports (RI/LO and LI/RO) are provided to allow expansion of the accumulator for words greater than four bits in length.

The A or B register can be parallel loaded from the four I/O ports. The B register can also be parallel loaded from the ALU as an accumulator register and in addition, the B register can be serially loaded from either the RI/LO or the LI/RO ports.

The SN54LS681 is characterized for operation over the full military temperature range from 55˚C to 125 C. The SN74LS681 is characterized for operation from 0°C to 70°C.

3

TTL DEVICES

TEXAS
INSTRUMENTS

functional block diagram

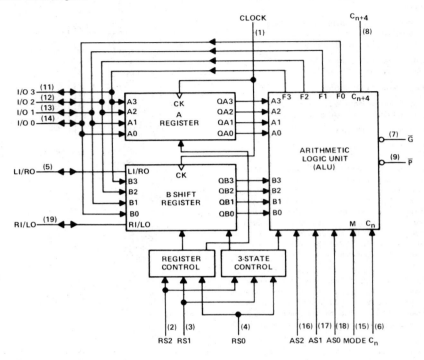

schematics of inputs and outputs

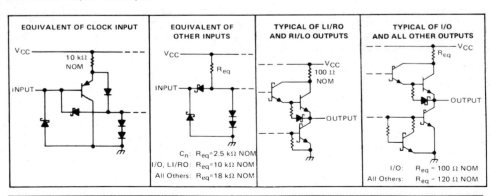

FUNCTION TABLES

TABLE 1 – ARITHMETIC FUNCTIONS

Mode Control (M) = Low

ALU SELECTION			ACTIVE-HIGH DATA	
AS2	AS1	AS0	C_n = H (with carry)	C_n = L (no carry)
L	L	L	F_j = L	F_j = H
L	L	H	F = B MINUS A	F = B MINUS A MINUS 1
L	H	L	F = A MINUS B	F = A MINUS B MINUS 1
L	H	H	F = A PLUS B PLUS 1	F = A PLUS B
H	L	L	F = B PLUS 1	$F_j = B_j$
H	L	H	F = $\overline{B}$ PLUS 1	$F_j = \overline{B}_j$
H	H	L	F = A PLUS 1	$F_j = A_j$
H	H	H	F = $\overline{A}$ PLUS 1	$F_j = \overline{A}_j$

TABLE 2 – LOGIC FUNCTIONS

Mode Control (M) = High

ALU SELECTION			ACTIVE-HIGH DATA	
AS2	AS1	AS0	C_n = H (with carry)	C_n = L (no carry)
L	L	L	F_0 = H, F_1 = F_2 = F_3 = L	F_j = L
L	L	H	$F_j = A_j \oplus B_j$ PLUS 1	$F_j = A_j \oplus B_j$
L	H	L	$F_j = \overline{A_j \oplus B_j}$ PLUS 1	$F_j = \overline{A_j \oplus B_j}$
L	H	H	F_j = L	F_j = H
H	L	L	$F_j = A_j B_j$ PLUS 1	$F_j = A_j B_j$
H	L	H	$F_j = \overline{A_j + B_j}$ PLUS 1	$F_j = \overline{A_j + B_j}$
H	H	L	$F_j = \overline{A_j B_j}$ PLUS 1	$F_j = \overline{A_j B_j}$
H	H	H	$F_j = A_j + B_j$ PLUS 1	$F_j = A_j + B_j$

TABLE 3 – REGISTER FUNCTIONS

FUNCTION	INPUTS BEFORE L TO H CLOCK TRANSITION								INTERNAL OUTPUTS AFTER L TO H CLOCK TRANSITION												
	REGISTER SELECTION			DATA INPUTS						A REGISTER				B SHIFT REGISTER						ALU			
	RS2	RS1	RS0	LI/RO	I/O 3	I/O 2	I/O 1	I/O 0	RI/LO	QA3	QA2	QA1	QA0	LI/RO	QB3	QB2	QB1	QB0	RI/LO	F3	F2	F1	F0
ACCUM	L	L	L	Z	F3	F2	F1	F0	Z	$QA3_0$	$QA2_0$	$QA1_0$	$QA0_0$	Z	$F3_n$	$F2_n$	$F1_n$	$F0_n$	Z	F3	F2	F1	F0
LOAD B	L	L	H	Z	b3	b2	b1	b0	Z	$QA3_0$	$QA2_0$	$QA1_0$	$QA0_0$	Z	b3	b2	b1	b0	Z	Z	Z	Z	Z
LEFT SHIFT LOGICAL	L	H	L	li	F3	F2	F1	F0	QB0	$QA3_0$	$QA2_0$	$QA1_0$	$QA0_0$	li	li	$QB3_n$	$QB2_n$	$QB1_n$	$QB1_n$	F3	F2	F1	F0
LEFT SHIFT ARITH	L	H	H	li	F3	F2	F1	F0	QB0	$QA3_0$	$QA2_0$	$QA1_0$	$QA0_0$	li	$QB3_n$	li	$QB2_n$	$QB1_n$	$QB1_n$	F3	F2	F1	F0
RIGHT SHIFT LOGICAL	H	L	L	QB3	F3	F2	F1	F0	ri	$QA3_0$	$QA2_0$	$QA1_0$	$QA0_0$	$QB2_n$	$QB2_n$	$QB1_n$	$QB0_n$	ri	ri	F3	F2	F1	F0
RIGHT SHIFT ARITH	H	L	H	QB2	F3	F2	F1	F0	ri	$QA3_0$	$QA2_0$	$QA1_0$	$QA0_0$	$QB1_n$	$QB3_n$	$QB1_n$	$QB0_n$	ri	ri	F3	F2	F1	F0
HOLD	H	H	L	Z	F3	F2	F1	F0	Z	$QA3_0$	$QA2_0$	$QA1_0$	$QA0_0$	Z	$QB3_0$	$QB2_0$	$QB1_0$	$QB0_0$	Z	$F3_0$	$F2_0$	$F1_0$	$F0_0$
LOAD A	H	H	H	Z	a3	a2	a1	a0	Z	a3	a2	a1	a0	Z	$QB3_0$	$QB2_0$	$QB1_0$	$QB0_0$	Z	Z	Z	Z	Z

H = high level (steady state)

L = low level (steady state)

Z = high impedance (output off)

a0 . . . a3, b0 . . . b3 = the level of steady - state condition at I/O 0 thru I/O 3, respectively and intended as A or B input data

F0 . . . F3 = internal ALU results

$QA0_0$ . . . $QB0_0$, $F0_0$ . . . $F3_0$ = the level of QA0 thru QB3 and F0 thru F3, respectively, before the indicated steady-state input conditions were established

$QA0_n$ . . . $QB3_n$ = the level of QA0 thru QB3 before the most recent ↑ transition of the clock

ri, li = the level of steady-state conditions at RI/LO or LI/RO, respectively

3

TTL DEVICES

TEXAS
INSTRUMENTS

3-1081

logic symbol

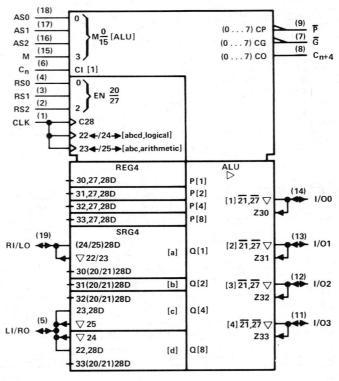

Pin numbers shown on logic notation are for DW, J or N packages.

absolute maximum ratings over operating free-air temperature range (unless otherwise noted)

Supply voltage, V_{CC} (see Note 1) . . . . 7 V
Input voltage . . . . 7 V
Operating free-air temperature range: SN54LS681 . . . . −55°C to 125°C
SN74LS681 . . . . 0°C to 70°C
Storage temperature range . . . . −65°C to 150°C

NOTE 1: Voltage values are with respect to the network ground terminal.

TEXAS
INSTRUMENTS

recommended operating conditions

		SN54LS681 MIN	NOM	MAX	SN74LS681 MIN	NOM	MAX	UNIT
Supply voltage, V_{CC}		4.5	5	5.5	4.75	5	5.25	V
High-level output current, I_{OH}	LI/RO, I/O, RI/LO			−1			−2.6	mA
	$\overline{P}, \overline{G}, C_{n+4}$			−0.4			−0.4	mA
Low-level output current, I_{OL}	I/O			12			24	
	C_{n+4}, LI/RO, RI/LO			4			8	mA
	$\overline{P}$			8			8	
	$\overline{G}$			16			16	
Clock frequency, f_{clock}		0	20		0		20	MHz
Width of clock pulse, $t_{w(clock)}$		25			25			ns
Setup time, t_{su}	RS0-RS2 to CLK↑	30			30			ns
	Data I/O to CLK↑	25			25			
Hold time, t_h		0			0			ns
Operating free-air temperature, T_A		−55		125	0		70	°C

electrical characteristics over recommended operating free-air temperature range (unless otherwise noted)

PARAMETER		TEST CONDITIONS[†]		SN54LS681 MIN	TYP[‡]	MAX	SN74LS681 MIN	TYP[‡]	MAX	UNIT
V_{IH}	High-level input voltage			2			2			V
V_{IL} Low-level input voltage	C_n					0.7			0.7	V
	All others					0.7			0.8	
V_{IK}	Input clamp voltage	V_{CC}=MIN, I_I=−18 mA				−1.5			−1.5	V
V_{OH} High-level output voltage	All I/O	V_{CC}=MIN, V_{IH}=2 V, $V_{IL}=V_{IL}$ max,		2.4	3.1		2.4	3.2		V
	$\overline{P}, \overline{G}, C_{n+4}$	I_{OH}=MAX		2.5	3.4		2.7	3.4		
V_{OL} Low-level output voltage	I/O	V_{CC}=MAX, V_{IH}=2 V, $V_{IL}=V_{IL}$ max	I_{OL}=12 mA		0.25	0.4		0.25	0.4	V
			I_{OL}=24 mA					0.35	0.5	
	LI/RO, RI/LO, C_{n+4}		I_{OL}=4 mA		0.25	0.4		0.25	0.4	
			I_{OL}=8 mA					0.35	0.5	
	$\overline{P}$		I_{OL}=8 mA		0.35	0.5		0.35	0.5	
	$\overline{G}$		I_{OL}=16 mA		0.35	0.5		0.35	0.5	
I_{OZH} Off-state output current, high-level voltage applied	I/O, LI/RO, RI/LO	V_{CC}=MAX, V_{IH}=2 V, $V_{IL}=V_{IL}$ max, V_O=2.7 V				40			40	µA
I_{OZL} Off-state output current, low-level voltage applied	I/O, LI/RO	V_{CC}=MAX, V_{IH}=2 V, $V_{IL}=V_{IL}$ max, V_O=0.4 V				−0.8			−0.8	mA
	RI/LO					−0.4			−0.4	
I_I Input current at maximim input voltage	All I/O	V_{CC}=MAX	V_I=5.5 V			0.1			0.1	mA
	C_n		V_I=7 V			0.5			0.5	
	All others					0.1			0.1	
I_{IH} High-level input current	C_n	V_{CC}=MAX, V_I=2.7 V				100			100	µA
	All I/O					40			40	
	All others					20			20	
I_{IL} Low-level input current	C_n	V_{CC}=MAX, V_I=0.4 V				−4			−4	mA
	I/O, LI/RO					−0.8			−0.8	
	CLK					−0.2			−0.2	
	All others					−0.4			−0.4	
I_{OS} Short-circuit output current[§]	I/O	V_{CC}=MAX		−30		−130	−30		−130	mA
	LI/RO, RI/LO, $\overline{P}, \overline{G}, C_{n+4}$			−20		−100	−20		−100	
I_{CC}	Supply current	V_{CC}=MAX, RS0 at 4.5 V, All other I/O at 0 V			100	150		100	150	mA

[†] For conditions shown as MIN or MAX, use the appropriate value specified under recommended operations.
[‡] All typical values are at V_{CC} = 5 V, T_A = 25 °C.
[§] Not more than one output should be shorted at a time, and duration of the short circuit should not exceed one second.

3

TTL DEVICES

switching characteristics, V_{CC} = 5 V, T_A = 25°C

PARAMETER¶	FROM (INPUT)	TO (OUTPUT)	TEST CONDITIONS		MIN	TYP	MAX	UNIT
t_{PLH}	CLOCK↑	$\overline{P}$	R_L = 667 Ω,	C_L = 45 pF		25	40	ns
t_{PHL}						30	45	
t_{PLH}		$\overline{G}$	R_L = 667 Ω,	C_L = 45 pF		26	40	ns
t_{PHL}						27	40	
t_{PLH}		I/O				27	40	ns
t_{PHL}						29	40	
t_{PLH}		C_n+4				36	55	ns
t_{PHL}						34	50	
t_{PLH}		LI/R0	R_L = 2 kΩ,	C_L = 15 pF		25	40	ns
t_{PHL}						23	35	
t_{PLH}		RI/L0				19	30	ns
t_{PHL}						17	30	
t_{PLH}	AS0-AS2	$\overline{P}$	R_L = 667 Ω,	C_L = 45 pF		30	45	ns
t_{PHL}						30	45	
t_{PLH}		$\overline{G}$	R_L = 667 Ω,	C_L = 45 pF		27	35	ns
t_{PHL}						28	35	
t_{PLH}		I/O				31	45	ns
t_{PHL}						29	45	
t_{PLH}		C_n+4	R_L = 2 kΩ,	C_L = 15 pF		39	55	ns
t_{PHL}						34	50	
t_{PLH}	C_n	$\overline{P}$	R_L = 667 Ω,	C_L = 45 pF		9	25	ns
t_{PHL}						9	20	
t_{PLH}		I/O				17	35	ns
t_{PHL}						13	20	
t_{PLH}		C_n+4	R_L = 2 kΩ,	C_L = 15 pF		20	30	ns
t_{PHL}						16	25	
t_{PLH}	MODE	$\overline{P}$	R_L = 667 Ω,	C_L = 45 pF		28	40	ns
t_{PHL}						29	40	
t_{PLH}		$\overline{G}$	R_L = 667 Ω,	C_L = 45 pF		21	30	ns
t_{PHL}						23	30	
t_{PLH}		I/O				30	45	ns
t_{PHL}						28	40	
t_{PLH}		C_n+4	R_L = 2 kΩ,	C_L = 15 pF		40	60	ns
t_{PHL}						37	50	
t_{PZH}	RS0-RS2	I/O	R_L = 667 Ω	C_L = 45 pF		28	45	ns
t_{PZL}						28	45	
t_{PHZ}				C_L = 5 pF		35	65	ns
t_{PLZ}						39	65	
t_{PZH}		LI/R0	R_L = 2 kΩ	C_L = 15 pF		25	40	ns
t_{PZL}						22	40	
t_{PHZ}				C_L = 5 pF		21	40	ns
t_{PLZ}						34	60	
t_{PZH}		RI/L0	R_L = 2 kΩ	C_L = 15 pF		22	40	ns
t_{PZL}						24	40	
t_{PHZ}				C_L = 5 pF		11	30	ns
t_{PLZ}						16	40	

¶ t_{PLH} = Propagation delay time, low-to-high-level input
t_{PHL} = Propagation delay time, high-to-low-level input
t_{PZL} = Output enable time to low level
t_{PZH} = Output enable time to high level
t_{PLZ} = Output disable time from low level
t_{PHZ} = Output disable time from high level

NOTE 2: See General Information Section for load circuits and voltage waveforms.

TEXAS
INSTRUMENTS

- Compares Two 8-Bit Words
- Choice of Totem-Pole or Open-Collector Outputs
- Hysteresis at P and Q Inputs
- 'LS682 and 'LS683 have 20-kΩ Pullup Resistors on the Q Inputs
- 'LS686 and 'LS687 . . . New JT and NT 24-Pin, 3000-Mil Packages

TYPE	P = Q	P > Q	OUTPUT ENABLE	OUTPUT CONFIGURATION	20-kΩ PULLUP
'LS682	yes	yes	no	totem-pole	yes
'LS683	yes	yes	no	open-collector	yes
'LS684	yes	yes	no	totem-pole	no
'LS685	yes	yes	no	open-collector	no
'LS686	yes	yes	yes	totem-pole	no
'LS687	yes	yes	yes	open-collector	no
'LS688	yes	no	yes	totem-pole	no
'LS689	yes	no	yes	open-collector	no

SN54LS686, SN54LS687 . . . JT PACKAGE
SN74LS686, SN74LS687 . . . DW, JT OR NT PACKAGE
(TOP VIEW)

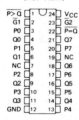

SN54LS686, SN54LS687 . . . FK PACKAGE
SN74LS686, SN74LS687 . . . FN PACKAGE
(TOP VIEW)

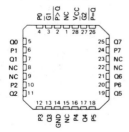

NC - No internal connection

SN54LS682 THRU SN54LS685 . . . J PACKAGE
SN74LS682 THRU SN74LS685 . . . DW, J OR N PACKAGE
(TOP VIEW)

SN54LS682 THRU SN54LS685 . . . FK PACKAGE
SN74LS682 THRU SN74LS685 . . . FK PACKAGE
(TOP VIEW)

SN54LS688, SN54LS689 . . . J PACKAGE
SN74LS688, SN74LS689 . . . DW, J OR N PACKAGE
(TOP VIEW)

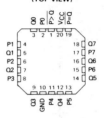

SN54LS688, SN54LS689 . . . FK PACKAGE
SN74LS688, SN74LS689
(TOP VIEW)

3

TTL DEVICES

TEXAS
INSTRUMENTS

TYPES SN54LS682 THRU SN54LS689, SN74LS682 THRU SN74LS689
8–BIT MAGNITUDE/IDENTITY COMPARATORS

description

These magnitude comparators perform comparisons of two eight-bit binary or BCD words. All types provide $\overline{P = Q}$ outputs and the 'LS682 thru 'LS687 provide $\overline{P > Q}$ outputs as well. The 'LS682, 'LS684, 'LS686, and 'LS688 have totem-pole outputs, while the 'LS683, 'LS685, 'LS687, and 'LS689 have open-collector outputs. The 'LS682 and 'LS683 feature 20-kΩ pullup termination resistors on the Q inputs for analog or switch data.

FUNCTION TABLE

INPUTS			OUTPUTS	
DATA	ENABLES			
P, Q	$\overline{G}$, $\overline{G1}$	$\overline{G2}$	$\overline{P = Q}$	$\overline{P > Q}$
P = Q	L	X	L	H
P > Q	X	L	H	L
P < Q	X	X	H	H
P = Q	H	X	H	H
P > Q	X	H	H	H
X	H	H	H	H

NOTES: 1. The last three lines of the function table applies only to the devices having enable inputs, i.e., 'LS686 thru 'LS689.
2. The P < Q function can be generated by applying the P = Q and P > Q outputs to a 2-input NAND gate.
3. For 'LS686, 'LS687 G1 enables P = Q, and G2 enables P > Q.

logic symbols

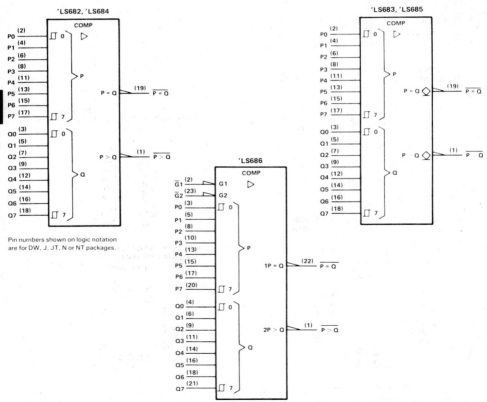

Pin numbers shown on logic notation are for DW, J, JT, N or NT packages.

TEXAS INSTRUMENTS

logic symbols (continued)

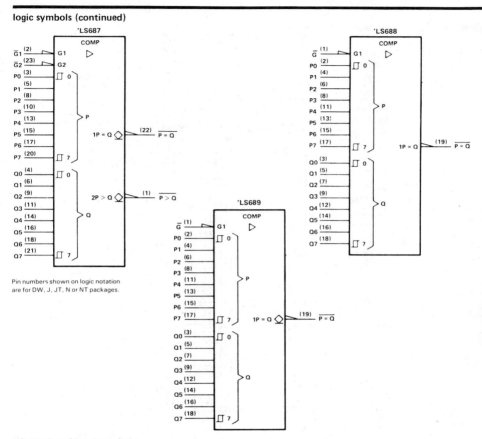

Pin numbers shown on logic notation
are for DW, J, JT, N or NT packages.

schematics of inputs and outputs

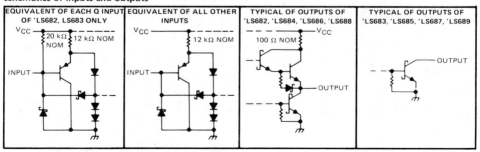

EQUIVALENT OF EACH Q INPUT OF 'LS682, LS683 ONLY	EQUIVALENT OF ALL OTHER INPUTS	TYPICAL OF OUTPUTS OF 'LS682, 'LS684, 'LS686, 'LS688	TYPICAL OF OUTPUTS OF 'LS683, 'LS685, 'LS687, 'LS689

'LS682 thru 'LS685 logic diagram (positive logic)

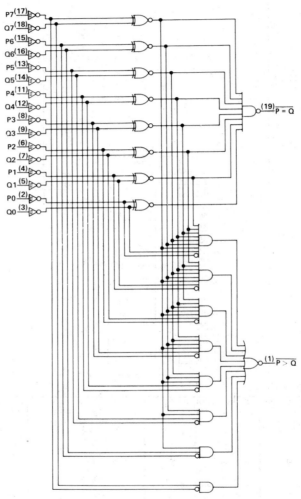

Pin numbers shown on logic notation are for DW, J or N packages

TEXAS
INSTRUMENTS

'LS686, 'LS687 logic diagram (positive logic)

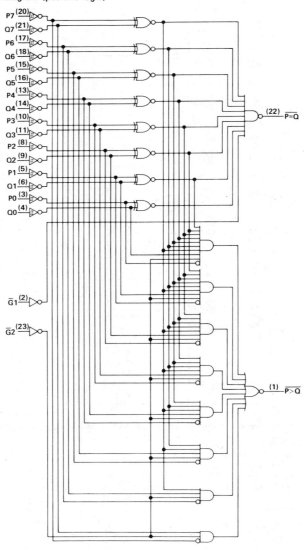

Pin numbers shown on logic notation are for DW, JT, or NT packages.

'LS688, 'LS689 logic diagram (positive logic)

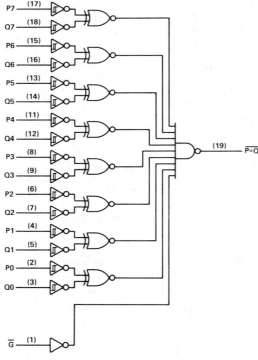

Pin numbers shown on logic notation are for DW, J or N packages.

absolute maximum ratings over operating free-air temperature range (unless otherwise noted)

Supply voltage (see Note 1)	7 V
Input voltage: Q inputs of 'LS682 and 'LS683	5.5 V
All other inputs	7 V
Off-state output voltage: 'LS683, 'LS685, 'LS687, 'LS689	7 V
Operating free-air temperature range: SN54LS682 thru SN54LS689	−55°C to 125°C
SN74LS682 thru SN74LS689	0°C to 70°C
Storage temperature range	−65°C to 150°C

NOTE 1: Voltage values are with respect to network ground terminal.

TEXAS
INSTRUMENTS

'LS682, 'LS684, 'LS686, 'LS688

recommended operating conditions

	SN54LS' MIN	SN54LS' NOM	SN54LS' MAX	SN74LS' MIN	SN74LS' NOM	SN74LS' MAX	UNIT
Supply voltage, V_{CC}	4.5	5	5.5	4.75	5	5.25	V
High-level output current, I_{OH}			−400			−400	µA
Low-level output current, I_{OL}			12			24	mA
Operating free-air temperature, T_A	−55		125	0		70	°C

electrical characteristics over recommended operating free-air temperature range (unless otherwise noted)

PARAMETER		TEST CONDITIONS[†]		SN54LS' MIN	SN54LS' TYP[‡]	SN54LS' MAX	SN74LS' MIN	SN74LS' TYP[‡]	SN74LS' MAX	UNIT
V_{IH}	High-level input voltage			2			2			V
V_{IL}	Low-level input voltage					0.7			0.8	V
$V_{T+} - V_{T-}$	Hysteresis P or Q inputs	V_{CC} = MIN			0.4			0.4		V
V_{IK}	Input clamp voltage	V_{CC} = MIN,	I_I = −18 mA			−1.5			−1.5	V
V_{OH}	High-level output voltage	V_{CC} = MIN, V_{IL} = V_{IL}max,	V_{IH} = 2 V, I_{OH} = −400 µA	2.5			2.7			V
V_{OL}	Low-level output voltage	V_{CC} = MIN, V_{IH} = 2 V, V_{IL} = V_{IL}max	I_{OL} = 12 mA		0.25	0.4		0.25	0.4	V
			I_{OL} = 24 mA					0.35	0.5	
I_I	Input current at maximum input voltage Q inputs, 'LS682	V_{CC} = MAX,	V_I = 5.5 V			0.1			0.1	mA
	All other inputs	V_{CC} = MAX,	V_I = 7 V							
I_{IH}	High-level input current	V_{CC} = MAX,	V_I = 2.7 V			20			20	µA
I_{IL}	Low-level input current Q inputs, 'LS682	V_{CC} = MAX,	V_I = 0.4 V			−0.4			−0.4	mA
	All other inputs					−0.2			−0.2	
I_{OS}[§]	Short-circuit output current	V_{CC} = MAX,	V_O = 0	−20		−100	−20		−100	mA
I_{CC}	Supply current 'LS682	V_{CC} = MAX,	See Note 2		42	70		42	70	mA
	'LS684				40	65		40	65	
	'LS686				44	75		44	75	
	'LS688				40	65		40	65	

‡All typical values are at V_{CC} = 5 V, T_A = 25°C.
§ Not more than one output should be shorted at a time, and duration of the short-circuit should not exceed one second.
NOTE 2: I_{CC} is measured with any $\overline{G}$ inputs grounded, all other inputs at 4.5 V, and all outputs open.

switching characteristics, V_{CC} = 5 V, T_A = 25°C

PARAMETER[#]	FROM (INPUTS)	TO (OUTPUT)	TEST CONDITIONS	'LS682 MIN	'LS682 TYP	'LS682 MAX	'LS684 MIN	'LS684 TYP	'LS684 MAX	'LS686 MIN	'LS686 TYP	'LS686 MAX	'LS688 MIN	'LS688 TYP	'LS688 MAX	UNIT
t_{PLH}	P	$\overline{P = Q}$			13	25		15	25		13	25		18	27	ns
t_{PHL}					15	25		17	25		20	30		20	30	
t_{PLH}	Q	$\overline{P = Q}$			14	25		16	25		13	25		18	27	ns
t_{PHL}					15	25		15	25		21	30		20	30	
t_{PLH}	$\overline{G}$, $\overline{G}$1	$\overline{P = Q}$	R_L = 667 Ω, C_L = 45 pF,								11	20		12	18	ns
t_{PHL}			All other inputs low,								19	30		13	20	
t_{PLH}	P	$\overline{P > Q}$	See Note 3		20	30		22	30		19	30				ns
t_{PHL}					15	30		17	30		15	30				
t_{PLH}	Q	$\overline{P > Q}$			21	30		24	30		18	30				ns
t_{PHL}					19	30		20	30		19	30				
t_{PLH}	$\overline{G}$2	$\overline{P > Q}$									21	30				ns
t_{PHL}											16	25				

#t_{PLH} ≡ propagation delay time, low-to-high-level outputs; t_{PHL} ≡ propagation delay time, high-to-low-level output.
NOTE 3: See General Information Section for load circuits and voltage waveforms.

TEXAS INSTRUMENTS

recommended operating conditions 'LS683, 'LS685, 'LS687, 'LS689

	SN54LS'			SN74LS'			UNIT
	MIN	NOM	MAX	MIN	NOM	MAX	
Supply voltage, V_{CC}	4.5	5	5.5	4.75	5	5.25	V
High-level output voltage, V_{OH}			5.5			5.5	V
Low-level output current, I_{OL}			12			24	mA
Operating free-air temperature, T_A	−55		125	0		70	°C

electrical characteristics over recommended operating free-air temperature range (unless otherwise noted)

PARAMETER		TEST CONDITIONS†		SN54LS'			SN74LS'			UNIT
				MIN	TYP‡	MAX	MIN	TYP‡	MAX	
V_{IH}	High-level input voltage			2			2			V
V_{IL}	Low-level input voltage					0.7			0.8	V
$V_{T+} - V_{T-}$	Hysteresis	P or Q inputs	V_{CC} = MIN	0.4			0.4			V
V_{IK}	Input clamp voltage		V_{CC} = MIN, $I_I = -18$ mA			−1.5			−1.5	V
I_{OH}	High-level output voltage		V_{CC} = MIN, $V_{IH} = 2$ V, $V_{IL} = V_{IL}$max, $V_{OH} = 5.5$ V			250			100	μA
V_{OL}	Low-level output voltage		V_{CC} = MIN, $V_{IH} = 2$ V, $V_{IL} = V_{IL}$max	$I_{OL} = 12$ mA	0.25	0.4		0.25	0.4	V
				$I_{OL} = 24$ mA				0.35	0.5	
I_I	Input current at maximum input voltage	Q inputs, 'LS683	V_{CC} = MAX, $V_I = 5.5$ V		0.1			0.1		mA
		All other inputs	V_{CC} = MAX, $V_I = 7$ V							
I_{IH}	High-level input current		V_{CC} = MAX, $V_I = 2.7$ V			20			20	μA
I_{IL}	Low-level input current	Q inputs, 'LS683	V_{CC} = MAX, $V_I = 0.4$ V			−0.4			−0.4	mA
		All other inputs				−0.2			−0.2	
I_{CC}	Supply current	'LS683	V_{CC} = MAX, See Note 2		42	70		42	70	mA
		'LS685			40	65		40	65	
		'LS687			44	75		44	75	
		'LS689			40	65		40	65	

†For conditions shown as MIN or MAX, use the appropriate value specified under recommended operating conditions.
‡All typical values are at V_{CC} = 5 V, T_A = 25°C.
NOTE 2: I_{CC} is measured with any $\overline{G}$ inputs grounded, all other inputs at 4.5 V, and all outputs open.

switching characteristics, V_{CC} = 5 V, T_A = 25°C

PARAMETER¶	FROM (INPUTS)	TO (OUTPUT)	TEST CONDITIONS	'LS683			'LS685			'LS687			'LS689			UNIT
				MIN	TYP	MAX	MIN	TYP	MAX	MIN	TYP	MAX	MIN	TYP	MAX	
t_{PLH}	P	$\overline{P = Q}$	$R_L = 667$ Ω, $C_L = 45$ pF, All other inputs low, See Note 3		30	45		30	45		24	35		24	40	ns
t_{PHL}					20	30		19	35		20	30		22	35	
t_{PLH}	Q	$\overline{P = Q}$			24	35		24	45		24	35		24	40	ns
t_{PHL}					23	35		23	35		20	30		22	35	
t_{PLH}	$\overline{G}, \overline{G}1$	$\overline{P = Q}$									21	35		22	35	ns
t_{PHL}											18	30		19	30	
t_{PLH}	P	$\overline{P > Q}$			31	45		32	45		24	35				ns
t_{PHL}					17	30		16	35		16	30				
t_{PLH}	Q	$\overline{P > Q}$			30	45		30	45		24	35				ns
t_{PHL}					21	30		20	35		16	30				
t_{PLH}	$\overline{G}2$	$\overline{P > Q}$									24	35				ns
t_{PHL}											15	30				

¶ $t_{PLH} \equiv$ propagation delay time, low-to-high-level output; $t_{PHL} \equiv$ propagation delay time, high-to-low-level output.
NOTE 3: See General Information Section for load circuits and voltage waveforms.

3 TTL DEVICES

TYPES SN54LS690, SN54LS691, SN54LS693, SN74LS690, SN74LS691, SN74LS693
SYNCHRONOUS COUNTERS WITH OUTPUT REGISTERS
AND MULTIPLEXED 3-STATE OUTPUTS

D2423, JANUARY 1981

- **4-Bit Counters/Registers**
- **Multiplexed Outputs for Counter of Latched Data**
- **3-State Outputs Drive Bus Lines Directly**
- **'LS690 .. Decade Counter, Direct Clear**
  'LS691 .. Binary Counter, Direct Clear
  'LS693 .. Binary Counter, Synchronous Clear

description

These low-power Schottky LSI devices incorporate synchronous counters, four-bit D-type registers, and quadruple two-line to one-line multiplexers with three-state outputs in a single 20-pin package. The counters can be programmed from the data inputs and have enable P inputs and enable T inputs and a ripple-carry output for easy expansion. The register/counter select input, R/C̄, selects the counter when low or the register when high for the three-state outputs, Q_A, Q_B, Q_C, and Q_D. These outputs are rated at 12 and 24 milliamperes (54LS/74LS) for good bus-driving performance.

Individual clock and clear inputs are provided for both the counter and the register. Both clock inputs are positive-edge triggered: The clear line is active low and is asynchronous on the 'LS690 and 'LS691, synchronous on the 'LS693. Loading of the counter is accomplished when LOAD is taken low and a positive-transition occurs on the counter clock CCK.

Expansion is easily accomplished by connecting RCO of the first stage to ENT of the second stage, etc. All ENP inputs can be tied common and used as a master enable or disable control.

SN54LS690, SN54LS691, SN54LS693 ... J PACKAGE
SN74LS690, SN74LS691,
SN74LS693 ... DW, J OR N PACKAGE
(TOP VIEW)

CCLR̄	1	20	V_{CC}
CCK	2	19	RCO
A	3	18	Q_A
B	4	17	Q_B
C	5	16	Q_C
D	6	15	Q_D
ENP	7	14	ENT
RCLR̄	8	13	LOAD̄
RCK	9	12	Ḡ
GND	10	11	R/C̄

SN54LS690, SN54LS691, SN54LS693 ... FK PACKAGE
SN74LS690, SN74LS691, SN74LS693
(TOP VIEW)

Pins (clockwise): A, CCK, CCLR̄, V_{CC}, RCO (top row 3 2 1 20 19)

B	4	18	Q_A
C	5	17	Q_B
D	6	16	Q_C
ENP	7	15	Q_D
RCLR̄	8	14	ENT

Bottom pins (9 10 11 12 13): RCK, GND, R/C̄, Ḡ, LOAD̄

schematics of inputs and outputs

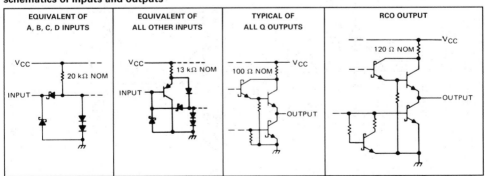

EQUIVALENT OF A, B, C, D INPUTS	EQUIVALENT OF ALL OTHER INPUTS	TYPICAL OF ALL Q OUTPUTS	RCO OUTPUT

PRODUCTION DATA
This document contains information current as of publication date. Products conform to specifications per the terms of Texas Instruments standard warranty. Production processing does not necessarily include testing of all parameters.

TEXAS
INSTRUMENTS

3-1093

TTL DEVICES — 3

logic diagrams

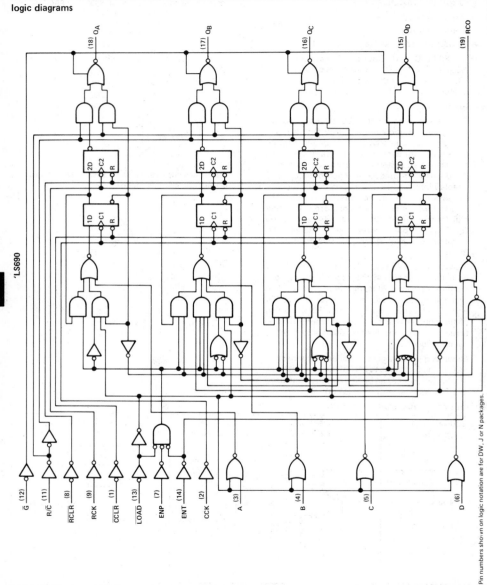

'LS690

TTL DEVICES

3

Pin numbers shown on logic notation are for DW, J or N packages.

TEXAS
INSTRUMENTS

logic diagrams (continued)

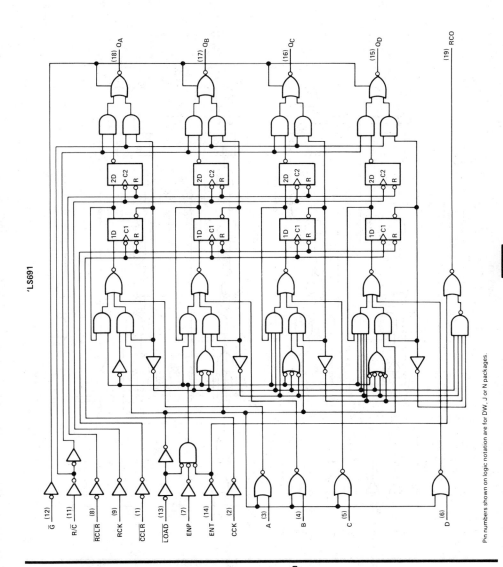

'LS691

Pin numbers shown on logic notation are for DW, J or N packages.

TTL DEVICES

3

3-1095

logic diagrams (continued)

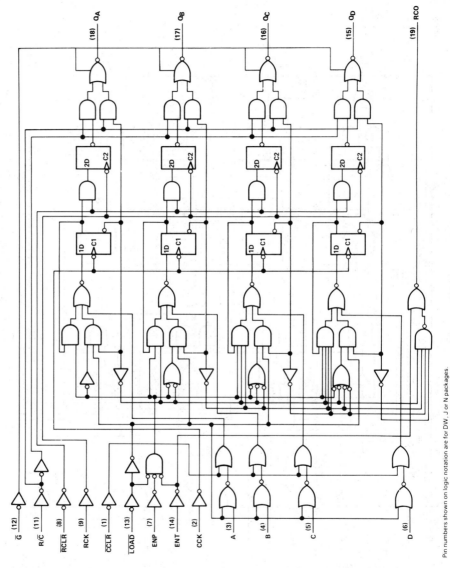

Pin numbers shown on logic notation are for DW, J or N packages

3 TTL DEVICES

'LS693

TEXAS
INSTRUMENTS

logic symbols

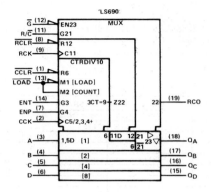

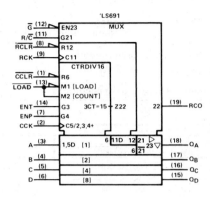

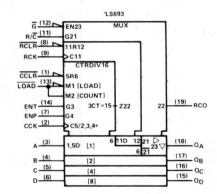

Pin numbers shown on logic notation are for DW, J or N packages.

3

TTL DEVICES

TEXAS
INSTRUMENTS

absolute maximum ratings over operating free-air temperature range (unless otherwise noted)

Supply voltage, V_{CC} (see Note 1) . . . . 7 V
Input voltage . . . . 7 V
Off-state output voltage . . . . 5.5 V
Operating free-air temperature range: SN54LS690, SN54LS691, SN54LS691 . . −55°C to 125°C
SN74LS690, SN74LS691, SN74LS693 . . . . . 0°C to 70°C
Storage temperature range . . . . −65°C to 150°C

Note 1: Voltage values are with respect to network ground terminal.

recommended operating conditions

			SN54LS' MIN	SN54LS' NOM	SN54LS' MAX	SN74LS' MIN	SN74LS' NOM	SN74LS' MAX	UNIT
V_{CC}	Supply voltage		4.5	5	5.5	4.75	5	5.25	V
V_{IH}	High-level input voltage		2			2			V
V_{IL}	Low-level input voltage				0.7			0.8	V
I_{OH}	High-level output current	Q			−1			−2.6	mA
		RCO			−0.4			−0.4	mA
I_{OL}	Low-level output current	Q			12			24	mA
		RCO			4			8	mA
f_{clock}	Clock frequency	CCK	0		20	0		20	MHz
		RCK	0		20	0		20	MHZ
t_w	Pulse duration	CCK high or low	25			25			ns
		RCK high or low	25			25			
	'LS690, 'LS691	$\overline{RCLR}$ low	20			20			
		$\overline{CCLR}$ low	20			20			
t_{su}	Setup time before CCK↑	A thru D	30			30			ns
		ENP or ENT	30			30			
		$\overline{LOAD}$↓	30			30			
	'LS693	$\overline{CCLR}$↓	40			40			
	'LS690, 'LS691	$\overline{CCLR}$↑ inactive	25			25			
t_{su}	Setup time before RCK↑	CCK↑ (see Note 2)	30			30			ns
	'LS690, 'LS691	$\overline{RCLR}$↑ inactive	25			25			
	'LS693	RCLR↓	20			20			
t_h	Hold time	Any input from CCK↑ or RCK↑	0			0			ns
T_A	Operating free-air temperature		−55		125	0		70	°C

NOTE 2: This set up time ensures the register will see stable data from the counter outputs. The clocks may be tied together in which case the register state will be one clock pulse behind the counter.

TEXAS
INSTRUMENTS

TYPES SN54LS690, SN54LS691, SN54LS693, SN74LS690, SN74LS691, SN74LS693
SYNCHRONOUS COUNTERS WITH OUTPUT REGISTERS
AND MULTIPLEXED 3-STATE OUTPUTS

electrical characteristics over recommended operating free-air temperature range (unless otherwise noted)

PARAMETER		TEST CONDITIONS†		SN54LS' MIN	TYP‡	MAX	SN74LS' MIN	TYP‡	MAX	UNIT
V_{IK}		V_{CC} = MIN, I_I = − 18 mA				− 1.5			− 1.5	V
V_{OH}	Any Q	V_{CC} = MIN, V_{IH} = 2 V, V_{IL} = MAX	I_{OH} = − 1 mA	2.4	3.1					V
	Any Q		I_{OH} = − 2.6 mA				2.4	3.1		
	RCO		I_{OH} = − 0.4 mA	2.5	3.2		2.7	3.2		
V_{OL}	Any Q	V_{CC} = MIN, V_{IH} = 2 V, V_{IL} = MAX	I_{OL} = 12 mA		0.25	0.4		0.25	0.4	V
	Any Q		I_{OL} = 24 mA					0.35	0.5	
	RCO		I_{OL} = 4 mA		0.25	0.4		0.25	0.4	
	RCO		I_{OL} = 8 mA					0.35	0.5	
I_{OZH}	Any Q	V_{CC} = MAX, V_{IH} = 2 V, V_{IL} = MAX, V_O = 2.7 V				20			20	µA
I_{OZL}	Any Q	V_{CC} = MAX, V_{IH} = 2 V, V_{IL} = MAX, V_O = 0.4 V				− 20			− 20	µA
I_I		V_{CC} = MAX, V_I = 7 V				0.1			0.1	mA
I_{IH}		V_{CC} = MAX, V_I = 2.7 V				20			20	µA
I_{IL}	A thru D	V_{CC} = MAX, V_I = 0.4 V				− 0.4			− 0.4	mA
	All others					− 0.2			− 0.2	
I_{OS}§	Any Q	V_{CC} = MAX, V_O = 0 V		− 30		− 130	− 30		− 130	mA
	RCO			− 20		− 100	− 20		− 100	
I_{CCH}		V_{CC} = MAX, All outputs open	See Note 3		46	65		46	65	mA
I_{CCL}			See Note 4		48	70		48	70	
I_{CCZ}			See Note 5		48	70		48	70	

† For conditions shown as MIN or MAX, use the appropriate value specified under recommended operating conditions.
‡ All typical values are at V_{CC} = 5 V, T_A = 25°C.
§ Not more than one output should be shorted at a time and duration of short-circuit should not exceed one second.

NOTES: 3. I_{CCH} is measured after two 4.5 V to 0-V to 4.5-V pulses have been applied to CCK and RCK while $\overline{G}$ is grounded and all other inputs are at 4.5 V.
4. I_{CCL} is measured after two 0-V to 4.5-V to 0-V pulses have been applied to CCK and RCK while all other inputs are grounded.
5. I_{CCZ} is measured after two 0-V to 4.5-V to 0-V pulses have been applied to CCK and RCK while $\overline{G}$ is at 4.5 V and all other inputs are grounded.

TEXAS INSTRUMENTS

TYPES SN54LS690, SN54LS691, SN54LS693, SN74LS690, SN74LS691, SN74LS693
SYNCHRONOUS COUNTERS WITH OUTPUT REGISTERS
AND MULTIPLEXED 3-STATE OUTPUTS

switching characteristics, V_{CC} = 5 V, T_A = 25°C (see note 6)

PARAMETER	FROM (INPUT)	TO (OUTPUT)	TEST CONDITIONS	'LS690, 'LS691 MIN	TYP	MAX	'LS693 MIN	TYP	MAX	UNIT
t_{PLH}	CCK↑	RCO	R_L = 2 kΩ, C_L = 15 pF		23	40		23	40	ns
t_{PHL}					23	40		23	40	
t_{PLH}	ENT	RCO			13	20		13	20	ns
t_{PHL}					13	20		13	20	
t_{PLH}	CCK↑	Q			12	20		12	20	ns
t_{PHL}					17	25		17	25	
t_{PLH}	RCK↑	Q			12	20		12	20	ns
t_{PHL}					17	25		17	25	
t_{PHL}	$\overline{CCLR}$↓	Q			23	40				ns
t_{PHL}	$\overline{RCLR}$↓	Q	R_L = 667 Ω, C_L = 45 pF		20	30				ns
t_{PLH}	R/$\overline{C}$	Q			16	25		16	25	ns
t_{PHL}					16	25		16	25	
t_{PZH}	$\overline{G}$↓	Q			19	30		19	30	ns
t_{PZL}					19	30		19	30	
t_{PHZ}	$\overline{G}$↑	Q	R_L = 667 Ω, C_L = 5 pF		17	30		17	30	ns
t_{PLZ}					17	30		17	30	

NOTE 6: See General Information Section for load circuits and voltage waveforms.

t_{PLH} ≐ Propagation delay time, low-to-high-level output
t_{PHL} ≐ Propagation delay time, high-to-low-level output
t_{PZH} ≐ Output enable time to high level
t_{PZL} ≐ Output enable time to low level
t_{PHZ} ≐ Output disable time from high level
t_{PLZ} ≐ Output disable time from low level

3

TTL DEVICES

TEXAS
INSTRUMENTS

typical operating sequences

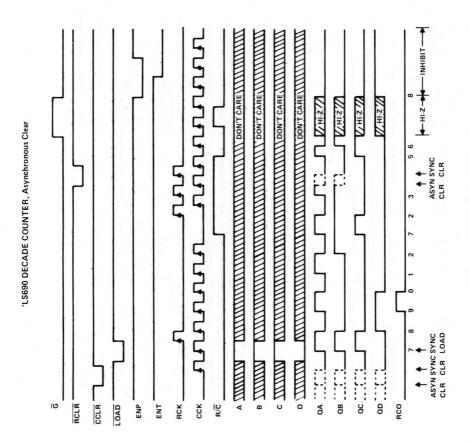

'LS690 DECADE COUNTER, Asynchronous Clear

TTL DEVICES

3

typical operating sequences (continued)

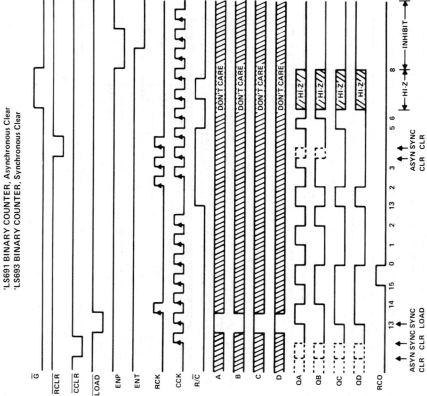

TYPES SN54LS696, SN54LS697, SN54LS699, SN74LS696, SN74LS697, SN74LS699
SYNCHRONOUS UP/DOWN COUNTERS
WITH OUTPUT REGISTERS AND MULTIPLEXED 3-STATE OUTPUTS

D2424, JANUARY 1981

- **4-Bit Counters/Registers**
- **Multiplexed Outputs for Counter of Latched Data**
- **3-State Outputs Drive Bus Lines Directly**
- **'LS696 .. Decade Counter, Direct Clear**
  'LS697 .. Binary Counter, Direct Clear
  'LS699 .. Binary Counter, Synchronous Clear

SN54LS696, SN54LS697, SN54LS699 ... J PACKAGE
SN74LS696, SN74LS697,
SN74LS699 ... DW, J OR N PACKAGE
(TOP VIEW)

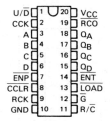

SN54LS696, SN54LS697, SN54LS699 ... FK PACKAGE
SN74LS696, SN74LS697, SN74LS699
(TOP VIEW)

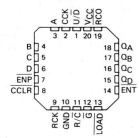

description

These low-power Schottky LSI devices incorporate synchronous up/down counter, four-bit D-type registers, and quadruple two-line to one-line multiplexers with three-state outputs in a single 20-pin package. The up/down counters are programmable from the data inputs and feature enable $\overline{P}$ and enable $\overline{T}$ and a ripple-carry output for easy expansion. The register/counter select input R/$\overline{C}$, selects the counter when low and the register when high for the three-state outputs, Q_A, Q_B, Q_C, and Q_D. These outputs are rated at 12 and 24 milliamperes (54LS/74LS) for good bus driving performance.

Both the counter clock CCK and register clock RCK are positive-edge triggered. The counter clear $\overline{CCLR}$ is active low and is asynchronous on the 'LS696 and 'LS697, synchronous on the 'LS699. Loading of the counter is accomplished when $\overline{LOAD}$ is taken low and a positive transition occurs on the counter clock CCK.

Expansion is easily accomplished by connecting $\overline{RCO}$ of the first stage to $\overline{ENT}$ of the second stage, etc. All $\overline{ENP}$ inputs can be tied common and used as a master enable or disable control.

schematics of inputs and outputs

EQUIVALENT OF A, B, C, D INPUTS	EQUIVALENT OF ALL OTHER INPUTS	TYPICAL OF ALL Q OUTPUTS	RCO OUTPUT

TEXAS INSTRUMENTS

3 TTL DEVICES

logic symbols

'LS696

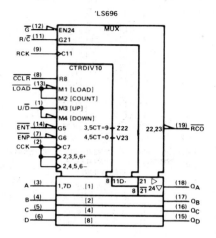

'LS697

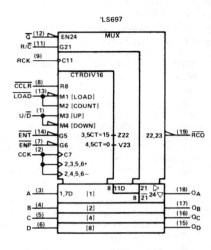

'LS699

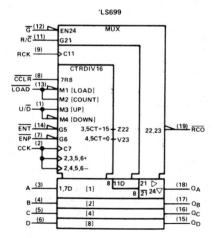

Pin numbers shown on logic notation are for DW, J or N packages.

TEXAS
INSTRUMENTS

logic diagrams

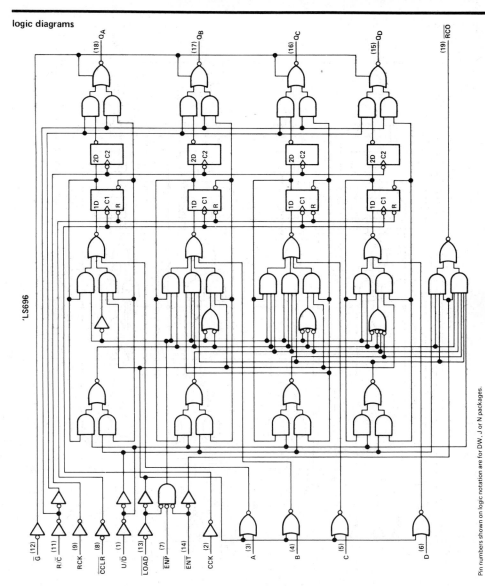

'LS696

TTL DEVICES

3

logic diagrams (continued)

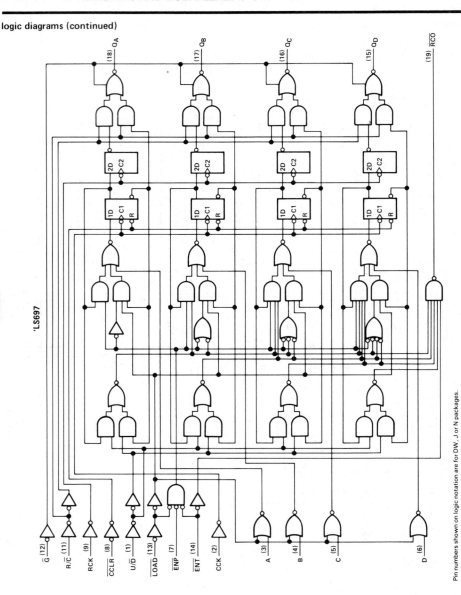

Pin numbers shown on logic notation are for DW, J or N packages.

'LS697

3

TTL DEVICES

TEXAS
INSTRUMENTS

logic diagrams (continued)

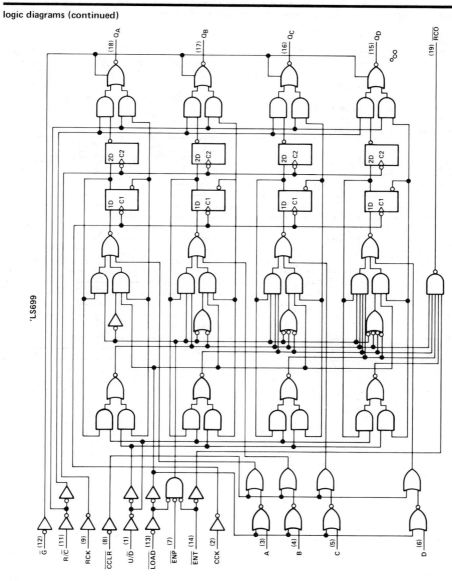

'LS699

Pin numbers shown on logic notation are for DW, J or N packages.

TTL DEVICES

3

TYPES SN54LS696, SN54LS697, SN54LS699, SN74LS696, SN74LS697, SN74LS699
SYNCHRONOUS UP/DOWN COUNTERS
WITH OUTPUT REGISTERS AND MULTIPLEXED 3-STATE OUTPUTS

absolute maximum ratings over operating free-air temperature range (unless otherwise noted)

Supply voltage, V_{CC} (see Note 1) .... 7 V
Input voltage .... 7 V
Off-state output voltage .... 5.5 V
Operating free-air temperature range: SN54LS696, SN54LS697, SN54LS699 .. −55°C to 125°C
SN74LS696, SN74LS697, SN74LS699 ..... 0°C to 70°C
Storage temperature range .... −65°C to 150°C

Note 1: Voltage values are with respect to network ground terminal.

recommended operating conditions

			SN54LS'			SN74LS'			UNIT
			MIN	NOM	MAX	MIN	NOM	MAX	
V_{CC}	Supply voltage		4.5	5	5.5	4.75	5	5.25	V
I_{OH}	High-level output current	Q			−1			−2.6	mA
		$\overline{RCO}$			−0.4			−0.4	
I_{OL}	Low-level output current	Q			12			24	mA
		$\overline{RCO}$			4			8	
f_{clock}	Clock frequency	CCK	0		20	0		20	MHz
		RCK	0		20	0		20	
t_w	Pulse duration	CCK high or low	25			25			ns
		RCK high or low	25			25			
		'LS696, 'LS697 $\overline{CCLR}$ low	20			20			
t_{su}	Setup time before CCK↑	A thru D	30			30			ns
		$\overline{ENP}$ or $\overline{ENT}$	30			30			
		$\overline{LOAD}$	30			30			
		$U/\overline{D}$	35			35			
		'LS696, 'LS697, $\overline{CCLR}$ inactive	25			25			
		'LS699, $\overline{CCLR}$	30			30			
t_{su}	Setup time CCK↑ before RCK↑ (see Note 2)		30			30			ns
t_h	Hold time		0			0			ns
T_A	Operating free-air temperature		−55		125	0		70	°C

NOTE 2: This set up time ensures the register will see stable data from the counter outputs. The clocks may be tied together in which case the register state will be one clock pulse behind the counter.

electrical characteristics over recommended operating free-air temperature range (unless otherwise noted)

PARAMETER		TEST CONDITIONS[†]		SN54LS' MIN	SN54LS' TYP[‡]	SN54LS' MAX	SN74LS' MIN	SN74LS' TYP[‡]	SN74LS' MAX	UNIT
V_{IH}	High-level input voltage			2			2			V
V_{IL}	Low-level input voltage					0.7			0.8	V
V_{IK}	Input clamp voltage	V_{CC}=MIN, I_I=−18 mA				−1.5			−1.5	V
V_{OH}	High-level output voltage	Any Q / V_{CC}=MIN, V_{IH}=2 V, V_{IL}=V_{IL} max	I_{OH}=−1 mA	2.4	3.1					V
		Any Q	I_{OH}=−2.6 mA				2.4	3.1		
		$\overline{RCO}$	I_{OH}=−400 μA	2.5	3.2		2.7	3.2		
V_{OL}	Low-level output voltage	Any Q / V_{CC}=MIN, V_{IH}=2 V, V_{IL}=V_{IL} max	I_{OL}=12 mA		0.25	0.4		0.25	0.4	V
		Any Q	I_{OL}=24 mA					0.35	0.5	
		$\overline{RCO}$	I_{OL}=4 mA		0.25	0.4		0.25	0.4	
		$\overline{RCO}$	I_{OL}=8 mA					0.35	0.5	
I_{OZH}	Off-state output current, high-level voltage applied	Any Q	V_{CC}=MAX, $\overline{G}$ at 2 V, V_O=2.7 V			20			20	μA
I_{OZL}	Off-state output current, low-level voltage applied	Any Q	V_{CC}=MAX, $\overline{G}$ at 2 V, V_O=0.4 V			−20			−20	μA
I_I	Input current at maximum input voltage		V_{CC}=MAX, V_I=7 V			0.1			0.1	mA
I_{IH}	High-level input current		V_{CC}=MAX, V_I=2.7 V			20			20	μA
I_{IL}	Low-level input current	A thru D	V_{CC}=MAX, V_I=0.4 V			−0.4			−0.4	mA
		All others				−0.2			−0.2	
I_{OS}	Short-circuit output current[§]	Any Q	V_{CC}=MAX, V_O=0 V	−30		−130	−30		−130	mA
		$\overline{RCO}$		−20		−100	−20		−100	
I_{CCH}	Supply current, outputs high	V_{CC}=MAX, All outputs open	See Note 3		46	65		46	65	mA
I_{CCL}	Supply current, outputs low		See Note 4		48	70		48	70	
I_{CCZ}	Supply current, outputs off		See Note 5		48	70		48	70	

[†] For conditions shown as MIN or MAX, use the appropriate value specified under recommended operating conditions.

[‡] All typical values are at V_{CC} = 5 V, T_A = 25°C.

[§] Only one output should be shorted at a time, and duration of the short-circuit should not exceed one second.

NOTES: 3. I_{CCH} is measured after two 4.5 V to 0 V to 4.5 V pulses have been applied to CCK and RCK while $\overline{G}$ is grounded and all other inputs are at 4.5 V.
      4. I_{CCL} is measured after two 0 V to 4.5 V to 0 V pulses have been applied to CCK and RCK while all other inputs are grounded.
      5. I_{CCZ} is measured after two 0 V to 4.5 V to 0 V pulses have been applied to CCK and RCK while $\overline{G}$ is at 4.5 V and all other inputs are grounded.

switching characteristics, V_{CC} = 5 V, T_A = 25°C (see note 6)

PARAMETER	FROM (INPUT)	TO (OUTPUT)	TEST CONDITIONS	'LS696, 'LS697 MIN	'LS696, 'LS697 TYP	'LS696, 'LS697 MAX	'LS699 MIN	'LS699 TYP	'LS699 MAX	UNIT
t_{PLH}	CCK↑	$\overline{RCO}$	R_L = 2 kΩ, C_L = 15 pF		23	40		23	40	ns
t_{PHL}					23	40		23	40	ns
t_{PLH}	$\overline{ENT}$	$\overline{RCO}$			13	20		13	20	ns
t_{PHL}					13	20		13	20	ns
t_{PLH}	CCK↑	Q			12	20		12	20	ns
t_{PHL}					17	25		17	25	ns
t_{PLH}	RCK↑	Q			12	20		12	20	ns
t_{PHL}					17	25		17	25	ns
t_{PHL}	$\overline{CCLR}$↓	Q	R_L = 667 Ω, C_L = 45 pF		23	40				ns
t_{PLH}	R/$\overline{C}$	Q			16	25		16	25	ns
t_{PHL}					16	25		16	25	ns
t_{PZH}	$\overline{G}$↓	Q			19	30		19	30	ns
t_{PZL}					19	30		19	30	ns
t_{PHZ}	$\overline{G}$↑	Q	R_L = 667 Ω, C_L = 5 pF		17	30		17	30	ns
t_{PLZ}					17	30		17	30	ns

NOTE 6: See General Information Section for load circuits and voltage waveforms.

TEXAS INSTRUMENTS

3

TTL DEVICES

3-1109

typical operating sequences

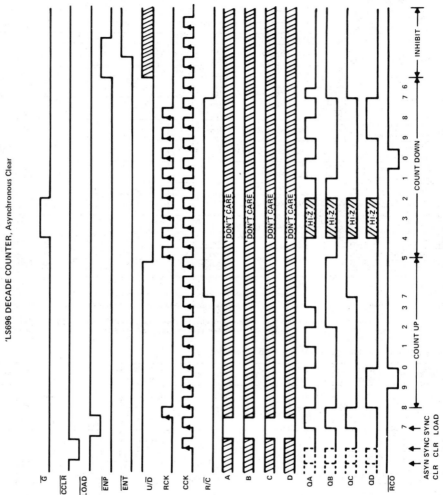

'LS696 DECADE COUNTER, Asynchronous Clear

TEXAS
INSTRUMENTS

typical operating sequences (continued)

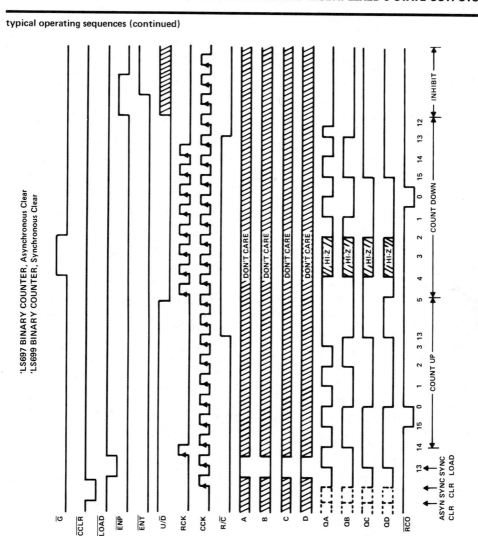

'LS697 BINARY COUNTER, Asynchronous Clear
'LS699 BINARY COUNTER, Synchronous Clear

TTL DEVICES

3

General Information   **1**

Functional Index   **2**

TTL Devices   **3**

Mechanical Data   **4**

4

MECHANICAL DATA

ORDERING INSTRUCTIONS

Electrical characteristics presented in this data book, unless otherwise noted, apply for circuit type(s) listed in the page heading regardless of package. The availability of a circuit function in a particular package is denoted by an alphabetical reference above the pin-connection diagram(s). These alphabetical references refer to mechanical outline drawings shown in this section.

Factory orders for circuits described in this catalog should include a four-part type number as explained in the following example.

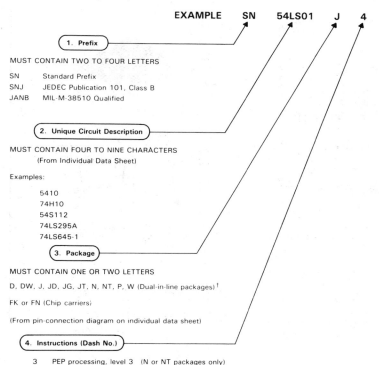

EXAMPLE   SN   54LS01   J   4

1. Prefix

MUST CONTAIN TWO TO FOUR LETTERS

SN   Standard Prefix
SNJ   JEDEC Publication 101, Class B
JANB   MIL-M-38510 Qualified

2. Unique Circuit Description

MUST CONTAIN FOUR TO NINE CHARACTERS
    (From Individual Data Sheet)

Examples:

        5410
        74H10
        54S112
        74LS295A
        74LS645-1

3. Package

MUST CONTAIN ONE OR TWO LETTERS

D, DW, J, JD, JG, JT, N, NT, P, W (Dual-in-line packages) †

FK or FN (Chip carriers)

(From pin-connection diagram on individual data sheet)

4. Instructions (Dash No.)

        3   PEP processing, level 3   (N or NT packages only)

---

† These circuits in dual-in-line packages are shipped in one of the carriers shown below. Unless a specific method of shipment is specified by the customer (with possible additional costs), circuits will be shipped in the most practical carrier. Please contact your TI sales representative for the method that will best suit your particular needs.

Dual-in-line (D, DW, J, JD, JG, JT, N, NT, P, W)

— A-Channel Plastic Tubing
  Tape and Reel
— Barnes Carrier (W only)

TEXAS INSTRUMENTS

4

MECHANICAL DATA

MECHANICAL DATA

D plastic dual-in-line packages

Each of these dual-in-line packages consists of a circuit mounted on a lead frame and encapsulated within a plastic compound. The compound will withstand soldering temperature with no deformation, and circuit performance characteristics will remain stable when operated in high-humidity conditions. Leads require no additional cleaning or processing when used in soldered assembly.

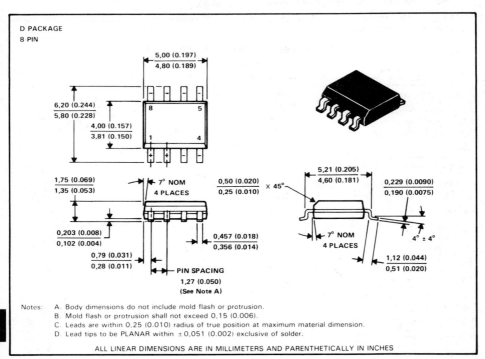

D PACKAGE
8-PIN

Notes: A. Body dimensions do not include mold flash or protrusion.
        B. Mold flash or protrusion shall not exceed 0,15 (0.006).
        C. Leads are within 0,25 (0.010) radius of true position at maximum material dimension.
        D. Lead tips to be PLANAR within ±0,051 (0.002) exclusive of solder.

ALL LINEAR DIMENSIONS ARE IN MILLIMETERS AND PARENTHETICALLY IN INCHES

4

MECHANICAL DATA

TEXAS
INSTRUMENTS

D plastic dual-in-line packages

Each of these dual-in-line packages consists of a circuit mounted on a lead frame and encapsulated within a plastic compound. The compound will withstand soldering temperature with no deformation, and circuit performance characteristics will remain stable when operated in high-humidity conditions. Leads require no additional cleaning or processing when used in soldered assembly.

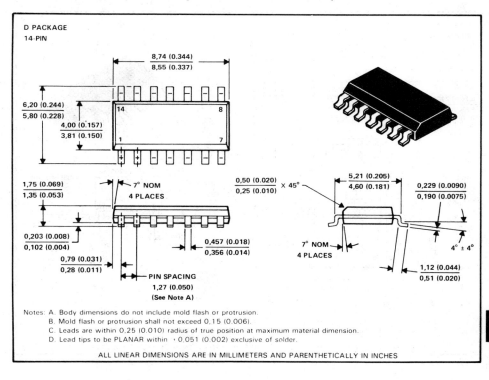

D PACKAGE
14-PIN

8,74 (0.344)
8,55 (0.337)

6,20 (0.244)
5,80 (0.228)

4,00 (0.157)
3,81 (0.150)

1,75 (0.069)
1,35 (0.053)

7° NOM
4 PLACES

0,203 (0.008)
0,102 (0.004)

0,50 (0.020)
0,25 (0.010) × 45°

0,457 (0.018)
0,356 (0.014)

0,79 (0.031)
0,28 (0.011)

PIN SPACING
1,27 (0.050)
(See Note A)

5,21 (0.205)
4,60 (0.181)

0,229 (0.0090)
0,190 (0.0075)

7° NOM
4 PLACES

4° ± 4°

1,12 (0.044)
0,51 (0.020)

Notes: A. Body dimensions do not include mold flash or protrusion.
B. Mold flash or protrusion shall not exceed 0,15 (0.006).
C. Leads are within 0,25 (0.010) radius of true position at maximum material dimension.
D. Lead tips to be PLANAR within ±0.051 (0.002) exclusive of solder.

ALL LINEAR DIMENSIONS ARE IN MILLIMETERS AND PARENTHETICALLY IN INCHES

4

MECHANICAL DATA

TEXAS
INSTRUMENTS

MECHANICAL DATA

D plastic dual-in-line packages

Each of these dual-in-line packages consists of a circuit mounted on a lead frame and encapsulated within a plastic compound. The compound will withstand soldering temperature with no deformation, and circuit performance characteristics will remain stable when operated in high-humidity conditions. Leads require no additional cleaning or processing when used in soldered assembly.

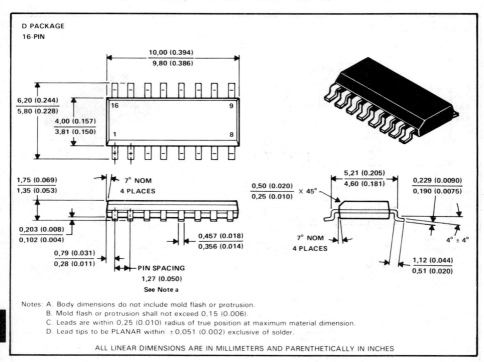

D PACKAGE
16-PIN

Notes: A. Body dimensions do not include mold flash or protrusion.
      B. Mold flash or protrusion shall not exceed 0,15 (0.006).
      C. Leads are within 0,25 (0.010) radius of true position at maximum material dimension.
      D. Lead tips to be PLANAR within ±0,051 (0.002) exclusive of solder.

ALL LINEAR DIMENSIONS ARE IN MILLIMETERS AND PARENTHETICALLY IN INCHES

4

MECHANICAL DATA

TEXAS
INSTRUMENTS

DW plastic dual-in-line packages

Each of these dual-in-line packages consists of a circuit mounted on a lead frame and encapsulated within a plastic compound. The compound will withstand soldering temperature with no deformation, and circuit performance characteristics will remain stable when operated in high-humidity conditions. Leads require no additional cleaning or processing when used in soldered assembly.

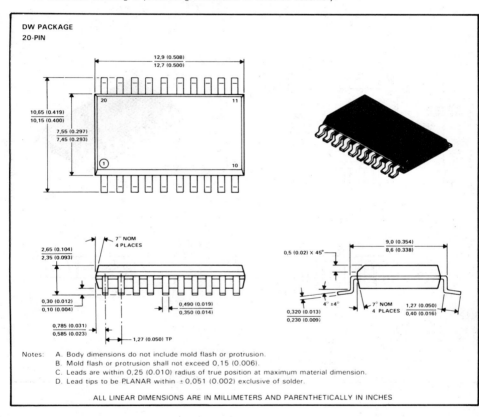

DW PACKAGE
20-PIN

Notes: A. Body dimensions do not include mold flash or protrusion.
B. Mold flash or protrusion shall not exceed 0,15 (0.006).
C. Leads are within 0,25 (0.010) radius of true position at maximum material dimension.
D. Lead tips to be PLANAR within ±0,051 (0.002) exclusive of solder.

ALL LINEAR DIMENSIONS ARE IN MILLIMETERS AND PARENTHETICALLY IN INCHES

4

MECHANICAL DATA

MECHANICAL DATA

DW plastic dual-in-line packages

Each of these dual-in-line packages consists of a circuit mounted on a lead frame and encapsulated within a plastic compound. The compound will withstand soldering temperature with no deformation, and circuit performance characteristics will remain stable when operated in high-humidity conditions. Leads require no additional cleaning or processing when used in soldered assembly.

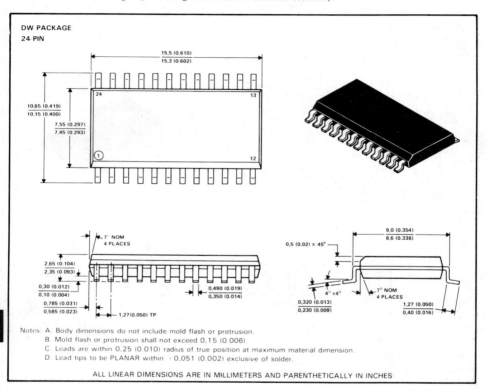

DW PACKAGE
24-PIN

Notes: A. Body dimensions do not include mold flash or protrusion.
B. Mold flash or protrusion shall not exceed 0,15 (0.006).
C. Leads are within 0,25 (0.010) radius of true position at maximum material dimension.
D. Lead tips to be PLANAR within ·0,051 (0.002) exclusive of solder.

ALL LINEAR DIMENSIONS ARE IN MILLIMETERS AND PARENTHETICALLY IN INCHES

TEXAS INSTRUMENTS

4

MECHANICAL DATA

FK ceramic chip carrier packages

Each of these hermetically sealed chip carrier packages has a three-layer ceramic base with a metal lid and braze seal. The packages are intended for surface mounting on solder lands on 1,27 (0.050-inch) centers. terminals require no additional cleaning or processing when used in soldered assembly.

FK package terminal assignments conform to JEDEC Standards 1 and 2.

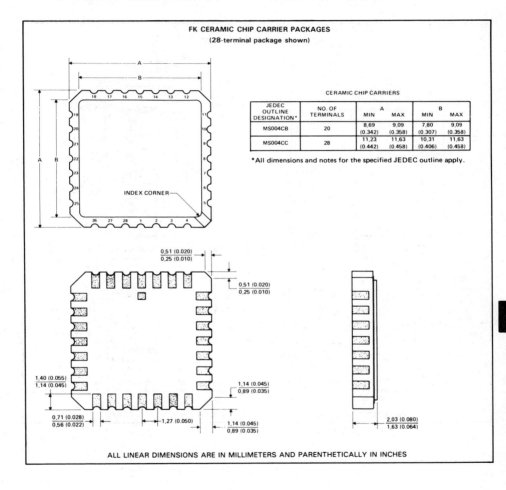

FK CERAMIC CHIP CARRIER PACKAGES
(28-terminal package shown)

CERAMIC CHIP CARRIERS

JEDEC OUTLINE DESIGNATION*	NO. OF TERMINALS	A		B	
		MIN	MAX	MIN	MAX
MS004CB	20	8,69 (0.342)	9,09 (0.358)	7,80 (0.307)	9,09 (0.358)
MS004CC	28	11,23 (0.442)	11,63 (0.458)	10,31 (0.406)	11,63 (0.458)

*All dimensions and notes for the specified JEDEC outline apply.

INDEX CORNER

0,51 (0.020) / 0,25 (0.010)

0,51 (0.020) / 0,25 (0.010)

1,40 (0.055) / 1,14 (0.045)

1,14 (0.045) / 0,89 (0.035)

0,71 (0.028) / 0,56 (0.022)

1,27 (0.050)

1,14 (0.045) / 0,89 (0.035)

2,03 (0.080) / 1,63 (0.064)

ALL LINEAR DIMENSIONS ARE IN MILLIMETERS AND PARENTHETICALLY IN INCHES

4

MECHANICAL DATA

FN plastic chip carrier package

Each of these chip carrier packages consists of a circuit mounted on a lead frame and encapsulated within an electrically nonconductive plastic compound. The compound withstands soldering temperatures with no deformation, and circuit performance characteristics remain stable when the devices are operated in high-humidity conditions. The packages are intended for surface mounting on solder lands on 1,27 (0.050) centers. Leads require no additional cleaning or processing when used in soldered assembly.

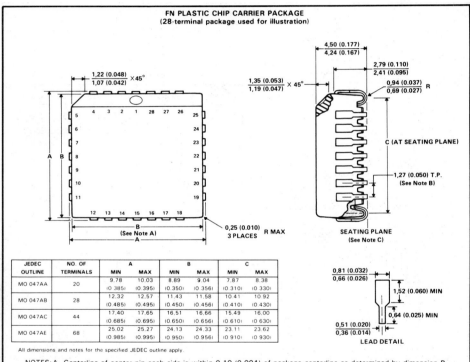

FN PLASTIC CHIP CARRIER PACKAGE
(28-terminal package used for illustration)

JEDEC OUTLINE	NO. OF TERMINALS	A		B		C	
		MIN	MAX	MIN	MAX	MIN	MAX
MO 047AA	20	9.78 (0.385)	10.03 (0.395)	8.89 (0.350)	9.04 (0.356)	7.87 (0.310)	8.38 (0.330)
MO 047AB	28	12.32 (0.485)	12.57 (0.495)	11.43 (0.450)	11.58 (0.456)	10.41 (0.410)	10.92 (0.430)
MO 047AC	44	17.40 (0.685)	17.65 (0.695)	16.51 (0.650)	16.66 (0.656)	15.49 (0.610)	16.00 (0.630)
MO 047AE	68	25.02 (0.985)	25.27 (0.995)	24.13 (0.950)	24.33 (0.956)	23.11 (0.910)	23.62 (0.930)

All dimensions and notes for the specified JEDEC outline apply.

NOTES: A. Centerline of center pin each side is within 0,10 (0.004) of package centerline as determined by dimension B.
  B. Location of each pin is within 0,127 (0.005) of true position with respect to center pin on each side.
  C. The lead contact points are planar within 0,10 (0.004).

ALL LINEAR DIMENSIONS ARE IN MILLIMETERS AND PARENTHETICALLY IN INCHES

4

MECHANICAL DATA

TEXAS
INSTRUMENTS

J ceramic packages (including JT dual-in-line package)

Each of these hermetically sealed dual-in-line packages consists of a ceramic base, ceramic cap, and a lead frame. Hermetic sealing is accomplished with glass. The JT packages are intended for insertion in mounting-hole rows on 7,62 (0.300) centers. Once the leads are compressed and inserted sufficient tension is provided to secure the package in the board during soldering. Tin-plated ("bright-dipped") leads require no additional cleaning or processing when used in soldered assembly.

NOTE: For the 14-, 16-, and 20-pin packages, the letter J is used by itself since these packages are available only in the 7,62 (0.300) row spacing. For the 24-pin packages, if no second letter or row spacing is specified, the package is assumed to have 15,24 (0.600) row spacing.

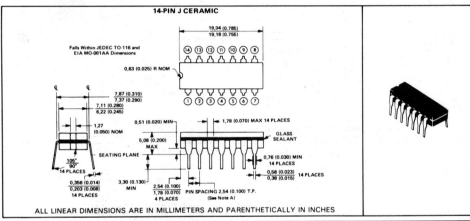

14-PIN J CERAMIC

ALL LINEAR DIMENSIONS ARE IN MILLIMETERS AND PARENTHETICALLY IN INCHES

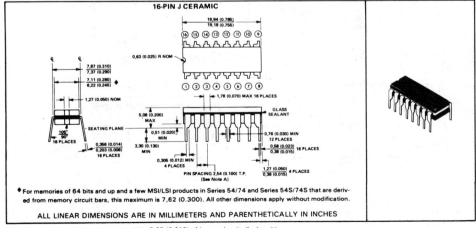

16-PIN J CERAMIC

◆ For memories of 64 bits and up and a few MSI/LSI products in Series 54/74 and Series 54S/74S that are derived from memory circuit bars, this maximum is 7,62 (0.300). All other dimensions apply without modification.

ALL LINEAR DIMENSIONS ARE IN MILLIMETERS AND PARENTHETICALLY IN INCHES

NOTE A: Each pin centerline is located within 0,25 (0.010) of its true longitudinal position.

J ceramic dual-in-line packages (continued)

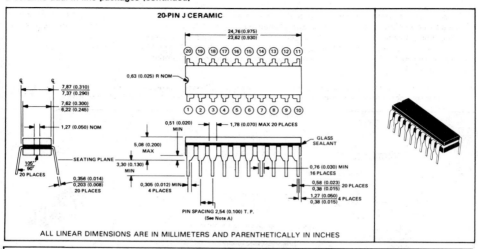

20-PIN J CERAMIC

ALL LINEAR DIMENSIONS ARE IN MILLIMETERS AND PARENTHETICALLY IN INCHES

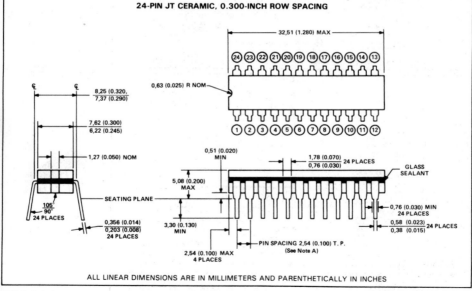

24-PIN JT CERAMIC, 0.300-INCH ROW SPACING

ALL LINEAR DIMENSIONS ARE IN MILLIMETERS AND PARENTHETICALLY IN INCHES

NOTE A: Each pin centerline is located within 0,25 (0.010) of its true longitudinal position.

TEXAS
INSTRUMENTS

J ceramic dual-in-line packages (continued)

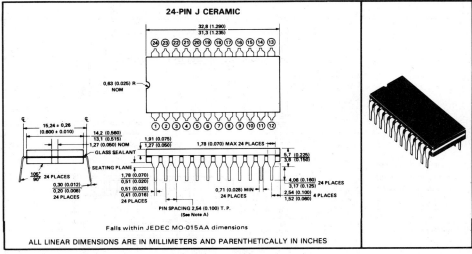

24-PIN J CERAMIC

Falls within JEDEC MO-015AA dimensions

ALL LINEAR DIMENSIONS ARE IN MILLIMETERS AND PARENTHETICALLY IN INCHES

NOTE A: Each pin centerline is located within 0,25 (0.010) of its true longitudinal position.

TEXAS INSTRUMENTS

MECHANICAL DATA

4

ceramic packages – side-braze (JD suffix)

This is a hermetically sealed ceramic package with a metal cap and side-brazed tin-plated leads.

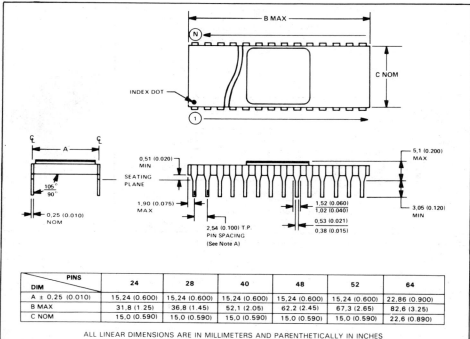

DIM \ PINS	24	28	40	48	52	64
A ± 0,25 (0.010)	15,24 (0.600)	15,24 (0.600)	15,24 (0.600)	15,24 (0.600)	15,24 (0.600)	22,86 (0.900)
B MAX	31,8 (1.25)	36,8 (1.45)	52,1 (2.05)	62,2 (2.45)	67,3 (2.65)	82,6 (3.25)
C NOM	15,0 (0.590)	15,0 (0.590)	15,0 (0.590)	15,0 (0.590)	15,0 (0.590)	22,6 (0.890)

ALL LINEAR DIMENSIONS ARE IN MILLIMETERS AND PARENTHETICALLY IN INCHES

NOTE A: Each pin centerline is located within 0,25 (0.010) of its true longitudinal position.

4

MECHANICAL DATA

TEXAS INSTRUMENTS

JG ceramic dual-in-line package

This hermetically sealed dual-in-line package consists of a ceramic base, ceramic cap, and 8-lead frame. Hermetic sealing is accomplished with glass. The package is intended for insertion in mounting-hole rows on 7,62 (0.300) centers (see Note a). Once the leads are compressed and inserted, sufficient tension is provided to secure the package in the board during soldering. Non-shiny tin-plated leads require no additional cleaning or processing when used in soldered assembly.

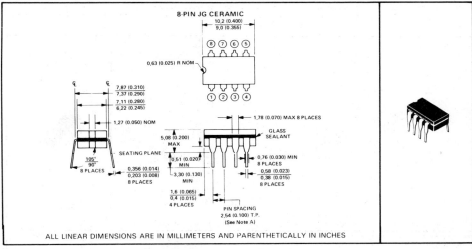

8-PIN JG CERAMIC

ALL LINEAR DIMENSIONS ARE IN MILLIMETERS AND PARENTHETICALLY IN INCHES

NOTE A: Each pin centerline is located within 0.25 (0.010) of its true longitudinal position.

TEXAS INSTRUMENTS

MECHANICAL DATA

4

N plastic packages (including NT dual-in-package)

Each of these dual-in-line packages consists of a circuit mounted on a lead frame and encapsulated within an electrically nonconductive plastic compound. The compound will withstand soldering temperature with no deformation and circuit performance characteristics remain stable when operated in high-humidity conditions. The packages are intended for insertion in mounting-hole rows on 7,62 (0.300) centers for the NT package. Once the leads are compressed and inserted, sufficient tension is provided to secure the package in the board during soldering. Leads require no additional cleaning or processing when used in soldered assembly.

NOTE: For the 14-, 16-, 20-, and 28-pin packages, the letter N is used by itself since these packages are available in only one row-spacing width – 7,62 (0.300) for the 14-, 16-, 18-, and 20-pin packages and 15,24 (0.600) for the 28-pin package. For the 24-pin package, if no second letter or row spacing is specified, the package is assumed to have 15,24 (0.600) row spacing.

14-PIN N PLASTIC

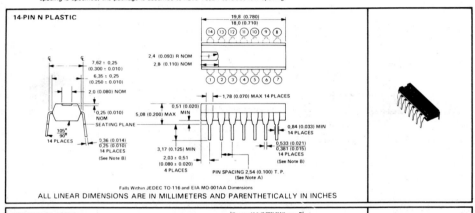

Falls Within JEDEC TO-116 and EIA MO-001AA Dimensions

ALL LINEAR DIMENSIONS ARE IN MILLIMETERS AND PARENTHETICALLY IN INCHES

16-PIN N PLASTIC

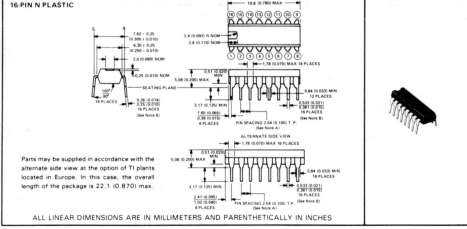

Parts may be supplied in accordance with the alternate side view at the option of TI plants located in Europe. In this case, the overall length of the package is 22,1 (0.870) max.

ALL LINEAR DIMENSIONS ARE IN MILLIMETERS AND PARENTHETICALLY IN INCHES

NOTES: A. Each pin centerline is located within 0,25 (0.010) of its true longitudinal position.
 B. For solder dipped leads, this dimension applies from the lead tip to the standoff.

TEXAS INSTRUMENTS

4

MECHANICAL DATA

N package

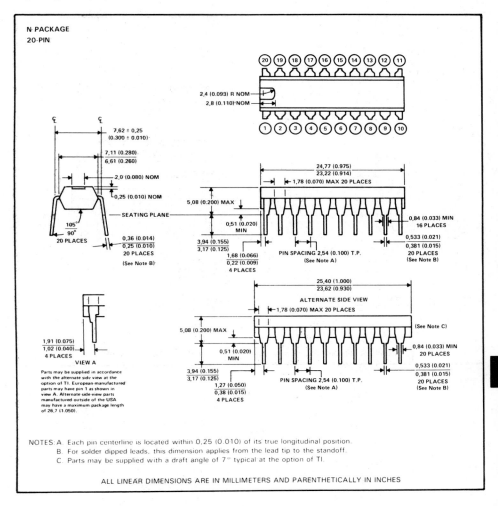

N PACKAGE
20-PIN

2,4 (0.093) R NOM
2,8 (0.110) NOM

7,62 ± 0,25
(0.300 ± 0.010)

7,11 (0.280)
6,61 (0.260)

2,0 (0.080) NOM

0,25 (0.010) NOM

SEATING PLANE

105°
90°
20 PLACES

0,36 (0.014)
0,25 (0.010)
20 PLACES
(See Note B)

24,77 (0.975)
23,22 (0.914)

1,78 (0.070) MAX 20 PLACES

5,08 (0.200) MAX

0,51 (0.020)
MIN

3,94 (0.155)
3,17 (0.125)

1,68 (0.066)
0,22 (0.009)
4 PLACES

PIN SPACING 2,54 (0.100) T.P.
(See Note A)

0,84 (0.033) MIN
16 PLACES

0,533 (0.021)
0,381 (0.015)
20 PLACES
(See Note B)

1,91 (0.075)
1,02 (0.040)
4 PLACES

VIEW A

Parts may be supplied in accordance
with the alternate side view at the
option of TI. European-manufactured
parts may have pin 1 as shown in
view A. Alternate-side-view parts
manufactured outside of the USA
may have a maximum package length
of 26,7 (1.050).

25,40 (1.000)
23,62 (0.930)

ALTERNATE SIDE VIEW

1,78 (0.070) MAX 20 PLACES

5,08 (0.200) MAX

0,51 (0.020)
MIN

3,94 (0.155)
3,17 (0.125)

1,27 (0.050)
0,38 (0.015)
4 PLACES

PIN SPACING 2,54 (0.100) T.P.
(See Note A)

(See Note C)

0,84 (0.033) MIN
20 PLACES

0,533 (0.021)
0,381 (0.015)
20 PLACES
(See Note B)

NOTES: A. Each pin centerline is located within 0,25 (0.010) of its true longitudinal position.
B. For solder dipped leads, this dimension applies from the lead tip to the standoff.
C. Parts may be supplied with a draft angle of 7" typical at the option of TI.

ALL LINEAR DIMENSIONS ARE IN MILLIMETERS AND PARENTHETICALLY IN INCHES

4

MECHANICAL DATA

TEXAS
INSTRUMENTS

MECHANICAL DATA

NT package

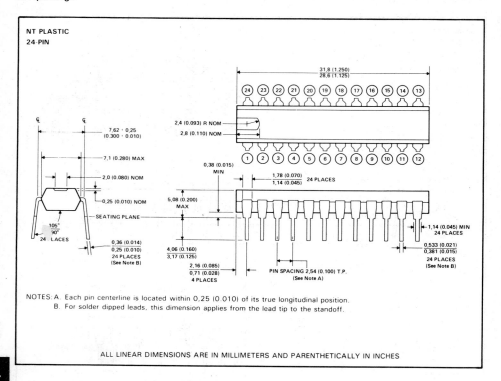

**NT PLASTIC
24-PIN**

31,8 (1.250)
28,6 (1.125)

7,62 · 0,25
(0.300 · 0.010)

7,1 (0.280) MAX

2,0 (0.080) NOM

0,25 (0.010) NOM

SEATING PLANE

105°
90°
24 PLACES

0,36 (0.014)
0,25 (0.010)
24 PLACES
(See Note B)

2,4 (0.093) R NOM
2,8 (0.110) NOM

0,38 (0.015)
MIN

5,08 (0.200)
MAX

4,06 (0.160)
3,17 (0.125)

2,16 (0.085)
0,71 (0.028)
4 PLACES

1,78 (0.070)
1,14 (0.045) 24 PLACES

1,14 (0.045) MIN
24 PLACES

0,533 (0.021)
0,381 (0.015)
24 PLACES
(See Note B)

PIN SPACING 2,54 (0.100) T.P.
(See Note A)

NOTES: A. Each pin centerline is located within 0,25 (0.010) of its true longitudinal position.
B. For solder dipped leads, this dimension applies from the lead tip to the standoff.

ALL LINEAR DIMENSIONS ARE IN MILLIMETERS AND PARENTHETICALLY IN INCHES

4

MECHANICAL DATA

TEXAS
INSTRUMENTS

N plastic dual-in-line packages (continued)

24-PIN N PLASTIC

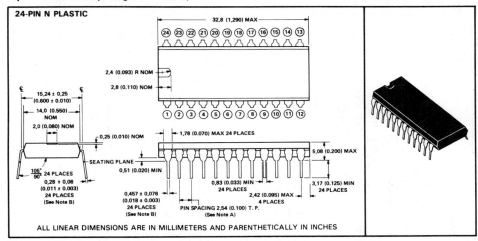

32,8 (1,290) MAX

2,4 (0.093) R NOM
2,8 (0.110) NOM
15,24 ± 0,25 (0.600 ± 0.010)
14,0 (0.550) NOM
2,0 (0.080) NOM
0,25 (0.010) NOM
1,78 (0.070) MAX 24 PLACES
5,08 (0.200) MAX
SEATING PLANE
0,51 (0.020) MIN
105° 90° 24 PLACES
0,28 ± 0,08 (0.011 ± 0.003) 24 PLACES (See Note B)
0,83 (0.033) MIN 24 PLACES
3,17 (0.125) MIN 24 PLACES
0,457 ± 0,076 (0.018 ± 0.003) 24 PLACES (See Note B)
2,42 (0.095) MAX 4 PLACES
PIN SPACING 2,54 (0.100) T.P. (See Note A)

ALL LINEAR DIMENSIONS ARE IN MILLIMETERS AND PARENTHETICALLY IN INCHES

NOTES: A. Each pin centerline is located within 0,25 (0.010) of its true longitudinal position.
B. For solder-dipped leads, this dimension applies from the lead tip to the standoff.

TEXAS INSTRUMENTS

4

MECHANICAL DATA

N plastic packages (continued)

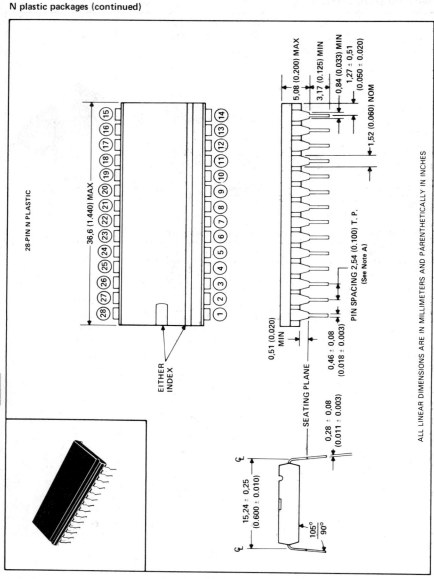

28-PIN N PLASTIC

ALL LINEAR DIMENSIONS ARE IN MILLIMETERS AND PARENTHETICALLY IN INCHES

NOTE A: Each pin centerline is located within 0.25 (0.010) of its true longitudinal position.

4

MECHANICAL DATA

TEXAS
INSTRUMENTS

N plastic packages (continued)

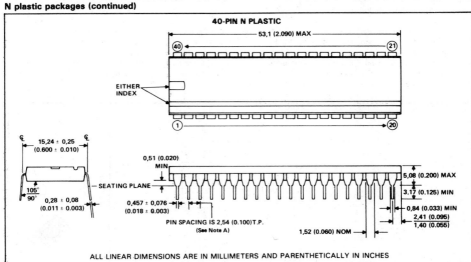

40-PIN N PLASTIC

53,1 (2.090) MAX

EITHER INDEX

15,24 ± 0,25 (0.600 ± 0.010)

105°
90°

0,28 ± 0,08 (0.011 ± 0.003)

SEATING PLANE

0,51 (0.020) MIN

0,457 ± 0,076 (0.018 ± 0.003)

PIN SPACING IS 2,54 (0.100) T.P. (See Note A)

5,08 (0.200) MAX

3,17 (0.125) MIN

0,84 (0.033) MIN

2,41 (0.095)
1,40 (0.055)

1,52 (0.060) NOM

ALL LINEAR DIMENSIONS ARE IN MILLIMETERS AND PARENTHETICALLY IN INCHES

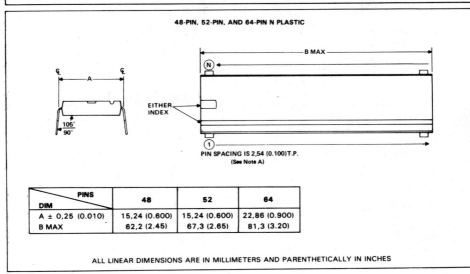

48-PIN, 52-PIN, AND 64-PIN N PLASTIC

B MAX

A

EITHER INDEX

105°
90°

PIN SPACING IS 2,54 (0.100) T.P. (See Note A)

PINS DIM	48	52	64
A ± 0,25 (0.010)	15,24 (0.600)	15,24 (0.600)	22,86 (0.900)
B MAX	62,2 (2.45)	67,3 (2.65)	81,3 (3.20)

ALL LINEAR DIMENSIONS ARE IN MILLIMETERS AND PARENTHETICALLY IN INCHES

NOTE A: Each pin centerline is located within 0,25 (0.010) of its true longitudinal position.

TEXAS INSTRUMENTS

MECHANICAL DATA

P plastic dual-in-line package

This dual-in-line package consists of a circuit mounted on an 8-lead frame and encapsulated within a plastic compound. The compound will withstand soldering temperature with no deformation and circuit performance characteristics remain stable when operated in high-humidity conditions. The package is intended for insertion in mounting-hole rows on 7,62-mm (0.300) centers (see Note A). Once the leads are compressed and inserted, sufficient tension is provided to secure the package in the board during soldering. Solder-plated leads require no additional cleaning or processing when used in soldered assembly.

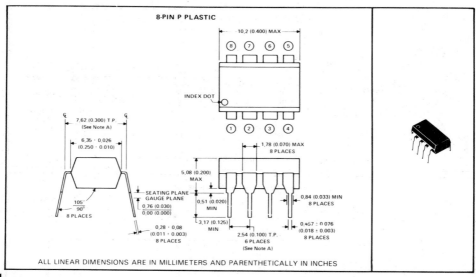

8-PIN P PLASTIC

ALL LINEAR DIMENSIONS ARE IN MILLIMETERS AND PARENTHETICALLY IN INCHES

NOTE A: Each pin is within 0,13 (0.0005) radius of true position (TP) at the gauge plane with maximum material condition and unit installed.

TEXAS
INSTRUMENTS

W ceramic flat packages

These hermetically sealed flat packages consist of an electrically nonconductive ceramic base and cap and a lead frame. Hermetic sealing is accomplished with glass. Leads require no additional cleaning or processing when used in soldered assembly.

14-PIN W CERAMIC

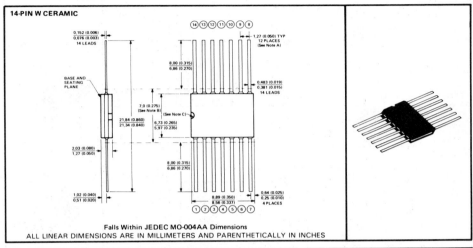

Falls Within JEDEC MO-004AA Dimensions
ALL LINEAR DIMENSIONS ARE IN MILLIMETERS AND PARENTHETICALLY IN INCHES

16-PIN W CERAMIC

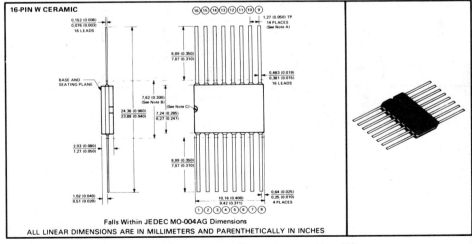

Falls Within JEDEC MO-004AG Dimensions
ALL LINEAR DIMENSIONS ARE IN MILLIMETERS AND PARENTHETICALLY IN INCHES

NOTES: A. Leads are within 0,13 (0.005) radius of true position (TP) at maximum material condition.
B. This dimension determines a zone within which all body and lead irregularities lie.
C. Index point is provided on cap for terminal identification only.

TEXAS
INSTRUMENTS

4

MECHANICAL DATA

W ceramic flat package (continued)

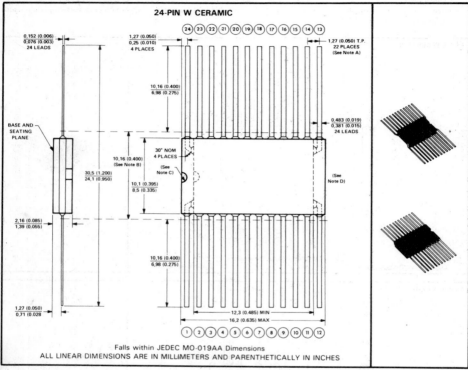

24-PIN W CERAMIC

Falls within JEDEC MO-019AA Dimensions
ALL LINEAR DIMENSIONS ARE IN MILLIMETERS AND PARENTHETICALLY IN INCHES

NOTES: A. Leads are within 0,13 (0.005) radius of true position (TP) at maximum material condition.
B. This dimension determines a zone within which all body and lead irregularities lie.
C. Index point is provided on cap for terminal identification only.
D. End configuration of 24-pin package is at the option of TI.

TEXAS
INSTRUMENTS